MW00654902

This companion workbook is meant to be used alongside Thinkwell's CD-ROM and web-based Precalculus text. For more information about this please contact support@thinkwell.com.

Senior Editor:
Sarah Flood Ryland

Contributing Editor:
Joaquin Salazar

Text and Cover design:
Peat Duggins, Martin Turzik, Amy Bryant

Production Guru:
Samantha Webber

Technical Guru:
Palo Chalupka

Spiritual Leaders:
Carl Tyson, Kent Fuka, and Martin Kahn

Project Manager:
Amy Bryant

With Special Thanks to:
Hank Cathey
Peat Duggins
Justin Kauffman
Vera Renkiewicz
Kristy Summers
Scout and Bingle

Thinkwell's Precalculus

with Edward Burger

To Kent Fuka and Carl Tyson

PREFACE

To The Student:

How to Use this workbook to succeed:
Congratulations! You are about to add a new dimension to your college learning experience - one that is more engaging, more thorough, and more effective than any textbook assignment you've ever received.

This printed workbook is designed to help you take maximum advantage of Thinkwell's Precalculus by providing a streamlined version of the multimedia content of the Thinkwell text. It also can serve as a useful place to record your own notes, examples, questions, and ideas.

Concepts, theories, and examples from the Precalculus video lectures are outlined here in order to streamline referencing and reviewing the material. Precalculus vocabulary terms are defined as they are used, repeated at the end of subchapters, and appear in the glossary at the end of this book. A searchable index is also available on the Thinkwell Precalculus website.

This workbook is not a substitute for viewing the lectures. It's a tool to help you to navigate the course with maximum success. Many students have found that a workbook helps them follow the video lectures more attentively, allowing them to pause and make their own notes as they watch the videos.

For more help with the CD-ROM or online components of Thinkwell's Precalculus, consult the Student User's Guide, available online in the Help Center, or contact us at technicalsupport@thinkwell.com.

The following tips are offered to help you with the transition from a traditional text to Thinkwell's next-generation textbook. Many of these suggestions, however, are reliable, time-tested study habits that work in just about any situation.

Get Organized:
Survey your coming semester from beginning to end. Using a calendar, make a full-semester study schedule for all of your courses. Include midterms, assignments, and study times. Often, instructors assume that you will spend at least three hours on homework for every hour you spend in class. Find out what your instructors' estimates are for your classes and plan accordingly. Schedule this time on your calendar. Plan to study during those times of the day when you're the least tired and least likely to be distracted. Find a quiet, private place to study to help ensure that noise and surprise distractions will not interrupt you.

Also schedule time to work on long-term assignments and projects. Plan to start working on them as early as possible so that you have plenty of time to ask questions, research, problem-solve, and make any revisions.

View the Thinkwell lectures actively:
Research shows that students who interact with course content, rather than passively reading, listening, or viewing it, are much more likely to gain a far superior understanding of that content. Allow yourself about 30 minutes to view a typical 10-to-15 minute Thinkwell video lecture. This extra time allows you to stop the lecture whenever you feel a need to review the material again or jot down a question or comment. Try watching each lecture once without stopping. Then watch it a second time, using this workbook and taking your own notes. Highlight the key concepts as they are discussed and any important points or details that will help you remember and understand this critical content. Write down new terms along with their definitions.

Also pay close attention to the text and graphic elements of the Thinkwell video lecture on your screen. For instance, the key concept box, contains the main ideas of the lecture around which sub-points, examples, and definitions are built. These key concepts also appear on the subchapter pages of this workbook. Most of the Thinkwell video lectures also contain a definitions area. Here you'll find terms, formulas, laws, or other discipline-specific language you should know.

Finally, the content area, on the right-hand side of your screen, contains some of the same information that appears in the online notes and in this workbook. The text and graphics in this area of the video builds as the Thinkwell presenter delivers the lecture. Pay special attention to headings, charts, bulleted lists, and diagrams, for they contain distillations of important material.

Utilize Thinkwell's Website resources:
Your Thinkwell website contains hundreds of on-line exercises and test questions, which your instructor can activate. Depending on how your instructor uses them, these automatically-graded questions will exercise or test your knowledge of the course content. Many of these exercises contain hints and explanations concerning any questions that you might answer incorrectly.

The Thinkwell website provides you with an online searchable index and glossary of key terms. The searchable index tells you in which lecture or exercise a term appears. The glossary database provides you with the definitions of all key terms. Be sure you know the meaning of all terms introduced in the lectures as well as any additional terms your instructor may have mentioned.

Every lecture also provides you with online notes. These are digital versions of much of the content of this workbook in a lecture-by-lecture format.

Take In-class notes:
If your instructor lectures in class, note-taking is critical. Studies show that you are far more likely to remember and comprehend material if you take notes in addition to listening to a lecture. Try to take notes that are readable and complete, and when possible, structure your notes according to the structure of the lecture. Your instructor may be speaking from prepared notes, so try to listen for the main headings and subheadings. Pay attention to lists and diagrams.

Try to find a moment immediately after the lecture to review and flesh out your notes. Most students' memories of even the major points of a lecture begins to fade after about thirty minutes. This 10-to-20 minute exercise is an extremely good use of time and one that you'll appreciate when you review your notes prior to an exam.

Prepare for exams:
Your notes reflect your ongoing understanding of and progression through the course content. One of the most effective ways to study is to cumulatively outline your notes. This method works best if you write your outlines by hand, even if you took them first on your computer.

Start with the notes you made in class (or from your Thinkwell lectures), and make a new set of notes that summarizes these in outline format. Begin making summary outline notes after the forth or fifth lecture. Try to keep the summary outline notes to three or four pages. Retain important headings, subheadings, lists, and any brief explanations you need to understand each key idea or concept.

After the next four or five lectures, revise your summary outline notes from the first group of lectures, and add your summary outline notes from the next group so that the entire summary outline is still just four pages long. Each time you revise your four-page summary outline, you are organizing and revisiting the important ideas of the coursecand learning them. It might look as though you're trying to distill the essentials of a course down to a few pages, but in fact you will be learning, managing, and understanding the core content of the course.

Another useful study technique is to try to predict the questions that will be on the exam. Base this exercise on the key points from your notes. This isn't as hard as it sounds and is a very good way to prepare. Some instructors may make previous exam questions available. You don't want to be surprised when you sit down to take the exam.

Finally, for problem-solving courses, it's very important to know the method for solving every kind of problem you might encounter on an exam. Work as many practice problems as you can, making sure you haven't forgotten any types or special cases. Most importantly, listen attentively for any guidance that your instructor might provide concerning the types of questions you can expect to see on the exam.

From all of us at Thinkwell who are committed to engaging your interest and ensuring your success, Good luck!

Thinkwell's Precalculus

with Edward Burger

Table of Contents:

Induction

Combinations and Probability

1

Basic Algebra Review

Concepts of Inequality

- $<$ is the symbol meaning that the number on the left is **less than** the number on the right.
- $>$ is the symbol meaning that the number on the left is **greater than** the number on the right.
- $\leq$ means that the number on the left is either **less than or equal to** the number on the right.
- $\geq$ means that the number on the left is either **equal to or greater than** the number on the right.
- The **transitive property** means that if A is larger than B and B is larger than C, then A is larger than C. The property also means if A is smaller than B and B is smaller than C, then A is smaller than C.
- Adding the same number to both sides of an inequality maintains the inequality. Subtracting the same number from both sides also maintains the inequality.
- Multiplying or dividing both sides of an inequality by a positive number maintains the inequality. Multiplying or dividing both sides by a negative number reverses the inequality.

$A < B$ smaller (less than) larger (greater than)	In reading inequality symbols, the symbol always opens toward the larger number.
The Transitive Property: **if $a < b$ and $b < c$, then $a < c$** $A < B \quad B < C \Longrightarrow A < C$	Any number that is smaller than one number which, in turn, is smaller than a third number will always turn out also to be smaller than the third number. Likewise, any number that is greater than a number which, in turn, is greater than a third number will also be greater than that third number.
$A < B$ $A + C < B + C$ the inequality remains the same	You can add or subtract the same amount from both sides of the inequality without changing the nature of the inequality.
$-3 < 2$ $(-3)(5) < (2)(5)$ *multiply both sides by 5* $-15 < 10$ *signs are still correct*	Multiplying or dividing by any positive number maintains the inequality that existed before the multiplication. In this example, you start with -3 is less than 2. When you multiply by 5, you get -15 is less than 10 and the inequality is maintained.
multiplying an inequality by a negative number flips the inequality sign $-3 < 2$ $(-3)(5) < (2)(5)$ $-15 < 10$ $(-3)(-5) \quad (2)(-5)$ *multiply both sides by –5* $15 > -10$	Multiplying or dividing by any negative number reverses the order of inequality that existed before the multiplication. In this example, you can see that multiplying by -5 alters the inequality.

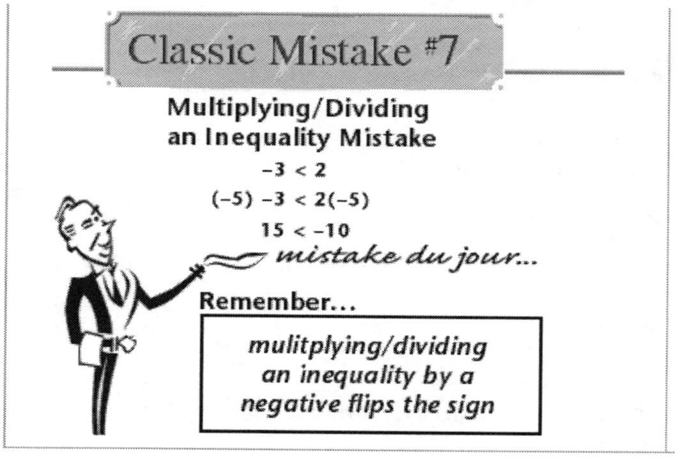

One of the most common mistakes in algebra is misapplying inequalities when multiplying or dividing by a negative number.

Sample problems:

1. True or false: $-\frac{5}{3} < -2$

   Solution: False

   Explanation: Express -2 as a fraction where the denominator is 3: $-2 = \frac{6}{3}$. Replace -2 with $-\frac{6}{3}$ in the inequality, then compare: $-\frac{5}{3} < -\frac{6}{3}$. Now the fractions have the some denominator, so ingnore the denominator and compare the numerators: $-\frac{5}{3} < -\frac{6}{3} \Rightarrow -5 < -6$. Multiply the inequality by -1: $-1(-5 < -6)$; $5 > 6$, which is a false statement.

2. If $3x < y$ and $y < \frac{2}{5}w$, what can be assumed about $3x$ and $\frac{2}{5}w$?

   Solution: $3x < \frac{2}{5}w$

   Explanation: The transitive property states that if $a < b$ and $b < c$, then $a < c$ must also be true. Thus, $3x < \frac{2}{5}w$.

3. True or false: If $x > 5$, then $-3x < -15$.

   Solution: True

   Explanation: Multiply the inequality $x > 5$ by -3 (remember to flip the inequality since the inequality is be multiplied by a negative number): $x > 5$; $-3(x > 5)$; $-3x < -15$. Thus, the statement is true.

Practice problems: *(Answers on page: 729)*

1. True or false: $\frac{1}{11} > 0.09$
2. True or false: $\left(-\frac{2}{3}\right)\left(\frac{3}{4}\right) \geq -\frac{4}{5}$
3. True or false: If $-x \geq 0.2$, then $x \geq -0.2$

Review questions: *(Answers to odd questions on page: 729)*

1. True or false: $0.4 < \frac{5}{12}$
2. True or false: $\frac{1}{5} < \frac{3}{8}$

3. True or false: $\frac{2}{5}-\frac{1}{6}>\frac{2}{7}$

4. True or false: $\frac{1}{4}-\frac{1}{3}>\frac{1}{12}$

5. True or false: $18\left(-\frac{2}{3}\right)>-4-7$

Inequalities and Interval Notation

- $<$: The number on the left of this sign must be less than the number on the right side.
- $\leq$: The number on the left must be less than or equal to the number on the right side.
- $>$: The number on the left must be larger than the number on the right side.
- $\geq$: The number on the left must be larger than or equal to the number on the right.
- **Interval**: The range of values on the number line that are possible solutions for x in a particular problem.
- (or **o**: On a number line, either of these indicates a boundary which x cannot equal.
- [or •: On a number line, either of these indicates a boundary that x can equal.
- **Interval Notation**: Two numbers enclosed by a parentheses, brackets, or one of each, indicating the range of possible solutions for x.
- **Infinity**: The symbols ∞ and $-\infty$, called positive and negative infinity, are not numbers. They are just symbols that indicate that the number line never ends in either the positive or negative direction.

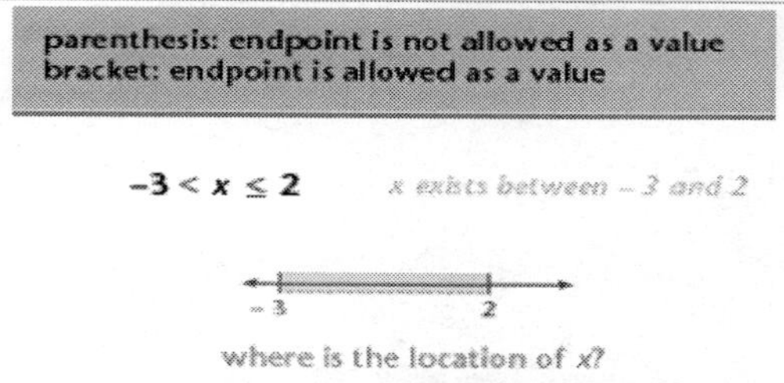	An **interval** designates the range from which values of x can come. In this case, any number down to, but not including, -3 and up to and including +2 will work as a value for x. The number on the left is the lower boundary of the interval and the number on the right is the upper boundary of the interval.
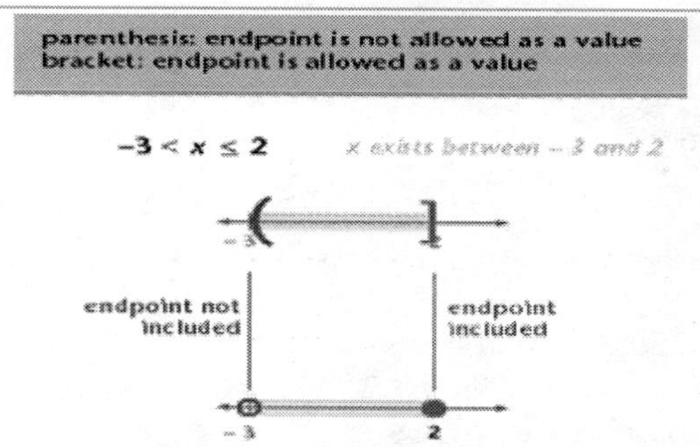	(or ***o*** on a number line indicates that the x can approach that value, but not equal it. In this example, x can approach but not equal -3. [or • on a number line indicates that the x can both approach and equal that value. Here, x can both approach and equal +2.
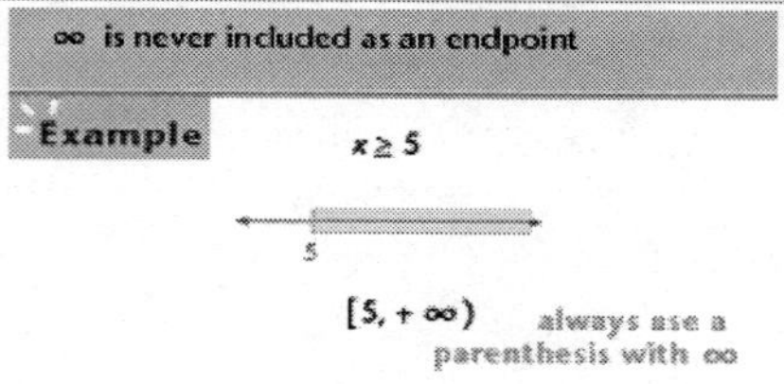	Infinity (∞) is never included as an endpoint. There is no way for any variable to actually equal infinity. The interval **($-\infty$,∞)** indicates that x can be any and every value in the number system.

Sample problems:

1. True or false: [1, 3) represents the inequality $1 \leq x < 3$.
   Solution: True
   Explanation: In the interval [1, 3) the bracket indicates that 1 is included in the inequality and the closing parenthesis indicates the 3 in not included in the inequality. The inequality $1 \leq x < 3$ includes all values between 1 and 3, including 1 but not 3.

2. Express the following inequality in interval notation: $0 \le x \le \frac{1}{2}$.

   Solution: $[0, \frac{1}{2}]$

   Explanation: The inequality $0 \le x \le \frac{1}{2}$ includes all values between 0 and $\frac{1}{2}$, including 0 and $\frac{1}{2}$. In order to include 0 and $\frac{1}{2}$ in the interval notation, brackets are needed on each side.

3. True or false: $[-8, 8]$ represents $x \ge -8$ and $x \le 8$.

   Solution: True

   Explanation: These intervals represents the inequalities $x \le 8$ and $x \ge -8$ respectively: $(-\infty, 8]$ and $[-8, \infty)$. Intersect the two intervals to find the values which satisfy both inequalities: $(-\infty, 8] \cap [-8, \infty) = [-8, 8]$.

Practice problems: *(Answers on page: 729)*

1. True or false: $[5,7)$ represents $5 \le x < 7$.
2. True or false: The intervals $(-\infty, 3)$ and $(3, \infty)$ represent $x \ne 3$.
3. True or false: The intervals $(-\infty, -2)$ and $(4, \infty)$ represent $-2 < x < 4$.

Review questions: *(Answers to odd questions on page: 729)*

1. True or false: $(-\infty, 6]$ represents $x \le 6$
2. True or false: $(2, \infty)$ represents $x < 2$
3. True or false: $[8, 11)$ represents $8 \le x < 11$
4. True or false: The intervals $(-\infty, -2)$ and $(4, \infty)$ represent $-2 < x < 4$
5. True or false: The interval $(5,8)$ represents the inequalities $-2x < -10$ and $3x < 24$

Properties of Absolute Value

- **Absolute value**: The non-negative value of any real number.
- In terms of distance, absolute value measures how far a number is along the number line from zero, without regard to which direction away from zero the number is located.

Absolute value of a positive = the same Absolute value of a negative = the opposite $\lvert 5 \rvert = 5$ $\lvert -7 \rvert = 7$ what is the absolute value? $\lvert N \rvert = \begin{cases} N \text{ if } N \ge 0 \\ -N \text{ if } N < 0 \end{cases}$ a negative of a negative is a positive DON'T TRUST ANY UNKNOWN TO BE POSITIVE!	The **absolute value** of a positive number is itself. The absolute value of a negative number is its opposite, i.e., the positive version of itself. Or you can say it's the negative of itself, which is positive because the negative of a negative makes a positive. **NEVER** take it for granted that a variable within absolute value signs is positive. Always consider the negative possibility as well.
the absolute value of: a product/quotient = product/quotient of absolute value $\lvert A \rvert \ge 0$ $\lvert AB \rvert = \lvert A \rvert \lvert B \rvert$ $\left\lvert \frac{A}{B} \right\rvert = \frac{\lvert A \rvert}{\lvert B \rvert}$	The absolute value of a product of two numbers is equal to the product of the absolute values of the numbers. The absolute value of a fraction or a division problem is the absolute value of the numerator divided by the absolute value of the denominator.

$\|A + B\| = \|A\| + \|B\|$ — A Classic Mistake $\|-5 + 3\|$ $= \|-2\|$ $= 2$ $\|-5\| + \|3\|$ $= 5 + 3$ $= 8$ $2 \neq 8$	Adding is different. The absolute value of a sum is ALWAYS less than or equal to the sum of the absolute values of the two numbers involved. Absolute value always adds positive numbers, while adding inside the absolute value signs may add a positive with a negative. In the example, you can see the difference between adding two terms within absolute value and adding the absolute values of two separate terms.
$\|A + B\| \leq \|A\| + \|B\|$ — triangle inequality	In general, the absolute value of a sum of two numbers will be less than or equal to the sum of the absolute values of the numbers. They are equal when the two numbers have the same sign.

Sample problems:

1. Simplify: $|-27| \div 3$
   Solution: 9
   Explanation: Take the absolute value of each term, then divide: $|-27| \div |3| = 27 \div 3 = 9$.

2. Simplify: $|-4| - |-18| \div |-8+2|$
   Solution: 1
   Explanation: Begin with the absolute value that contains an operation, $|-8+2|$ and don't make the classic mistake $|-8+2| \neq 8+2$. Simplify the term discussed above: $|-4| - |-18| \div |-8+2| =$ $|-4| - |-18| \div |-6|$. Now take the absolute value of each term: $|-4| - |-18| \div |-6| = 4 - 18 \div 6$.
   Follow the order of operation, so divide then subtract: $4 - 18 \div 6 = 4 - 3 = 1$.

3. Evaluate $\dfrac{|a| - |b|}{-b}$ when $a = 7$ and $b = -2$.
   Solution: $\dfrac{5}{2}$
   Explanation: Substitute the a and b values into the expression and simplify the absolute value:
   $\frac{|7| - |-2|}{-(-2)} = \frac{7-2}{-(-2)} = \frac{5}{2}$.

Practice problems: *(Answers on page: 729)*

1. Simplify: $|-2| \cdot |-30 + 4|$
2. Simplify: $|5| - 3|-11|$
3. Evaluate $|a + b|$ when $a = \dfrac{1}{3}$ and $b = -\dfrac{1}{4}$.

Review questions: *(Answers to odd questions on page: 729)*

1. Simplify: $|-13|$
2. Simplify: $|3 - 12|$
3. Simplify: $|6 - 3| + |1 - 7|$
4. Simplify: $|3 - 5| - |7 - 1| + |-5 + 2|$

5. Simplify: $\left|\dfrac{|15-3| \div |-3|}{0-4}\right|$

Evaluating Absolute Value Expressions

- The **absolute value** of any number represents its positive distance to 0 on a number line.
- If the quantity inside the absolute value notation is positive or equal to 0, its absolute value is just itself.
- If the quantity inside the absolute value notation is negative, then its absolute value is the negative of itself.
- **Absolute value notation** is two vertical lines around the quantity; e.g., $|7|$, $|a - 2c - 5|$.

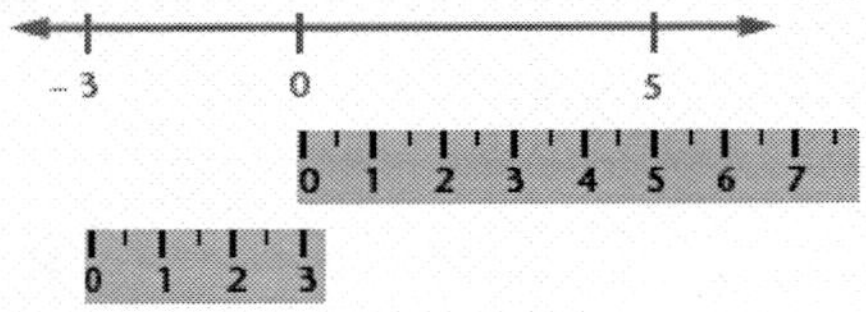	Always remember that the point of **absolute value** is to measure distance.
evaluate: $\lvert\pi - 3\rvert$ *distance between π and 3* $\lvert 3.14 - 3\rvert$ *since that result would be positive* $\lvert\pi - 3\rvert = \pi - 3$	If a quantity can be shown to be positive, you can remove the **absolute value notation** and work with the expression as is. In this case you know you are dealing with a positive quantity because π is larger than 3. That means you will have a positive answer after you subtract.
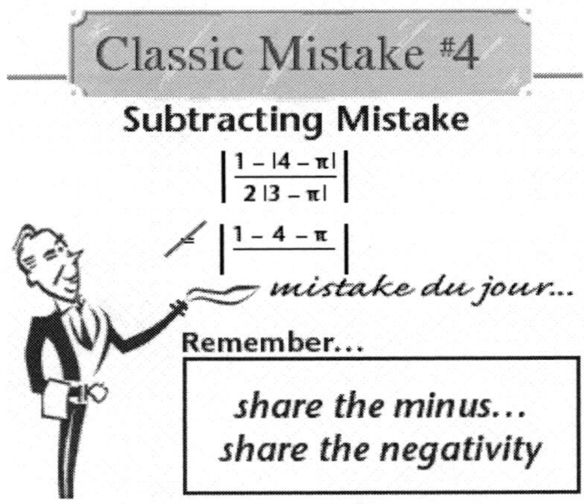	Always remember to distribute any negative sign across all the terms in the affected expression. Not doing this accurately is a major cause of arithmetic mistakes in algebra problems.
• multiply each term within a bracket • often it makes sense to keep the denominator factored **Example** $\left\lvert\frac{1-\lvert 4-\pi\rvert}{2\lvert 3-\pi\rvert}\right\rvert$ $= \left\lvert\frac{1-(4-\pi)}{2(-(3-\pi))}\right\rvert$ *distribute the negative* $= \left\lvert\frac{1-4+\pi}{2(-3+\pi)}\right\rvert$ $= \left\lvert\frac{-3+\pi \cdot 1}{2(-3+\pi)}\right\rvert = \left\lvert\frac{1}{2}\right\rvert = \frac{1}{2}$	This problem reminds you that sometimes a factoring possibility shows up unexpectedly. In that case do not multiply through. Your answer will simplify down more completely if you let the factors cancel. Also, this problem is an example of having a positive quantity within the absolute value notation. You note that the absolute value of the quantity 1/2 is itself.

the absolute value of a negative = its opposite **Example** if $t < 3$, find $\|t-3\|$ know: $t < 3$ $-3 \quad -3$ $t-3<0$ $\|t-3\| = -(t-3)$	This problem shows you how a negative quantity within the absolute value signs is handled. You note that the absolute value of this negative value is the negative of itself. **Remember:** Distribute the negative sign across the parentheses onto every term in the group.
when increasing/decreasing 2 sides of an inequality by the same amount, the inequality remains **Example** if $x < -2$, find $\|6-5x\|$ know: $x < -2$ $(-5) \quad (-5)$ *multiply through by −5* $-5x > 10$ $+6 \quad +6$ *add 6 to both sides* $6-5x > 16$ $\|6-5x\| = 6-5x$	In this example, you must determine whether the expression inside the absolute value signs is positive or negative. By starting with the inequality, and multiplying and adding to produce the expression in the absolute value, you determine that that expression is positive. From there you know that the absolute value of the quantity is itself.

Sample problems:

1. Simplify: $\dfrac{2|5-\pi|}{8-|2-\pi|-\pi}$

   Solution: 1

   Explanation: The first step is to remove the absolute values. So, find the sign of each expression within the absolute value: $5-\pi = 5-3.14... =$ positive and $2-\pi = 2-3.14... =$ negative. Since $5-\pi$ is positive, replace the $|5-\pi|$ with $(5-\pi)$ and since $2-\pi$ is negative, replace $|2-\pi|$ with $-(2-\pi)$: $\dfrac{2|5-\pi|}{8-|2-\pi|-\pi} = \dfrac{2(5-\pi)}{8--(2-\pi)-\pi}$.

   Use the distributive property to simplify the numerator: $\dfrac{2(5-\pi)}{8--(2-\pi)-\pi} = \dfrac{10-2\pi}{8--(2-\pi)-\pi}$.

   To simplify the denominator, replace $--$ with +, then add and subtract:
   $\dfrac{10-2\pi}{8--(2-\pi)-\pi} = \dfrac{10-2\pi}{8+(2-\pi)-\pi} = \dfrac{10-2\pi}{8+2-\pi-\pi} = \dfrac{10-2\pi}{10-2\pi} = 1$.

2. If $y > -4$ find $|-y-4|$.

   Solution: $y+4$

   Explanation: Begin with the inequality: $y > -4$. Multiply both sides by -1 and flip the inequality (since the multiplication is by a negative number): $y > -4$; $-y < 4$. Add -4 to both sides of the inequality: $-y < 4$; $-y-4 < 0$. According to that inequality, $-y-4$ is negative, therefore the expression inside the absolute value is also negative. Use the definition of absolute value: $|-y-4| = -(-y-4) = y+4$.

3. If $x > 3$, find $|-2x+1|$.

   Solution: $2x-1$

   Explanation: Multiply $x > 3$ by -2 (remember to flip the inequality since the inequality is being multiplied by a negative number): $-2(x<3)$; $-2x < -6$. Add 1 to both sides of the inequality: $-2x < -6$; $-2x+1 < -6+1$; $-2x+1 < -5$. The expression $-2x+1$ is less than -5, thus the expression must be negative. Multiply the expression by -1: $-1(-2x+1) = 2x-1$. Thus, $|-2x+1| = 2x-1$ when $x > 3$.

Practice problems: *(Answers on page: 729)*

1. If $x < -1$, find $|-4x+1|$.

2. Simplify: $\dfrac{\pi|2-\pi|}{|\pi-2|}$

3. If $x > 2$, find $|5-3x|$.

Review questions: *(Answers to odd questions on page: 729)*

1. If $x < -2$, find $|x-1|$.
2. If $x > 8$ find $|x-8|$.
3. If $x < 5$, find $|11-2x|$.
4. Simplify: $|2\pi - 6|$
5. Simplify: $\left|\dfrac{|1-\pi|+2}{3|\pi+1|}\right|$

An Introduction to Exponents

- **Exponents**: A shortcut way to write multiplication problems in which a number multiplies with itself. The exponent tells how many times the number is multiplying with itself.
- **Powers**: Another name for exponents.

x^5	**Exponents** are written as smaller numbers to the right and above (superscripted) the number or variable which they have counted.
$xxxxx = x^5$ Can be written as	Exponents indicate how many times that number is multiplied with itself.
 The power of exponents: Troublesome figures become short and concise.	Exponents are sometimes called "**powers.**"

Sample problems:

1. Simplify: $5^2 + 2^3$
   Solution: 33
   Explanation: Follow order of operations: $5^2 + 2^3 = 5\cdot5 + 2\cdot2\cdot2 = 25 + 8 = 33$.

2. Simplify: $(1+5)^2 + 10^2$
   Solution: 136
   Explanation: Follow order of operations: $(1+5)^2 + 10^2 = (6)^2 + 10^2 = 6\cdot6 + 10\cdot10 = 36 + 100 = 136$.

3. Simplify: $\dfrac{1^4 + (3+4)^2 + 9^2 + 1^{10}}{4^2}$
   Solution: $\dfrac{33}{4}$
   Explanation: Follow order of operations: $\dfrac{1^4 + (3+4)^2 + 9^2 + 1^{10}}{4^2} = \dfrac{1^4 + (7)^2 + 9^2 + 1^{10}}{4^2}$

$= \dfrac{1+49+81+1}{16} = \dfrac{132}{16} = \dfrac{33}{4}$.

Practice problems: *(Answers on page: 729)*

1. Simplify: $20+3^2$
2. Simplify: $(3+5)^2+(6-1)^3$
3. Simplify: $\dfrac{6+(5-1)^3}{10^1}+3^2$

Review questions: *(Answers to odd questions on page: 729)*

1. Simplify: 5^3
2. Simplify: $(-4)^2$
3. Simplify: -7^2
4. True or false: $(-6)^3=216$
5. True or false: $-(-12)^2=144$

Evaluating Exponential Expressions

- **Exponents**: The superscripted (or small, raised) numbers which often are attached to the right side of a number or variable. They indicate how many times that number or variable is multiplied with itself. Ex., $2^4=2\cdot 2\cdot 2\cdot 2$.
- **Exponentiation**: The notation of using the superscripted numbers instead of writing a number out however many times as a multiplication problem.
- **Order of Operations**: When evaluating an expression that contains more than one operation, first check to see what must be done within parentheses. Perform the work required by exponents next. Then do multiplication and division working from left to right. Finally, finish up with the addition and subtraction, again working from left to right.

Exponential Expressions: $A^4=AAAA$	**Exponents** tell you how many times a number is multiplying with itself.
Classic Mistake #10 Squaring Negative Mistake $-3^2=9$  mistake du jour... Remember... a minus ain't squared unless it's been snared	**Note:** Watch signs carefully. In this example, you cannot assume that you are squaring –3. You must assume that the negative is separate from the 3 so that you will square and have a negative answer, -9. Does $-x^2$ mean $(-x)^2$ or $-(x^2)$? It means $-(x^2)$. The negative is added after squaring unless it is included in parentheses.
Evaluating Exponential Expressions: *(order matters)* **exponentiate before multiplying**	The order in which you do arithmetic matters. 1. Always do the multiplication indicated by **exponents** first. 2. Then, do the regular multiplication and division. 3. Finally, do the adding and subtracting.

Sample problems:

1. Simplify: $-5^2+(-3)^2-1^3$
   Solution: -17
   Explanation: Begin by evaluating the exponents and be careful of the negatives:
   $-5^2+(-3)^2-1^3=-(5)(5)+(-3)(-3)-(1)(1)(1)=-25+9-1=-16-1=-17.$

2. Simplify: $4(2-7)^2+10(3)^2$
   Solution: 190
   Explanation: Follow order of operations to simplify. Parentheses: $4(2-7)^2+10(3)^2=4(-5)^2+10(3)^2$.
   Exponents: $4(-5)^2+10(3)^2=4(-5)(-5)+10(3)(3)=100+90=190.$

3. Simplify: $\dfrac{-4^2+6(1-3)^3-5(3)^2-1^{17}}{1-3(-2)^2}$
   Solution: 10
   Explanation: Follow order of operations to simplify: $\dfrac{-4^2+6(1-3)^3-5(3)^2-1^{17}}{1-3(-2)^2}=$
   $\dfrac{-4^2+6(-2)^3-5(3)^2-1^{17}}{1-3(-2)^2}=\dfrac{-16+6(-8)-5(9)-1}{1-3(4)}=\dfrac{-16+-48-45-1}{1-12}=\dfrac{-110}{-11}=10.$

Practice problems: *(Answers on page: 729)*

1. Simplify: $5(-2)^2-4^2$
2. Simplify: $-(5-2)^3-1^4+(-3)^2$
3. Simplify: $\dfrac{5(3+7)^2-9^2+1^5}{-2^2}$

Review questions: *(Answers to odd questions on page: 729)*

1. Simplify: $-3(4)^2$
2. Simplify: $-5^2(-3)^3(-2^4)$
3. Simplify: $6\left[(3)^3-(2)^3\right]$
4. Simplify: $3(7-2)^2+10(2)+(-1)^4$
5. Simplify: $\dfrac{10+2(3)^2-4}{5+1}$

Applying the Rules of Exponents

- **Multiplying with Exponents**: Add the exponents attached to the same bases. You're still just counting how many times a particular number is going to multiply with itself in a particular problem.
- **Base**: The number or variable to which an exponent is attached.
- **Grouping with Exponents**: All the bases that carry the same exponent can be written together in parenthesis with the exponent written once and attached to the parenthesis.
- **Ungrouping with Exponents**: You can ungroup bases enclosed in parentheses with an exponent attached if you carefully apply the exponent to each base as you remove the parentheses. Multiply the exponents for individual terms with the one for the whole group so that you maintain an accurate count of how many times each base number is used in the problem.

Rules of the road $A^n\ A^m = A^{n+m}$  **Rules of the road with Exponents** $2^3 \cdot 2^5 \neq 2^{15}$ $= 22222222$ — *Add Exponents* $= 2^8$ ← *Answer* $= 2^{3+5}$	**Multiplying with Exponents**: Add exponents attached to the same **bases**. You're not yet doing any multiplication to get an answer; you're still just counting how many numbers are going to multiply. **Remember:** The exponent is just a shortcut for how many times a number is multiplying with itself during a multiplication problem.
Rules of the road with Exponents $3^4 \cdot 5^4 = 15^8$ $= 3 \cdot 3 \cdot 3 \cdot 3 \cdot 5 \cdot 5 \cdot 5 \cdot 5$ $= (3 \cdot 5)(3 \cdot 5)(3 \cdot 5)(3 \cdot 5)$ $= 15^4$ ← *Answer*	**Multiplying with Exponents**: In this example, you cannot add any exponents because they are attached to different bases. Since the two bases are to the same power, you can group and multiply the bases instead.
Rules of the Road: Multilication $A^n B^n = (A \cdot B)^n$ Division $\frac{A^n}{B^n} = \left(\frac{A}{B}\right)^n$	**Grouping numbers** for multiplication or division is allowed if they carry the same exponent.
Rules of the Road: $(A^n)^m = A^{nm}$ **Example** $(2x^5 y^4)^3 = (2)^3 (x^5)^3 (y^4)^3$ $= 8 \cdot x^{15} \cdot y^{12}$ $= \boxed{8x^{15}y^{12}}$ ← *Answer*	To **ungroup numbers**, apply the exponent attached to the parenthesis to each factor that is within the parenthesis. **Note:** The outside exponent will multiply with each inside exponent because now you are counting for each factor in the group.

Sample problems:

1. True or false: $4^3\left(16^5\right) = 4^{30}$

   Solution: False

   Explanation: Express 16 as a power of 4: $16 = 4^2$. Replace 16 with 4^2 to create a common base: $4^3\left(16^5\right) = 4^3\left((4^2)^5\right)$. Apply the properties of exponents: $4^3\left((4^2)^5\right) = 4^3\left(4^{10}\right) = 4^{13}$.

2. Simplify: $(-3x^2y)^3$

   Solution: $-27x^6y^3$

   Explanation: Apply the properties of exponents: $(-3x^2y)^3 = (-3)^3(x^2)^3y^3 = -27x^6y^3$.

3. Simplify: $(3x^2y^5z)^3(-4xyz^2)^2$

   Solution: $432x^8y^{17}z^7$

   Explanation: Apply the properties of exponents:
   $(3x^2y^5z)^3(-4xyz^2)^2 = (27x^6y^{15}z^3)(16x^2y^2z^4) = 432x^8y^{17}z^7$.

Practice problems: *(Answers on page: 729)*

1. True or false: $3^7 \cdot 9^4 = 3^{15}$
2. Simplify: $\dfrac{\left(4xy^5\right)^2}{(4x)^2}$
3. Simplify: $(-5x)^2(3x^2y)^3(xy^2z^5)^4$

Review questions: *(Answers to odd questions on page: 729)*

1. True or false: $\left(5^8\right)^2 = 5^{16}$
2. Simplify: $x^2\left(x^5\right)$
3. Simplify: $\left(3x^2y\right)^2$
4. Simplify: $\dfrac{16x^4y}{10x^3}$
5. Simplify: $\left(-2a^2bc^3\right)^3$

Evaluating Expressions with Negative Exponents

- To **Divide with Exponents**: Subtract the exponent for any factor in the denominator from the exponent for the same factor in the numerator to get the exponent for that factor in the answer.
- **0 as an Exponent**: Any number to the 0 power equals 1; i.e. any $a^0 = 1$.
- **Negative Exponents**: The negative tells you that the base to which the exponent is attached belongs in the opposite level of the fraction. When you move the factor to the other level, the exponent becomes positive.

Example $\dfrac{2^5}{2^3} = \dfrac{2\cdot2\cdot2\cdot2\cdot2}{2\cdot2\cdot2\cdot1}$ ← Invisible one $= 2^2 = 4$	**Dividing with exponents** is a matter of subtracting the top exponent by the bottom (or dividing) exponent. What you are actually doing is canceling a number from the top and the bottom with each subtraction; i.e., you are reducing the fraction.
$A \neq 0$ $\dfrac{A}{A} = 1$ $1 = \dfrac{A^1}{A^1} = A^0$ Answer $\boxed{A^0 = 1}$ Any non-zero number raised to the zero power = 1	**0 as an exponent:** Any number raised to the 0 power, i.e., any a^0, equals 1. You can think about this fact by considering the fraction a^1/a^1. On one hand, the numerator and denominator of this fraction cancel, so the whole fraction is equal to 1. On the other hand, by subtracting exponents, this fraction is equal to $a^{1-1} = a^0$. Thus you can see that $a^0 = 1$. This is true for every non-zero number *a*.
A Fundamental Rule For Exponents $\dfrac{A^n}{A^m} = A^{n-m}$ **Example** $(-3)^{-2} =$ $\boxed{\dfrac{1}{(-3)^2} = \dfrac{1}{9}}$ ← Answer	**Negative Exponents**: A negative exponent attached to a base tells you that the base belongs in the opposite level of the fraction. Move it there and the exponent becomes positive. In this example, the exponent –2 becomes +2 when the base, (–3), moves from the numerator to the denominator. If you wish to move a number out of the denominator, use the same process. Change the sign of its exponent and move it to the numerator.

Sample problems:

1. True or false: $5^{-1}x^3y^{-2} = \dfrac{1}{5x^3y^2}$

   Solution: False

   Explanation: Express the factors with negative exponents as positive exponents by moving the base and the exponent to the denominator: $5^{-1}x^3y^{-2} = \frac{1}{5}\cdot x^3\cdot\frac{1}{y^2} = \frac{x^3}{5y^2}$.

2. Simplify: $\dfrac{2s^{-6}t^{-2}}{2^{-1}st^2}$

<u>Solution:</u> $\dfrac{4}{s^7t^4}$

<u>Explanation:</u> Use the fact that $\dfrac{A^n}{A^m} = A^{n-m}$ to simplify. Group the common bases: $\dfrac{2}{2^{-1}}\cdot\dfrac{s^{-6}}{s}\cdot\dfrac{t^{-2}}{t^2}$.

Express the division as subtraction of exponents: $\dfrac{2}{2^{-1}}\cdot\dfrac{s^{-6}}{s}\cdot\dfrac{t^{-2}}{t^2} = 2^{1--1}\cdot s^{-6-1}\cdot t^{-2-2} = 2^2\cdot s^{-7}\cdot t^{-4}$.

Simplify and express with positive exponents: $4s^{-7}t^{-4} = \dfrac{4}{s^7t^4}$.

3. Simplify: $\dfrac{\left(4a^2\right)^{-3}\left(6bc^4\right)^{-2}}{\left(2ab^2c^3\right)^{-2}}$

<u>Solution:</u> $\dfrac{b^2}{576a^4c^2}$

<u>Explanation:</u> Rewrite the expression with positive exponents: $\dfrac{\left(2ab^2c^3\right)^2}{\left(4a^2\right)^3\left(6bc^4\right)^2}$.

Apply the rules of exponents and simplify the denominator:

$$\frac{\left(2ab^2c^3\right)^2}{\left(4a^2\right)^3\left(6bc^4\right)^2} = \frac{4a^2b^4c^6}{\left(64a^6\right)\left(36b^2c^8\right)} = \frac{4a^2b^4c^6}{2304a^6b^2c^8}.$$

Subtract the exponents of the common bases: $\dfrac{4a^2b^4c^6}{2304a^6b^2c^8} = \dfrac{4}{2304}a^{2-6}b^{4-2}c^{6-8} = \dfrac{1}{576}a^{-4}b^2c^{-2}$.

Rewrite the expression with positive exponents: $\dfrac{1}{576}a^{-4}b^2c^{-2} = \dfrac{b^2}{576a^4c^2}$.

Practice problems: *(Answers on page: 729)*

1. Simplify: $(-4)^{-2}\cdot 3^{-1}$
2. Simplify: $\dfrac{8x^4y^{-2}z}{6x^{-1}y^{-3}z^2}$
3. Simplify: $\left(\dfrac{a^3b^{-2}c^{-3}}{a^{-5}bc^{-1}}\right)^{-1}$

Review questions: *(Answers to odd questions on page: 729)*

1. True or false: $512^0\cdot 2 = 2$
2. True or false: $\dfrac{5^{-7}}{5^4} = \dfrac{1}{5^{11}}$
3. True or false: $-7^{-3} = -\dfrac{1}{7^3}$
4. True or false: $\left(\dfrac{10}{3}\right)^{-1} = -\dfrac{10}{3}$
5. Simplify: $\dfrac{8a^3b^{-9}}{64a^{-8}b^{-9}}$

Converting between Decimal and Scientific Notation

- **Scientific Notation** means representing a really huge or really tiny number with its significant digits shown as a number less than 10 which is multiplying with 10 to whatever power would produce the actual number. The purpose is to avoid having to write lots of zeroes after a number that is huge or in front of a number that is tiny.
- Calculator presentation for scientific notation takes a shortcut because it has limited display space. It will display the significant digits, the symbol E, and the exponent for 10.
- Numbers larger than 10 will use positive exponents for 10 in scientific notation.
- Numbers including 1 and up to, but not including, 10 will use 0 for the exponent.
- Numbers less than 1 will use negative exponents for 10 in scientific notation.

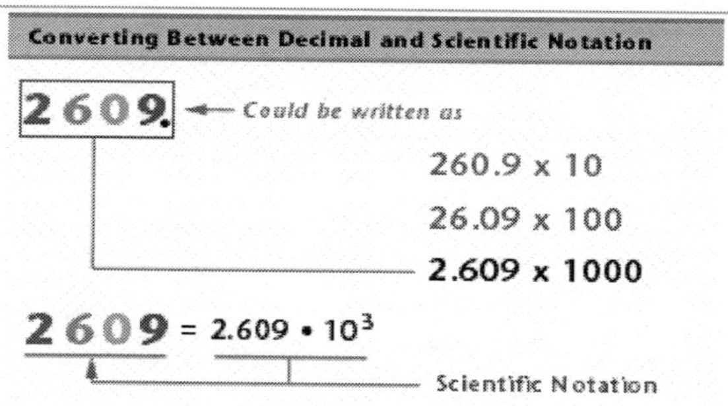

Converting to **scientific notation** involves

1. Writing the number with its decimal so that only one digit is to its left.
2. Write "x 10."
3. Calculate the exponent for 10 that is necessary so that the multiplication will produce the correct number.

(Easy secret: count the number of spaces the decimal would have to move, and that's your exponent.)

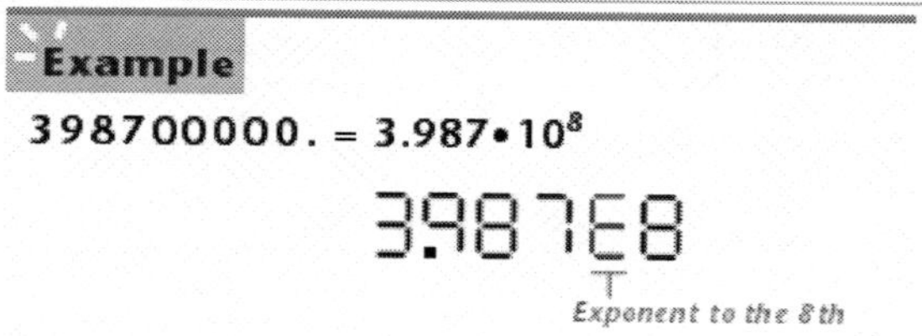

Calculator notation shows the significant digits with the decimal after the first digit. Then comes a symbol E followed by the exponent for 10. It does this because it has limited space.

Note: Do NOT write your answers as the calculator does. People won't like it because it doesn't portray the entire multiplication problem that the notation represents.

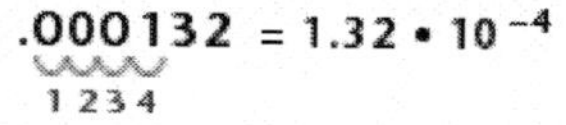

For small numbers, the exponent will be negative. Any time you want the decimal to move to the left of where it is in the scientific notation, the exponent for 10 will be negative because you are having to multiply by numbers that will make your base smaller.

Remember: $10^{-1} = 1/10$ and $10^{-2} = 1/100$, so you can see how multiplying by these fractions less than 1 would make any number smaller.

Sample problems:

1. True or false: $0.0048 = 4.8 \times 10^3$
   Solution: False
   Explanation: To write 0.0048 in scientific notation, rewrite the number so that the first non-zero digit is to the left of the decimal: $0.0048 = 4.8 \times 10^?$. Calculate the exponent for 10 by counting the number of spaces the decimal moved, which is 3. However, 0.0048 is a number less than 1, so the exponent must be negative $4.8 \times 10^{-3} = 0.0048$. Thus, the statement above is false.

2. Express 0.0000000573 in scientific notation.
   Solution: 5.73×10^{-8}
   Explanation: Rewrite 0.0000000573 so that the first non-zero digit is to the left of the decimal: $5.73 \times 10^?$. Calculate the exponent for 10 that is necessary so that $5.73 \times 10^? = 0.0000000573$ by counting the number of spaces that the decimal moved from 0.0000000573 to 5.73, which is 8. Since 0.0000000573 is less than 1, the exponent is negative. Thus, $0.0000000573 = 5.73 \times 10^{-8}$.

3. Express the product of 47,000 and 0.000002 in scientific notation.
   Solution: 9.4×10^{-2}
   Explanation: There are two common ways to solve this problem. 1. Complete the multplication and then write the product in scientific notation: $47{,}000(0.000002)=0.094=9.4\times10^{-2}$.
   2. Convert each factor to scientific notation first: $47{,}000(0.000002)=4.7\times10^{4}\left(2.0\times10^{-6}\right)$.
   Multiply using the properties of exponents: $4.7\times10^{4}\left(2.0\times10^{-6}\right)=4.7(2.0)\times10^{4-6}=9.4\times10^{-2}$.

Practice problems: *(Answers on page: 729)*

1. True or false: $5.09\times10^{-3}=0.00509$
2. Express 54,000,000 in scientific notation.
3. Express the product of 0.000571, 0.095, and 0.0000012 in scientific notation.

Review questions: *(Answers to odd questions on page: 729)*

1. Express in decimal notation: 3.81×10^{8}
2. True or false: $7.54\times10^{3}=754$
3. True or false: $1.46\times10^{6}=1{,}460{,}000$
4. Express in decimal notation: 4.42×10^{4}
5. Evaluate and express the result in scientific notation: 0.007×0.00082

Converting Rational Exponents and Radicals

- The **radical** is the symbol ($\sqrt{\ }$) indicating you are to find a root. The desired root is indicated by the number written in the "v" of the sign. A radical with no number in the "v" is asking for a square, or second root.
- **Rational Exponents** are exponents in fraction form, $a^{\frac{m}{n}}$. The fraction exponent is the equivalent of the radical notation, $a^{\frac{m}{n}} = (\sqrt[n]{a})^{m}$. The denominator states the root of the base. The numerator indicates the power of the base.
- Taking **roots** of numbers: To find the root of a number, determine the number that originally multiplied with itself some number of times to give you the number being "rooted."

For example: $8^{\frac{1}{3}}$ is asking: $x\cdot x\cdot x=8$, what is x? The answer is 2, so the cube root of 8 is 2, or $8^{\frac{1}{3}}=2$.

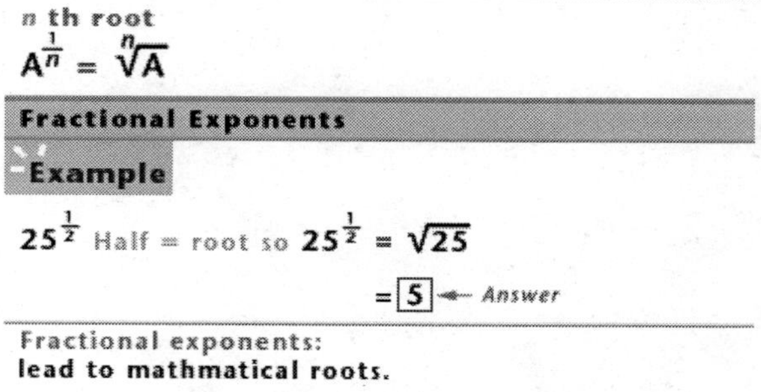

The exponent ½ asks for the square root of a number. It wants to know what number multiplied with itself will produce the base number.

The exponent 1/3 asks for the cube root of a number. It wants to know what number multiplied with itself and then multiplied again will produce the base number.

NOTE: The **square root** $\sqrt{\ }$ and the **rational exponent** ½ are asking for the same thing.

Fractional Exponents **Example** $\sqrt{2} \cdot \sqrt[3]{2} = 2^{\frac{1}{2}} \cdot 2^{\frac{1}{3}}$ *Same base so add exponents* $= 2^{\frac{1}{2}+\frac{1}{3}}$ $= \boxed{2^{\frac{5}{6}}}$ ← *Answer*	In algebra, it's generally easier to work with a problem if you rewrite the radicals using rational exponents.
Rational & Radical Exponent Principle: $(\sqrt[n]{A})^m = A^{\frac{m}{n}} = \sqrt[n]{A^m}$ **Fractional Exponents** **Example** $(-25)^{\frac{1}{2}}$ = *not a real number (can't be done)*	**REMEMBER:** There is no negative number that has a square root. This is true because there is no number that when you multiply it with itself gives a negative answer.

Sample problems:

1. Simplify: $36^{\frac{1}{2}}$
   Solution: 6
   Explanation: Convert the rational exponent to radical notation:
   $36^{\frac{1}{2}} = \sqrt[2]{36^1} = \sqrt{36} = 6.$

2. True or false: $\sqrt[3]{25} = 5^{\frac{2}{3}}$
   Solution : True
   Explanation : Express 25 as 5^2: $\sqrt[3]{25} = \sqrt[3]{5^2}$. Convert the radical to a rational exponent: $\sqrt[3]{5^2} = \left(5^2\right)^{\frac{1}{3}}$. Multiply the exponents: $\left(5^2\right)^{\frac{1}{3}} = 5^{2\cdot\frac{1}{3}} = 5^{\frac{2}{3}}$.

3. Simplify: $9^{-\frac{1}{2}}$
   Solution : $\frac{1}{3}$
   Explanation : Factor the exponent: $9^{-\frac{1}{2}} = 9^{-1\left(\frac{1}{2}\right)}$. Apply properties of exponents to simplify: $9^{-1\left(\frac{1}{2}\right)} = \left(\frac{1}{9}\right)^{\frac{1}{2}} = \frac{\sqrt{1}}{\sqrt{9}} = \frac{1}{3}$.

Practice problems: *(Answers on page: 729)*

1. Simplify: $100^{\frac{1}{2}}$
2. True or false: $\sqrt[5]{125} = 5^{\frac{5}{3}}$
3. Simplify: $64^{-\frac{1}{2}}$

Review questions: *(Answers to odd questions on page: 729)*

1. Simplify: $9^{\frac{1}{2}}$
2. Simplify: $144^{\frac{1}{2}}$
3. Simplify: $49^{-\frac{1}{2}}$
4. Simplify: $27^{-\frac{1}{3}}$

5. Simplify: $125^{-\frac{1}{3}}$

Simplifying Radical Expressions

- A **negative exponent** tells you to treat its base as a fraction and flip it over. Then the exponent becomes positive.
- When dealing with **rational exponents**:
  - the numerator tells you to raise the base to the indicated power.
  - the denominator tells you to find the indicated root.

Example Simplifying Radicals $\left(\frac{121}{100}\right)^{-\frac{3}{2}} = \left(\frac{100}{121}\right)^{\frac{3}{2}}$ *By flipping, the negative sign was removed*	This work involves remembering the things we've recently been learning. The **negative exponent** means flip the number over. Once you flip, the exponent becomes positive.
$\left(\frac{121}{100}\right)^{-\frac{3}{2}} = \left(\frac{100}{121}\right)^{\frac{3}{2}} = \left(\frac{\sqrt{100}}{\sqrt{121}}\right)^3$ $= \left(\frac{10}{11}\right)^3$	The denominator of the **rational exponent** asks for the root, i.e., the number that produced each of these bases. Figure that out and your new base will have a whole number exponent, i.e., the original numerator.
$= \boxed{\frac{1000}{1331}}$ ← *Answer*	Raise your new base to the power indicated by the exponent and you're done.
Example Simplifying Radicals $\sqrt[3]{64(3)^6(5)^3}$ $(64\cdot(3)^6\cdot(5)^3)^{\frac{1}{3}} = 64^{\frac{1}{3}}\cdot((3)^6)^{\frac{1}{3}}\cdot((5)^3)^{\frac{1}{3}}$ $= 4 \cdot 3^{\frac{6}{3}} \cdot 5^{\frac{3}{3}}$ $= 4 \cdot 3^2 \cdot 5^1$ $= 4 \cdot 9 \cdot 5$ $= \boxed{180}$ ← *Answer*	This is a great example of how using rational exponents can vastly simplify even a horrible-looking problem. Notice that applying the rational exponent to each factor resulted in small numbers so the actual multiplication was simple arithmetic.

Sample problems:

1. Simplify: $\dfrac{2}{100^{-\frac{1}{2}}}$

   Solution: 20

   Explanation: Write the problem with a positive exponent: $\dfrac{2}{100^{-\frac{1}{2}}} = 2\left(100^{\frac{1}{2}}\right)$.

   Express 100 as a base with an exponent and apply the rules of exponents:

   $$2\left(100^{\frac{1}{2}}\right) = 2\left(\left(10^2\right)^{\frac{1}{2}}\right) = 2\left((10)^{2\cdot\frac{1}{2}}\right) = 2\left((10)^{\frac{2}{2}}\right) = 2(10)^1 = 2(10) = 20.$$

2. Simplify: $\left(\dfrac{125}{8}\right)^{-\frac{2}{3}}$

   Solution: $\dfrac{4}{25}$

   Explanation: Convert to a positive exponent: $\left(\frac{125}{8}\right)^{-\frac{2}{3}} = \left(\frac{8}{125}\right)^{\frac{2}{3}}$. Express 8 and 125 as bases with exponents and apply the rules of exponents:

   $$\left(\tfrac{8}{125}\right)^{\frac{2}{3}} = \left(\tfrac{2^3}{5^3}\right)^{\frac{2}{3}} = \left(\left(\tfrac{2}{5}\right)^3\right)^{\frac{2}{3}} = \left(\tfrac{2}{5}\right)^{\frac{6}{3}} = \left(\tfrac{2}{5}\right)^2 = \tfrac{4}{25}.$$

3. Simplify: $\sqrt[3]{\dfrac{216}{343}}$

   Solution: $\dfrac{6}{7}$

   Explanation: $\sqrt[3]{\frac{216}{343}} = \frac{\sqrt[3]{216}}{\sqrt[3]{343}}$. Factor 216 and 343 into primes. Because $216 = 2^3 \cdot 3^3$ and $343 = 7^3$; $\frac{\sqrt[3]{216}}{\sqrt[3]{343}} = \frac{\sqrt[3]{2^3 \cdot 3^3}}{\sqrt[3]{7^3}} = \frac{2^{3/3} \cdot 3^{3/3}}{7^{3/3}} = \frac{2 \cdot 3}{7} = \frac{6}{7}$.

Practice problems: *(Answers on page: 730)*

1. Simplify: $\dfrac{3}{8^{-\frac{1}{3}}}$
2. Simplify: $\left(\dfrac{1}{4}\right)^{-\frac{3}{2}}$
3. Simplify: $\sqrt[4]{\dfrac{1}{16}}$

Review questions: *(Answers to odd questions on page: 730)*

1. Simplify: $\dfrac{1}{49^{-\frac{1}{2}}}$
2. Simplify: $\dfrac{1}{-64^{-\frac{1}{3}}}$
3. Simplify: $\sqrt{\dfrac{41}{81}}$
4. Simplify: $\dfrac{64^{-\frac{2}{3}}}{27}$
5. Simplify: $\left(\dfrac{64}{25}\right)^{-\frac{3}{2}}$

Simplifying Radical Expressions with Variables

- A **radical** is asking for a root. It can be rewritten with the base number taken to a rational exponent whose denominator is the root requested.
- Raising a number at one power to another power is done by multiplying the two exponents.
- **Grouping terms** with a common exponent can show prospects for canceling and simplifying the problem.

Radical Expressions with variables — Example	
$\sqrt{25x^6y^5} = (25x^6\,y^5)^{\frac{1}{2}}$ $= (25^{\frac{1}{2}})\,(x^6)^{\frac{1}{2}}\,(y^5)^{\frac{1}{2}}$ $= 5 \quad x^{\frac{6}{2}} \quad y^{\frac{5}{2}}$ $= 5x^3 \quad y^{2 \cdot \frac{1}{2}}$ $= \boxed{5x^3(y^2)(\sqrt{y})}$ Another answer	Converting radicals to **rational exponents** sometimes makes it easier to see how to simplify your problem – especially if you apply the rational exponent separately to each term in the expression. Try to get comfortable expressing the powers and roots either way. It helps you see connections.

Radical Expressions with variables

Example

$$\frac{\sqrt[4]{32r^6s}\;\sqrt[4]{2rs^4}}{\sqrt[4]{4r^3s^2}} = \left(\frac{32r^6s\;2rs^4}{4r^3s^2}\right)^{\frac{1}{4}}$$

Some of the ugliest numbers you'll ever see are these radical monsters.

This one already looks simpler just by switching to rational exponents and **grouping** the numbers under a common exponent.

$$\frac{\sqrt[4]{32r^6s}\;\sqrt[4]{2rs^4}}{\sqrt[4]{4r^3s^2}} = \left(\frac{\overset{16\,r^3}{\cancel{32}\cancel{r^6}s}\;\overset{s^2}{\cancel{2}rs^{\cancel{4}}}}{\cancel{4}\cancel{r^3}\cancel{s^2}}\right)^{\frac{1}{4}}$$

$$= \left(\frac{16r^4s^3}{1}\right)^{\frac{1}{4}}$$

$$= (16)^{\frac{1}{4}}\,(r^4)^{\frac{1}{4}}\,(s^3)^{\frac{1}{4}}$$

$$= 2rs^{\frac{3}{4}}$$

$$= \boxed{2r(\sqrt[4]{s})^3} \leftarrow \text{...or the Radical way}$$

Now, begin to cancel and simplify wherever you see an opportunity.

Remember:

1. Write large and neatly so you can cancel easily.
2. Write the results after each set of changes. This helps prevent mistakes.

You have the choice of writing your answer with either **rational exponents** or **radical signs**. They are equivalent and either way is OK.

Sample problems:

1. Simplify: $\sqrt{\dfrac{45x^4y^9}{5y}}$ (Assume $x \geq 0$ and $y > 0$.)

   Solution: $3x^2y^4$

   Explanation: Simplify the coefficients: $\sqrt{\dfrac{45x^4y^9}{5y}} = \sqrt{\dfrac{9x^4y^9}{y}} = \sqrt{\dfrac{3^2x^4y^9}{y}}$. Move the denominator to the numerator by converting the exponent to a negative exponent: $\sqrt{\dfrac{3^2x^4y^9}{y}} = \sqrt{3^2x^4y^9y^{-1}}$. Use rules of exponents to combine: $\sqrt{3^2x^4y^9y^{-1}} = \sqrt{3^2x^4y^{9-1}} = \sqrt{3^2x^4y^8}$. Express the radical as a rational exponent and simplify: $\sqrt{3^2x^4y^8} = \left(3^2x^4y^8\right)^{\frac{1}{2}} = 3^{\frac{2}{2}}x^{\frac{4}{2}}y^{\frac{8}{2}} = 3x^2y^4$.

2. Simplify: $\dfrac{\sqrt[3]{32x^2}\cdot\sqrt[3]{x^2y^8}}{\sqrt[3]{4xy^{-2}}}$ (Assume $x \neq 0$ and $y \neq 0$.)

   Solution: $2xy^3\sqrt[3]{y}$

   Explanation: Combine the expressions under the radicals, since they all have index 3: $\sqrt[3]{\dfrac{32x^2\cdot x^2y^8}{4xy^{-2}}}$.

   Divide the coefficients and subtract the exponents of common variables: $\sqrt[3]{\dfrac{32x^2\cdot x^2y^8}{4xy^{-2}}} = \sqrt[3]{8x^{4-1}y^{8--2}}$ $= \sqrt[3]{8x^3y^{10}}$. Express the coefficient as a base with an exponent and express the radical as a rational exponent: $\sqrt[3]{8x^3y^{10}} = \left(2^3x^3y^{10}\right)^{\frac{1}{3}} = 2^{\frac{3}{3}}x^{\frac{3}{3}}y^{\frac{10}{3}} = 2xy^{\frac{10}{3}}$. Separate $\frac{10}{3}$ into an integer and a fraction: $2xy^{\frac{10}{3}} = 2xy^{\frac{9}{3}+\frac{1}{3}} = 2xy^{\frac{9}{3}}y^{\frac{1}{3}} = 2xy^3\sqrt[3]{y}$.

Tyra Turner

3. Simplify: $\sqrt[5]{\dfrac{x^7y^{-8}z^3u^{13}}{x^{-3}y^3z^8u^{-2}}}$ (Assume x, y, z and $u \neq 0$.)

Solution: $\dfrac{x^2u^3}{y^2z\sqrt[5]{y}}$

Explanation: Move variables from denominator to numerator:

$\sqrt[5]{\dfrac{x^7y^{-8}z^3u^{13}}{x^{-3}y^3z^8u^{-2}}} = \sqrt[5]{x^7(x^3)y^{-8}(y^{-3})z^3(z^{-8})u^{13}(u^2)}$.

Combine like terms: $\sqrt[5]{x^7(x^3)y^{-8}(y^{-3})z^3(z^{-8})u^{13}(u^2)} = \sqrt[5]{x^{10}y^{-11}z^{-5}u^{15}}$.

Express the radical as a rational exponent: $\sqrt[5]{x^{10}y^{-11}z^{-5}u^{15}} = x^{\frac{10}{5}}y^{-\frac{11}{5}}z^{-\frac{5}{5}}u^{\frac{15}{5}}$.

Separate the exponent into an integer and fractional part if needed:

$x^{\frac{10}{5}}y^{-\frac{11}{5}}z^{-\frac{5}{5}}u^{\frac{15}{5}} = x^2y^{-2}y^{-\frac{1}{5}}z^{-1}u^3 = \dfrac{x^2u^3}{y^2z\sqrt[5]{y}}$.

Practice problems: *(Answers on page: 730)*

1. Simplify: $\sqrt{\dfrac{36a^3b^5}{a^2b}}$ (Assume $a > 0$ and $b > 0$.)

2. Simplify: $\sqrt{\dfrac{8tu^3v^3}{t^7uv^2}}$ (Assume $t > 0$, $u > 0$, and $v > 0$.)

3. Simplify: $\dfrac{\sqrt[3]{12x^7yz}\sqrt[3]{4x^4y^4z^3}}{\sqrt[3]{6x^2y^{-3}z}}$ (Assume $x \neq 0$, $y \neq 0$, and $z \neq 0$.)

Review questions: *(Answers to odd questions on page: 730)*

1. Simplify: $\sqrt[3]{\dfrac{1}{125}}$

2. Simplify: $\sqrt[3]{27x^6z^3}$

3. Simplify: $\sqrt{\dfrac{100x^3}{y^2}}$ (Assume $x \geq 0$ and $y > 0$.)

4. Simplify: $\sqrt[3]{\dfrac{64sr^5}{s^4r^2}}$ (Assume $s \neq 0$ and $r \neq 0$.)

5. Simplify: $\sqrt{\dfrac{75x^5y^8}{3xy^2}}$ (Assume $x > 0$ and $y > 0$.)

Rationalizing Denominators

- The number 1 can be written as a fraction with any number or expression as the numerator so long as the same number or expression is used as the denominator (except for 0).
  In other words, $1 = 78/78$ or $(3a + b)/(3a + b)$, and so on.
- Clearing a denominator of radicals means to multiply the fraction by a version of 1. Your version of 1 will be the radical over itself. So, the denominator multiplies out the radical to clear it, and the numerator gets a radical. This process is called **rationalizing the denominator**.
- The **conjugate** of a given binomial is a binomial that contains the same terms but with the opposite sign connecting the two terms; i.e., $(a - b)$ and $(a + b)$ are conjugates of each other. When you multiply a binomial by its conjugate, you are left with the difference of two squares and no middle terms.
- **FOIL**: Multiply binomials by multiplying
  - **F**irst terms
  - **O**uter terms
  - **I**nside terms
  - **L**ast terms, and combining like terms.

Multiply anything by one and it dosen't change anything. **Example** Rationalizing a Denominator $\frac{5}{\sqrt{3}} = \frac{5}{\sqrt{3}} \cdot \frac{\sqrt{3}}{\sqrt{3}}$	Mathematicians like to eliminate radicals from the denominators of fractions. It's easy. Multiply it by your version of 1, $\frac{\sqrt{3}}{\sqrt{3}}$.
$= \frac{5\sqrt{3}}{3}$	Now there is no radical in the denominator.
Conjugate: The second term of the denominator gets the opposite sign. Rationalizing a Binomial Denominator **Example** $\frac{3}{\sqrt{2}+1} = \frac{3}{\sqrt{2}+1} \cdot \frac{(\sqrt{2}-1)}{(\sqrt{2}-1)} =$ $= \frac{3(\sqrt{2}-1)}{(\sqrt{2}+1)(\sqrt{2}-1)}$	When the denominator is a binomial, you must be careful. Your version of 1 must use the **conjugate** of the denominator. In this case, the conjugate is $\left(\sqrt{2}-1\right)$.
$= \frac{3(\sqrt{2}-1)}{(\sqrt{2}+1)(\sqrt{2}-1)}$ $= \frac{3\sqrt{2}-3}{2+\sqrt{2}-\sqrt{2}-1}$ *Answers* $= \frac{3\sqrt{2}-3}{1} = \boxed{3\sqrt{2}-3}$ $= \boxed{3(\sqrt{2}-1)}$	**Remember:** You are multiplying binomials and use your **FOIL** properly so you get the right answer.

Sample problems:

1. Rationalize the denominator: $\frac{\sqrt{5}+1}{\sqrt{5}-1}$

   Solution: $\frac{3+\sqrt{5}}{2}$

   Explanation: Multiply by the conjugate of the denominator, $\frac{\sqrt{5}+1}{\sqrt{5}+1}$:

   $\frac{\sqrt{5}+1}{\sqrt{5}-1}\left(\frac{\sqrt{5}+1}{\sqrt{5}+1}\right)=\frac{(\sqrt{5}+1)(\sqrt{5}+1)}{(\sqrt{5}-1)(\sqrt{5}+1)}$.

   Use FOIL to simplify the numerator and the denominator:

   $\frac{(\sqrt{5}+1)(\sqrt{5}+1)}{(\sqrt{5}-1)(\sqrt{5}+1)}=\frac{\sqrt{25}+2\sqrt{5}+1}{\sqrt{25}-1}=\frac{5+2\sqrt{5}+1}{5-1}=\frac{6+2\sqrt{5}}{4}$.

   Factor the numerator to reduce: $\frac{6+2\sqrt{5}}{4}=\frac{2(3+\sqrt{5})}{4}=\frac{3+\sqrt{5}}{2}$.

2. Rationalize the denominator: $\frac{\sqrt{2}}{\sqrt{11}-\sqrt{2}}$

   Solution: $\frac{2+\sqrt{22}}{9}$

   Explanation: Multiply the expression by the conjugate of the denominator over itself:

   $\frac{\sqrt{2}}{\sqrt{11}-\sqrt{2}}\left(\frac{\sqrt{11}+\sqrt{2}}{\sqrt{11}+\sqrt{2}}\right)=\frac{\sqrt{22}+\sqrt{4}}{\sqrt{121}-\sqrt{4}}$.

   Simplify the radicals: $\frac{\sqrt{22}+\sqrt{4}}{\sqrt{121}-\sqrt{4}}=\frac{\sqrt{22}+2}{11-2}=\frac{2+\sqrt{22}}{9}$.

3. Rationalize the denominator: $\frac{6}{\sqrt{x}-5}$

   Solution: $\frac{6\sqrt{x}+30}{x-25}$

   Explanation: Multiply the expression by the conjugate of the denominator over itself and simplify: $\frac{6}{\sqrt{x}-5}=\frac{6}{\sqrt{x}-5}\left(\frac{\sqrt{x}+5}{\sqrt{x}+5}\right)=\frac{6\sqrt{x}+30}{x-25}$

Practice problems: *(Answers on page: 730)*

1. Rationalize the denominator: $\frac{11}{\sqrt{2}-1}$
2. Rationalize the denominator: $\frac{8-\sqrt{3}}{8+\sqrt{3}}$
3. Rationalize the denominator: $\frac{3}{\sqrt{2-y}+7}$

Review questions: *(Answers to odd questions on page: 730)*

1. Rationalize the denominator: $\frac{6}{\sqrt{2}}$
2. Rationalize the denominator: $\frac{3\sqrt{3}}{5\sqrt{3}}$

3. Rationalize the denominator: $\dfrac{\sqrt{3}}{\sqrt{2}-1}$

4. Rationalize the denominator: $\dfrac{6+\sqrt{5}}{6-\sqrt{5}}$

5. Rationalize the denominator: $\dfrac{18}{\sqrt{7}-1}$

Determining Components and Degree

- **Polynomial**: A sum or difference of terms that are products of numbers and variables raised to powers.
- **Coefficient**: A number multiplying with a variable.
- The **degree of a polynomial** in one variable is equal to the largest exponent used in the polynomial.

Polynomial a sum or dif. of terms with the same basic shape $a_n x^n + a_{n-1} x^{n-1} + \ldots + a_1 x + a_0$ some number multiplied by a variable raised to some power **A basic polynomial:** $4x^2 - 3x + \pi x^{100} + 10$	**Polynomials** can come in many shapes and sizes. They may include: 1. one or more terms 2. one or more variables 3. nonnegative, integral (not fractional) exponents 4. constants
$4x^2 - 3x + \pi x^{100} + 10$ *coefficients*	**Notice:** Negative and fractional exponents are excluded from polynomials. The **degree of a polynomial** in one variable is set by the largest exponent. So, for example, this is a polynomial of 100th degree. Usually (but not in the example to the left!), polynomials are written with the term with the largest exponent first followed by the other terms in decreasing order.
You can have as many variables in a polynomial as you want - as long as the exponents are zero or positive integers. **Flavors of polynomials** monomial: $3x$ (one term) binomial: $3x+5$ (two terms) trinomial: x^2+3x+5 (three terms) *... and so on*	Generally, three different types of polynomials are given specific names. The three most common are indicated. Their names are based on how many terms exist within each polynomial. There are many polynomials with even more terms than allowed in these three groups, but they are usually not grouped under any special name.

Sample problems:

1. True or false: The expression $x+5$ is a 1st degree binomial.
   Solution: True
   Explanation: The highest power of a variable is 1, so the degree is also 1. There are 2 terms in $x+5$, so it is a binomial.

2. True or false: The expression $\pi^3 + x + \pi x^2$ is a 3rd degree trinomial.
   Solution: False
   Explanation: The expression has 3 terms, so it is indeed a trinomial. However, the highest power of a variable is 2 (not 3 because π is not a variable), so the expression is a 2nd degree trinomial.

3. True or false: The expression $x^3 + 5x^{\frac{4}{2}} - x + 1$ is a polynomial.
   Solution: True
   Explanation: A polynomial cannot include a variable with a fractional or negative exponent. However, simplifying the expression clears the fractional exponent:
   $x^3 + 5x^{\frac{4}{2}} - x + 1 = x^3 + 5x^2 - x + 1$, so the expression is a polynomial.

Practice problems: *(Answers on page: 730)*

1. True or false: The expression $5x^2 - x + 3$ is a 2nd degree trinomial.
2. True or false: The expression $6x^{-1}$ is a monomial.
3. True or false: The expression $\pi x^4 - x^{\frac{6}{4}}$ is a binomial.

Review questions: *(Answers to odd questions on page: 730)*

1. True or false: The expression $2x^7 - 5x^3 + 6x$ is a 2nd degree trinomial.
2. True or false: The expression $\dfrac{2x^3 - 4x - 12}{11}$ is a 3rd degree trinomial.
3. True or false: The expression $\dfrac{1}{x^3} + \dfrac{1}{x^2} + \dfrac{1}{x}$ is a polynomial.
4. True or false: The expression $\dfrac{2}{9}x^4 + \sqrt{43}$ is a 4th degree binomial.
5. True or false: The expression $x^5 - x^4 - x^3 + \dfrac{1}{2x^2} - x - 1$ is a 5th degree polynomial.

Adding, Subtracting, and Multiplying Polynomials

- **Adding Polynomials** means that you combine all like terms.
- **Like terms** are either those which have the same variables to the same degree, or the constants.
- **Subtracting polynomials** is the same as adding except that the negative sign preceding the second polynomial changes every sign in that polynomial before you combine like terms.
- **FOIL**: A technique for multiplying binomials that is based on the distributive property.
  - F – multiply the first terms in each binomial.
  - O – multiply the outer terms in each binomial.
  - I – multiply the inner terms in each binomial.
  - L – multiply the last terms in each binomial.

Like Terms: Like terms have the same variable each raised to the same power.

ADDITION	SUBTRACTION
$3x^3 - 2x^2 + \quad x$	$3x^3 - 2x^2 + \quad x$
$+ \quad x^2 - 4x + 3$	$- \quad -x^2 + 4x - 3$
$3x^3 - 1x^2 - 3x + 3$	$3x^3 - 3x^2 + 5x - 3$
$3x^3 - x^2 - 3x + 3$	

Subtraction is the same as addition, only you change signs on all the subtracting terms before you add.

Adding polynomials means that you combine all **like terms** - all x^2s together, all xs together, all constants together.

If you had several x^3y^2s, you would combine them too, and so on.

Subtracting polynomials means that you have to change all the signs in the second polynomial before you add.

Note: Paying attention to signs is the best way to avoid mistakes with these problems.

FOIL (first outer inner last) $(2x-1)(3x+4)$ $6x^2+8x-3x-4$ $6x^2+5x-4$	The **FOIL** rule for multiplying binomials says: • F – multiply first terms: $2x$ with $3x$. • O – multiply outer terms: $2x$ with 4. • I – multiply inner terms: -1 with $3x$. • L – multiply last terms: -1 with 4. Then combine like terms for your answer.
Distributive Property $A(B+C)=AB+AC$ Using the Distributive Property $(2x-1)(3x+4)$ $(2x-1)(3x)+(2x-1)(4)$ $(6x^2-3x)+(8x+4)$ $6x^2+5x+4$	This example is done using the distributive property to show you the origins of FOIL, and how both techniques yield the same answer. If you like thinking of multiplication with binomials as distributing rather than FOILing, do so.

Sample problems:

1. Simplify: $[3b^4+(2b-7)-6b^2]-[17b-(3b^3+2b^2-5b)-3b(b-7)]$
   Solution: $3b^4+3b^3-b^2-41b-7$
   Explanation: Begin be eliminating the parentheses within the brackets.
   Distribute: $[3b^4+2b-7-6b^2]-[17b-3b^3-2b^2+5b-3b^2+21b]$
   Distribute again to subtract: $3b^4+2b-7-6b^2-17b+3b^3+2b^2-5b+3b^2-21b$
   Carefully group like terms: $(3b^4)+(3b^3)+(-6b^2+2b^2+3b^2)+(2b-17b-5b-21b)-7$
   Combine like terms: $3b^4+3b^3-b^2-41b-7$

2. Multiply: $(5x-4)(x+2)$
   Solution: $5x^2+6x-8$
   Explanation: To multiply two binomials, use the distributive property twice, then combine like terms. Rewrite by distributing the first term, $5x$, by the second binomial and the second term, -4, by the second binomial: $(5x-4)(x+2)=5x(x+2)-4(x+2)$. Distribute: $5x^2+10x-4x-8$. Combine like terms: $5x^2+6x-8$.

3. Multiply: $(7a-b^3)(7a+b^3)$
   Solution: $49a^2-b^6$
   Explanation: FOIL: $(7a-b^3)(7a+b^3)=49a^2+7ab^3-7ab^3-b^6$. Combine like terms: $49a^2-b^6$. Notice that the product is the difference of two squares.

Practice problems: *(Answers on page: 730)*

1. Simplify: $\left[3x-5\left(2x^2+x\right)-(6x+4)\right]-\left[x^2+1+3x\left(1-x^2\right)\right]+x$
2. Multiply: $(3x+1)\left(x^2+2x+5\right)$
3. Simplify: $(9-5p)^2$

Review questions: *(Answers to odd questions on page: 730)*

1. Simplify: $\left(7a^2b+3ab^2\right)-\left(11ab^2-6a^2b\right)$
2. Simplify: $8abc+\left[4ab^2-\left(-7a^2b+3abc+4ab^2\right)+5a^2b\right]-\left[\left(-5abc+12a^2b-ab^2\right)+10abc\right]$
3. Multiply: $\left(6a^2b+11ab^2-5a^2b^2\right)3ab$
4. Multiply: $(4x+2)(4x+5)$
5. Multiply: $\left[1+(6+x)-3x\right]^2$

Multiplying Big Products

- The **Distributive property** says $a(b+c)=ab+ac$.
- **Multiplying polynomials** with three or more terms involves applying the distributive property, then combining like terms.
- **Like terms** are those terms with the same variables to the same degree, or constants.

$(y+3)(y^2-y+1)=$ $(y+3)y^2-(y+3)y+(y+3)$ $=y^3+3y^2-(y^2+3y)+y+3$ $=y^3+3y^2-y^2-3y+y+3$ $=y^3+2y^2-2y+3$	In this example, the terms of (y^2-y+1) are multiplying individually with the terms of $(y+3)$: $y^2\cdot(y+3)=y^3+3y^2$ $-y\cdot(y+3)=-y^2-3y$ $+1\cdot(y+3)=y+3$ Then you combine like terms.
$(x-y+z)(2x^2-4y+z)$ $2x^3-4xy+xz$ x times right side	To use the distributive property in this problem, we are going to multiply one term at time from the first polynomial with each term in the second polynomial. See what results on the left when you distribute the x onto $(2x^2-4y+z)$.
$-2x^2y+4y^2-yz$ -y times right side	Now, multiply the second term in the first polynomial, the $-y$, with $(2x^2-4y+z)$. Again, we get three terms in the product.
$2x^3-4xy+xz$ $+\ -2x^2y+4y^2-yz$ $+\ 2x^2z-4yz+z^2$	The total product is the sum of these nine terms. To finish up, we could combine the like terms $-yz$ and $-4yz$.
(trinomial x trinomial)=(3•3)=9 monomial terms (binomial x binomial)=(2•2)=4 monomial terms	The patterns on the left give you a way to keep track of the total number of terms that should result when multiplying trinomials times trinomials and binomials times binomials.

Sample problems:

1. True or false: $(a+b)(c+d+e)=ac+ad+ae+bc+bd+be$
   Solution: True
   Explanation: Use the distributive property to multiply each term in the binomial by the trinomial: $(a+b)(c+d+e)=a(c+d+e)+b(c+d+e)$. Complete the multiplication: $a(c+d+e)+b(c+d+e)=ac+ad+ae+bc+bd+be$.

2. Simplify: $(a+3b+c)(a^2+b^2+c^2)$
   Solution: $a^3+ab^2+ac^2+3a^2b+3b^3+3bc^2+a^2c+b^2c+c^3$
   Explanation: Use the distributive property to multiply each term in the first trinomial by the second trinomial: $(a+3b+c)(a^2+b^2+c^2)=a(a^2+b^2+c^2)+3b(a^2+b^2+c^2)+c(a^2+b^2+c^2)=$
   $a^3+ab^2+ac^2+3a^2b+3b^3+3bc^2+a^2c+b^2c+c^3$.

3. Simplify: $(1+t^{-1}+t^{-2})(t-1+t^{-1})$
   Solution: $t+t^{-1}+t^{-3}$
   Explanation: Distribute: $(1+t^{-1}+t^{-2})(t-1+t^{-1})=1(t-1+t^{-1})+t^{-1}(t-1+t^{-1})+t^{-2}(t-1+t^{-1})$
   $=(t-1+t^{-1})+(t^0-t^{-1}+t^{-2})+(t^{-1}-t^{-2}+t^{-3})=t-1+t^{-1}+1-t^{-1}+t^{-2}+t^{-1}-t^{-2}+t^{-3}$.
   Combine like terms: $(-1+1)+t+(t^{-1}-t^{-1}+t^{-1})+(t^{-2}-t^{-2})+t^{-3}=(0)+(t)+(t^{-1})+(0)+t^{-3}=$
   $t+t^{-1}+t^{-3}$.

Practice problems: *(Answers on page: 730)*

1. Simplify: $(6-x)(x^3+x^2+3x)$
2. Simplify: $(3x^2+5x-1)(2x^2-x+4)$
3. Simplify: $(a+4+a^{-1})(3-a^{-1}+2a^{-2})$

Review questions: *(Answers to odd questions on page: 730)*

1. Simplify: $(-w+9)(-w+1)$
2. Simplify: $(z-1)(z^2+z+1)$
3. Simplify: $(2x^3+1)(x+1)$
4. Simplify: $(1+t^{-1}+t^{-2})(t-1+t^{-1})$
5. Simplify: $(9-x)\cdot(3x^2+4x-8)$

Using Special Products

- $(a+b)^2=a^2+2ab+b^2$
- $(a+b)^3=a^3+3a^2b+3ab^2+b^3$
- **Like terms** are those terms with the same variables to the same degree, or constants.
- **Distributive property**: $a(b+c)=ab+ac$.

$(A+B)^2=(A+B)(A+B)$ $=A^2+2AB+B^2$ **Example** $(2x+y)^2=(2x+y)(2x+y)$ $=4x^2+4xy+y^2$	You can **multiply binomials** using either the FOIL method or the distributive property. In this example, $2x$ will multiply with the second binomial's $2x$ and $+y$. Then $+y$ from the first binomial will multiply with the second binomial's terms. To get your final answer, combine like terms.

$(A+B)^3=(A+B)(A^2+2AB+B^2)$ $A^3+2A^2B+AB^2$ $+A^2B+2AB^2+B^3$ $=A^3+3A^2B+3AB^2+B^3$	To **cube a binomial**: 1. FOIL the binomial times itself, just as you did when the binomial was being squared. 2. Use that product times the third binomial to get to the cubed products. 3. Look for like terms to combine.
Example $(3x^2-2y)^3$ $=(3x^2-2y)(9x^4-12x^2y+4y^2)$ $=27x^6-36x^4y+12x^2y^2$ $-18x^4y+24x^2y^2-8y^3$ $=27x^6-54x^4y+36x^2y^2-8y^3$	Now try a real example. Multiplying $(3x^2\text{-}2y)$ times $(3x^2\text{-}2y)$ yields the product $(9x^4 - 12x^2y + 4y^2)$. Multiply that trinomial with the third $(3x^2\text{-}2y)$. This time you get some like terms to combine for your final answer. (There frequently are none because the exponents won't match.)

Sample problems:

1. Multiply: $\left(3x^2-5y^3\right)^2$
   Solution: $9x^4-30x^2y^3+25y^6$
   Explanation: Use the special product formula for the square of a binomial, $(A+B)^2=A^2+2AB+B^2$, with $A=3x^2$ and $B=-5y^3$: $\left(3x^2-5y^3\right)^2=\left(3x^2\right)^2+2\left(3x^2\right)\left(-5y^3\right)+\left(-5y^3\right)^2$.
   Apply the rules of exponents and simplify:
   $(3)^2\left(x^2\right)^2+(2)(3)(-5)\left(x^2\right)\left(y^3\right)+(-5)^2\left(y^3\right)^2=9x^4-30x^2y^3+25y^6$.

2. True or false: $(2a-5b)^3=8a^3-60a^2b+150ab^2-125b^3$
   Solution: True
   Explanation: Use the special product formula for the cube of a binomial, $(A+B)^3=A^3+3A^2B+3AB^2+B^3$, with $A=2a$ and $B=-5b$: $(2a-5b)^3=(2a)^3+3(2a)^2(-5b)+3(2a)(-5b)^2+(-5b)^3$.
   Apply the rules of exponents and simplify:
   $2^3\cdot a^3+3\cdot 2^2\cdot a^2\cdot -5b+3\cdot 2a(-5)^2\cdot b^2+(-5)^3\cdot b^3$
   $=8\cdot a^3+3\cdot 4\cdot a^2\cdot -5b+3\cdot 2a\cdot 25\cdot b^2+-125\cdot b^3$
   $=8a^3+3\cdot 4\cdot -5\cdot a^2b+3\cdot 2\cdot 25\cdot ab^2-125b^3$
   $=8a^3-60a^2b+150ab^2-125b^3$.

3. True or false: $(r^2+1)^3=r^3+3r^2+3r+1$
   Solution: False
   Explanation: Use the special product formula for the cube of a binomial, $(A+B)^3=A^3+3A^2B+3AB^2+B^3$, with $A=r^2$ and $B=1$: $(r^2+1)^3=(r^2)^3+3(r^2)^2(1)+3(r^2)(1)^2+(1)^3$.
   Apply the rules of exponents and simplify: $r^6+3r^4+3r^2+1$.

Practice problems: *(Answers on page: 730)*

1. Multiply: $\left(3w^2-v^5\right)^2$
2. Multiply: $\left[(3x-1)+y^2\right]^2$
3. Multiply: $(x-3y)^3$

Review questions: *(Answers to odd questions on page: 730)*

1. Multiply: $\left(y+y^{-1}\right)^3$
2. Multiply: $(z+1)^3$
3. Multiply: $(2c+11d)^2$
4. Multiply: $(3-4z)^2$
5. Multiply: $\left(5xy^3-7x^2\right)^2$

Factoring Using the Greatest Common Factor

- **Review:** The **greatest common factor** of a group of terms is the greatest factor that is present in every individual term.
- Polynomials can be factored using the greatest common factor:
  1. Find the greatest common factor of the individual terms or **monomials** in the polynomial.
  2. Write the polynomial as the product of the greatest common factor and the remaining terms.

Greatest Common Factor - **the largest like-term that all the terms have in common** **Example** $4x^3y^3 + 8x^4y^3 - 12x^2y^4$ $(4 \cdot 1)$ $(x^2 \cdot x)$ $(y^3 \cdot 1)$ $(4 \cdot 2)$ $(x^2 \cdot x^2)$ $(y^3 \cdot 1)$ $(4 \cdot 3)$ $(x^2 \cdot 1)$ $(y^3 \cdot y)$	One way to factor polynomials is to pull out, or unmultiply, the **greatest common factor** of all the individual terms. Take a look at this polynomial. The greatest constant factor present in every individual term is 4, the greatest power of x in every term is x^2, and the greatest power of y in every term is y^3. Therefore, the greatest common factor is equal to $4x^2y^3$.
$4x^3y^3 + 8x^4y^3 - 12x^2y^4$ $= 4x^2y^3(x + 2x^2 - 3y)$ GCF	Factor out the greatest common factor by unmultiplying to pull it out and writing what is left for each individual term. Your answer is a multiplication problem with a monomial times a trinomial.
Example $3AB^2 - 6A^2B^3$	Let's try another. What is the greatest common factor for this binomial?
$3AB^2 - 6A^2B^3$ $(3AB^2 \cdot 1)$ $(3AB^2 \cdot 2AB)$	The greatest constant factor in each term is 3. The greatest power of A in each term is A. The greatest power of B in each term is B^2. The greatest common factor is $3AB^2$!
$3AB^2 - 6A^2B^3$ $= 3AB^2(1 - 2AB)$	Just pull out the greatest common factor to factor the polynomial. Your answer is a multiplication problem with a monomial times a binomial.
$3AB^2 - 6A^2B^3$ ✓ $3AB^2(1 - 2AB)$ Check your work	**NOTICE:** You can always check your work by multiplying back out again. Your expect to get the original polynomial before you factored it.

Sample problems:

1. Factor: $3x^3y^2+6x^3y-3x^2$
   Solution: $3x^2(xy^2+2xy-1)$
   Explanation: The factors of $3x^3y^2$ are $3\cdot x\cdot x\cdot x\cdot y\cdot y$. The factors of $6x^3y$ are $3\cdot 2\cdot x\cdot x\cdot x\cdot y$. The factors of $-3x^2$ are $3\cdot -1\cdot x\cdot x$. The factors common to all three terms are $3\cdot x\cdot x$. The GCF is $3x^2$. Factor out the GCF: $3x^3y^2+6x^3y-3x^2=\frac{3x^2}{3x^2}\left(3x^3y^2+6x^3y-3x^2\right)=$
   $3x^2\left(\frac{3x^3y^2}{3x^2}+\frac{6x^3y}{3x^2}-\frac{3x^2}{3x^2}\right)=3x^2(xy^2+2xy-1)$.

2. Factor: $3(x+1)-2y(x+1)$
   Solution: $(x+1)(3-2y)$
   Explanation: The factors of $3(x+1)$ are $3\cdot(x+1)$. The factors of $2y(x+1)$ are $2\cdot y\cdot(x+1)$. So, the GCF is $x+1$. Factor out the GCF: $3(x+1)-2y(x+1)=\frac{(x+1)}{(x+1)}(3(x+1)-2y(x+1))=$
   $(x+1)\left(\frac{3(x+1)}{(x+1)}-\frac{2y(x+1)}{(x+1)}\right)=(x+1)(3-2y)$.

3. Factor: $5x^3(y+2)+6x^2(y+2)$
   Solution: $x^2(y+2)(5x+6)$
   Explanation: The GCF of the two terms is $x^2(y+2)$. Factor the GCF from each term:
   $\frac{x^2(y+2)}{x^2(y+2)}\left(5x^3(y+2)+6x^2(y+2)\right)=x^2(y+2)\left(\frac{5x^3(y+2)}{x^2(y+2)}+\frac{6x^2(y+2)}{x^2(y+2)}\right)=x^2(y+2)(5x+6)$.

Practice problems: *(Answers on page: 730)*

1. Factor: $60a^3b^4+36a^2b^5$
2. Factor: $2x^3(y-13)+x(y-13)-(y-13)$
3. Factor: $12a^5(1-b)-6a^4(1-b)$

Review questions: *(Answers to odd questions on page: 730)*

1. Factor: $6x-39$
2. Factor: $7x^2+56x$
3. Factor: $15a^3b^2-50a^2b^3+85a^2b^5$
4. Factor: $16x^4y^2+12x^3y^4+52x^3y^7$
5. Factor: $(5p-r)(8p+1)+(5p+r)(8p+1)$

Factoring by Grouping

- **Grouping terms** often enables a common term to be factored out of part of a polynomial.
- Deciding what to group is part of the art of this process.

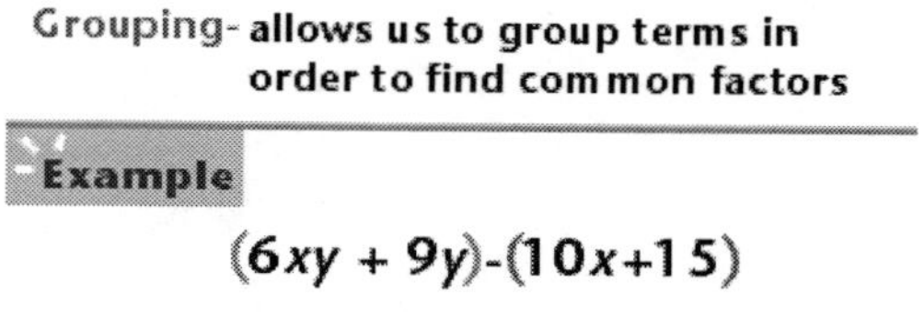

Grouping terms is very useful when a problem does not have a common factor for all its terms.

Here the first two and the last two terms have been grouped together. Notice that each group can be factored separately.

$(6xy + 9y) - (10x - 15)$ GCF → $3y$ GCF → 5 $3y(2x + 3) - 5(2x + 3)$ $(2x + 3)(3y - 5)$	As you can see in the example, sometimes a common factor becomes visible through grouping. Also, sometimes you can choose how you want to group so as to reveal a common factor.
Grouping- allows us to group terms in order to find common factors **Example** $15 - 5A^2 - 3B^2 + A^2B^2 =$ 3 A^2 $3(5 - B^2) + A^2(-5 + B^2) =$ Factor out -1 $3(5 - B^2) - A^2(5 - B^2) =$ $3(5 - B^2) - A^2(5 - B^2) =$ $(5 - B^2)(3 - A^2)$	**Remember:** Watch your exponents and signs carefully. No point in making mistakes with those. Notice that in this example, factoring is done once. Then you noticed something else you could factor, -1, and you did so. Factoring in stages like this is also helpful. You may not see everything to factor at first, and that's OK. You can always factor more as you work through the problem.

Sample problems:

1. Factor: $a^2b^3c - bc + a^3b^3 - ab$
   Solution: $b(a^2b^2 - 1)(c + a)$
   Explanation: First factor b from the polynomial, since b is common to all of the terms:
   $a^2b^3c - bc + a^3b^3 - ab = b[a^2b^2c - c + a^3b^2 - a]$.
   Factor c from the first two terms and a from the last two terms:
   $b[(a^2b^2c - c) + (a^3b^2 - a)] = b[c(a^2b^2 - 1) + a(a^2b^2 - 1)]$.
   Finally, factor out the $a^2b^2 - 1$: $b[c(a^2b^2 - 1) + a(a^2b^2 - 1)] = b(a^2b^2 - 1)(c + a)$.

2. Factor: $8u - 16y^3w^2 + 4w^2 - 32y^3u$
   Solution: $4[(1 - 4y^3)(2u + w^2)]$
   Explanation: Factor 4 from the polynomial: $8u - 16y^3w^2 + 4w^2 - 32y^3u$: $4(2u - 4y^3w^2 + w^2 - 8y^3u)$.
   Manipulate the terms: $4[(2u - 8y^3u) + (w^2 - 4y^3w^2)]$. Factor the GCF from each binomial:
   $4[2u(1 - 4y^3) + w^2(1 - 4y^3)]$. Factor out $(1 - 4y^3)$: $4[(1 - 4y^3)(2u + w^2)]$.

3. Factor: $36tu^3 + 15u^2 + 24tu + 10$
   Solution: $(12tu + 5)(3u^2 + 2)$
   Explanation: Factor $3u^2$ from the first two terms and 2 from the last two terms:
   $(36tu^3 + 15u^2) + (24tu + 10) = 3u^2(12tu + 5) + 2(12tu + 5)$.
   Factor $(12tu + 5)$ from each of the two remaining terms:
   $3u^2(12tu + 5) + 2(12tu + 5) = (12tu + 5)(3u^2 + 2)$.

Practice problems: *(Answers on page: 730)*

1. Factor: $6t^5v + 48v^2 + 5t^5 + 40v$
2. Factor: $30xy - 3xz + 6xyz - 15x$
3. Factor: $5a^2b^2c + 10a^2b - 5a^2b^2 - 10a^2bc$

Review questions: *(Answers to odd questions on page: 730)*

1. Factor: $8wv + 30w - 12v - 45$
2. Factor: $-3m^4 - 6mn^2 + 13m^3 + 26n^2$
3. Factor: $9r^2s - 33rs + 15r - 55$
4. Factor: $x^3 + 8x + 3x^2 + 24$
5. Factor: $21y^3 - 7y + 3y^2 - 1$

Factoring Trinomials

- **Trinomial**: A polynomial with three terms, generally a variable squared, a variable to the first power, and a constant.
- **Factoring To-Do List**:
  - Factor out any factors common to every term.
  - Look for a way to group terms and factor.
  - Break up squared terms.
- **FOIL**: A shortcut way to remember how to multiply when you have two binomials to multiply with each other. **FOIL** means that you multiply as follows:
  - **F**irst terms in each group multiply together.
  - **O**uter terms in each group multiply together.
  - **I**nside terms in each group multiply together.
  - **L**ast terms in each group multiply together.

  Now, combine any terms you can. Usually, the result will be a trinomial.
- Check signs and coefficients carefully.

Example	
$6y^2 - 48y - 120 =$ $6(y^2 - 8y - 20) =$ $6(y + 2)(y - 10) =$	First, can you factor any common factor out of every term? In this example, every term is a multiple of 6, so you factor the 6 out and group the terms in parentheses. Factoring is really un-multiplying. What two groups of two terms each could have multiplied to produce this trinomial as the answer? 1. Unmultiply the first term, y^2, and write the two answers, y and y, in the first spots in each set of ( )s. 2. Unmultiply the last term, 20, and write the two answers, 2 and 10, in the last spots of each set of ( )s. 3. The third term is –20 which means the signs connecting terms within the binomials don't match. So, write a "+" in one binomial as your connecting sign, and a "-" in the other. 4. Check your answer. Be sure you would get the three terms you started with. Check numbers and signs closely.

Example $5r^4 - 7r^2s - 6s^2$

$$5(r^2)^2 - 7(r^2)s - 6s^2 =$$

$$(5r^2 + 3s)(r^2 - 2s)$$

☺ $5r^4 - 7r^2s - 6s^2$

Sometimes you get trinomials with exponents larger than 2. As in this example, you can often factor these using FOIL.

See if you can group and rewrite the terms so that you wind up with:

1. some number squared in the first position,
2. that same number not squared in the second term and multiplying with something new,
3. the "something new" squared in the third slot.

Coefficients attached to these terms may vary from problem to problem. If so, factoring with FOIL will still work.

Remember: **FOIL**
(first, outer, inside, last)

Example

$$x^2 - 5x + 6 =$$

$$(x - 2)(x - 3)$$

Note: The middle term will tell you the signs of the last terms in the binomials.

Some things to watch:

1) If the last term of the trinomial is positive, it means:
   a) both binomials have the same sign separating their terms.
   b) the middle term of the trinomial is your indicator; use its sign in your binomials.

2) If the last term of the trinomial is negative, it means:
   a) the binomials have different signs separating their terms.
   b) you'll have to check your possibilities to find out which one is positive and which one is negative.

3) If your squared term has some coefficient other than 1, you have to check carefully as you factor to be sure that when you multiply your binomials:
   a) the middle term of the trinomial appears.
   b) the signs and coefficients are all correct.

Sample problems:

1. Factor: $-2x^2 - 12x + 32$

   Solution: $-2(x+8)(x-2)$

   Explanation: Factor the GCF from the terms: $-2x^2 - 12x + 32 = -2(x^2 + 6x - 16)$.

   Set up the parentheses and factor the first term: $-2(x^2 + 6x - 16) = -2(x \quad)(x \quad)$.
   List the factors of the last term (since 16 is negative, exactly one factor from each pair must be negative): $1 \cdot -16, 2 \cdot -8, 4 \cdot -4, -1 \cdot 16$, or $-2 \cdot 8$.
   To determine which pair belongs inside the parentheses, think: the sum of which factors of -16 equals $+6$? Place 8 & -2 (since their sum is 6) inside the parentheses:
   $-2(x \quad)(x \quad) \Rightarrow -2(x+8)(x-2)$. Use FOIL to check the factors:
   $-2(x+8)(x-2) = -2(x^2 + 6x - 16) = -2x^2 - 12x + 32$.
   Thus, $-2(x+8)(x-2)$ is the correct factorization.

2. Factor: $3x^2 - 13x - 10$
   Solution: $(3x+2)(x-5)$
   Explanation: Factor $3x^2$: $3x^2 - 13x - 10 = (3x \quad)(x \quad)$. Next, factor the last term, -10, and notice the sign: $10 \cdot -1$, $-10 \cdot 1$, $2 \cdot -5$, $-2 \cdot 5$. Use FOIL to check different pairs until the correct factors are found: $(3x+2)(x-5) = 3x^2 + 2x - 15x - 10 = 3x^2 - 13x - 10$.

3. Factor: $2a^2 + 11ab + 15b^2$
   Solution: $(2a+5b)(a+3b)$
   Explanation: Factor $2a^2$: $(2a)(a)$. Factor $15b^2$: $(b)(15b)$ or $(3b)(5b)$.
   List the combinations of factors in parentheses and foil to determine the correct factorization. The possibilities are: $(2a+\_)(a+\_) \Rightarrow (2a+\underline{3b})(a+\underline{5b})$; $(2a+\underline{5b})(a+\underline{3b})$; $(2a+\underline{b})(a+\underline{15b})$; or $(2a+\underline{15b})(a+\underline{b})$. Foil the binomials to check: $(2a+3b)(a+5b) = 2a^2 + 13ab + 15b^2$, so the first pair of binomials is incorrect, $(2a+5b)(a+3b) = 2a^2 + 11ab + 15b^2$, so $(2a+5b)(a+3b)$ is the correct factorization.

Practice problems: *(Answers on page: 730)*

1. Factor: $3g^2 - 18g - 48$
2. Factor: $2d^2 - 5d + 2$
3. Factor: $15x^2 + 29xy + 8y^2$

Review questions: *(Answers to odd questions on page: 730)*

1. Factor: $x^2 - x - 2$
2. Factor: $x^2 + 2x + 1$
3. Factor: $x^2 - 7x + 10$
4. Factor: $6y^2 - 54y + 84$
5. Factor: $10y^2 + 9y + 2$

Factoring Perfect Square Trinomials

- **Perfect square trinomial**: These expressions always take the form of $a^2 + 2ab + b^2$; i.e., (some value squared) + (2 times the first value times the second value) + (the second value squared).

$A^2 + 2AB + B^2$ is a perfect square	This trinomial demonstrates the pattern for a perfect square. The A and B are squared for the first and last terms. The middle term is $2AB$.

$$= A^2 + 2AB + B^2$$

something² ↑ (under A^2), ↑ 2 something something (under $2AB$), ↑ something² (under B^2)

$$(A + B)^2$$

Once the perfect square has been identified in a trinomial, factoring follows these steps:

1. Unsquare the first term and write it in the first position in your set of parentheses. In this example, A^2 goes to A.

2. Unsquare the third term and write it in the second position in your set of parentheses. Here B^2 goes to B.

3. Write the sign of the second term in the trinomial between the two terms in your parentheses. Here you choose "+" between A and B because $2AB$ has "+".

4. Check your answer. Multiply to square the terms in the parentheses. Check that the middle term and its sign match your original middle term.

Example

$$9x^2 - 30x + 25 =$$

$$(3x)^2 + 2(3x)(-5) + (-5)^2$$

something² ↑ (under $(3x)^2$), ↑ 2 something something (under $2(3x)(-5)$), ↑ something² (under $(-5)^2$)

$$= (3x - 5)^2$$

This example, again, shows you how the pattern fits a perfect square trinomial.

1. The first term, $9x^2$, is ($3x$) squared.

2. The last term, 25, is (-5) squared.

3. The third term is 2 times ($3x$) times (-5).

4. The sign of the middle term is "-".

As a result, you immediately know that the trinomial factors to $(3x-5)^2$.

Sample problems:

1. Factor: $25x^2 - 30x + 9$

   Solution: $(5x-3)^2$

   Explanation: The trinomial is a perfect square since it follows the pattern $A^2 + 2AB + B^2$: $A^2 = (5x)^2$, $B^2 = (-3)^2$, and $2AB = 2(5x)(-3) = -30x$. Therefore, it factors according to $(A+B)^2$: $(5x-3)^2$.

2. Factor the following perfect square trinomial: $9a^2b^2 + 30abc + 25c^2$

   Solution: $(3ab+5c)^2$

   Explanation: Since it is a perfect square trinomial use the pattern $A^2 + 2AB + B^2$ to find the factors. A is the square root of the first term: $\sqrt{9a^2b^2} = 3ab$. B is the square root of the last term: $\sqrt{25c^2} = 5c$. Thus, the perfect square is $(3ab+5c)^2$.

3. Factor: $(m+2n)^2 + 4(m+2n) + 4$

   Solution: $[(m+2n)+2]^2$

   Explanation: Check that the trinomial is a perfect square: $A^2 = (m+2n)^2$ and $B^2 = (2)^2$, so $2AB = 2(m+2n)(2) = 4(m+2n)$. Thus the trinomial is a perfect square. Factor according to $(A+B)^2$: $[(m+2n)+2]^2$.

Practice problems: *(Answers on page: 731)*

1. Factor: $w^2 + 2wt + t^2$
2. Factor: $81s^2 - 108s + 36$
3. Factor: $(3a+b)^4 - 20(3a+b)^2 + 100$

Review questions: *(Answers to odd questions on page: 731)*

1. Factor: $x^2 - 8x + 16$
2. Factor: $16a^2 - 24a + 9$
3. Factor: $9x^2 + 12x + 4$
4. Factor: $4z^2 - 2z + \frac{1}{4}$
5. Factor: $(m-2n)^2 - 4(m-2n) + 4$

Factoring the Difference of Two Squares

- Remember that combining like terms where possible simplifies your results.
- Learn to notice where you can rewrite terms so that a common pattern shows up and you can work the problem easily.

$A^2 - B^2 = (A+B)(A-B)$ Example $x^2 - 4 =$ $(x+2)(x-2)$ *Common Mistake: $(x+4)(x-4)$!*	The difference of two squares is easy to factor. It works nicely because the middle terms all cancel each other out. If you multiply out this problem, you will have the products: $x^2 - 2x + 2x - 4$. Once you combine like terms, you will have your $x^2 - 4$. Notice the Common Mistake made in factoring $x^2 - 4$. This occurs when people forget to factor the final term.
$A^2 - B^2 = (A+B)(A-B)$ Example $16x^2 - 81y^4 =$ $(4x)^2 - (9y^2)^2 =$ $(4x + 9y^2)(4x - 9y^2)$ $16x^2 + \cancel{36xy^2} - \cancel{36xy^2} - 81y^4$	Here's another example. It looks different but it's really the same type of problem. You just have to know how to look at it. Rewrite the terms so they are both some number squared and you know what to do. Again, you can see that the middle terms cancel out and leave you with the difference of two squares.
$A^2 - B^2 =$  good! $A^2 + B^2 =$  bad	This graphic is a subtle reminder that the difference of two squares gives you a nice, neat little answer. The sum of two squares is more complicated.

Sample problems:

1. Factor: $9a^2 - 49$
   Solution: $(3a+7)(3a-7)$
   Explanation: Check that the binomial is the difference of two squares: $A^2 = (3a)^2$ and $B = (7)^2$. Thus $9a^2 - 49$ is the difference of two squares. Factor according to $(A+B)(A-B)$: $(3a+7)(3a-7)$.

2. Factor: $16x^4 - y^2$
   Solution: $(4x^2 + y)(4x^2 - y)$
   Explanation: Check that the binomial is the difference of two squares: $A^2 = (4x^2)^2$ and $B = (y)^2$. Thus $16x^4 - y^2$ is the difference of two squares. Factor according to $(A+B)(A-B)$: $(4x^2 + y)(4x^2 - y)$.

3. Factor the difference of two squares: $p^8 - (3q+2)^2$
   Solution: $[p^4 + (3q+2)][p^4 - (3q+2)]$
   Explanation: Check that the binomial is the difference of two squares: $A^2 = (p^4)^2$ and $B^2 = (3q+2)^2$. Thus, $p^8 - (3q+2)^2$ is the difference of two squares. Factor according to $(A+B)(A-B)$: $[p^4 + (3q+2)][p^4 - (3q+2)]$.

Practice problems: *(Answers on page: 731)*

1. Factor: $a^2 - 4b^2$
2. Factor: $25r^4 - 9s^6$
3. Factor: $(y-3)^2 - 121$

Review questions: *(Answers to odd questions on page: 731)*

1. Factor: $x^2 - 9$
2. Factor: $4x^2 - 81$
3. Factor: $9x^2 - 1$
4. Factor: $x^2 - 64$
5. Factor: $(x-7)^2 - 16$

Factoring the Sums and Differences of Cubes

- **Sum of Two Cubes**: $a^3 + b^3 = (a + b)(a^2 - ab + b^2)$
- **Difference of Two Cubes**: $a^3 - b^3 = (a - b)(a^2 + ab + b^2)$

Difference of Two Cubes $x^3 - y^3 = (x - y)(x^2 + xy + y^2)$ *Check your work by distributing* $= x^3 + \cancel{x^2y} - \cancel{x^2y} + \cancel{xy^2} - \cancel{xy^2} - y^3$ **Difference of Two Cubes** $x^3 \ominus y^3 = (x \ominus y)(x^2 \oplus xy + y^2)$	When working with the **Difference of Two Cubes**, factoring follows this pattern: 1. The first parentheses hold the two cubes each reduced to first degree; i.e., uncubed. 2. These two terms are connected by the same sign as the cubes. 3. The second parentheses hold: a. the first term squared in the first position. b. the second term squared in the third position. c. a third term in the middle or second position which is the product of the two first terms. d. this middle term has the sign opposite that used in the first set of parentheses.
Sum of Two Perfect Cubes $x^3 + y^3 = (x + y)$ $x^3 + y^3 = (x + y)(x^2 \quad xy \quad y^2)$ $x^3 + y^3 = (x + y)(x^2 - xy + y^2)$	When working with the **Sum of Two Cubes**, factoring follows the same pattern: 1. The first parentheses hold the two cubes reduced to first degree connected by the same sign. 2. The second parentheses hold: a. the first term squared in the first position. b. the second term squared in the third position. c. a third term in the middle position that is the product of the first two terms. d. the middle term has the sign opposite that used in the first set of parentheses.
Sum of Two Perfect Cubes $x^3 \oplus y^3 = (x \oplus y)(x^2 \ominus xy + y^2)$ *Difference of Two Perfect Cubes* $x^3 \ominus y^3 = (x \ominus y)(x^2 \oplus xy + y^2)$	The pattern of signs that is noted here is the critical thing about factoring the sum or difference of cubes. The other difference you might notice is that the xy term does not have coefficient of 2, or some other number you might expect. Many people make the mistake of not noticing that.

Sample problems:

1. Factor: $8 + a^6$

   Solution: $\left(2 + a^2\right)\left(4 - 2a^2 + a^4\right)$

   Explanation: The binomial is the sum of two cubes since $8 = (2)^3$ and $a^6 = \left(a^2\right)^3$. Therefore $8 + a^6$ can be factored according to $\left(x^3 + y^3\right) = (x + y)\left(x^2 - xy + y^2\right)$. Find x: $8 = (2)^3$, so $x = 2$. Find y: $a^6 = \left(a^2\right)^3$, so $y = a^2$. Substitute $x = 2$ and $y = a^2$ into $(x + y)\left(x^2 - xy + y^2\right)$: $\left(2 + a^2\right)\left((2)^2 - (2)\left(a^2\right) + \left(a^2\right)^2\right)$. Simplify: $\left(2 + a^2\right)\left(4 - 2a^2 + a^4\right)$.

2. Factor the difference of two cubes: $8a^{12}-27b^6c^3$

   Solution: $\left(2a^4-3b^2c\right)\left(4a^8+6a^4b^2c+9b^4c^2\right)$

   Explanation: Any difference of two cubes can be factored using the pattern $(x^3+y^3)=$ $(x-y)\left(x^2+xy+y^2\right)$. Find x: $x^3=8a^{12}=\left(2a^4\right)^3$, so $x=2a^4$. Find y: $y^3=27b^6c^3=\left(3b^2c\right)^3$, so $y=3b^2c$. Substitute $x=2a^4$ and $y=3b^2c$ into $(x-y)\left(x^2+xy+y^2\right)$ to determine the factorization: $\left(2a^4-3b^2c\right)\left(\left(2a^4\right)^2+\left(2a^4\right)\left(3b^2c\right)+\left(3b^2c\right)^2\right)$. Simplify: $\left(2a^4-3b^2c\right)\left(4a^8+6a^4b^2c+9b^4c^2\right)$.

3. Factor the sum of two cubes: $(h+3k)^3+27$

   Solution: $\left[(h+3k)+3\right]\left[(h+3k)^2-3(h+3k)+9\right]$

   Explanation: Any sum of two cubes can be factored using the pattern $\left(x^3+y^3\right)=(x+y)\left(x^2-xy+y^2\right)$.
   Find x: $x^3=(h+3k)^3$, so $x=(h+3k)$. Find y: $y^3=27=(3)^3$, so $y=3$.
   Substitute $x=(h+3k)$ and $y=3$ into $(x-y)\left(x^2+xy+y^2\right)$ and simplify to determine the factorization:
   $\left[(h+3k)+3\right]\left[(h+3k)^2-(h+3k)(3)+(3)^2\right]=\left[(h+3k)+3\right]\left[(h+3k)^2-3(h+3k)+9\right]$.

Practice problems: *(Answers on page: 731)*

1. Factor: $27+z^3$
2. Factor: $125-64z^3$
3. Factor: $(a-b)^3-64c^6$

Review questions: *(Answers to odd questions on page: 731)*

1. Factor: x^3+8
2. Factor: t^3-125
3. Factor: $8x^3+y^3z^3$
4. Factor: $64x^3-1$
5. Factor: $(a-b)^3-64$

Factoring by Any Method

- Never get discouraged if your first technique for factoring doesn't work. It happens to everyone. Sometimes you need to use more than one method for factoring to factor a single polynomial.
- **Methods of factoring** –
  - Greatest Common Factor: the GCF is factored out of every term
  - Perfect Square Trinomials: $(a^2+2ab+b^2)=(a+b)^2$
  - Difference of Two Squares: $a^2-b^2=(a+b)(a-b)$
  - Difference of Two Cubes: $a^3-b^3=(a-b)(a^2+ab+b^2)$
  - Sum of Two Cubes: $a^3+b^3=(a+b)(a^2-ab+b^2)$

Example yx^3-yx^6	Look for the greatest common factor across the entire expression. It makes the rest of the expression easier to think about.
$yx^3(1-x^3)$	Factoring out the yx^3, leaves the expression as the difference of two cubes.

$yx^3(1 - x)(1 + x + x^2)$	Now use your patterns for cubes, and factor again.
Example $x^5 - 2x^4 + x^3 =$ $x^3(x^2 - 2x + 1) =$ $x^3(x - 1)(x - 1) =$ $x^3(x - 1)^2$	Try the same steps in this problem: 1. Factor out the greatest common factor, x^3. 2. Factor whatever is left completely.
Example $(x + y)^2 - (x - y)^2 =$ $((x+y) + (x-y))((x+y) - (x-y)) =$ $y - (-y) = 2y$ $(2x)$ $(2y)$ $(2x)(2y) = 4xy$	This example is included because it is simpler than it looks at first glance. First, factor using the differnece of the two squares pattern. In each case when you remove the inside parentheses and do the arithmetic, you get one-term results, easy to multiply for your final answer.
Example $x^4 - 3x^2 - 4$ *could also be written as:* $(x^2)^2 - 3(x^2) - 4$ | Let $A = x^2$: $A^2 - 3A - 4 =$ $(x^2 + 1)(x^2 - 4) =$ | $(A + 1)(A - 4) =$ *insert x^2 for A* $(x^2 + 1)(x^2 - 4) =$ *difference of 2 squares* $(x^2+1)(x+2)(x-2)$ | $(x^2+1)(x+2)(x-2)$	This example allows you to factor what you see by substituting. Let $A = x^2$ and it's easy to see how to use your factoring techniques. Then, when you get to $(x^2 - 4)$, you'll be ready to factor it too, without any stress. Your final answer shows the results of your double factoring.

Sample problems:

1. Factor: $-3xy - 30x^2y - 75x^3y$
   Solution: $-3xy(1+5x)^2$
   Explanation: Factor out the GCF: $-3xy(1+10x+25x^2)$.
   Recognize that the trinomial in the parentheses is a perfect square. Follow the pattern for factoring a perfect square trinomial, $a^2 + 2ab + b^2 = (a+b)^2$.
   Find a: $1 = (1)^2$, so $a = 1$. Find b: $25x^2 = (5x)^2$, so $b = 5x$.
   Write these factors along with the GCF into the form for a perfect square trinomial: $-3xy(1+5x)^2$.

2. Factor: $135a^3c^2 - 5b^3c^2$
   Solution: $5c^2(3a-b)(9a^2 + 3ab + b^2)$
   Explanation: Factor out the GCF: $5c^2(27a^3 - b^3)$.
   Recognize that the binomial in the parentheses is a difference of two cubes. Follow the pattern for factoring the difference of two cubes: $A^3 - B^3 = (A-B)(A^2 + AB + B^2)$.
   Find A: $27a^3 = (3a)^3$, so $A = 3a$. Find B: $b^3 = (b)^3$, so $B = b$. Write these factors along with the GCF into the form for a difference of two cubes: $5c^2(3a-b)(9a^2 + 3ab + b^2)$.

3. Factor: $48xz^2 + 6w^3xz^2 + 16yz^2 + 2w^3yz^2$
   Solution: $2z^2(3x+y)(2+w)(4-2w+w^2)$
   Explanation: Factor out the GCF: $2z^2(24x+3w^3x+8y+w^3y)$. Factor the polynomial within the parentheses by grouping: $2z^2[(24x+3w^3x)+(8y+w^3y)] = 2z^2[3x(8+w^3)+y(8+w^3)]$
   $= 2z^2(3x+y)(8+w^3)$. Notice that $(8+w^3)$ is the sum of two cubes. Factor $(8+w^3)$:
   $2z^2(3x+y)(8+w^3) = 2z^2(3x+y)(2+w)(4-2w+w^2)$.

Practice problems: *(Answers on page: 731)*

1. Factor: $125x^3 - 27$
2. Factor: $48x^2 + 6x^2y^3 + 56x + 7xy^3 - 40 - 5y^3$
3. Factor: $18w^3x^7z - 18x^7z - 50w^3xy^2z + 50xy^2z$

Review questions: *(Answers to odd questions on page: 731)*

1. Factor: $x^2 - 2x - 8$
2. Factor: $4k^2 - 3k - 1$
3. Factor: $2p^2 + p - 15$
4. Factor: $81y^2 - 49$
5. Factor: $2k^2(a+6b) - 3(a+6b)$

Rational Expressions and Domain

- A **rational expression** is a fraction that has a polynomial in the numerator, the denominator, or both.
- The **domain** is the set of all values that a variable can use in a polynomial or function.
- The **domain of a rational expression** is the set of all the values for x that do NOT create a denominator with a total value of 0.
- The denominator cannot equal 0 in any fraction of any form.

Domain: all the allowable values of x. **Finding the Domain of a Rational Function** $\frac{x-2}{x+5}$ $x \neq -5$ because that would make the denominator = 0. Domain = all real numbers except -5	For any **rational expression**, always first calculate what values of x must be excluded so that the *denominator* does NOT equal 0. In this example, set the denominator equal to 0 and solve for x to determine what values must be excluded from the domain of the expression. This work shows that x equals –5 when the denominator $x + 5$ equals 0. Therefore –5 must be excluded from the domain.

Example

$$\frac{3x-1}{x^2+2x-3} = \frac{3x-1}{(x+3)(x-1)}$$

$x+3=0$, $x=-3$ | $x-1=0$, $x=1$

Domain = all real numbers except 1 and -3

The **domain** for any x is the set of all the real numbers that will work for x in the given problem.

This problem requires factoring the denominator to determine what values for x must be excluded.

Remember: Anytime numbers multiply and the answer is 0, at least one of the numbers must itself be 0.

Set each factor equal to 0 and solve for x to determine what values must be excluded from the domain.

Every real number value except –3 and +1 can be used for x in this expression.

Sample problems:

1. True of false: The domain of $\dfrac{x-3}{2x^2+x-3}$ is all real numbers except $x=-\dfrac{3}{2}$ and $x=1$.
   Solution: True
   Explanation: Factor the denominator: $2x^2+x-3=(2x+3)(x-1)$. Set each factor equal to zero and solve each factor for x: $2x+3=0$ or $x-1=0$; $x=-\frac{3}{2}$ or $x=1$.

2. True or false: The domain of $\dfrac{9x^5-17}{x^3-10x^2+9x}$ is all real numbers except $x=9$ and $x=1$.
   Solution: False
   Evaluation: Factor the denominator: $x^3-10x^2+9x=x(x^2-10x+9)=x(x-9)(x-1)$. Set each factor equal to 0 and solve for x: $x=0$ or $x-9=0$ or $x-1=0$; $x=0$ or $x=9$ or $x=1$. Thus, the domain is all real numbers except 0, 9, and 1.

3. Find the domain of $\dfrac{1}{x^3-2x^2-4x+8}$.
   Solution: All real numbers except $x=2$ and $x=-2$
   Explanation: Factor the denominator by grouping: $x^3-2x^2-4x+8=x^2(x-2)-4(x-2)$ $=(x^2-4)(x-2)=(x+2)(x-2)(x-2)$. The same factor is repeated two times, so set $(x-2)$ and $(x+2)$ equal to zero and solve for x: $x-2=0$, $x=2$; $x+2=0$, $x=-2$.

Practice problems: *(Answers on page: 731)*

1. True or false: The domain of $\dfrac{1}{x^2+x}$ is all real numbers except $x=0$ and $x=-1$.

2. True or false: The domain of $\dfrac{1-5x^4}{4x^3-22x^2-12x}$ is all real numbers except $x=0$, $x=-\dfrac{1}{2}$ and $x=6$.

3. Find the domain of $\dfrac{5}{x^3+4x^2-x-4}$.

Review questions: *(Answers to odd questions on page: 731)*

1. True or false: The domain of $\dfrac{x}{x-1}$ is all real numbers except $x=1$.

2. True or false: The domain of $\dfrac{5x-1}{2x+16}$ is all real numbers except $x=-8$.

3. True or false: The domain of $\dfrac{x+1}{x^2-4}$ is all real numbers except $x = 2$.

4. True or false: The domain of $\dfrac{7x}{x^3-7x^2+10x}$ is all real numbers except $x = 5$, $x = 2$, or $x = 0$.

5. True or false: The domain of $\dfrac{9}{3x^2-14x-5}$ is all real numbers except $x = -\dfrac{1}{3}$ or $x = 5$.

Working with Fractions

- The **Common Denominator** is usually the lowest multiple shared by all the denominators in the fractions of the problem; i.e., all the denominators have exactly the same factors.
- To achieve a common denominator, multiply both the numerator and the denominator of each fraction by any factor missing in the denominator so that the denominator has all the factors that the other denominators have.
- **Canceling** in a fraction multiplication problem is the process for "reducing" by removing common factors from both the numerator and denominator. Because these factors multiply, it works to cancel across fractions, not just within one fraction.
- A **complex fraction** is a rational expression composed of fractions in the numerator, denominator or both.

Example $\frac{5}{6} - \frac{1}{10} = \frac{5}{2\cdot 3} - \frac{1}{2\cdot 5}$ factor the denominators $= \frac{5\cdot 5}{2\cdot 3\cdot 5} - \frac{1\cdot 3}{2\cdot 5\cdot 3}$ and multiply to get a common denominator	To add or subtract fractions: 1. Find a **common denominator**. 2. Add or subtract the numerators. 3. Reduce the answer, if possible. If one fraction is missing a factor in the denominator, multiply both its numerator and denominator by that factor. Do this for every fraction until all the denominators match.
Example don't forget the invisible 1 $\frac{5}{6} \cdot \frac{2}{15} = \frac{\cancel{5}\cdot\cancel{2}\cdot 1}{\underset{3}{\cancel{6}}\cdot\underset{3}{\cancel{15}}} = \boxed{\frac{1}{9}}$	Multiplication is easy: 1. Multiply the numerators. 2. Multiply the denominators. 3. Reduce the answer. Reduce in advance by **canceling** any factor in a numerator with itself in a denominator. **Remember:** When a number cancels, it is actually dividing it by itself and the answer is 1, not 0.
Example $\frac{\frac{2}{3}}{\frac{5}{7}} = \frac{2}{3} \div \frac{5}{7}$ flip it and multiply $= \frac{2}{3} \cdot \frac{7}{5}$ $= \frac{14}{15}$	Division is easy too: 1. Flip the dividing fraction on its head. 2. Multiply. **Remember:** Every fraction is a division problem with the number being divided on top and the number doing the dividing on the bottom.

Sample problems:

1. Simplify: $\frac{2}{21}+\frac{2}{7}\div\frac{1}{2}$

   Solution: $\frac{2}{3}$

   Explanation: First, complete the division.

   Flip the third fraction and multiply: $\frac{2}{21}+\frac{2}{7}\div\frac{1}{2}=\frac{2}{21}+\frac{2}{7}\cdot\frac{2}{1}=\frac{2}{21}+\frac{4}{7}$.

   Next, find the common denominator and multiply each fraction by the missing factor over itself.

   The common denominator is 21, so multiply the 2nd fraction by $\frac{3}{3}$:

   $\frac{2}{21}+\frac{4}{7}=\frac{2}{21}+\frac{4}{7}\left(\frac{3}{3}\right)=\frac{2}{21}+\frac{12}{21}$.

   Add the numerators and reduce:

   $\frac{2}{21}+\frac{12}{21}=\frac{14}{21}=\frac{\cancel{7}\cdot 2}{\cancel{7}\cdot 3}=\frac{2}{3}$.

2. Simplify: $2\left[\left(\frac{1}{3}\right)^2-\frac{5}{6}\right]$

   Solution: $-\frac{13}{9}$

   Explanation: Carefully follow the order of operations.

   Complete the exponent, subtract, then multiply by 2.

   First, square the fraction (multiply $\frac{1}{3}$ by itself): $2\left[\left(\frac{1}{3}\cdot\frac{1}{3}\right)-\frac{5}{6}\right]=2\left[\frac{1}{9}-\frac{5}{6}\right]$.

   Before subtracting, the common denominator must be found: $2\left[\frac{1}{9}\cdot\frac{2}{2}-\frac{5}{6}\cdot\frac{3}{3}\right]=2\left[\frac{2}{18}-\frac{15}{18}\right]=2\left[-\frac{13}{18}\right]$.

   Last, multiply by 2 and remember to cancel any common factors: $2\left[-\frac{13}{18}\right]=\frac{2}{1}\cdot-\frac{13}{18}=\frac{\cancel{2}(-13)}{\cancel{2}(9)}=-\frac{13}{9}$.

3. Simplify: $\frac{\frac{3}{4}(1-\frac{5}{3})^2}{5}$

   Solution: $\frac{1}{15}$

   Explanation: Carefully follow order of operations:

   $\frac{\frac{3}{4}(1-\frac{5}{3})^2}{5}=\frac{\frac{3}{4}(\frac{3}{3}-\frac{5}{3})^2}{5}=\frac{\frac{3}{4}(-\frac{2}{3})^2}{5}=\frac{\frac{3}{4}(\frac{4}{9})}{5}=\frac{\frac{12}{36}}{5}=\frac{\frac{1}{3}}{5}=\frac{1}{3}\div 5=\frac{1}{3}\div\frac{5}{1}=\frac{1}{3}\cdot\frac{1}{5}=\frac{1}{15}$.

Practice problems: *(Answers on page: 731)*

1. Simplify: $5\left(\frac{7}{15}\right)-\left(\frac{2}{3}\right)\div\left(\frac{4}{5}\right)$

2. Simplify: $\frac{3-\left(\frac{1}{2}\right)^2}{\frac{5}{6}}$

3. Simplify: $\frac{8(\frac{1}{2})^2}{\frac{3}{5}}-1$

Review questions: *(Answers to odd questions on page: 731)*

1. Simplify: $-\frac{1}{9}-\frac{2}{9}$
2. Simplify: $\frac{5}{21}+\frac{3}{14}$
3. Simplify: $20\div\frac{1}{2}$
4. Simplify: $6\left(\frac{3}{4}\right)-12\left(\frac{1}{6}\right)$
5. Simplify: $\dfrac{4+\left(\frac{1}{3}\right)^2}{-\frac{5}{6}}$

Writing Rational Expressions in Lowest Terms

- A **rational expression** is a $\dfrac{\textit{polynomial}}{\textit{polynomial}}$.
- Factor out any quantity common across the numerator and the denominator as your first step in reducing a rational expression.
- Remember that the denominator can never equal zero.

Example $\frac{2x+2}{2}=$ $\frac{2(x+1)}{2}=\frac{2}{2}\bullet\frac{(x+1)}{1}$ $=x+1$	In canceling factors to reduce a rational expression, first you must factor out the common quantity from everything in the numerator and everything in the denominator. Then you can cancel because what you have created is 2/2, which is a fraction equal to 1. Multiplying by 1 has no effect, so it can be eliminated.
Example $\frac{20x+10}{30x+15}=$ $\frac{10(2x+1)}{15(2x+1)}=\frac{2}{3}$	In this example, factoring out the obvious numbers, 20 and 15, reveals an expression that can be cancelled. The result is a simple fraction for the answer.
Rational Function : $\frac{\text{POLYNOMIAL}}{\text{POLYNOMIAL}}$ Domain : all allowable values of x. Simplify: $\frac{A^2-4A+4}{A^2+A-6}=$ $\frac{(A-2)(A-2)}{(A+3)(A-2)}=\frac{A-2}{A+3}$ $A\neq -3, 2$ because that would make the denominator 0.	**Remember:** Any time you have a variable in the denominator, you must exclude from its domain any value that sets the denominator equal to zero. In this case, –3 and +2 must be excluded. You can see that if $A=-3$, then $(A+3)=0$ or if $A=2$, then $(A-2)=0$. Remember that those exclusions carry forward into the answer as well as being initial conditions of the problem.

Sample problems:

1. Simplify: $\dfrac{y^2+2y-3}{y^2+4y+3}$

   Solution: $\dfrac{y-1}{y+1},\ y \neq -3,\ -1$

   Explanation: Factor the numerator and denominator: $\dfrac{y^2+2y-3}{y^2+4y+3}=\dfrac{(y-1)(y+3)}{(y+3)(y+1)}$.
   First, find the domain by setting each factor in the denominator equal to zero and solving for y: $y+3=0$ or $y+1=0$, $y=-3$ or $y=-1$.
   So the domain is all real numbers except $y=-3$ or $y=-1$.

   Next, reduce the rational expression: $\dfrac{(y-1)\cancel{(y+3)}}{\cancel{(y+3)}(y+1)}=\dfrac{y-1}{y+1},\ y\neq -3,\ -1.$

2. Simplify: $\dfrac{2x^2+11x+5}{2x^2-3x-2}$

   Solution: $\dfrac{x+5}{x-2},\ x\neq -\dfrac{1}{2},\ 2$

   Explanation: Factor the numerator and denominator: $\dfrac{2x^2+11x+5}{2x^2-3x-2}=\dfrac{(2x+1)(x+5)}{(2x+1)(x-2)}$.

   Set each factor in the denominator equal to zero and solve for x: $2x+1=0$ or $x-2=0$; $x=-\dfrac{1}{2}$ or $x=2$.

   So, the domain is all numbers except $x=-\dfrac{1}{2}$ or 2.

   Now, reduce the rational expression: $\dfrac{\cancel{(2x+1)}(x+5)}{\cancel{(2x+1)}(x-2)}=\dfrac{x+5}{x-2},\ x\neq -\dfrac{1}{2},\ 2.$

3. Simplify: $\dfrac{2a^3-54}{2a^2-18}$

   Solution: $\dfrac{a^2+3a+9}{a+3},\ a\neq 3,-3$

   Explanation: Factor the numerator and denominator: $\dfrac{2a^3-54}{2a^2-18}=\dfrac{2(a-3)(a^2+3a+9)}{2(a+3)(a-3)}$.

   Cancel the common factors: $\dfrac{\cancel{2}\cancel{(a-3)}(a^2+3a+9)}{\cancel{2}(a+3)\cancel{(a-3)}}=\dfrac{a^2+3a+9}{a+3},\ a\neq 3,\ -3.$

Practice problems: *(Answers on page: 731)*

1. Simplify: $\dfrac{3t^2-10t-8}{6t^2+13t+6}$

2. Simplify: $\dfrac{z^2+6z+9}{z^2-9}$

3. Simplify: $\dfrac{a^3-27}{a^2-9}$

Review questions: *(Answers to odd questions on page: 731)*

1. Simplify: $\dfrac{6(a+4)}{(a+4)(a+2)}$

2. Simplify: $\dfrac{(r-3)(r+2)}{(r+3)(r+2)}$

3. Simplify: $\dfrac{5x-5}{7x-7}$

4. Simplify: $\dfrac{z^2-7z+10}{3z-15}$

5. Simplify: $\dfrac{a^3-27}{a^2-9}$

Multiplying and Dividing Rational Expressions

- Multiplying and dividing rational expressions is the same process as multiplying and dividing fractions composed of real numbers.
- **Multiplying rationals** means: $\frac{a}{b}\cdot\frac{c}{d}=\frac{ac}{bd}$, and reduce if possible.
- **Dividing rationals** means: $\frac{a}{b}\div\frac{c}{d}=\frac{a}{d}\cdot\frac{d}{c}=\frac{ac}{bc}$, and reduce if possible.
- Remember that factoring a polynomial must remove the factored value from every term in the expression, not just the first one.
- Remember to watch signs carefully when factoring.

Example $\frac{5t^2+25t}{2}\bullet\frac{4}{6t+30}=$ $\frac{(5t^2+25t)\cancel{4}\,2}{\cancel{2}(6t+30)}=\frac{2\bullet 5t\cancel{(t+5)}}{6\cancel{(t+5)}}$ $=\frac{2\bullet 5t}{6}=\frac{5t}{3}$	In this example, multiplying across produces one fraction with factors to simplify. Then, remove factors from the binomials, and simplify some more. Finally, factor and cancel a pair of 2s to reach the final answer.
Example $\frac{x^2+x}{5}\div\frac{xy+y}{25}=$ $\frac{x^2+x}{5}\bullet\frac{25}{xy+y}=\frac{(x^2+x)\,25}{5\,(xy+y)}=$ $\frac{x\cancel{(x+1)}\,\cancel{25}\,5}{\cancel{5}y\cancel{(x+1)}}=\frac{5x}{y}$	The first step in dividing these rational expressions is to flip the second expression over. Next, multiply across the numerator and the denominator. Finally look for and find ways to factor more to simplify the final answer.
Example Simplify: $\frac{k^2+3k+2}{k^2+5k+4}\div\frac{k^2+5k+6}{k^2+10k+24}=$ $\frac{\cancel{(k+2)}\cancel{(k+1)}}{\cancel{(k+4)}\cancel{(k+1)}}\bullet\frac{(k+6)\cancel{(k+4)}}{\cancel{(k+2)}(k+3)}=\frac{k+6}{k+3}$	This example is a division problem with lots of factoring. So, the steps will be: 1. Flip the second fraction over. 2. Factor all the terms into binomials. 3. Cancel wherever possible. 4. Check the result and simplify further if possible.

Sample problems:

1. Simplify: $\dfrac{z^2-9}{z^2-9z+18} \div \dfrac{z^2+5z+6}{z^2-z-30}$

   Solution: $\dfrac{z+5}{z+2}$, $z \neq 3,\ z \neq 6,\ z \neq -2,\ z \neq -3$

   Explanation: Since the operation is division, multiply by the reciprocal:

   $\dfrac{z^2-9}{z^2-9z+18} \cdot \dfrac{z^2-z-30}{z^2+5z+6}$. Factor all polynomials: $\dfrac{(z+3)(z-3)}{(z-3)(z-6)} \cdot \dfrac{(z+5)(z-6)}{(z+2)(z+3)}$.

   Next, cancel the common factors: $\dfrac{\cancel{(z+3)}\cancel{(z-3)}(z+5)\cancel{(z-6)}}{\cancel{(z-3)}\cancel{(z-6)}(z+2)\cancel{(z+3)}} = \dfrac{(z+5)}{(z+2)}$.

   Set each factor in the denominator equal to 0 to determine the domain:
   $z-3=0;\ z-6=0;\ z+2=0;\ z+3=0$.
   Solve for z: $z \neq 3,\ z \neq 6,\ z \neq -2,\ z \neq -3$.

2. Simplify: $\dfrac{6x+3}{6x^2+30x+36} \div \dfrac{2x+1}{2x^2+14x+20}$

   Solution: $\dfrac{x+5}{x+3}$, $x \neq -3,\ -2,\ -\dfrac{1}{2}$

   Explanation: Since the operation is division, multiply by the reciprocal:

   $\dfrac{6x+3}{6x^2+30x+36} \cdot \dfrac{2x^2+14x+20}{2x+1} = \dfrac{3(2x+1)}{6(x+3)(x+2)} \cdot \dfrac{2(x+5)(x+2)}{2x+1}$.

   Cancel all common factors: $\dfrac{\cancel{3} \cdot \cancel{2}\,\cancel{(2x+1)}(x+5)\cancel{(x+2)}}{\cancel{6}(x+3)\cancel{(x+2)}\cancel{(2x+1)}} = \dfrac{x+5}{x+3}$.

   Determine the domain: $x \neq -3,\ x \neq -2,\ x \neq -\dfrac{1}{2}$.

3. Simplify: $\dfrac{x^3-1}{3x+12} \cdot \dfrac{6x+6}{x^2-1} \div 4x^2+4x+4$

   Solution: $\dfrac{1}{2x+8}$, $x \neq -4,\ x \neq -1,\ x \neq 1$

   Explanation: Express the term being divided as a term being multiplied then factor and cancel:

   $\dfrac{x^3-1}{3x+12} \cdot \dfrac{6x+6}{x^2-1} \cdot \dfrac{1}{4x^2+4x+4} = \dfrac{\cancel{(x-1)}\cancel{(x^2+x+1)}(6)\cancel{(x+1)}}{3(x+4)\cancel{(x+1)}\cancel{(x-1)}(4)\cancel{(x^2+x+1)}}$

   $= \dfrac{6}{12(x+4)} = \dfrac{1}{2(x+4)} = \dfrac{1}{2x+8}$.

   Determine the domain: $x \neq -1,\ x \neq 1, x \neq -4$

Practice problems: *(Answers on page: 731)*

1. Simplify: $\dfrac{t^2+7t+12}{t^2-t-20} \div \dfrac{t^2+9t+18}{t^2-9t+20}$

2. Simplify: $\dfrac{x^2-16}{2x^3-12x^2+16x} \cdot \dfrac{x^3+x^2-6x}{x^2-9}$

3. Simplify: $\dfrac{5x+10}{x^2-9} \cdot \dfrac{x^2+x-6}{10x+5} \div \dfrac{x^2-4}{2x^2-5x-3}$

Review questions: *(Answers to odd questions on page: 731)*

1. Simplify: $\dfrac{4x+8}{x} \div \dfrac{8}{x}$

2. Simplify: $\dfrac{9}{m^2-2m} \div \dfrac{5m}{6m-12}$

3. Simplify: $\dfrac{w^2+3w}{4w+4} \cdot \dfrac{16w+16}{w^2+2w-3}$

4. Simplify: $\dfrac{r^2-4}{r^2-1} \div \dfrac{r^2-r-2}{r^2+2r+1}$

5. Simplify: $\dfrac{2v^2-5v-3}{v^2+8v-33} \cdot \dfrac{v^2+9v-22}{2v^2-3v-2}$

Adding and Subtracting Rational Expressions

- Always find the common denominator for the rational expressions before you add or subtract.
- The **least common denominator** is the smallest multiple common to all the denominators in the problem.
- The **least common multiple** is the smallest number that contains every factor in the denominators. It is usually used as the common denominator.
- To change the denominator, multiply by 1 in some form; i.e., multiply by a fraction that has the same expression for both numerator and denominator.
- As a general rule, let denominators stay factored because you might see an opportunity to cancel one or more factors after you do the arithmetic.

Adding Rational Expressions **Example** Simplify: $\dfrac{1}{x+z} + \dfrac{1}{x-z}$	In this example, the two fractions have no common factors in their denominators.
$\left(\dfrac{x-z}{x-z}\right)\left(\dfrac{1}{x+z}\right) + \left(\dfrac{1}{x-z}\right)\left(\dfrac{x+z}{x+z}\right) =$	To create a common denominator, use 1 in some form. A fraction equal to 1 has the same numerator as it has denominator. In this case, use two forms of 1: $\dfrac{x-z}{x-z}$ and $\dfrac{x+z}{x+z}$ to create your common denominator in the two fractions.
$\dfrac{x-z}{(x+z)(x-z)} + \dfrac{x+z}{(x+z)(x-z)} = \dfrac{2x}{(x+z)(x-z)}$ $= \dfrac{2x}{x^2-z^2}$	Multiplying to create the common denominator brings $(x-z)$ and $(x+z)$ to the numerator. As you remove the parentheses and add terms, follow the signs carefully. As your final step, you may choose to multiply out the denominator.
Example Simplify: $\dfrac{1}{t^2+t-12} - \dfrac{1}{t^2-7t+12} + \dfrac{1}{t^2-16} =$ $\dfrac{1}{(t+4)(t-3)} - \dfrac{1}{(t-3)(t-4)} + \dfrac{1}{(t+4)(t-4)}$	The message of this problem is that each denominator must be factored so you can see what is needed to create a common denominator.

$\text{LCM} = (t+4)(t-3)(t-4)$ $\left(\frac{t-4}{t-4}\right)\left(\frac{1}{(t+4)(t-3)}\right) - \left(\frac{t+4}{t+4}\right)\left(\frac{1}{(t-3)(t-4)}\right) + \left(\frac{t-3}{t-3}\right)\left(\frac{1}{(t+4)(t-4)}\right)$	Factoring the denominator enables you to see what form of 1 to multiply each fraction with in order to create the common denominator. The lowest common multiple (LCM) will be the smallest number that multiplies every factor used in the denominators. In this case the LCM multiplies $(t-4)$, $(t+4)$ and $(t-3)$.
$\frac{t-4}{(t+4)(t-3)(t-4)} - \frac{t+4}{(t+4)(t-3)(t-4)} + \frac{t-3}{(t+4)(t-3)(t-4)} =$ $\frac{t-11}{(t+4)(t-3)(t-4)}$	Always distribute carefully through the parentheses when multiplying for denominators. The arithmetic mistakes that happen because signs were not changed when multiplying across parentheses are common and painful.
$\frac{t-11}{(t+4)(t-3)(t-4)}$	Remember to exclude from your domain for t any values that would result in the denominator having a value of 0. In this case, exclude $t = 4, -4$, and 3.

Sample problems:

1. Simplify: $\dfrac{z+4}{z-1} - \dfrac{z}{z+3}$

   Solution: $\dfrac{8z+12}{(z-1)(z+3)}$

   Explanation: Find the common denominator: $\dfrac{z+4}{z-1} - \dfrac{z}{z+3} = \left(\dfrac{z+3}{z+3}\right)\dfrac{z+4}{z-1} - \left(\dfrac{z-1}{z-1}\right)\dfrac{z}{z+3}$.

   Subtract: $\dfrac{(z+3)(z+4)}{(z+3)(z-1)} - \dfrac{z(z-1)}{(z-1)(z+3)} = \dfrac{(z+3)(z+4) - z(z-1)}{(z+3)(z-1)}$.

   Simplify the numerator: $\dfrac{(z+3)(z+4) - z(z-1)}{(z+3)(z-1)} = \dfrac{(z^2+7z+12) - (z^2 - z)}{(z+3)(z-1)} = \dfrac{8z+12}{(z-1)(z+3)}$.

2. Simplify: $\dfrac{x-1}{x^2-x-12} + \dfrac{3-x}{x^2-3x-4}$

   Solution: $\dfrac{8}{(x+1)(x+3)(x-4)}$

   Explanation: Factor the denominator of each term:

   $\dfrac{x-1}{x^2-x-12} + \dfrac{3-x}{x^2-3x-4} = \dfrac{x-1}{(x+3)(x-4)} + \dfrac{3-x}{(x-4)(x+1)}$.

   Find a common denominator: $\left(\dfrac{x+1}{x+1}\right) \cdot \dfrac{x-1}{(x+3)(x-4)} + \left(\dfrac{x+3}{x+3}\right) \cdot \dfrac{3-x}{(x-4)(x+1)}$.

   Multiply the factors together: $\dfrac{x^2-1}{(x+1)(x+3)(x-4)} + \dfrac{9-x^2}{(x+1)(x+3)(x-4)}$.

   Add the two terms together: $\dfrac{(x^2-1)+(9-x^2)}{(x+1)(x+3)(x-4)} = \dfrac{8}{(x+1)(x+3)(x-4)}$.

3. Simplify: $\dfrac{2}{x^2-9}+\dfrac{1}{x^2+2x-15}-\dfrac{3}{x^2+8x+15}$

Solution: $\dfrac{22}{(x+3)(x-3)(x+5)}$

Explanation: Factor each denominator: $\dfrac{2}{(x+3)(x-3)}+\dfrac{1}{(x+5)(x-3)}-\dfrac{3}{(x+5)(x+3)}$.

Find the common denominator: $\left(\dfrac{x+5}{x+5}\right)\cdot\dfrac{2}{(x+3)(x-3)}+\left(\dfrac{x+3}{x+3}\right)\cdot\dfrac{1}{(x+5)(x-3)}-\dfrac{(x-3)}{(x-3)}\cdot\dfrac{3}{(x+5)(x+3)}$.

Combine the terms: $\dfrac{2(x+5)+1(x+3)-3(x-3)}{(x+3)(x-3)(x+5)}$.

Simplify the numerator: $\dfrac{2x+10+x+3-3x+9}{(x+3)(x-3)(x+5)}=\dfrac{22}{(x+3)(x-3)(x+5)}$.

Practice problems: *(Answers on page: 732)*

1. Simplify: $\dfrac{3}{k+8}-\dfrac{3}{k-8}$
2. Simplify: $\dfrac{x+7}{x+1}+\dfrac{2x-5}{x-2}$
3. Simplify: $\dfrac{1}{x+4}+\dfrac{3}{x^2-16}-\dfrac{5}{x^2+9x+20}$

Review questions: *(Answers to odd questions on page: 732)*

1. Simplify: $\dfrac{k+8}{3}-\dfrac{k-8}{3}$
2. Simplify: $\dfrac{3}{5x}+\dfrac{5}{3x}$
3. Simplify: $\dfrac{1}{t-2}+\dfrac{1}{3t}$
4. Simplify: $\dfrac{w+9}{w^2+6w-16}-\dfrac{w-9}{w^2+10w+16}$
5. Simplify: $\dfrac{1}{4y}-\dfrac{1}{y+7}+\dfrac{1}{y-1}$

Rewriting Complex Fractions

- The first step in simplifying a **complex fraction** is to put in place a common denominator within the numerator and also within the denominator.
- Two ways to simplify a complex fraction:
  - Set up a common denominator in both the numerator and the denominator, then invert and multiply.
  - Multiply both numerator and denominator of the complex fraction by the least common multiple for the denominators of both levels of the complex fraction.

Example $\dfrac{2-\frac{2}{t}}{2+\frac{2}{t}}$	The common denominator in both the numerator and denominator of this example is *t*.

Example Method 1: Invert the denominator and multiply $\dfrac{(\frac{t}{t})(2)-\frac{2}{t}}{(\frac{t}{t})(2)+\frac{2}{t}} = \dfrac{\frac{2t}{t}-\frac{2}{t}}{\frac{2t}{t}+\frac{2}{t}} = \dfrac{\frac{2t-2}{t}}{\frac{2t+2}{t}}$	The first step is to multiply by *t/t* to get the common denominator in place. Once the common denominator is in place, invert and multiply as required for the division.
$\dfrac{2t-2}{\not t} \bullet \dfrac{\not t}{2t+2} = \dfrac{\not 2(t-1)}{\not 2(t+1)} = \dfrac{t-1}{t+1}$	In this example, once the second fraction is inverted to multiply, the single *t*s can cancel. Also, 2s can factor out and cancel.
Example Method 2: Multiply the numerator and denominator of the complex fraction by the least common multiple $\dfrac{1+\frac{1}{x}}{1-\frac{1}{x^2}} = \dfrac{(1+\frac{1}{x})x^2}{(1-\frac{1}{x^2})x^2}$	In this case, the least common multiple for all the denominators in the problem is x^2. Multiply by x^2/x^2 and the complex fraction simplifies to a normal fraction.
$\dfrac{x^2+x}{x^2-1} = \dfrac{x\cancel{(x+1)}}{\cancel{(x+1)}(x-1)} = \dfrac{x}{x-1}$	Check the simplified fraction for any factoring that would further reduce the fraction.

Sample problems:

1. Simplify: $\dfrac{\frac{1}{z-4}+\frac{2}{z+1}}{\frac{2}{z+1}+\frac{3}{z-4}}$

   Solution: $\dfrac{3z-7}{5z-5}$

   Explanation: Multiply by the common denominator:

$$\frac{\frac{1}{z-4}+\frac{2}{z+1}}{\frac{2}{z+1}+\frac{3}{z-4}}\cdot\left(\frac{(z+1)(z-4)}{(z+1)(z-4)}\right)=\frac{\frac{(z+1)(z-4)}{z-4}+\frac{2(z+1)(z-4)}{z+1}}{\frac{2(z+1)(z-4)}{z+1}+\frac{3(z+1)(z-4)}{z-4}}.$$

Cancel common factors from each term:

$$\frac{\frac{(z+1)\cancel{(z-4)}}{\cancel{z-4}}+\frac{2\cancel{(z+1)}(z-4)}{\cancel{z+1}}}{\frac{2\cancel{(z+1)}(z-4)}{\cancel{z+1}}+\frac{3(z+1)\cancel{(z-4)}}{\cancel{z-4}}}=\frac{(z+1)+2(z-4)}{2(z-4)+3(z+1)}.$$

Simplify: $\dfrac{(z+1)+2(z-4)}{2(z-4)+3(z+1)}=\dfrac{z+1+2z-8}{2z-8+3z+3}=\dfrac{3z-7}{5z-5}.$

2. Simplify: $\dfrac{\dfrac{1}{x^2+5x+6}}{\dfrac{1}{x+3}-\dfrac{1}{x+2}}$

Solution: -1

Explanation: Factor the expression in the numerator: $\dfrac{\dfrac{1}{(x+2)(x+3)}}{\dfrac{1}{x+3}-\dfrac{1}{x+2}}$.

Multiply by the common denominator: $\dfrac{\dfrac{1}{(x+2)(x+3)}}{\dfrac{1}{x+3}-\dfrac{1}{x+2}}\cdot\left(\dfrac{(x+2)(x+3)}{(x+2)(x+3)}\right)=\dfrac{\dfrac{(x+2)(x+3)}{(x+2)(x+3)}}{\dfrac{(x+2)(x+3)}{x+3}-\dfrac{(x+2)(x+3)}{x+2}}$.

Cancel common factors from each term and simplify:

$$\frac{\dfrac{\cancel{(x+2)}\,\cancel{(x+3)}}{\cancel{(x+2)}\,\cancel{(x+3)}}}{\dfrac{(x+2)\cancel{(x+3)}}{\cancel{x+3}}-\dfrac{\cancel{(x+2)}(x+3)}{\cancel{x+2}}}=\frac{1}{(x+2)-(x+3)}=\frac{1}{-1}=-1.$$

3. Simplify: $\dfrac{\dfrac{3}{x^2+3x+2}+\dfrac{5}{x+1}}{\dfrac{1}{x^2+6x+5}-\dfrac{2}{x^2+7x+10}}$

Solution: $\dfrac{5x^2+38x+65}{-x}$

Explanation: Factor each denominator: $\dfrac{\dfrac{3}{(x+2)(x+1)}+\dfrac{5}{x+1}}{\dfrac{1}{(x+5)(x+1)}-\dfrac{2}{(x+5)(x+2)}}$.

Multiply by the common denominator:

$$\frac{\dfrac{3}{(x+2)(x+1)}+\dfrac{5}{x+1}}{\dfrac{1}{(x+5)(x+1)}-\dfrac{2}{(x+5)(x+2)}}\cdot\frac{(x+2)(x+1)(x+5)}{(x+2)(x+1)(x+5)}=\frac{\dfrac{3(x+2)(x+1)(x+5)}{(x+2)(x+1)}+\dfrac{5(x+2)(x+1)(x+5)}{x+1}}{\dfrac{1(x+2)(x+1)(x+5)}{(x+5)(x+1)}-\dfrac{2(x+2)(x+1)(x+5)}{(x+5)(x+2)}}.$$

Cancel common factors from each term:

$$\frac{\dfrac{3\cancel{(x+2)}\,\cancel{(x+1)}(x+5)}{\cancel{(x+2)}\,\cancel{(x+1)}}+\dfrac{5(x+2)\cancel{(x+1)}(x+5)}{\cancel{x+1}}}{\dfrac{1(x+2)\cancel{(x+1)}\,\cancel{(x+5)}}{\cancel{(x+5)}\,\cancel{(x+1)}}-\dfrac{2\cancel{(x+2)}(x+1)\cancel{(x+5)}}{\cancel{(x+5)}\,\cancel{(x+2)}}}=\frac{3(x+5)+5(x+2)(x+5)}{(x+2)-2(x+1)}.$$

Simplify the numerator and the denominator:

$$\frac{3x+15+5(x^2+7x+10)}{(x+2)-2x-2}=\frac{3x+15+5x^2+35x+50}{x+2-2x-2}=\frac{5x^2+38x+65}{-x}.$$

Practice problems: *(Answers on page: 732)*

1. Simplify: $\dfrac{\dfrac{1}{n}-\dfrac{1}{3-n}}{\dfrac{1}{n}}$

2. Simplify: $\dfrac{\dfrac{2}{x^2+3x-10}+\dfrac{1}{x+5}}{\dfrac{1}{x-2}}$

3. Simplify: $\dfrac{\dfrac{2}{x+3}-\dfrac{1}{x^2-2x-15}}{\dfrac{1}{x^2+7x+12}+\dfrac{4}{x^2-x-20}}$

Review questions: *(Answers to odd questions on page: 732)*

1. Simplify: $\dfrac{\frac{4}{3}}{\frac{16}{9}}$

2. Simplify: $\dfrac{\frac{1}{x+h}-\frac{1}{x}}{h}$

3. Simplify: $\dfrac{1}{\frac{1}{x}-\frac{1}{y}}$

4. Simplify: $\dfrac{\frac{5}{k^2-9}+1}{\frac{1}{k+3}+\frac{5}{k-3}}$

5. Simplify: $\dfrac{2+\frac{1}{2x+1}}{3+\frac{1}{2+\frac{1}{x}}}$

Introducing and Writing Complex Numbers

- Numbers like $\sqrt{-4}$ or $\sqrt{-9.5}$ that involve the square root of a negative number are called **imaginary numbers**.
- Imaginary numbers can be written in terms of the number i, which is equal to the square root of -1: $i=\sqrt{-1}$.
- A **complex number** has the form $\boldsymbol{a+bi}$ where $\boldsymbol{a}$ is a real number and $\boldsymbol{bi}$ is some number multiplying with $\boldsymbol{i}$, an imaginary number.

$\sqrt{-9}$ *not real*	When you see a number under a square root sign, you are being asked for the value that multiplied with itself to give the number under the radical sign; i.e., the root that produced the number under the radical sign. There is no real number that multiplies with itself and gives a negative answer. So, the square root of any negative number must be an imaginary number.
$\sqrt{-9}=\sqrt{(-1)(9)}$	You can easily factor the negative out of a number.
$=\sqrt{-1}\sqrt{9}$	Then you can separate the factors so that you have a positive square root to find and the square root of the -1.
$\sqrt{-1}=i$	Because the square root of any negative number is **imaginary**, mathematicians have developed a special set of numbers.
Example $\sqrt{-9}=\sqrt{(-1)(9)}$ $=\sqrt{-1}\sqrt{9}$ $=3i$	The -1 is represented in the answer by i. The square root of 9 is the 3. Without the use of i, we would be unable to eliminate this radical.

Sample problems:

1. Simplify: $\sqrt{-36}$
   Solution: $6i$

   Explanation: Begin by factoring the radicand: $\sqrt{-36} = \sqrt{(6)^2} \cdot \sqrt{-1}$. Next, find the square root of each factor: $\sqrt{(6)^2} \cdot \sqrt{-1} = 6i$.

2. Simplify: $\sqrt{-49} + 2$
   Solution: $7i + 2$
   Explanation: Factor the randicand then find the root of each factor:
   $\sqrt{-49} + 2 = \left(\sqrt{7 \cdot 7} \cdot \sqrt{-1}\right) + 2 = 7i + 2$

3. Simplify: $5\sqrt{-200} + \sqrt{-32}$
   Solution: $54i\sqrt{2}$
   Explanation: Simplify each radical:
   $5\sqrt{-200} + \sqrt{-32} = 5\sqrt{2 \cdot 100 \cdot -1} + \sqrt{2 \cdot 16 \cdot -1}$
   $= 5(\sqrt{2})(\sqrt{100})(\sqrt{-1}) + (\sqrt{2})(\sqrt{16})(\sqrt{-1})$
   $= 5(\sqrt{2})(10)(i) + (\sqrt{2})(4)(i)$
   $= 50i\sqrt{2} + 4i\sqrt{2} = 54i\sqrt{2}$.

Practice problems: *(Answers on page: 732)*

1. Simplify: $\sqrt{-20}$
2. Simplify: $9 + \sqrt{-18}$
3. Simplify: $\sqrt{-300} + 4\sqrt{-75}$

Review questions: *(Answers to odd questions on page: 732)*

1. Simplify: $\sqrt{-121}$
2. Simplify: $3 - \sqrt[3]{-27}$
3. Simplify: $\sqrt{-1} + 7$
4. Simplify: $4 + \sqrt{-325}$
5. Simplify: $2\sqrt{-125} + 7\sqrt{20}$

Rewriting Powers of i

- $i = \sqrt{-1}$. The number ***i*** is an example of an **imaginary number**.
- $i^2 = -1$.
- $i^3 = i \cdot i^2 = i \cdot -1 = -i$.
- $i^4 = (i^2)^2 = -1 \cdot -1 = 1$.
- Every power of ***i*** is equal to one of these four values: ***i***, -1, - ***i***, or 1.

$i = \sqrt{-1}$	*i* is called an **imaginary number** because in our number system there is no number which can multiply by itself and still be negative.

$i^2=-1$	i^2 turns that imaginary number, i, into an imaginary number with a real number value, not by any magic, but by using normal multiplication rules: $\sqrt{-1}\cdot\sqrt{-1}=(\sqrt{-1})^2=-1$
$i^3=i^2\bullet i=-i$	i^3 can be read as $i\cdot i^2$. That's a good idea since we know the value of both of those. Substituting -1 for i^2, gives us our value.
$i^4=1$	i^4 equals $i^2\cdot i^2$, which is -1 -1. Doing the multiplication, you get 1 as the product. There are no more values beyond i^4. i and i^2 are defined. i^3 and i^4 are combinations of i and i^2 that provide unique answers.
To find the equivalent to any power of i : • divide the power by four • your answer will = $i^{(\text{remainder})}$ $i=\sqrt{-1}$ $i^2=-1$ $i^3=-i$ $i^4=1$ **Example** $i^{40}=i^{4\cdot 10}=(i^4)^{10}=1^{10}=1$ **Example** $i^{223}=i^{4\cdot 55+3}=(i^4)^{55}\bullet i^3$ $=(1)^{55}\bullet -i$ $=-i$	Starting with i^5, the values start over because everything is some combination of the first four values. The values make a loop that starts over every four terms. Your value will always be wherever you fall in that loop. Divide the power given for i in your problem by 4. The value you need will be the value for i using the remainder as your power.

Sample problems:

1. Simplify: i^{10}

   Solution: -1

   Explanation: Divide the exponent by 4 (the answer will be $i^{(\text{remainder})}$) :

   $i^{10}=i^{4\cdot 2+2}=(i^4)^2\cdot i^2$.

   Recall that $i^4=1$: $(i^4)^2\cdot i^2=(1)^2\cdot i^2=1\cdot i^2=i^2$.

   Recall that $i^2=-1$. Thus, $i^{10}=-1$.

2. Simplify: i^{-22}

   Solution: -1

   Explanation: Express i^{-22} with a positive exponent: $i^{-22}=\frac{1}{i^{22}}$.

   Divide the exponent by 4 (the answer will be $i^{(\text{remainder})}$):

   $\frac{1}{i^{22}}=\frac{1}{i^{4\cdot 5+2}}=\frac{1}{(i^4)^5\cdot i^2}=\frac{1}{(1)^5\cdot i^2}=\frac{1}{1\cdot i^2}=\frac{1}{i^2}$.

   Recall that $i^2=-1$: $\frac{1}{i^2}=\frac{1}{-1}=-1$. Thus, $i^{-22}=-1$.

3. Simplify: $-i^{-494}$

   Solution: 1

   Explanation: Express $-i^{-494}$ with a positive exponent: $-i^{-494}=-\frac{1}{i^{494}}$.

   Divide the exponent by 4: $-\frac{1}{i^{494}}=-\frac{1}{i^{4\cdot 123+2}}=-\frac{1}{(i^4)^{123}\cdot i^2}=-\frac{1}{(1)^{123}\cdot i^2}$

   $=\frac{1}{i^2}=-\frac{1}{-1}=-(-1)=1.$

Practice problems: *(Answers on page: 732)*

1. Simplify: i^{-3}
2. Simplify: i^{-33}
3. Simplify: $-i^{-168}$

Review questions: *(Answers to odd questions on page: 732)*

1. Simplify: i^{4}
2. Simplify: i^{15}
3. Simplify: i^{23}
4. Simplify: i^{-35}
5. Simplify: i^{122}

Adding and Subtracting Complex Numbers

- A **Complex Number** is a binomial composed of a variable or constant with an imaginary, or i -number, being added or subtracted.
- When **adding complex numbers**, add like terms according to the normal rules. Add constants to constants, variables to variables, and imaginary numbers to imaginary numbers.
- When **subtracting complex numbers**, subtract like terms according to the normal rules, paying attention to sign changes across parentheses as you combine constants with constants, variables with variables, and imaginary numbers with imaginary numbers.

Example $(5-i)+(9-2i)=14-3i$ $5-i$ $+\ 9-2i$ $14-3i$	**Adding complex numbers** means that you add like terms: • Variables with variables • i 's with i 's • Constants with constants
Example $(7-3i)-(-5-i)=12-2i$ $7-3i$ $-\ (-5-i)$ $12-2i$	**Subtracting complex numbers** follows the same rules: • Variables with variables • i 's with i 's • Constants with constants **Remember:** Watch your signs and use your parentheses correctly. It may even pay to write out the numbers with their signs changed before you do any combining. This one mistake creates more errors with this type of numbers than any other action.

Sample problems:

1. Simplify: $5+3(1-8i)-10i$
   Solution: $8-34i$
   Explanation: Use the distributive property, then combine like terms:
   $5+3(1-8i)-10i=5+3-24i-10i=8-34i.$

2. Simplify: $(5+9i)-(12+13i)$
   Solution: $-7-4i$
   Explanation: Distribute the negative, then combine like terms:
   $(5+9i)-(12+13i)=5+9i-12-13i=-7-4i.$

3. Simplify: $(1-10i)+2(5+9i)-5(2+3i)$
   Solution: $1-7i$
   Explanation: Distribute the 2 and the negative, then combine like terms:
   $(1-10i)+2(5+9i)-5(2+3i)=1-10i+10+18i-10-15i=1-7i.$

Practice problems: *(Answers on page: 732)*

1. Simplify: $(6i+4)+(2i-7)$
2. Simplify: $(i+2)-(5i-1)$
3. Simplify: $(6i+1)-2(i-3)+5(2i+7)$

Review questions: *(Answers to odd questions on page: 732)*

1. Simplify: $(6-i)+(-3+i)$
2. Simplify: $(5-2i)+(3+7i)$
3. Simplify: $(2-5i)-(5+2i)$
4. Simplify: $(11+2i)-(9-4i)$
5. Simplify: $2(2-3i)-(4+8i)+15i$

Multiplying Complex Numbers

- $i=\sqrt{-1}$. This is called an imaginary number because there are no examples of a number which multiplies with itself to produce a negative number. Therefore, no one knows what the square root of a negative might be; it must be **imaginary**.
- $i^2=-1$. This follows from the definition of a square root. If you multiply a square root times itself, you get the base being rooted.
- **FOIL**: Multiply binomials by multiplying
  First terms together
  Outer terms together
  Inside terms
  Last terms, and adding all the products together.

$i=\sqrt{-1} \quad i^2=-1$	Here are ***i*** and ***i***^{2} defined for you. Learn them. They turn up wherever complex numbers turn up.
Example $(2+3i)(6-5i)$ $12+18i-10i-15i^2(-1)$ $=27+8i$	Multiplying with complex numbers works just like **FOIL** with a binomial. Note the i^2 becomes -1 which means that the -15 becomes +15.
Example $(3+5i)^2=$ $(3+5i)(3+5i)=$ $9+15i+15i+25i^2\ -25$ $=-16+30i$	The only new thing to remember is that when you get an ***i***^{2} change it to –1. The net effect is to create a constant with the opposite sign. Once you've done that, if there are other constants, combine them.

Sample problems:

1. Express the following complex number in standard form: $(3-i)^2$
   Solution: $8-6i$
   Explanation: Use the FOIL method to multiply: $(3-i)^2 = (3-i)(3-i) = 9-6i+i^2$.
   Use $i^2 = -1$ to further simplify the expression: $9-6i+i^2 = 9-6i+(-1) = 8-6i$.

2. Express the following complex number in standard form: $\left(\sqrt{3}+2i\right)\left(\sqrt{3}-2i\right)$
   Solution: 7
   Explanation: Multiply: $\left(\sqrt{3}+2i\right)\left(\sqrt{3}-2i\right) = \sqrt{9}-2i\sqrt{3}+2i\sqrt{3}-4i^2 = 3-4i^2$.
   Use $i^2 = -1$ to further simplify: $3-4i^2 = 3-4(-1) = 3+4 = 7$.

3. Express the following complex number in standard form: $i(5-2i)(i+4)$
   Solution: $3+22i$
   Explanation: FOIL the binomials: $i(5-2i)(i+4) = i(5i+20-2i^2-8i)$. Distribute the i and simplify: $i(5i+20-2i^2-8i) = 5i^2+20i-2i^3-8i^2 = -3i^2+20i-2i^3 = -3(-1)+20i-2(-1)i =$
   $3+20i+2i = 3+22i$.

Practice problems: *(Answers on page: 732)*

1. Express the following complex number in standard form: $(5+2i)^2$
2. Express the following complex number in standard form: $\left(\sqrt{5}+i\right)\left(\sqrt{5}-i\right)$
3. Express the following complex number in standard form: $i(5+2i)(i-1)$

Review questions: *(Answers to odd questions on page: 732)*

1. Express the following in standard form: $(1+i)^2$
2. Express the following in standard form: $(-1-5i)^2$
3. Express the following in standard form: $(2-2i)(-3+3i)$
4. Express the following in standard form: $i(4-i)(5+2i)$
5. Express the following in standard form: $(4+i)(2+i)$

Dividing Complex Numbers

- Clearing a denominator of radicals means to multiply the fraction by a version of 1. Your version of 1 will be the radical over itself. So, the denominator multiplies out the radical to clear it, and the numerator gets a radical.
- A **conjugate** is used when fractions have radicals or imaginary numbers in their denominators as a means of clearing those values from the denominators, or **rationalizing the denominator**.
- $i = \sqrt{-1}$
- $i^2 = -1$

Example $\frac{4+i}{3+5i} = \left(\frac{(4+i)}{(3+5i)}\right)\cdot\left(\frac{(3-5i)}{(3-5i)}\right) =$ $\frac{12+3i-20i+5}{9-15i+15i+25} = \frac{17-17i}{34}$	The first step in dividing with complex numbers is to clear the complex values from the denominator. So, multiply both top and bottom of the fraction by the **conjugate** of the denominator. This process leaves all real numbers in the denominator and adds a complex number to the numerator.

$=\frac{17(1-i)}{34}$ $=\frac{1-i}{2}$ $=\frac{1}{2}-\frac{1}{2}i$ real — imaginary	Once you've cleared the undesirable numbers from the denominator, you can proceed to solve the problem quite nicely.
Example $\frac{1}{2+i}\left(\frac{(2-i)}{(2-i)}\right)=\frac{2-i}{4-2i+2i-i^2}=\frac{2-i}{4+1}$ $=\frac{2-i}{5}$ $=\frac{2}{5}-\frac{1}{5}i$	Let's try another one. Multiply the top and bottom of the fraction by $2-i$, the conjugate of the denominator. This one leads you into the paths that are common with imaginary numbers and radicals. It's not difficult, but the answer is unexpected.

Sample problems:

1. Express the following complex number in standard form: $\frac{15-9i}{3i}$

   Solution: $-3-5i$

   Explanation: To express a complex number in standard form, $a+bi$, simplify and write the constant term then the imaginary term. Notice that a 3 will factor from the numerator: $\frac{15-9i}{3i}=\frac{3(5-3i)}{3i}=\frac{5-3i}{i}$. Next, since there is an imaginary number in the denominator, rationalize the denominator by multiplying the expression by $\frac{i}{i}$: $\frac{5-3i}{i}=\frac{5-3i}{i}\cdot\frac{i}{i}=\frac{i(5-3i)}{i^2}=\frac{5i-3i^2}{i^2}$. Subsitiute -1 in for i^2 to further simplify: $\frac{5i-3i^2}{i^2}=\frac{5i-3(-1)}{(-1)}=\frac{5i+3}{(-1)}=-3-5i$.

2. Express the following complex number in standard form: $\frac{8}{9+4i}$

   Solution: $\frac{72}{97}-\frac{32}{97}i$

   Explanation: The denominator is a binomial with an imaginary number, so in order to simplify first rationalize this denominator by multiplying the expression by the conjugate over itself, $\frac{9-4i}{9-4i}$: $\frac{8}{9+4i}=\frac{8}{9+4i}\cdot\frac{9-4i}{9-4i}=\frac{8(9-4i)}{(9+4i)(9-4i)}=\frac{72-32i}{81-16i^2}$. Further simplify by substituting -1 for i^2: $\frac{72-32i}{81-16i^2}=\frac{72-32i}{81-16(-1)}=\frac{72-32i}{97}$.
   The standard form of a complex number is $a+bi$, so express as $\frac{72}{97}-\frac{32}{97}i$.

3. Express the following complex number in standard form: $\frac{7+2i}{3+5i}$

   Solution: $\frac{31}{34}-\frac{29}{34}i$

   Explanation: Multiply by the conjugate to rationalize the denominator, then simplify: $\frac{7+2i}{3+5i}=\frac{7+2i}{3+5i}\cdot\frac{3-5i}{3-5i}=\frac{21-29i-10i^2}{9-25i^2}$. Further simplify by substituting -1 for i^2: $\frac{21-29i-10(-1)}{9-25(-1)}=\frac{21-29i-10(-1)}{9-25(-1)}=\frac{21-29i+10}{9+25}=\frac{31-29i}{34}$.
   The standard form of a complex number is $a+bi$, so express as $\frac{31}{34}-\frac{29}{34}i$.

Practice problems: *(Answers on page: 732)*

1. Express the following complex number in standard form: $\dfrac{2+3i}{3+2i}$

2. Express the following complex number in standard form: $\dfrac{-5+2i}{-1+3i}$

3. Express the following complex number in standard form: $\dfrac{-4-5i}{-8-7i}$

Review questions: *(Answers to odd questions on page: 732)*

1. Express the following in standard form: $\dfrac{1+i}{5}$

2. Express the following in standard form: $\dfrac{2}{4-7i}$

3. Express the following in standard form: $\dfrac{2-i}{2+i}$

4. Express the following in standard form: $\dfrac{1+3i}{5-i}$

5. Express the following in standard form: $\dfrac{5+i}{11-i}$

2

Equations and Inequalities

An Introduction to Solving Equations

- **Equation**: two values are shown to be equal, or perfectly balanced, as signified by their being connected across an equal sign.
- **Variable**: an unknown value in an expression or equation that is represented usually by a letter.
- ***x***: letter most commonly used as a variable.
- **Constant**: a regular number; e.g., 7, which always has the same value.
- **Solving an equation**: finding the value(s) for the variable(s) that makes the equation true.
- **Proving an answer**: Using the value you found in the equation, in place of the variable, to see whether the equation really is balanced and whether the left side really has the same value as the right side even though they are probably not written using the same numbers.

$4x - 3 = 2x + 5$

$16 = 16$ ← TRUE

$16 = 15$ ← FALSE

Think of an **equation** as representing two versions of exactly the same number, one on each side of the equal sign.

Find: the value of *x* that makes the statement true or balanced

$4x - 3 = 2x + 5$

$4? - 3 = 2? + 5$

Solving an equation in algebra means figuring out what number must be substituted for the unknown number represented by the **variable**.

The variable can be any symbol you wish. People have been known to use pennies, empty boxes, happy faces, ducks, and a host of other objects.

Most commonly, the unknown value is represented by some letter, usually x.

Find: value of *x* that makes the statement true/balanced
Need to: add, subtract, multiply or divide to get *x* isolated on one side

$$\begin{aligned} 4x - 3 &= 2x + 5 \\ -2x \quad &= -2x \\ \hline 2x - 3 &= 5 \\ +3 &= +3 \\ \hline 2x &= 8 \end{aligned}$$

add 3 to both sides

divide both sides by 2

To solve for x you get all the variables on one side of the equation, usually the left, and everything else on the right side.

You do this by adding and subtracting the same amounts to both sides of the equation so the variable shifts to the left side and the **constants** shift to the right side.

In this case, add $-2x$ and $+3$ to both sides. When you are done, you will have the variables all together on one side and the constants all together on the other side.

$$\begin{aligned} 4x - 3 &= 2x + 5 \\ -2x \quad &= -2x \\ \hline 2x - 3 &= 5 \\ +3 &= +3 \\ \hline \frac{\cancel{2}x}{\cancel{2}} &= \frac{8}{2} \end{aligned}$$

$$\boxed{x = 4}$$

add 3 to both sides

divide both sides by 2

cancel and simplify

Next, you'll multiply or divide both sides of the equation by the same number. Your goal is to have one x isolated on its side of the equation.

In this example, divide both sides by +2.
The result is $x = 4$.

You don't worry about the right side; you'll have whatever number is the answer there when you've finished getting down to just x on the left side.

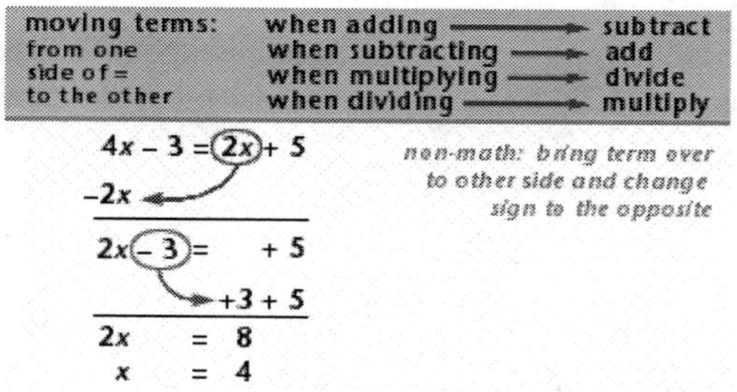

Want a shortcut? Use opposites.

On the left side add the opposite of every variable found on the right. On the right side, add the opposite of every constant found on the left. In this case, add $-2x$ to the left and $+3$ to the right.

Then multiply or divide to find out what value x has. In this case, divide both sides by 2 to find out that $x = 4$.

Sample problems:

1. Solve for x: $5x+4=-x+7$

   Solution: $\frac{1}{2}$

   Explanation: Add x to both sides: $5x+4+x=-x+7+x$; $6x+4=7$. Subtract 4 from both sides: $6x+4-4=7-4$; $6x=3$. Divide each side by 6: $\frac{6x}{6}=\frac{3}{6}$; $x=\frac{3}{6}=\frac{1}{2}$.

2. True or false: The solution of $4(x+6)-7x=2(x+3)-2$ is $x=-4$.
   Solution: False
   Explanation: Substitute -4 into the equation for each x and simplify:
   $4(-4+6)-7(-4)=2(-4+3)-2$; $4(2)+28=2(-1)-2$;
   $8+28=-2-2$; $36 \neq -4$.
   Substituting -4 results in a false statement, thus $x=-4$ is not a solution.

3. Solve for y: $y+3=2y-8$
   Solution: 11
   Explanation: Subtract $2y$ from each side: $y+3-2y=2y-8-2y$; $-y+3=-8$. Subtract 3 from each side: $-y+3-3=-8-3$; $-y=-11$. Multiply each side by -1: $(-1)(-y)=(-1)(-11)$; $y=11$.

Practice problems: *(Answers on page: 732)*

1. Solve for y: $4-y=15$
2. True or false: The solution of $\frac{3(x+1)}{9}+3x=27-2x$ is $x=5$.
3. Solve for x: $x-6=3x+10$

Review questions: *(Answers to odd questions on page: 732)*

1. Solve for x: $x+5=-11$
2. Solve for x: $4x=7x-6$
3. Solve for x: $2x-t=4p$
4. Solve for x: $9x+2=6x-3$
5. Solve for x: $15(2x+3)=2(x+8)-3$

Solving a Linear Equation

- **Linear equation**: All variables are to the 1st power and the graph forms a line.
- **Cross-multiplying**: Multiplying the denominator of one side of the equation with the numerator of the other side so the denominator disappears.

Example $2x - 5 = x + 7$ *find x*

TO ISOLATE X

$$\begin{array}{rcl} 2x - 5 &=& x + 7 \\ -x & & -x \\ \hline \end{array}$$

subtract x from both sides

Goal: find the value of x that satisfies this equation.

Process: Get all the x's on one side of the equals sign and everything else on the other side.

$$\begin{array}{rcl} x - 5 &=& 7 \\ +5 &=& +5 \\ \hline \boxed{x} &\boxed{=}& \boxed{12} \end{array}$$

add 5 to both sides

You can always add the same value to both sides without changing the "balance" of the equation.

$2(12) - 5 = 12 + 7$
$24 - 5 = 19$
$19 = 19$

plug answer into equation to check accuracy

Always check your answer. Substitute your value for x into the original equation, do the arithmetic, and expect the same value on both sides of the equals sign.

Example $5(y + 3) + 4y - 5 = -(2y - 4)$ *find y*

$5(y + 3) + 4y - 5 = -1(2y - 4)$ *distribute*

$5y + 15 + 4y - 5 = -2y + 4$

$$\begin{array}{rcl} 9y + 10 &=& -2y + 4 \\ +2y & & +2y \\ \hline 11y + 10 &=& 4 \\ -10 & & -10 \\ \hline \frac{11y}{11} &=& \frac{-6}{11} \end{array}$$

add 2y to both sides

subtract each side by 10

divide each side by 11

$$\boxed{y = \frac{-6}{11}}$$

check the answer by plugging it into the equation

$5(\frac{-6}{11} + 3) + (4)(\frac{-6}{11}) - 5 = -((2)(\frac{-6}{11}) - 4)$

Remember: distribute carefully with signs and multiplying across parentheses.

Notice: Put a box or circle around your variable and its answer. There is so much writing on the page that this practice makes it much easier to spot the significant values.

multiplying each side of an equation by the same number doesn't change the equality

Example $\frac{2t + 5}{5} = \frac{t + 2}{3}$ *find t*

multiply each side by the same number to eliminate the fractions

$15\left(\frac{2t + 5}{5}\right) = \left(\frac{t + 2}{3}\right)15$ *cancel*

distribute

$$\begin{array}{rcl} 6t + 15 &=& 5t + 10 \\ -5t & & -5t \\ \hline t + 15 &=& +10 \\ -15 &=& -15 \\ \hline \boxed{t} &\boxed{=}& \boxed{-5} \end{array}$$

subtract both sides by 5t

subtract both sides by 15

Most people dislike working with fractions. The problems always seem harder.

So multiply across to make the denominators cancel and solve your simpler, non-fraction equation. Then follow all your normal steps.

You'll get the same answer without as much stress.

Sample problems:

1. Solve for y: $3 + 2[y - 10(1 - 4y)] = 7y + 133$

   Solution: 2

   Explanation:

Begin with the given expression:	$3 + 2[y - 10(1 - 4y)] = 7y + 133$
Distribute to remove the inner-most parentheses:	$3 + 2[y - 10 + 40y] = 7y + 133$
Distribute again to remove the brackets:	$3 + 2y - 20 + 80y = 7y + 133$
Combine like terms:	$82y - 17 = 7y + 133$
Add $-7y$ to both sides to combine the variables:	$-7y \quad -7y$
	$75y - 17 = 133$
Isolate the variable by adding 17 to each side:	$75y = 150$
Divide each side by 75:	$\frac{75}{75}y = \frac{150}{75};\ y = 2$

2. Solve for w: $\frac{3w+8}{5}+2=\frac{3w}{2}$

Solution: 4

Explanation: Find the LCM of 5 and 2: LCM(5, 2) = 10. Multiply the equation by 10 to eliminate the fractions: $10\left(\frac{3w+8}{5}+2\right)=\left(\frac{3w}{2}\right)10$; $\frac{10(3w+8)}{5}+10(2)=\frac{10(3w)}{2}$. Simplify: $2(3w+8)+20=5(3w)$; $6w+16+20=15w$; $6w+36=15w$. Solve for w: $6w+36-6w=15w-6w$; $36=9w$; $\frac{36}{9}=\frac{9w}{9}$; $w=4$.

3. Solve for x: $\frac{x}{2}-\frac{5}{6}=\frac{x+1}{4}-\frac{3x}{8}$

Solution: $\frac{26}{15}$

Explanation: Find the LCM of the denominators: LCM(2,4,6,8) = 24. Multiply the equation by 24 to eliminate fractions: $24\left(\frac{x}{2}-\frac{5}{6}\right)=24\left(\frac{x+1}{4}-\frac{3x}{8}\right)$; $\frac{24(x)}{2}-\frac{24(5)}{6}=\frac{24(x+1)}{4}-\frac{24(3x)}{8}$. Simplify: $\frac{24(x)}{2}-\frac{24(5)}{6}=\frac{24(x+1)}{4}-\frac{24(3x)}{8}$; $12x-20=6(x+1)-9x$; $12x-20=6x+6-9x$; $12x-20=-3x+6$. Solve for x: $12x-20=-3x+6$; $12x-20+3x=-3x+6+3x$; $15x-20=6$; $15x=26$; $x=\frac{26}{15}$.

Practice problems: *(Answers on page: 732)*

1. Solve for x:
   $\frac{7-2x}{4}=\frac{3(x+5)}{9}$
2. Solve for x:
   $\frac{5x}{4}+\frac{1}{2}=x-\frac{1}{2}$
3. Solve for w: $\frac{w}{4}-\frac{w-2}{2}=1-\frac{5w-9}{8}$

Review questions: *(Answers to odd questions on page: 732)*

1. Solve for t: $4(4-2t)+1=7(t+2(1-t))$
2. Solve for z: $-3(z+1)+z=4z+5$
3. Solve for y: $7(2-y)+5=1+3(y+8)$
4. Solve for x: $\frac{5x}{4}+\frac{1}{2}=x-\frac{1}{2}$
5. Solve for x: $\frac{3x}{2}-\frac{1}{6}=\frac{2x-1}{4}+\frac{x}{12}$

Solving a Linear Equation with Rationals

- Remove variables from the denominator by multiplying the entire equation by the denominator.
- **Cross-multiplying**: When you have an equation with one fraction equal to another fraction, as in ratios, you can multiply the denominator of one fraction with the numerator of the other fraction both ways and eliminate the denominators.

Example

$$\frac{3}{x+2} = \frac{5}{2x-7}$$ *multiply each side by x + 2*

$$\cancel{(x+2)}\left(\frac{3}{\cancel{x+2}}\right) = \frac{5}{2x-7}(x+2)$$ *cancel*

$$3 = \frac{5(x+2)}{2x-7}$$ *distribute*

$$(2x-7)\,3 = \left(\frac{5(x+2)}{\cancel{2x-7}}\right)\cancel{(2x-7)}$$ *multiply both sides by 2x − 7* *cancel*

$$3(2x-7) = 5(x+2)$$

When a problem has the variable in the denominator, multiply the entire equation by the denominator. Multiplying both sides of the equation by the same number keeps things "balanced."

If there are variables in the denominator on both sides, cross-multiply.

$$3(2x-7) = 5(x+2)$$ *distribute terms*

$$6x - 21 = 5x + 10$$

Parentheses are vital in a case like this. Distribute carefully to avoid a wrong answer.

$$6x - 21 = 5x + 10$$ *subtract 5x from both sides*

$$-5x$$

$$x - 21 = 10$$ *add 21 to both sides*

$$+21$$

$$\boxed{x = 31}$$

Once the denominators are eliminated, solve as usual:

1. isolate the x ; and

2. determine what value x equals.

$$\frac{3}{31+2} = \frac{5}{2(31)-7}$$ *check answer by plugging 31 into the equation*

$$\frac{3}{33} = \frac{5}{55}$$

$$\frac{1}{11} = \frac{1}{11}$$

Check the answer by substituting it in the original equation to make sure the answer produces a true statement.

Remember: Eliminate any value that would have a denominator equal 0.

Method 2

multiply

$$\frac{3}{x+2} \times \frac{5}{2x-7}$$ *multiply each side by x + 2*

$$\cancel{(x+2)}\left(\frac{3}{\cancel{x+2}}\right) = \frac{5}{2x-7}(x+2)$$ *cancel*

$$3 = \frac{5(x+2)}{2x-7}$$ *distribute*

$$(2x-7)\,3 = \left(\frac{5(x+2)}{\cancel{2x-7}}\right)\cancel{(2x-7)}$$ *multiply both sides by 2x − 7* *cancel*

$$3(2x-7) = 5(x+2)$$ *the fractions have been eliminated*

Cross-multiplying works if both sides of your equation have denominators.

Cross-multiplying eliminates both denominators in one step. It works only when there is exactly one rational expression on each side of the equal sign.

Once the denominators are eliminated, proceed using all the usual tricks to solve for x.

Example $\frac{3x}{x+4} = 2 - \frac{12}{x+4}$ **find x**

$$\frac{3x}{x+4} = 2 - \frac{12}{x+4}$$ *can't cross multiply here*

In this example cross-multiplying will NOT work. Part of the equation is not a fraction so cross-multiplying will ruin the balance of the equation.

$$\frac{3x}{x+4} = 2 - \frac{12}{x+4}$$ *can't cross multiply here*

$$\cancel{(x+4)}\left(\frac{3x}{\cancel{x+4}}\right) = (x+4)\left(2 - \frac{12}{x+4}\right)$$ *multiply each side by x + 4* *cancel*

$$3x = (x+4)2 - \cancel{(x+4)}\left(\frac{12}{\cancel{x+4}}\right)$$ *distribute* *cancel*

$$3x = 2x + 8 - 12$$ *subtract both sides by 2x*

$$-2x$$

$$\boxed{x = -4}$$

Solve this by multiplying both sides of the equation with the denominator.

Then, use the regular tricks to solve for x.

$$\frac{3(-4)}{-4+4} = 2 - \frac{12}{-4+4}$$ check answer by plugging in for x

$$\frac{-12}{0} = 2 - \frac{12}{0}$$ ← can't divide by 0 !

NOT A SOLUTION

$x = -4$

WARNING: No denominator can EVER equal zero.

If the solution is a value that makes a denominator equal to zero, that value cannot be a solution.

If that value is the only solution, then the equation cannot be solved.

This is where the practice of checking every answer pays off in a correct conclusion!

Sample problems:

1. Solve: $\dfrac{-6}{y+2} - 7 = \dfrac{3y}{y+2}$

   Solution: No Solution

   Explanation: Multiply by the common denominator: $(y+2)\left(\dfrac{-6}{y+2} - 7\right) = \left(\dfrac{3y}{y+2}\right)(y+2)$;

   $\dfrac{-6(y+2)}{y+2} - 7(y+2) = \dfrac{3y(y+2)}{y+2}$. Cancel common factors from each term: $-6 - 7(y+2) = 3y$.

   Simplify: $-6 - 7y - 14 = 3y$; $-7y - 20 = 3y$. Solve for y: $-10y - 20 = 0$; $-10y = 20$; $y = -2$.

   Check the solution: $\frac{-6}{-2+2} - 7 = \frac{3(-2)}{-2+2}$; $-\frac{6}{0} - 7 = -\frac{6}{0}$ ⇒ There is no solution, since the denominator is 0.

2. Solve: $\dfrac{-1}{2x+3} = \dfrac{2}{3x-20}$

   Solution: 2

   Explanation: Cross multiply: $\dfrac{-1}{2x+3} = \dfrac{2}{3x-20}$; $-1(3x-20) = 2(2x+3)$.

   Distribute: $-3x + 20 = 4x + 6$. Solve for x: $-7x + 20 = 6$; $-7x = -14$; $x = 2$.

   To determine the validity of the solution, substitute 2 into the original equation for x:

   $\dfrac{-1}{2(2)+3} = \dfrac{2}{3(2)-20}$; $-\frac{1}{7} = -\frac{2}{14}$; $-\frac{1}{7} = -\frac{1}{7}$.

3. Solve: $\dfrac{3}{x} - 1 = \dfrac{5}{4x} - \dfrac{1}{3x}$

   Solution: $\dfrac{25}{12}$

   Explanation: Multiply by the common denominator: $12x\left(\dfrac{3}{x} - 1\right) = \left(\dfrac{5}{4x} - \dfrac{1}{3x}\right)12x$;

   $\dfrac{3(12x)}{x} - 1(12x) = \dfrac{5(12x)}{4x} - \dfrac{1(12x)}{3x}$. Cancel common factors from each term:

   $36 - 12x = 15 - 4$. Simplify and solve for x: $36 - 12x = 11$; $-12x = -25$; $x = \dfrac{25}{12}$.

Practice problems: *(Answers on page: 732)*

1. Solve: $\dfrac{7y}{y+9} - 2 = \dfrac{2}{y+9}$

2. Solve: $1 + \dfrac{4}{x+5} = \dfrac{7}{3} - \dfrac{2x}{x+5}$

3. Solve: $\frac{6}{x+4}+1=\frac{x}{x+6}$

Review questions: *(Answers to odd questions on page: 733)*

1. Solve for z: $\frac{z+1}{6-z}=\frac{2}{3}$
2. Solve for x: $\frac{2}{x}+\frac{4x-3}{x}=10$
3. Solve for y: $\frac{3}{y}+2=\frac{1}{2y}-\frac{2}{3y}$
4. Solve for x: $\frac{3x-1}{4}=\frac{10-x}{5}$
5. Solve for x: $\frac{2x-6}{x-1}+\frac{4}{x-1}=8$

Solving a Linear Equation That Has Restrictions

- Denominators cannot equal 0.
- When working with equations, the two sides of each equation must stay balanced. So, when making a change, always operate on both sides of the equation in the same way.
- Some equations have no solution. This happens if working with the equation leads to an equation that is untrue. It also happens if the solution produces a denominator equal to zero.

Example $\frac{4x-3}{2x}=\frac{2x-4}{x-2}$ *find x* *factor distribute cancel* $\frac{4x-3}{2x}=\frac{2(x-2)}{x-2}$ $2x-4$ $\frac{4x-3}{2x}=2$	**Remember:** Any time a variable is found in a denominator, determine what values for x must be excluded from the domain. If possible, simplify one or both sides of the problem before multiplying with the denominators. The hope is to be able to cancel some factors. In this example, one denominator cancels.
$(2x)\left(\frac{4x-3}{2x}\right)=2(2x)$ *multiply each side by 2x and cancel* $4x-3=4x$ $-4x$ *subtract 4x from each side*	Now follow the normal steps to solve for x. In this example, multiply both sides to cancel out the remaining denominator. Add and subtract to simplify and isolate variables from constants.
$-3=0$	And… if a problem worked with no mistakes produces a false statement, the equation has no solution.
• always check your answer... especially when there is a denominator $\frac{4x-3}{2x}=\frac{2x-4}{x-2}$ *find x* ↑ THERE IS NO SOLUTION	Arriving at a conclusion of "no solution" is OK; there are problems like that out there. Just be sure to double-check for mistakes before declaring the finding.

Sample problems:

1. Solve: $\dfrac{8}{1-z}+\dfrac{7z+4}{z-1}=4$
   Solution: 0
   Explanation: Multiply by the common denominator: $(1-z)(z-1)(\frac{8}{1-z}+\frac{7z+4}{z-1})=4(1-z)(z-1)$; $8(z-1)+(7z+4)(1-z)=4(1-z)(z-1)$. Simplify: $8z-8+(-7z^2+3z+4)=-4+8z-4z^2$; $-7z^2+11z-4=-4+8z-4z^2$. Isolate the z's on the left side by adding 4 and $4z^2$ to both sides and subtracting $8z$ from each side: $-7z^2+11z-4+4-8z+4z^2=0$; $-3z^2+3z=0$. Factor and solve for z: $-3z(z-1)=0 \Rightarrow -3z=0$ or $z-1=0$; $z=0$ or $z=1$. However, $z=1$ is an invalid solution since it is not included in the domain. Thus $x=0$ is the only solution.

2. Solve: $\dfrac{7}{x}-\dfrac{7}{x-1}=\dfrac{2}{x^2}$
   Solution: $\dfrac{2}{9}$
   Explanation: Multiply by the common denominator:
   $(x^2)(x-1)\left(\dfrac{7}{x}-\dfrac{7}{x-1}\right)=\left(\dfrac{2}{x^2}\right)(x^2)(x-1)$;
   $\dfrac{7(x^2)(x-1)}{x}-\dfrac{7(x^2)(x-1)}{x-1}=\dfrac{2(x^2)(x-1)}{x^2}$.
   Cancel common factors:
   $\dfrac{7(x\cdot \cancel{x})(x-1)}{\cancel{x}}-\dfrac{7(x^2)\cancel{(x-1)}}{\cancel{x-1}}=\dfrac{2(\cancel{x^2})(x-1)}{\cancel{x^2}}=7x(x-1)-7x^2=2(x-1)$.
   Simplify and solve for x: $7x^2-7x-7x^2=2(x-1)$; $-7x=2x-2$; $-9x=-2$; $x=\dfrac{2}{9}$.

3. Solve: $\dfrac{x}{1-x}=1-\dfrac{x-3}{x-1}$
   Solution: -2
   Explanation: Multiply by the common denominator:
   $(1-x)(x-1)\left(\dfrac{x}{1-x}\right)=\left(1-\dfrac{x-3}{x-1}\right)(1-x)(x-1)$;
   $\dfrac{x(1-x)(x-1)}{1-x}=(1-x)(x-1)-\dfrac{(x-3)(1-x)(x-1)}{x-1}$;
   Cancel common factors: $\dfrac{x\cancel{(1-x)}(x-1)}{\cancel{1-x}}=(1-x)(x-1)-\dfrac{(x-3)(1-x)\cancel{(x-1)}}{\cancel{x-1}}=$
   Simplify: $x(x-1)=(1-x)(x-1)-(x-3)(1-x)$
   Distribute: $x^2-x=-1+2x-x^2+3-4x+x^2$; $x^2-x=2-2x$.
   Isolate the terms, factor, and solve for x: $x^2-x=2-2x$; $x^2+x-2=0$;
   $(x+2)(x-1)=0$; $x+2=0$ or $x-1=0$; $x=-2$ or $x=1$.
   However, $x=1$ is not in the domain, so $x=-2$ is the only solution.

Practice problems: *(Answers on page: 733)*

1. Solve: $\dfrac{3}{w-1}+\dfrac{3}{2w+5}=\dfrac{10}{2w+5}-\dfrac{1}{w-1}$
2. Solve: $\dfrac{7}{2x+3}+\dfrac{5}{x+1}=\dfrac{9}{x+1}-\dfrac{1}{2x+3}$
3. Solve: $\dfrac{3}{2t}-\dfrac{7}{t-1}=\dfrac{1}{t}$

Review questions: *(Answers to odd questions on page: 733)*

1. Solve for z: $\dfrac{3(z+1)}{10} = \dfrac{z}{5}$
2. Solve for z: $\dfrac{z+2}{4z+8} = \dfrac{1}{7-z}$
3. Solve for x: $4(x+2) - 3x = x + 12$
4. Solve for x: $\dfrac{5x-10}{x-2} = \dfrac{3x}{x+1}$
5. Solve for x: $\dfrac{1}{x-2} = \dfrac{3}{x+2} - \dfrac{6x}{x^2-4}$

An Introduction to Solving Word Problems

- Working a word problem requires both the mathematical skills and the ability to restate the facts as variables in equations.
- **Word Problem Solving Process**:
  1. Determine the facts
  2. Define the variables
  3. Create an equation
  4. Solve the equation
  5. Check your answer

The challenging part of solving a word problem is translating the words into a mathematical equation.

Working a word problem is first of all a translation process. You must:

1. Determine your facts.
2. Define the variables.
3. Create an equation.

Only then do you perform the steps to solve for the requested information.

Advice for solving a word problem:

- **Pay attention to the specifics**
- **Read and re-read**
- **Don't rush**

Working a word problem requires that you read carefully and think about what the words are telling you.

Constantly think about what the problem is telling you. Stick very closely to the facts as presented.

Separate the facts. You might want to make a list.

Note what is being asked for so you can define your variables.

Also note any stray information that you will not use. Many word problems include information that is interesting but not needed to solve for the requested answers.

Solving for Perimeter

- **Word Problems** require translation from English, or some language, into math numbers and symbols.
- **Formula**: a generalized equation for a characteristic or action that works in every situation of its kind. You use a formula by choosing it for the situation you have and then substituting into the formula the specific facts of your situation, and solving for what you need to know.
- Always check when you're done to be sure:
  1. You have every answer asked for in the problem.
  2. The answer works with the facts in the problem.
- The most important part of working with any word problem is the translation process that creates the equation you will work with.

The length of a Pop-Tart is 3 cm less than twice its width. If it has a perimeter of 54cm, then what is the measurement of its width? 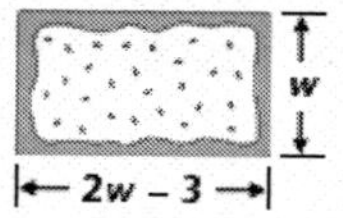	Read the words carefully. Draw a sketch. Write out the facts you know and what you are being asked to find.
Perimeter : The sum of the lengths of the sides. **PER = $2w - 3 + w + 2w - 3 + w = 54$**	Now take all those facts and convert them into an equation using the formula that you've decided on.
$6w - 6 = 54$ $\frac{6w}{6} = \frac{60}{6}$ $w = 10$ cm	Solve the equation for the variable. Are you done? Is the value for w all you need? Check it out to be sure.

Sample problems:

1. A rectangular strip of paper has a perimeter of 26 centimeters. The sum of the length and twice the width is 16. How wide is the strip of paper?
   Solution: 3 cm
   Explanation: Substitute 26 into the formula for perimeter: $p = 2w + 2l$: $26 = 2l + 2w$. The sum of the length and twice the width is 16 so, $l + 2w = 16$. Solve the equation for l: $l + 2w = 16$; $l = 16 - 2w$. Substitute the expression for l, which is $16 - 2w$, into the formula for perimeter: $26 = 2w + 2(16 - 2w)$. Distribute to remove the perentheses, simplify and solve the equation for w: $26 = 2w + 2(16 - 2w)$; $26 = 2w + 32 - 4w$; $26 = 32 - 2w$; $-6 = -2w$; $w = 3$. The width of the strip of paper is 3 cm.

2. Ceralda has 52ft of fence to enclose a rectangular garden. She wants the width of the garden to be 1 foot longer than $\frac{1}{4}$ of the length. What should the dimensions of the garden be so that all the fence will be used?
   Solution: $l = 20$ and $w = 6$
   Explanation: Substitute 52 into the formula for perimeter: $52 = 2l + 2w$. The width is 1 foot longer than $\frac{1}{4}$ of the length, so $w = 1 + \frac{1}{4}l$; $w - 1 = \frac{1}{4}l$; $l = 4w - 4$. Substitute the expression for l, $4w - 4$, into the perimeter formula: $52 = 2(4w - 4) + 2w$. Simplify and solve the equation for w: $52 = 2(4w - 4) + 2w$; $52 = 8w - 8 + 2w$; $52 = 10w - 8$; $10w = 60$; $w = 6$. Now find the length by substituting 6 into $l = 4w - 4$ and simplify: $l = 4(6) - 4 = 20$. Thus, the length must be 20ft and the width must be 6ft in order to use all 52ft of fence.

3. A piece of paper is 1.7 times as long as it is wide. It has an area of 27.2 centimeters squared. What is the perimeter of the piece of paper?
Solution: 21.6 cm
Explanation: Translate "1.7 times as long as it is wide" into an equation: $l = 1.7w$. If the area is 27.2 cm^2, then $lw = 27.2$. Substitute the expression for l, $1.7w$, into $lw = 27.2$ and solve for w: $(1.7w) = 27.2$; $1.7w^2 = 27.2$; $w^2 = 16$; $\sqrt{w^2} = \sqrt{16}$; $w = 4$. Now find the length by substituting 4 into $l = 1.7w$: $l = 1.7(4) = 6.8$. Find the perimeter by substituting 6.8 and 4 into the formula for perimeter, $p = 2l + 2w$: $p = 2(6.8) + 2(4) = 13.6 + 8 = 21.6$, so the perimeter of the paper is 21.6 cm.

Practice problems: *(Answers on page: 733)*

1. Suppose $\frac{1}{2}$ of the length of a rectangle is 1 cm longer than the width and the perimeter of this rectangle is 28 cm. Find the length of the rectangle.
2. A plaque has a perimeter of 17.5 inches. It is three quarters as tall as it is wide. What is its width in inches?
3. The area of rectangular garden is 640 ft^2. The sum of the width and twice the length is 72 ft. Find the possible length of the garden.

Review questions: *(Answers to odd questions on page: 733)*

1. The width of a rectangular pool is 20 feet less than the length and the perimeter is 100 feet. What is the length of the pool?
2. The perimeter of a rectangle is 38 inches. If the length of the rectangle is six inches less than four times the width, find the dimensions.
3. A poster has a perimeter of 72 inches. It is twice as long as it is wide. What is the width of the poster?
4. A photograph has a frame for which the difference between the length and half of the width is 2 centimeters. The width is exactly one-fourth the value of the perimeter. What is the perimeter of the photograph?
5. A painting is stretched over a rectangular wooden frame whose length is two-and-a-half times its width in feet. The sum of the length and the width is 7 feet. The wood for the frame came from one piece that was cut into four pieces. How long was the original piece of wood in feet?

Solving a Linear Geometry Problem

- A **right circular cylinder** is the shape of a can of food. It has round tops and bottoms that are the same size. The height forms a right angle with the top and bottom.
- The **volume** of a right cylinder can be found using $V = \pi r^2 h$.

A right circular cylinder has a radius of 6 inches. If the volume is 144π inches³, what is the height? 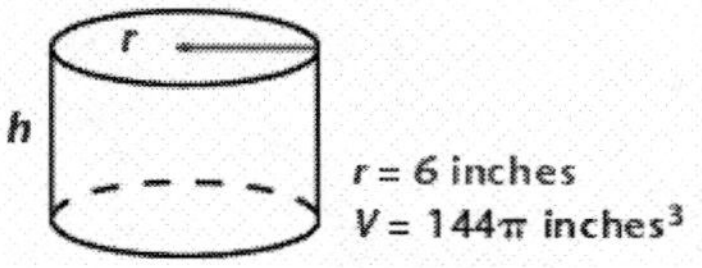	Define the variables: h = the height of the cylinder. r = the distance from the center of the top or bottom to its edge.

$V = \pi r^2 h$ 6^2 $144\pi = \pi 36 h$ 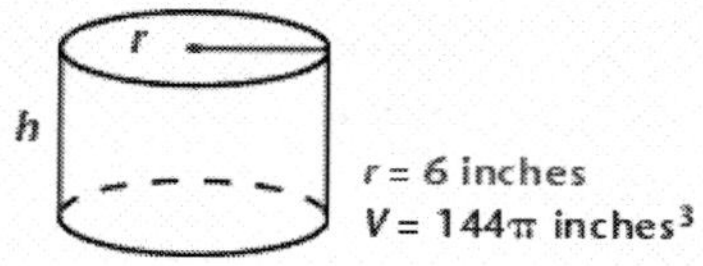	In this problem, the radius squared is 36, so our volume formula becomes π times 36 times h.
$\frac{144\pi}{36\pi} = \frac{\pi 36 h}{\pi 36}$ $h = 4$ inches 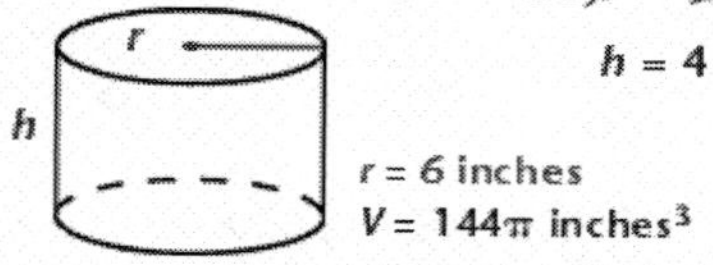	The height (h) will be found by dividing both sides by 36π. In this case, the height is 4 inches.

Sample problems:

1. Find the height of a paint can if the volume is 192π in^3 and the diameter is 8 in.
   Solution: 12 in
   Explanation: A paint can is a cylinder and the formula for the volume of a cylinder is $V = \pi r^2 h$. The diameter of the can is 8, so the radius is 4. Substitute $V = 192\pi$ and $r = 4$ into the formula, then solve for h: $192\pi = \pi(4)^2 h$; $192\pi = 16\pi h$; $h = \frac{192\pi}{16\pi} = 12$. Thus, the height of the can is 12 in.

2. Let s_1, s_2, and s_3 represent the length of the three sides of a triangle with a perimeter of 86 cm. Suppose s_2 is half of s_1 and s_3 is 6 cm longer than the shortest side. Find the length of each side.
   Solution: 40 cm, 20 cm, and 26 cm
   Explanation: The perimeter of a triangle is the sum of the sides. Write an equation for the perimeter: $s_1 + s_2 + s_3 = 86$. It is known that s_2 is half of s_1, so $s_2 = \frac{1}{2}s_1$. Furthermore, s_3 is 6cm longer than the shortest side. The shortest side must be s_2 (since it is $\frac{1}{2}s_1$), so $s_3 = s_2 + 6 = \frac{1}{2}s_1 + 6$. Substitute the expressions for s_2 and s_3 into the perimeter equation: $s_1 + \left(\frac{1}{2}s_1\right) + \left(\frac{1}{2}s_1 + 6\right) = 86$. Simplify and solve for s_1: $s_1 + \frac{1}{2}s_1 + \frac{1}{2}s_1 + 6 = 86$; $2s_1 + 6 = 86$; $2s_1 = 80$; $s_1 = 40$. Now find the lengths of the other two sides: $s_2 = \frac{1}{2}s_1 = \frac{1}{2}(40) = 20$ and $s_3 = s_2 + 6 = 20 + 6 = 26$. Thus the lengths of the sides are 40, 20, and 26.

3. The area of a trapezoid is 63 cm^2. The height is 9 cm and b_1 is $\frac{2}{5}$ of b_2. Find the length of b_1 and b_2.
   Solution: 10 cm, 4 cm
   Explanation: Substitute $A = 63$ and $h = 9$ into the formula for the area of a trapezoid, $A = \frac{1}{2}(b_1 + b_2)h$: $63 = \frac{1}{2}(b_1 + b_2)(9)$. Since b_1 is $\frac{2}{5}$ of b_2, $b_1 = \frac{2}{5}b_2$. Substitute the expression for b_1 into the formula and solve for b_2: $63 = \frac{1}{2}(\frac{2}{5}b_2 + b_2)(9)$; $63 = \frac{9}{2}(\frac{7}{5}b_2)$; $63 = \frac{63}{10}b_2$; $b_2 = 63(\frac{10}{63}) = 10$.
   Find b_1: $b_1 = \frac{2}{5}b_2 = \frac{2}{5}(10) = 4$. Thus the length of the bases are 10cm and 4cm.

Practice problems: *(Answers on page: 733)*

1. The volume of a cone is 75π cm^3. If the radius of the cone is 5 cm, find the height.
2. Let s_1, s_2, s_3, and s_4 represent the 4 sides of a quadralateral with perimeter 64 cm. Suppose that s_1 is $\frac{3}{5}$ of s_4, s_3 is $\frac{1}{2}$ of s_4, and s_2 is 2 cm longer than s_4. Find the length of each side.
3. The length of a painting is 28 in and the perimeter is 96 in. The painting is enclosed in a frame that is 4 in wide. Find the area of the entire surface of the frame.

Review questions: *(Answers to odd questions on page: 733)*

1. Find the area of a triangle if the base is 7 cm and the height is 11 cm.
2. Keri's Saturday morning jog follows a triangular path. Two legs of the path are equal, and the third is 2 miles shorter than each of the other legs. If the total path is 13 miles long, find the length of each leg.
3. Let s_1, s_2, and s_3 represent the length of the three sides of a triangle with a perimeter of 25 cm. Suppose s_2 is one-third of s_1 and s_3 is 5 cm longer than the shortest side. Find the length of each side.
4. The diameter of a cylinder is 13 inches and the volume is 102π in^3. Find the height.
5. An aquarium is 22 in long, 12 in wide and 24 in high. The volume of water in the aquarium is 1584 in^3. How deep is the water?

Solving for Consecutive Numbers

- **Consecutive numbers**: Counting numbers that follow one after another. For example, 6, 7, 8, 9,... are consecutive numbers. Consecutive numbers take the form: $x, x + 1, x + 2, \ldots$
- **Consecutive even numbers**: Counting number multiples of 2 that follow each other; e.g., 2, 4, 6, ... Consecutive even numbers take the form: $2x, 2x + 2, 2x + 4, \ldots$
- **Consecutive odd numbers**: Counting numbers not multiplies of 2 that follow each other; e.g., 5, 7, 9, ... Consecutive odd numbers take the form: $2x + 1, 2x + 3, 2x + 5, \ldots$

Find three consecutive odd natural numbers whose sume is 99. **Important Facts:** • odd • consecutive	Read the problem. In this example, it's short and to the point. Determine the facts. Because the requested numbers are odd, they come every other number in the counting sequence. So the problem sets up as the first number, that one plus 2, and that one plus 2 more.
1st number $2s + 1$ *2nd number* $2s + 3$ *3rd number* $2s + 5$ $6s + 9 = 99$	Define the variable. Guarantee the numbers are odd by using $2s$, which as a multiple of 2 would be even, then plus 1 to make the number an odd one. Write the equation. In this example, it is the sum of the three numbers.
$6s + 9 = 99$ $\frac{6s}{6} = \frac{90}{6}$ $s = 15$	Now, solve the equation. **NOTE:** The variable may not be the answer. Use its value to get the requested information.
1st number $2s + 1 = \boxed{31}$ *2nd number* $2s + 3 = \boxed{33}$ *3rd number* $2s + 5 = \boxed{35}$	**Remember:** Check to see that the requested information has been discovered. Check the answers to see that they work.

Sample problems:

1. Given three consecutive odd natural numbers, the sum of twice the first, $\frac{1}{5}$ of the second, and three times the third is 288. Find the numbers.
   Solution: 53, 55, 57
   Explanation: Let $2n+1$, $2n+3$, and $2n+5$ be the three consecutive odd natural numbers.
   Translate each part of the description into an expression: "twice the 1st" $\Rightarrow 2(2n+1)$, "$\frac{1}{5}$ of the 2nd" $\Rightarrow \frac{1}{5}(2n+3)$, and "three times the third" $\Rightarrow 3(2n+5)$.
   The sum is 288, so add the 3 expressions and set it equal to 288:
   $2(2n+1)+\frac{1}{5}(2n+3)+3(2n+5)=288$. Multiply the equation by 5 to eliminate the fraction:
   $5(2(2n+1))+5(\frac{1}{5}(2n+3))+5(3(2n+5))=5(288)$; $10(2n+1)+(2n+3)+15(2n+5)=1440$.
   Simplify and solve for n: $20n+10+2n+3+30n+75=1440$; $52n+88=1440$;
   $52n=1352$; $n=26$. Find the 1st natural number: $2(26)+1=53$.
   Thus, the three consecutive odd natural numbers are 53,55, and 57.
   Check: $2(53)+\frac{1}{5}(55)+3(57)=106+11+171=288$.

2. The product of two consecutive natural numbers is 5 more than the square of the smaller one. Find the numbers.
   Solution: 5, 6
   Explanation: Let n, $n+1$ be the consecutive natural numbers. Translate "product of two consecutive natural numbers": $n(n+1)$ and "5 more than the square of the smaller one": n^2+5, since the smaller one is n. Set the two expressions equal to each other, then simplify and solve for n: $n(n+1)=n^2+5$; $n^2+n=n^2+5$. Add $-n^2$ to each side: $n=5$, so $n+1=6$.

3. The difference of the squares of two consecutive odd natural numbers is 128. Find the numbers.
   Solution: 31, 33
   Explanation: Let $2n+1$ and $2n+3$ be the consecutive odd natural numbers. So, the square of each number is $(2n+1)^2$ and $(2n+3)^2$. Translate "the difference of the squares [of the numbers] is 128:" $(2n+3)^2-(2n+1)^2=128$. Use the FOIL method to simplify each binomial, then combine like terms: $(2n+3)(2n+3)-(2n+1)(2n+1)=128$; $(4n^2+12n+9)-(4n^2+4n+1)=128$; $4n^2+12n+9-4n^2-4n-1=128$; $8n+8=128$; $8n=120$; $n=15$. Find the first number: $2n+1=2(15)+1=31$. Thus the two consecutive odd natural numbers are 31 and 33.

Practice problems: *(Answers on page: 733)*

1. Given four consecutive natural numbers, the sum of the first, one-third of the second, three-fifth of the third, and one-half of the fourth is 59. Find the numbers.
2. Find four consecutive even natural numbers such that their sum is two more than five times the smallest natural number.
3. The product of two consecutive even integers is 40 less than the square of the large number. Find the numbers.

Review questions: *(Answers to odd questions on page: 733)*

1. Find the two consecutive natural numbers whose sum is 87.
2. One-third of the sum of three consecutive odd integers is 91. Find the integers.
3. Twice the sum of two consecutive even natural numbers is 6 times the smaller number. Find the numbers.
4. Find three consecutive odd integer whose sum is 183.

5. Find two consecutive even integers such that the sum of $\frac{1}{2}$ of the first and $\frac{1}{4}$ of the second is 80.

Solving to Find the Average

- **To find the average:**
  - Add all the terms.
  - Divide by the number of terms in the total.
- **To get a desired average, you must:**
  - Add all known terms plus a variable for each unknown item.
  - Divide the total by the number of items being added.
  - Set the division problem as equal to the average desired.
  - Solve for the variable.

A student has earned the following grades on his first four of five tests: 80, 82, 94, and 71. If he wants to finish the class with an 85 average, what must he score on his fifth test?	Step one: read the problem and determine the facts.
Average : Compute by adding all the grades and dividing by the number of grades. **? = grade on the fifth test**	Step two: define the variable. In this case the variable is "?" and represents the grade on the test not yet taken.
all the grades / number of grades $\frac{80 + 82 + 94 + 71 + ?}{5} = 85$	Step three: create the equation.
$5\left(\frac{327 + ?}{5}\right) = (85)5$ $327 + ? = 425$ $\boxed{? = 98}$	Step four: solve the equation, as usual. Step five: check the answer. Substitute it back into the equation to make it sure it produces a true statement. Finally, circle or box the answer, so it's easy to spot.

Sample problems:

1. Jenny likes to average 3 hours a day each day at her part-time job at the mall. She worked 10 hours on Saturday and 8 hours on Sunday. How many total hours does she need to work from Monday to Friday to make her average?
   Solution: 3 hours
   Explanation: Let x be her total hours from Monday through Friday. The average is over 7 days, so: $\frac{10+8+x}{7} = 3$. Multiply each side by 7: $18 + x = 21$. Solve the equation for x: $x = 3$ hrs.

2. Jeff's grade in class is determined by 3 exams and a final which is worth twice as much as each exam. If his exam grades are 81, 92, and 84 percent, what percentage does he need to get on the final to get a 90 percent for the course?
   Solution: 96.5%
   Explanation: Let x be the percentage on the final exam. The final counts as 2 exams, so the average is: $\frac{81+92+84+x+x}{5} = 90$. Combine like terms: $\frac{257+2x}{5} = 90$. Multiply each side by 5 and solve for x: $257 + 2x = 450$; $2x = 193$; $x = \frac{193}{2}$; $x = 96.5\%$.

3. Brandon took 4 tests and made the following scores: 72, 84, 0, 63. He took two more tests and the score of the sixth test was twice the fifth. If the average of all six tests is a 59, what were the scores on the fifth and sixth tests?
   Solution: 45, 90
   Explanation: Let x = the fifth test score and $2x$ = the sixth test score. Write an equation for the average and solve for x: $\frac{72+84+63+x+2x}{6} = 59;\; 219+3x = 354;\; 3x = 135;\; x = 45.$
   So, the fifth test score was 45 and the sixth was $2(45) = 90$.

Practice problems: *(Answers on page: 733)*

1. A volleyball league has a 5 week season averaging 6 games per week. The Slammin' Spikers played 4 games, 7 games, 2 games, and 5 games, during the first 4 weeks. How many games will they play during the last week?
2. Bob is taking an 8 week course with weekly quizzes. He has taken 5 quizzes with scores of 79, 94, 63, 84, and 87. What does he need to average on the last 3 quizzes to have an overall average of 85?
3. Suppose Al scored progressively higher on four tests. The score of the second test was 10 points higher than the first, the third test score was twice the second, and the fourth was 5 points higher than the third. If the average of the four test scores was 58.75, what were the scores?

Review questions: *(Answers to odd questions on page: 733)*

1. A computer programmer works a flexible schedule. She works Monday through Friday, but she can work any number of hours each day as long as her weekly average is 8 hours per day. If her Monday through Thursday hours are 9, 6.5, 10.1, and 8.4, how many hours does she need to work on Friday?
2. Teri joined a CD club requiring her to purchase an average of 4 CDs per year for 3 years. She bought 7 CDs the first year but only 3 CDs the second year. How many will she need to purchase during the last year of the plan?
3. Nicole has received grades of 73, 68, 82, and 85, on four exams in her class. If she wants an average of 80, what grade does she need on the next exam?
4. Debbie is running laps at the track. She wants to average 100 seconds per lap on her last set of 4. For the first 3 laps, she ran 98 seconds, 103 seconds, and 101 seconds. How fast does she need to run the last lap?
5. Todd wants to average 4 hours of study time each day from Monday through Friday. If he studies 2 hours, 5 hours, 6 hours, and 1 hour, respectively on Monday, Tuesday, Wednesday, and Thursday, how many hours should he study on Friday to maintain the average?

Solving for Constant Velocity

- A **constant velocity problem** involves travel at a steady speed.

Bob leaves from Chicago on a plane traveling to Los Angeles at 540 mph. One hour later, Mary leaves Los Angeles for Chicago traveling 660 mph. If the distance between Chicago and L.A. is 1800 miles, how long will Bob travel before the two planes pass each other? Also, how far from Chicago are they at that moment?

Notice in this problem that both parties travel at a constant speed. However, each party travels at his or her own speed.

Also, notice how the distance factor is defined. You know the total distance between the two cities but not how far each individual traveled. As a result you define your distance variables to use the facts you know.

Distance is defined as D = RT ├— 1800 – d —┼— d —┤ L.A. 1800 miles Chicago d = Distance that Bob travels to the meeting point *(Mary's distance)* **(1800 – d)**	For this problem, you will fall back on an old formula you already know: distance = rate x time. You need one variable, *d*, which represents the distance one of the two people travels. For this example, Dr. Burger chose *d* to equal the distance that Bob travels. Since the total distance is 1800 miles, the distance Mary travels will be 1800 miles less the distance Bob travels. In math terms, that means (1800 - *d*).
Distance is defined as D = RT d = Distance that Bob travels to the meeting point t = Time that Bob travels to the meeting point *Mary* (1800 – d) (t – 1)	You need a second variable, *t*, to indicate the time that is used in the travels. Dr. Burger assigned *t* to be the amount of time that Bob travels. The problem says that Mary travels one hours less than Bob, so her time will be (t -1).
D = RT *(Mary's distance)* $(1800 - d) = 660(t - 1)$ **D = RT** *(Bob's distance)* $d = 540t$	Now that you have defined your variables you can set up an equation for Bob and one for Mary using your formula. This gives you two equations in two variables.
$(1800 - d) = 660(t - 1)$ $1800 - 540t = 660t - 660$ $\frac{2460}{1200} = \frac{1200t}{1200}$ $t = \frac{123}{60}$ **D = RT** *(Bob's distance)* $d = 540t$	Since Bob's equation gives you a convenient expression for *d*, substitute that expression for *d* in Mary's equation. That substitution gives you an equation in one unknown and allows you to solve for *t*. **Remember:** *t* is defined as Bob's travel time.
$t = \frac{123}{60}$ t = 2 hours 3 minutes **D = RT** *(Bob's distance)* $d = 540t$ $d = 540\left(\frac{123}{60}\right)$ d = 1107 miles	Next you can use Bob's travel time, which you have just discovered, to solve for the distance from Chicago. Substitute the 2 hr. 3 min. into the formula for Bob's distance and do the arithmetic. Once you know this answer, check your problem. You should now have the two pieces of information you were asked to find.

Sample problems:

1. Jack leaves from Nashville on a train traveling to Memphis, 210 miles away, at 80 mph. Henry leaves Memphis 1 hour and 30 minutes later on a train traveling 75 mph. If the trains travel at a constant speed, how long after Jack leaves will the two trains to pass each other?
   Solution: 2 hours and 5 min
   Explanation: Define Jack's distance as d and Henry's distance as $210 - d$. Define the time Jack traveled as t and the time Henry traveled as $t - 1.5$. Next, substitute these variables and the speeds into $d = rt$: Jack $\Rightarrow d = 80t$ and Henry $\Rightarrow 210 - d = 75(t - 1.5)$. The goal is to have a one variable equation, so substitute the expression for d, which is $80t$, into $210 - d = 75(t-1.5)$: $210 - (80t) = 75(t - 1.5)$. Simplify and solve the equation for t: $210 - 80t = 75(t - 1.5)$; $210 - 80t = 75t - 112.5$; $210 - 155t = -112.5$; $-155t = -322.5$; $t = 2.08$. Lastly, convert that decimal into minutes: $(.08)(60) = 4.8 \approx 5$ minutes. The trains pass after 2 hours and 5 minutes.

2. An airplane leaves the airport at 200 kilometers per hour. Another airplane leaves an hour later traveling the same route. 3 hours after the first plane took off, the second plane caught up with it. How fast is the second plane traveling?
   Solution: 300 km/hr
   Explanation: To find the distance traveled by Plane 1, substitute $r = 200$ and $t = 3$ into $d = rt$: $d = 200(3) = 600$ miles. The planes traveled the same distance, so Plane 2 also traveled 600 miles, but in 2 hours. To determine the speed of Plane 2 substitute $d = 600$ and $t = 2$ into $d = rt$ and solve for r: $600 = r(2)$; $600 = 2r$; $r = 300$. The speed of Plane 2 is 300 km/hr.

3. Kelly and Chris are shopping in the city. Chris leaves for home in his car at 3:00 traveling at 48 miles per hour, but Kelly is engrossed in a shoe store and doesn't leave until 3:15. If she drives at 66 miles per hour, how long after she leaves does she catch up with Chris?
   Solution: 40 min
   Explanation: Let t represent the time after Kelly left the shoe store. Kelly drove at 66 mph, so $d_k = 66t$. Chris left 15 minutes earlier, $\frac{1}{4}$ of an hour, and drove at 48 mph, so $d_c = 48(t + \frac{1}{4})$. The distance traveled by each person is the same, so $d_k = d_c$ or $66t = 48(t + \frac{1}{4})$. Simplify and solve for t: $66t = 48t + 12$; $18t = 12$; $t = \frac{12}{18} = \frac{2}{3}$, and $\frac{2}{3}$ of an hour is 40 minutes.

Practice problems: *(Answers on page: 733)*

1. A runner is training by sprinting up a long hill then slowly jogging down. He runs uphill at 240 meters per minute and comes back down at 160 meters per minute. If one trip up the hill and back down takes 30 minutes, how far is a one-way trip?
2. Suppose Ben leaves his house and walks to meet Anna. Anna leaves her house 30 minutes later and walks to meet Ben. Anna's average walking speed is 3mph and Ben's is 4mph. When they meet, Ben has walked twice as far as Anna. Find the total distance they walked.
3. Troy and Phil agree to meet at the movies. Phil leaves at 3:00 and drives 24 miles to the theater. Troy leaves at 3:20 and rides his bike at 15mph the 5 miles to the theater. They arrive at the theater at the same time. How fast did Phil drive?

Review questions: *(Answers to odd questions on page: 733)*

1. Steve leaves Denver at 1:00 and at 3:00 has gone 96 miles. Find his average speed.
2. Janet rides her bike to work at a speed of 12 miles per hour. It takes her 1/3 hour to get there from her house. How long is her ride to work?
3. Bob roller blades 9 miles each morning. Today, he averaged 10 miles per hour for the first 6 miles but then slowed to 5 miles per hour for the remaining 3 miles. How long did the entire trip take?
4. Two cars begin to drive in the same direction at the same time, one traveling at 55 miles per hour and one at 45 miles per hour. After 3 hours, how far apart are the cars?
5. Wendy kayaks downstream for 1/4 of an hour at an average speed of 10 miles per hour, then stops for lunch and paddles back upstream. If the return trip takes an hour, what is her average speed on the way back?

Solving a Problem about Work

- A **linear work problem** calculates work performed at an average rate over a period of time by one or more workers.

Professor Burger's mother can build a fence in 8 hours. Working together, she and Professor Burger can build the same fence in 5 hours. How long would it take Professor Burger to build the fence alone? 	This type of problem asks that two rates be linked to complete usually one job. The rates are set up in fractions with the number of hours required to finish the job working alone as the denominator and the number of hours actually worked as the numerator.
t = number of hours of work $\frac{t}{8}$ = portion of the fence that mother builds **If she works 8 hours, then $t = 8$ and** $\frac{t}{8} = \frac{8}{8} = 1$ fence	Since the problem asks about time, define a variable, t, for time used. Since Ms. B. could build the entire fence in 8 hours, set up a fraction: t = time Mrs. Burger will use 8 = hours used if Mrs. Burger worked alone
r = Professor Burger's rate $\frac{t}{r}$ = portion of the fence that Professor Burger builds	Next assign a variable, r, to represent Dr. Burger's fence-building speed. Then set up a fraction for his rate to match the fraction for his mother's rate.
$\frac{t}{8} + \frac{t}{r} = 1$	As the last step, set up an equation for building the fence. Add the two fractions to get 1. The 1 represents one job completed, in this case one fence built.
When $t = 5$ hours $\frac{t}{8} + \frac{t}{r} = 1$ $\frac{5}{8} + \frac{5}{r} = 1$ $\frac{5}{r} = \frac{3}{8}$ $3r = 40$ $r = \frac{40}{3} = \boxed{\text{13 hours 20 minutes}}$	The problem states that if they build the fence together it will take five hours. So, $t = 5$. Now solve the equation for r. The value for r is Dr. Burger's rate and that answers the question that the problem posed

Sample problems:

1. Carl and Zoe are cleaning motel rooms. If Carl works alone he can clean one room in 20 minutes. If Carl and Zoe work together they can clean 7 rooms in 1 hour and 24 minutes. If Zoe is working alone, how long will it take for her to clean one room?
   Solution: 30 minutes
   Explanation: Carl can clean 1 room in 20 minutes, so Carl's rate is $\frac{1}{20}$. Let z be the time it takes Zoe to clean one room, so Zoe's rate is $\frac{1}{z}$. Zoe and Carl can clean 7 rooms in 84 minutes. One equation that decribes this situation is: $84\left(\frac{1}{20}\right) + 84\left(\frac{1}{z}\right) = 7$. Multiply the equation by the common denominator: $20z\left[84\left(\frac{1}{20}\right) + 84\left(\frac{1}{z}\right)\right] = (7)20z$; $84z + 1680 = 140z$. Solve for z: $-56z + 168 = 0$; $-56z = -1680$; $z = 30$.

2. Two teachers are grading math homework. One teacher can grade a stack of papers in 75 minutes and the other can complete the job in 90 minutes. How long does it take them to grade all the papers if the first teacher grades alone for 20 minutes, then they work together to finish?
   Solution: 50 min.
   Explanation: The rate for teacher 1 is $\frac{1}{75}$ and the rate for teacher 2 is $\frac{1}{90}$. Teacher 1 grades alone for 20 minutes: $20\left(\frac{1}{75}\right)$. Let t be the time the teachers grade together. Set up an equation for completing the job: $20\left(\frac{1}{75}\right)+t\left(\frac{1}{75}\right)+t\left(\frac{1}{90}\right)=1$. Multiply the equation by the common denominator: $450\left[20\left(\frac{1}{75}\right)+t\left(\frac{1}{75}\right)+t\left(\frac{1}{90}\right)\right]=(1)450$; $120+6t+5t=450$. Simplify and solve for t: $120+11t=450$; $11t=330$; $t=30$. Therefore, the total time is: 20 + 30 = 50 minutes.

3. A leaky bucket is being filled with water from a hose. All of the water can leak out in 18 minutes, and the hose could fill a non-leaking bucket in 12 minutes. If the leak is plugged in 4 minutes after turning on the water, how long after the leak is plugged does it take to fill the bucket?
   Solution: 10 min. 40 sec.
   Explanation: The rate of water to fill the bucket is $\frac{1}{12}$. The rate of water leaking out of the bucket is $-\frac{1}{18}$. Since the water is leaving the bucket, the rate is negative. Water filled the leaking bucket for 4 minutes: $4\left(\frac{1}{12}\right)-4\left(\frac{1}{18}\right)$. Let t be the time it takes to fill the bucket after the leak is plugged. Set up an equation: $\frac{4}{12}-\frac{4}{18}+\frac{t}{12}=1$. Multiply the equation by the common denominator: $36\left(\frac{4}{12}-\frac{4}{18}+\frac{t}{12}\right)=(1)36$; $12-8+3t=36$. Solve for t: $4+3t=36$; $3t=32$; $t=10\frac{2}{3}$. It will take 10 minutes and 40 seconds to fill the bucket after the leak is plugged.

Practice problems: *(Answers on page: 733)*

1. Morgan and Rebekah work in a stable. Morgan can clean a horse stall in 40 minutes. Rebekah can clean a horse stall in one hour. How long will it take for Morgan and Rebekah to clean a stall together?
2. Terri and Judy run a lawn mowing business. If Terri can mow a large lawn in 8 hours and Judy can mow the same lawn in 12 hours, how long will it take them together to mow the lawn?
3. Two water faucets are being used to fill a water tank, and one faucet lets in water twice as fast as the other. If the faucets fill the tank together in 46 minutes, how long would it take to fill the tank with only the bigger faucet?

Review questions: *(Answers to odd questions on page: 733)*

1. Bob can paint a room in 3 hours, and Suzie can paint one in 2 hours. How long will it take them together to paint a room?
2. Bobby and Chuck are playing in the back yard, busily filling a big bucket with mud. If they could fill the bucket together in 15 minutes and it would take Bobby 40 minutes to fill it alone, how long would it take Chuck to fill the bucket?
3. A pond is being drained through an outlet pipe, then will be filled through an inlet pipe. If the inlet pipe can fill the pond in 9 hours and the outlet pipe can empty the pond in 15 hours, how long would it take to fill the pond if the outlet pipe was left open?

4. George and Stanley are building a stone fence. They can complete the fence together in 8 hours, and George can complete it in 24 hours working alone. If they work together for 6 hours, then Stanley goes to the pub for a pint, how much longer must George work to finish the fence?

5. One press can run the day's newspapers in 6 hours while another can do it in 8 hours. If they are both running for 2 hours, at which time the faster one breaks, how much longer must the other press run to finish the newspapers?

Solving a Mixture Problem

- **Mixture problems**: Word problems that set up equations involving various substances mixed together.
- **Tricks for mixture problems:**
  - Make sure the amounts are all measured in the same unit.
  - Convert any percents to two-place decimals.
- **Remember:** the translation process from words to an equation is the true math in word problems and where the real thinking occurs.
- In defining the variable, usually one amount is the variable and the other amount involves addition or subtraction with the variable.

How many grams of pure silver does a silversmith need to mix with a 45% silver alloy to produce 200g of a 50% silver alloy? 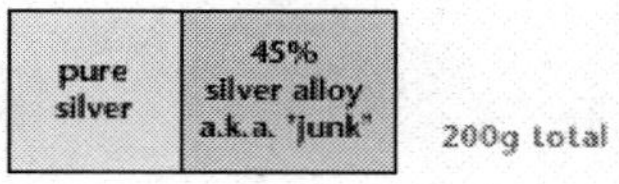	Read the problem. Draw a sketch. Write the known facts. In this problem: 1. There are 200 g of metal that is 50% silver. 2. This 200 g was made by mixing pure silver with 45% silver metal.
s = amount of silver $200-s$ = amount of 45% silver alloy, a.k.a. "junk"	Define the variable and create the equation. Read the problem carefully at this point.
$s+0.45(200-s)=100$	Remember to change any percents into decimals.
$s+\frac{45}{100}\cdot 200-0.45s=100$ $s+\frac{45^{90}}{1\not{0}\not{0}}\cdot 2\not{0}\not{0}-0.45s=100$ $\frac{0.55s}{0.55}=\frac{10}{0.55}$ $\boxed{s=18\frac{2}{11}\text{ g}}$	Solving this equation is straightforward. Pay careful attention to: 1. arithmetic with the decimals 2. distribution across parentheses.

Sample problems:

1. How many liters of sports drink which is 70% water should be added to a 6 liter drink which is 90% water to get a drink which is 85% water?
   Solution: 2 liters
   Explanation: Let x = the number of liters of 70% water sports drink to be added. The final drink, of which there is $x+6$ cups at .85% water, is a mixture of 6 liters at 90% and x liters at 70%, or $0.85(x+6)=.9(6)+.7x$. Simplify and solve for x: $.85(x+6)=5.4+.7x$; $.85x+5.1=5.4+.7x$; $.15x=.3$; $x=2$. Thus, 2 liters of sports drink that is 70% water needs to be added.

2. Tickets for a concert cost \$24, \$30, or \$40 depending on the seat location. A total of \$41,160 was collected from ticket sales. If 1400 tickets were sold, with 6 times as many \$24 tickets as \$30 tickets, and the rest being \$40 tickets, how many \$24 tickets were sold?
Solution: 840
Explanation: Let x = the number of \$24 tickets, y = the number of \$30 tickets, and z = the number of \$40 tickets sold. The total collected from ticket sales was \$41,160, so $24x + 30y + 40z = 41,160$. And, 400 total tickets were sold, so $x + y + z = 400$. There were 6 times as many \$24 tickets sold as \$30 tickets, so $x = 6y$. To write an expression for z in terms of y, substitute $x = 6y$ into $x + y + z = 1400$ and solve for z: $6y + y + z = 1400$; $7y + z = 1400$; $z = 1400 - 7y$.
Now substitute the expression for z, $1400 - 7y$, and the expression for x, $6y$, into $24x + 30y + 40z = 41,160$ for y: $24(6y) + 30y + 40(1400 - 7y) = 41,160$. Now that there is an equation with one variable, solve the equation for y: $144y + 30y + 56,000 - 280y = 41,160$; $56,000 - 106y = 41,160$; $-106y = -14,840$; $y = 140$. Find the number of \$24 tickets sold: $x = 6y = 6(140) = 840$. Thus, 840 \$24 tickets were sold.

3. A chemist has 4 liters of a 12% saline solution. How much must she pour out and replace with a 20% saline solution to produce 4 liters of 15% saline solution?
Solution: 1.5 liters
Explanation: Let x = the number of liters she pours out/replaces. The final solution, of which she has 4 liters at 15% saline, is a mixture of $(4 - x)$ liters at 12% and x liters at 20%, or $.15(4) = .12(4 - x) + .2x$. Simplify and solve for x: $.6 = .48 - .12x + .2x$; $.6 = .48 + .08x$; $.12 = .08x$; $x = 1.5$. Thus, she needs to pour out and replace 1.5 liters.

Practice problems: *(Answers on page: 733)*

1. Julie is mixing orange juice. She adds water to the concentrate until she has 2 liters of juice which is 60% concentrate. She then adds some leftover juice which is 75% concentrate. If the result is 65% concentrated juice, how much of the stronger mix did she add?
2. Eddie spills his cash register drawer on the floor and has to sweep up the coins. He has 742 coins which are a mixture of pennies, nickels, dimes, and quarters. There are 10 times as many pennies as dimes, and half as many quarters as dimes. If he has \$24.60 how many dimes are there?
3. Bernie is a baker and he is making chocolate chip cookie dough. He combines 2 cups of dough that contains 25% chocolate chips with 5 cups of dough that contains 20% chips. How many additional cups of chocolate chips must he add to the dough to make it 35% chocolate chips?

Review questions: *(Answers to odd questions on page: 733)*

1. How much pure gold should be melted into 5 g of a 62% gold alloy to make it an 85% gold alloy?
2. How much water should be added to 10 ml of a 10% acid solution to make it a 5% solution?
3. A chemist has 4 liters of a 12% saline solution. How much must she pour out and replace with a 20% saline solution to produce 4 liters of 15% saline solution?
4. Bobby has a bag containing 2 sizes of marbles. The big ones weigh 8 g and the small ones weigh 2 g. If there are twice as many small ones as big ones and the bag weighs 324 g, how many big marbles does he have?
5. A scientist wants to dilute a 60% acid solution by adding some 20% solution. If she starts with 60 ml of the 60% solution, how much 20% solution does she need to add to get a resulting 45% acid solution?

Solving an Investment Problem

- **Investment problem**: A word problem that requests a solution involving interest on investments.

A White House intern invests part of her \$6000 bonus into a 5% simple interest account. She invests the remainder into an 8.5% simple interest account. After one year, the two accounts earn her \$370 in interest. How much did she invest into each account?	Reading the question is always the most important part for any word problem. In this example there is \$6,000 to invest. Part of the \$6,000 is invested at 5%. The remainder is invested at 8.5%
F = amount in the 5% interest account $6000 - F$ = amount in the 8.5% interest account	Define the variable as the amount invested at one rate of interest. The second amount will be (\$6,000 – the variable).
$5\%F + 8.5\%(6000 - F) = 370$ $0.05F + 0.085(6000 - F) = 370$	Set up the equation. In this example, add the two amounts to equal the gain, \$370. **Remember:** Convert percents to decimals.
$1000(0.05F + 0.085(6000 - F)) = (370)1000$	Multiply through by multiples of 10 to remove the decimal. In this example, multiply through by 1000. Everybody likes working with whole numbers better than decimals.
$50F + 85(6000 - F) = 370{,}000$ $50F + 510{,}000 - 85F = 370{,}000$ $\frac{-35F}{-35} = \frac{-140{,}000}{-35}$ $F = \$4000$ in the 5% account	Once the equation is set up, solve it through. Check the answer to see that: 1. it works in the equation, and 2. it answers the problem.
\$2000 in the 8.5% account; $F = \$4000$ in the 5% account	Frequently, the problem asks for two answers. In this case, solving for the variable reveals that \$4,000 was invested at 5%. Subtract for the amount invested at 8.5%, \$2000.

Sample problems:

1. Alan invests some of his retirement savings in a fund earning 6% simple interest and invests twice as much in a fund earning 9% simple interest. If he earns \$480 combined interest from the accounts after one year, how much did he invest in the 6% account?
   Solution: \$2000
   Explanation: Let x = the amount invested in the 6% account. Then the amount invested in the 9% account is $2x$, since twice as much was invested in this account. Write the investment equation: $0.06x + 0.09(2x) = 480$. Simplify and solve for x: $0.06x + 0.18x = 480$; $0.24x = 480$; $x = 2000$, so he invested \$2000 in the 6% account.

2. Amy receives a gift of \$4000, but has to pay 12.5% income tax on the gift. She invests the remaining money in 2 accounts earning 3% and 5% simple interest. If she earns \$147 in interest after one year, how much was invested in each account?
   Solution: \$1400 at 3%, \$2100 at 5%
   Explanation: Find the amount invested: $4000 - (\text{tax}) = 4000 - 0.125(4000) = 4{,}000 - 500 = 3500$, so she invested \$3500. Let A = the amount invested in the 3% account. So the amount invested in the 5% account is $(3500 - A)$. Write the investment equation: $0.03(A) + 0.05(3500 - A) = 147$. Simplify and solve for A: $0.03(A) + 0.05(3500 - A) = 147$; $0.03A + 175 - 0.05A = 147$; $-0.02A + 175 = 147$; $-0.02A = -28$; $A = 1400$, so \$1400 was invested at 3%. Determine the amount invested at 5%: $3500 - A = 3500 - 1400 = 2100$, so \$2100 was invested at 5%.

3. Mike bought two houses for a total of \$460,000. He made 13% profit after selling the first and lost 8% on the second house. His total profit was \$7,300. How much did he pay for the second house?
Solution: \$250,000
Explanation: Let $p=$ the price of the 1st house. Then, $(460,000-p)$ is the price of the 2nd house. His total profit is the profit from the 1st house minus the loss from the 2nd house, or $7{,}300 = 0.13p - 0.08(460{,}000 - p)$. Simplify and solve for p: $7{,}300 = 0.13p - 36{,}800 + .08p$; $.21p = 44{,}100$; $p = 210{,}000$. Find the price of the second house: $460{,}000 - 210{,}000 = 250{,}000$, so he paid \$250,000 for the 2nd house.

Practice problems: *(Answers on page: 733)*

1. Bobby has a bond earning 11% yearly interest and another bond worth 3 times as much earning 10% interest. If the total yearly interest is \$307.50, find the value of each bond.
2. After Terri wins a \$100,000 payout in the lottery, she must pay 30% in taxes. She then donates 20% to charity, gives 25% to her family and friends, and spends 14.5% on herself. The remainder is in accounts earning 14% and 11% simple interest. If her total interest is \$1335 after one year, how much was invested in each account?
3. Sam invested \$3,000 in one account and \$5,000 in a 2nd account. The combined interest rates of the two accounts was 12.2%. After 1 year the two accounts earned a total of \$500 in interest. What was the interest rate of the second account?

Review questions: *(Answers to odd questions on page: 733)*

1. Jennifer invests her savings of \$8000 in an account earning 7% simple interest. How much interest does she earn in a year?
2. A business has \$8600 invested at 12% and \$7000 at 9.5% interest. How much interest is earned in one year?
3. Kelly has \$800, which she divides between two savings accounts. One account earns 2% simple interest and the other earns 5% simple interest. If she earns \$31 in interest after one year between the two accounts, how much money was invested in each account?
4. Mike bought two houses for a total of \$460,000. He made 13% profit after selling the first and lost 8% on the second house. His total profit was \$7300. How much did he pay for the second house?
5. Sally has \$600 from her piggy bank. She keeps half of it in a savings account and the other half in a second account earning 1% more. If she earns \$27 a year in interest for the year, what is the interest rate on each account?

Solving Business Problems

- **Solving problems involving prices:**
  - Define the variable as the unknown price.
  - The change in price will then be a percent of the variable.
  - The variable and its change will equal the known price.

"Gobbles" the Beanie Baby currently sells at a price of \$750. If the price of Gobbles fell 20% this year, what was the price last year?	**Remember:** As always, reading the word problem for its facts and relationships is the crucial piece in getting to the answer. What are the facts? What is requested? Will a sketch be useful?

P = price of Gobbles last year	Define the variable.
$P - 0.2P = 750$	Set up the equation.
 $\frac{0.8P}{0.8} = \frac{750}{0.8}$ $P = \$937.50$	Solve the equation. Check the answer to be sure: • it's reasonable; • it works arithmetically with the facts; • all the answers asked for have been supplied.

Sample problems:

1. A company's profit was 15% lower in June than in May. If the total profit for the two months was $32,375, find the profit for each month.
   Solution: $17,500 and $14,875
   Explanation: Let m = May profits and j = June profits. The total profit for the two months was $32,375, so $m + j = 32{,}375$. The profit was 15% lower in June than in May, so $j = m - .15m$. Substitute the expression for j, $m - .15m$, into $m + j = 32{,}375$ and solve for m: $m + (m - .15m) = 32{,}375$; $1.85m = 32{,}375$; $m = 17{,}500$. Now find the profit in June: $j = m - .15m = 17{,}500 - (.15)(17{,}500) = 17{,}500 - 2{,}625 = 14{,}875$. Thus, the profit in May was $17,500 and June's profit was $14,875.

2. A clock factory has fixed costs of $18,900 per day, plus cost of $11 per clock produced. The clocks sell for $32 each. How many must they sell to break even?
   Solution: 900 clocks
   Explanation: Let c = the number of clocks made/sold. In order to "break even" the expenses must equal the sales. So, write an equation for total expenses, e, and an equation for total sales, s: $e = 18900 + 11c$ and $s = 32c$. The company will break even when $e = s$, or when $18900 + 11c = 32c$. Solve this equation for c: $18900 + 11c = 32c$; $18900 = 21c$; $c = 900$. Thus, they must sell 900 clocks to break even.

3. If the cost to make a single pizza is $0.75/pizza and a pizza sells for $6.25, how many pizzas must be sold to earn a profit of $4,400?
   Solution: 800 pizzas
   Explanation: Let x = the number of pizzas made/sold. Profit is sales minus expenses, or $p = s - e$. Write an equation for expenses and an equation for sales: $e = 0.75x$ and $s = 6.25x$. Substitute these expressions for e and s, along with 4,400 for profit into $p = s - e$: $4{,}400 = 6.25x - 0.75x$; $4{,}400 = 5.5x$; $x = 800$. Thus, they must sell 800 pizzas to make $4,400 in profit.

Practice problems: *(Answers on page: 733)*

1. Grace purchases a ski pass and must also rent her skis. The cost of the ski pass is $60 more than the rental fee, and she spends a total of $81.90. How much was the rental fee?
2. Shelley must pay $85 per day to rent the stand where she sells bead necklaces. The beads for each necklace cost $3.50, and she can sell each necklace for $9. How many must she sell to make a profit of $245 per day?
3. Amy takes out a loan of $6500 to start a business building and selling rocking chairs. If the chairs cost $35 to build and she can sell them for $100 each, how many must she sell to pay off the loan?

Review questions: *(Answers to odd questions on page: 733)*

1. A shirt is marked 20% off and the sale price is $32.00. What was the original price?
2. Kelly earns 20% more than her sister, and together they earn $880 per week. How much does Kelly earn per week?

3. If Hank pays \$3.75 for each bunch of lillies and then sells the lillies for \$10.25/bunch, how many bunches must he sell in order to make \$250 in profit?
4. A car was worth \$15000 when purchased, but is now only worth \$5250. Find the percent that its value has decreased.
5. A factory produces straw baskets which sell for \$12.50 each. If the cost of production is \$8,000 each day, how many baskest are sold to make a profit of \$17,000 each day?

Solving Quadratics by Factoring

- **Quadratic equations** have a squared variable, but no higher exponents
- One method for solving a quadratic equation is factoring:
  - Group all the terms together, so the equation equals 0.
  - Factor.
  - Set each factor equal to 0 and solve.

Example $x^2 = 25$ $x^2 - 25 = 0$	Quadratic equations introduce the idea that there is more than one specific answer for an equation. To be sure you find all the answers, add and subtract everything over to the left side of the equal with only 0 remaining on the right.
$(x+5)(x-5) = 0$ *difference of two squares*	Then factor your numbers.
$x + 5 = 0$ OR $x - 5 = 0$ $x = -5$ $x = 5$ **Note:** The only way a product can equal 0, is if either the first or second number is 0.	Set each factor equal to 0, and solve for the variable in each situation. You've got all your answers, generally two of them in a quadratic equation.
Example $3x^2 - 7x = 0$ $x(3x - 7) = 0$ *factor out common factor* $x = 0$ OR $3x - 7 = 0$ $3x = 7$ $x = \frac{7}{3}$ ✓ *Check by plugging in answer:* $3(\frac{49}{9}) - 7(\frac{7}{3}) = 0$ $\frac{49}{3} - \frac{49}{3} = 0$	In this case one of your factors is a monomial, which is OK. It can still equal 0, which gives you a value for x. **Remember:** Check each of your answers to be sure it satisfies the equation.
Example $2x^2 - 5x - 3 = 0$ $(2x + 1)(x - 3) = 0$ *check your work by using FOIL!* $2x + 1 = 0$ $x - 3 = 0$ $2x = -1$ $x = 3$ $x = \frac{-1}{2}$	In this example, we use the same process. We just have to think a little harder to accommodate the coefficient 2 on the x^2.
Example $x^2 - 4x + 4 = 0$ $(x - 2)(x - 2) = 0$ $x - 2 = 0$ OR $x - 2 = 0$ $x = 2$	What situations might there be when you only get one answer to a quadratic equation? In this example, we see one. There are two answers and they are the same number.

Sample problems:

1. Solve for t: $6t^2 - 17t + 5 = 0$

   Solution: $\frac{1}{3}$ or $\frac{5}{2}$

   Explanation: Factor: $(3t-1)(2t-5)=0$. Set each factor equal to 0 and solve each equation for t: $3t-1=0$ or $2t-5=0$; $3t=1$ or $2t=5$; $t=\frac{1}{3}$ or $t=\frac{5}{2}$.

2. Solve for x: $4x^2 = 25$

   Solution: $\frac{5}{2}$ or $-\frac{5}{2}$

   Explanation: Set the equation equal to 0: $4x^2 - 25 = 0$. Factor: $(2x-5)(2x+5)=0$. Set each factor equal to 0 and solve for x: $2x-5=0$ or $2x+5=0$; $2x=5$ or $2x=-5$; $x=\frac{5}{2}$ or $x=-\frac{5}{2}$. An alternative method for solving the equation is to divide both sides by 4, then find the square root of each side: $4x^2 = 25$; $x^2 = \frac{25}{4}$; $\sqrt{x^2} = \sqrt{\frac{25}{4}}$; $x = \pm\frac{5}{2}$.

3. Solve for x: $-12x = 27 + x^2$

   Solution: -3 or -9

   Explanation: Set the equation equal to 0 by adding $12x$ to both sides: $0 = 27 + 12x + x^2$ or $x^2 + 12x + 27 = 0$. Factor: $(x+3)(x+9)=0$. Set each factor equal to 0 and solve for x: $x+3=0$ or $x+9=0$; $x=-3$ or $x=-9$.

Practice problems: *(Answers on page: 733)*

1. Solve for x: $x^2 - 10x = 24$
2. Solve for y: $(y-3)^2 = 0$
3. Solve for y: $-12 + 32y - 5y^2 = 0$

Review questions: *(Answers to odd questions on page: 733)*

1. Solve for x: $x^2 - 2x - 8 = 0$
2. Solve for w: $4w^2 = 4w + 3$
3. Solve for y: $6y^2 + 5y = 4$
4. Solve for t: $6t^2 - 17t + 5 = 0$
5. Solve for x: $x^3 - 3x^2 - 4x = 0$

Solving Quadratics by Completing the Square

- **Completing the square** is a process used to solve quadratic equations. In this method
  1. Move constants across the equal sign away from the variable.
  2. Divide the coefficient of the unsquared term by two and square that answer.
  3. Add that answer to both sides of the equation to create a perfect square trinomial with the variable.
  4. Factor the perfect square trinomial.
  5. Take the square root of both sides.
  6. Add or subtract constants as necessary to solve for the variable.

Remember: $x^2 = 25$ ↓ *take the square root* $x = \pm\sqrt{25} = \pm 5$	You have two ways to solve this problem. You can move the 25 to the left side and then factor. Or, as shown here, you can square root both sides of the equation. Either way you will find that $x = 5, -5$. **Remember:** You get both a positive and a negative root.
Example solve for *x* $x^2 + 6x + 1 = 0$ ~~(x)(x)~~ *will not factor*	A problem like this one invites you to factor it so you can solve for *x*. However, it won't factor.
move constant $x^2 + 6x \quad = -1$ *what is added to one side, must be added to the other*	Remembering the problem above, you begin to look for a way to square root here too. **Step one:** Move the +1 to the right side.
complete square $x^2 + 6x + 9 = -1 + 9$ *take* $\frac{1}{2}$ *and square it* → $+\frac{6}{2} = (+3)^2 = +9$	**Step Two:** Divide the coefficient of the 6*x* by 2 and square to get 9. **Step Three:** Add 9 to both sides of the equation.
$(x + 3)(x + 3) = 8$ $(x + 3)^2 = 8$	You have created a perfect square on the side with the variable. **Step Four:** Factor your perfect square.
$x + 3 = \pm\sqrt{8}$	**Step Five:** Square root both sides of the equation.
$x = -3 \pm \sqrt{8}$ $8 = 4 \cdot 2$ $\sqrt{8} = \sqrt{4} \cdot \sqrt{2}$ $= 2\sqrt{2}$	**Step Six:** Subtract +3 to isolate *x*. This gives you two answers for *x*, as expected. **Note:** In this specific example, you can simplify the radical rather than leaving 8 under the radical.

Sample problems:

1. Solve for *w*: $w^2 - 6w + 1 = 0$
   Solution: $3 + 2\sqrt{2}$ or $3 - 2\sqrt{2}$
   Explanation: Notice that $w^2 - 6w + 1$ will not factor. To solve by completing the square, move the constant term to the right side in order to isolate the variables: $w^2 - 6w = -1$. Next, identify the coefficient of the unsquared term (also known as the linear term): -6. Square half of -6: $\left(\frac{-6}{2}\right)^2 = (-3)^2 = 9$. Add 9 to each side: $w^2 - 6w + 9 = -1 + 9$. Factor and simplify: $(w-3)^2 = 8$. Now, solve for *w*: $\sqrt{(w-3)^2} = \sqrt{8}$; $w - 3 = \sqrt{4} \cdot \sqrt{2}$; $w - 3 = \pm 2\sqrt{2}$; $w = 3 \pm 2\sqrt{2}$.

2. Solve for x: $x^2 + 22x - 2 = 0$
   Solution: $-11+\sqrt{123}$ or $-11-\sqrt{123}$
   Explanation: Notice that $x^2 + 22x - 2$ will not factor. Move the constant term to the right side: $x^2 + 22x = 2$. Next, square half of the linear coefficient: $\left(\frac{22}{2}\right)^2 = (11)^2 = 121$. Add 121 to each side, factor, and simplify: $x^2 + 22x + 121 = 2 + 121$; $(x+11)^2 = 123$. Now, solve for x: $\sqrt{(x+11)^2} = \pm\sqrt{123}$; $x + 11 = \pm\sqrt{123}$; $x = -11 \pm \sqrt{123}$. So, $x = -11 + \sqrt{123}$ or $x = -11 - \sqrt{123}$.

3. Solve for y: $y^2 + 10y - 20 = 0$
   Solution: $-5 + 3\sqrt{5}$ or $-5 - 3\sqrt{5}$
   Explanation: Notice that it will not factor. Move the constant term to the right side: $y^2 + 10y = 20$. Next, to complete the square, square half of the linear coefficient and add that to each side: $\left(\frac{10}{2}\right)^2 = (5)^2 = 25$, $y^2 + 10y + 25 = 20 + 25$. Factor, simplify, and solve for y: $(y+5)^2 = 45$; $\sqrt{(y+5)^2} = \sqrt{45}$; $y + 5 = \sqrt{9} \cdot \sqrt{5}$; $y + 5 = \pm 3\sqrt{5}$; $y = -5 \pm 3\sqrt{5}$.

Practice problems: *(Answers on page: 734)*

1. Solve for x: $(x+15)^2 = 81$
2. Solve for w: $w^2 + 6w - 7 = 0$
3. Solve for t: $t^2 - 4t + 4 = 121$

Review questions: *(Answers to odd questions on page: 734)*

1. Solve for x: $(3-2x)^2 = 25$
2. Solve for x: $x^2 + 4x - 5 = 0$
3. Solve for x: $x^2 - 6x + 8 = 0$
4. Solve for x: $x^2 = 4 - 3x$
5. Solve for x: $x(x-6) = 4$

Completing the Square: Another Example

- When a square term has a coefficient other than 1, divide the entire equation by that coefficient to eliminate having to consider it with the squared term.
- When completing the square, keep all the terms with the variable you are solving for on the left and move all the other terms to the right of the equal sign.

Reducing a Quadratic Equation divide the equation by the coefficient of x^2 *reduce* $\frac{2x^2 + 4x - 1}{2} = \frac{0}{2}$ $x^2 + 2x - \frac{1}{2} = 0$	Completing the square works with x^2 where the coefficient is 1. So, in this case eliminate the 2 by dividing the entire equation by 2.
move constant $x^2 + 2x \quad = \frac{1}{2}$	Next, move the constant term to the right side of the equal sign. This allows you to complete the square for the terms remaining on the left side.

ve stant $x^2 + 2x + 1 = \frac{1}{2} + 1$ plete ire take $\frac{1}{2}$ and square $2 \cdot \frac{1}{2} = (1)^2 = 1$ $x^2 + 2x + 1 = \frac{3}{2}$	To complete the square: 1. Divide the coefficient of the unsquared term, the 2 in this example, in half: 2/2 = 1. 2. Square that half: $(1)^2 = 1$. 3. Add that newly found number to both sides of the equation: add 1 to both sides.
$(x + 1)^2 = \frac{3}{2}$	Now, rewrite the left side as the square of a binomial.
take the square root $x + 1 = \pm\sqrt{\frac{3}{2}}$	Once you've got a square on the left, just take the square root of both sides to get to x.
$x = -1 \pm \sqrt{\frac{3}{2}}$	Then move the constant with x to the right side. And, you've indicated your two answers with the ± sign, so you're done, almost.
$x = -1 \pm \sqrt{\frac{3}{2}}$ Rationalize the Denomintator $\frac{\sqrt{3}}{\sqrt{2}} \cdot \frac{\sqrt{2}}{\sqrt{2}} = \frac{\sqrt{6}}{2}$	**Remember:** Most people dislike radicals in the denominator. So, take the extra step to eliminate those from your answers.
$x = -1 + \frac{\sqrt{6}}{2}$ or $x = -1 - \frac{\sqrt{6}}{2}$	And here are your two finished answers.

Sample problems:

1. Solve for x: $12 - 3x - x^2 = 0$

   Solution: $\dfrac{-3+\sqrt{57}}{2}$ or $\dfrac{-3-\sqrt{57}}{2}$

   Explanation: Since the coefficient of x^2 is not 1, divide each side by -1: $x^2 + 3x - 12 = 0$. Move the constant term to the right side: $x^2 + 3x = 12$. Next, to complete the square, square half of the linear coefficient and add that to both sides: $\left(\frac{3}{2}\right)^2 = \frac{9}{4}$, $x^2 + 3x + \frac{9}{4} = 12 + \frac{9}{4}$. Now factor, simplify, and solve for x: $(x + \frac{3}{2})^2 = \frac{57}{4}$; $\sqrt{(x+\frac{3}{2})^2} = \sqrt{\frac{57}{4}}$; $x + \frac{3}{2} = \pm\frac{\sqrt{57}}{2}$; $x = -\frac{3}{2} \pm \frac{\sqrt{57}}{2}$; $x = \frac{-3\pm\sqrt{57}}{2}$.

2. Solve for y: $4 - 11y - 2y^2 = 0$

   Solution: $\dfrac{-11+3\sqrt{17}}{4}$ or $\dfrac{-11-3\sqrt{17}}{4}$

   Explanation: Divide each side by -2: $-2 + \frac{11}{2}y + y^2 = 0$. Move the constant term: $y^2 + \frac{11}{2}y = 2$. Next, to complete the square, square half of the linear coefficient and add that to both sides: $\left(\frac{11}{2} \div 2\right)^2 = \left(\frac{11}{4}\right)^2 = \frac{121}{16}$; $y^2 + \frac{11}{2}y + \frac{121}{16} = 2 + \frac{121}{16}$. Now factor, simplify,and solve for y: $(y + \frac{11}{4})^2 = \frac{153}{16}$; $\sqrt{(y+\frac{11}{4})^2} = \sqrt{\frac{153}{16}}$; $y + \frac{11}{4} = \pm\frac{3\sqrt{17}}{4}$; $y = -\frac{11}{4} \pm \frac{3\sqrt{17}}{4}$; $y = \frac{-11\pm3\sqrt{17}}{4}$.

3. Solve for *x*: $3x^2 + 12x - 4 = 0$

<u>Solution:</u> $-2 + \frac{4\sqrt{3}}{3}$ or $-2 - \frac{4\sqrt{3}}{3}$

<u>Explanation:</u> Divide each side by 3: $x^2 + 4x - \frac{4}{3} = 0$. Move the constant term: $x^2 + 4x = \frac{4}{3}$. Next, to complete the square, square half of the linear coefficient and add that to both sides: $\left(\frac{4}{2}\right)^2 = 2^2 = 4$; $x^2 + 4x + 4 = \frac{4}{3} + 4$. Now factor, simplify, and solve for *y*: $(x+2)^2 = \frac{16}{3}$; $\sqrt{(x+2)^2} = \sqrt{\frac{16}{3}}$; $x + 2 = \pm\frac{4}{\sqrt{3}}$; $x = -2 \pm \frac{4}{\sqrt{3}}$. There is a radical in the denominator, so rationalize the denominator: $x = -2 \pm \frac{4}{\sqrt{3}} \cdot \frac{\sqrt{3}}{\sqrt{3}}$; $x = -2 \pm \frac{4\sqrt{3}}{3}$.

Practice problems: *(Answers on page: 734)*

1. Solve for t: $-7t^2 - 42t - 63 = 0$
2. Solve for y: $30y - 9y^2 = 25$
3. Solve for y: $2y^2 - 2y = 8$

Review questions: *(Answers to odd questions on page: 734)*

1. Solve for *x*: $-x^2 + 6x + 10 = 0$
2. Solve for *x*: $2x^2 - 8x = 22$
3. Solve for *x*: $2x^2 = x + 1$
4. Solve for *x*: $3x^2 - 2 = 5x$
5. Solve for *x*: $4x^2 = 12x - 7$

Proving the Quadratic Formula

- Completing the square for a generalized quadratic equation gives us a very powerful formula for solving all quadratic equations.
- **Quadratic formula:** $x = \frac{-b \pm \sqrt{b^2 - 4ac}}{2a}$

solve for x: $ax^2 + bx + c = 0$ (a, b, c: any numbers)	Begin with a generalized equation, one that is solving for *x* and using letters rather than specific numbers in each position.
reduce $x^2 + \left(\frac{b}{a}\right)x + \frac{c}{a} = 0$	Step one in completing the square is to divide the entire equation by any coefficient of x^2 other than 1, in this case, *a*.
move constant $x^2 + \left(\frac{b}{a}\right)x \quad = -\frac{c}{a}$	Next step is to move the constant, in this case *c*/*a* to the right side of the equation.
move constant $x^2 + \left(\frac{b}{a}\right)x \quad = -\frac{c}{a}$ *take $\frac{1}{2}$ and square* $\frac{1}{2} \cdot \frac{b}{a} = \left(\frac{b}{2a}\right)^2 = \frac{b^2}{4a^2}$	Now for the biggie. Divide the coefficient of *x* by 2: $(b/a) \div 2 = b/2a$. Then square the number: $\frac{b^2}{4a^2}$.
complete the square $x^2 + \left(\frac{b}{a}\right)x + \frac{b^2}{4a^2} = -\frac{c}{a} + \frac{b^2}{4a^2}$	Next add that squared number to both sides of the equation.

$(x + \frac{b}{2a})^2 =$	Write the left side as the square of a binomial.
take the square roots $x + \frac{b}{2a} = \frac{\pm\sqrt{b^2 - 4ac}}{\sqrt{4a^2}}$	Take the square root of both sides.
$x = \frac{-b \pm \sqrt{b^2 - 4ac}}{2a}$	Finally, move the constant on the left side to the right side and you have your two final answers. Remember also to rationalize the denominator. You rarely have to develop the quadratic formula in this fashion. However, you will use it frequently.

Using the Quadratic Formula

- Using the **quadratic formula** allows solutions for equations that cannot be factored or solved by easier methods.
- **Quadratic equation:** $ax^2 + bx + c = 0$
- **Quadratic formula:** $x = \frac{-b \pm \sqrt{b^2 - 4ac}}{2a}$.
- "**a**" is the coefficient of the squared term (quadratic term) in the equation.
- "**b**" is the coefficient of the unsquared term (linear term) in the equation.
- "**c**" is the constant in the equation.

Example solve for x $3x^2 - 5x + 3 = 0$ (a b c) $x = \frac{-b \pm \sqrt{b^2 - 4ac}}{2a}$	As a practice, try to factor first. It is a shorter and easier process. Generally, use the **quadratic formula** when nothing else works. Using the formula involves simply substituting in the values for *a*, *b*, and *c* that you find in the equation.
$x = \frac{5 \pm \sqrt{25 - 36}}{6}$ $x = \frac{5 \pm \sqrt{-11}}{6}$ $x = \frac{5 \pm \sqrt{11}i}{6}$ *the Quadratic Formula can give imaginary numbers as solutions*	Then, do the arithmetic. Expect two answers. Frequently, the two answers include an imaginary element.
Example solve for x $\sqrt{2}x^2 + 3x + \sqrt{2} = 0$ (a b c) $x = \frac{-3 \pm \sqrt{9 - 4(2)}}{2\sqrt{2}}$	In this example, both a and c are radicals. Identify *a*, *b*, and *c*. Substitute those values into the formula.
$x = \frac{-3 + 1}{2\sqrt{2}} = \frac{-2}{2\sqrt{2}} = \frac{-1}{\sqrt{2}} \cdot \frac{\sqrt{2}}{\sqrt{2}} = \frac{-\sqrt{2}}{2}$ $x = \frac{-3 - 1}{2\sqrt{2}} = \frac{-4}{2\sqrt{2}} = \frac{-2}{\sqrt{2}} \cdot \frac{\sqrt{2}}{\sqrt{2}} = \frac{-2\sqrt{2}}{2} = -\sqrt{2}$	Do the arithmetic to find your two answers. Note here you must rationalize the denominator because of the $\sqrt{2}$.

Sample problems:

1. Solve for y: $3y^2 - \sqrt{7}y + 1 = 0$

   Solution: $\frac{\sqrt{7} + i\sqrt{5}}{6}$ or $\frac{\sqrt{7} - i\sqrt{5}}{6}$

   Explanation: Be sure the equation is set equal to 0, then identify the coefficients: $a = 3$, $b = -\sqrt{7}$, and $c = 1$. Use the quadratic formula, $y = \frac{-b \pm \sqrt{b^2 - 4ac}}{2a}$, to solve for y. Substitute the a, b, and c values into the formula and simplify:
   $y = \frac{-(-\sqrt{7}) \pm \sqrt{(-\sqrt{7})^2 - 4(3)(1)}}{2(3)} = \frac{\sqrt{7} \pm \sqrt{7 - 12}}{6} = \frac{\sqrt{7} \pm \sqrt{-5}}{6} = \frac{\sqrt{7} \pm i\sqrt{-5}}{6}$.

2. Solve for k: $k^2 + \sqrt{2}k - 6 = 0$

   Solution: $\frac{-\sqrt{2} + \sqrt{26}}{2}$ or $\frac{-\sqrt{2} - \sqrt{26}}{2}$

   Explanation: Be sure the equation is set equal to 0, then identify the coefficients: $a = 1$, $b = \sqrt{2}$, and $c = -6$. Use the quadratic formula to solve for y:
   $k = \frac{-(\sqrt{2}) \pm \sqrt{(\sqrt{2})^2 - 4(1)(-6)}}{2(1)} = \frac{-\sqrt{2} \pm \sqrt{2 + 24}}{2} = \frac{-\sqrt{2} \pm \sqrt{26}}{2}$.

3. Solve for x: $\sqrt{5}x^2 - 7x = \sqrt{5} - 4x$

   Solution: $\frac{3\sqrt{5} + \sqrt{145}}{10}$ or $\frac{3\sqrt{5} - \sqrt{145}}{10}$

   Explanation: Before identifying the coefficients, set the equation equal to 0: $\sqrt{5}x^2 - 3x - \sqrt{5} = 0$, so $a = \sqrt{5}$, $b = -3$, and $c = -\sqrt{5}$. Use the quadratic formula to solve for x: $x = \frac{-(-3) \pm \sqrt{(-3)^2 - 4(\sqrt{5})(-\sqrt{5})}}{2(\sqrt{5})} = \frac{3 \pm \sqrt{9 + 20}}{2\sqrt{5}} = \frac{3 \pm \sqrt{29}}{2\sqrt{5}}$.

   Rationalize the denominator: $x = \frac{3 \pm \sqrt{29}}{2\sqrt{5}} \cdot \frac{\sqrt{5}}{\sqrt{5}} = \frac{3\sqrt{5} \pm \sqrt{29} \cdot \sqrt{5}}{2(5)} = \frac{3\sqrt{5} \pm \sqrt{145}}{10}$.

Practice problems: *(Answers on page: 734)*

1. Solve for y: $y^2 + 3y - 1 = 0$
2. Solve for t: $t^2 + t + 1 = 0$
3. Solve for x: $\frac{1}{2}x^2 + \frac{5}{4}x - \frac{5}{4} = 0$

Review questions: *(Answers to odd questions on page: 734)*

1. Solve for x: $9 - 4x - x^2 = 0$
2. Solve for y: $8y^2 + 4y - 2 = 0$
3. Solve for z: $12z - 9z^2 = 6$
4. Solve for w: $(w - 5)^2 = 2w$
5. Solve for z: $\frac{z^2}{2} - \frac{z}{3} + \frac{7}{6} = 0$

Predicting the Type of Solutions Using the Discriminant

- The **discriminant** is the quantity under the radical in the quadratic formula.
- The discriminant for the equation $ax^2 + bx + c = 0$, is $b^2 - 4ac$.
- The discriminant is important because we can analyze it to determine in advance the number and nature of the solutions of the quadratic equation in question.
  - If the discriminant = 0, there is only one real solution to the equation.
  - If the discriminant is positive, there are two real solutions.
  - If the discriminant is negative, there are two complex solutions.
- Evaluating the discriminant is very useful, BUT it does NOT give you the answers, just information about the answers.

D > 0, then 2 real solutions **D = 0, only 1 solution** $(x = \frac{-b}{2a})$ **D < 0, then 2 complex solutions** **Example** How many solutions will there be? *(Compute discriminant)* $2x^2 - 5x - 7 = 0$ $D = b^2 - 4ac$ $= (5)^2 - 4(2)(-7)$ $= 25 - 4\cdot$ ~~14~~ (-14) $= 25 + 56$	Doing this analysis is a simple matter: 1. Substitute your a, b, and c values into the discriminant. 2. Do the arithmetic to see if the quantity is 0, > 0, or < 0. 3. Evaluate the number and type of solutions your equation has.
$= 81 > 0$, **2 real** solutions	The quantity is positive so there will be two solutions, both of them real numbers.
Example $3x^2 - 2x + 10 = 0$ $D = (-2)^2 - 4(3)(10)$ $= 4 - 4(30)$ $= 4 - 120$ $= -116$, **2 complex** solutions	Here's a second example. It works the same way: 1. Substitute in your a, b, c values. 2. Do the arithmetic. 3. Evaluate.
Example $x^2 - 20x + 100 = 0$ $D = (-20)^2 - 4(1)(100)$ $= 400 - 400$ $= 0$, **1** solution	This third example is slightly different. Substitute in your values. When you do the arithmetic, you get 0. Your conclusion: there is only one solution.

Sample problems:

1. How many solutions are there for $\frac{1}{2}x^2 - 5x + 4 = 0$?

   Solution: 2 distinct real solutions

   Explanation: To determine the number of solutions find the discriminant $\left(b^2 - 4ac\right)$, then based on that quantity identify the number of solutions. Since the equation $\frac{1}{2}x^2 - 5x + 4 = 0$ is already set equal to zero, the coefficients are: $a = \frac{1}{2}$, $b = -5$, and $c = 4$. Substitute these values into the discriminant formula: $b^2 - 4ac = (-5)^2 - 4\left(\frac{1}{2}\right)(4) = 25 - 8 = 17$. The discriminant is positive, so there must be 2 real solutions.

2. How many solutions are there for $3w^2 + w = \frac{-1}{12}$?
   Solution: 1 real solution
   Explanation: The equation must be set equal to zero before the coefficients are identified: $3w^2 + w + \frac{1}{12} = 0$. So, $a = 3$, $b = 1$, and $c = \frac{1}{12}$. Calculate the discriminant: $b^2 - 4ac = (1)^2 - 4(3)(\frac{1}{12}) = 1 - 1 = 0$. Since the discriminant is 0, there must be one real solution.

3. How many solutions are there for $x^2 + x = 4x - 5$?
   Solution: 2 complex solutions
   Explanation: Set the equation equal to 0: $x^2 - 3x + 5 = 0$. Identify the coefficients: $a = 1$, $b = -3$, and $c = 5$. Calculate the discriminant: $b^2 - 4ac = (-3)^2 - 4(1)(5) = 9 - 20 = -11$. The discriminant is negative, so there must be 2 imaginary solutions.

Practice problems: *(Answers on page: 734)*

1. How many solutions are there for $x^2 + x = 6$?
2. How many solutions are there for $4y^2 + 25 = 20y$?
3. How many solutions are there for $\sqrt{7}t^2 + t = -\sqrt{7}$?

Review questions: *(Answers to odd questions on page: 734)*

1. Determine the discriminant of $y^2 = 8y - 16$.
2. Determine the discriminant of $\frac{1}{2}x^2 + \frac{6}{5}x = 8$.
3. How many solutions are there for $3y = y^2 - 7$?
4. How many solutions are there for $3x^2 + 60x = -300$?
5. How many solutions are there for $2w^2 - \sqrt{5}w + 3 = 0$?

Solving for a Squared Variable

- **Quadratic formula:** $x = \frac{-b \pm \sqrt{b^2 - 4ac}}{2a}$
- The example used in this lecture shows you a problem where a variable is treated as a number. In this case, y is part of the answer when you solve for x.
- The quadratic formula gives us an easy way to solve equations that might appear unsolvable and that certainly involve messy numbers. You can use it for any quadratic equation.

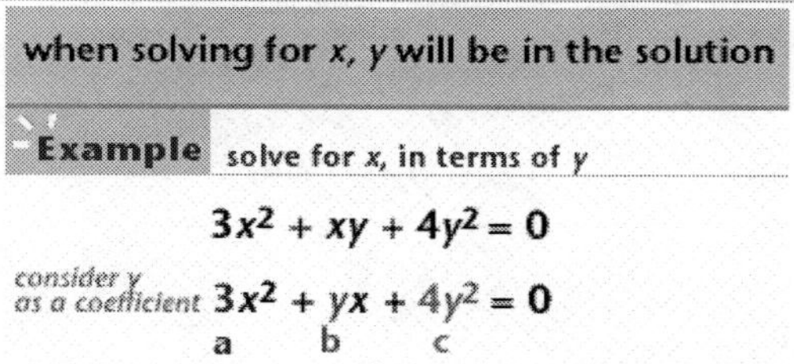

Here's an example using the quadratic formula:
$ax^2 + bx + c = 0$.

In this problem,
$a = 3$
$b = y$ (It's OK to have a variable as a coefficient so long as it is NOT the variable you are solving for.)
$c = 4y^2$

Now, you are ready to use the formula, a matter of simple substitution.

$x = \dfrac{-y \pm \sqrt{y^2 - 4 \cdot 12y^2}}{6}$	Here's what this problem looks like after you've substituted its "numbers" into the formula.
$x = \dfrac{-y \pm \sqrt{y^2(1 - 48)}}{6}$ ← *y is factored out* $x = \dfrac{-y \pm y\sqrt{-47}}{6}$	Next simplify in whatever ways are possible.
$x = \dfrac{y(-1 \pm \sqrt{47}\,i)}{6}$ ← *y is factored out* $(i = \sqrt{-1})$	And here's your answer. You have solved for x in terms of y. Because this answer includes a negative constant, you are using "i".

Sample problems:

1. Solve for z in terms of x, y, and w: $x = \dfrac{y^2}{(z+2w)^2}$

   Solution: $\dfrac{-2wx + y\sqrt{x}}{x}$ or $\dfrac{-2wx - y\sqrt{x}}{x}$

   Explanation: Multiply each side by $(z+2w)^2$: $x(z+2w)^2 = y^2$. Divide each side by x: $(z+2w)^2 = \dfrac{y^2}{x}$.

   Take the square root of each side: $z + 2w = \pm\sqrt{\dfrac{y^2}{x}}$; $z = -2w \pm \dfrac{y}{\sqrt{x}}$.

   Express with a common denominator: $z = \dfrac{-2wx \pm y\sqrt{x}}{x}$.

2. Solve for x in terms of y: $5x^2 + 2xy + y^2 = 0$

   Solution: $\dfrac{-y + 2yi}{5}$ or $\dfrac{-y - 2yi}{5}$

   Explanation: Use the quadratic formula to solve the quadratic equation. Identify the coefficients of x: $a = 5$, $b = 2y$, and $c = y^2$. Since the equation is being solved for x <u>in terms of y</u> it is ok for y to be the coefficient. Substitute the a, b, and c values into the quadratic formula:

   $$x = \frac{-(2y) \pm \sqrt{(2y)^2 - 4(5)(y^2)}}{2(5)} = \frac{-2y \pm \sqrt{4y^2 - 20y^2}}{10} = \frac{-2y \pm \sqrt{16y^2}}{10} = \frac{-2y \pm 4yi}{10} = \frac{-y \pm 2yi}{5}.$$

3. Solve for t in terms of v, g, and y: $y = -\frac{1}{2}gt^2 + vt$

   Solution: $\dfrac{v + \sqrt{v^2 - 2gy}}{g}$ or $\dfrac{v - \sqrt{v^2 - 2gy}}{g}$

   Explanation: Set the equation equal to 0, then identify a, b, and c: $0 = -\frac{1}{2}gt^2 + vt - y$, so $a = -\frac{1}{2}g$, $b = v$, $c = -y$. Use the quadratic formula to solve for t:

   $$t = \frac{-v \pm \sqrt{v^2 - 4(-\frac{1}{2}g)(-y)}}{2(-\frac{1}{2}g)} = \frac{-v \pm \sqrt{v^2 - 2gy}}{-g} = \frac{v \pm \sqrt{v^2 - 2gy}}{g}.$$

Practice problems: *(Answers on page: 734)*

1. Solve for z: $x = \dfrac{y^2}{(z+2w)^2}$

2. Solve for x: $3x^2 + yx + 4 = 0$

3. Solve for L: $g = \dfrac{L - RL}{L^2 - 1}$

Review questions: *(Answers to odd questions on page: 734)*

1. Solve for y: $(y-5)^2 = 3 - x$
2. Solve for r: $A = \pi(R^2 - r^2)$
3. Solve for x: $x^2 + 8x + 16 = 25$
4. Solve for t: $S = V_0 t - 16t^2$
5. Solve for r: $p = \dfrac{-r - rs}{r^2 + 4}$

Finding Real Number Restrictions

- The denominator can never have a value of zero. That stipulation restricts the domain of the variable to exclude any values that yield a value of zero for the denominator.
- The domain of the variable is the set of all real numbers that the variable can use.
- To find any value of the variable that makes the denominator equal zero, set the denominator equal to zero and solve that equation. This value(s) must be excluded from the domain of the variable.

Example Find the Domain $\dfrac{3 - 2x}{3x^2 - 19x - 14}$ $3x^2 - 19x - 14 = 0$ $(3x+2)(x-7) = 0$ $3x + 2 = 0$ or $x - 7 = 0$ $x = \frac{-2}{3}$ $\quad$ $x = 7$ **Domain:** $x \neq \frac{-2}{3}, 7$	To find the domain of an expression, first factor the denominator. Next set each factor equal to zero to see what values of x must be eliminated from the domain. If an equation is too complex to be easily factored, use the quadratic formula. It will show you every number that must be excluded.
Example Find the Domain $\dfrac{-18x}{25x^2 - 30x + 9}$ $25x^2 - 30x + 9 = 0$ $(5x - 3)(5x - 3) = 0$ $5x - 3 = 0$ $x = \frac{3}{5}$ **Domain:** $x \neq \frac{3}{5}$	To find the domain for this expression, factor the denominator. Then set the factor(s) equal to zero and solve for x. This solution is the one real number that must be excluded from the domain of x.
Example Find the Domain $\dfrac{x}{x^2 + 1}$ *Where does $x^2 + 1$ equal 0?* $x^2 = -1$ *this is imaginary* **Domain:** all real numbers	This example shows you a different result. This denominator can equal zero only when x has the value of an imaginary number. Therefore, no real numbers are excluded and the domain is all real numbers.

Sample problems:

1. Determine the domain of $\dfrac{38}{z^2 - 5z}$.

   Solution: $z \neq 0, 5$

   Explanation: To find the values of z that make the denominator zero, set the denominator equal to 0 and solve for z: $z^2 - 5z = 0$; $z(z-5) = 0$; $z = 0$ or $z - 5 = 0$; $z = 0$ or $z = -5$. So, $z \neq 0$ or 5

2. Find the real number restrictions on w in the expression $\dfrac{7w-6}{(w-1)^2 - 4}$.

   Solution: 3 or -1

   Explanation: Set the denominator equal to 0 and solve for w: $(w-1)^2 - 4 = 0$; $(w-1)^2 = 4$; $\sqrt{(w-1)^2} = \sqrt{4}$; $w - 1 = \pm 2$; $w = 1 \pm 2$. These are the restrictions on w: $w = 3$ or $w = -1$.

3. Find the real number restrictions on w in the expression $\dfrac{13w}{w^2 + 6w + 2}$.

   Solution: $-3 + \sqrt{7}$ and $-3 - \sqrt{7}$

   Explanation: Set the denominator equal to 0: $w^2 + 6w + 2 = 0$. Notice that this expression can't be factored, so use the quadratic formula to solve for w:

   $$w = \frac{-6 \pm \sqrt{(6)^2 - 4(1)(2)}}{2(1)} = \frac{-6 \pm \sqrt{36-8}}{2} = \frac{-6 \pm \sqrt{28}}{2} = \frac{-6 \pm \sqrt{4}\sqrt{7}}{2} = \frac{-6 \pm 2\sqrt{7}}{2} = -3 \pm \sqrt{7}.$$

Practice problems: *(Answers on page: 734)*

1. Find the real number restrictions on x in the expression $\dfrac{2}{-4 + 4x - x^2}$.
2. Find the real number restrictions on y in the expression $\dfrac{-1}{3y^2 + 12}$.
3. Find the real number restrictions on y in the expression $\dfrac{4 - y}{y^2 - 5y + 13}$.

Review questions: *(Answers to odd questions on page: 734)*

1. Find the real number restrictions on z in the expression $\dfrac{12z}{z^2 - 13z + 36}$.
2. Find the real number restrictions on x in the expression $\dfrac{x^2}{x^2 - 14x + 49}$.
3. Find the real number restrictions on t in the expression $\dfrac{t+1}{t^2 + 3t - 4}$.
4. Find the real number restrictions on y in the expression $\dfrac{3y + 6}{\sqrt{2}y^2 - 5y + \sqrt{2}}$.
5. Find the real number restrictions on x in the expression $\dfrac{-8}{5x^2 - x + 1}$.

Solving Fancy Quadratics

- Frequently an equation that appears to be of higher degree than a squared term, can be rewritten so that your quadratic techniques allow you to solve it.
- Be creative with your use of variables. Look for ways to use them so that you can see your equation as a quadratic and use all your tools.
- Remember that whenever you solve an equation by substituting in a new variable, you must replace that variable when you have found its solution. At that point, you reinsert the original variable and solve for its values from this much simplified equation.

fancy quadratic equations

Example solve for x

$$x^4 - 9x^2 + 14 = 0$$
$$(x^2)^2 - 9x^2 + 14 = 0$$
Let $G = x^2$
$$G^2 - 9G + 14 = 0$$
$$(G - 2)(G - 7) = 0$$
$$G - 2 = 0 \qquad G - 7 = 0$$
$$G = 2 \qquad G = 7$$
$$x^2 = 2 \qquad x^2 = 7$$
$$x = \pm\sqrt{2} \qquad x = \pm\sqrt{7}$$
an equation with a power of 4, can have 4 solutions

Since you have x^2 and its square x^4 in this equation, substitute in a new variable that equals x^2.

Now solve the equation as a quadratic.

Substitute x^2 back in for the variable.

Solve for x. Expect four answers because your variable was originally raised to the fourth degree.

fancy quadratic equations

Example solve for x

$$x^6 + x^3 - 6 = 0$$
$$(x^3)^2 + (x^3) - 6 = 0$$
Let $G = x^2$
$$G^2 + G - 6 = 0$$
$$(G + 3)(G - 2) = 0$$
$$G = -3 \qquad G = 2$$
$$x^3 = -3 \qquad x^3 = 2$$
$$\sqrt[3]{x^3} = \sqrt[3]{-3} \qquad \sqrt[3]{x^3} = \sqrt[3]{2}$$
$$x = -\sqrt[3]{3} \qquad x = \sqrt[3]{2}$$

This example works much the same way.

Since you have x^3 and its square x^6, you can substitute in a new variable for x^3.

Then solve the equation.

Finally, put the x^3 back in and solve for it.

Sample problems:

1. Find all real solutions for x: $x^8 + 3x^4 - 4 = 0$

   Solution: ± 1

   Explanation: Since x^8 is the square of x^4, let $G = x^4$. Substitute G into the equation for x^4: $G^2 + 3G - 4 = 0$. Solve for G: $(G+4)(g-1) = 0$; $G + 4 = 0$ or $G - 1 = 0$; $G = -4$ or $G = 1$. Now substitute x^4 into each equation for G and solve for x: 1) $x^4 = -4$; $x = \sqrt[4]{-4} \Rightarrow$; this is an imaginary number so it is not included with the real solutions. 2) $x^4 = 1$; $x = \sqrt[4]{1} = \pm 1$. So the real solutions are 1 and -1.

2. Find all real solutions for x: $(x+2)^4 - 5(x+2)^2 + 4 = 0$
   Solution: $-4,\ -3,\ -1,\ 0$
   Explanation: Since $(x+2)^4$ is the square of $(x+2)^2$, let $G = (x+2)^2$. Substitute G into the equation and solve for G: $G^2 + 5G + 4 = 0$; $(G-4)(G-1) = 0$; $G - 4 = 0$ or $G - 1 = 0$; $G = 4$ or $G = 1$. Substitute $(x+2)^2$ into each equation and solve for x:
   1) $(x+2)^2 = 4$; $\sqrt{(x+2)^2} = \sqrt{4}$; $x+2 = \pm 2$; $x = -2 \pm 2; x = 0$ or $x = -4$.
   2) $(x+2)^2 = 1$; $\sqrt{(x+2)^2} = \sqrt{1}$; $x+2 = \pm 1$; $x = -2 \pm 1$; $x = -1$ or $x = -3$.
   So $x = -4,\ -3,\ -1,\ 0$.

3. Find all real solutions for x: $9(x+1)^2 + 21(x+1) + 10 = 0$.
   Solution: $-\frac{5}{3},\ -\frac{8}{3}$
   Explanation: Since $(x+1)^2$ is the square of $(x+1)$, let $G = x+1$. Substitute G into the equation and solve for G: $9G^2 + 21G + 10 = 0$; $(3G+2)(3G+5) = 0$; $3G + 2 = 0$ or $3G + 5 = 0$; $G = -\frac{2}{3}$ or $G = -\frac{5}{3}$. Substitute $x+1$ into each equation for G and solve for x: $x + 1 = -\frac{2}{3}$ or $x + 1 = -\frac{5}{3}$; $x = -\frac{2}{3} - 1$ or $x = -\frac{5}{3} - 1$; $x = -\frac{5}{3}$ or $x = -\frac{8}{3}$.

Practice problems: *(Answers on page: 734)*

1. Find all real solutions for x: $x^6 - 3x^3 - 4 = 0$
2. Find all real solutions for y: $\frac{6}{y^2} - \frac{7}{y} - 3 = 0$
3. Find all real solutions for z: $5z - 11\sqrt{z} + 2 = 0$

Review questions: *(Answers to odd questions on page: 734)*

1. Find all real solutions for x: $9(x+1)^2 + 21(x+1) + 10 = 0$
2. Find all real solutions for z: $z^{10} - 8z^5 + 15 = 0$
3. Find all real solutions for x: $\frac{4}{x^4} - \frac{9}{x^2} + 2 = 0$
4. Find all real solutions for x: $2x^{\frac{2}{5}} - x^{\frac{1}{5}} - 1 = 0$
5. Find all real solutions for x: $3(x+1)^2 + 13(x+1) = 10$

Solving a Quadratic Geometry Problem

- **Process for solving word problems**:
  - Define the variable.
  - Write what facts you know.
  - Create the equation.
  - Solve the equation.
  - Check your answer.
- Geometry problems generally use at least one of the many formulas everyone knows for area, surface area, circumference, volume, etc. They help you set up your equations.

Solve the Word Problem **The perimeter of the the dorm is 34 ft, and its area is 60 Square ft.** **What are is the dimensions of the room?** Dorm Room 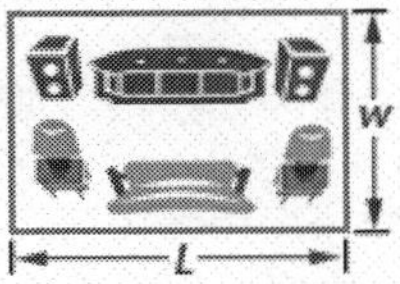	In reading this problem, you find several facts and know that you are being asked to find the dimensions of the room; i.e., its length and width.
w = **Width of the dorm room** L = **Length of the dorm room** The perimeter of the the dorm is 34 ft, and its area is 60 Square ft. What is the dimension of the room? Dorm Room 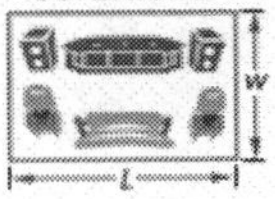 $2L+2w = 34$ $L+w = 17$ ← *Divided by 2 to simplify*	Now you can define your variables and set up the equation for the perimeter. You can even simplify the equation by noticing that 2 factors out of everything.
The perimeter of the dorm is 34 ft. $L+w = 17$ $w = 17-L$ **The area of the dorm is 60 ft.** $L \cdot w = 60$ Substitute and solve for L $L(17-L) = 60$ $17L-L^2 = 60$ $0 = L^2-17L+60$ $0 = (L-5)(L-12)$ or $L-5 = 0$ $L-12 = 0$ *Answer* → L = **5 feet**, w = **12 feet**	You can also set up an equation for the area of the room. Knowing this gives you two equations. Now, solve one equation for *w*, in terms of *L*. Substitute that into the other equation and solve for *L*. In solving this equation, you will find two values for L, 5 and 12. By substituting these back into w = 17 – L, you can determine the actual values for the length and width of the room.

Sample problems:

1. A rectangular swimming pool is 10ft longer than it is wide, and it has a surrounding deck of width 3ft on each side. If the area of the pool and deck is 1,656 ft^2, find the dimensions of the outside edge of the deck.

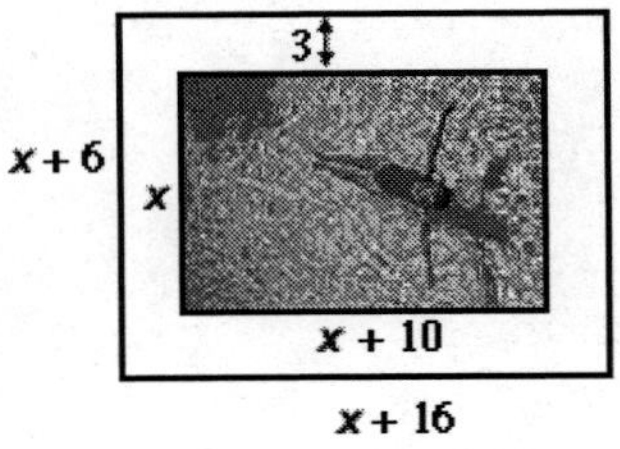

Solution: 36ft × 46ft
Explanation: Let x and $x+10$ be the width and length of the pool. Then the dimensions of the outside of the deck will be $x+6$ and $x+16$. Area: $A=(x+6)(x+16)=1{,}656$. Bring all the terms to one side. $x^2+22x+96-1{,}656=0$; $x^2+22x-1{,}560=0$. Factor the left side. $(x+52)(x-30)=0$; $x=-52$ or $x=30$. x cannot be negative. Solution: $x+6=36$ft. $x+16=46$ft.

2. Joey's Science Fair project requires him to keep bugs in 3 rectangular enclosures seperated and surrounded by 400 in. of partition. The area of the entire project is 4800 $in.^2$. What are the dimensions of his project?

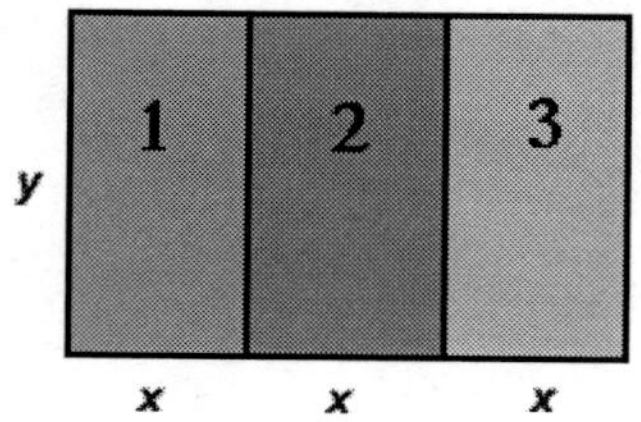

Solution: 80 in. × 60 in. or 120 in. × 40 in.
Explanation: Substitute 4800, $3x$, and y into $A = lw$: $4800 = 3xy$. Write an explanation for the amount of partition wall: $4y + 6x = 400$. Solve the 2nd equation for y: $4y = 400 - 6x$; $y = \frac{400-6x}{4}$; $y = \frac{200-3x}{2}$. Substitute the expression for y into the area equation: $4800 = 3x(\frac{200-3x}{2})$. Multiply by 2 and simplify: $9600 = 3x(200 - 3x)$; $9600 = 600x - 9x^2$; (divide by -3) $-3200 = -200x + 3x^2$. Set the equation to equal zero and solve for x: $0 = 3x^2 - 200x + 3200$; $0 = (3x - 80)(x - 40)$; $3x - 80 = 0$ or $x - 40 = 0$; $x = \frac{80}{3}$ or $x = 40$. Substitute each value into $y = \frac{200-3x}{2}$ to find the other dimension: $y = \frac{200-3(\frac{80}{3})}{2} = \frac{200-80}{2} = 60$ or $y = \frac{200-3(40)}{2} = 40$. One side of the large rectangle is represented by y and the other is $3x$, so multiply the x values by 3 to get the length of the side of the rectangle. Thus the dimensions are 80 in. × 60 in. or 120 in. × 40 in.

3. A gardener wants to fence in her plot in two equal rectangular sections. If she has 48 yards of fence and the area of the entire plot is 96yd^2, find the dimensions of the garden.

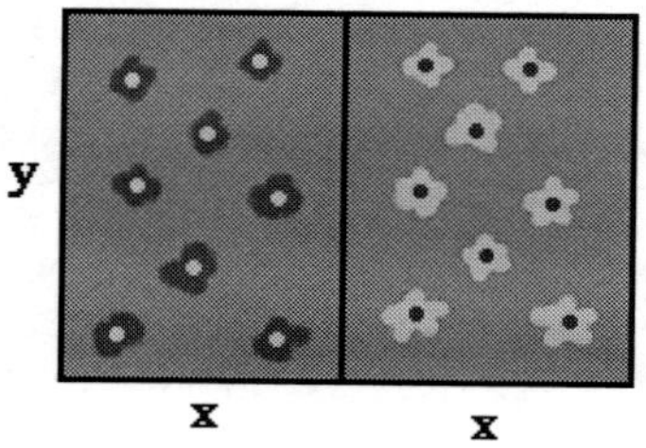

Solution: 12 yd × 8 yd
Explanation: The formula for the area of a rectangle is $A = lw$. Substitute 96 into the formula for A, $2x$ in for l and y in for the width: $96 = 2xy$. Next, write an equation using the total fence: $48 = 4x + 3y$. Solve one of the equations for one of the variables, so solve the 2nd equation for y: $48 - 4x = 3y$; $y = \frac{48-4x}{3}$. Substitute this expression for y into the other equation: $96 = 2x(\frac{48-4x}{3})$. Multiply the equation by 3: $288 = 2x(48 - 4x)$. Simplify: $96x - 8x^2 = 288$. Divide the equation by -8, then set it equal to zero: $-12x + x^2 = -36$; $x^2 - 12x + 36 = 0$. Solve for x: $(x - 6)(x - 6) = 0$; $x - 6 = 0$; $x = 6$. To find the other dimension, substitute 6 into $y =$ for x: $y = \frac{48-4(6)}{3} = \frac{48-24}{3} = 8$. So the garden is 12 yd × 8 yd.

Practice problems: *(Answers on page: 734)*

1. The shorter parallel side of a trapezoid is equal to its height, and the longer side is $\frac{3}{2}$ times as long. If the area is 80, find the length of the shorter side.

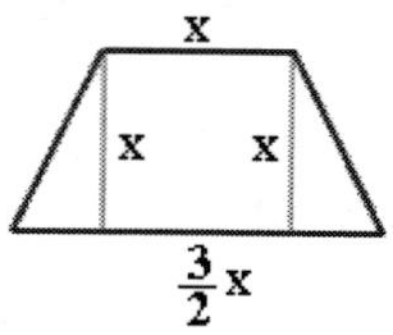

2. A flyer is printed on $18 \text{ in} \times 20 \text{ in}$ paper, and there are 120 in^2 of printed area on the flyer. If the margin is the same width on all sides, what are the dimensions of the printed area?

3. A rectangular field is enclosed on 3 sides by a fence, while the 4th side is a stream. The fence opposite the stream is 150m longer than the other sides. If the area of the field is 70,000m^2, find its dimensions.

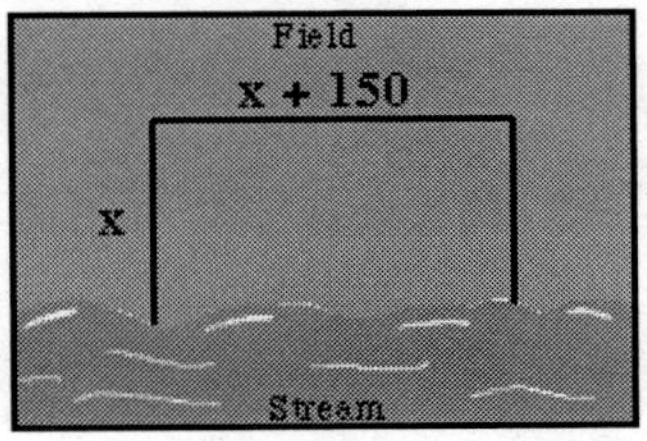

Review questions: *(Answers to odd questions on page: 734)*

1. A rectangle has length 4 inches more than its width and an area of 77 inches. Find its dimensions.
2. A triangle has height equal to its base, and its area is 18 in^2. Find the base and height of the triangle.
3. A rectangle has an area of 55 inches squared. Joey measures and finds that the length is 6 inches longer than the width. What are the dimensions of the rectangle?
4. A picture frame has thickness x, and the dimensions of the unframed picture are 18 in $\times$ 24 in. If the area of the picture and frame together is 720 in^2, find the thickness of the frame.
5. Joe's rectangular backyard has a perimeter of 60 yards and an area of 200yd^2. Find its dimensions.

Solving with the Pythagorean Theorem

- The **Pythagorean Theorem** states that the sum of the squares of the two sides of a right triangle is equal to the square of the hypotenuse: $a^2 + b^2 = c^2$.

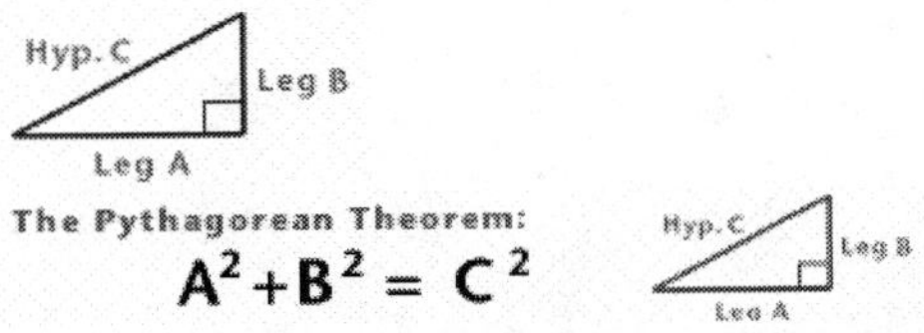	This splendid theorem is used frequently and in a variety of circumstances throughout math. You will be amazed at how often some process is an application or derivation of the Pythagorean Theorem.
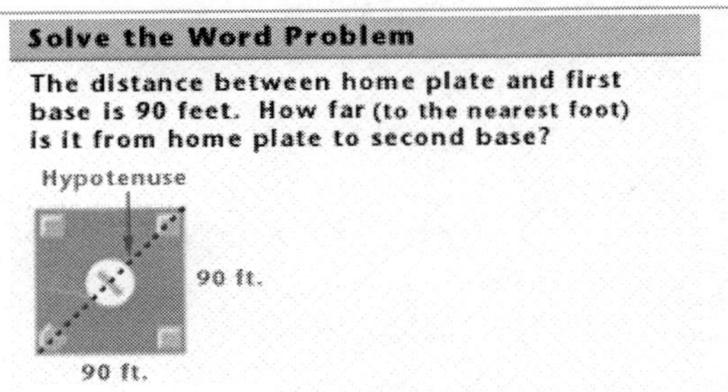	This example involves a triangle that is 90 feet on each side. You are asked to find the hypotenuse. In terms of the Pythagorean Theorem, you know that $a = 90$ and $b = 90$. What c equals is your problem to solve.
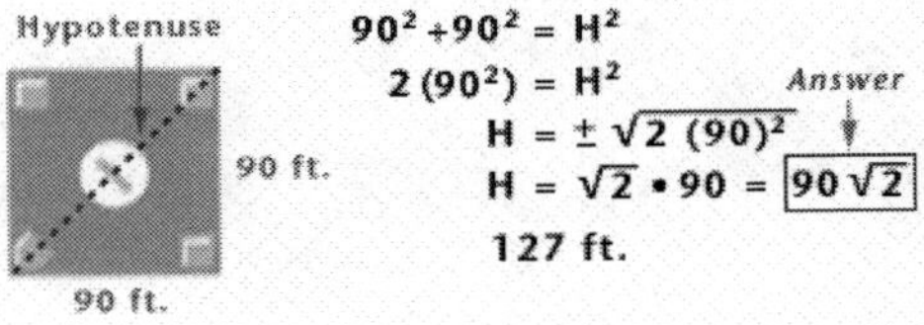	Substitute the known values into the theorem. Then do the arithmetic to solve for the unknown value. **Remember:** Length or distance is always positive so you can dismiss negative possibilities.

Sample problems:

1. Find the length x given the right triangle.

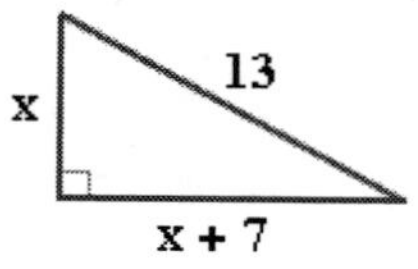

Solution: 5
Explanation: Use the Pythagorean Theorem to set up an equation where $a = x$, $b = x+7$ and $c = 13$: $x^2 + (x+7)^2 = 13^2$. Simplify: $x^2 + x^2 + 14x + 49 = 169$; $2x^2 + 14x + 49 = 169$. Set the equation to equal 0: $2x^2 + 14x - 120 = 0$. Divide the equation by 2: $x^2 + 7x - 60 = 0$. Factor and solve for x: $(x+12)(x-5) = 0$; $x+12 = 0$ or $x-5 = 0$; $x = -12$ or $x = 5$. x cannot be negative, so the only solution is $x = 5$.

2. Find the length of three equal sides of an equilateral triangle with height 10.

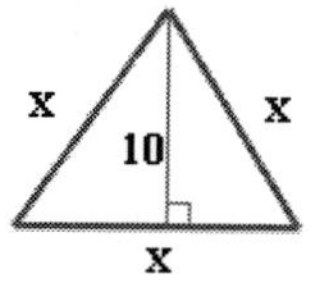

Solution: $\frac{20\sqrt{3}}{3}$
Explanation: The three sides of the right triangle are x, 10, and $\frac{1}{2}x$ where x is the hypotenuse. Set up the equation using the Pythagorean Theorem: $\left(\frac{1}{2}x\right)^2 + 10^2 = x^2$. Simplify: $\frac{1}{4}x^2 + 100 = x^2$. Multiply the equation by 4: $x^2 + 400 = 4x$. Solve for x: $400 = 3x^2$; $x^2 = \frac{400}{3}$; $\sqrt{x^2} = \sqrt{\frac{400}{3}}$; $x \frac{\pm 20}{\sqrt{3}}$. Use only the positive solution, so $x = \frac{20\sqrt{3}}{3}$.

3. Two cars leave an intersection at the same time. One drives east while the other travels south at 10 miles per hour faster than the other. After 2 hours, the cars are 100 miles apart. How fast is the southbound car driving?

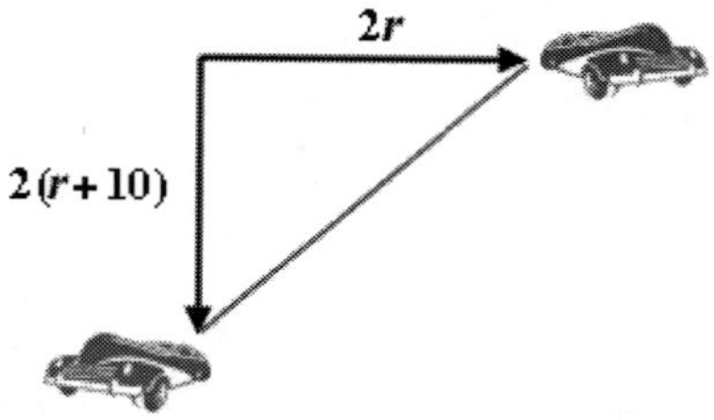

Solution: 40 mph
Explanation: The three sides of the right triangle are d_1, the distance traveled by the east bound car, d_2, the distance traveled by the southbound car, and 100, the distance between the two cars. Use $d = rt$ to write equations for d_1 and d_2: $d_1 = 2r$ and $d_2 = 2(r+10)$, since both cars traveled for 2 hours and the southbound car drove 10mph faster than the eastbound car. Use the expressions for d_1 and d_2 in the Pythagorean Theorem with 100 as the hypotenuse: $(2r)^2 + \left(2(r+10)\right)^2 = 100^2$. Simplify: $4r^2 + 4(r^2 + 20r + 100) = 10,000$; $4r^2 + 4r^2 + 80r + 400 = 10,000$; $8r^2 + 80r + 400 = 10,000$. Divide the equation by 8: $r^2 + 10r + 50 = 1250$. Set the equation equal to 0 and solve for r: $r^2 + 10r - 1200 = 0$; $(r+40)(r-30) = 0$; $r+40 = 0$ or $r-30 = 0$; $r = -40$ or $r = 30$. The speed cannot be negative, so the speed of the eastbound car is 30mph. Thus, the speed of the southbound car is 40mph.

Practice problems: *(Answers on page: 734)*

1. Find x, given the right triangle:

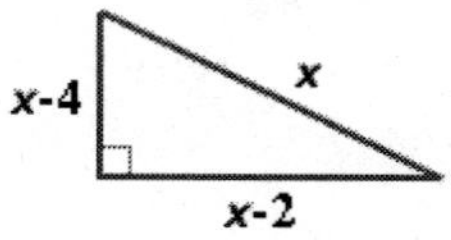

2. A boat is tied to a dock by a 25 ft. rope. The distance from the dock to the boat along the water is 3 more than 3 times the height of the dock. How high is the dock?

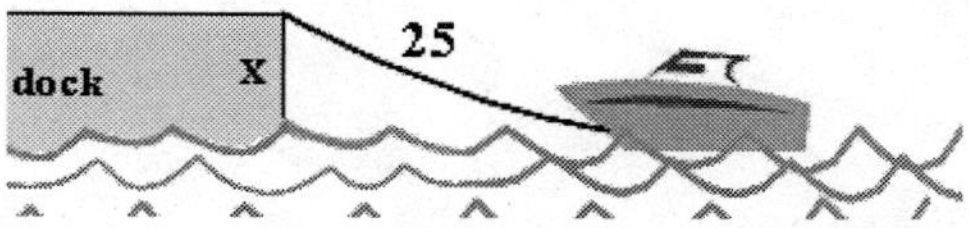

3. One airplane leaves Denver southbound while another plane leaves at the same time heading due west and travelling 40 miles per hour faster than the first plane. After 3 hours, they are 600 miles apart. How fast is the southbound airplane travelling?

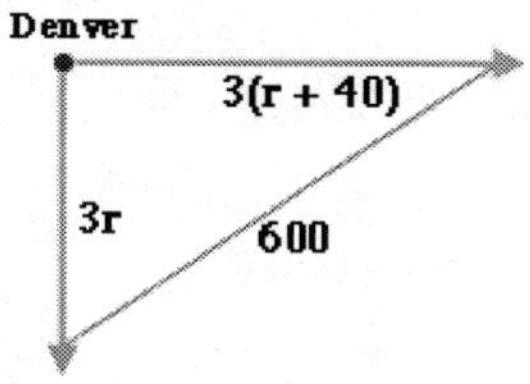

Review questions: *(Answers to odd questions on page: 734)*

1. Find the length of this isosceles right triangle with hypotenuse of length 12.

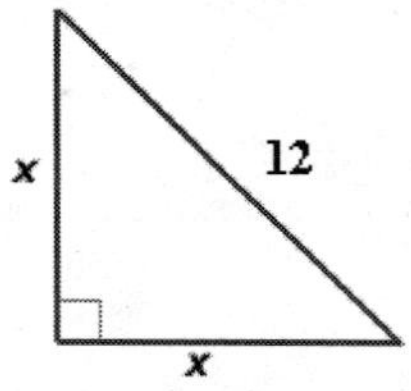

2. Solve for the length x for this right triangle.

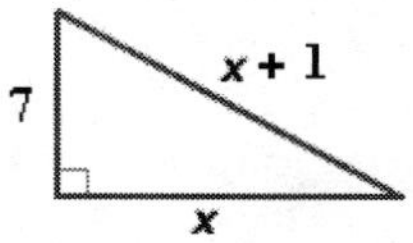

3. Solve for x, given the following right triangle:

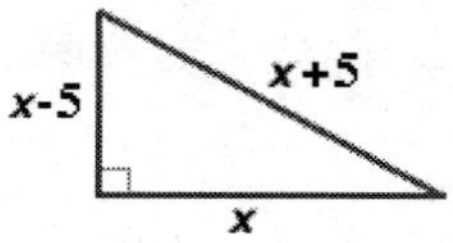

4. Train A and Train B leave the station at the same time. Train A is northbound, and Train B is eastbound travelling 20 miles per hour faster than Train A. After 2 hours, they are 200 miles apart. How fast is Train A travelling?

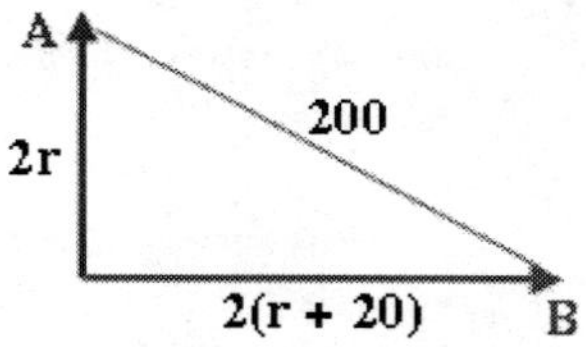

5. Edie is out flying her kite. If the height of the kite is 6 more than twice the distance from Edie to a point below the kite, and she has let out 39 feet of string, how high is the kite?

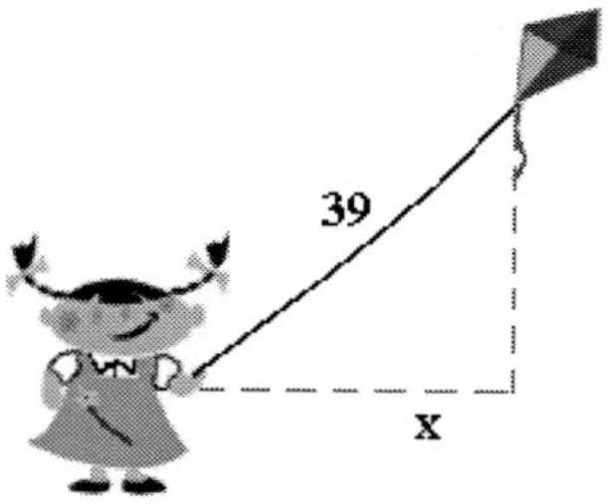

Solving a Motion Problem

- **Process for solving word problems**:
  - Define the variable.
  - Write what facts you know.
  - Create the equation.
  - Solve the equation.
  - Check your answer.
- This type of motion problem works with average speed over a given distance or time.

Solve the Word Problem A student drove to see his "special friend." He drove the first 105 miles of the trip in an hour more than it took to drive the last 90 miles, because of a keen anticipation of seeing the special friend. The average rate of the last 90 miles was 10 miles per hour faster than the average rate during the first 105 miles. How long did it take to get to his special friend's house? 	The first thing to do, always, is to read the problem to see what you are looking for and what you know. In this problem, you are asked how long did the student travel? Your variable, *t*, will be defined as the student's travel time. You know two distance facts and something about two rates, defined with variable *r*.
Distance = rate•time D = RT 90 miles: $r+10$	105 miles: r= rate t=time	You know that you will likely use the tried and true formula connecting distance, speed and time.
Second: $90 = (r+10)t$ First: $105 = r(t+1)$	This much information allows you to set up two equations, one for each leg of the trip.
Second: $90 = (r+10)t$ $90 = \left(\frac{105}{t+1}+10\right)t$ First: $105 = r(t+1)$ $\frac{105}{t+1} = r$ Plugged in for r	You want to eliminate one variable, if possible, so you can solve the equation. The equation for the first leg of the trip can be solved for *r*. Then, substitute that value for *r* into the equation for the second leg of the trip.
$90 = \left(\frac{115+10t}{t+1}\right)t$ $90t+90 = 115t+10t^2$ $(0 = 10t^2+25t-90) \div 5$ $0 = 2t^2+5t-18$ $= (2t+9)(t-2)$ $2t+9 = 0$ or $t-2 = 0$ ~~$t = -\frac{9}{2}$~~ $\boxed{t = 2}$ ← Answer?	Now solve for *t*. You find that $t = -9/2$ or 2. However, you eliminate the negative answer because time cannot be negative. So, you know that $t = 2$ hrs. And that gives you the time for the second leg of the trip.

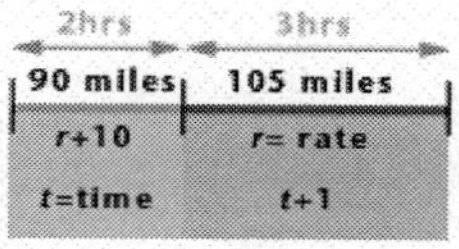

Since the first leg of the trip was defined to be $t + 1$, that means it took 3 hours. Therefore, the total time required for the student's trip was $2 + 3 = 5$ hrs.

Sample problems:

1. Debbie begins her daily run slowly for the first 3 miles, then accelerates to 2 miles per hour faster for the last 4 miles. If both parts take the same amount of time, how fast did she start her run?
   Solution: 6 mph
   Explanation: Use $d = rt$ to write 2 equations, one equation for the first 3 miles and a second equation for the last 4 miles. For the first 3 miles, $3 = rt$, where r is Debbie's speed and t is the time it takes for her to run those 3 miles. For the last 4 miles, $4 = (r+2)t$, since the speed is 2 mph faster for the last 4 miles and t is the same in both equations. Solve the first equation for t: $t = \frac{3}{r}$. Substitute this expression for t into the second equation: $(r+2)(\frac{3}{r}) = 4$. Multiply each side by r: $(r+2)(3) = 4r$. Simplify and solve for r: $3r + 6 = 4r$; $r = 6$ mph.

2. Jay's flight to Miami has 2 legs. The first part of the trip is 250 miles on one plane, followed by 420 miles on a plane traveling 40 miles per hour faster. If the second part of the trip takes $\frac{1}{2}$ hour more than the first part, find the total time for Jay's trip.
   Solution: $5\frac{1}{2}$ hours or 3 hours
   Explanation: The distance traveled during the first part is 250 miles, so $250 = rt$, where r is the speed of the first plane and t is the time spent on the first part of the trip. During the second part of the trip the distance is 420 miles, the speed is 40 mph faster than r and the time is $\frac{1}{2}$ hour longer than t, so $420 = (r+40)(t+\frac{1}{2})$. Solve the first equation for r: $r = \frac{250}{t}$. Substitute this expression for r into the second equation, then multiply the equation by $2t$: $420 = (\frac{250}{t}+40)(t+\frac{1}{2})$; $2t\left[420 = (\frac{250}{t}+40)(t+\frac{1}{2})\right]$; $2t(420) = t(\frac{250}{t}+40)\cdot 2(t+\frac{1}{2})$; $840t = (250+40t)(2t+1)$. Multiply and set the equation equal to 0: $840t = 500t + 250 + 80t^2 + 40t$; $80t^2 - 300t + 250 = 0$. Divide each term by 10: $8t^2 - 30t + 25 = 0$. Factor then solve for t: $(2t-5)(4t-5) = 0$; $2t - 5 = 0$ or $4t - 5 = 0$; $t = \frac{5}{2}$ or $t = \frac{5}{4}$. Total time for the trip is $T = t + (t + \frac{1}{2})$. Substitute in the two values for t and simplify: $T = \frac{5}{2} + (\frac{5}{2} + \frac{1}{2})$ or $T = \frac{5}{4} + (\frac{5}{4} + \frac{1}{2})$.; $T = 5\frac{1}{2}$ or $T = 3$.

3. It takes Joanne 1 hour longer to hike up a 6-mile trail than it takes Lisa to hike a 5-mile trail. If Lisa hikes 2 miles per hour faster than Joanne, how fast does Joanne hike?
   Solution: 3 mph
   Explanation: For Joanne's hike, $6 = rt$ and for Lisa's hike, $5 = (r+2)(t-1)$, since Lisa's speed is 2 mph faster than Joanne's speed and Lisa's time was 1 hour faster than Joanne's time. Solve for t in Joanne's equation: $t = \frac{6}{r}$. Substitute this value of t into Lisa's equation: $(r+2)(\frac{6}{r} - 1) = 5$. Multiply each side by r: $(r+2)(6-r) = 5r$. Multiply, set the equation equal to 0, and solve for r: $-r^2 + 4r + 12 = 5r$; $r^2 + r - 12 = 0$; $(r-3)(r+4) = 0$; $r - 3 = 0$ or $r + 4 = 0$; $r = 3$ or $r = -4$. Since Joanne's speed cannot be negative, $r = 3$ mph.

Practice problems: *(Answers on page: 735)*

1. Eric drives to a town 350 miles away, then returns driving 20 miles per hour faster. If the return trip takes him 2 hours less, how fast was he driving during the drive out?

2. It takes the A-Train $\frac{1}{2}$ hour less to make its 270 mile route than it takes the B-Train to make its 350 mile route. If the A-Train is 10 miles per hour slower than the B-Train, which of the following could be the speed of the B-Train?

3. A biker's trail takes him uphill for 15 miles, then downhill for 10 miles. If his downhill rate is 10 miles per hour faster than his uphill rate and the downhill portion took 1 hour less than the uphill stretch, what is his downhill speed?

Review questions: *(Answers to odd questions on page: 735)*

1. Chris drives 200 miles, then increases his speed by 25 miles per hours for 450 miles. If the second part of the drive took 2 hours longer than the first part, find his average speed for the entire drive.
2. Carol commutes to work each day. She drives 12 miles to the Park 'n' Ride, then rides the bus for 48 miles at a speed which is 20 miles per hour slower than she drives. If the bus ride takes 1 hour longer than her drive, find her average speed for the trip to work.
3. Kelly rollerblades for 12 miles, then slows down by 4 miles per hour for another 6 miles. The slower portion takes 15 minutes less than the first part. Find the total time she spent rollerblading, if you know it was not more than 1 hour and 30 minutes.
4. Suzanne rides the chairlift to the top of a 4 mile hill, then skis down at 8 miles per hour faster than the lift travels. The trip down is 8 minutes faster than the ride up. Find her average speed for the entire trip.
5. Two planes make a 1000 mile flight, one flying 75 miles per hour faster than the other. The quicker plane makes the trip 3 hours faster. How long did it take the slower plane to complete the flight?

Solving a Projectile Problem

- **Quadratic formula:** $x = \dfrac{-b \pm \sqrt{b^2 - 4ac}}{2a}$

Solve the Word Problem **A disgruntled Algebra student kicks her algebra book across the south quad of the student Union. How long was the algebra book in the air?**	This situation involves a quadratic equation which measures the impact of gravity on a moving object.
$s = -16t^2 + 88t + 2$ *s = position of book*	This formula solves for s as the position of the object off the ground. The time, t, is used in seconds.
$s = -16t^2 + 88t + 2$ *Where $t = 0$, Answer: 2 feet*	At the start, when $t = 0$, you can solve for s and discover that the book is 2 feet above the ground. Apparently, the student was holding it before she kicked it.
$s = -16t^2 + 88t + 2 = 0$ $8t + 44t + 1 = 0$ ← *Factor to solve*	You can work with smaller numbers if you divide the formula through by 2, the largest common factor for the equation. You know that $s = 0$ for this problem, because you are being asked about the book as it returns to the ground. You are solving for t, the time the book was in the air.

$8t+44t+1 = 0$ $t = \frac{-44 \pm \sqrt{(44)^2-4(-8)(1)}}{-16}$ $t = \frac{-44 \pm \sqrt{1968}}{-16}$ $t = \frac{-44 \pm 44.36}{-16}$	Now solve for *t*. You find that *t* = -9/2 or 2. However, you eliminate the negative answer because time cannot be negative. So, you know that *t* = 2 hrs. And that gives you the time for the second leg of the trip.
$t = \frac{-44 \pm \sqrt{1968}}{-16}$ $t = \frac{-44 - 44.36}{-16}$ ~~$\frac{-44+44.36}{-16}$~~ Positive sign is the extraneous root	Time is always positive, unless you're going backwards in time, so you can throw away any answer which is negative. In this case using the positive value from the radical, 44.36, will create a negative answer. So, you get to forget about using +44.36 and have only one answer.
$t = \frac{-44 \pm \sqrt{1968}}{-16}$ $t = \frac{-44 - 44.36}{-16} \approx$ 5.52...Sec. ← Answer	You can leave your answer in fraction form, reduced to lowest terms of course, or find the approximate decimal value for your answer.

Sample problems:

1. A baseball player throws a baseball straight up into the air. The formula for the height h of the ball after t seconds is $h = -16t^2 + 48t$. How high is the ball after 1 second?
   Solution: 32 feet
   Explanation: Substitute $t = 1$ into the formula: $h = -16(1)^2 + 48(1) = -16 + 48 = 32$ feet.

2. Rob throws a rock off a 96-foot cliff. The height of the rock above the ground is given by: $h = -16t^2 + 32t + 96$. How long does it take for the rock to hit the ground?
   Solution: 3.65 seconds
   Explanation: The rock hits the ground when the height is zero, so substitute $h = 0$ into the equation: $0 = -16t^2 + 32t + 96$. Divide each term by -16: $0 = t^2 - 2t - 6$.
   Use the quadratic formula: $a = 1$, $b = -2$, $c = -6$. $t = \frac{2 \pm \sqrt{4 - 4(1)(-6)}}{2} = \frac{2 \pm \sqrt{4 + 24}}{2}$;
   $t = \frac{2 \pm \sqrt{28}}{2} = \frac{2 \pm \sqrt{(4)(7)}}{2} = \frac{2 \pm 2\sqrt{7}}{2} = 1 \pm \sqrt{7}$. The time cannot be negative, so $t = 1 + \sqrt{7} \approx 3.65$ seconds.

3. Larry is flying his hot air balloon 480 feet high when he decides to release a sandbag so that he can go higher. The height in feet of the sandbag above ground is given by $h = -16t^2 + 8t + 480$. How long does it take the bag to fall 120 feet?
   Solution: 3 seconds
   Explanation: If the bag falls 120 feet, it is 360 feet above the ground. So, substitute 360 into the equation for h: $-16t^2 + 8t + 480 = 360$. Set the equation equal to 0: $-16t^2 + 8t + 120 = 0$. Divide by -8 and solve to t: $2t^2 - t - 15 = 0$; $-8(2t + 5)(t - 3) = 0$; $2t + 5 = 0$ or $t - 3 = 0$; $t = -\frac{5}{2}$ or $t = 3$. Since time cannot be negative, $t = 3$ seconds.

Practice problems: *(Answers on page: 735)*

1. Davey drops a water balloon from the top of a 400-foot building. The formula for its height above the ground t seconds later is $h = -16t^2 + 400$. How high is the balloon after 2 seconds?
2. After his final exam, a student goes to the top of a building and throws his book into the air. The height h in feet of the book above the ground is given by: $h = -16t^2 + 32t + 128$. How long is the book in the air?

3. Kim is standing on top of a 96-foot cliff with her slingshot. She shoots a rock into the air over the edge of the cliff, so that the height above ground of the rock is given by: $h = -16t^2 + 32t + 96$. After how many seconds is the rock at 64 feet?

Review questions: *(Answers to odd questions on page: 735)*

1. An astronaut (who played baseball in high school) throws his own baseball upward while standing on the moon. The height in feet of the ball t seconds later is given by $h = -2.7t^2 + 21.6t$. How long before the ball returns to the surface of the moon?
2. An astronaut (who played baseball in high school) throws his own baseball upward while standing on the moon. The height in feet of the ball t seconds later is given by: $h = -2.7t^2 + 21.6t$. After how many seconds is the height equal to 40.5 feet?
3. Davey drops a water balloon from the top of a 400-foot building. The formula for its height above the ground t seconds later is $h = -16t^2 + 400$. How long until the balloon hits the ground?
4. A talk show host drops a watermelon from the observation tower of the Empire State Building. If the height of the watermelon above the ground after t seconds is given by the equation $s = -16t^2 + 1224$, how long will it take the watermelon to hit the ground? Express your answer to the nearest tenth of a second.
5. After a punter kicks a football, its height in feet above the ground is given by $s = -16t^2 + 20t + 1$, where t is in seconds. How long will the football be in the air, to the nearest hundredth of a second?

Solving Other Problems

- **Quadratic formula:** $x = \dfrac{-b \pm \sqrt{b^2 - 4ac}}{2a}$
- When working with problems with decimals, many people will multiply through by 10, 100, or whatever power of 10 required to "clear" the decimals from the problem. As long as you multiply both sides of the equation, this procedure is valid and protects the balance of the equation. Clearing the decimals helps you think about the numbers involved since most of us prefer to work with whole numbers.

Solve the Word Problem To determine the landing speed of a small plane, all that is required is the length of the runway. If s is the initial landing speed in ft. per second, and L is the length of the runway then $.1s$ squared minus $3s + 22 = D$. So if the landing speed is too fast, the pilot may run out of runway; if the landing speed is too slow the plane may stall. If the runway is 800 ft. long, what is the appropriate landing speed? 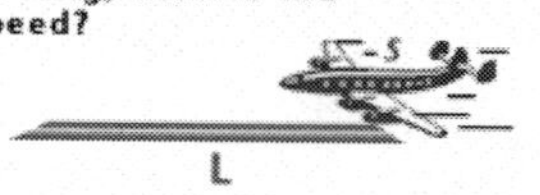	In landing an aircraft the pilot must balance two things, the distance available for the landing and the speed needed to land safely without stalling.
$L = .1s^2 - 3s + 22$	The formula for this problem is set in s, the plane's speed, and L, the length of the runway.
$L = .1s^2 - 3s + 22 = 800$	The problem tells us the runway is 800 feet long, so we know that $L = 800$.
$L = .1s^2 - 3s + 22 = 800$ $s^2 - 30s + 220 = 8000$ ← Multiply through by 10 to clear decimal	Before you start working, you may want to multiply through by 10 to clear the decimals.

$L = .1s^2-3s+22 = 800$ $s^2-30s+220 = 8000$ $s^2-30s-7780 = 0$ ← *Now solve*	Once you have cleared the decimals, move everything to one side of the equation. Then you find the values you need for the quadratic formula: $a = 1$, $b = -30$, $c = -7780$.
$s = \frac{30 \pm \sqrt{(-30)^2+4(7780)}}{2}$	Substitute those values into the formula and solve.
Extraneous root (You can't fly an airplane at a negative speed) ~~$30-\sqrt{(-30)^2+4(7780)}$~~	You'll find you cannot use the negative value under the radical because it makes the whole answer negative. Time is rarely negative. So you discard that answer.
$s = \frac{30 + \sqrt{(-30)^2+4(7780)}}{2}$ ≈ 104.47 ft./sec. ← *Answer*	You are left with one valid answer. Approximate its value in decimals to find the speed, in feet/second, the plane must use.

Sample problems:

1. Solve for x: $0.2x^4 - 0.65x^2 + 0.01 = 0.04$.
   Solution: $\pm 1.815,\ 0.308i$
   Explanation: Begin by multiplying the equation by 100 to clear the decimals: $20x^4 - 65x^2 + 1 = 4$. Set the equation equal to 0: $20x^4 - 65x^2 - 3 = 0$. Since x^4 is the square of x^2, let $G = x^2$ and substitute G into the equation: $20G^4 - 65G^2 - 3 = 0$. Now solve for G using the quadratic formula:
   $G = \frac{-(-65)\pm\sqrt{(-65)^2-4(20)(-3)}}{2(20)} = \frac{65\pm\sqrt{4465}}{40} = \frac{65\pm 66.82}{40}$, so $G = 3.296$ or $G = -0.095$. Next, substitute x^2 into each equation for G and solve for x: 1) $x^2 = 3.296$; $\sqrt{x^2} = \sqrt{3.296}$; $x = \pm 1.815$. 2) $x^2 = -0.095$; $\sqrt{x^2} = \sqrt{-0.095}$; $x = 0.308i$. Thus, $x = \pm 1.815,\ 0.308i$.

2. Given the function $f(x) = 0.1x \ + 1.2x + 3.3$, find x when $f(x) = 1.3$.
   Solution: $-10,\ -2$
   Explanation: Substitute 1.3 into the function for $f(x)$: $1.3 = .1x^2 + 1.2x + 3.3$. Multiply the equation by 10: $13 = x^2 + 12x + 33$. Set the equation equal to 0: $0 = x^2 + 12x + 20$. Solve for x by factoring: $(x = 10)(x + 2) = 0$; $x = 10 = 0$ or $x + 2 = 0$; $x = -10$ or $x = -2$.

3. Suppose the area of a rectangle is 7.2ft^2 and the length of the rectangle is 6 inches longer than the width. Find the length and width of the rectangle.
   Solution: $L = 2.945$ and $w = 2.445$
   Explanation: This geometry problem gives the area of the rectangle, 7.2ft^2, so use the formula for the area of a rectangle: $A = Lw \Rightarrow 7.2 = Lw$. Next, translate the description of the length into an equation: $L = w + .5$ (use .5 since 6 inches is $\frac{1}{2}$ of a foot). Now, substitute $w + .5$ into the formula for L: $7.2 = (w + .5)w$. Simplify: $7.2 = w^2 + .5w$. Multiply the equation by 10: $72 = 10w^2 + 5w$. Set the equation to 0: $0 = 10w^2 + 5w$. Solve for w using the quadratice formula:
   $w = \frac{-5\pm\sqrt{(5)^2-4(10)(-72)}}{2(10)} = \frac{-5\pm\sqrt{25+2880}}{20} = \frac{-5\pm 53.9}{20}$; $w = 2.945$ or $w = 2.445$. Use each width to find the possible lengths: $L = w + .5 \Rightarrow L = 2.945 + .5$ or $L = 2.445 + .5$, so $L = 3.445$ when $w = 2.945$ or $L = 2.945$ when $w = 2.445$. However, the first pair does not create a rectangle with the area 7.2ft^2, so the only solution is $L = 2.945$ and $w = 2.445$.

Practice problems: *(Answers on page: 735)*

1. A toaster factory has revenues which follow the formula $R = -x^2 + 2{,}400x - 1{,}320{,}00$ where x is the number of toasters sold each month. How much does the factory earn if 1,000 toasters are sold each month?

2. The popluation of a small town is monitored starting in 1980, and the data follows the quadratic equation $P = 50x^2 + 10,000 (x \geq 0)$, where x is the number of years after 1980. How many residents were there in 1987?
3. A manufacturer develops a formula to determine the demand for its product depending on the price in dollars. The formula is $D = 1,000 + 200P - 4P^2$, where P is the price per unit and D is the number of units in demand. At what price will the demand drop to 584 units?

Review questions: *(Answers to odd questions on page: 735)*

1. A manufacturer develops a formula to determine the demand for its product depending on the price in dollars. The formula is $D = 1,000 + 200P - 4P^2$, where P is the price per unit and D is the number of units in demand. How many units will be sold if the price is \$30?
2. A science experiment involves changing the temperature in a small room using a heat source. The temperature starts at 70°, and follows the quadratic model $T = 70 + 14t - 2t^2$ where t is elapsed time in hours. After how many hours is the temperature back to 70°?
3. During a downhill ski race, the distance (in yards) a skier has travelled since leaving the starting gate follows this quadratic equation: $D = 5t^2 + 32t + 1,000t$ is the time in seconds measuring her run. After how many seconds has she skied 2,000 yards?
4. A company finds that its profits can be modelled with the formula $P = 67.2x - 4.2x^2$, where P is the profit in millions of dollars and x is the production (in thousand of units). At what production level are the profits \$200 million?
5. A company finds that its profits can be modelled with the formula $P = 67.2x - 4.2x^2$, where P is profit in millions of dollars and x is the production (in thousands of units). At what profit level is the model valid? Hint: Look at the Discriminant.

Determining Extraneous Roots

- **Extraneous** roots are solutions that don't work when you use them in the original equation.
- Always check all solutions in the original equation so you can determine which ones work and which ones do not work.
- Always check your answer when you have a variable in the denominator because the denominator can never have a value of zero.

x=2 *given*	This basic example worked out on the left is used to make the point that some solutions don't work and are therefore what are known as extraneous roots.
x=2 **x²=4** *stoopidly square both sides*	Take what is given and square it. (This is not something you would ordinarily do, but we're making a point here.)

$x^2-4=0$ $(x+2)(x-2)=0$ $x=-2 \quad x=2$ *two possible solutions*	Solve the resulting equation for x. And, as usual, you get two answers.
Extraneous roots: **false solutions that arise from squaring both sides in order to solve an equation** ~~$x=-2$~~ $x=2$ *Remember to check your answers when you see a radical in the equation or a variable in the denominator.* 	Check both answers in the original equation and it is obvious that one of them, -2, doesn't work. Therefore, -2 is an extraneous root, not a solution.

Solving an Equation Containing a Radical

- To solve an equation containing a radical, first eliminate the radical.
- If one side of the equation is nothing but a radical, squaring both sides instantly eliminates the radical. At the same time there will be significant changes on the other side of the equation.
- Extraneous roots do exist for these equations. Always check your answers to see which, if any, are really solutions for your equations.

Example $x=\sqrt{15-2x}$ $x^2=15-2x$	The easiest way to eliminate a radical is to square both sides. You must square both sides to keep the equation balanced.
$x^2+2x-15=0$ $(x+5)(x-3)=0$ *factor*	Now, move everything to the left side and set it equal to 0. Then, you're ready to solve the equation. In this case, factoring works.
$x+5=0$ or $x-3=0$ $x=-5 \quad x=3$	Set each factor equal to 0, and solve for x. Now, you have your two solutions.
Check your answers $x=\sqrt{15-2x}$ $3\stackrel{?}{=}\sqrt{15-6}$ $3=\sqrt{9}=3$ $x+5=0$ or $x-3=0$ $x=-5 \quad x=3$	Remember to check each solution to be sure it works. Checking one answer, 3, we find that it works. So we have at least one solution; we know that $x = 3$.
Check your answers $x\stackrel{?}{=}\sqrt{15-2x}$ $-5\stackrel{?}{=}\sqrt{15+10}=\sqrt{25}$ $-5\neq5$ ~~$x=-5$~~ *extraneous root* $x=3$	One of your answers, -5, doesn't work. So it is an extraneous root.
Example $x=3+\sqrt{3-x}$ $x-3=\sqrt{3-x}$ *bring 3 over to isolate radical*	When you have some term(s) on the same side of the equation as the radical, your first step has to be to move them to the other side.
$(x-3)^2=3-x$ $x^2-6x+9=3-x$ $x^2-5x+6=0$ $(x-2)(x-3)=0$ $x-2=0$ or $x-3=0$ $x=2$ or $x=3$	Once you have isolated your radical on its side of the equation, then you do your squaring-both-sides trick. Now you are ready to solve.

$x=3+\sqrt{3-x}$ $2\overset{?}{=}3+\sqrt{3-2}$ $2\overset{?}{=}3+\sqrt{1}=4$ $2\neq 4$ $x=3+\sqrt{3-x}$ $3\overset{?}{=}3+\sqrt{3-3}$ $3\overset{?}{=}3+0=3$ ✓	Check both of your answers to see if both, only one, or neither is a solution for the original equation.
$x-2=0$ or $x-3=0$ ~~$x=2$~~ ($x=3$) *extraneous root*	Once you have checked, you find you have one solution: $x=3$. You have one extraneous root: $x=2$.

Sample problems:

1. Solve for w: $\sqrt{4w}=w-3$
   Solution: 9
   Explanation: Since the radical is isolated, begin by squaring each side of the equation. Use FOIL to square the binomial: $\left(\sqrt{4w}\right)^2=(w-3)^2$; $4w=w^2-6w+9$. Set the equation equal to 0 by subtracting $4w$ from each side: $0=w^2-10w+9$, which is the same as $w^2-10w+9=0$. In order to solve for w, first factor, then set each factor equal to 0, and solve each equation for w: $(w-9)(w-1)=0$; $w-9=0$ or $w-1=0$; $w=9$ or $w=1$. Check for extraneous roots by checking each value of w:
   Check $w=9$: $\sqrt{4\cdot 9}=9-3$; $\sqrt{36}=6$; $6=6$, so $w=9$ is a solution because it satisfies the equation.
   Check $w=1$: $\sqrt{4\cdot 1}=1-3$; $\sqrt{4}=-2$; $2\neq -2$, so $w=1$ is not a solution.

2. Solve for x: $\sqrt{32-x}-x+2=0$
   Solution: 7
   Explanation: Isolate the radical: $\sqrt{32-x}=x-2$. Square both sides: $\left(\sqrt{32-x}\right)^2=(x-2)^2$; $32-x=x^2-4x+4$. Set the equation equal to 0: $x^2-3x-28=0$. Factor, set each factor equal to 0, and solve each equation for x: $(x-7)(x+4)=0$; $x-7=0$ or $x+4=0$; $x=7$ or $x=-4$. Check for extraneous roots: the only solution is $x=7$, since $x=-4$ results in a false statement.

3. Solve for x: $\sqrt[3]{5x-2}=2$
   Solution: 2
   Explanation: Cube both sides: $\sqrt[3]{5x-2}=2$; $\left(\sqrt[3]{5x-2}\right)^3=(2)^3$; $5x-2=8$. Solve as usual: $5x-2=8$; $5x=10$; $x=2$.

Practice problems: *(Answers on page: 735)*

1. Solve for x: $\sqrt{2x}-x=-4$
2. Solve for w: $\sqrt{3w+14}+6=3w$
3. Solve for x: $\sqrt[3]{5x-8}=3$

Review questions: *(Answers to odd questions on page: 735)*

1. Solve for y: $\sqrt{2y+1}=3$
2. Solve for x: $\sqrt{3x-2}=x$
3. Solve for y: $\sqrt{15-4y}-y=y-6$
4. Solve for x: $\sqrt{2x+1}+1=x$

5. Solve for x: $\sqrt{5-x}+1=x-2$

Solving an Equation with Two Radicals

- Solving a radical equation generally means that we try to isolate the radical and square the equation so that the radical disappears.
- When an equation has two radicals, you will have to do the isolating and squaring process twice in order to eliminate the radicals.
- Once you have solved your non-radicalized equation, be sure to check your answers to see if both, one, or neither is a true solution for the original radical equation.

$\sqrt{2x+3}=1+\sqrt{x+1}$ $(\sqrt{2x+3})^2=(1+\sqrt{x+1})^2$ $2x+3=(1+\sqrt{x+1})(1+\sqrt{x+1})$ $2x+3=1+2\sqrt{x+1}+(\sqrt{x+1})^2$ $2x+3=1+2\sqrt{x+1}+x+1$ $2x+3=2+x+2\sqrt{x+1}$	In this example, we have two radicals. So, isolate one of them and square the equation. Notice that the expression on the right is a binomial. Be sure you FOIL correctly. You still have some radicals remaining. So, repeat the process.
$x+1=2\sqrt{x+1}$ $(x+1)^2=(2\sqrt{x+1})^2$ $x^2+2x+1=4(x+1)$	Move all the non-radical terms to the left side of the equation, and combine like terms. Square a second time to eliminate all radicals.
$x^2+2x+1=4x+4$ $x^2-2x-3=0$ $(x+1)(x-3)=0$ $x=-1 \quad x=3$	Now you solve for your answers, expecting and getting two answers for your quadratic equation.
$\sqrt{2x+3}=1+\sqrt{x+1}$ 	Remember to check your answers to see if they work. They both do check in this example, and you find you have two solutions for this equation.

Sample problems:

1. Solve for x: $\sqrt{2x+5}-1=\sqrt{2x-3}+1$
   Solution: 2
   Explanation: Isolate one of the radicals: $\sqrt{2x+5}=\sqrt{2x-3}+2$.
   Square each side, then simplify:
   $\left(\sqrt{2x+5}\right)^2=\left(\sqrt{2x-3}+2\right)^2$; $2x+5=(2x-3)+4\sqrt{2x-3}+4$; $2x+5=2x+1+\left(4\sqrt{2x-3}\right)$.
   Isolate the remaining radical, then square each side:
   $4=4\sqrt{2x-3}$; $(4)^2=\left(4\sqrt{2x-3}\right)^2$; $16=16(2x-3)$.
   Cancel the 16 from each side and solve for x: $1=2x-3$; $4=2x$; $x=2$.
   Check to determine if 2 is an extraneous root:
   $\sqrt{2(2)+5}-1=\sqrt{2(2)-3}+1$; $\sqrt{9}-1=\sqrt{1}+1$; 2=2
   $x=2$ is the solution.

2. Solve for x: $\sqrt{2x+7} = \sqrt{x+7} - 1$
   Solution: -3
   Explanation: Square each side of the equation:
   $\left(\sqrt{2x+7}\right)^2 = \left(\sqrt{x+7} - 1\right)^2$; $2x+7 = (x+7) - 2\sqrt{x+7} + 1$.
   Isolate the remaining radical: $2x+7 = x+8-2\sqrt{x+7}$; $x-1 = -2\sqrt{x+7}$.
   Square each side: $(x-1)^2 = \left(-2\sqrt{x+7}\right)^2$; $x^2-2x+1 = (-2)^2\left(\sqrt{x+7}\right)^2$;
   $x^2-2x+1 = 4(x+7)$; $x^2-2x+1 = 4x+28$.
   Set the equation equal to 0, then factor:
   $x^2-6x-27=0$; $(x-9)(x+3)=0$.
   Set each factor equal to 0 and solve each equation for x:
   $x-9=0$ or $x+3=0$; $x=9$ or $x=-3$.
   Check for extraneous roots by checking each value of x.
   Check $x=9$: $\sqrt{2\cdot 9+7} = \sqrt{9+7}-1$; $\sqrt{18+7} = \sqrt{16}-1$; $\sqrt{25} = 4-1$; $5 \neq 3$, so 9 is not a solution.
   Check $x=-3$: $\sqrt{2\cdot -3+7} = \sqrt{-3+7}-1$; $\sqrt{-6+7} = \sqrt{4}-1$; $\sqrt{1} = 2-1$; $1=1$, so -3 is a solution.

3. Solve for y: $\sqrt{y-3} - \sqrt{8-y} = -1$
   Solution: 4
   Explanation: Isolate one of the radicals by adding $\sqrt{8-y}$ to both sides:
   $\sqrt{y-3} - \sqrt{8-y} = -1$; $\sqrt{y-3} = \sqrt{8-y} - 1$. Square each side of the equation:
   $\left(\sqrt{y-3}\right)^2 = \left(\sqrt{8-y}-1\right)^2$; $y-3 = (8-y) - 2\sqrt{8-y} + 1$. Isolate the remaining radical: $y-3-8+y-1 = -2\sqrt{8-y}$; $2y-12 = -2\sqrt{8-y}$; $-y+6 = \sqrt{8-y}$.
   Square each side: $y^2-12y+36 = 8-y$. Bring all the terms to one side and factor:
   $y^2-11y+28 = (y-4)(y-7) = 0$; $y=4$ or $y=7$.
   Since $y=7$ does not satisfy the equation, $y=4$ is the only solution.

Practice problems: *(Answers on page: 735)*

1. Solve for z: $\sqrt{3z} = \sqrt{2z-8} + 2$
2. Solve for w: $\sqrt{3w+1} - 3 = \sqrt{w-4}$
3. Solve for x: $\sqrt{2x-11} - \sqrt{3x+6} = -3$

Review questions: *(Answers to odd questions on page: 735)*

1. Solve for y: $\sqrt{y-3} = \sqrt{8-y} - 1$
2. Solve for y: $\sqrt{y-2} = \sqrt{y+5} - 1$
3. Solve for x: $\sqrt{x+5} = \sqrt{4x+5} + 1$
4. Solve for y: $\sqrt{y} = \sqrt{y+15} - 1$
5. Solve for x: $\sqrt{x-16} = \sqrt{x} - 2$

Solving an Equation with Rational Exponents

- To solve an equation containing a rational exponent, isolate the expression with the rational exponent then raise each side to the reciprocal of that rational exponent.
- Extraneous roots do exist for these equations. Always check your answers to see which, if any, are real solutions for your equations.
- Use substitution to express a non-quadratic equation in a quadratic form.

Equations with rational exponents

•isolate the object that has the fractional exponent
•raise both sides to the appropriate power to get rid of this exponent

Example

$$(5x^2-6)^{1/4}=x$$
$$((5x^2-6)^{1/4})^4=x^4$$
$$5x^2-6=x^4$$
$$0=x^4-5x^2+6$$

pull everything to one side and set equal to zero

Remember, the key to solving an equation with a rational exponent is to 1) isolate the expression with the rational exponent and 2) raise each side to the reciprocal of that rational exponent.

In this example, to solve for x apply the appropriate exponent to each side. In this example the exponent is ¼, so raise each side to the 4th power in order to eliminate the rational exponent.

Simplify each side—notice that the radical exponent cancels out.

Manipulate the terms so that the equation is set equal to zero. Notice that the equation is similar to a quadratic equation.

$$(5x^2-6)^{1/4}=x$$
$$((5x^2-6)^{1/4})^4=x^4$$
$$5x^2-6=x^4$$
$$0=x^4-5x^2+6$$
$$0=(x^2)^2-5(x^2)+6$$

Let $A=x^2$
$$0=A^2-5A+6$$
$$0=(A-2)(A-3)$$
$$A=2 \quad A=3$$

Express the equation in terms of x^2.

Let $A=x^2$, substitute A into the equation and solve the new quadratic equation by factoring.

$$(5x^2-6)^{1/4}=x$$
$$((5x^2-6)^{1/4})^4=x^4$$
$$5x^2-6=x^4$$
$$0=x^4-5x^2+6$$
$$0=(x^2)^2-5(x^2)+6$$
$$x^2=2 \text{ or } x^2=3$$
$$x=\pm\sqrt{2} \text{ or } x=\pm\sqrt{3}$$

four possibilities

Let $A=x^2$
$$0=A^2-5A+6$$
$$0=(A-2)(A-3)$$
$$A=2 \quad A=3$$

To find the possible values of x, substitute the values for A into the equation $A=x^2$ and solve each equation for x.

$$(5x^2-6)^{1/4}=x$$
$$((5x^2-6)^{1/4})^4=x^4$$
$$5x^2-6=x^4$$
$$0=x^4-5x^2+6$$
$$0=(x^2)^2-5(x^2)+6$$
$$x^2=2 \text{ or } x^2=3$$
$$x=\pm\sqrt{2} \text{ or } x=\pm\sqrt{3}$$

four possibilities

Let $A=x^2$
$$0=A^2-5A+6$$
$$0=(A-2)(A-3)$$
$$A=2 \quad A=3$$

check $x=\sqrt{2}$
$$(5\cdot 2-6)^{1/4}\stackrel{?}{=}\sqrt{2}$$
$$(4)^{1/4}\stackrel{?}{=}\sqrt{2}$$
$$4^{\frac{1}{2}\cdot\frac{1}{2}}$$
$$\left(4^{\frac{1}{2}}\right)^{\frac{1}{2}}=(\sqrt{4})^{1/2}$$
$$=\sqrt{2}$$

The answer checks!

Check for extraneous roots by substituting each of the four solutions back into the original equation and simplifying.

Sample problems:

1. Solve for w: $(w^2+7w+12)^{\frac{1}{5}}=(w^2+3)^{\frac{1}{5}}$

   Solution: $-\frac{9}{7}$

   Explanation: To eliminate the exponents raise each side of the equation to the 5th power:
   $\left[(w^2+7w+12)^{\frac{1}{5}}\right]^5=\left[(w^2+3)^{\frac{1}{5}}\right]^5$; $w^2+7w+12=w^2+3$.
   Set the equation equal to 0 by subtracting w^2 from each side, then solve for w:
   $7w+12=3$; $7w=-9$; $w=-\frac{9}{7}$.
   Determine if this is an extraneous root by checking in the original equation.
   Subsititute $-\frac{9}{7}$ into the equation for w: $\left[\left(-\frac{9}{7}\right)^2+7\left(-\frac{9}{7}\right)+12\right]^{\frac{1}{5}}=\left[\left(-\frac{9}{7}\right)^2+3\right]^{\frac{1}{5}}$;
   $\left[\frac{81}{49}-9+12\right]^{\frac{1}{5}}=\left[\frac{81}{49}+3\right]^{\frac{1}{5}}$; $\left[\frac{81}{49}+3\right]^{\frac{1}{5}}=\left[\frac{81}{49}+3\right]^{\frac{1}{5}}$.
   Since this is a true statement, $-\frac{9}{7}$ is the solution.

2. Solve for y: $(3y)^{\frac{2}{5}}=(21y+18)^{\frac{1}{5}}$

   Solution: $-\frac{2}{3}$ or 3

   Explanation: Raise each side to the 5th power: $\left[(3y)^{\frac{2}{5}}\right]^5=\left[(21y+18)^{\frac{1}{5}}\right]^5$;
   $(3y)^2=21y+18$; $9y^2=21y+18$.
   Bring all the terms to one side: $9y^2-21y-18=0$.
   Factor: $3(3y^2-7y-6)=0$; $3(3y+2)(y-3)=0$.
   Use the zero factor property and solve:
   $3y+2=0$ or $y-3=0$; $3y=-2$ or $y=3$; $y=-\frac{2}{3}$ or $y=3$.
   Check for extraneous roots:
   Check $y=3$ into $9y^2=21y+18$: $9(3)^2=21(3)+18$; $81=81$.
   Check $y=-\frac{2}{3}$ into $9y^2=21y+18$: $9(-\frac{2}{3})^2=21(-\frac{2}{3})+18$; $9(\frac{4}{9})=-14+18$; $4=4$.
   Both solutions check, therefore $y=-\frac{2}{3}$ or 3 is the solution.

3. Solve for x: $(x^2+2x-20)^{\frac{1}{3}}=(1-2x)^{\frac{1}{3}}$

   Solution: -7 or 3

   Explanation: Raise each side to the 3rd power: $x^2+2x-20=1-2x$.
   Bring all the terms to one side and simplify: $x^2+2x-20-1+2x=0$; $x^2+4x-21=0$.
   Factor and solve for x: $(x+7)(x-3)=0$; $x+7=0$ or $x-3=0$; $x=-7$ or $x=3$.
   Check for extraneous roots: $x=-7$ or 3.

Practice problems: *(Answers on page: 735)*

1. Solve for x: $(x^2-4x)^{\frac{1}{4}}=(-2x^2+9x-4)^{\frac{1}{4}}$
2. Solve for z: $(2z)^{\frac{2}{3}}=(6-10z)^{\frac{1}{3}}$
3. Solve for y: $y^{\frac{1}{4}}=4y^{\frac{3}{4}}$

Review questions: *(Answers to odd questions on page: 735)*

1. Solve for w: $(w-2)^{\frac{2}{3}}=9$
2. Solve for x: $(3x+1)^{\frac{1}{3}}=(4x+9)^{\frac{1}{3}}$

3. Solve for w: $(5-w)^{\frac{1}{5}} = (2w-1)^{\frac{1}{5}}$

4. Solve for x: $(x^2 - 4x + 3)^{\frac{1}{3}} = x^{\frac{2}{3}}$

5. Solve for x: $(3x^2 - x - 3)^{\frac{1}{5}} = x^{\frac{2}{5}}$

An Introduction to Variation

- **Variation** is the notion that two quantities can increase or decrease in relation or proportion to each other.
- If two quantities are **directly proportional**, it means that if one changes by a certain percentage, the other changes in the same way and by the same percentage.
- Two quantities usually are directly proportional without being the same size.
- If two quantities are **inversely** or **indirectly proportional**, it means that if one grows by a certain percentage, the other decreases by the same percentage.
- The constant of change is usually referred to as "***k***".
- The variable x is **directly proportional** to y if $x = ky$.
- The variable x is **inversely proportional** to y if $x = k/y$.

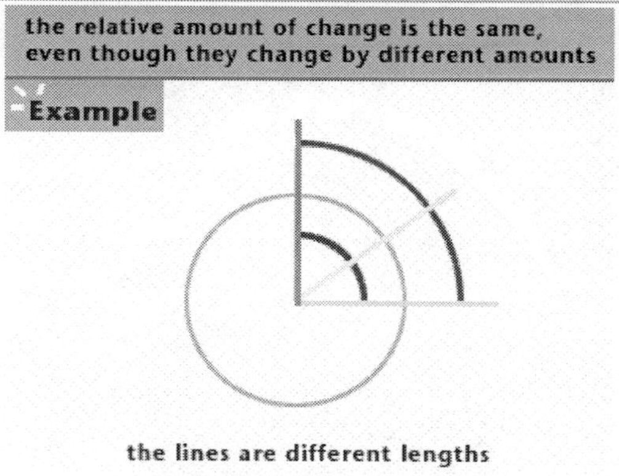

In this example, the spread between the dark line and its perpendicular line cuts arcs representing 25% of each circle.

You would expect that the three 25% arcs are different lengths because their circles are different sizes. However, since they represent the same amount of their circle, they are **directly proportional** to each other.

Now, move the lighter of the two straight lines and the arcs change length becoming shorter. You can expect that all the arcs will shorten proportionately to each other.

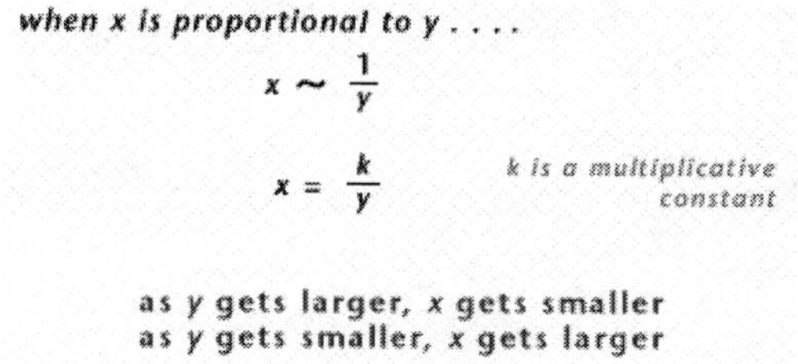

In terms of the circle used above as an example, we could say that the outer arc was **inversely proportional** to the inner arc if, whenever the outer arc grew longer by some percentage, the inner arc grew smaller by the same percentage.

Being inverse or indirectly proportional means the two quantities change opposite to each other.

Direct Proportion

- **Hooke's Law** says that the distance a spring stretches varies directly to the force applied.
- If two quantities are **directly proportional**, it means that if one changes by a certain percentage, the other changes in the same way and by the same percentage.
- Two quantities usually are directly proportional without being the same size.
- The constant of change is usually referred to as "***k***".
- The variable x is directly proportional to y if $x = ky$.

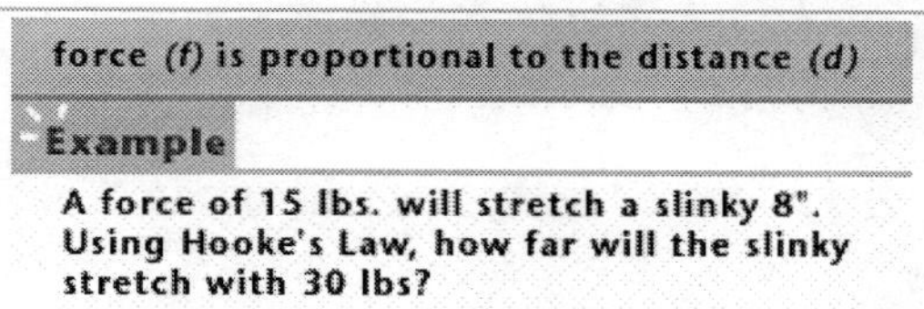

Reading this problem tells that the distance of stretch will vary directly with the amount of weight attached to the spring.

This problem will use the $x = ky$ proportion.

$d = kf$ *find the constant* $8 = k(15)$ $\therefore k = \frac{8}{15}$ ← constant	First calculate what the constant of stretch, k, will be. Set up the equation substituting in the values given. Let x be d for distance stretched and y be f for force applied. Then, solve for k.
$d = \frac{8}{15} f$ $d = \frac{8}{\cancel{15}} (\cancel{30}^{2})$ $\boxed{d = 16"}$	To answer the question in the problem, substitute k in the original equation and use the force given to calculate its appropriate distance. In this example, the force is 30 pounds. Substitute 30 for f. Calculate the stretched distance.

Sample problems:

1. The pressure exerted by a liquid on an object varies directly with the depth of the object. If an object at depth 3 meters undergoes a pressure of 485 kg/m^2, find the pressure on an object at 7m.
   Solution: 1132 kg/m^2
   Explanation: Let P represent the pressure and d represent the depth. Then $P = kd$, since P varies directly with d. Begin by finding k. Substitute the known values from the first situation into $P = kd$ and solve for k: $485 = k(3)$; $k = \frac{485}{3}$. Next, substitute the known value from the second situation and the value of k into $P = kd$ and solve for P:
   $P = \frac{485}{3} \cdot 7 = \frac{3395}{3} \approx 1132$ kg/m^2.

2. The power dissipated by a resistor is directly proportional to the square of the current flowing through it. If 100 watts of power is dissipated when the current is 5 amps, then how much power is dissipated when the current is increased to 10 amps?
   Solution: 400 watts
   Explanation: Let P represent the power and I represent the current. Then $P = kI^2$, since P is directly proportional to I^2. Begin by finding k. Substitute the known values from the first situation into $P = kI^2$ and solve for k: $100 = k(5^2)$; $25k = 100$; $k = 4$. Next, substitute the known value from the second situation and the value of k into $P = kI^2$ and solve for P: $P = 4 \cdot 10^2 = 400$ watts.

3. Suppose z varies directly with the sum of x and y. Furthermore, z is 42 when x is 2 and y is 5. Find x when z is 48 and y is 1.
   Solution: 7
   Explanation: Find k: $z = k(x+y) \Rightarrow 42 = k(2+5)$; $42 = 7k$; $k = 6$. Find x when $z = 48$ and $y = 1$: $z = 6(x+y) \Rightarrow 48 = 6(x+1)$; $48 = 6x + 6$; $6x = 42$; $x = 7$.

Practice problems: *(Answers on page: 735)*

1. Income tax varies directly with income. If a person earning $30,000/year pays $8,400 in taxes, how much will a person earning $42,000/year pay?
2. The distance that an object falls is directly proportional to the square of the time of the fall. If an object falls 25 feet in 3.5 seconds, how far will it fall in 5 seconds?
3. Suppose a varies directly with the square root of b and b is 9 when a is 15. Find b when a is 30.

Review questions: *(Answers to odd questions on page: 735)*

1. A measurement of distance in kilometers varies directly as measurement in miles. If a 5 kilometer race is 3.1 miles, how many kilometers is a marathon (26.2 miles)?
2. Simple interest on a bank account varies directly as the amount of principal in the account. If a \$1,200 investment earns \$84, how much does a \$5,000 investment earn?
3. A kite company produces kites whose lengths vary directly with the widths. If a kite with length 80 cm has width 65 cm, find the width of a 96 cm long kite.
4. Two values d and g are directly proportional. If $d = 16$ when $g = 14$, what is the value of g when d is 25?
5. Volume measured in liters varies directly as volume measured in gallons. A 5 gallon container is approximately the same as a 19 liter container. Approximately how many liters will a 15 gallon container hold?

Inverse Proportion

- If two quantities are **inversely** or **indirectly proportional**, it means that if one grows by a certain percentage, the other decreases by the same percentage.
- The variable x is inversely proportional to y if $x = k/y$.
- The intensity of the illumination of light is inversely proportional to the square of the distance over which it shows an object. The constant, k, of variation will change with each source of light being considered.

Example at 5m the flashlight's illumination is 70 candela. what is the illumination at 12m?	Inverse proportion works with light in that the farther away the viewer is from the light source, the weaker the illumination from the light appears to be. To work with this problem, use the indirect equation: $x = k/y$.
d = distance when: d = 5m I = illumination I = 70 candela $I = \frac{k}{d^2}$ $70 = \frac{k}{5^2}$ find the constant (k) $k = 25 \cdot 70$ $k = 1750$ ← the constant for this flashlight	First read the problem and define the variables. Then, substitute into the definition to find out what the constant k is for this problem.
as the distance gets greater, the illumination gets less $I = \frac{1750}{d^2}$ $I = \frac{1750}{144}$ $I = 12.1527...$ candela	Now, substitute the value for k into the equation and solve for the illumination at the distance of 12 meters.

Sample problems:

1. If x varies inversely with the square of y and x is $\frac{5}{2}$ when y is 2, what is x when y is 5?

   Solution: $\frac{2}{5}$

   Explanation: Since x varies inversely with the square of y, $x = \frac{k}{y^2}$.

   Find k: $\frac{5}{2} = \frac{k}{2^2}$; $\frac{5}{2} = \frac{k}{2^2}$; $4 \cdot \frac{5}{2} = k$; $k = 10$.

   Find x when y is 5: $x = \frac{10}{5^2} = \frac{10}{25} = \frac{2}{5}$.

2. If a pendulum of 99cm has a frequency of $1/2$ Hz, find the frequency of a 4m pendulum given that the frequency varies inversely with the square root of the length.
   Solution: 0.25 Hz
   Explanation: Let f represent the frequency and L represent the length. Then $f = \frac{k}{\sqrt{L}}$, since f varies inversely with the square root of L. Begin by finding k. Substitute the known values from the first situation into $f = \frac{k}{\sqrt{L}}$ and solve for k: $\frac{1}{2} = \frac{k}{\sqrt{99}}$; $k = \frac{\sqrt{99}}{2}$. Next, substitute the known value from the second situation (L is in centimeters, so 4 meter must be converted to cm: 4 m = 400 cm) and the value of k into $f = \frac{k}{\sqrt{L}}$ and solve for f: $f = \frac{\frac{\sqrt{99}}{2}}{\sqrt{400}} = \frac{\frac{\sqrt{99}}{2}}{20} = \frac{\sqrt{99}}{2} \div 20 = \frac{\sqrt{99}}{2} \cdot \frac{1}{20} = \frac{\sqrt{99}}{40} \approx 0.25$ Hz.

3. If x varies inversely with the cube of y, how does x change when y is doubled?
   Solution: $x_2 = \frac{1}{8} x_1$
   Explanation: If x varies inversely with the cube of y then $x = \frac{k}{y^3}$. When y is doubled $y = zy$, so $x = \frac{k}{(2y)^3} = \frac{k}{2^3 y^3} = \frac{k}{8y^3} = \frac{1}{8} \cdot \frac{k}{y^3}$. So, when y is doubled, x is $\frac{1}{8}$ of the original x, or $x_2 = \frac{1}{8} x_1$.

Practice problems: *(Answers on page: 735)*

1. The illumination from a lightbulb varies inversely with the square of the distance d from the lightbulb. If the illumination is 85 candela at 5m, what is the illumination at 15m?
2. If x varies inversely with $\sqrt{y}$, and $x = 2$ when $y = 289$, find x when $y = 10{,}000$.
3. The frequency of the oscillations of a pendulum varies inversely with the square root of the length. How does the frequency change if the pendulum's length is increased to 4 times the previous length?

Review questions: *(Answers to odd questions on page: 735)*

1. The power in an electric circuit varies inversely with the resistance. If the power is 1000 watts when the resistance is 12 ohms, find the power when the resistance is 5 ohms.
2. The frequency of oscillations of a pendulum varies inversely as the square root of the length of the pendulum. If a pendulum of length 25 feet oscillates with a frequency of 100 swings per minute, what would be the frequency of a pendulum of length 16 feet?
3. The loudness in decibels of a noise source varies inversely as the square of the distance d to the source. If a listener at 5ft hears 22 decibels, how loud is the sound at 10ft?
4. The intensity of sound, in decibels, varies inversely as the square of the distance from the source. If the intensity of the sound from a rock band is 100 decibels at a distance of 50 feet from the stage, what would be the intensity at a distance of 62.5 feet from the stage?
5. The volume of a fixed amount of gas varies directly with the temperature and inversely with pressure. If a gas has volume 3L when the temperature is 270 K and the pressure is $1000 \frac{\text{N}}{\text{m}^2}$, find its volume at 330 K at $10{,}000 \frac{\text{N}}{\text{m}^2}$.

An Introduction to Solving Inequalities

- $\leq$ indicates that the quantity on the left is less than or equal to the quantity on the right.
- $<$ indicates that the quantity on the left is strictly less than the quantity on the right.
- $\geq$ indicates that the quantity on the left is greater than or equal to the quantity on the right.
- $>$ indicates that the quantity on the left is strictly greater than the quantity on the right.
- Adding or subtracting the same amounts to both sides of an inequality does not change the inequality.
- Multiplying or dividing by a positive number does not affect the inequality.
- Multiplying or dividing by a negative number reverses the inequality.

$2(x+3) < 4x+10$ $2x+6 < 4x+10$ $-4x \quad = -4x$ $-2x+6 < \quad 10$ $-6 = \quad -6$ $\frac{-2x}{-2} \; (<) \; \frac{4}{-2}$ *flip* $\boxed{x > -2}$	Solving an inequality follows the usual rules. In this case, first distribute the 2 to eliminate the parentheses. Then add to get all the *x*'s on one side of the inequality and all the constants on the other side. Now, divide by the coefficient of *x* for your final answer.
$\boxed{x > -2}$	**Notice:** Dividing (or multiplying) by a negative number reverses the inequality.
$\boxed{x > -2}$ 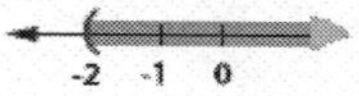 $(-2, +\infty)$	**Note again:** There are three different notations for the answer, each used in specific situations. When solving algebraically, the notation on the left is most used.
$2-3x \leq x+14$ $2-4x \leq 14$ $\frac{-4x}{-4} \; (\leq) \; \frac{12}{-4}$ *subtract 2 from both sides* $x \geq -3$ 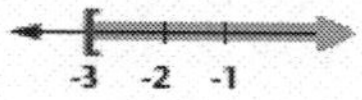 $[-3, +\infty)$	Here is another example for solving: 1. Isolate your *x*'s on one side. 2. Divide by *x*'s coefficient, -4 in this case. (Remember to reverse the inequality.) Indicate the numbers in the solution using one of the three notations.
Check your answer: $2-3(0) \leq 0+14$ $2 \leq 14$ ✓	**Always remember:** Check your answer to be sure it works in the original equation.

Sample problems:

1. Given $4 \geq \frac{z}{3} - \frac{2z}{3}$, solve the inequality and express the solution in interval notation.
   Solution: $[-12, \infty)$
   Explanation: Multiply each term by 3: $3(4) \geq 3\left(\frac{z}{3}\right) - 3\left(\frac{2z}{3}\right)$; $12 \geq z - 2z$. Simplify and solve for z: $12 \geq -z$. Each side will be divided by -1, so reverse the inequality: $12 \geq -z$; $-12 \leq z$ or $z \geq -12$. Express in interval notation: $[-12, \infty)$.

2. Given $\frac{w-1}{5} > \frac{3w}{10}$, solve the inequality and express the solution in interval notation.
   Solution: $(-\infty, -2)$
   Explanation: To cancel the denominators, multiply each side by the GCF of 5 & 10, which is 10: $10\left(\frac{w-1}{5}\right) > \left(\frac{3w}{10}\right)10$; $2(w-1) > 3w$. Simplify and solve for w: $2w - 2 > 3w$; $-w - 2 > 0$; $-w > 2$. Divide each side by -1 and reverse the inequality: $w < -2$. Express in interval notation: $(-\infty, -2)$.

3. Given $x^2 - 6x + 4 < x^2 + 2x$, solve the inequality and express the solution in interval notation.

   Solution: $\left(\frac{1}{2}, \infty\right)$

   Explanation: Subtract x^2 from each side: $x^2 - 6x + 4 < x^2 + 2x$; $-6x + 4x < 2x$.
   Solve for x: $-8x + 4 < 0$; $-8x < -4$. Divide each side by -8 and reverse the inequality:
   $x > \frac{-4}{-8} = \frac{1}{2}$. Use interval notation. $\left(\frac{1}{2}, \infty\right)$.

Practice problems: *(Answers on page: 735)*

1. Given $3 - 4z \le 7z + 1$, solve the inequality and express the solution in interval notation.
2. Given $\frac{5x-1}{2} + \frac{1}{3} > 1 + 3(x+2)$, solve the inequality and express the solution in interval notation.
3. Given $x^2 - 6 \ge x^2 - 3(x+4)$, solve the inequality and express the solution in interval notation.

Review questions: *(Answers to odd questions on page: 735)*

1. Given $7 - x < 2$, solve the inequality and express the solution in interval notation.
2. Given $2x + 1 > 5x - 7$, solve the inequality and express the solution in interval notation.
3. Given $2(p+1) \ge 26 - p$, solve the inequality and express the solution in interval notation.
4. Given $x^2 - 6x + 4 < x^2 + 2x$, solve the inequality and express the solution in interval notation.
5. Given $\frac{5(q+1)}{2} - \frac{3q}{5} \le \frac{7q-2}{10}$, solve the inequality and express the solution in interval notation.

Solving Compound Inequalities

- A **compound inequality** consists of two inequalities linked by a connective word, "and" or "or."
- "**And**" means that both inequalities must be satisfied at the same time. This relationship is sometimes called the **intersection** where both inequalities hold true.
- Graphing both solutions on a number line is the easiest way to see the intersection, or the entire range where both inequalities hold true.
- "**Or**" means that either inequality must be satisfied, not necessarily both. This relationship is called a **union** because it can be said to unite the two sets of solutions.
- The term **empty set** indicates that there are no numbers which satisfy the terms of the compound inequality.

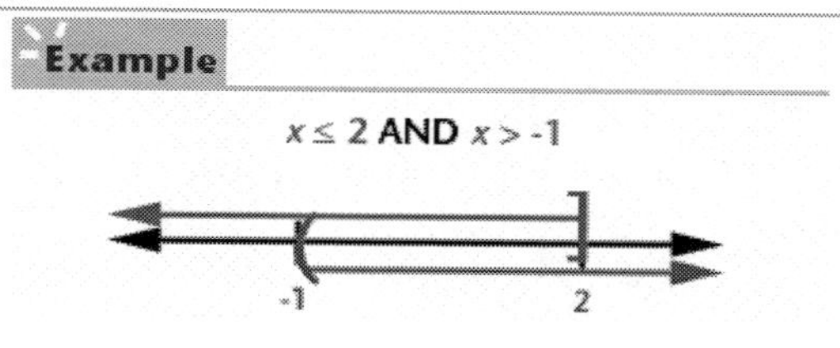	For this **compound inequality**, we want to see all the numbers that satisfy both expressions. On the number line we can see the two separate sets of solutions. The set that works for both inequalities is clearly all the numbers larger than –1 that are smaller than +2; i.e., $-1 < x < 2$.
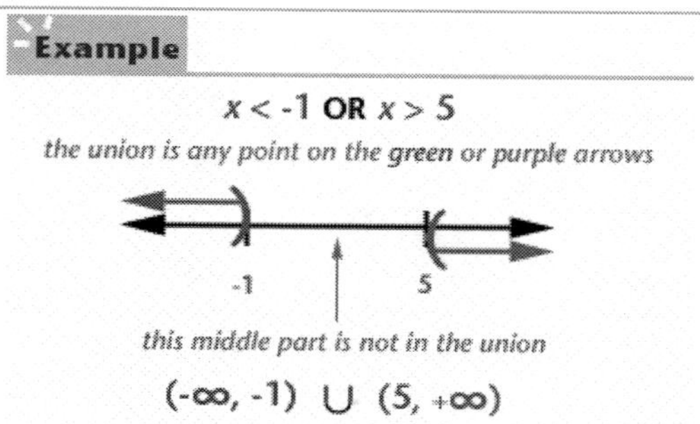	**Note:** Graphing is almost always the best way to check that you are really comprehending the full set of the solution's range. In this example, one inequality is satisfied by all the numbers less than –1. The other inequality is satisfied by all the numbers greater than +5. So, the solution will be all the numbers less than –1 or greater than +5; i.e., $-1 > x > 5$.

Example

$x \geq 3$ AND $x < 0$

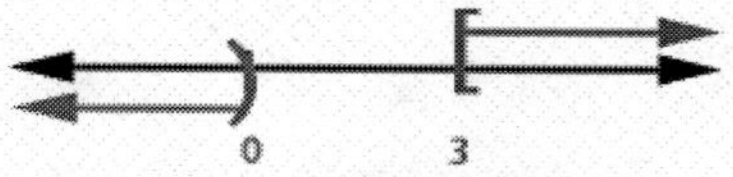

there are no values for x that will satisfy both x≥3 AND x<0 at the same time

The word "**and**" asks for all the numbers that satisfy both inequalities.

There are none.

So your solution is an **empty set**.

Sample problems:

1. Express the solution of the compound inequality $x \leq -1$ and $x \geq -3$ in interval notation.
   Solution: $[-3, -1]$
   Explanation: The solution of "$x \leq -1$ and $x \geq -3$" is the intersection of the two inequalities. To find the intersection, determine the numbers that are included in both inequalities, or all numbers between -1 and -3, including -1 and -3. So, $[-3, -1]$ is the solution.

2. Express the solution of the compound inequality $x > 6$ and $6 > x$ in interval notation.
   Solution: $\varnothing$
   Explanation: The solution of "$x > 6$ and $6 > x$" is the intersection of $x > 6$ and $x < 6$. There are no numbers common to both inequalities, so the solution is the empty set.

3. Express the solution of the compound inequality $x \geq 7$ or $x < 9$ in interval notation.
   Solution: $(-\infty, \infty)$
   Explanation: The solution of "$x \geq 7$ or $x < 9$" is the union of $x \geq 7$ and $x < 9$, or all numbers greater than or equal to 7 and all numbers less than 9. The union of these two inequalities is all real numbers, or $(-\infty, \infty)$.

Practice problems: *(Answers on page: 735)*

1. Express the solution of the compound inequality $x \geq 7$ and $x < 10$ in interval notation.
2. Express the solution of the compound inequality $x \geq 3.5$ and $x < 4$ in interval notation.
3. Express the solution of the compound inequality $x > 1$ or $x \leq 0$ in interval notation.

Review questions: *(Answers to odd questions on page: 735)*

1. Express the solution of the compound inequality $w \geq 1$ or $w < 3$ in interval notation.
2. Express the solution of the compound inequality $x > 3$ and $x < 7$ in interval notation.
3. Express the solution of the compound inequality $w \geq 1$ and $w > -3$ in interval notation.
4. Express the solution of the compound inequality $z > \frac{17}{5}$ or $z \leq 4$ in interval notation.
5. Express the solution of the compound inequality $p \leq \frac{20}{3}$ and $p > 6$ in interval notation.

More on Compound Inequalities

- Remember to reverse the inequality if you multiply or divide by a negative number.

Example

$1-2x < 0$ or $6+3x < 0$

$\frac{-2x}{-2} < \frac{-1}{-2}$ $\qquad$ $\frac{3x}{3} < \frac{-6}{3}$ *divide by 3*

$x > \frac{1}{2}$ or $x < -2$

In this "**or**" example, our solution set will be all numbers which satisfy either of the inequalities.

 $(-\infty, -2) \cup (\frac{1}{2}, +\infty)$	The best way to comprehend the total solution set is to graph both sets on a number line.
AND - intersection OR - union **Example** $0 \le 2x+6 < 18$ $-6 = \quad -6 = -6$ $\frac{-6}{2} \le \frac{2x}{2} < \frac{12}{2}$ $-3 \le x < 6$ 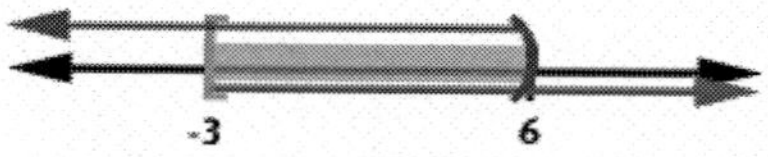 [-3, 6)	A **compound inequality** can be written as one algebraic sentence with two inequalities, as is the case here. Solve it by changing all three sides the same until you have a solution for x. This is easy so long as you are careful with your arithmetic, your signs, and any inequality reversals caused by multiplying with a negative number. This is an "**and**" situation. We can consider the solution to be ONLY those numbers that satisfy both unequal relationships.

Sample problems:

1. Solve for x: $-11 \le 5x - 1 \le 4$
   Solution: $[-2,\ 1]$
   Explanation: Apply the usual solving steps to all three sides of the compound inequality.
   Add 1 to each side: $-11 \le 5x - 1 \le 4$; $-10 \le 5x \le 5$. Divide each side by 5: $-10 \le 5x \le 5$; $-2 \le x \le 1$.
   Express the compound inequality in interval notation: $x \ge -2$ and $x \le 1 \Rightarrow [-2, \infty) \cap (-\infty, 1] \Rightarrow [-2,\ 1]$.

2. True or false: The solution of $0 < 5(6 - x) \le 10$ is $4 \ge x > 6$.
   Solution: False
   Explanation: Simplify: $0 < 5(6 - x) \le 10$; $0 < 30 - 5x \le 10$.
   Apply the usual solving steps to all three sides of the compound inequality:
   $0 < 30 - 5x \le 10$; $-30 < -5x \le -20$. Divide all three sides by -5 and reverse both inequalities:
   $-30 < -5x \le -20$; $6 > x \ge 4$, or $4 \le x < 6$, but not $4 \ge x > 6$.

3. Solve for x: $-5 \le \dfrac{-8x - 1}{9} \le -4$
   Solution: $\left[\frac{35}{8}, \frac{11}{2}\right]$
   Explanation: Multiply each side by 9 to clear the denominator: $-45 \le -8x - 1 \le -36$. Solve for x as usual: $-44 \le -8x \le -35$; $\frac{44}{8} \ge x \ge \frac{35}{8}$; $\frac{11}{2} \ge x \ge \frac{35}{8}$. Express this inequality in interaval notation:
   $-\dfrac{11}{2} \le x$ and $x \le -\dfrac{35}{8} \quad \Rightarrow \quad \left[\frac{35}{8}, \infty\right) \cap \left(-\infty, \frac{11}{2}\right] = \left[\frac{35}{8}, \frac{11}{2}\right]$.

Practice problems: *(Answers on page: 736)*

1. Solve for w: $2 < 3w - 1 < 14$
2. Solve for z: $-2 < \dfrac{1 - 3z}{7} \le 10$
3. True or false: The solution of $0 \le \dfrac{6 - x}{5} \le 4$ is $[-14, -6]$

Review questions: *(Answers to odd questions on page: 736)*

1. Solve for x: $2 \le 5x - 1 < 9$

2. Solve for x: $1-3x \le 13$ or $x+1 \le 10$
3. Solve for y: $-2y+5 \le 8$ or $7y-1 < 6$
4. Solve for x: $-7 \le \dfrac{1-x}{2} \le 4$
5. Solve for q: $\dfrac{5q}{3} \le 4$ or $\dfrac{1-2q}{5} \le 1$

Solving Word Problems Involving Inequalities

- **Word problem solving process**:
  - Determine the facts
  - Define the variables
  - Create an equation
  - Solve the equation
  - Check your answer

How many sales per week does Ed have to make so that Plan A will yield a higher paycheck? A  B  \$100/wk + \$8/sale \$250/wk + \$3.50/sale	Read the problem and see what facts you have and what you are being asked to figure out.
Let s = number of sales per week How many sales per week does Ed have to make so that Plan A will yield a higher paycheck? A  B  \$100/wk + \$8/sale \$250/wk + \$3.50/sale 100 + 8s \$250 + 3.5s	As usual step one is to define the variable. In this example, "*s*" equals the number of sales per week.
$100 + 8s > 250 + 3.5s$	Then use the variable and the facts you know to write the equation. Our concern here is to find out when the left side is larger than the right side.
$100 + 4.5s > 250$ $\dfrac{4.5s}{4.5} > \dfrac{150}{4.5}$ $s > \dfrac{150}{4.5}$ $s > 33\frac{1}{3}$	Now, solve the equation for the answer to the question in the problem. In this example, we never have to reverse the inequality because we don't multiply or divide by a negative number.
$s > \dfrac{150}{4.5}$ $s > 33\frac{1}{3}$ the smallest number of sales that is greater than thirty three and a third is 34.	To answer our question we need a whole number because sales don't come in parts. So, the answer to the question will be the next larger whole number; i.e., 34. Check the answer by substituting 34 into the equation to verify that the left side really is more money than the right side.

Sample problems:

1. Kelly's cellular phone plan charges her \$8 per month plus \$0.25 per minute of phone usage. Chris's plan charges him \$20/month but only \$0.10 per minute. For how many minutes must Chris use his cell phone in one month to make his plan cheaper than Kelly's?
   Solution: 81 minutes
   Explanation: Let x be the number of minutes of cell phone usage in a month. Kelly's charge can be represented by $8+.25x$ and Chris's by $20+.10x$. Chris pays less than Kelly when: $20+.10x<8+.25x$. Solve for x: $20+.10x<8+.25x$; $20-.15x<8$; $-.15x<-12$; $x>80$. Chris's plan is cheaper when he uses 81 minutes or more per month.

2. Tickets to a museum cost \$7.00 for adults and \$3.50 for children. A group of children and 9 adults are taking a trip to a museum. If the group has \$160.00 to spend on tickets, what is the greatest possible number of children's tickets they can buy?
   Solution: 27
   Explanation: Let x be the number of children tickets. The total amount spent on tickets can be represented by $7(9)+3.5x$, or $63+3.5x$. The amount spent on tickets must be less than or equal to \$160, or $63+3.5x\leq 160$. Solve for x: $63+3.5x\leq 160$; $3.5x\leq 97$; $x\leq 27.7$. So, they can buy 27 children tickets.

3. Every month John spends $\frac{1}{4}$ of his salary on rent and $\frac{1}{5}$ of his salary on utility bills. If he spends at least \$525 on rent and bills each month, find John's lowest possible salary.
   Solution: \$1,166.67
   Explanation: Let x be John's salary. The amount he spends on rent and bills must be at least 525, or $\frac{1}{4}x+\frac{1}{5}x\geq 525$. Multiply the equation by 20 to clear the denominators, then solve for x: $20(\frac{1}{4}x+\frac{1}{5}x)\geq 20(525)$; $5x+4x\geq 10,500$; $9x\geq 10,500$; $x\geq 1,166.67$.
   Thus, John must make at least \$1,166.67.

Practice problems: *(Answers on page: 736)*

1. Troy and Phil are renting a car to go on a vacation for one week. They have a choice of paying \$100/week and \$0.20 per mile or \$50/week with \$0.30 per mile for the rental car. How many miles per week should they plan to drive if they decide to pick the first option?
2. The student council is sponsoring a concert as a fund raiser. Tickets are \$2 for students and \$8 for non-students. The student council wants to raise at least \$600. If 150 students attend, how many non-students must attend to reach the goal?
3. Sarah makes and sells pottery bowls. She has costs totaling \$10,000 per year plus a cost of \$7 for each bowl she makes. If she sells the bowls for \$25 each, how many must she sell each year to earn at least a \$25,000 profit?

Review questions: *(Answers to odd questions on page: 736)*

1. A car salesman earns a \$22,000 salary each year plus a commission of \$350 on each car he sells. How many cars must he sell each year to earn at least \$50,000?
2. A bank account has \$9000 and earns 8% simple interest. How many years must pass before the account holds more than \$12,000?
3. A yo-yo factory has fixed operating costs of \$5000 per day plus costs of \$2 per yo-yo produced. If a yo-yo sells for \$5.50, how many must be sold in a day to earn a profit?
4. A long-distance phone company offers two plans. Plan A charges a monthly fee of \$5 plus 11¢ per minute of usage. Plan B charges \$10 per month plus 8¢ per minute of usage. How many minutes of usage per month would be required in order for Plan B to be the less expensive option?

5. A store sells candy bars for 65¢ and gumballs for 8¢. Martha Zo has \$2 and wants to buy one candy bar and some gumballs. What is the greatest number of gumballs Martha Zo can buy?

Solving Quadratic Inequalities

- Solving inequalities:
  - Factor where possible.
  - Determine the points where each factor equals zero.
  - Determine what intervals produce results that satisfy the inequality as originally stated.
- Remember that multiplying or dividing by a negative number reverses the inequality.
- Remember that graphing on a number line is the best way to spot all the possibilities.

Example $2x^2+5x-12 \geq 0$ $(2x-3)(x+4) \geq 0$ $2x-3=0$ $x+4=0$ $2x=3$ $x=-4$ $x=3/2$	In this example, you are able to factor easily. By factoring you can solve for the points where the polynomial equals zero
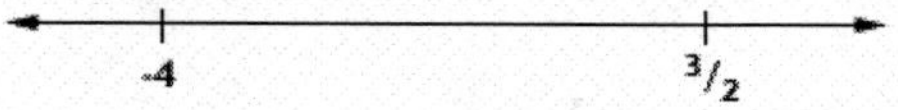	Now, use a number line to determine the points in the solution. For this example, your main concern is that the product be greater than 0. To get a product greater than 0, multiply numbers with the same signs; i.e., either both positive or both negative.
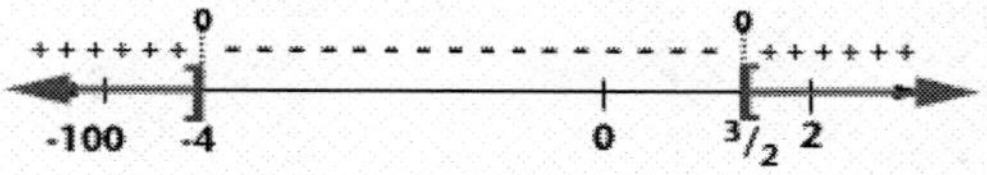 $(-\infty, -4] \cup [\frac{3}{2}, +\infty)$	To determine your solution, pick a number from each interval and substitute it in for x. In this example, your intervals are: (1) all the numbers < -4; (2) all the numbers between -4 and $+3/2$; (3) all the numbers $> +3/2$. Do the arithmetic and see if your result matches the inequality. For example, try -5 from the left interval, 0 from the middle interval, and $+3$ from the right interval. Doing this you will get: -5: (-10-3)(-5+4) = 13, > 0; it works. 0: (0-3)(0+4) = -12, < 0. +3: (6-3)(3+4) = 21, > 0; it works. This shows that your solution set is all the numbers less than -4 and greater than 3/2.

Sample problems:

1. Solve for x: $9x^2+1>0$

   Solution: $(-\infty, \infty)$

   Explanation: Solve $9x^2+1=0$. Subtract 1 from both sides: $9x^2=-1$.

   Divide both sides by 9: $x^2=-\frac{1}{9}$. There are no solutions. If $x=0$, then $9(0)+1=1>0$. So $9x^2+1$ is always positive. The solution is $(-\infty, \infty)$.

2. Solve for y: $y^2+2\le 0$
   Solution: $\varnothing$ (empty set)
   Explanation: Solve $y^2+2=0$. Subtract 2 from both sides: $y^2=-2$. There are no solutions. y^2+2 is never zero. Check $y=0$: $0+2=2$. So y^2+2 is always positive. The solution is $\varnothing$.

3. Solve for x: $7x^2+77x+126\le 0$
   Solution: $[-9,-2]$
   Explanation: Solve $7x^2+77x+126=0$ for x. Divide the equation by 7: $x^2+11x+18=0$. Factor: $(x+9)(x+2)=0$. Set each factor equal to zero and solve for x: $x+9=0$ or $x+2=0$; $x=-9$ or $x=-2$. Set up a number line and check a value from each interval in the original inequality. The solution is $[-9,-2]$.

Practice problems: *(Answers on page: 736)*

1. Solve for x: $(2x+1)(x-9)\ge 0$
2. Solve for x: $-x^2+x+6>0$
3. Solve for y: $3y^2-26y<77$

Review questions: *(Answers to odd questions on page: 736)*

1. Solve for x: $(x-3)(x+2)>0$
2. Solve for w: $w^2-9<0$
3. Solve for x: $-3x^2-3x+60<0$
4. Solve for x: $6x^2-23x-4>0$
5. Solve for p: $2p^2-p-15\ge 0$

Solving Quadratic Inequalities: Another Example

- Solving inequalities:
  - Factor where possible.
  - Determine the points where each factor equals zero.
  - Determine what intervals produce results that satisfy the inequality as originally stated.
- Remember that multiplying or dividing by a negative number reverses the inequality.
- Remember that graphing on a number line is the best way to spot all the possibilities.

$3x^2<-10-13x$	Your original inequality asks for all the values of x that make $3x^2$ smaller than (-10 -13x).
$3x^2+13x+10<0$ $(3x+10)(x+1)<0$ $3x+10=0$ $3x=-10$ $x=-\frac{10}{3}$ $x=-1$	To solve, do your usual steps for solving a quadratic equation: 1. Move everything to one side and set it equal to 0. 2. Factor if possible. 3. Set each factor equal to 0 and solve for x.

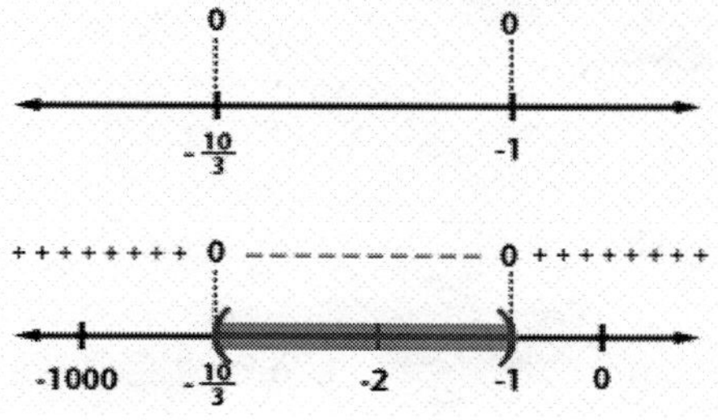

$\left(-\frac{10}{3}, -1\right)$

Then do your steps for inequalities:

1. Set up a number line with the points marked where the factors equal 0. In this case, that means you mark –10/3 and –1. Setting two points creates three intervals on the number line.
2. Choose a random point from each interval on the number line.
3. Substitute that point for x in the original equation.
4. Check to see which intervals yield the results indicated by the original equation.

For example, choose and test with:
-5: (-15 + 10)(-5 + 1) = 20, > 0.
-2: (-6 + 10)(-2 + 1) = -4, < 0; it works.
0: (0 + 10)(0 + 1) = 10, > 0.

Mark the number line and/or use other notation to show which intervals are solutions.

Sample problems:

1. Solve for w: $-x^2 < -(x+12)$
   Solution: $(-\infty,-3) \cup (4,\infty)$
   Explanation: Set the inequality equal to 0 by adding $(x+12)$ to both sides: $-x^2+x+12<0$. Divide by -1 and reverse the inequality: $x^2-x-12>0$. Solve $x^2-x-12=0$ for x: $(x-4)(x+3)=0$; $x-4=0$ or $x+3=0$; $x=4$ or $x=-3$. Set up a number line and check a value from each interval in the original inequality. The solution is $(-\infty,-3) \cup (4,\infty)$.

2. Solve for y: $y^2+2y \ge 35$.
   Solution: $(-\infty,-7]\cup[5,\infty)$
   Explanation: $y^2+2y-35=0$. Bring all the terms to one side. Solve: $y^2+2y-35=0$; $(y+7)(y-5)=0$. Factor the left side. $y+7=0$ or $y-5=0$. $y=-7$ or $y=5$. Sign chart: $x=-8:(-8)^2+2(-8)-35=64-16-35=13$; $x=0:0^2+2(0)-35=-35$; $x=6:6^2+2(6)-35=36+12-35=13$. Solution: $(-\infty,-7]\cup[5,\infty)$.

3. Which values satisfy the quadratic inequality $8x^2-6x-35>0$?
   Solution: $x>\frac{5}{2}$ or $x<-\frac{7}{4}$
   Explanation: Factor the inequality: $(4x+7)(2x-5)>0$. Solve for x: $4x+7=0$; $4x=-7$; $x=-\frac{7}{4}$; or $2x-5=0$; $2x=5$; $x=\frac{5}{2}$. Mark these two points on a number line and choose any point from each of the three intervals: $x=-3:8(-3)^2-6(-3)-35=72+18-35=55$; $x=0:8(0)^2-6(0)-35=0+0-35=-35$; $x=3:8(3)^2-6(3)-35=72-18-32=19$. The two outer regions of the number line satisfy the inequality. The solution is: $x>\frac{5}{2}$ or $x<-\frac{7}{4}$.

Practice problems: *(Answers on page: 736)*

1. Solve for v: $-35v \le 5v^2+30$

2. Solve for x: $25-3x^2>x^2$
3. Solve for p: $24p^2<-14p+3$

Review questions: *(Answers to odd questions on page: 736)*

1. Solve for z: $5z^2\le -17z-6$
2. Solve for x: $-2x^2-5x\ge -3$
3. Solve for y: $-2y^2-16y\ge 24$
4. Solve for x: $4x^2+14>15x$
5. Solve for x: $6x^2-11x-35\ge 0$

Solving Rational Inequalities

- **Solving inequalities**:
  - Factor where possible.
  - Determine the points where each factor equals zero.
  - Determine the points that cause the denominator to equal zero and must be excluded from the domain for x.
  - Determine what intervals produce results that satisfy the inequality as originally stated.
- The extra step involved with rational expressions is to find a common denominator if necessary.
- Inequalities state their answer sets using interval notation.
- Remember that multiplying or dividing by a negative number reverses the inequality.

Example Find all values for x $\frac{3x+4}{x+1}\le 2$ $\frac{3x+4}{x+1}-2\le 0$ $\frac{3x+4}{x+1}-\frac{2(x+1)}{x+1}\le 0$ $\frac{3x+4-2(x+1)}{x+1}\le 0$	In this example, the first step will be to move the 2 to the left side so the entire equation is expressed in relation to 0. Then, do the multiplying necessary to set up a common denominator. Next, simplify the expression.
$\frac{x+2}{x+1}<0$ *denominator = 0 at -1, fraction is undefined*	**Remember:** With the variable in the denominator, exclude from the domain of x any value that sets the denominator equal to 0. In this case that value is –1.
	Now, mark the points where the expression equals 0. In this case that is the one point at which x equals –2. Also, mark the points where the expression is undefined; i.e., where the denominator equals 0. In this example that is the one point at which x equals –1.
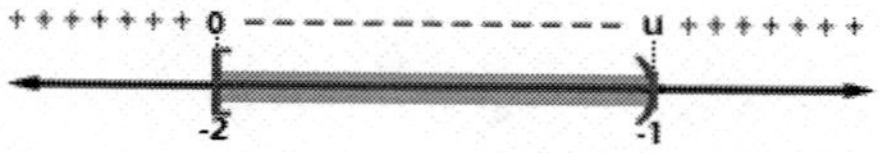	Now test a random point from each of the regions. Since this problem states that the expression is less than or equal to 0, the solution will be the points which produce a negative value for the expression: from the left region: -3 produces +½ from the middle region: -1½ produces -1; it works from the right region: 0 produces +2 Only the middle interval, (-2,-1) works.

[-2, -1) *interval notation*	Include –2 in the solution; when x equals -2, the expression equals 0 which is included in the ≤ relationship. **NOTE:** -1 would be included also, except that it is excluded from the domain.

Sample problems:

1. Solve for v: $\frac{10}{3-2v} \geq \frac{5}{3-2v}$

   Solution: $\left(-\infty, \frac{3}{2}\right)$

   Explanation: Express the inequality in relation to 0: $\frac{10}{3-2v} - \frac{5}{3-2v} \geq 0$. Simplify the numerator: $\frac{10-5}{3-2v} \geq 0$; $\frac{5}{3-2v} \geq 0$. Find the values where $\frac{5}{3-2v}$ is a) zero or b) undefined: a) Set the numerator $= 0$ and solve for v: $5 \neq 0$, the expression never equals 0, b) Set the denominator $= 0$ and solve for v: $3-2v=0$; $-2v=-3$; $v \neq \frac{3}{2}$. Note this critical value on a number line. Choose a random value from each region and test in $\frac{5}{3-2v} \geq 0$. Testing any value from $v < \frac{3}{2}$ gives a true result. Testing any value from $v > \frac{3}{2}$ gives a false result. Therefore, the solution set is $(-\infty, \frac{3}{2})$.

2. Solve for x: $\frac{3x-1}{x-5} \geq -4$

   Solution: $(-\infty, 3] \cup (5, \infty)$

   Explanation: Express the inequality in relation to 0: $\frac{3x-1}{x-5} + 4 \geq 0$. Multiply by the common denominator: $\frac{3x-1}{x-5} + 4 \cdot \frac{(x-5)}{(x-5)} \geq 0$; $\frac{3x-1}{x-5} + \frac{4(x-5)}{(x-5)} \geq 0$. Add: $\frac{3x-1+4(x-5)}{x-5} \geq 0$. Simplify the numerator: $\frac{3x-1+4x-20}{x-5} \geq 0$; $\frac{7x-21}{x-5} \geq 0$. Find the values where $\frac{7x-21}{x-5}$ is a) zero or b) undefined: a) Set the numerator $= 0$ and solve for x: $7x-21=0$; $7x=21$; $x=3$. b) Set the denominator $= 0$ and solve for x: $x-5=0$; $x \neq 5$. Note these critical values on a number line. Choose a random value from each region and test in $\frac{7x-21}{x-5} \geq 0$. Testing any value from $x \leq 3$ gives a true result, values from $3 \leq x < 5$ give a false result, and values from $x > 5$ give a true result. Therefore, the solution set is $(-\infty, 3] \cup (5, \infty)$.

3. Solve for x: $\dfrac{7}{x+2} \geq \dfrac{1}{x-1}$

<u>Solution</u>: $(-2,1) \cup \left[\dfrac{3}{2}, \infty\right)$

<u>Explanation</u>: Express the inequality in relation to 0: $\dfrac{7}{x+2} - \dfrac{1}{x-1} \geq 0$. Multiply by the common denominator: $\dfrac{(x-1)}{(x-1)}\left(\dfrac{7}{x+2}\right) - \dfrac{(x+2)}{(x+2)}\left(\dfrac{1}{x-1}\right) \geq 0$; $\dfrac{7(x-1)-(x+2)}{(x+2)(x-1)} \geq 0$. Simplify the numerator: $\dfrac{7x-7-x-2}{(x+2)(x-1)} \geq 0$; $\dfrac{6x-9}{(x+2)(x-1)} \geq 0$. Find the values where $\dfrac{6x-9}{(x+2)(x-1)}$ is a) zero or b) undefined: a) $6x-9=0$; $6x=9$; $x=\dfrac{9}{6}=\dfrac{3}{2}$, b) $x+2=0$ or $x-1=0$; $x \neq -2$ or $x \neq 1$.

Note these critical values on a number line and test a value from each region in $\dfrac{6x-9}{(x+2)(x-1)} \geq 0$.

The solution set is $(-2,1) \cup \left[\dfrac{3}{2}, \infty\right)$.

Practice problems: *(Answers on page: 736)*

1. Solve for x: $\dfrac{5}{2x+7} \geq \dfrac{x}{2x+7}$
2. Solve for x: $\dfrac{x-3}{x+6} \leq 2$
3. Solve for x: $\dfrac{5}{x+3} \geq \dfrac{4}{x+1}$

Review questions: *(Answers to odd questions on page: 736)*

1. Solve for w: $\dfrac{w+7}{w-11} \geq 0$
2. Solve for x: $\dfrac{1}{x-2} < 1$
3. Solve for y: $\dfrac{1}{y-3} < \dfrac{1}{4}$
4. Solve for x: $\dfrac{1}{x} > x$
5. Solve for w: $\dfrac{3}{4w-1} < -\dfrac{1}{w}$

Solving Rational Inequalities: Another Example

- Solving inequalities:
  - Factor where possible.
  - Determine the points where each factor equals zero.
  - Determine the points that cause the denominator to equal zero and must be excluded from the domain for x.
  - Determine what intervals produce results that satisfy the inequality as originally stated.
- Remember to carefully watch that you distribute and use signs correctly.
- Remember that multiplying or dividing by a negative number reverses the inequality.

Find all values for X $\dfrac{x^2+x-6}{x-4} \geq 0$	The mission, in this problem, is to find all values of x so that the given expression has a value greater than or equal to 0.

$\dfrac{x^2+x-6}{x-4} \ge 0$ $\dfrac{(x+3)(x-2)}{x-4} \ge 0$ *we can factor.*	Factoring the numerator helps find the places where the expression will equal 0. In this problem, the expression equals 0 when x equals -3 and when x equals 2. Also note that the denominator equals 0 when x equals 4. Therefore, exclude 4 from the domain for x because the expression is undefined at that point.
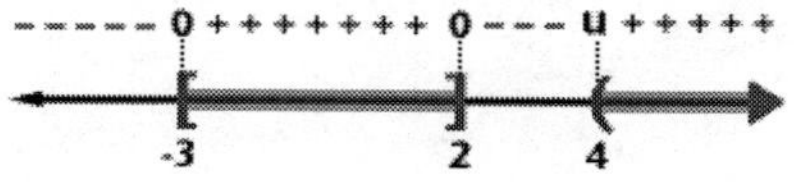	Mark on the number line the points where the expression equals 0 or is undefined; i.e., -3, 2, and 4 for this example. The inequality wants values that give the expression a value greater than 0. So, pick from each region and see: -5 produces -14/9, <0. 0 produces +3/2, >0, it works. +3 produces -6, <0. +5 produces +24, >0, it works.
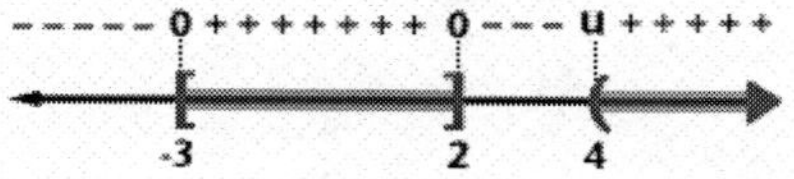 $[-3, 2] \cup (4, +\infty)$	The solution interval covers all the numbers between and including –3 and +2 plus all the numbers larger than, but not including, +4. Both the number line graph and the union notation clearly state the solution values.

Sample problems:

1. Solve for w: $\dfrac{w^2+1}{w-3} \le \dfrac{1}{w-3}$

   Solution: $(-\infty,\ 3)$

   Explanation: Express the inequality in relation to 0: $\dfrac{w^2+1}{w-3} - \dfrac{1}{w-3} \le 0$. Subtract:

   $\dfrac{w^2+1-1}{w-3} \le 0$; $\dfrac{w^2}{w-3} \le 0$. Find the values where $\dfrac{w^2}{w-3}$ is a) zero or b) undefined:

   a) $w^2=0$; $w=0$, b) $w-3=0$; $w \ne 3$. Note these critical values on a number line.

   Choose a random value from each region and test in $\dfrac{w^2}{w-3} \le 0$. The solution set is $(-\infty, 3)$.

2. Solve for x: $\dfrac{x^2-6x-14}{x+1} \ge -2$

   Solution: $[-2,-1) \cup [6,\infty)$

   Explanation: Express the inequality in relation to 0 and combine the terms:

   $\frac{x^2-6x-14}{x+1} + 2 \ge 0$; $\frac{x^2-6x-14}{x+1} + (2)\frac{(x+1)}{(x+1)} \ge 0$; $\frac{x^2-6x-14+2(x+1)}{x+1} \ge 0$. Simplify the numerator: $\frac{x^2-6x-14+2x+2}{x+1} \ge 0$. Factor the numerator: $\frac{(x-6)(x+2)}{x-1} \ge 0$. Find the values where $\frac{(x-6)(x+2)}{x-1}$ is a) zero and b) undefined: a) $x-6=0$ or $x+2=0$; $x=6$ or $x=-2$, b) $x+1=0$; $x \ne 1$. Note these critical values on a number line and test values from each region in $\frac{(x-6)(x+2)}{x-1}$. The solution set is $[-2,-1) \cup [6,\infty)$.

3. Solve for x: $\frac{x+2}{x+6} \leq \frac{3}{x+1}$

Solution: $(-6,-4] \cup (-1,4]$

Explanation: Express the inequality in relation to 0 and combine the terms: $\frac{x+2}{x+6} - \frac{3}{x+1} \leq 0$;

$\frac{(x+1)}{(x+1)}\left(\frac{x+2}{x+6}\right) - \frac{(x+6)}{(x+6)}\left(\frac{3}{x+1}\right) \leq 0$; $\frac{(x+1)(x+2)-3(x+6)}{(x+1)(x+6)} \leq 0$. Find the critical values:

a) $x+4=0$ or $x-4=0$; $x=-4$ or $x=4$, b) $x+1=0$ or $x+6=0$; $x \neq -1$ or $x \neq -6$. Note these critical values on a number line and test a value from each region in $\frac{(x+4)(x-4)}{(x+1)(x+6)} \leq 0$.

These solution set is $(-6,-4] \cup (-1,4]$.

Practice problems: *(Answers on page: 736)*

1. Solve for w: $\frac{w^2-9w+25}{w+3} \leq \frac{w+1}{w+3}$
2. Solve for x: $\frac{x^2+11x-2}{x-3} \leq 4$
3. Solve for y: $\frac{y-4}{2y+10} \geq -\frac{1}{y+3}$

Review questions: *(Answers to odd questions on page: 736)*

1. Solve for y: $\frac{y^2+6y+9}{y-4} \geq 0$
2. Solve for x: $\frac{3x^2+12-10}{2x-1} \geq \frac{3x+2}{2x-1}$
3. Solve for z: $\frac{z^2-7z+20}{z+3} < \frac{3z-5}{z+3}$
4. Solve for w: $\frac{5}{w-3} > \frac{3}{w+1}$
5. Solve for s: $\frac{2s+5}{s+1} > \frac{s+1}{s-1}$

Determining the Domains of Expressions with Radicals

- The **domain** is the set of all values that can be used for x in an expression.
- The **radicand** is the value or expression under the radical sign. It must be positive in order to have a real number root.
- Solving inequalities:
  - Factor where possible.
  - Determine the points where each factor equals zero.
  - Determine what intervals produce results that satisfy the inequality as originally stated.

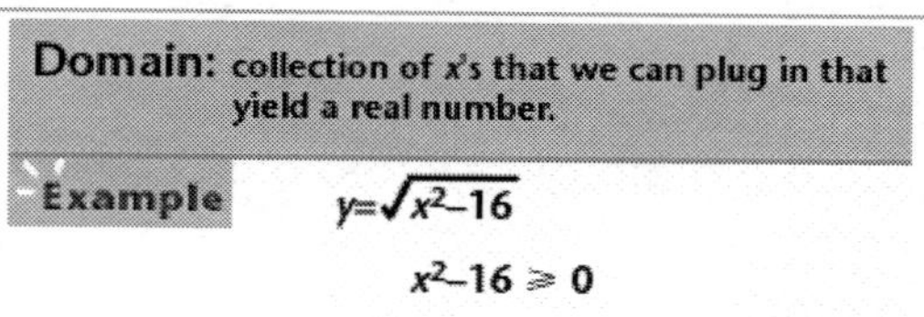

In this type of problem, find out what values of x will help out.

$x^2 - 16$ must be positive, or there is no real number square root. That fact leads to setting up an inequality to solve for x.

(x+4)(x–4) ≥ 0 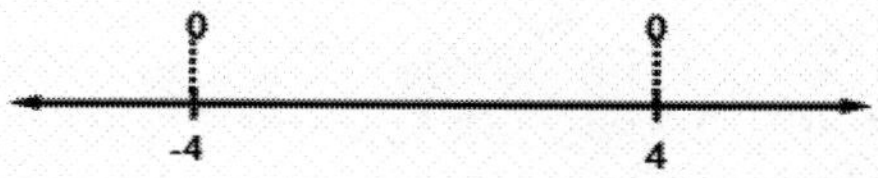 	Resort to the usual inequality tricks: 1. Factor to get $(x + 4)$ and $(x - 4)$. 2. Set each factor equal to 0. 3. Solve for x . 4. Mark those values on a number line. 5. Choose random points from each interval to determine which of them satisfy the inequality: -5 from the left: produces +9, >0; it works. 0 from the middle: produces -16, < 0. +5 from the right: produces +9, >0; it works.
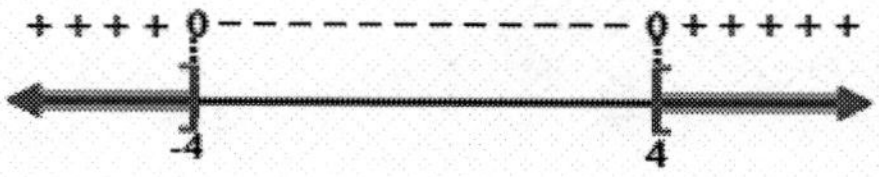 **(-∞, -4] U [4, +∞)**	Mark the left and right intervals as solutions on the number line and include both –4 and +4 because the expression equals 0 at those points. What this means is that values between -4 and +4 have been excluded from the domain of x because they create a negative value under the radical.

Sample problems:

1. Find the domain: $A(y)=\sqrt{y^2-12y+36}$
   Solution: $(-\infty,\infty)$
   Explanation: $A(y)$ is defined wherever the expression under the radical is non-negative. Thus the domain is the solution of the inequality: $y^2-12y+36\geq 0$. Solve for y by factoring, then set each factor equal to zero: $y^2-12y+36=0$; $(y-6)^2=0$; $y=6$. Note this critical value on a number line. Choose a random value from each region and test in $y^2-12y+36\geq 0$. For example, test $y=0$: $0^2-12(0)+36\geq 0$; $0-0+36\geq 0$; $36\geq 0$, this is a true statement so that region is included in the domain. Test a value from the other region, for example $y=7$: $7^2-12(7)+36\geq 0$; $49-84+36\geq 0$ $1\geq 0$, which is also a true statement. Thus, the domain is all real numbers: $(-\infty,\infty)$.

2. Find the domain: $w(x)=\sqrt{\dfrac{x}{2x-5}}$
   Solution: $(-\infty,0]\cup\left(\frac{5}{2},\infty\right)$
   Explanation: The domain is the solution of the inequality $\frac{x}{2x-5}\geq 0$. Find all the values of x where $\frac{x}{2x-5}$ is a) zero or b) undefined: a) $x=0$, b) $2x-5=0$; $2x=5$; $x=\frac{5}{2}$. Note these critical values on a number line. Choose a random value from each region and test in $\frac{x}{2x-5}\geq 0$. The domain is $(-\infty,0]\cup\left(\frac{5}{2},\infty\right)$.

3. Find the domain: $f(x)=\sqrt{\dfrac{x^2-9}{x+4}}$
   Solution: $(-4,-3]\cup[3,\infty)$
   Explanation: The domain is the solution of the inequality $\dfrac{x^2-9}{x+4}\geq 0$.
   Find all values of x where the inequality is a) zero or b) undefined:
   a) $x^2-9=0$; $(x+3)(x-3)=0$; $x+3=0$ or $x-3=0$; $x=-3$ or $x=3$
   b) $x+4=0$; $x\neq -4$.
   Note these critical values on a number line and test the regions.
   The solution set is $(-4,-3]\cup[3,\infty)$

Practice problems: *(Answers on page: 736)*

1. Find the domain: $h(x)=\sqrt{x^2-2x-15}$
2. Find the domain: $f(x)=\sqrt{\dfrac{1-z}{z+2}}$
3. Find the domain: $g(x)=\sqrt{\dfrac{x^2-4x-21}{x-2}}$

Review questions: *(Answers to odd questions on page: 736)*

1. Find the domain of the function: $g(x)=\sqrt{(2x-3)(x-6)}$
2. Find the domain of the function: $f(x)=\sqrt{x^2-25}$.
3. Find the domain of the function: $f(x)=\sqrt{\dfrac{2x-7}{5+3x}}$
4. Find the domain of the function: $g(x)=\sqrt{\dfrac{2x-3}{x+5}}$
5. Find the domain of the function: $f(x)=\sqrt{\dfrac{2x^2-13x-7}{x+2}}$

Matching Number Lines with Absolute Values

- **Absolute value** is the distance a number is from 0 on the number line. It is always positive or equal to 0.
- An **absolute value with a "less than"** statement indicates that all the solution values are between the endpoints approaching 0.
- An **absolute value with a "greater than"** statement indicates that all the solution values are outside the endpoints moving away from 0.
- The solution set for any inequality is shown by a line covering all possible values. The endpoints are shown with hollow dots or parentheses if the endpoints are not included in the solution set. The endpoints are shown with solid dots or square brackets if the endpoints are included in the solution.

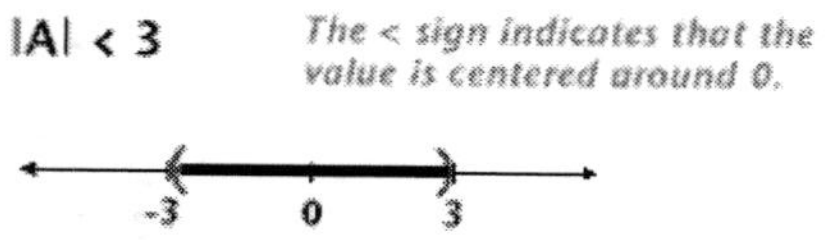	Notice that the solution for this problem is shown by the bold line with the parentheses on –3 and +3. The bold line indicates that any value between –3 and +3 will satisfy the problem. The parentheses show that the endpoints are NOT included in the solution set. The variable can go to any value between –3 and +3 up to, but not including, those endpoints themselves.
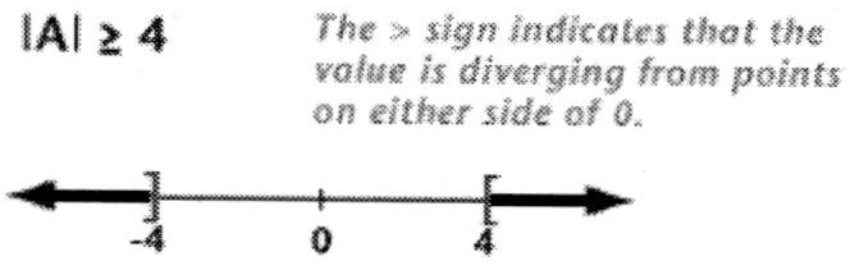	In this problem, you see the bold lines indicating the solution set again. The square brackets on +4 and –4 indicate that they ARE included in the solution set for the problem. So this problem is solved by any value larger than and including +4 or smaller than and including –4.
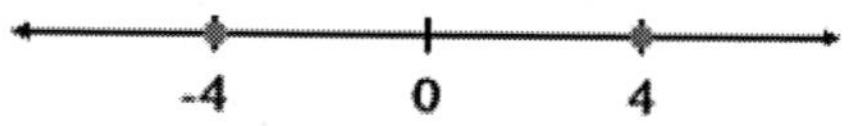	Notice the solid dots here. They tell you that +4 and –4 are included in the solution set. The solid dots are an alternative to the square brackets.
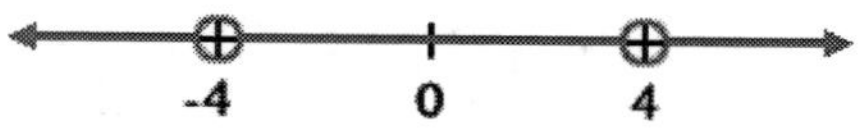	In this case, the hollow circles on +4 and –4 indicate that those values are NOT included in the solution set. They are an alternative to the parentheses.

Sample problems:

1. True or false: The graph of $|x| \geq 3$ is shown below.

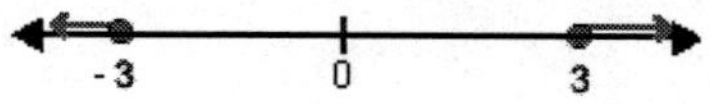

Solution: True
Explanation: An absolute value with a greater than indicates an "or" compound inequality. Express $|x| \geq 3$ as a compound inequality: $x \geq 3$ or $-x \geq 3$. Solve the 2nd inequility for x: $-x \geq 3$; $x \leq -3$. The graph must describe "$x \geq 3$ or $x \leq -3$". Thus, the graph includes 3 and -3 and all values outside these endpoints moving away from 0, which is shown above.

2. True or false: The graph of $|x| < 5$ is shown below.

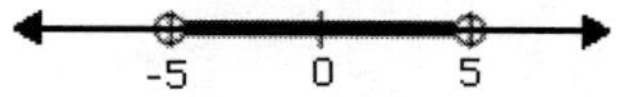

Solution: True
Explanation: Express $|x| < 5$ as an "and" compound inequality: $x < 5$ and $-x < 5$.
Solve the 2nd inequality for $x: -x < 5$; $x > -5$. The graph must describe "$x < 5$ and $x > -5$". Thus, the graph includes all values between -5 and 5, but not including those endpoints, which is shown above.

3. True or false: The graph of $|x| \leq -2$ is shown below.

Solution: False
Explanation: Logically the absolute value of a number can never be negative, and therefore is never less than -2. Thus the solution is the empty set, not the graph above. Expressing $|x| \leq -2$ as an "and" compound inequility will yield the same result.

Practice problems: *(Answers on page: 736)*

1. True or false: The graph of $|x| \leq 0$ is shown below.

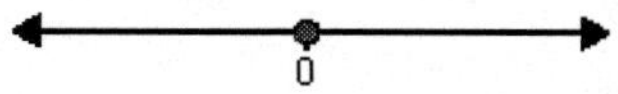

2. True or false: The graph of $|x| < 1$ is shown below.

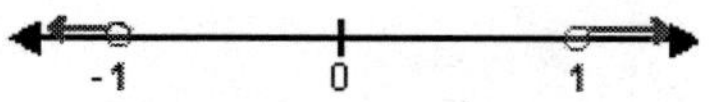

3. True or false: The graph of $|x| > 10$ is shown below.

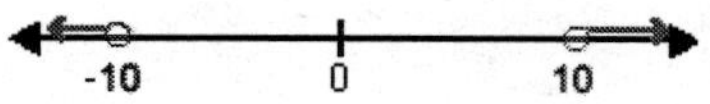

Review questions: *(Answers to odd questions on page: 736)*

1. True or false: The graph of $|x| \geq 5$ is shown below.

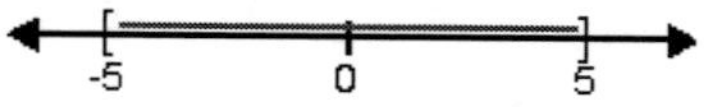

2. True or false: The graph of $|x| < 0$ is shown below.

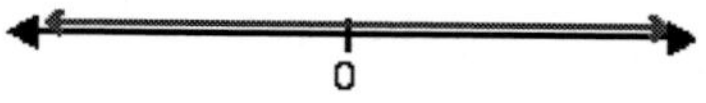

3. True or false: The graph of $|x| = 1$ is shown below.

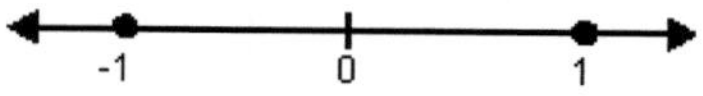

4. True or false: The graph of $|x| \neq 10$ is shown below.

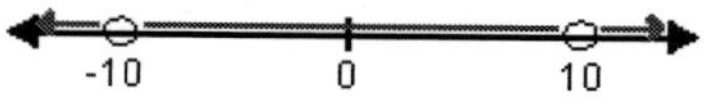

5. True or false: The graph of $|x| = -10$ is shown below.

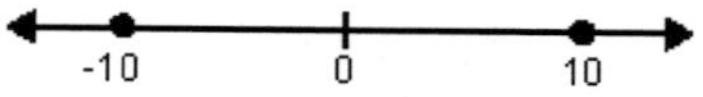

Solving Absolute Value Equations

- The **absolute value** of a number states how far that number lies on the number line from 0. It does not indicate in which direction the number lies; i.e., whether it is positive or negative.
- The notation for absolute value places a vertical line on each side of the variable, number or expression for which absolute value is denoted; e.g., $|x|$ indicates "absolute value of x."
- If the absolute value of a number is equal to a value, you know that the number lies that many units from 0 in one direction or the other.

If: $\|A\| = ?$ Then: $A = ?$ or $A = -?$ *there are two possible values of A* **Example** $\|3x - 1\| = 2$ *set up two equations* $3x - 1 = 2$ or $3x - 1 = -2$ $3x = 3$ $3x = -1$ $x = 1$ $x = \frac{-1}{3}$	The **absolute value** in this case indicates that the expression (3*x* - 1) equals +2 or –2. You must solve for both. Set up the equations for each possibility. Solve for *x* in each equation.
$\|3(1) - 1\| = 2$ $\|3(-\frac{1}{3}) - 1\| = 2$ $\|3 - 1\| = 2$ $\|-1 - 1\| = 2$ $\|2\| = 2$ $\|-2\| = 2$	When you substitute each of these values into the expression, you find that both work. When $x = 1$, your expression is $\|2\|$ which is 2. When $x = -1/3$, your expression is $\|-2\|$ which is also 2.

Example $\left\lvert \frac{5}{x-3} \right\rvert = 10$ *set up two equations* $\frac{5}{x-3} = \frac{10}{1}$ or $\frac{5}{x-3} = \frac{-10}{1}$ $10(x-3) = 5$ $-10(x-3) = 5$ $10x - 30 = 5$ $-10x + 30 = 5$ $10x = 35$ $-10x = -25$ $x = \frac{35}{10} = \boxed{\frac{7}{2}}$ $x = \frac{25}{10} = \boxed{\frac{5}{2}}$	The process is the same with this example. However, you will have additional steps because of the rational expression. Set up both equations. Cross multiply to eliminate the denominators. Solve for x. Remember to check your answers.

Sample problems:

1. Solve for w: $|w-3| = -1$
   Solution: No solutions
   Explanation: This equation has no solutions since the absolute value must always be non-negative. If the equation is solved, the solutions are $w = 2$ or $w = 4$. But, neither value works in the equation

2. Solve for x: $\left\lvert \frac{x+1}{4} \right\rvert = 2$
   Solution: 7 or -9
   Explanation: Set up the equation for the positive possibility: $\frac{x+1}{4} = 2$. Solve for x: $x+1 = 8$; $x = 7$. Set up the equation for the negative possibility: $\frac{x+1}{4} = -2$. Solve for x: $x+1 = -8$; $x = -9$.

3. Solve for x: $|x^3| = 8$
   Solution: -2 or 2
   Explanation: Set up the two equations and solve each for x: $x^3 = 8$; $x = \sqrt[3]{8}$; $x = 2$, or $x^3 = -8$; $x = \sqrt[3]{-8}$; $x = -2$. Thus, $x = 2$ or $x = -2$.

Practice problems: *(Answers on page: 736)*

1. Solve for y: $\left\lvert \frac{3(1-x)}{5} \right\rvert = 6$

2. Solve for z: $\left\lvert \frac{4}{z-1} \right\rvert = 2$

3. Solve for w: $54 = |2x^3|$

Review questions: *(Answers to odd questions on page: 736)*

1. Solve for x: $|x| = 17$

2. Solve for z: $|z-6| = 6$

3. Solve for w: $\left\lvert \frac{3-w}{7} \right\rvert = 1$

4. Solve for x: $\left\lvert \frac{2}{2x+1} \right\rvert = 3$

5. Solve for y: $\left\lvert \frac{y-5}{3} \right\rvert = 2$

Solving Equations with Two Absolute Value Expressions

- Some equations have two absolute value expressions in them. Once you have tried all the possible combinations, you will find there are only two distinct equations involved.
- Set up your two possible equations and solve for the variable.
- Check your answers in the original absolute value equation.

Consider an Equation with Two Absolute Values

$$|3 - 2x| = |5 - 4x|$$

set up two equations

$$3 - 2x = 5 - 4x \quad \text{or} \quad 3 - 2x = -(5 - 4x)$$

$$2x + 3 = 5 \qquad 3 - 2x = -5 + 4x$$

$$2x = 2 \qquad -6x = -8$$

$$\boxed{x = 1} \qquad x = \frac{8}{6} \qquad \boxed{x = \frac{4}{3}}$$

Your problem has two absolute value expressions.

Create your two equations to handle all the combinations.

Solve for x.

Absolute Value of a Fraction

$$\left|\frac{3A - 4}{2A + 3}\right| = 1$$

set up two equations

$$\frac{3A - 4}{2A + 3} = \frac{1}{1} \quad \text{or} \quad \frac{3A - 4}{2A + 3} = -1$$

$$3A - 4 = 2A + 3 \qquad 3A - 4 = -(2A + 3)$$

$$\boxed{A = 7} \qquad 3A - 4 = -2A - 3$$

$$5A = 1$$

$$\boxed{A = \frac{1}{5}}$$

Again you have two absolute value expressions. In this example, however, they compose a rational expression.

Set up your two equations.

Solve for your variable, in this case A, in each equation.

$A = 7$ ✔

$$\left|\frac{3(7) - 4}{2(7) + 3}\right| = 1 \qquad \left|\frac{21 - 4}{14 + 3}\right| = 1 \qquad \left|\frac{17}{17}\right| = 1 \qquad |1| = 1$$

$A = \frac{1}{5}$ ✔

$$\left|\frac{3(1/5) - 4}{2(1/5) + 3}\right| = 1 \qquad \left|\frac{(3/5 - 4)5}{(2/5 + 3)5}\right| = 1 \qquad \left|\frac{3 - 20}{2 + 15}\right| = 1 \qquad \left|\frac{-17}{17}\right| = 1 \quad |-1| = 1$$

Remember to check your work. This, as always, is one of the most important steps for your accuracy.

One at a time, substitute each of your values for A, 7 and 1/5, into the original equation and see if you get a true statement with either, none or both of them.

Sample problems:

1. Solve for x: $|4x - 9| = |7x + 2|$

   Solution: $\frac{7}{11}$ or $-\frac{11}{3}$

   Explanation: Set up the equation for the positive possibility: $4x - 9 = 7x + 2$. Solve for x: $-3x - 9 = 2$; $-3x = 11$; $x = -\frac{11}{3}$. Set up the equation for the negative possibility: $4x - 9 = -(7x + 2)$. Solve for x: $4x - 9 = -7x - 2$; $11x - 9 = -2$; $11x = 7$; $x = \frac{7}{11}$.

2. Solve for x: $\left|\frac{5x + 1}{6 - x}\right| = 4$

   Solution: $\frac{23}{9}$ or -25

   Explanation: Set up the equation for the positive possibility: $\frac{5x+1}{6-x} = 4$. Multiply both sides by $6 - x$ and solve for x: $5x + 1 = 4(6 - x)$; $5x + 1 = 24 - 4x$; $9x + 1 = 24$; $9x = 23$; $x = \frac{23}{9}$. Set up the equation for the negative possibility: $\frac{5x+1}{6-x} = -4$. Solve for x: $5x + 1 = -4(6 - x)$; $5x + 1 = -24 + 4x$; $x + 1 = -24$; $x = -25$.

3. Solve for x: $|x^2+6x-20| = |x^2|$

   Solution: -5, 2, or $\frac{10}{3}$

   Explanation: Set up the positive possibility: $x^2+6x-20 = x^2$. Subtract x^2 from each side and continue to solve for x: $6x-20=0$; $6x=20$; $x=\frac{20}{6}=\frac{10}{3}$. Set up the negative possibility: $x^2+6x-20=-x^2$. Add x^2 to both sides: $2x^2+6x-20=0$. Divide the equation by 2: $x^2+3x-10=0$. Factor and solve for x: $(x+5)(x-2)=0$; $x+5=0$ or $x-2=0$; $x=-5$ or $x=2$.

Practice problems: *(Answers on page: 736)*

1. Solve for y: $|y+2| = |3y-1|$
2. Solve for x: $\left|\frac{2x+4}{x-7}\right| = 1$
3. Solve for x: $|2x^2+4x-8| = |2x^2|$

Review questions: *(Answers to odd questions on page: 737)*

1. Solve for x: $|x+1| = |x-3|$
2. Solve for w: $|w+4| = |2w+14|$
3. Solve for p: $\left|\frac{p-1}{4-p}\right| = 2$
4. Solve for x: $\left|\frac{7x-3}{2x+1}\right| = 5$
5. Solve for v: $\left|\frac{v+7}{6v-1}\right| = -1$

Solving Absolute Value Inequalities

- **Absolute values** within inequalities are best discerned using a number line graph. Sketch one out for each problem so you can visually study the possibilities.
- If the absolute value is less than the value stated, your absolute value expression will be greater than the negative value and smaller than the positive value stated; i.e., **|A| < B means -B < A < B**. The expression's value is inside the boundaries set by the positive and negative value of the inequality.
- If the absolute value is greater than the value stated, your absolute value expression will be smaller than the negative value and larger than the positive value stated; i.e., **|A| > B means A < -B or A > B**. The expression's value is outside the boundaries set by the positive and negative value of the inequality.

Example $|3x+1| \geq 7$ 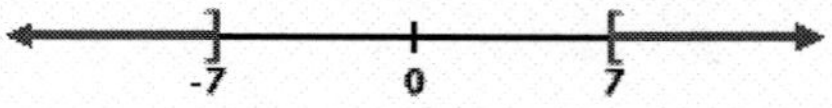 $3x+1 \geq 7$ or $3x+1 \leq -7$	Because the absolute value is greater than or equal to the stated value of 7, its solutions lie outside the boundaries set at –7 and +7. This fact creates the two equations to solve.
$3x+1 \geq 7$ or $3x+1 \leq -7$ $3x \geq 6$ $3x \leq -8$ $x \geq \frac{6}{3}$ $\boxed{x \leq \frac{-8}{3}}$ $\boxed{x \geq 2}$	Solve the two equations. Remember to check your answers to be sure they work in the original equation.

$|A| < B$ can be converted to $-B < A < B$
$|A| > B$ can be converted to $A > B$ or $A < -B$

Example

$$|6x + 4| < 1$$

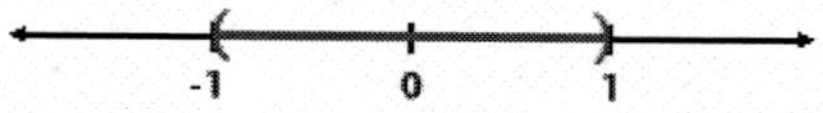

$$-1 < 6x + 4 < 1$$
$$-4 \quad -4 \quad -4$$
$$\frac{-5}{6} < \frac{6x}{6} < \frac{-3}{6}$$
$$\boxed{\frac{-5}{6} < x < \frac{-1}{2}}$$

In a "less than" inequality, all the possible solutions for the absolute value expression $|6x + 4|$ will lie within the boundaries set at -1 and +1.

This sets up your two equations. Notice that in this problem you've used an alternate notation showing two relationships within one sentence. This is sometimes used to save writing. Be sure your thinking stays accurate as you work towards your solutions.

Remember to check your answers.

Sample problems:

1. Solve for x: $|2+3x| \le 11$

   Solution: $-\frac{13}{3} \le x \le 3$

   Explanation: Use the fact that "$|A| > B$ can be converted to $-B < A < B$" to convert $|2+3x| \le 11$ into a compound inequality: $-11 \le 2+3x \le 11$. Solve for x by applying each solving step to all three sides: $-11 \le 2+3x \le 11$; $-13 \le 3x \le 9$; $-\frac{13}{3} \le x \le 3$.

2. Solve for x: $|5-4x| \le 19$

   Solution: $-\frac{7}{2} \le x \le 6$

   Explanation: Convert $|5-4x| \le 19$ into a compound inequality: $-19 \le 5-4x \le 19$.
   To solve for x, subtract 5 from each side: $-19 \le 5-4x \le 19$; $-24 \le -4x \le 14$.
   Divide each side by -4 and reverse the inequality: $-24 \le -4x \le 14$; $6 \ge x \ge -\frac{14}{4}$.
   Reduce the fraction and rewrite the compound inequality beginning with the smallest endpoint:
   $6 \ge x \ge -\frac{14}{4}$; $-\frac{7}{2} \le x \le 6$.

3. Solve for x: $|6x-5+6-8x| \ge 7$

   Solution: $x \le -3$ or $x \ge 4$

   Explanation: Simplify inside the absolute value: $|6x-5+6-8x| \ge 7$; $|1-2x| \ge 7$. Use the fact that "$|A| > B$ can be converted to $A > B$ or $A < -B$" to convert $|1-2x| \ge 7$ into a compound inequality:
   $1-2x \ge 7$ or $1-2x \ge -7$. Solve each inequality for x:
   $1-2x \ge 7$; $-2x \ge 6$; $x \le -3$, or
   $1-2x \le -7$; $-2x \le -8$; $x \ge 4$.

Practice problems: *(Answers on page: 737)*

1. Solve for w: $|5-2w| \ge 21$
2. Solve for y: $|6-y| \le 1$
3. Solve for x: $|6(1-x)| \ge 14$

Review questions: *(Answers to odd questions on page: 737)*

1. Solve for v: $|v| \le 1$

2. Solve for z: $|z-1|<3$
3. Solve for x: $3|2x-1|\geq 15$
4. Solve for x: $|7x+6|>10$
5. Solve for x: $|3-5x|\leq 7$

Solving Absolute Value Inequalities: More Examples

- The best way to work with absolute value inequalities is to think through what each one means and graph out the range of solutions on a number line.
- **Remember:** When an equation offers an absolute value expression in relationship with other terms in addition to the inequality, isolate the absolute value before setting up your solution possibilities.
- Any absolute value will be positive or equal to zero.

Example $|5y+2|-4<10$ *isolate the absolute value* $|5y+2|<14$	First add +4 to both sides to isolate the absolute value.
	Graphically show what the possibilities are. In this case, because you are given a "<" inequality, all possible solutions are between the boundaries of –14 and +14.
$-14<5y+2<14$	Set up your equation for your two possible relationships.
$-14<5y+2<14$ $-2 \quad\quad -2 \quad -2$ $\frac{-16}{5}<\frac{5y}{5}<\frac{12}{5}$ $\boxed{\frac{-16}{5}<y<\frac{12}{5}}$	Solve your two equations for two answers. **Remember:** Check your answers to be sure they give you true statements when substituted into the original problem.
Example Solve the Inequality *This value can be any number except 0.* $|2x-6|>0$ $2x-6\neq 0$ $2x\neq 6$ $x\neq 3$ Therefore, x = all real numbers except 3	This one allows a different procedure. Since you know $|2x-6|$ is greater than 0, $(2x-6)$ must be either greater or less than 0. For sure, $(2x-6)$ does NOT equal 0. If you set up the sentence as shown and solve it, you get all your solution possibilities quickly.
...Or, You Could Solve It This Way  $2x-6<0$ or $2x-6>0$ $2x<6 \quad\quad 2x>6$ $x<3 \quad\quad x>3$ Therefore, x = all real numbers except 3	Here is the same problem worked the way you have worked the other problems. $(2x-6)$ is either greater than 0 or less than 0, so you set up the two equations. Solving those equations, you find your set of solutions.

Sample problems:

1. Solve for x: $\frac{1}{3}|1-2x|-7 \geq 6$

   Solution: $x \leq -19$ or $x \geq 20$

   Explanation: Isolate the absolute value: $\frac{1}{3}|1-2x|-7 \geq 6$; $\frac{1}{3}|1-2x| \geq 13$; $|1-2x| \geq 39$.
   Convert the absoute value inequality into a compound inequality: $1-2x \geq 39$ or $1-2x \leq -39$.
   Solve each inequality for x:
   $1-2x \geq 39$; $-2x \geq 38$; $x \leq -19$
   $1-2x \leq -39$; $-2x \leq -40$; $x \geq 20$.

2. Solve for x: $5-4|2x+3| \geq -7$

   Solution: $-3 \leq x \leq 0$

   Explanation: Isolate the absolute value: $5-4|2x+3| \geq -7$; $-4|2x+3| \geq -12$.
   Divide each side by -4 and reverse the inequality: $-4|2x+3| \geq -12$; $|2x+3| \leq 3$.
   Convert the absolute value inequality into a compound inequality and solve for x:
   $-3 \leq 2x+3 \leq 3$; $-6 \leq 2x \leq 0$; $-3 \leq x \leq 0$.

3. Solve for x: $3-\frac{2}{5}|8-6x| \geq -1$

   Solution: $-\frac{1}{3} \leq x \leq 3$

   Explanation: Isolate the absolute value: $3-\frac{2}{5}|8-6x| \geq -1$; $-\frac{2}{5}|8-6x| \geq -4$. Multiply both sides by $-\frac{5}{2}$ and reverse the inequality: $|8-6x| \leq -4(-\frac{5}{2})$; $|8-6x| \leq 10$. Convert the absolute value inequality into a compound inequality and solve for x: $-10 \leq 8-6x \leq 10$; $-18 \leq -6x \leq 2$; $3 \geq x \geq -\frac{1}{3}$.

Practice problems: *(Answers on page: 737)*

1. Solve for x: $1-\frac{1}{3}|2x+5| \geq -8$
2. Solve for x: $2|5x+1|-3 > 15$
3. Solve for x: $1-\frac{3}{4}|5-2x| \leq 0$

Review questions: *(Answers to odd questions on page: 737)*

1. Solve for x: $2|x-1| < 6$
2. Solve for x: $3|2-x| < 6$
3. Solve for p: $|p-3|+2 \geq 9$
4. Solve for x: $\frac{1}{4}|3x-1|-1 \leq 4$
5. Solve for y: $\left|7y+\frac{2}{3}\right|-\frac{1}{3} > \frac{4}{3}$

3

Relations and Functions

Using the Cartesian System

- ***x*-Axis**: The horizontal scale for measuring change on a graph.
- ***y*-Axis**: The vertical scale for measuring change on a graph.
- **Origin**: The point where the two scales cross and both have a value of 0. The coordinates of the origin are **(0,0)**.
- **Cartesian Plane**: The name for the system that uses the *x*- and *y*-axes.
- **Quadrants**: The four areas that are created by drawing *x*- and *y*-axes on a plane.
- **Ordered Pairs**: The address of each point. It states the *x*-value first, then the *y*-value **(*x*,*y*)**. By using this protocol, everyone in the world knows to start at the origin, (0,0) and move sideways as indicated by the ***x*-value** and vertically as indicated by the ***y*-value**.

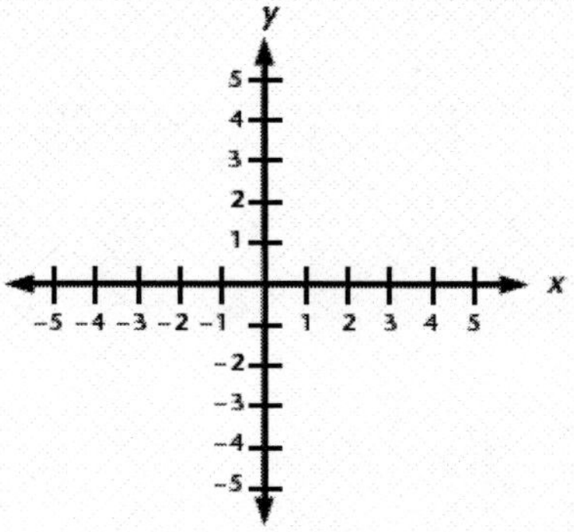

The ***x*-Axis** is a horizontal number line. It measures to the right positively and to the left negatively.

The ***y*-Axis** vertical number line. It measures up positively and down negatively.

Where these two line cross is called the **Origin**. Its address is **(0,0)**.

This system is called a **Cartesian plane** because a mathematician named Descartes invented it.

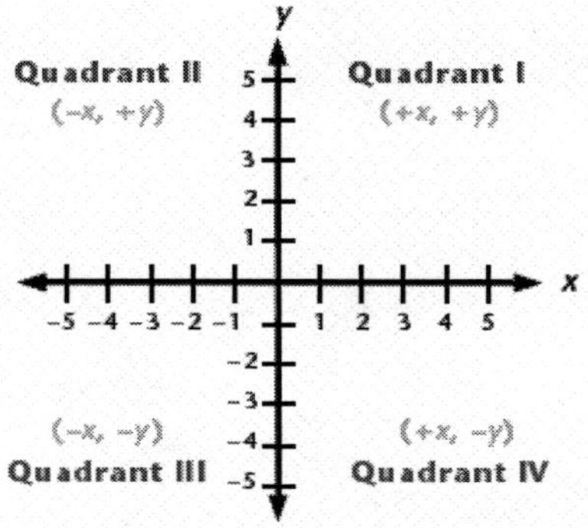

The two axes divide the plane into four areas, or quadrants.

Quadrant I contains all points where the *x* and *y* coordinates are positive.

Quadrant II contains all points where the *x* coordinates are negative and the *y* coordinates are positive.

Quadrant III contains all points where the *x* and *y* coordinates are negative.

Quadrant IV contains all points where the *x* coordinates are positve and the *y* coodinates are negative.

Example

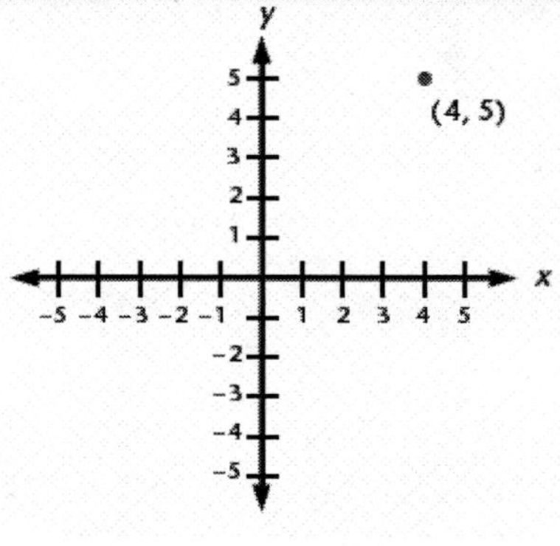

A point's location is stated with a number showing how far horizontally from the origin the point is located, and a second number showing how far vertically the point is from the origin. The information is always horizontal (*x*) first, and vertical (*y*) second: (*x*,*y*). That's why it's called "ordered."

Plotting points is a matter of counting from the origin, (0,0), the indicated distance horizontally and vertically and plotting your point to mark the spot.

Sample problems:

1. In what quadrant is the point (−4, 7) located?
   Solution: Quadrant II
   Explanation: The point (−4, 7) is located 4 units to the left of the origin and then 7 units up from the *x*-axis, which is in quadrant II.

2. What are the coordinates of a point located in the third quadrant 5 units from each axis?
   Solution: $(-5,-5)$
   Explanation: Points in quadrant III have negative x and y values. So, a point in quadrant III that is five units from each axis will have the coordinates $(-5,-5)$.

3. What are the coordinates of the resulting point when $(-3,7)$ is reflected across the x-axis?
   Solution: $(-3,-7)$
   Explanation: A reflection across the x-axis changes only the y-coordinate, so the x-coordinate is still -3. The y-coordinate has the opposite sign. Thus, the result of reflecting $(-3,7)$ across the x-axis is $(-3,-7)$.

Practice problems: *(Answers on page: 737)*

1. True or false: The point below is located at $(-8,-12)$.

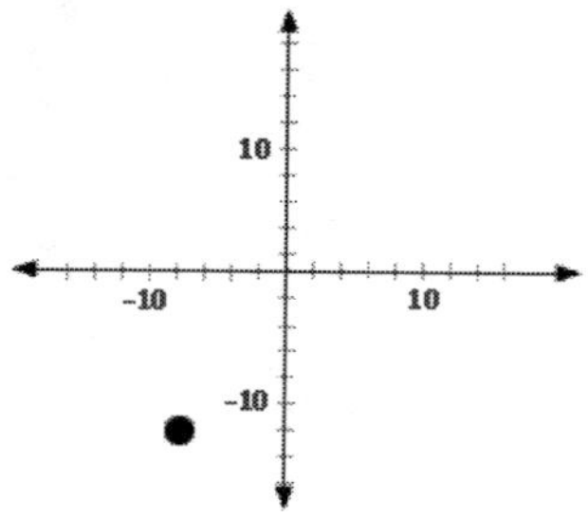

2. In what quadrant is the point $(10.3,-0.2)$ located?
3. What are the coordinates of a point located in the second quadrant and 2 units away from each axis?

Review questions: *(Answers to odd questions on page: 737)*

1. True or false: The point below is located at $(1,-2)$.

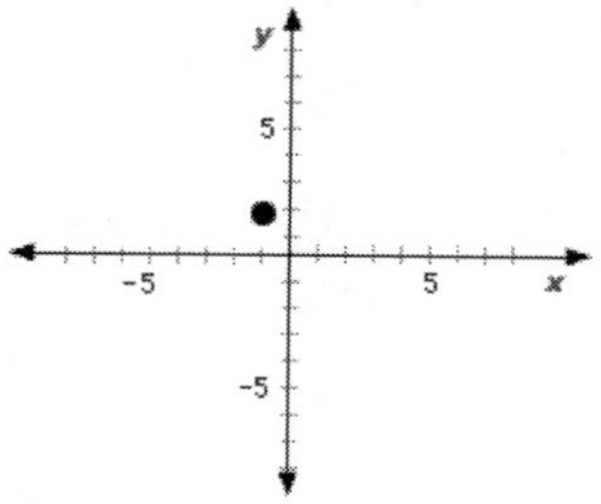

2. True or false: The point below is located at $(-10,10)$.

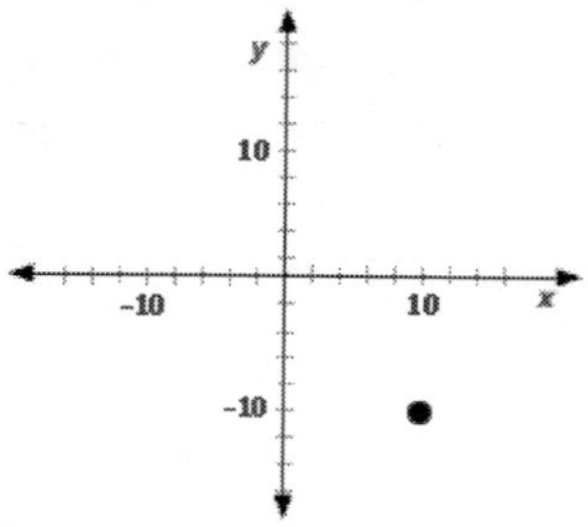

3. What are the coordinates of a point located in the fourth quadrant and 5 units away from each axis?
4. What are the coordinates of a point located in the third quadrant and 4 units away from each axis?
5. In what quadrant does the point $(3,-7)$ lie?

Thinking Visually

- An **axis** is the scale which measures the distance along one dimension, either width, height, or depth.
- The **origin** is the point where the axes of a system intersect.
- A **horizontal axis** measures horizontal distance from the origin on a plane. It is usually designated by x and is referred to as the x-axis.
- A **vertical axis** measures vertical distance from the origin on a plane. It is usually designated by y and is referred to as the y-axis.
- A **plane** is a level surface usually considered to have width and height but no depth. A plane is created whenever two axes intersect.
- A **point** is a specific location with no width, height, or depth on a surface. Its designation and location are given by the ordered pair (x,y) which gives the measurements for both its horizontal and its vertical location from the origin on the plane.
- **Plotting a point** is the process of locating a point on an axis system.
- A **line** is the straight path that passes through and beyond two specific points.
- A **circle** is a completely symmetrical figure which is composed of all the points a fixed distance from a specific point.

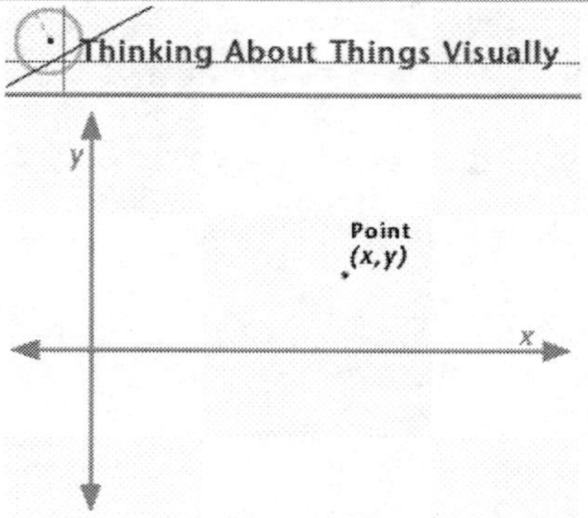

Most of our graphing is done on a **plane** (level surface) with an x-axis and an y-axis. The distance is measured from the **origin**.

Any point can be located by stating its coordinates (x,y) which describe its location as x units from the origin horizontally and then y units vertically.

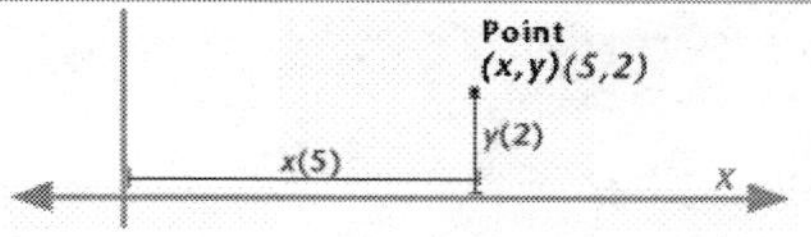

For example, this is the point (5,2). That means it is located horizontally 5 units to the right of the origin and vertically 2 units above the origin.

Only one point will have this exact location.

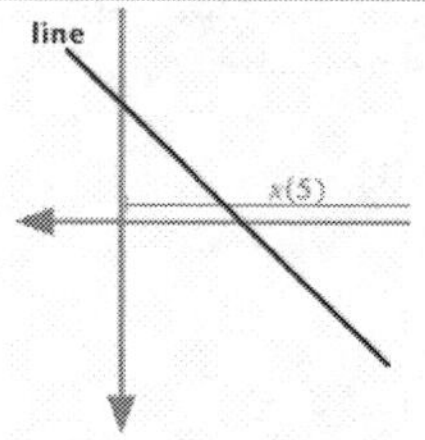

You can also graph a line. Each line has a graph which describes its unique path across the axis system.

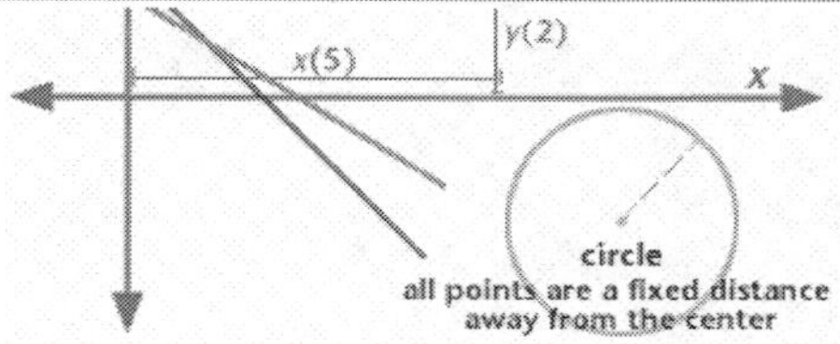

We can also find an equation for figures on the axis plane. In this example, a **circle** is shown. It will have an equation that uniquely describes its size and location on the surface.

Finding the Distance between Two Points

- **Distance formula**:

  $d = \sqrt{(x_2 - x_1)^2 + (y_2 - y_1)^2}$
- The distance formula is an application of the Pythagorean Theorem, which states that the hypotenuse of a right triangle equals the square root of the sum of the other sides squared.
- **Midpoint formula**:

  $(\frac{x_1 + x_2}{2}, \frac{y_1 + y_2}{2})$
- The midpoint formula determines the point in the middle of the line segment formed by 2 points.

What is the distance between the two points?

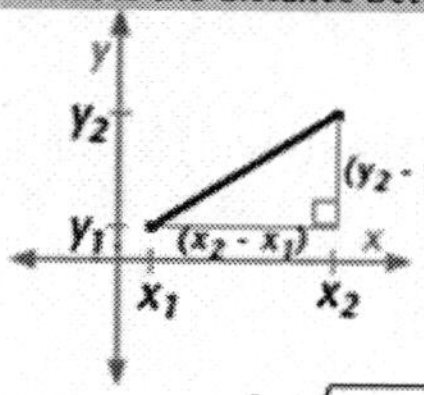

$d = \sqrt{(x_2 - x_1)^2 + (y_2 - y_1)^2}$

Draw your given line segment first.

Then draw a vertical line from one end and a horizontal line from the other end. This creates a right triangle.

The length of the triangle's horizontal side can be found by taking the difference of the two x-values because they measure horizontal movement.

The length of the vertical side can be found by taking the difference of the two y-values because they measure vertical movement.

Now, using the Pythagorean Theorem,
(first side)^2 + (second side)^2 = (hypotenuse)^2.
$(x_2 - x_1)^2 + (y_2 - y_1)^2 = d^2$. So,
$d = \sqrt{(x_2 - x_1)^2 + (y_2 - y_1)^2}$

Example Find the distance between two points

(6,4) and (-8,11)

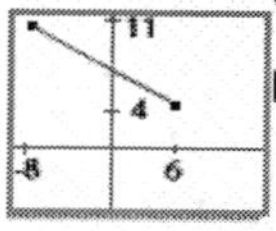

$\text{Dist.} = \sqrt{(6 - -8)^2 + (4 - 11)^2}$

$= \sqrt{14^2 + (-7)^2}$

$= \sqrt{196 + 49}$

$= \sqrt{245} = 15.65$

Now that you know the formula, just substitute in the values from each point and solve for your length.

It doesn't matter which point is identified as (x_1,y_1) and (x_2,y_2).

In this case (6, 4) is (x_2,y_2).

Example Find the midpoint

(1, -1) and (5,5)

$\text{Midpoint} = (\frac{1+5}{2}, \frac{-1+5}{2})$

$= (\frac{6}{2}, \frac{4}{2}) = (3,2)$

Finding the midpoint of a line segment means finding the average between the two endpoints:

Add the x-values and divide by 2.

Add the y-values and divide by 2.

These answers are the ordered pair of your midpoint.

Sample problems:

1. Given the points $P=(3,10)$ and $Q=(-1,0)$, find the length of the line segment from P to Q.
   Solution: 10.8
   Explanation: Use the distance formula, $d=\sqrt{(x_2-x_1)^2+(y_2-y_1)^2}$, to find the length of a line segment. Substitute the x and y values into the formula and simplify:
   $d=\sqrt{(-1-3)^2+(0-10)^2}=\sqrt{(-4)^2+(-10)^2}=\sqrt{116}=10.8.$
   In this case point Q was identified as (x_2,y_2). Notice that identifying P as (x_2,y_2) yields the same distance: $d=\sqrt{(3--1)^2+(10-0)^2}=\sqrt{116}=10.8.$

2. Given the points $A=(-4,10)$ and $B=(2,-6)$, find the coordinates of the point that is one-fourth of the distance from A to B.
   Solution: $\left(-\frac{5}{2},6\right)$
   Explanation: To find the point that is $\frac{1}{4}$ of the distance from A to B first find the midpoint, C, then find the midpoint between A and C. First, substitute the x and y values from A and B into the midpoint formula: $\left(\frac{x_1+x_2}{2},\frac{y_1+y_2}{2}\right)\Rightarrow\left(\frac{-4+2}{2},\frac{10+-6}{2}\right)=(-1,2)=C.$
   Next substitute the x and y values from A and C into the midpoint formula: $\left(\frac{-4+-1}{2},\frac{10+2}{2}\right)=\left(-\frac{5}{2},6\right).$

3. A soccer player kicks a ball from the point (10, 12) towards the point (50, 40), but an opponent stops the ball when it is only half way to its destination. How far is the blocker from the kicker? Assume the units are in yards.

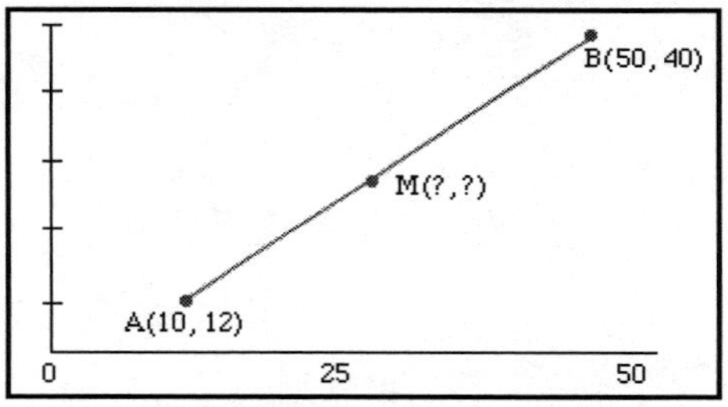

   Solution: 24.4 yards
   Explanation: First, find the coordinates of the midpoint: $\left(\frac{10+50}{2},\frac{12+40}{2}\right)=(30,26).$
   Then use the distance formula to compute the distance from $A(10,12)$ to the midpoint $(30,26)$: $d=\sqrt{(30-10)^2+(26-12)^2}=\sqrt{20^2+14^2}=\sqrt{400+196}=\sqrt{596}=24.4.$

Practice problems: *(Answers on page: 737)*

1. Given the points $A=(-3.4,\ -2.7)$ and $B=(10.5,\ -7.8)$ find the length of the line segment from A to B.
2. Given the points $A=(3\sqrt{2},-2\sqrt{5})$ and $B=(-2\sqrt{2},3\sqrt{5})$, find the distance between A and B.
3. Find the midpoint of the segment AB.

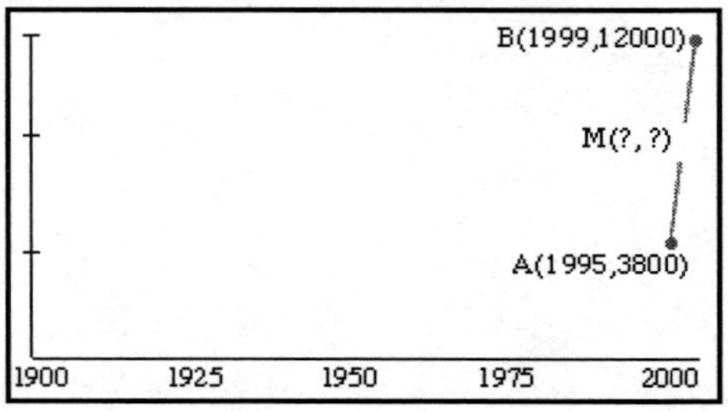

Review questions: *(Answers to odd questions on page: 737)*

1. Find the midpoint between the two intercepts of a line if the intercepts are $(-6,0)$ and $(0,-14)$.
2. Find the distance between the two points $(-3,11)$ and $(4,-15)$.
3. Find the length of the line segment between the points $(12.1,-1.1)(-4.7,3.3)$.
4. Find the distance between the points $(2.2,3.5)$ and $(1.5,0.9)$.
5. Find the distance between the points $(-3.4,-2.7)$ and $(10.5,-7.8)$.

Finding the Second Endpoint of a Segment

- **Midpoint formula**: $\left(\frac{x_1+x_2}{2}, \frac{y_1+y_2}{2}\right)$
- Any point's location is given by the ordered pair (x,y) where x measures horizontal distance from the origin and y measures vertical distance from the origin.

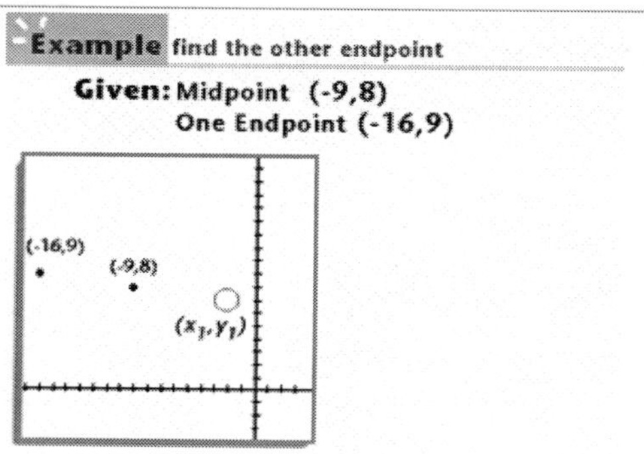

If you are given an endpoint and a midpoint, you set up a generic point for the second end. Label this point as (x_1,y_1). It always helps to sketch a graph so you can visually understand the situation you are working with.

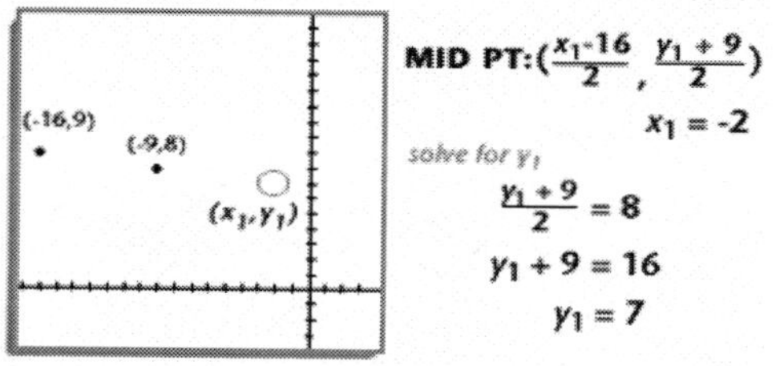

Now use the **midpoint formula**. Substitute in your values and solve for the missing x and y.

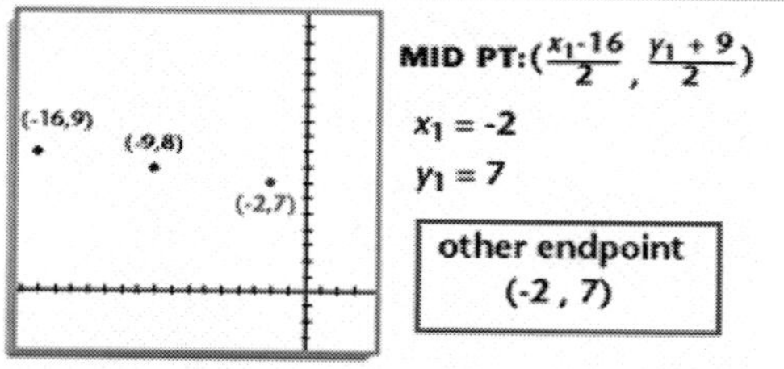

Once you find the missing x and y, you can set the ordered pair for the endpoint and graph it.

Sample problems:

1. The point $(4,-2)$ is the midpoint of line segment AB. If the coordinates of B are $\left(\frac{2}{3},-\frac{1}{2}\right)$, find the coordinates of A.

   Solution: $\left(\frac{22}{3},-\frac{7}{2}\right)$

   Explanation: Let the coordinates of A be (x,y).

   Use the midpoint formula to write two equations: $\dfrac{x+\frac{2}{3}}{2}=4$ and $\dfrac{y+-\frac{1}{2}}{2}=-2$.

   Solve for x: $\dfrac{x+\frac{2}{3}}{2}=4;\ x+\frac{2}{3}=8;\ 3x+2=24;\ 3x=22;\ x=\frac{22}{3}$.

   Solve for y: $\dfrac{y+-\frac{1}{2}}{2}=-2;\ y-\frac{1}{2}=-4;\ 2y-1=-8;\ 2y=-7;\ y=-\frac{7}{2}$.

   The coordinates of point A are $\left(\frac{22}{3},-\frac{7}{2}\right)$.

2. The point $(5,3)$ is the midpoint of (a,b) and $(-4,2)$. Find the value of value of $a+b$.

   Solution: 18

   Explanation: Use the midpoint formula to write two equations: $\frac{-4+a}{2}=5$ and $\frac{2+b}{2}=3$.

   Solve for a: $\frac{-4+a}{2}=5;\ -4+a=10;\ a=14$. Solve for b: $\frac{2+b}{2}=3;\ 2+b=6;\ b=4$.

   The value for $a+b$ is $14+4=18$.

3. The point $\left(2w,\frac{1}{2}w+4\right)$ is the midpoint of line segment PQ. If the coordinates of P are $(3w,7)$, find the coordinates of Q.

   Solution: $(w,w+1)$

   Explanation: Let the coordinates of Q be (x,y). Use the midpoint formula to write two equations: $\dfrac{3w+x}{2}=2w$ and $\dfrac{7+y}{2}=\frac{1}{2}w+4$. Solve for x: $\dfrac{3w+x}{2}=2w$; $3w+x=4w;\ x=w$. Solve for y: $\dfrac{7+y}{2}=\frac{1}{2}w+4;\ 7+y=w+8;\ y=w+1$.

   Thus, the coordinates of Q are $(w,w+1)$.

Practice problems: *(Answers on page: 737)*

1. The point $\left(\frac{11}{4},-\frac{1}{2}\right)$ is the midpoint of line segment AB. If the coordinates of A are $(5,0)$, find the coordinates of B.
2. The point $(3,-1)$ is the midpoint of (x,y) and $(-1,1)$. Find the value of value of $x-y$.
3. The point $\left(n+\frac{3}{2},2n\right)$ is the midpoint of line segment PQ. If the coordinates of P are $(2-n,5n)$, find the coordinates of Q.

Review questions: *(Answers to odd questions on page: 737)*

1. The point $\left(-\frac{3}{4},7\right)$ is the midpoint of line segment AB. If the coordinates of A are $\left(-\frac{5}{2},2\right)$, find the coordinates of B.
2. The point $(-1,2)$ is the midpoint of (x,y) and $(6,0)$. Find the value of value of $\frac{x}{y}$.
3. The point $\left(\frac{3}{2},0\right)$ is the midpoint of (x,y) and $(5,1)$. Find the value of value of $y-x$.
4. The point $(d,d+1)$ is the midpoint of line segment AB. If the coordinates of A are $(3-d,5d)$, find the coordinates of B.

5. The point $\left(\frac{1}{2}-\frac{1}{6}z, \frac{1}{4}z+\frac{5}{2}\right)$ is the midpoint of line segment AB. If the coordinates of A are $\left(1-z, \frac{1}{2}z+5\right)$, find the coordinates of B.

Collinearity and Distance

- Points that fall on the same line are **collinear** points.
- Three points are collinear if, for some pair of lengths between two points, their sum is equal to the remaining third length between two points.
- Three points are not collinear if, for every pair of lengths between two points, their sum is greater than the remaining third length between two points. This result indicates that the points form a triangle.
- **Pythagorean Theorem**: $a^2 + b^2 = c^2$
- If you are given three points and you square the three lengths between pairs of points, you can tell that the points form a right triangle if the sum of any two of the squared lengths equals the third squared length.
- **Distance formula**: $d = \sqrt{(x_2 - x_1)^2 + (y_2 - y_1)^2}$
- The distance between any two points is found by squaring the difference in their x-values and adding it to the squared difference in their y-values, then finding the square root of the sum.

Example are these points collinear? 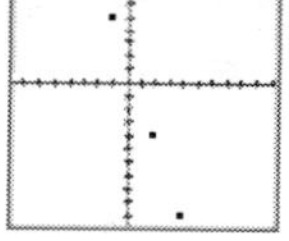 A(-1,5) B(2,-4) C(4,-10) Dist(A,B) $= \sqrt{(2 - -1)^2 + (-4-5)^2}$ $= \sqrt{9+81}$ $= \sqrt{90}$ $= \sqrt{9}\,\sqrt{10} = 3\sqrt{10}$	Figuring out whether these points are collinear becomes a matter of calculating the three lengths and checking to see if any two of them add up to the third one. So, let's calculate the distance between points A and B. Set up the formula and solve for the value.
Dist(A,C) $= \sqrt{(4 - -1)^2 + (-10-5)^2}$ $= \sqrt{25+225}$ $= \sqrt{250}$ $= \sqrt{25}\,\sqrt{10} = 5\sqrt{10}$ Dist(B,C) $= \sqrt{(4-2)^2 + (-10 - -4)^2}$ $= \sqrt{4+36}$ $= \sqrt{40}$ $= \sqrt{4}\,\sqrt{10} = 2\sqrt{10}$	Next, let's find the distance between a second pair of points, A and C. Finally, find the distance between the third pair of points, B and C.
Example are these points collinear? **Yes !** 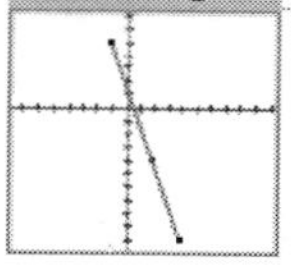 A(-1,5) B(2,-4) C(4,-10) $3\sqrt{10} + 2\sqrt{10} = 5\sqrt{10}$ Dist (A,B) + Dist (B,C) = Dist (A,C)	When you compare the three lengths, you see that two of them added together equal the third. Your conclusion is that the points are collinear. Your conclusion is supported by the graph showing the location of the three points.

Sample problems:

1. Are the points $A(-2,-7)$, $B(0,3)$ and $C(1,8)$ collinear?
   Solution: yes
   Explanation: The points A, B, and C are collinear if $AB + BC = AC$, so use the distance formula, $d = \sqrt{(x_1 - x_2)^2 + (y_1 - y_2)^2}$, to find AB, BC, and AC.
   Find AB: $AB = \sqrt{(-2-0)^2 + (-7-3)^2} = \sqrt{104} = 2\sqrt{26}$.
   Find BC: $BC = \sqrt{(0-1)^2 + (3-8)^2} = \sqrt{26}$.
   Find AC: $AC = \sqrt{(-2-1)^2 + (-7-8)^2} = \sqrt{234} = 3\sqrt{26}$.
   Check that $AB + BC = AC$: $2\sqrt{26} + \sqrt{26} = 3\sqrt{26} = AC$. Thus, the points are collinear.

2. Are the points $A(-8,-12)$, $B(0,0)$ and $C(4,6)$ collinear?
   Solution: yes
   Explanation: Find AB: $AB=\sqrt{(-8-0)^2+(-12-0)^2}=\sqrt{208}=4\sqrt{13}$.
   Find BC: $BC=\sqrt{(0-4)^2+(0-6)^2}=\sqrt{52}=2\sqrt{13}$.
   Find AC: $AC=\sqrt{(-8-4)^2+(-12-6)^2}=\sqrt{468}=6\sqrt{13}$.
   Check that $AB+BC=AC$: $4\sqrt{13}+2\sqrt{13}=6\sqrt{13}=AC$. Thus, the points are collinear.

3. Are the points $A(-\frac{1}{3},2)$, $B(0,1)$ and $C(\frac{5}{3},\frac{2}{3})$ collinear?
   Solution: no
   Explanation: Find AB: $AB=\sqrt{\left(-\frac{1}{3}-0\right)^2+(2-1)^2}=\sqrt{\frac{10}{9}}=\frac{\sqrt{10}}{3}$.
   Find BC: $BC=\sqrt{\left(0-\frac{5}{3}\right)^2+\left(1-\frac{2}{3}\right)^2}=\sqrt{\frac{26}{9}}=\frac{\sqrt{26}}{3}$.
   Find AC: $AC=\sqrt{\left(-\frac{1}{3}-\frac{5}{3}\right)^2+\left(2-\frac{2}{3}\right)^2}=\sqrt{\frac{52}{9}}=\frac{2\sqrt{13}}{3}$.
   Check that $AB+BC=AC$: $\frac{\sqrt{10}}{3}+\frac{\sqrt{26}}{3}=\frac{\sqrt{10}+\sqrt{26}}{3}\neq AC$. Thus, the points are not collinear.

Practice problems: *(Answers on page: 737)*

1. Are the points $A(2,7)$, $B(0,1)$ and $C(-3,-8)$ collinear?
2. Are the points $A(-9,5)$, $B(-3,1)$ and $C(3,-4)$ collinear?
3. Are the points $A(6,1)$, $B(8,\frac{1}{3})$ and $C(10,-\frac{1}{3})$ collinear?

Review questions: *(Answers to odd questions on page: 737)*

1. Are the points $A(-2,-1)$, $B(-2,\frac{5}{3})$ and $C(-2,6)$ collinear?
2. Are the points $A(5,-7)$, $B(-2,0)$ and $C(-3,0)$ collinear?
3. Are the points $A(-3,7)$, $B(1,3)$ and $C(5,-1)$ collinear?
4. Are the points $A(-2,-17)$, $B(1,-2)$ and $C(3,12)$ collinear?
5. Are the points $A(-3,-5)$, $B(-1,-\frac{5}{3})$ and $C(2,\frac{10}{3})$ collinear?

Triangles

- **Collinear**: any two or more points that fall on the same line.
- **Distance formula**: $d=\sqrt{(x_2-x_1)^2+(y_2-y_1)^2}$
- Three points are collinear any time that the sum of any two lengths between two points is equal to the third length between two points.
- Three points form a triangle any time that the sum of any two lengths between points is longer than the third length between two points.
- **Pythagorean Theorem**: $a^2+b^2=c^2$
- Three points form a right triangle any time any two lengths squared add up to the third length squared.

Example are these points collinear? 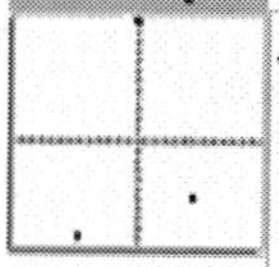 A(-3,-5) B(3, -3) C(0,6) Dist (A,B) $= \sqrt{(3 - -3)^2 + (-3 - -5)^2}$ $= \sqrt{6^2 + 2^2}$ $= \sqrt{36 + 4}$ $= \sqrt{40} = 6.32...$	Calculate the three lengths between each pair of points.Here are the calculations for (A,B).
Dist (A,C) $= \sqrt{(0 - -3)^2 + (6 - -5)^2}$ $= \sqrt{3^2 + 11^2}$ $= \sqrt{9 + 121}$ $= \sqrt{130} = 11.40...$ Dist (B,C) $= \sqrt{(0 - 3)^2 + (6 - -3)^2}$ $= \sqrt{(-3)^2 + 9^2}$ $= \sqrt{9 + 81}$ $= \sqrt{90} = 9.48...$	Here are the calculations for (A,C) and (B,C).
are these points collinear? **No !** A(-3,-5) B(3, -3) C(0,6) $6.32 + 11.40 \neq 9.48$ $9.48 + 11.40 \neq 6.32$ $6.32 + 9.48 \neq 11.40$	These points are not collinear because no two sums add up to the third one.
Example Are the points a right triangle? **Yes!** 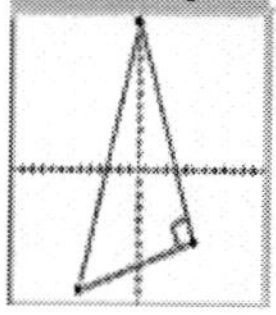 A(-3,-5) B(3, -3) C(0,6) $(\sqrt{40})^2 + (\sqrt{90})^2 = (\sqrt{130})^2$ $40 + 90 = 130$	The three points meet the test for being a right triangle: two of their lengths squared do add up to the third length squared.

Sample problems:

1. True or false: Triangle ABC is a right triangle.

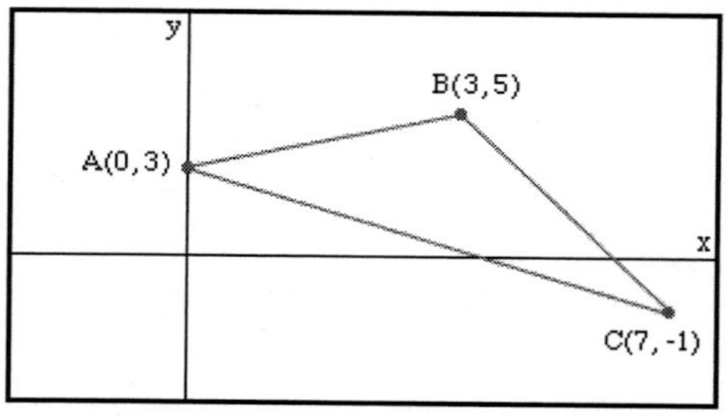

Solution: True

Explanation: Use the Pythagorian Theorem to determine if triangle ABC is a right triangle.

Find the lengths of the three sides: $AC = \sqrt{(0-7)^2 + (3+1)^2} = \sqrt{49+16} = \sqrt{65}$, $AB = \sqrt{(0-3)^2 + (3-5)^2} = \sqrt{9+4} = \sqrt{13}$, $BC = \sqrt{(3-7)^2 + (5+1)^2} = \sqrt{16+36} = \sqrt{52}$.

Substitute the three lengths into $c^2 = a^2 + b^2$, where c is the hypotenuse and longest side: $\left(\sqrt{65}\right)^2 = \left(\sqrt{13}\right)^2 + \left(\sqrt{52}\right)^2$; $65 = 13 + 52$; $65 = 65$, so the triangle is right.

2. Do the points $A(-6,-4)$, $B(0,-2)$, and $C(-10,8)$ form the vertices of a right triangle?
   Solution: yes

   Explanation: Find the lengths of the three sides: $AB=\sqrt{(-6-0)^2+(-4--2)^2}=\sqrt{40}$,
   $BC=\sqrt{(0--10)^2+(-2-8)^2}=\sqrt{200}$, $AC=\sqrt{(-6--10)^2+(-4-8)^2}=\sqrt{160}$.
   Use the Pythagorean Theorem to determine if the three sides form a right triangle:
   $\left(\sqrt{40}\right)^2+\left(\sqrt{160}\right)^2=\left(\sqrt{200}\right)^2$; $40+160=200$, so triangle ABC is a right triangle.

3. Do the points $A(-4,1)$, $B(1,4)$, and $C(-6,-1)$ form the vertices of a right triangle?
   Solution: no

   Explanation: Find the lengths of the three sides: $AB=\sqrt{(-4-1)^2+(1-4)^2}=\sqrt{34}$,
   $BC=\sqrt{(1--6)^2+(4--1)^2}=\sqrt{74}$, $AC=\sqrt{(-4--6)^2+(1--1)^2}=\sqrt{8}$.
   Use the Pythagorean Theorem to determine if the three sides form a right triangle:
   $\left(\sqrt{34}\right)^2+\left(\sqrt{8}\right)^2=\left(\sqrt{74}\right)^2$; $34+8\neq 74$, so triangle ABC is not a right triangle.

Practice problems: *(Answers on page: 737)*

1. True or false: Triangle ABC is a right triangle.

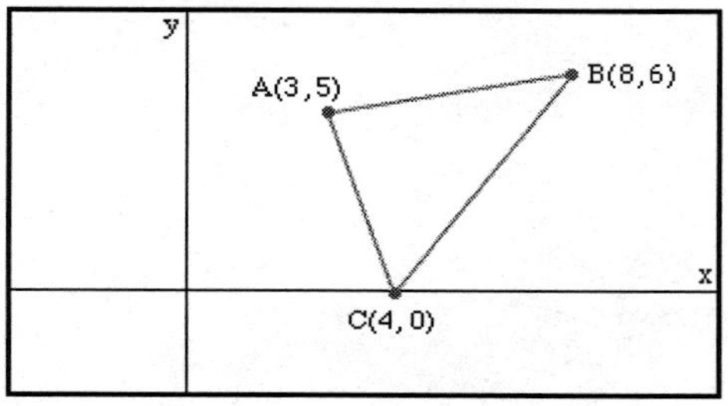

2. Do the points $A(-2,5)$, $B(12,3)$, and $C(10,-11)$ form the vertices of a right triangle?
3. Do the points $A(-5,3)$, $B(6,0)$, and $C(5,7)$ form the vertices of a right triangle?

Review questions: *(Answers to odd questions on page: 737)*

1. Do the points $A(4,-3)$, $B(0,-3)$, and $C(4,2)$ form the vertices of a right triangle?
2. Do the points $A(-2,5)$, $B(1,3)$, and $C(-1,0)$ form the vertices of a right triangle?
3. Do the points $A(0,0)$, $B(2,1)$, and $C(3,-7)$ form the vertices of a right triangle?
4. Do the points $A(-6,3)$, $B(3,-5)$, and $C(-1,5)$ form the vertices of a right triangle?
5. Do the points $A(4,-3)$, $B(7,1)$, and $C(2,1)$ form the vertices of a right triangle?

Finding the Center-Radius Form of the Equation of a Circle

- A **circle** is the set of all points on a plane which are the same distance from a given point, the center of the circle.
- The **center of a circle** is usually given as the ordered pair **(*h*,*k*)** where h is the x-value and k is the y-value of the centerpoint.
- Any point (x,y) mentioned in relation to a circle is found on the circumference of the circle.
- **Radius** is the distance from the center of a circle to any point on its circumference.
- The **equation of a circle** $(x-h)^2+(y-k)^2=r^2$

<table>
<tr><td>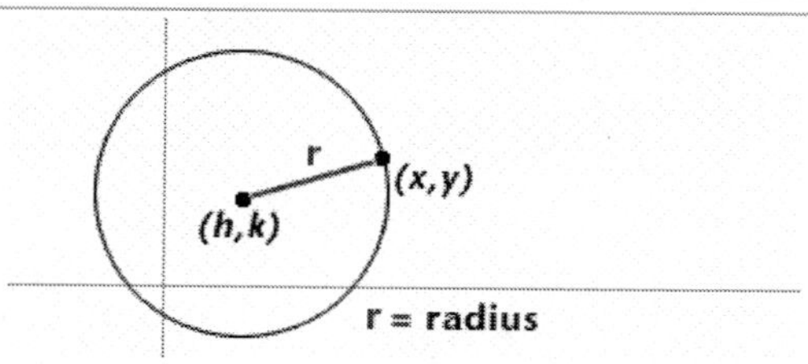
</td><td>This diagram shows the major parts of a circle.</td></tr>
<tr><td>$\sqrt{(x - h)^2 + (y - k)^2} = r$</td><td>You can find the length of the radius by using the distance formula with the endpoints (h,k) and (x,y).</td></tr>
<tr><td>Example find the equation for the circle
radius 5 , center (-2,3)
r h k
$(x - h)^2 + (y - k)^2 = r^2$
$(x - -2)^2 + (y - 3)^2 = 5^2$
$(x + 2)^2 + (y - 3)^2 = 25$
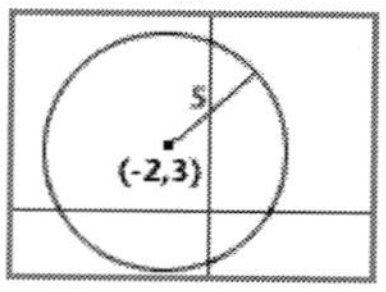
</td><td>When you are given the center and the radius, creating the equation for the circle is a matter of substituting into the standard equation for a circle.Here you're given the center (h,k) is (-2,3), so we substitute –2 for h and 3 for k into the equation.

Notice: The signs change because h and k are subtracting in the standard equation. You are given the radius is 5 so you substitute that into the equation and square it.The graph shows a sketch of the circle.</td></tr>
</table>

Sample problems:

1. Write the equation of a circle if the center is at $(-3,\ 5)$ and the radius is 6.
   Solution: $(x+3)^2+(y-5)^2=36$
   Explanation: Substitute the radius, 6, and the $(h,\ k)$ values from the center into the equation of a circle, $(x-h)^2+(y-k)^2=r^2$: $(x--3)^2+(y-5)^2=6^2$. Simplify: $(x+3)^2+(y-5)^2=36$.

2. Write the equation of a circle if the center is at the origin and a point on the circle is $\left(0,\ 2\frac{1}{2}\right)$.

   Solution: $x^2+y^2=6\frac{1}{4}$
   Explanation: The radius of the circle is the distance between the center of the circle and a point on the circle. In this case, the distance is from the origin, (0,0), and $\left(0,\ 2\frac{1}{2}\right)$, so the radius is $2\frac{1}{2}$.
   Substitute that radius and the $(h,\ k)$ values from the center, (0, 0), into the equation of a circle: $(x-0)^2+(y-0)^2=\left(2\frac{1}{2}\right)^2$. Simplify: $x^2+y^2=6\frac{1}{4}$.

3. Write the equation of a circle if the center is at $(1,-2)$ and a point on the circle is $(5,-2)$.
   Solution: $(x-1)^2+(y+2)^2=16$
   Explanation: The radius of the circle is the length of the vertical line between $(1,-2)$ and $(5,-2)$, so $r=4$. Substitute that radius and the $(h,\ k)$ values from the center into the equation of a circle, then simplify: $(x-1)^2+(y--2)^2=4^2$; $(x-1)^2+(y+2)^2=16$.

Practice problems: *(Answers on page: 737)*

1. Write the equation of the circle with a center at $(3,-2)$ and radius $\sqrt{5}$.
2. Write the equation of a circle if the center is at the origin and the *diameter* is 10.
3. True or false: The equation $x^2+(y+2)^2=1$ describes a circle with the center at (0, 2) and the radius is 1.

Review questions: *(Answers to odd questions on page: 737)*

1. Write the equation of a circle with a center at $(-4,2)$ and a diameter of 10.
2. Write the equation of a circle with a center at $(0,0)$ and a radius of $\sqrt{7}$.
3. Write the equation of the circle in which the endpoints of its diameter are $A(0,0)$ and $B(0,6)$.
4. Write the equation of the circle with a radius of $\frac{5}{2}$ and a center at the origin.
5. Write the equation of the circle with a radius of 3 and a center at $(4,2)$.

Finding the Center and Radius of a Circle

- The **equation of a circle**: $(x-h)^2+(y-k)^2=r^2$
- Completing the square:
  - Reduce the equation, if there is a coefficient in front of x^2.
  - Move the constant to the right.
  - Complete the square.
- Watch your signs when stating the center of the circle from the equation.
  The equation reads $(x - h)$ and $(y - k)$ so the signs change from the equation to the ordered pair notation.

Example Find the Center and Radius $x^2+6x+y^2+8y+9=0$ $x^2+6x+y^2+8y=-9$ $x^2+6x+\underline{9}+y^2+8y+\underline{\quad}=-9+\underline{9}+\underline{\quad}$ *add to both sides* *take $\frac{1}{2}$ and square* $\frac{1}{2}\cdot 6=3$ $3^2=9$	Frequently you are given an equation that you think is for a circle because it has terms with both x^2 and y^2. Try to convert the equation to your standard form for a circle by completing the square. Do the completing the square process once for the x-terms and a second time for the y-terms. Here note that $6/2 = 3$ and $3^2 = 9$. So 9 is added to the equation for the x -terms.
$x^2+6x+\underline{9}+y^2+8y+\underline{16}=-9+\underline{9}+\underline{16}$	Next work with the y-terms. You can see that $8/2 = 4$, and $4^2 = 16$. So, 16 is being added to the equation.
$(x+3)^2+(y+4)^2=16$	Now write the completed squares as binomials and that gives the left side of the circle equation. The total on the right side represents the radius squared.
Center: $(-3,-4)$ **Radius:** $\sqrt{16}=4$	In this form you know your center and your radius.
Example Find the Center and Radius $x^2-4x+y^2+12y=-4$ $x^2-4x+\underline{4}+y^2+12y+\underline{36}=-4+\underline{4}+\underline{36}$ **watch your signs !** $(x-2)^2+(y+6)^2=36$ **Center:** $(+2,-6)$ **Radius:** $\sqrt{36}=6$	This example works the same way. 1. Complete the square for the x-terms. 2. Complete the square for the y-terms. 3. Write the binomials on the left side. 4. Note the center and the radius.

Sample problems:

1. Determine the center and the radius of the circle described by $3x^2-18x+3y^2+30y=-27$.
   Solution: $(3,-5)$; $r=5$

Explanation: Express the equation $3x^2-18x+3y^2+30y=-27$ in the form of the equation of a circle, $(x-h)^2+(y-k)^2=r^2$, by completing the square for both x and y.
Divide the equation by 3: $x^2-6x+y^2+10y=-9$.
Add 9 to both sides, since $\left(\frac{-6}{2}\right)^2=9$: $(x^2+6x+9)+y^2+10y=-9+9$.
Add 25 to both sides, since $\left(\frac{10}{2}\right)^2=25$: $(x^2-6x+9)+(y^2+10y+25)=-9+9+25$.
Factor each trinomial and simplify the right side: $(x-3)^2+(y+5)^2=25$.
Now, consider the general equation of a circle, $(x-h)^2+(y-k)^2=r^2$ to determine the center, $(h,\ k)$, and the radius. The center is $(3,-5)$ and $r^2=25$, so $r=5$.

2. Determine the center and the radius of the circle described by $x^2-x+y^2-3y=-\frac{3}{2}$.

Solution: $\left(\frac{1}{2},\frac{3}{2}\right)$; $r=1$

Explanation: Complete the square of the x-terms by adding $\frac{1}{4}$ to both sides, since $\left(\frac{-1}{2}\right)^2=\frac{1}{4}$: $\left(x^2-x+\frac{1}{4}\right)+y^2-3y=-\frac{3}{2}+\frac{1}{4}$. Complete the square of the y-terms by adding $\frac{9}{4}$ to both sides, since $\left(-\frac{3}{2}\right)^2=\frac{9}{4}$: $\left(x^2-x+\frac{1}{4}\right)+\left(y^2-3y+\frac{9}{4}\right)=-\frac{3}{2}+\frac{1}{4}+\frac{9}{4}$. Factor each trinomial and simplify the right: $\left(x-\frac{1}{2}\right)^2+\left(y-\frac{3}{2}\right)^2=1$. Determine the center and radius of the circle from the equation: $\left(\frac{1}{2},\frac{3}{2}\right)$ is the center and $r^2=1$, so $r=1$.

3. Determine the center and the radius of the circle described by $x^2-2\sqrt{2}x+y^2-4\sqrt{2}y=6$.
Solution: $(\sqrt{2},\ 2\sqrt{2})$; $r=4$
Explanation: Complete the square for x and y: $(x^2-2\sqrt{2}x+2)+(y^2-4\sqrt{2}y+8)=6+2+8$.
Factor and simplify: $(x-\sqrt{2})^2+(y-2\sqrt{2})^2=16$. So the center is at $(\sqrt{2},2\sqrt{2})$ and $r^2=16$, so $r=\sqrt{16}=4$.

Practice problems: *(Answers on page: 737)*

1. Determine the center and the radius of the circle described by $4x^2-24x+4y^2+8y=12$.
2. Determine the center and the radius of the circle described by $x^2-\frac{2}{3}x+y^2-\frac{4}{3}y=\frac{31}{9}$.
3. Determine the center and the radius of the circle described by $x^2-\frac{4}{3}x+y^2-y=\frac{11}{36}$.

Review questions: *(Answers to odd questions on page: 737)*

1. Determine the center and the radius of the circle described by $x^2-6x+y^2+8y=3$.
2. Determine the center and the radius of the circle described by $x^2-4x+y^2-6y=-9$.
3. Determine the center and the radius of the circle described by $x^2+4\sqrt{3}x+y^2+2\sqrt{3}y=-6$.
4. Determine the center and the radius of the circle described by $\left(x^2-4x+4\right)+\left(y^2+6y+9\right)=16$.

5. Determine the center and the radius of the circle described by $x^2 - x - y^2 + \frac{2}{3}y = -\frac{1}{9}$.

Decoding the Circle Formula

- **Equation of a circle**: $(x-h)^2 + (y-k)^2 = r^2$
- The **center of a circle** is represented by the point (h,k).
- The **radius** is the distance from the center of a circle to any point on its circumference.

Example Find the Center and Radius **Suppose:** *you are given a equation* $(x - 4)^2 + (y + 6)^2 = 49$	When you first look at an equation, a natural question is what kind of line or curve is it representing.
Using the Equation for a Circle **center is *(h,k)*** **radius is *r*** $(x - 4)^2 + (y + 6)^2 = 49$ $(y - (-6))^2$ ***So, we have a Circle*** **Center: (4 ,-6)** *take the opposite sign*	An equation that has an x^2 and a y^2 with terms being added together positively will likely be a circle. When defining the center of the circle remember to change the signs from the standard form of the equation. The equation states $(x - h)$ and $(y - k)$, showing both center values as negative, while the ordered pair (h,k) shows both values as positive.
Radius: $\sqrt{49} = 7$ *must be positive*	The radius will be the square root of the constant on the right side of the equation. It will always be positive because it represents a distance.
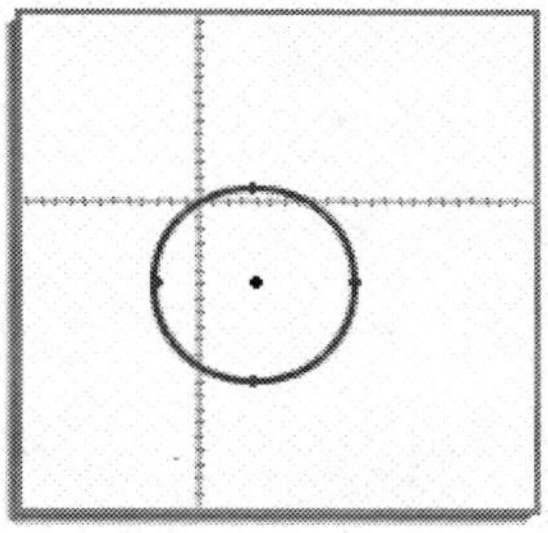	And once you know the center and the radius of a circle, you can easily sketch its graph.

Sample problems:

1. Given the equation $(x+1)^2 + (y-5)^2 = 9$, find the center and the radius of the circle.
   Solution: $(-1,5)$; $r = 3$
   Explanation: Consider the standard form of the equation of a circle: $(x-h)^2 + (y-k)^2 = r^2$.
   Express the given equation in standard form: $(x-(-1))^2 + (y-5)^2 = 3^2$. Identify the center and radius of the circle from the equation: $(-1,5)$ and $r = 3$

2. True or false: The equation $(x-1)^2 + (y+2)^2 = 4$ describes the graph below.

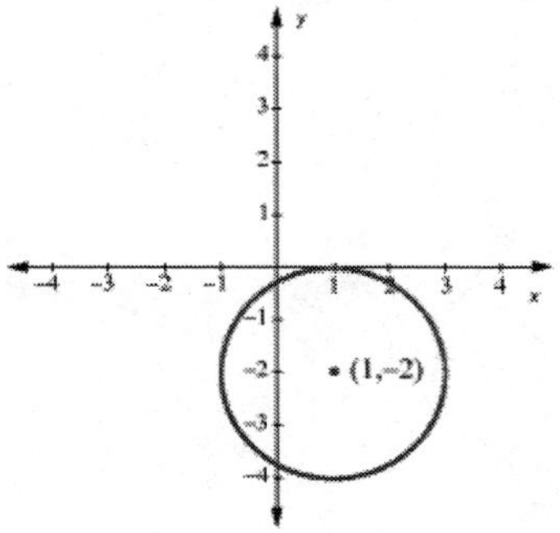

Solution: True
Explanation: Identify the center and radius from the equation expressed in standard form: $(x-1)^2+(y-(-2))^2$. So, the center is at $(1,-2)$ and the radius is 2. That center and radius agree with the circle in the graph.

3. True or false: The equation $(x+4)^2+(y+1)^2=4$ describes the graph below.

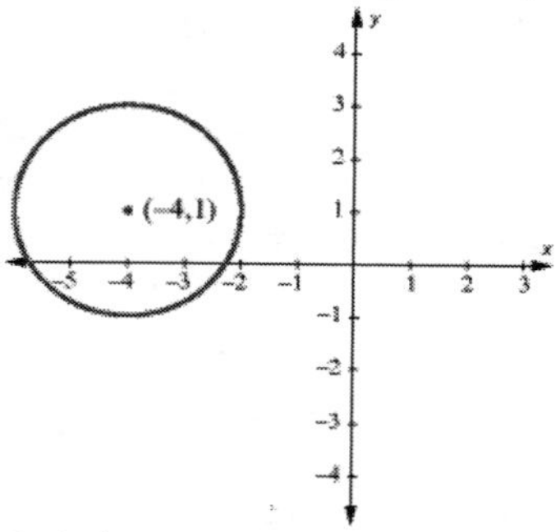

Solution: False
Explanation: Identify the center and radius from the equation expressed in standard form: $(x-(-4))^2+(y-(-1)^2)$. So, the center of this circle is at $(-4,-1)$, but the center of the graphed circle is at $(-4,\ 1)$.

Practice problems: *(Answers on page: 738)*

1. Find the center and radius of the circle $(x-2)^2+y^2=9$.
2. Sketch a graph of the equation $(x+1)^2+(y-2)^2=4$.
3. Find the center and radius of the circle $(x+4)^2+(y-1)^2=5$.

Review questions: *(Answers to odd questions on page: 738)*

1. Find the center and radius of the circle $(x+3)^2+(y-4)^2=3$.
2. Find the center and radius of the circle $(x-3)^2+(y+5)^2=27$.
3. Find the center and radius of the circle $(x-9)^2+(y-3)^2=36$.
4. Find the center and radius of the circle $x^2+y^2=4.44$.
5. Find the center and radius of the circle $x^2+(y+4)^2=121$.

Solving Word Problems Involving Circles

- **Equation of a circle**: $(x-h)^2+(y-k)^2=r^2$
- **Distance Formula**: $d=\sqrt{(x_2-x_1)^2+(y_2-y_1)^2}$
- **Midpoint Formula**: $\left(\dfrac{x_1+x_2}{2},\dfrac{y_1+y_2}{2}\right)$

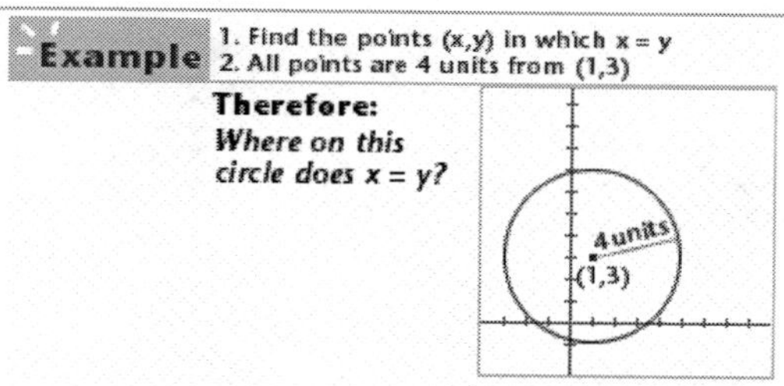

In this problem, you know there is a line representing $x=y$ which you have used before.

And you know that all points 4 units from (1,3) describe a circle.

Equation for Circle $(x-1)^2+(y-3)^2=16$ *if x = y, then* $(x-1)^2+(x-3)^2=16$ *FOIL* $x^2-2x+1+x^2-6x+9=16$ *Combine like terms* $2x^2-8x-6=0$ *Divide by two* $x^2-4x-3=0$ *Use Quadratic Formula* $x=\frac{4\pm\sqrt{16-4(-3)}}{2}=\frac{4\pm\sqrt{28}}{2}$	Begin with the equation for a circle with the center and radius substituted into it. Then substitute x for y in the equation, since they are equal. Now solve. Because the equation won't factor, use the quadratic formula.
$\left(\frac{4+\sqrt{28}}{2}, \frac{4+\sqrt{28}}{2}\right)$ $\left(\frac{4-\sqrt{28}}{2}, \frac{4-\sqrt{28}}{2}\right)$ 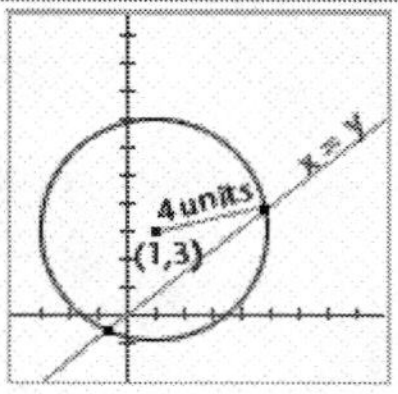 line represents where x = y. **The answers are the points where the line intersects the circle**	The result is that there are two answers. When you graph the line and the circle, you can easily where the two points lie.
Example Find the equation of a circle having the smallest radius that includes points (1,4)(-3,2) 1. To find the smallest circle, the points should be on opposite sides of the circle. 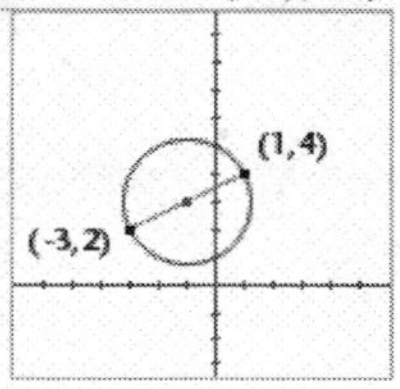 2. Center = Midpoint $\left(\frac{-2}{2},\frac{6}{2}\right)=(-1,3)$ 3. Radius: $\sqrt{(-1-(-3))^2+(3-2)^2}$ $\sqrt{2^2+1^2}=\sqrt{4+1}=\sqrt{5}$ 4. Find the Equation $(x+1)^2+(y-3)^2=5$	In this example, you are given two points on the circle. Your task is to find the center and radius so you can set up the equation. Finding the center is the easiest. It is the midpoint between the two points. Finding the radius is a matter of finding the distance between the center and one of the points. Writing the equation involves substitution.

Sample problems:

1. Find the equation of the circle with the smallest radius that contains the points $(2,4)$ and $(-4,2)$.
   Solution: $(x+1)^2+(y-3)^2=10$
   Explanation: The smallest circle that contains these points must have a diameter with (2,4) and (–4,2) as endpoints. So, the midpoint of (2,4) and (–4,2) will be the center of the circle.
   Use the midpoint formula to find the center: $\left(\frac{-4+2}{2},\frac{2+4}{2}\right)=(-1,3)$.
   To find the radius, compute the distance from the center to either of the given points using the distance formula: $r=\sqrt{(2+1)^2+(4-3)^2}=\sqrt{10}$. Now, substitute $(-1,3)$ for (h,k) and $\sqrt{10}$ for r into the standard equation of a circle, $(x-h)^2+(y-k)^2=r^2$, and simplify: $(x-(-1))^2+(y-3)^2=\left(\sqrt{10}\right)^2$; $(x+1)^2+(y-3)^2=10$.

2. Given a circle with radius 3 and center $(-2, 5)$, find all points (x, y) on that circle in which $y=-2x$.
   Solution: $(-1.073, 2.146)$ and $(-3.727, 7.454)$

Explanation: All the points on the circle where $y = -2x$ can be represented graphically.
Visualize the graph of the circle and the line $y = -2x$. The points on the circle where $y = -2x$ are the point(s) where the line and circle intersect. Therefore, in order to determine the points where $y = -2x$, solve the system of equations: $(x+2)^2 + (y-5)^2 = 9$ and $y = -2x$.
Solve the system using the substitution method, so substitute $-2x$ into the equation of the circle for y: $(x+2)^2 + (-2x-5) = 9$. Next, simplify: $x^2 + 4x + 4 + 4x^2 + 20x + 25 = 9$; $5x^2 + 24x + 29 = 9$.
Set the equation equal to zero: $5x^2 + 24x + 20 = 0$. Solve for x using the quadratic formula:

$$x = \frac{-2 \pm \sqrt{(24)^2 - 4(5)(20)}}{2(5)} = \frac{-24 \pm \sqrt{176}}{10} = \frac{-24 \pm 13.27}{10} = -1.073 \text{ or } -3.727.$$

So the x-coordinates of the 2 points on the circle where $y = -2x$ are -1.073 and -3.727.
Find the y-coordinates by substituting those x-values into $y = -2x$:
$y = -2(-1.073) = 2.146$ and $y = -2(-3.727) = 7.454$.
So the points on the circle in which $y = -2x$ are $(-1.073,\ 2.146)$ and $(-3.727,\ 7.454)$.

3. Let the center of the circle defined by $(x+5)^2 + (y+4)^2 = 1$ be point A.
And let the center of the circle defined by $(x-3)^2 + (y-2)^2 = 1$ be point B.
Write the equation of the circle whose diameter endpoints are at A and B.
Solution: $(x+1)^2 + (y+1)^2 = 25$
Explanation: Find the coordinates of A and B.
Point A is the center of the circle whose equation is $(x+5)^2 + (y+4)^2 = 1$, so $A = (-5,-4)$.
Point B is the center of the circle whose equation is $(x-3)^2 + (y-2)^2 = 1$, so $B = (3,\ 2)$.
Use the midpoint formula to determine the center of the new circle, since the center is the midpoint between A and B: center $= \left(\frac{-5+3}{2}, \frac{-4+2}{2}\right) = (-1,-1)$. Substitute the values from the new center and either A or B into the distance formula to determine the radius:
$r = \sqrt{(3--1)^2 + (2--1)^2} = \sqrt{16+9} = \sqrt{25} = 5$. Now, write the equation of the circle using the center, $(-1,-1)$ and the radius, 5: $(x+1)^2 + (y+1)^2 = 25$.

Practice problems: *(Answers on page: 738)*

1. Given a circle with center $(5,-1)$ and radius $2\sqrt{10}$, find all points on that circle such that $-x = y$.
2. Write the equation of a circle whose diameter endpoints are
1) the center of the circle given by the equation $x^2 + y^2 - 2x + 6y = 15$ and
2) the point (7, 5).
3. Write the equation of a circle whose diameter endpoints are the points on a circle with center (0,0) and radius 1, where $y = 1 - x$.

Review questions: *(Answers to odd questions on page: 738)*

1. Find the equation of a circle whose diameter endpoints are $(1,7)$ and $(5,3)$.
2. Find the equation of the circle whose diameter endpoints are $(0,0)$ and $(4,6)$.
3. Find the equation of the circle with the smallest possible radius that contains the points $(-2,6)$ and $(4,-10)$.
4. Find the distance from the center of the circle described by $x^2 + y^2 - 2x + 6y = 15$ to the point $(3,-2)$.
5. Find the distance between the centers of the two circles whose equations are
$x^2 + y^2 = 25$ and $x^2 - 32x + y^2 - 24y = -175$.

Graphing Equations by Locating Points

- One way to graph a line is to pick some x-values, substitute them into the function to find the corresponding y-values, and graph the points.
- Whenever you see one variable squared and the other variable not squared, expect your graph to be a parabola. If it is the x that is squared, the parabola will open up or down. If it is the y that is squared, the parabola will open to one side.
- Whenever you see a variable inside an absolute value, expect a V-shaped graph

$y = 2x+1$

x	y
−2	−3
−1	−1
0	1
1	3
2	5

Usually, you set up an x-y chart showing the values used.

In this example, -2,-1,0,1, and 2 were chosen for x. When each value was substituted into the equation, the resulting y-values were –3,-1,1,3, and 5. You can see how they are paired in the chart.

$y = 2x+1$

x	y
−2	−3
−1	−1
0	1
1	3
2	5

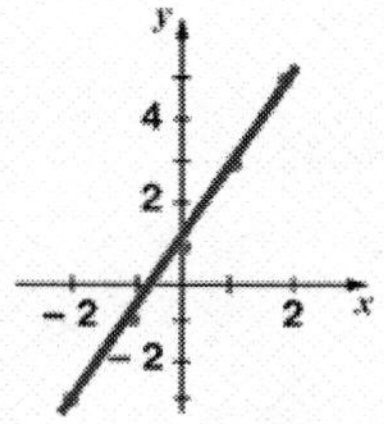

Each x-y pair is the ordered pair (x,y) for the points you graph. So, this line will included the points (-2,-3), (-1,-1), (0,1), (1,3), and (2,5).

Plot those points. Then you can easily draw the line.

$y = 3x^2$

x	y
−2	12
−1	3
0	0
1	3
2	12

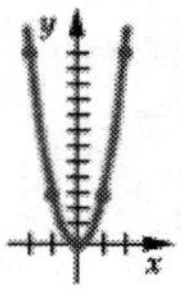

When you see an equation with one of its two variables squared, the graph will be a parabola.

The same technique works for more than just line graphs. This graph shows a basic parabola, $y = 3x^2$.

$x = y^2$

x	y
4	−2
1	−1
0	0
1	1
4	2

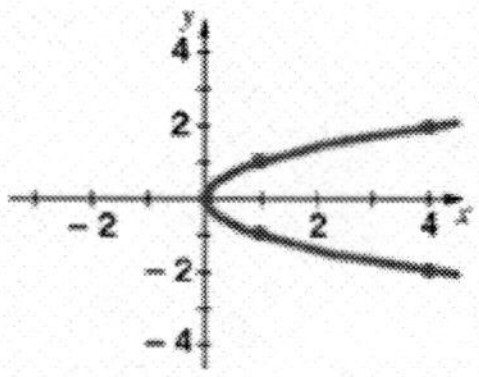

When you have an equation where the y is squared and the x is not, expect a parabola that opens to one side.

$y = |x|$

x	y
−2	2
−1	1
0	0
1	1
2	2

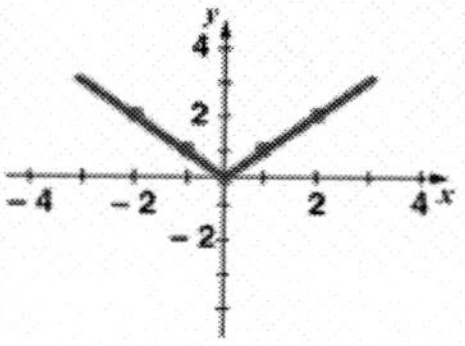

Here is an example that graphs as a "V". One example of the effect of the absolute value is to pair both –2 and 2 for x with 2 for y.

Sample problems:

1. Sketch the graph of $y = 5 - |x|$.
   Solution:

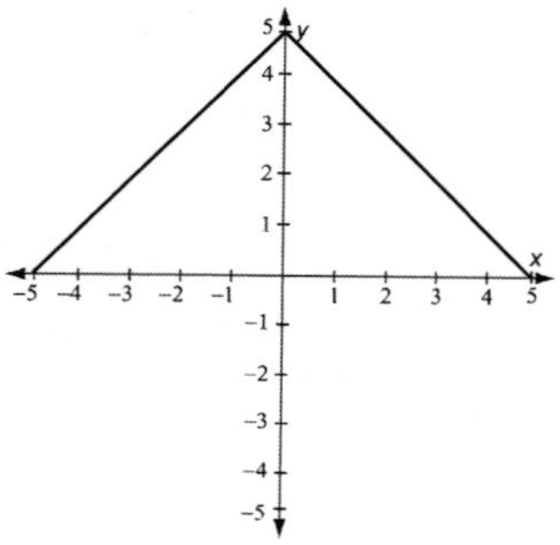

Explanation: Make a table to determine several coordinate pairs. Any value of x may be used in the table, however typically -2, -1, 0, 1, and 2 are chosen.
Substitute each x value into $y = 5 - |x|$:

$x = -2$: $y = 5 - |-2| = 5 - 2 = 3 \Rightarrow (-2,3)$
$x = -1$: $y = 5 - |-1| = 5 - 1 = 4 \Rightarrow (-1,4)$
$x = 0$: $y = 5 - |0| = 5 - 0 = 4 \Rightarrow (0,5)$
$x = 1$: $y = 5 - |1| = 5 - 1 = 4 \Rightarrow (1,4)$
$x = 2$: $y = 5 - |2| = 5 - 2 = 3 \Rightarrow (2,3)$

Plot the points to sketch the graph.

x	y
-2	3
-1	4
0	5
1	4
2	3

2. Sketch the graph of $x = (y+1)(y+2)$.
   Solution:

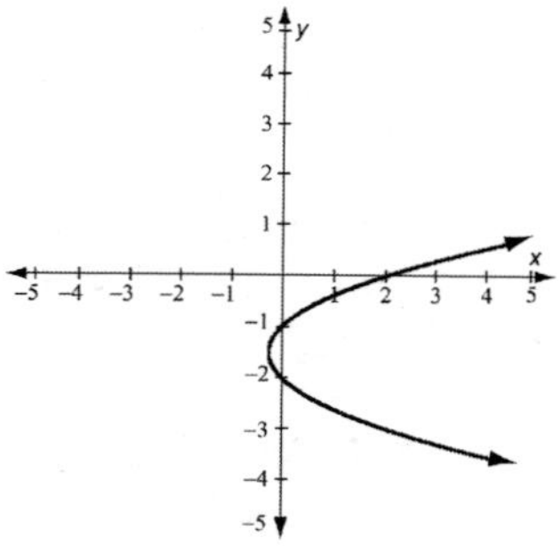

Explanation: Make a table to determine several coordinate pairs. Since x is a function of y, choose values for y and substitute each one into the equation to find the corresponding x. Plot the points to sketch the graph.

x	y
0	-2
0	-1
2	0
6	1
12	2

3. Sketch the graph of $y = -2(x-1)^2 + 1$.

Solution:

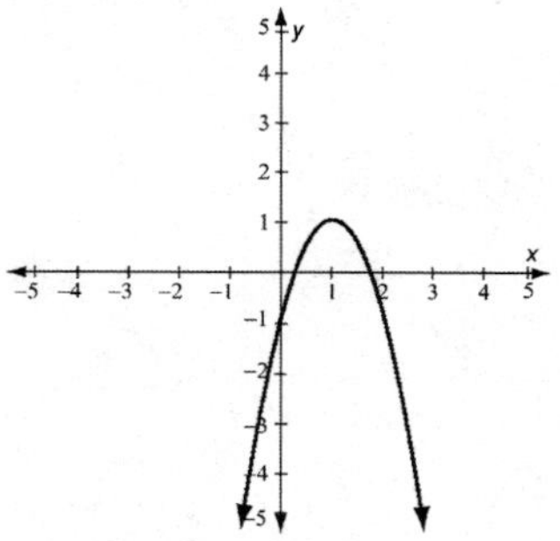

Explanation: Make a table to determine several coordinate pairs. Choose five values for x and substitute each one into the equation to find the corresponding y-values. Plot the points from the table to sketch the graph.

x	y
-2	-17
-1	-7
0	-1
1	1
2	-1

Practice problems: *(Answers on page: 738)*

1. Sketch the graph of $y = 4 - x$.
2. Sketch the graph of $y = x^2 + 3$.
3. Sketch the graph of $x = y^2 - y + 1$.

Review questions: *(Answers to odd questions on page: 738)*

1. Sketch the graph of $y = 5 - 2x$.
2. Sketch the graph of $y = |x-1|$.
3. Sketch the graph of $y = (x+1)(x-3)$.
4. Sketch the graph of $x = y(y+2)$.
5. Sketch the graph of $x = y^3 - 5$.

Finding the x- and y-Intercepts of an Equation

- An ***x*-intercept** is a point where a curve crosses the x-axis.
- A ***y*-intercept** is a point where a curve crosses the y-axis.
- A line will have one x-intercept and one y-intercept (with the exception of horizontal or vertical lines).
- A curve may have more than one of either intercept. A curve may have none of either or both intercepts.

x intercept is where the line crosses the *x* axis.
y intercept is where the line crosses the *y* axis.

Finding the *x* and *y* Intercepts

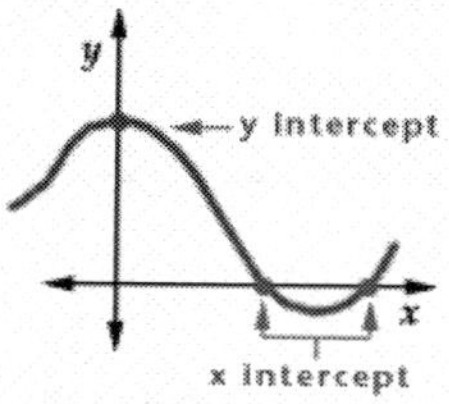

Significant points on any curve are the points where the curve crosses each of the two axes.

The curve crosses the y-axis at any point where $x = 0$.

The curve crosses the x-axis at any point where $y = 0$.

Example

$2x+5y = 12$
$2x = 12$
$x = 6$ ← *The x intercept*

To find the x-intercept, let $y = 0$, and solve for x.

In this case, $x = 6$ where $y = 0$.

So the x-intercept is at the point (6, 0).

$2x+5y = 12$
$5y = 12$
$y = \frac{12}{5}$ ← *The y intercept*

$x = 6$

To find the y-intercept, let $x = 0$, and solve the equation for y.

In this example, $y = 12/5$ when $x = 0$.

So the y-intercept is at the point $(0, \frac{12}{5})$.

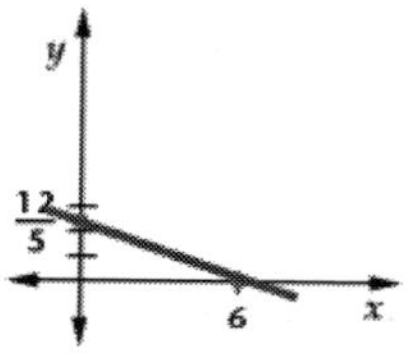

Now that you have two points on the line, graphing the line becomes fairly simple.

Example

$y = x^2 - 4x+3$
$y = 3$ ← *The y intercept*

To find the y-intercept, let $x = 0$ and solve.

In this case, $y = 3$ is a quick find.

$y = x^2 - 4x+3$
$(x-3)(x-1) = 0$
$x = 3 \quad x = 1$
Two x intercepts

To find the x-intercept, let $y = 0$ and solve.

Factoring is required to find there are two x intercepts, $x = 3$ and $x = 1$.

$y = 3$
$x = 3$
$x = 1$

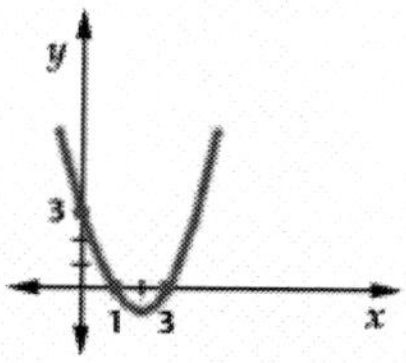

Now draw a quick sketch of the curve to see what we have. It's a matter of placing the points and connecting the dots to show us that we have a parabola for this equation.

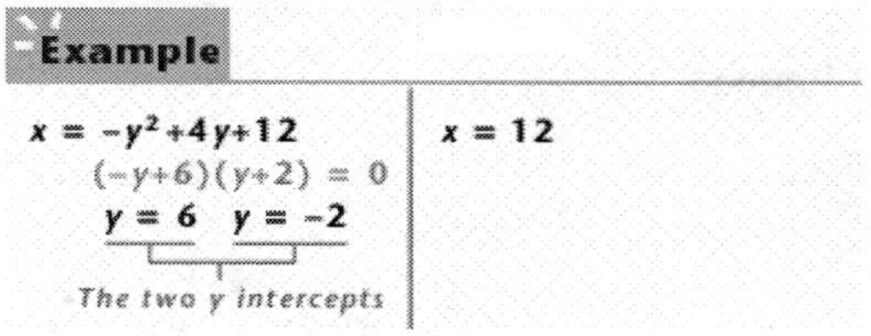

This equation follows the exact same procedures as the two examples above.

Find an x-intercept: when $y = 0$, $x = 12$. Find y-intercepts: when $x = 0$, $y = 6$ and $y = -2$.

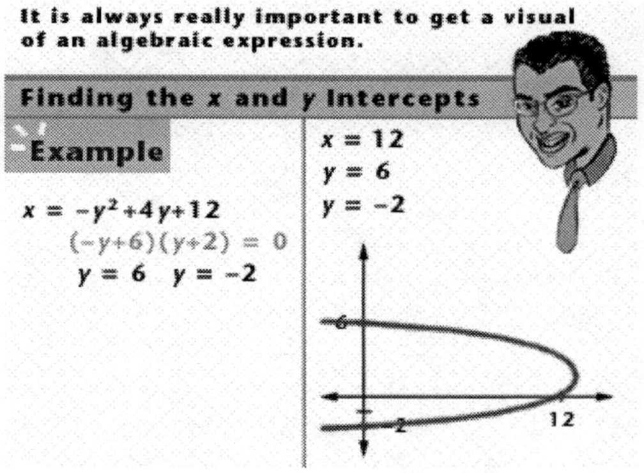

Graphing this one again reveals a parabola, but one opening to the left.

Using these intercepts gives a quick and easy way to sketch the graph of an equation. Using them lets us visually understand what the equation is saying.

Sample problems:

1. Find the y-intercept of $9y = 2x^2 - 18$.
   Solution: $(0, -2)$
   Explanation: To find the y-intercept, substitute $x = 0$ into $9y = 2x^2 - 18$ and solve for y: $9y = 2(0)^2 - 18$; $9y = -18$; $y = -2$. So, the y-intercept is located at $(0, -2)$.

2. Find the x and y-intercepts of $y = 2x^2 + x - 1$.
   Solution: x-intercepts: $\frac{1}{2}$ and -1, y-intercept: -1
   Explanation: To find the x-intercept, substitute $y = 0$ into $y = 2x^2 + x - 1$ and solve for x: $2x^2 + x - 1 = 0$. Solve this equation by factoring the trinomial, then set each factor equal to 0, and then solve each equation for x: $(2x-1)(x+1) = 0$; $2x - 1 = 0$ or $x + 1 = 0$; $2x = 1$ or $x = -1$; $x = \frac{1}{2}$ or $x = -1$. Thus, the x-intercepts are $\frac{1}{2}$ and -1. To find the y-intercept, substitute $x = 0$ into $y = 2x^2 + x - 1$ and solve for y: $y = 2(0)^2 + (0) - 1 = 2(0) + 0 - 1 = -1$. Thus, the y-intercept is -1.

3. Find the x and y-intercepts of $\frac{x^2}{4} + \frac{y^2}{9} = 1$.
   Solution: x-intercepts: ± 2, y-intercept: ± 3
   Explanation: To find the x-intercept, substitute $y = 0$ into the equation and solve for x: $\frac{x^2}{4} + \frac{(0)^2}{9} = 1$; $\frac{x^2}{4} + 0 = 1$; $\frac{x^2}{4} = 1$; $x^2 = 4$; $\sqrt{x^2} = \sqrt{4}$; $x = \pm 2$. Thus, the x-intercepts are 2 and -2. To find the y-intercept, substitute $x = 0$ into the equation and solve for y: $\frac{(0)^2}{4} + \frac{y^2}{9} = 1$; $0 + \frac{y^2}{9} = 1$; $\frac{y^2}{9} = 1$; $y^2 = 9$; $\sqrt{y^2} = \sqrt{9}$; $y = \pm 3$. Thus, the y-intercepts are 3 and -3.

Practice problems: *(Answers on page: 738)*

1. Find the x-intercepts for the equation $y = x^2 + 2x - 3$.
2. Given the equation $y = -\frac{1}{3}x + \frac{5}{3}$, find the y-intercept.
3. Given the equation $\frac{x^2}{36} + \frac{y^2}{4} = 1$, find a y-intercept.

Review questions: *(Answers to odd questions on page: 738)*

1. Find the y-intercept for the equation $y = x^2 - 8$
2. Find the y-intercept for the equation $y = -x^2 - 2$
3. Find the x-intercepts for the equation $y = 2x^2 - 6x$
4. Find the x-intercepts for the equation $y = x^2 + 6x + 8$
5. Find the y-intercept for the equation $y = 2x^2 + 4x + 3$

Functions and the Vertical Line Test

- A **relation** is a set of ordered pairs in which any given x-value may be paired with more than one y-value.
- A **function** is a set of ordered pairs in which each x-value is matched with exactly one y-value.

with a function, if the x value is known, you can find the y value **Example** $y = x^2 + 10x + 25$ *if $x = 1$ find y* $y = 1^2 + 10(1) + 25$ $y = 1 + 10 + 25$ $\boxed{y = 36}$	If each time you use a specific value for x in an equation, you get exactly one value for y, then the equation is a function. In this example, solving for a random value, $x = 1$, you get exactly one answer, $y = 36$. Only one y-value is possible for this or any other x, so the equation qualifies as a function.
Example $y = x^2 + 10x + 25$ *if $x = 2$ find y* $y = 2^2 + 10(2) + 25$ $y = 4 + 20 + 25$ $\boxed{y = 49}$	In this example, if you solve for $x = 2$, you get exactly one answer, $y = 49$. Only one y-value is possible for this or any other x, so the equation qualifies as a function.
Example $y = x^2 + 10x + 25$ *if $x = \$5$ find y* $y = (\$5)^2 + 10(\$5) + 25$ $y = \$25 + \$50 + 25$ $\boxed{y = \$100}$	In this example, if you solve for $x = \$5$, you get exactly one answer, $y = \$100$. Only one y-value is possible for this or any other x, so the equation qualifies as a function.
function: has one unique value for y relation: has more than one value for y 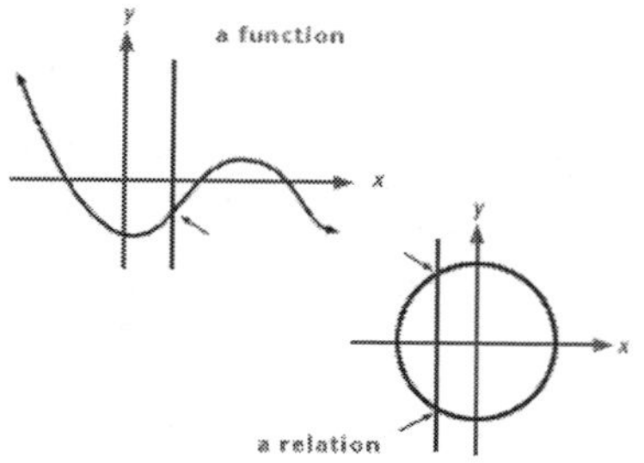	The graph on the left represents a function. No matter where you place the vertical line it passes through only one point on the curve. For each x there is only one (x,y) point. The graph on the right does not represent a function because the vertical line passes through more than one point. This type of graph represents a relation.

Sample problems:

1. True or false: The following is a graph of a function.

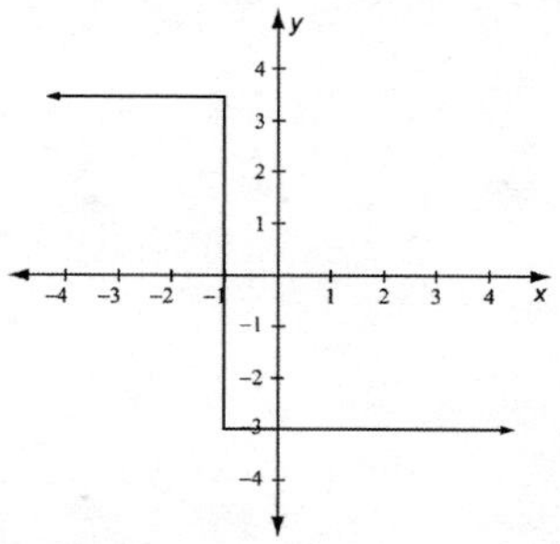

Solution: False

Explanation: Using the vertical line test we can see that at the value $x = -1$, there are multiple values for y. Therefore, it fails the vertical line test and is not a function.

2. True or false: The following is a graph of a function.

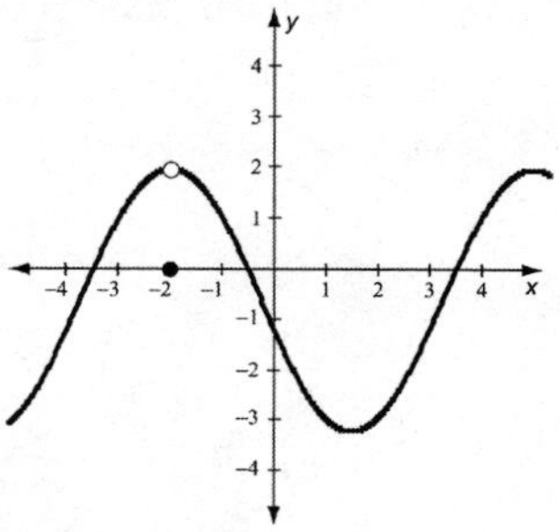

Solution: True

Explanation: Using the vertical line test we can determine that for the given graph every value of x leads to only one value of y (even at $x = -2$ when the function jumps from a height of $y = 2$ down to $y = 0$). Therefore, the given graph is of a function.

3. True or false: The following is a graph of a function.

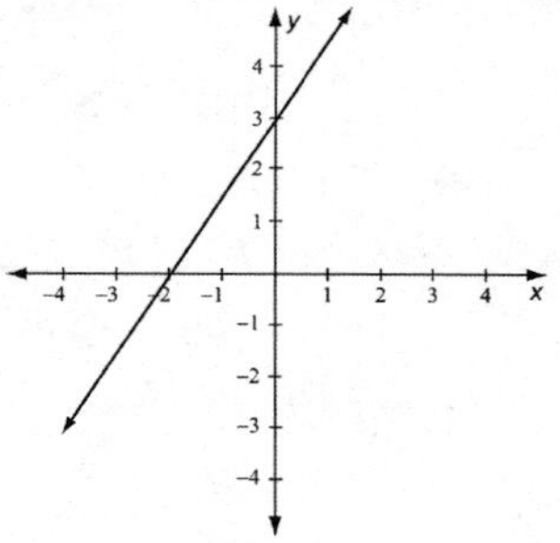

Solution: True

Explanation: Using the vertical line test we can determine that for the given graph every value of x leads to only one value of y. Therefore, the given graph is of a function.

Practice problems: *(Answers on page: 738)*

1. True or false: The following is a graph of a function.

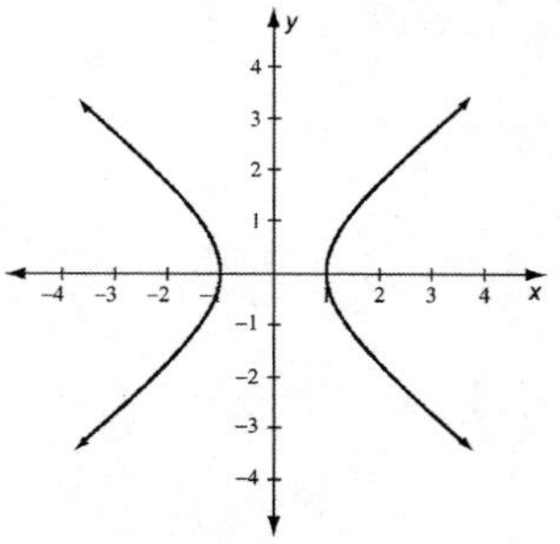

2. True or false: The following is a graph of a function.

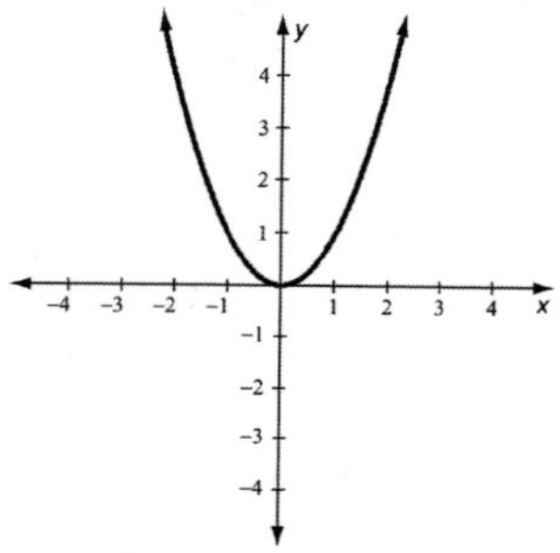

3. True or false: The following is a graph of a function.

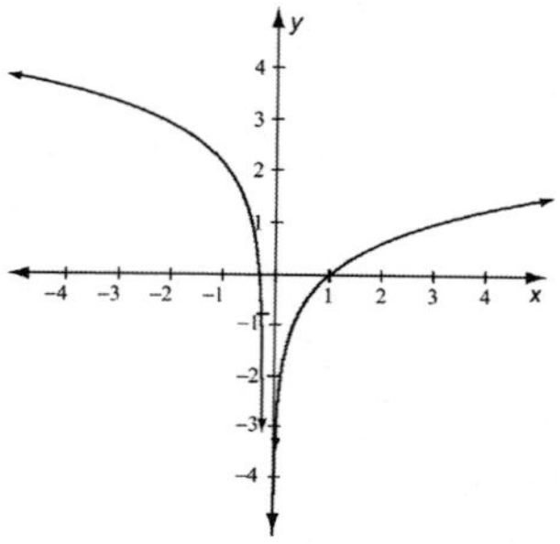

Review questions: *(Answers to odd questions on page: 738)*

1. Let $f = \{(-1,3),(-2,5),(-3,7)\}$. Is f a function?
2. True or false: The following is a graph of a function.

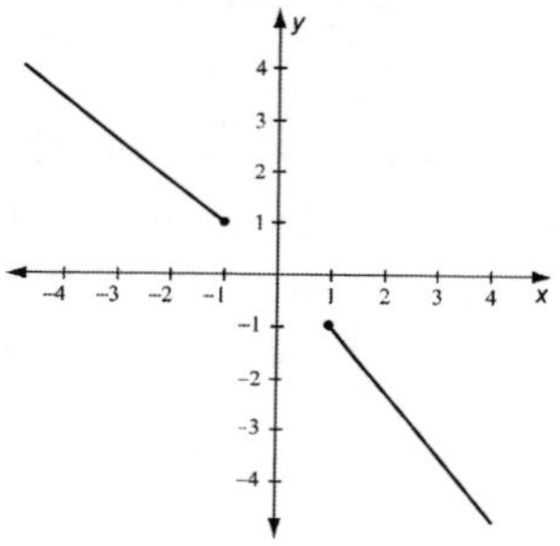

3. True or false: The following is a graph of a function.

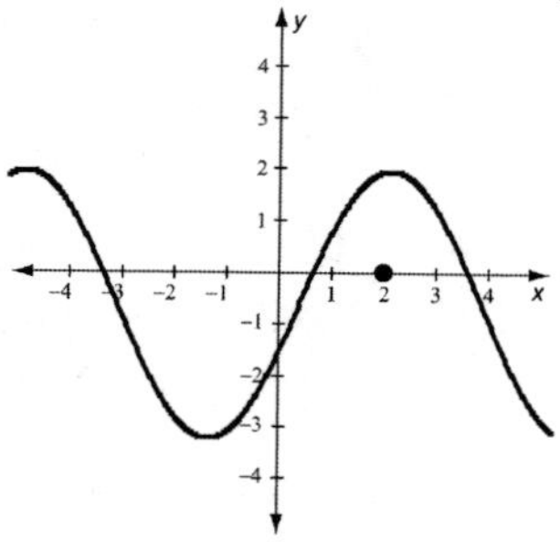

4. True or false: The following graph is a function.

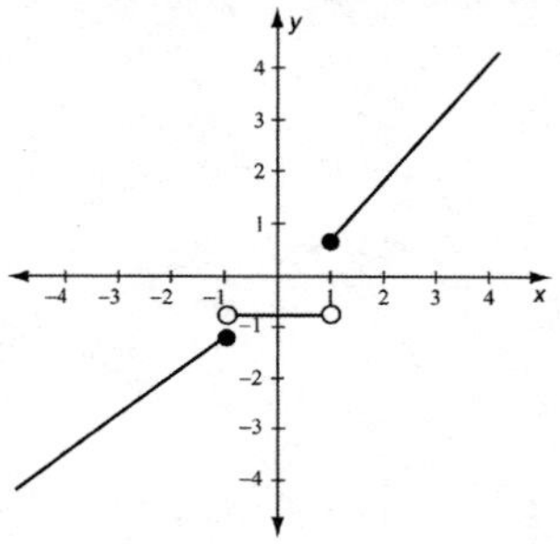

5. True or false: The following table represents a function.

x	y
-2	16
-1	4
0	0
1	4
2	16

Identifying Functions

- A **function** is an equation where you get exactly one result for each value you put in.
- **Vertical line test** for a function of x means that for every value of x there exists at most one value of y.

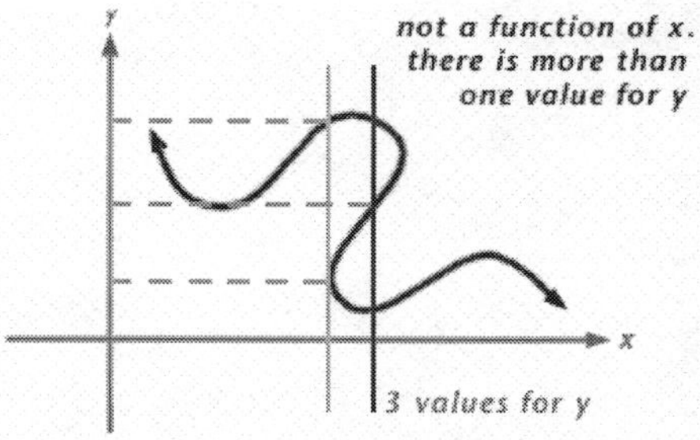

For an equation to be a function of x, it must pass the vertical line test. This means that every value of x has no more than one value of y; i.e., a vertical line will intersect a given curve no more than once.

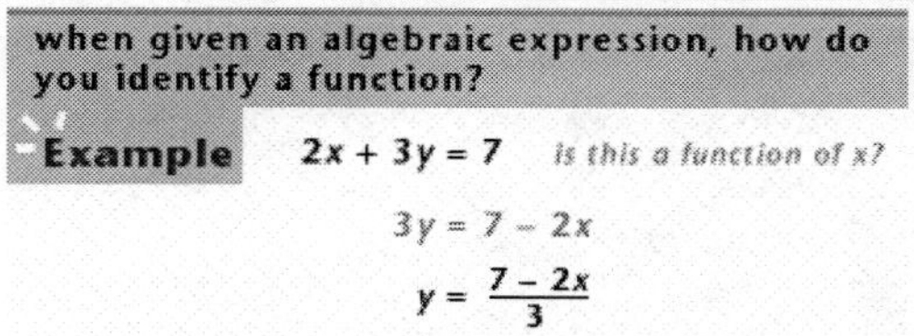

In identifying a function, the question is whether for every value of x, there is only one or no values of y.

First transform this equation into a statement that shows what y equals in terms of x.

Then, you know that this one is a function of x; no matter what you use for x, you will derive only one y.

Example $y = x^2 - 4$ *is this a function of x?*

yes *ask: when substituting for x do you get one value for y?*

This example meets the function test because, once again, for each value of x you use there will be exactly one value of y.

the function as a graph:

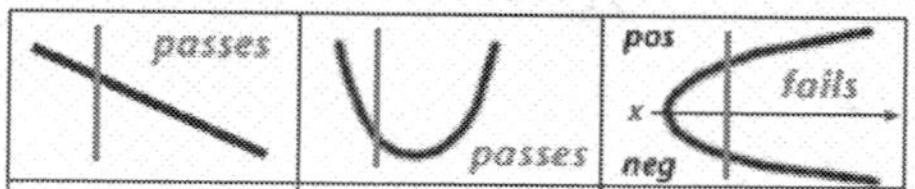

$2x + 3y = 7$	$y = x^2 - 4$	$-x + y^2 = 2$
$y = \frac{7 - 2x}{3}$	yes	$y = \pm\sqrt{2 + x}$
yes		No

It is easy to check each example using the vertical line test.

The first two examples verify graphically what you found out algebraically. They show there is only one y-value for each x-value; i.e., that a vertical line intersects the curve at most once.

The third example verifies graphically that the curve fails the vertical line test and, therefore, cannot be considered a function of x.

Sample problems:

1. Given $y = \frac{1}{x^2}$, determine algebraically if y is a function of x.
   Solution: y is a function of x
   Explanation: Determine if there is more than one y - value for any given x - value. Choose any x - value, for example $x = 3$, and substitute it into the equation to find the corresponding y - value:
   $y = \frac{1}{(3)^2} = \frac{1}{9}$. Since the x - value produces only one y - value, $y = \frac{1}{x^2}$ is a function of x.

2. Given $y - x^3 = 0$, solve for y and determine algebraically if y is a function of x.
   Solution: y is a function of x
   Explanation: Solve the equation for y: $y - x^3 = 0 \Rightarrow y = x^3$. Determine if there is more than one y - value for any given x - value. Choose any x - value, for example $x = -5$, and substitute it into the equation to find the corresponding y - value:
   $y = (-5)^3 = -125$. Since the x - value raised to the third power produces only one y - value as a result, $y - x^3 = 0$ is a function of x.

3. Given $x^4 - y^4 = 1$, solve for y and determine algebraically if y is a function of x.
   Solution: y is not a function of x
   Explanation: Solve the equation for y: $x^4 - y^4 = 1 \Rightarrow y^4 = x^4 - 1$; $y = \pm\sqrt[4]{(x^4 - 1)}$.
   Determine if there is more than one y - value for any given x - value. Choose any x - value, for example $x = 2$, and substitute it into the equation to find the corresponding y - value: $y = \pm\sqrt[4]{(2^4 - 1)} = \pm\sqrt[4]{15}$. Therefore, the equation does not describe a function of x, since there is an x - value that corresponds to two y - values.

Practice problems: *(Answers on page: 738)*

1. Given $y = \frac{5}{1 - x}$, determine algebraically if y is a function of x.

2. Given $3x + 2y^2 = 1$, solve for y and determine algebraically if y is a function of x.

3. Given $x^2 - 2y = 0$, solve for y and determine algebraically if y is a function of x.

Review questions: *(Answers to odd questions on page: 738)*

1. Given $y = \dfrac{x+1}{x^2}$, determine algebraically if y is a function of x.

2. Given $y = \sqrt[4]{\dfrac{1}{x}}$, determine algebraically if y is a function of x.

3. Given $\frac{1}{2}x - y^2 = x^2$, solve for y and determine algebraically if y is a function of x.

4. Given $\dfrac{3x^4 - 5y^4}{2} = 1$, solve for y and determine algebraically if y is a function of x.

5. Given $x - \frac{2}{3}y = x^2$, solve for y and determine algebraically if y is a function of x.

Function Notation and Finding Function Values

- **Function notation** replaces the "y =" in an equation with "$f(x)$ =" which shows that each y-value depends on the value used for x.
- *f(x)* shows the y-value for the given x and shows that the y-value can be found when an x-value is known and used in the equation. Other letters are frequently used as well, so that you may find $g(x)$, $h(x)$, and so on.
- *f(x)* is read "f of x." The expression $f(2)$ is read as "f of 2". $f(2)$ indicates the value that y has in this function when $x = 2$.

$f(x)$ = the value of y written in terms of a function of x "f of x" **Example** $y = 2x^2 - 1$ what does this mean? $f(2) =$ insert 2 for x $f(2) = 2(2)^2 - 1 = 7$ Original Question: Find the value for y when $x = 2$ New Notation: Find f of 2	For this function, $f(2)$ means to substitute 2 in each place that you find an x in the expression. Then solve for the value of the expression to determine $f(2)$. $f(2)$ is the y-value for the point where $x = 2$ in this expression. Since this $f(2) = 7$, on a graph, you would find the point (2,7). This notation replaces the old "y =" notation.
$f(1) = 2(1)^2 - 1 = 1$ plug in 1 for x	This $f(1)$ uses 1 for every x to determine that $f(1)$, or y, equals 1. On a graph this is the point (1,1).
$f(0) = 2(0)^2 - 1 = -1$ plug in 0 for x	Now $f(0)$ replaces x with 0 and it turns out that $f(0)$ equals −1. On a graph this is the point (0,-1).
Example $g(x) = \dfrac{1}{x+3}$ evaluate: $g(2) = \dfrac{1}{2+3} = \dfrac{1}{5}$ substitute 2 for x	For this function, g(2) equals 1/5. On a graph, this is the point (2,1/5)

Example $h(x) = \sqrt{x^2 - 1}$ *function doesn't have to be f* **evaluate:** $h(1) = \sqrt{1^2 - 1}$ $h(1) = \sqrt{0}$ $h(1) = 0$ $h(2) = \sqrt{2^2 - 1}$ $h(2) = \sqrt{3}$	For this function, $h(2)$ equals $\sqrt{3}$. On a graph, this is the point $(2, \sqrt{3})$.

Sample problems:

1. Given $g(x) = \dfrac{x+5}{2}$, find $g(2a-5)$.

   Solution: a

   Explanation: Substitute $2a-5$ for x in $g(x) = \dfrac{x+5}{2}$ and simplify:

   $$g(2a-5) = \frac{(2a-5)+5}{2} = \frac{2a}{2} = a.$$

2. Given $f(x) = |2x-5|$, find the value of $f(4) - f(1)$.

   Solution: 0

   Explanation: Substitute 4 and 1 for x in $f(x) = |2x-5|$, simplify each function, and then subtract:

   $f(4) - f(1) = |2(4)-5| - |2(1)-5| = |3| - |-3| = 3 - 3 = 0.$

3. Given $f(x) = 1 - 2x^2$, find $\dfrac{f(x+h) - f(x)}{h}$.

   Solution: $-4x - 2h$

   Explanation: In this problem the function $f(x) = 1 - 2x^2$ is used twice, once substituting $(x+h)$ and once as is. Complete the substitution:

   $\dfrac{f(x+h) - f(x)}{h} = \dfrac{[1 - 2(x+h)^2] - [1 - 2x^2]}{h}$. Simplify:

   $$\frac{[1 - 2x^2 - 4xh - 2h^2] - [1 - 2x^2]}{h} = \frac{1 - 2x^2 - 4xh - 2h^2 - 1 + 2x^2}{h} = \frac{-4xh - 2h^2}{h} = -4x - 2h.$$

Practice problems: *(Answers on page: 739)*

1. Given $h(x) = \dfrac{2}{x} + x$, find $h(a+1)$.
2. Given $f(x) = x^2 - 2x$ find $f(x+h)$.
3. Given $f(x) = x^2 + 3$, find $\dfrac{f(x) - f(x+2)}{-4}$.

Review questions: *(Answers to odd questions on page: 739)*

1. If $f(x) = x^3 - 5x - 2$, find $f(-2)$.
2. If $f(x) = x^3 - 5x - 2$, find $f\left(\dfrac{3}{2}\right)$.
3. If $f(x) = \dfrac{x^3 + 2x}{x - 1}$, find $f(-2)$.

4. If $f(x) = (x-2)^2 + 3$, find $f(a+1) - f(1)$.

5. If $f(x) = \dfrac{(3x-1)}{4x+2}$, find $f\left(\dfrac{x-1}{x+2}\right)$.

Determining Intervals Over Which a Function Is Increasing

- A **function is decreasing** if the graph drops as the x-values get larger.
- A **function is increasing** if the graph rises as the x-values get larger.
- A **function is constant** if it is neither increasing nor decreasing over a given interval.
- A **maximum** is a high point that occurs when an increasing curve begins decreasing.
- A **minimum** is a low point that occurs when a decreasing curve begins increasing.
- Whether a function is increasing or decreasing is determined as the graph is viewed from left to right.
- Some functions increase and decrease many times over their curve.

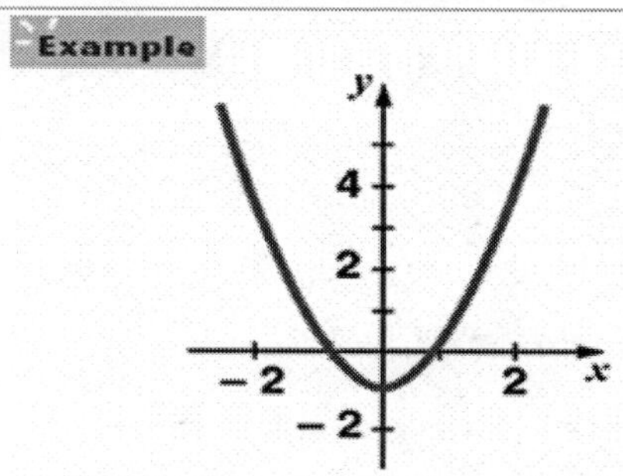	This function is **decreasing** for all the x-values smaller than 0. As you view the portion of the curve to the left of the y-axis, reading it from left to right, it is falling.The function is **increasing** for all x-values larger than 0. As you view the portion of the curve to the right of the y-axis, reading it also from left to right, it is rising.The point where the curve turns is a **minimum**.
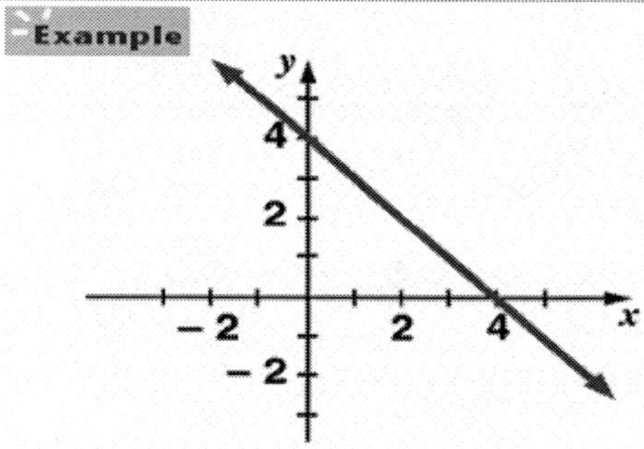	This function is always decreasing. Remember to read the curve from left to right as you make your judgement.It has no maximum or minimum points because it never turns.
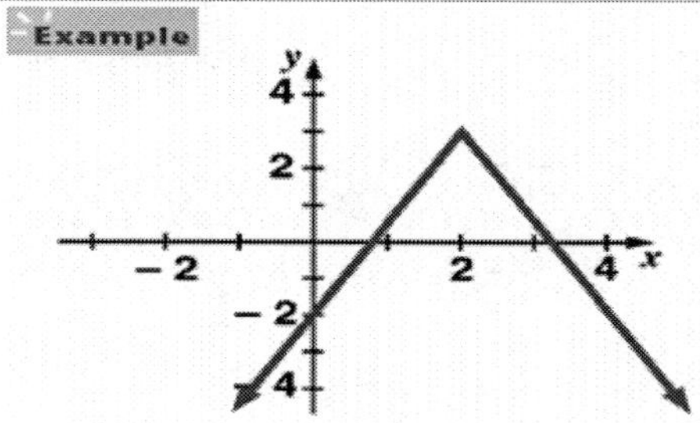	This function is increasing for all x-values less than +2. The function is decreasing for all x-values greater than +2.
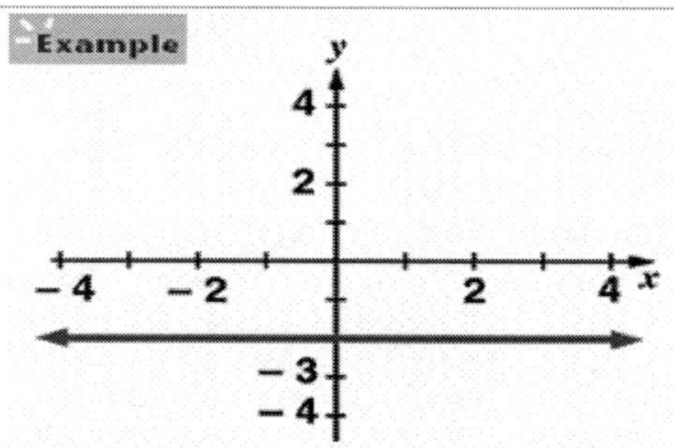	This function is always constant. It neither rises nor falls.

<table>
<tr>
<td>
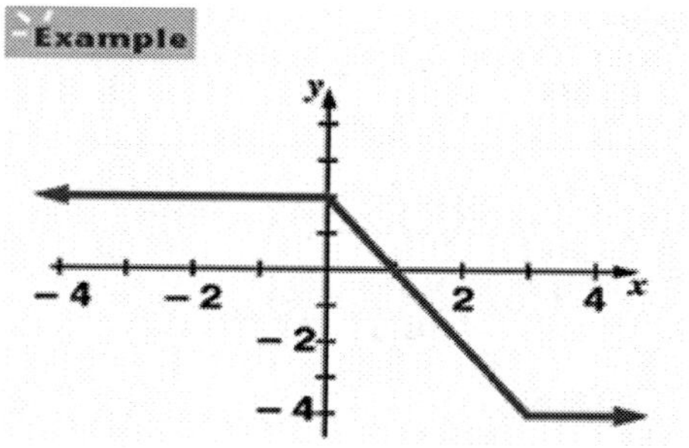

</td>
<td>
This function is constant for all x-values less than or equal to 0. It is also constant for all x-values greater than or equal to 3.

The function is decreasing over the interval $0 < x < 3$.
</td>
</tr>
<tr>
<td>
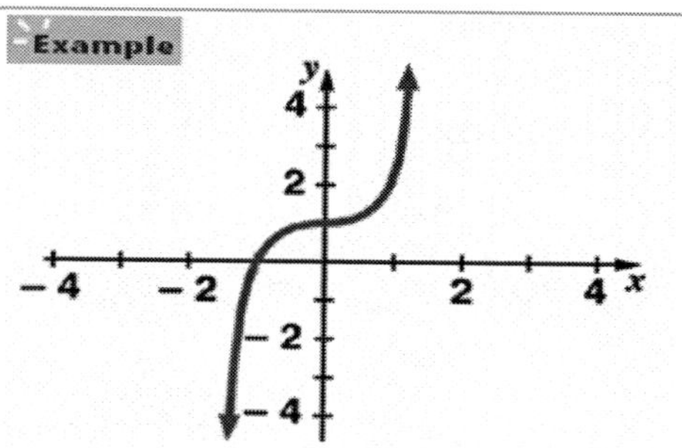

</td>
<td>
This function is increasing over its entire curve. Remember you are reading from left to right. Your analysis is whether the point to the right is higher than your point of reference for each point on the curve.
</td>
</tr>
<tr>
<td>
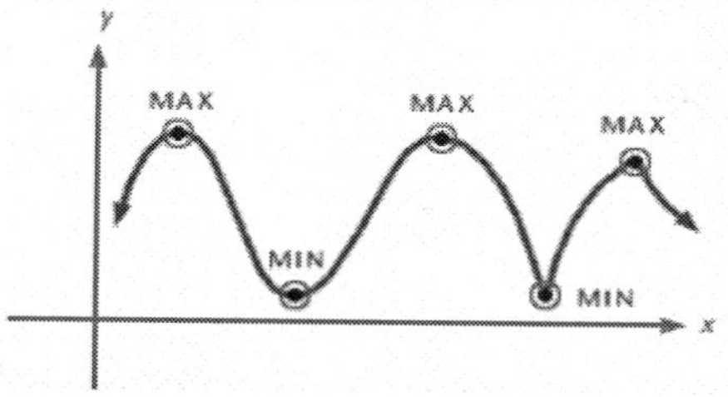

</td>
<td>
Functions that change between increasing and decreasing have high and low points.

This function has three maxima and two minima that you can see over the pictured interval. This function is turning frequently.
</td>
</tr>
</table>

Sample problems:

1. Given the graph of $f(x) = \dfrac{x^2(8 - x^2)}{4}$, determine the interval of x where $f(x)$ is increasing.

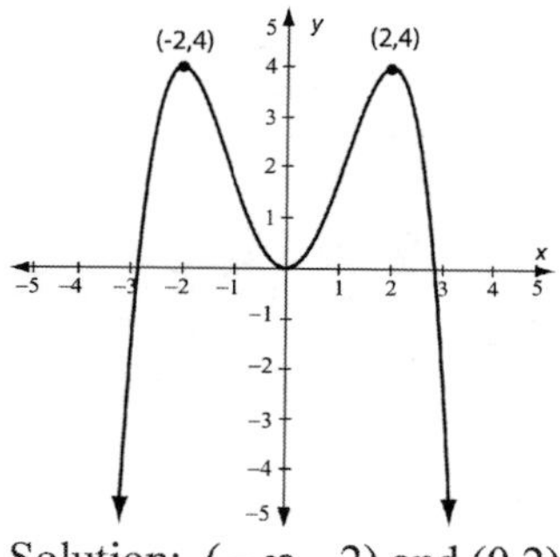

Solution: $(-\infty, -2)$ and $(0,2)$

Explanation: Observe the graph from left to right. The curve rises for x from $-\infty \rightarrow -2$, then begins decreasing. Then again the curve rises for x from $0 \rightarrow 2$, then decreases. Express these x-values in interval notation: $(-\infty, -2)$ and $(0,2)$.

2. Given the graph of $f(x) = \dfrac{x^2 + 4}{2x}$, determine the interval of x where $f(x)$ is increasing.

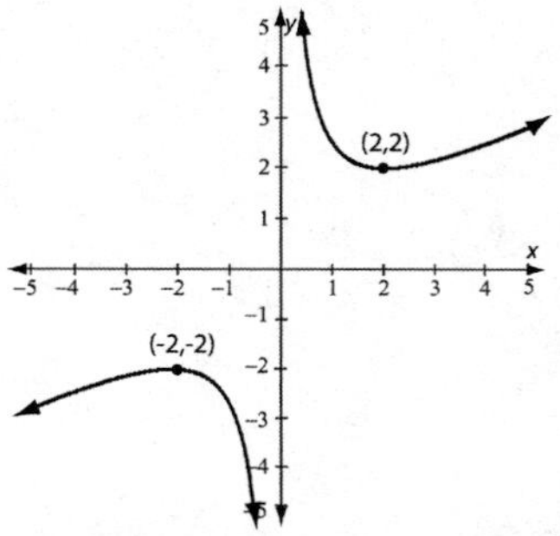

Solution: $(-\infty,-2)$ and $(2,\infty)$
Explanation: The curve rises for x from $-\infty \rightarrow -2$, then again from $2 \rightarrow \infty$. Express these x-values in interval notation: $(-\infty,-2)$ and $(2,\infty)$.

3. Given the graph of $f(x)=x^3-3x$, determine the interval of x where $f(x)$ is decreasing and the interval of x where $f(x)$ is constant.

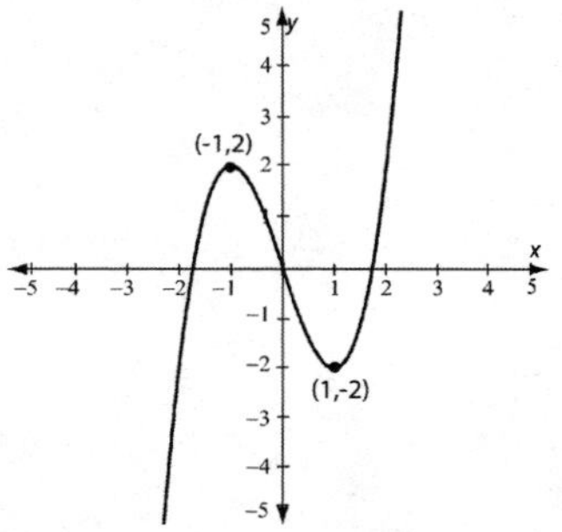

Solution: $(-1,1)$, $f(x)$ is never constant
Explanation: The curve *decreases* for x from $-1 \rightarrow 1$. Express these x-values in interval notation: $(-1,1)$. A function is constant where its graph is horizontal, however this function is never constant.

Practice problems: *(Answers on page: 739)*

1. Given the graph of $f(x)=-x^2+4$, determine the interval of x where $f(x)$ is decreasing.

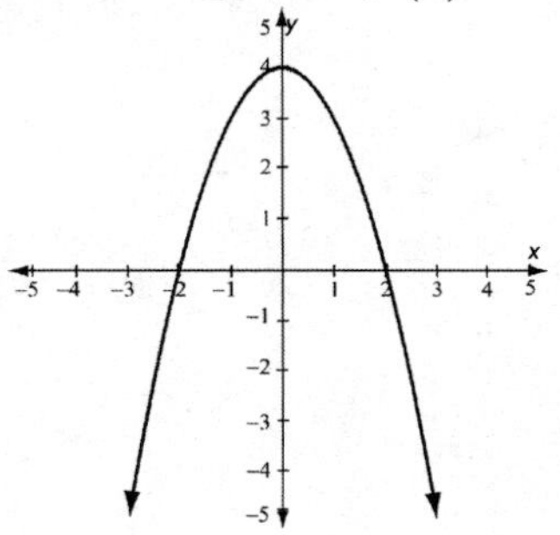

2. Given the graph of $f(x)=x^3-2$, determine the interval of x where $f(x)$ is increasing.

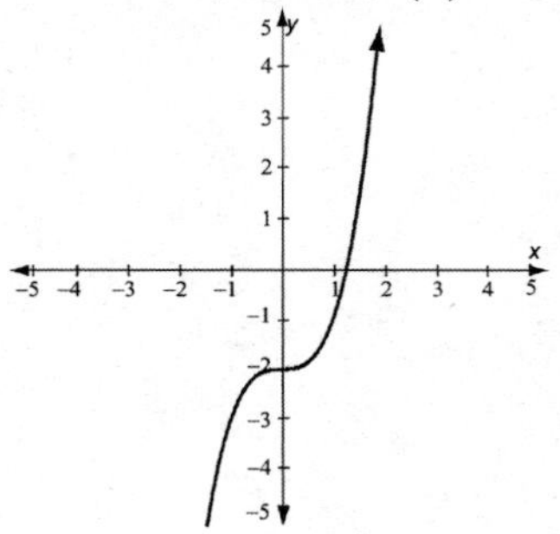

3. Given the graph $f(x)$ below, determine the interval of x where $f(x)$ is constant.

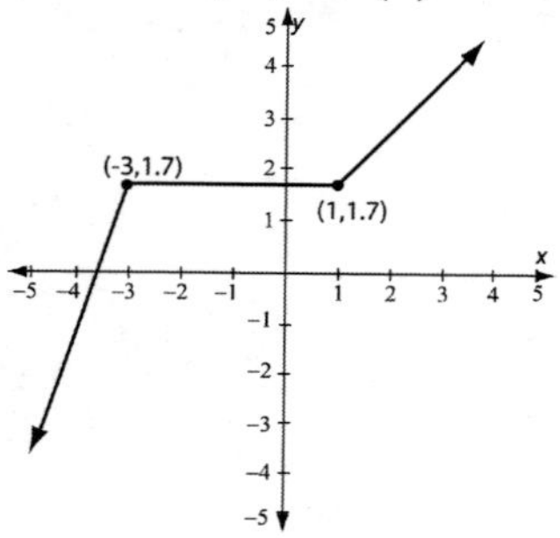

Review questions: *(Answers to odd questions on page: 739)*

1. Given the graph of $f(x)=|x|$, determine the interval of x where $f(x)$ is increasing.

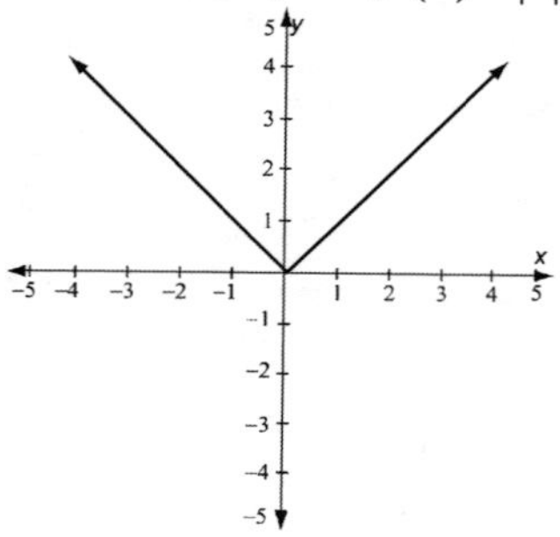

2. Given the graph of $f(x)=1-x^3$, determine the interval of x where $f(x)$ is increasing.

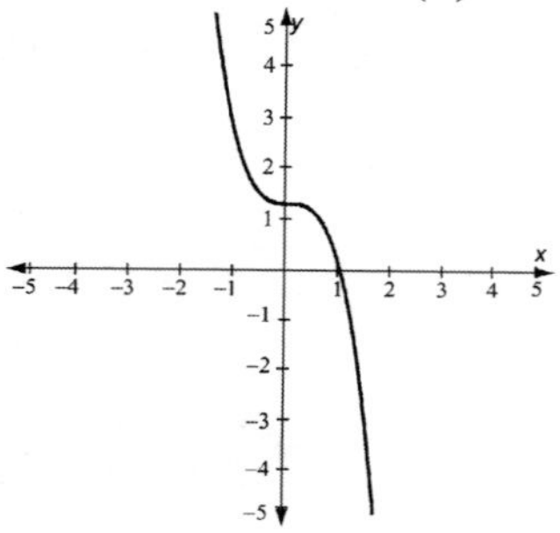

3. Given the graph of $f(x)=\frac{2}{3}x+1$, determine the interval of x where $f(x)$ is increasing.

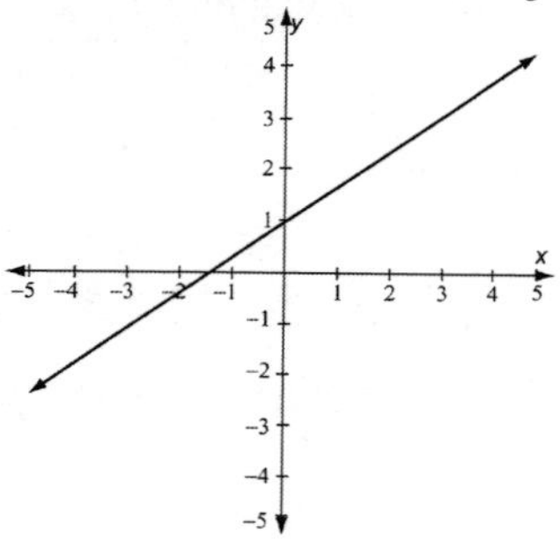

4. Given the graph $f(x)$ below, determine the interval of x where $f(x)$ is decreasing.

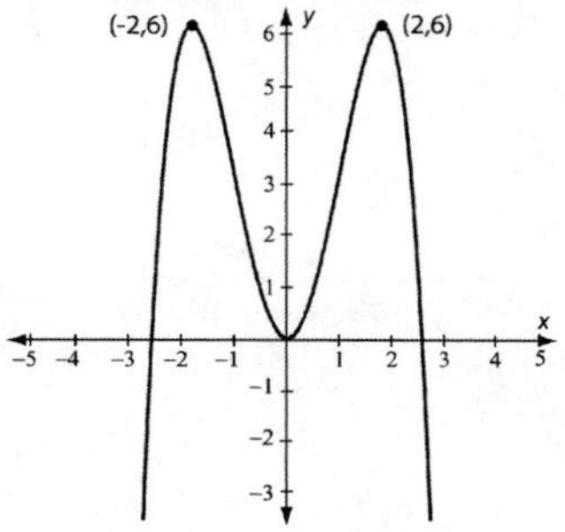

5. Given the graph $f(x)$ below, determine the interval of x where $f(x)$ is constant.

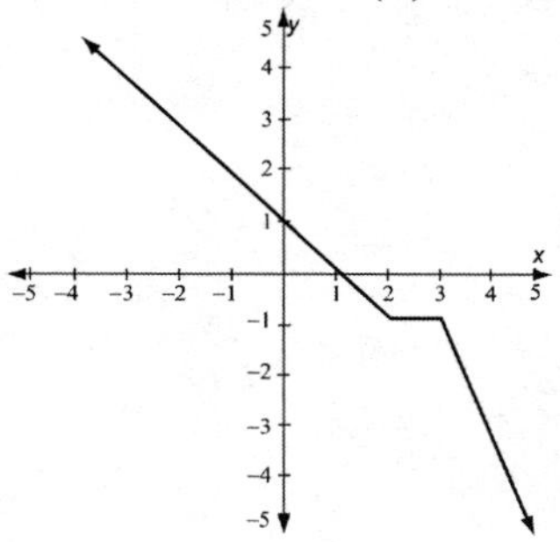

Evaluating Piecewise-Defined Functions for Given Values

- A **piecewise-defined function** is defined using different equations for different intervals in its **domain**.
- To evaluate a piecewise-defined function at a particular x-value, determine the interval that the x-value is in and use the corresponding piece of the function.
- To graph a piecewise-defined function, you combine the graphs of each piece while paying attention to the intervals where the pieces are defined.

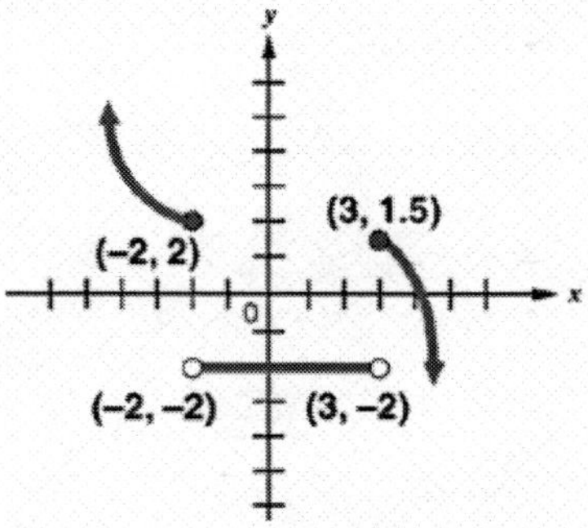

Up to this point you have only seen the graphs of relatively tame functions.

Take a look at the graph of this strange function. It's pretty wild!

After recovering from the shock (or not), you might ask yourself: How can you write down an equation for this function? The answer is to put together three separate functions, one for each piece of the graph.

whether the value is ≥ or < 2 will determine which formula to use

Example $f(x) = \begin{cases} 3x^2 + 1 \text{ if } x \geq 2 \\ \frac{-1}{2}x + 14 \text{ if } x < 2 \end{cases}$

evaluate:

$f(5) = 3x^2 + 1 \qquad 5 \geq 2$

$f(2) = 3x^2 + 1 \qquad 2 \geq 2$

$f(0) = \frac{-1}{2}x + 14 \qquad 0 < 2$

Here's an example of a function that pieces together two separate functions; functions defined in this way are called **piecewise-defined functions**.

To evaluate a piecewise-defined function at a particular x-value, you need to know which formula (or piece) to use. In this case, if $x > 2$, you use the first formula. If $x < 2$, you use the second formula.

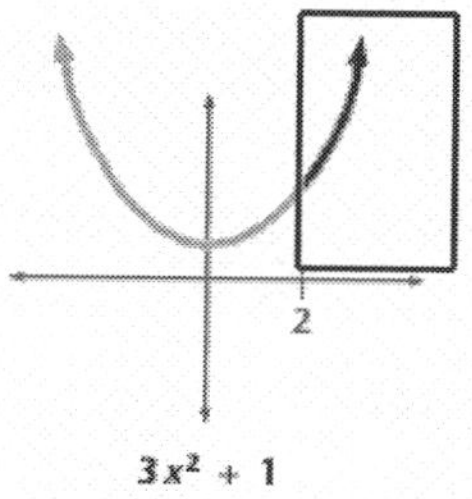 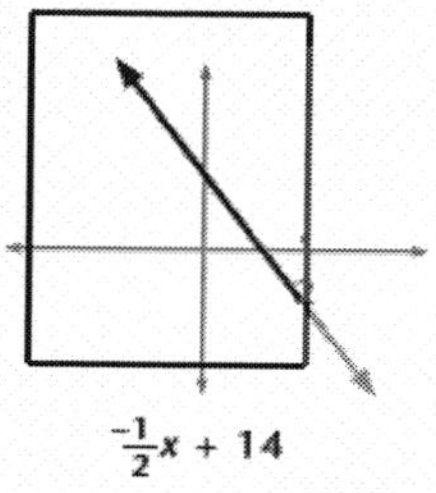	Here are the graphs of the two pieces each by itself. For the entire piecewise-defined function, you combine the graph of the first function for $x > 2$ with the graph of the second function for $x < 2$. **NOTE:** If you aren't comfortable graphing functions yet, don't worry – you'll get to that soon.
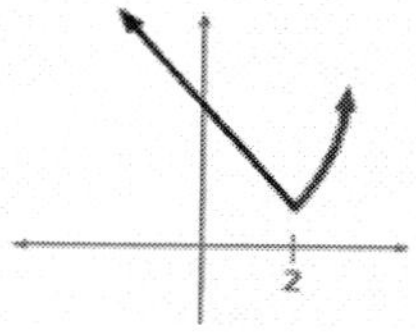	Put the two pieces together and you get the graph of the piecewise-defined function!

Sample problems:

1. Given the function $f(x) = \begin{cases} x+1 \text{ if } x > 2 \\ -2x+5 \text{ if } x \le 2 \end{cases}$, determine the interval of x in which $f(x)$ is decreasing.

   Solution: $(-\infty, 2]$

   Explanation: Consider the graph of the first part, $f(x) = x+1$. The graph is increasing. Consider the graph of the second part, $f(x) = -2x+5$. The graph is decreasing. This part of the function applies when $x \le 2$. Express this inequality in interval notation: $(-\infty, 2]$.

2. Given the function $f(x) = \begin{cases} -2x & \text{if} \quad x < -3 \\ -3x-1 & \text{if} \ -3 \le x \le 2 \\ -4x & \text{if} \quad x > 2 \end{cases}$, evaluate $f(-1)$.

   Solution: 2

   Explanation: To evaluate $f(-1)$, determine which part of the function is indicated by the given domain value, -1. Since -1 is in $-3 \le x \le 2$, evaluate $f(-1)$ using the second part, $f(x) = -3x-1$: $f(-1) = -3(-1)-1 = 2$.

3. Given the function $f(x) = \begin{cases} \frac{1}{2}x^2 & \text{if} \ x < -7 \\ 5-x & \text{if} \ -7 \le x < 0 \\ x^3+1 & \text{if} \ x \ge 0 \end{cases}$, evaluate $f(0)$.

   Solution: 1

   Explanation: Since 0 is in $x \ge 0$, evaluate $f(0)$ using the third part, $f(x) = x^3+1$: $f(0) = 0^3+1 = 1$.

Practice problems: *(Answers on page: 739)*

1. Given the function $g(x) = \begin{cases} x^2 \text{ if } x \le -1 \\ x \text{ if } -1 < x < 1 \\ -x \text{ if } x \ge 1 \end{cases}$, determine the interval of x in which $f(x)$ is decreasing.

2. Given the function $f(x) = \begin{cases} x+4 \ \text{ if } x < -4 \\ \frac{1}{x} \text{ if } -4 \le x \le 0 \\ x^2 - x \text{ if } x > 0 \end{cases}$, evaluate $f(-3)$.

3. Given the function $f(x) = \begin{cases} x^2+4x+1 \ \text{ if } x < 2 \\ 5-x \text{ if } x = 2 \\ x^2-1 \text{ if } x > 2 \end{cases}$, evaluate $f(-1)$.

Review questions: *(Answers to odd questions on page: 739)*

1. Given the function $f(x)=\begin{cases}3x & \text{if } x\le 0\\ 2 & \text{if } 0<x<1\\ -x & \text{if } x\ge 1\end{cases}$, determine the interval of x in which $f(x)$ is constant.

2. Given the function $f(x)=\begin{cases}4+x & \text{if } x\le -2\\ x^2 & \text{if } -2<x<3\\ x^3 & \text{if } x\ge 3\end{cases}$, determine the interval of x in which $f(x)$ is increasing.

3. Given the function $f(x)=\begin{cases}2x+4 & \text{if } x<-1\\ x & \text{if } -1\le x\le 0\\ x^2-3x & \text{if } x>0\end{cases}$, evaluate $f(-7)$.

4. Given the function $f(x)=\begin{cases}x^3 & \text{if } x<5\\ |x-2| & \text{if } 5\le x\le 9\\ 4 & \text{if } x>9\end{cases}$, evaluate $f(10)$.

5. Given the function $f(x)=\begin{cases}x^3 & \text{if } x<5\\ |x-2| & \text{if } 5\le x\le 9\\ 4 & \text{if } x>9\end{cases}$, evaluate $f(-2)$.

Solving Word Problems Involving Functions

- Function thinking allows you to solve a problem with two unknowns by setting up an equation with one unknown defined in terms of the other unknown. Then, when you can determine a value for the one unknown, you can solve for the other unknown.
- $f(x)$ means a function defined in terms of x. It also means the value an expression has for a given quantity, x.
- The perimeter of a rectangle equals the sum of the sides.
- The area of a rectangle equals length times width.

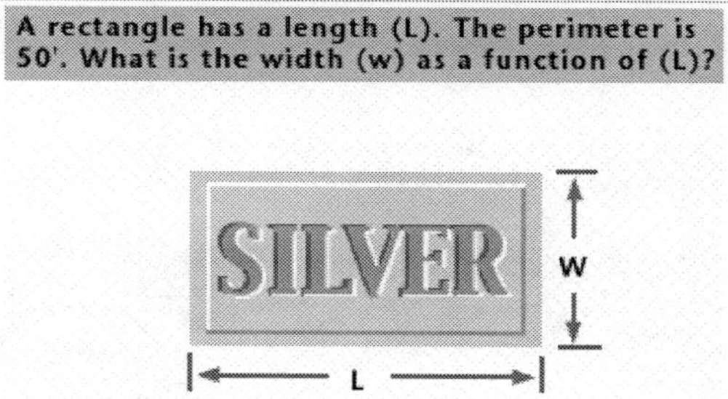

For any rectangle, Perimeter = $2l + 2w$; Area = $l \cdot w$

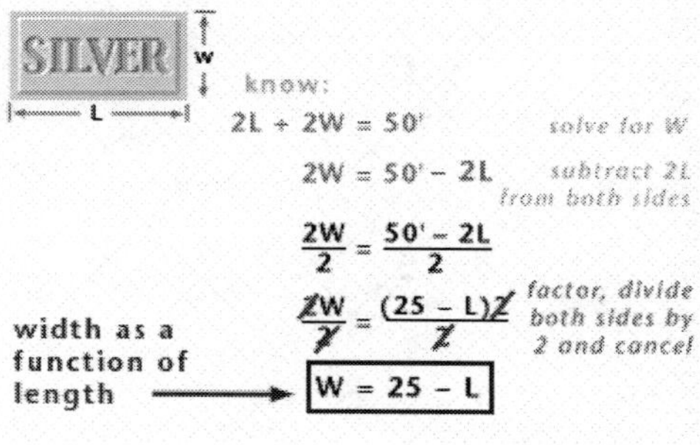

Once we know that the perimeter equals 50, we know

$P = 50 = 2l + 2w$

We can easily solve for w using this information. At any specific length (l) we can now solve for the width (w).

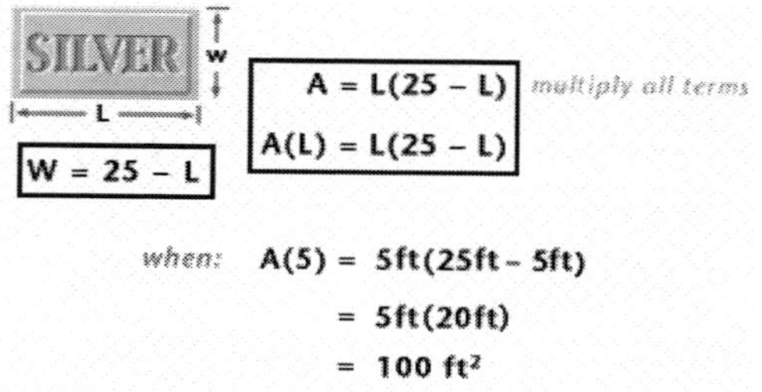

Once we have a statement for w, we can define the area in terms of the other variable L. Our notation is $A(L)$ which is read "area in terms of length," or the function "A of L."

Then, at any specific length, in this case when $L = 5$, we can calculate the area.

Sample problems:

1. Determine the area of the region that lies between the x-axis and $f(x) = \begin{cases} 7 \text{ for } 0 \le x \le 4 \\ 6 \text{ for } 4 \le x \le 8 \\ 2 \text{ for } 8 \le x \le 10 \end{cases}$.

   Solution: 56 units^2
   Explanation: Sketch the region. The function $f(x)$ produces a set of three rectangles, so find the sum of the areas of each rectangle: $(7)(4)+(6)(4)+(2)(2)=56$ units^2.

2. A piece of rope that is 10 feet long is cut into two pieces. One piece is used to form a circle and the other is used to form a square. Write a function for the sum of the areas of the square and the circle as a function of the radius of the circle.

   Solution: $\pi r^2 + \left(\frac{5-\pi r}{2}\right)^2$
   Explanation: Let r be the radius of the circle and s be the length of a side of the square. The circumference of the circle is $2\pi r$ and the perimeter of the square is $4s$. Since the length of the rope is 10 feet, $2\pi r + 4s = 10$. Solve for s: $s = \dfrac{10-2\pi r}{4} = \dfrac{5-\pi r}{2}$.
   Write a function for the sum of the areas of the circle and the square: $A = \pi r^2 + s^2$.
   Substitute the expression for s into the area function: $A = \pi r^2 + \left(\frac{5-\pi r}{2}\right)^2$.

3. A rectangle is inscribed in a semicircle with its length lying along the diameter of the circle as shown in the figure. The equation of the circle is $x^2 + y^2 = 25$. Write a function for the area of the rectangle in terms of x.

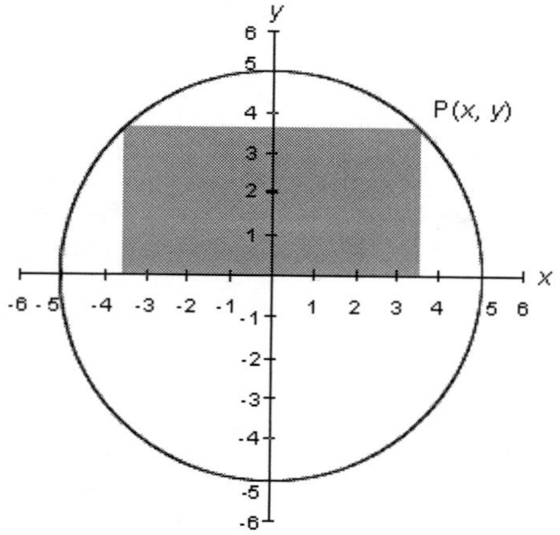

   Solution: $2x\sqrt{25-x^2}$
   Explanation: The base of the rectangle is $2x$ and the height is y. So, the area of the rectangle is given by $A = 2xy$. Solve the circle equation for y: $y = \sqrt{25-x^2}$.
   Substitute the expression for y into the area function: $A = 2xy = 2x\sqrt{25-x^2}$.

Practice problems: *(Answers on page: 739)*

1. Determine the area of the region that lies between the x-axis and $f(x)=\begin{cases}10 \text{ for } 0\le x\le 1\\ 12 \text{ for } 1\le x\le 5.\\ 3 \text{ for } 5\le x\le 7\end{cases}$
2. Write a function for the volume of a sphere in terms of the surface area, S, of the sphere.
3. Write a function for the area of a rectangle in terms of the width, w, if the perimeter of the rectangle is 20 cm.

Review questions: *(Answers to odd questions on page: 739)*

1. Determine the area of the region that lies between the x-axis and $f(x)=\begin{cases}1 \text{ for } 0\le x\le 1\\ 8 \text{ for } 1\le x\le 7\\ 2 \text{ for } 7\le x\le 10\end{cases}$.
2. The perimeter of the given rectangle is 28 feet. Let y be the width and x the length. Find the area as a function of the length (x).
3. The area of a circle is $A=\pi r^2$ and the circumference is $C=2\pi r$. Write an equation for the area of a circle as a function of the circumference .
4. A rectangle is in the 1st quadrant with one vertex at the origin, another on the x-axis, a third on the y-axis, and the final vertex on the line $3x+2y=6$. Find a formula for the area of the rectangle as a function of x.

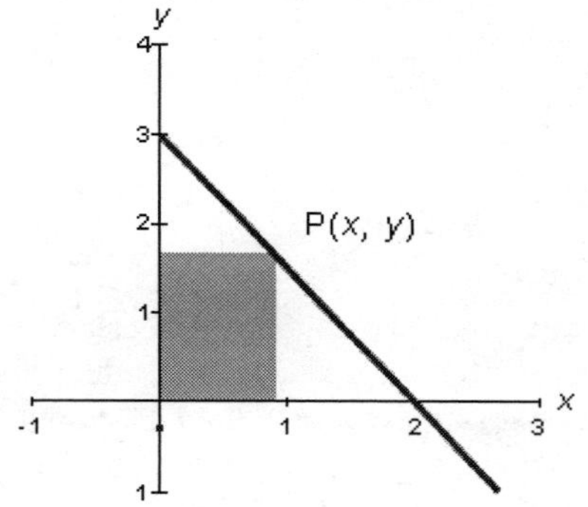

5. A rectangular metal sheet 10 inches by 8 inches is made into an open box by cutting out square corners on all four vertices of length x. Find a formula for the volume of the rectangular box .

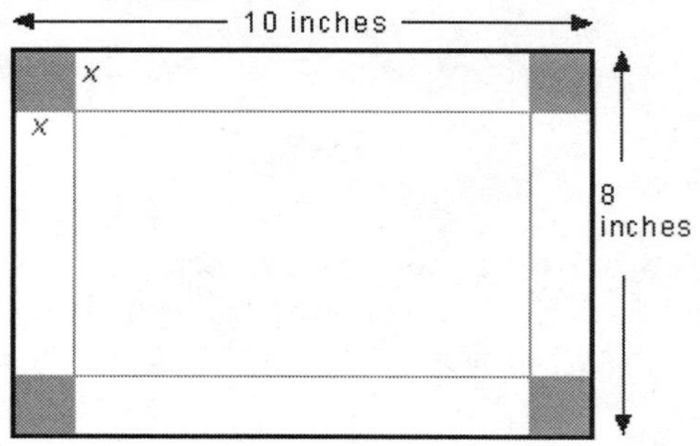

Finding the Domain and Range of a Function

- The **domain** of a function is the set of all x-values that can be used as inputs for the function.
- The **range** of a function is the set of all possible y-values, or outputs, for a function.
- Values excluded from the domain include values that result in a negative number under a square root sign and values that cause a denominator to equal zero.

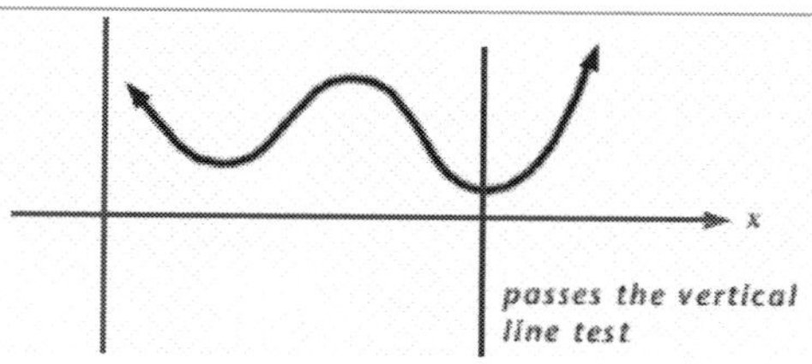

To be judged a function, an equation must have no more than one y-value for every x- value. Graphically, this notion means that if you place a vertical line anywhere on the curve, it will intersect the curve in only one point.

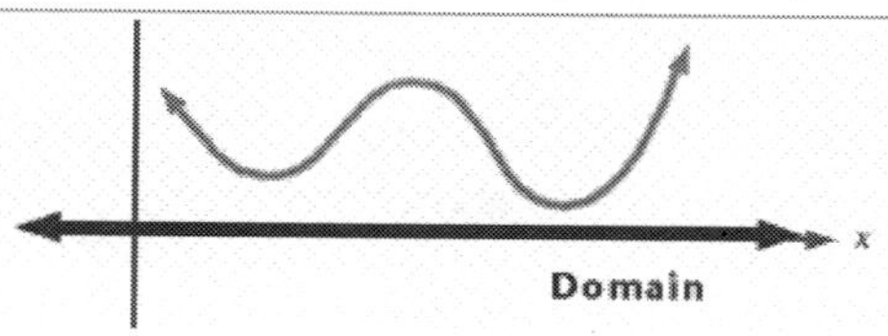

In this case, the **domain** is all the real numbers because the curve goes on forever to both the right and the left. As a result, every x there is will have some y on the curve.

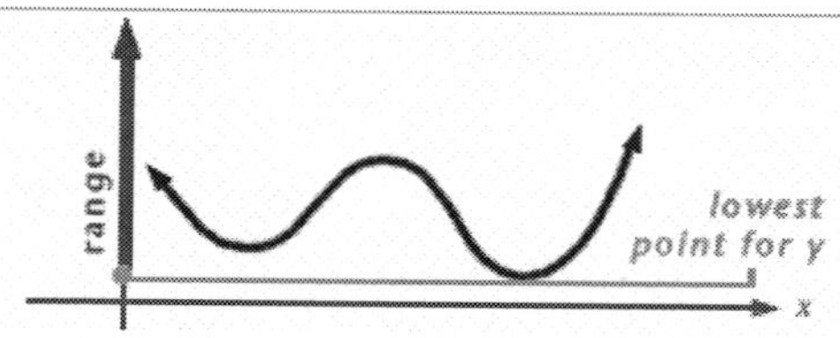

The **range** is all the real numbers that are used as y-values for a curve. In this example, there will not be any negative y values nor even any positive y values just barely above the x-axis.

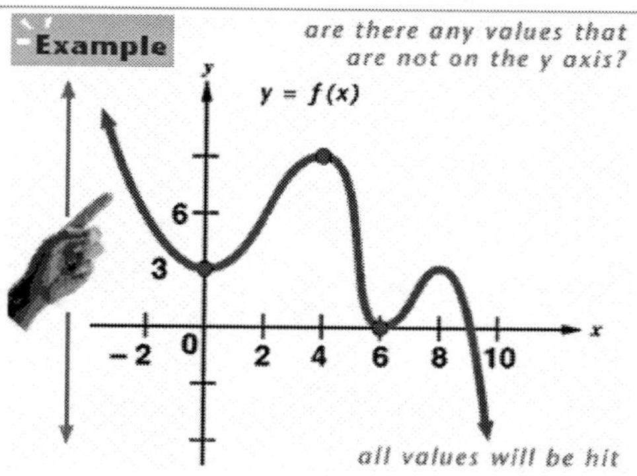

In this example, the domain is all the values of x, and the range is all the values of y. There are no values that will be missed or excluded in either direction.

Domain: $-\infty < x < \infty$
Range: $-\infty < y < \infty$

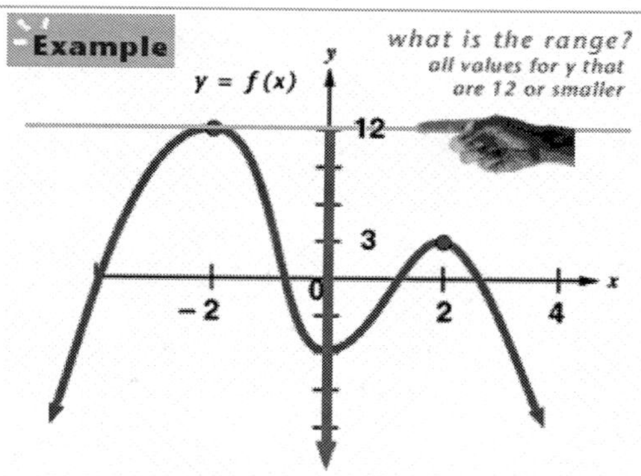

In this example, the domain will be all the x- values. The range, however, will not include any values larger than +12 because the curve does not rise any higher than that point. So, the range is all the y-values less than or equal to +12.

Domain: $-\infty < x < \infty$
Range: $y \le 12$

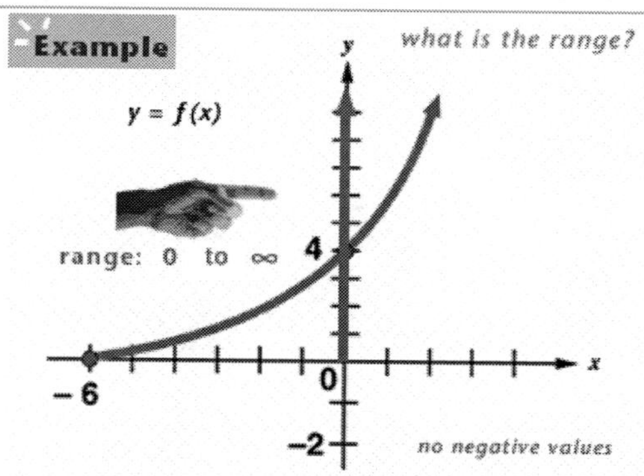

In this example, the domain will be all x-values greater than or equal to –6 because the curve stops and does not pass left of –6. The range will be 0 and all positive numbers because the curve does not move below the x-axis but does touch the x-axis.

Domain: $x \ge -6$
Range: $y \ge 0$

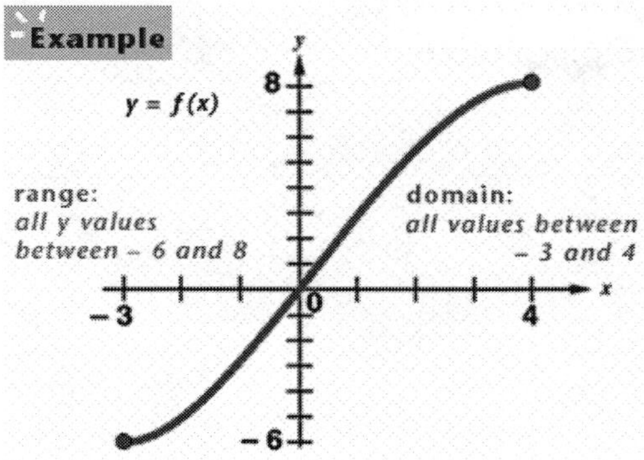

In this example of a curve segment, the endpoints are (-3,-6) and (4,8). Since the curve is continuous between those two points, all values between the two points are used on the curve. As a result the domain will include all values between –3 and 4. The range will include all values between -6 and 8.

Domain: $-3 \le x \le 4$
Range: $-6 \le y \le 8$

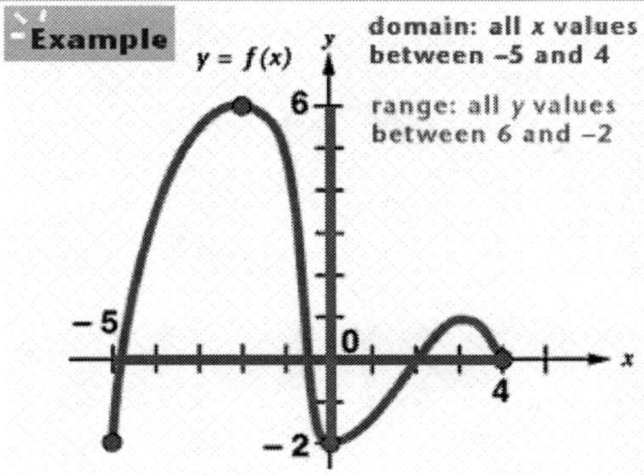

This curve is continuous and moves between (–5,–2) and (4,0). The domain is limited to include all values between or equal to –5, the left end of the curve, and +4, the right end of the curve. The range is limited to include all values between or equal to –2, the lowest point on the curve, and +6, the highest point on the curve.

Domain: $-5 \le x \le 4$
Range: $-2 \le y \le 6$

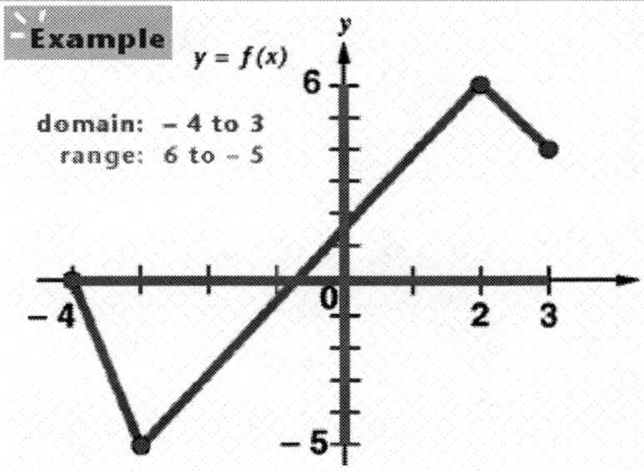

This unusual curve has endpoints at (–4,0) and (3,4). That fact will limit its values as shown. Its domain will be all the values between or equal to –4 and +3. Its range will be all the values between or equal to –5 and +6.

Domain: $-4 \le x \le 3$
Range: $-5 \le y \le 6$

Sample problems:

1. Find the domain of the function $y = x^4 - 2x^3 - 9x^2 + 8$.

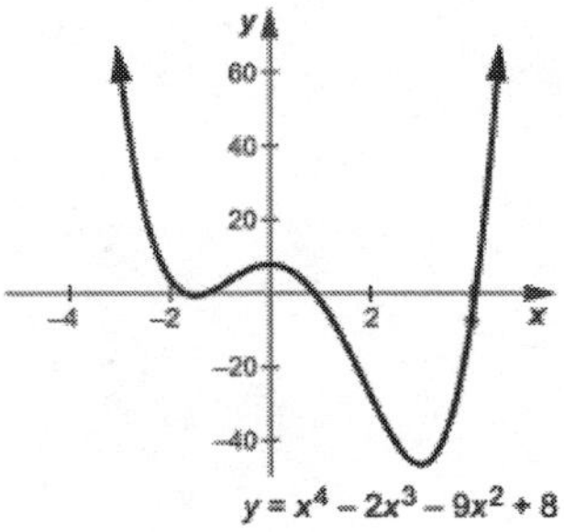

Solution: $-\infty < x < \infty$
Explanation: In the graph the arrows indicate that the graph extends infinitely in both the negative and positive directions, thus the possible x values are all real numbers. Additionally, in the equation, x is defined for all real numbers. Therefore, the domain is $-\infty < x < \infty$.

2. Given $y = f(x) = \sqrt{\dfrac{x+8}{2}}$, use this equation and the graph below to find the domain of the function f.

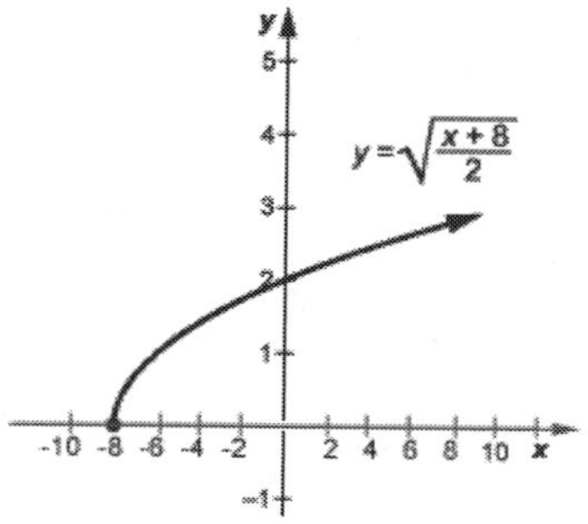

Solution: $x \geq -8$

Explanation: In the graph the possible values of x are any value -8 or larger. Thus, the domain is $x \geq -8$.

3. Find the domain and range of the function graphed below.

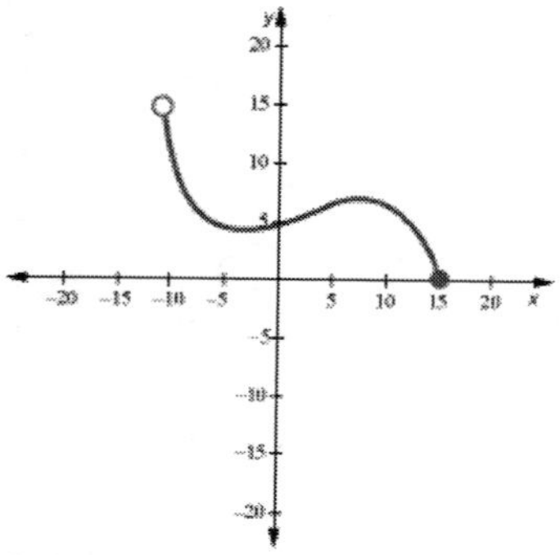

Solution: Domain: $-10 < x \leq 15$

Range: $0 \leq y < 15$

Explanation: The open circle at $(-10,\ 15)$ indicates that the point is not included in the domain/range. The domain (possible x-values) extends from -10 to 15, including 15, but not -10, or $-10 < x \leq 15$. The range (possible y-values) extends from 0 to 15, but not including 15, or $0 \leq y < 15$.

Practice problems: *(Answers on page: 739)*

1. Find the domain of the function $f(x) = x^2 + 2x - 3$.

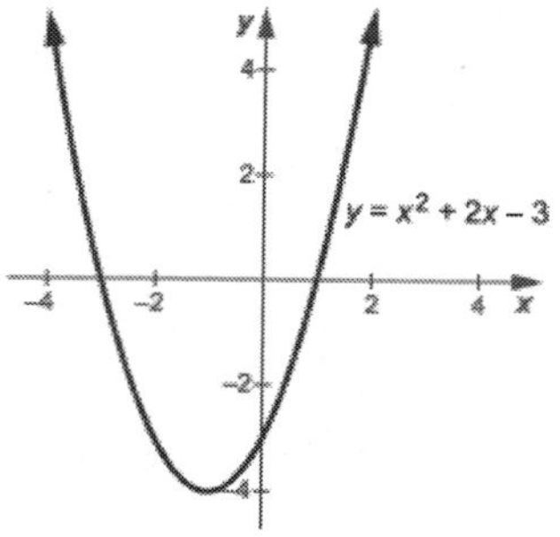

2. What is the domain of the following function?

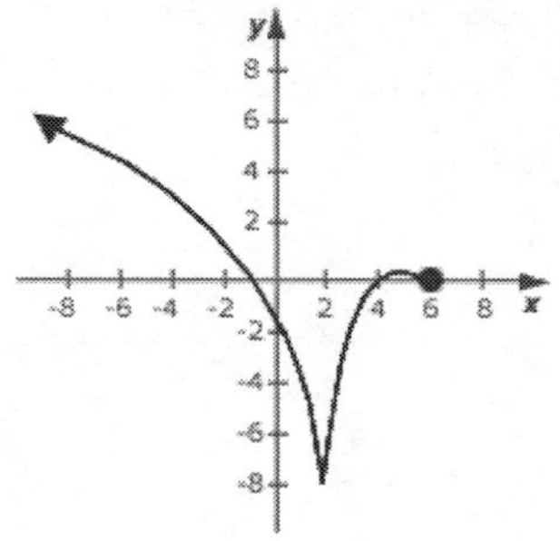

3. Find the domain and range of the function graphed below.

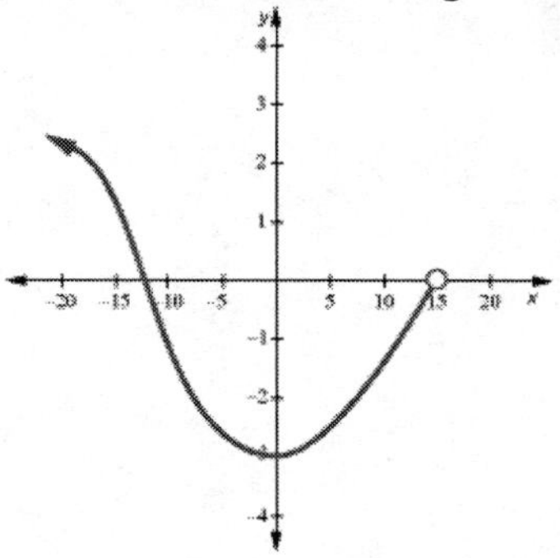

Review questions: *(Answers to odd questions on page: 739)*

1. From the graph of $f(x) = x^2 + 2x - 3$, find the range of f.

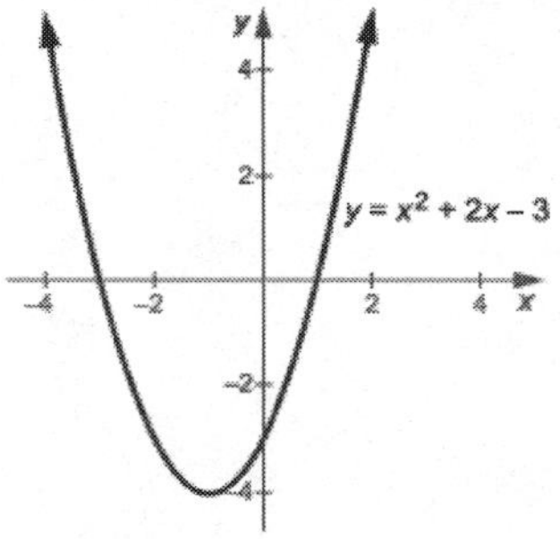

2. What is the range for the function graphed as shown?

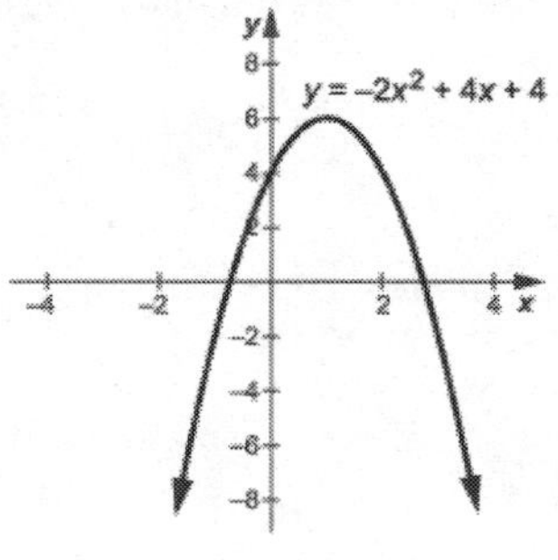

3. What is the domain for the function graphed as shown?

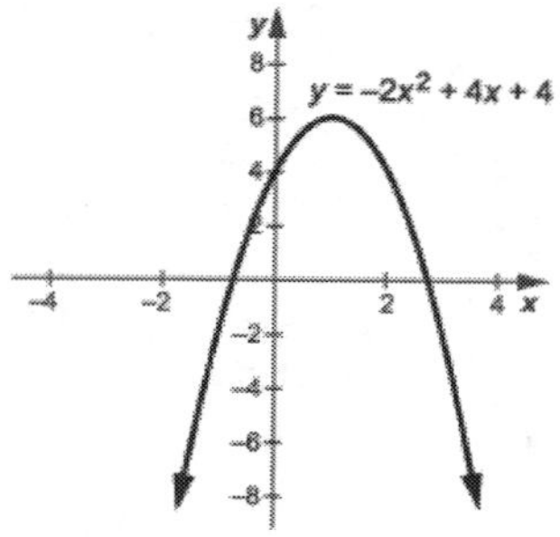

4. What is the domain for the function graphed as shown?

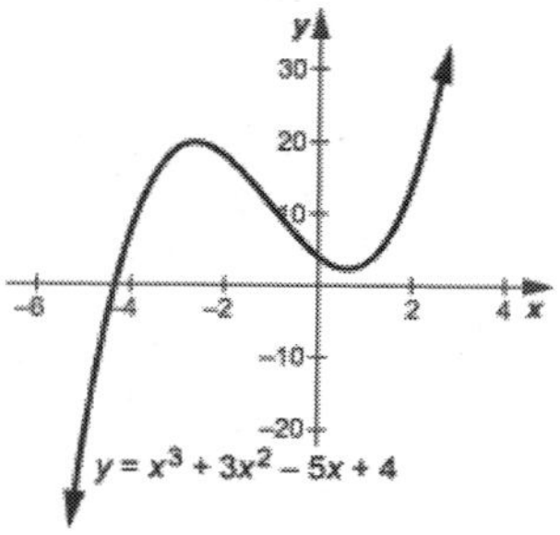

5. What is the range for the function graphed as shown?

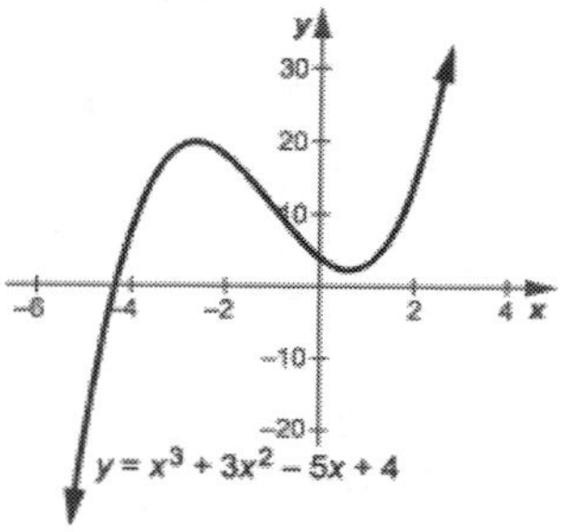

Domain and Range: One Explicit Example

- The **domain** for a function is the set of all real numbers that can be used for x.
- Values must be excluded from the domain if they create either a denominator equal to zero or a negative total under a square root sign.
- The **range** for a function is the set of all real numbers that are possible for y.
- $\mathbb{R}$ is the notational symbol for the set of all real numbers.

Example $f(x) = 2x + 5$ Find the domain — *there are no undefined values for x* domain = $\mathbb{R}$ — *all x values are allowed*	Any number can be multiplied with 2. There is no denominator to be considered. Therefore, no real numbers are excluded. The domain for this example is the set of all real numbers. Another notation for $-\infty > x < \infty$ is $\mathbb{R}$.

$f(x) = 2x + 5$ **Find the domain** — domain = $\mathbb{R}$ can $f(x) = 23$? $2x + 5 = 23$ $2x = 18$ $x = 9$ **Find the range** — check answer: $f(9) = 2(9) + 5$ $= 23$	Finding the range is a matter of ascertaining what values are possible for y. In this example, is it possible that y could equal 23? It turns out that 23 works nicely. And, in working with 23 you can see that any number placed in that position will work out to involve only real numbers. Therefore, the range for this function is also the set of all real numbers.
$f(x) = 2x + 5$ domain = $\mathbb{R}$ range = $\mathbb{R}$ 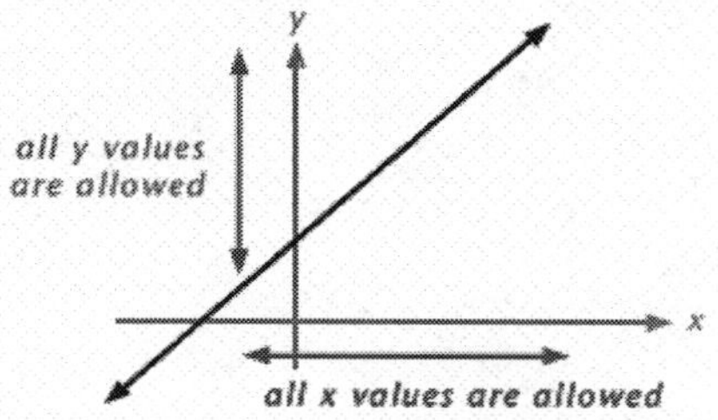	Looking at your conclusions graphically, you see that the function represents a line that is continuous throughout the plane. With a graph it is easy to visualize the fact that some point on the line will use every possible x-value. Likewise, some point on the line will use every possible y-value. You can visually see that declaring your domain and range each to be the full set of real numbers is the correct conclusion.

Sample problems:

1. Given the function $f(x) = 5 - \dfrac{2x-7}{3x^2}$, find the domain.
   Solution: all real numbers except 0
   Explanation: The domain is the set of all real numbers excluding those values that either: (1) lead to a negative number under a radical, or (2) create a denominator equal to 0. The first condition does not exclude any values in this function because the function does not ask for the square root of any value. The second condition does apply because the denominator contains a variable. Solve the denominator for any value(s) which make it equal 0 and exclude those values: $3x^2 = 0$; $x^2 = 0$; $x = 0$. Therefore, the domain is the set of all real numbers except 0.

2. Given the function $y = \dfrac{x^2 - 3x - 28}{x + 4}$, find the domain.
   Solution: All real numbers except -4
   Explanation: Since the denominator contains a variable, solve the denominator for any value(s) which make it equal 0 and exclude those values from the domain. Set the denominator equal to 0 and solve for x: $x + 4 = 0$; $x = -4$. Therefore, the domain is the set of all real numbers except -4.

3. Given the function $y = \left|x^2 + 4\right|$, find the domain and range.
   Solution: Domain: $\mathbb{R}$; Range: $y \geq 4$
   Explanation: The domain is all possible x-values. Any number can be squared, thus the domain is all real numbers. The range is all possible y-values. The absolute value of any number is positive, so obviously the range must include only positive numbers. Furthermore, the result of squaring any number is also positive, thus the value inside the absolute value is always greater than or equal to 4. Thus, the range is $y \geq 4$.

Practice problems: *(Answers on page: 739)*

1. Given the function $y = \dfrac{x^2 - 3x - 28}{x + 4}$, find the domain.
2. Given the function $y = \sqrt{x - 5}$, find the domain.
3. Given the function $y = -x^2$, find the domain and range.

Review questions: *(Answers to odd questions on page: 739)*

1. Determine the domain for the following relation: $y = x^2 + 2$
2. Determine the range for the following relation: $y = x^2 + 2$
3. Determine the domain and range for the following relation: $y = x^3 + 1$
4. Determine the domain and range for the following relation: $y = \sqrt{x + 2}$
5. Determine the domain and range for the following relation: $y = \dfrac{1}{x - 3}$

Satisfying the Domain of a Function

- The **domain** is the set of all real number values that can be used for x.
- $\mathbb{R}$ is the notational symbol for the set of all real numbers.
- $\mathbb{R} \setminus \{a_1, a_2, \ldots\}$ is the notation for a domain or range of all real numbers except certain ones.

Example $f(x) = x^2 - x + 1$ *find the domain* *ask: when input into the machine, what are the x values that will produce real numbers?* Domain = $\mathbb{R}$	In this example, all real numbers can be used for x because any number can be squared and then subtracted.
Example $g(x) = \sqrt{3 - 4x}$ *find the domain* $3 - 4x \geq 0$ *solve as an inequality* $-3 \quad -3$ *subtract 3 from each side* $\dfrac{-4x}{-4} \geq \dfrac{-3}{-4}$ *divide each side by −4* $x \leq \dfrac{+3}{4}$	In this problem if you try using a value larger than ¾, you will have a negative number under the square root sign. The domain does not allow you to include anything like that. It is OK to create 0 under the square root sign because the square root of 0 is 0. So, you are restricted in your domain for this function to numbers that are less than or equal to +3/4, as shown.
Example $h(x) = \dfrac{x - 1}{x^2 - 5x + 6}$ *find the domain* $x^2 - 5x + 6 = 0$ *identify when denominator = 0 first, set to = 0* $(x - 2)(x - 3) = 0$ *factor the denominator* $x = 2 \quad x = 3$ *values that cause the denominator to = 0* domain = all numbers except domain = $\mathbb{R} \setminus \{2, 3\}$ *another way to write it*	This example shows values eliminated from the domain because they create denominators that equal 0. Notice these excluded values for x are discovered by setting the denominator equal to 0 and solving for x by factoring. Here is one notation for the domain when specific values are excluded.

Example $k(x) = \frac{x-2}{x^2+3x-10}$ find the domain

domain = $\mathbb{R}\setminus\{-5, 2\}$ all real numbers except −5 and 2

another way to do the problem:

$k(x) = \frac{x-2}{(x+5)(x-2)}$ factor denominator immediately and cancel

$= \frac{1}{x+5}$

$x \neq 5$ $x \neq 2$ is 2 allowable?

remember the promise:

you can only cancel when not dividing by 0

In this example, first factor the denominator and notice you can cancel one factor with itself in the numerator.

Remember: Even if an expression is factored out, any value for x that would make the cancelled expression equal 0 must still be excluded.

Any activity performed with a rational expression must clearly state what values are to be excluded.

Sample problems:

1. Given $f(x) = \sqrt{4+2x}$, find the domain for the function f.
   Solution: $x \geq -2$
   Explanation: The domain is the set of all real numbers excluding those values that either: (1) lead to a negative number under a radical, or (2) create a denominator equal to 0. Since the radical contains a variable, determine the value(s) of x that will create a negative number in the radical. Set the the expression under the radical greater than or equal to 0 and solve for x: $4+2x \geq 0$; $2x \geq -4$; $x \geq -2$. So, the domain is the set of all real numbers greater than or equal to -2.

2. Given $f(x) = \dfrac{2x+5}{x^3+6x^2-16x}$, find the domain for the function f.
   Solution: $\mathbb{R}\setminus\{-8, 0, 2\}$
   Explanation: Since the denominator contains a variable, determine the value(s) of x that will create 0 in the denominator. Set the denominator equal to 0 and solve for x:
   $x^3+6x^2-16x = 0$; $x(x+8)(x-2) = 0$; $x = 0$, $x = -8$ or $x = 2$.
   So, the domain is the set of all real numbers except -8, 0, and 2.

3. Given $f(x) = \dfrac{\sqrt{2x-3}}{x^2-8x+15}$, find the domain of the function f.
   Solution: $x \geq \frac{3}{2} \setminus \{3,\ 5\}$
   Explanation: The expression under the radical must be greater than or equal to 0:
   $2x-3 \geq 0$; $2x \geq 3$; $x \geq \frac{3}{2}$. Thus, the domain includes only those values greater than or equal to $\frac{3}{2}$. However, there are further restrictions since the denominator cannot equal 0. Set the expression in the denominator equal to 0 and solve for x:
   $x^2-8x+15 = 0$; $(x-5)(x-3) = 0$; $x = 5$ or $x = 3$. Thus, the domain is all real numbers greater than or equal to $\frac{3}{2}$, excluding 3 and 5, or $x \geq \frac{3}{2} \setminus \{3,\ 5\}$.

Practice problems: *(Answers on page: 739)*

1. Given $f(x) = \sqrt{x+5}$ find the domain for the function f.
2. Given $f(x) = \dfrac{5x}{x^2+6x+9}$ find the domain for the function f.
3. Given $f(x) = \dfrac{\sqrt{5-x}}{x^2-x-20}$, find the domain of the function f.

Review questions: *(Answers to odd questions on page: 739)*

1. Given $f(x) = \dfrac{1}{x-4}$, find its domain.
2. Given $f(x) = \dfrac{1}{x^2 - x}$, find its domain.
3. Given $f(x) = \sqrt{9-x^2}$, find its domain.
4. Given $f(x) = \dfrac{x}{\sqrt{x+1}}$, find its domain.
5. Given $f(x) = \dfrac{\sqrt{2+x}}{3-x}$, find its domain.

An Introduction to Slope

- The graph of any **linear function** is a straight line.
- In Algebra the degree of steepness of a line is called its **slope**.

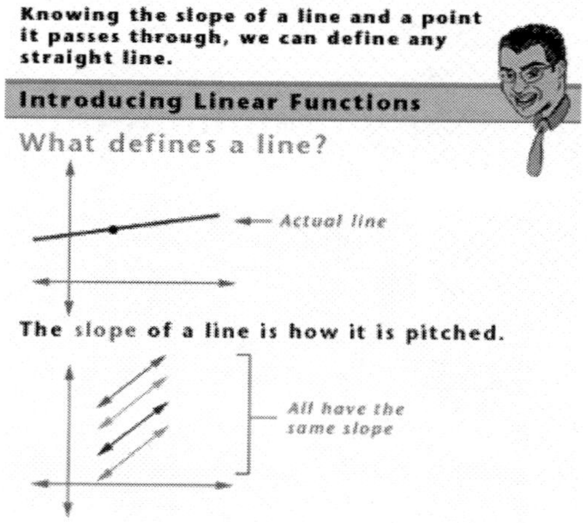

Every line has some degree of steepness, or slope. The degree of steepness ranges from horizontal, or flat, through all the levels to vertical, or upright.

Many lines can have the same slope.

If you know a line's slope and any one point on the line, you can tell exactly where to locate the line on a graph. And that line is a unique line.

Remember: You can identify and locate any unique line by knowing two things about it:
1. Its slope, and
2. any one of its points.

Finding the Slope of a Line Given Two Points

- **Slope** is the change from one point to another on a line. It is stated as a ratio (fraction) with change vertically over change horizontally. This is frequently referred to as ***rise/run***.
- Slope is the measure of pitch or steepness of a line. The larger the slope the steeper the line. A vertical line is so steep that the sideways change cannot be measured and its slope is undefined.
- **Slope (m)** = $\dfrac{y_2 - y_1}{x_2 - x_1} = \dfrac{\Delta y}{\Delta x} = \dfrac{\text{change in } y\text{s}}{\text{change in } x\text{s}}$. Δ is a notation for "change in" .

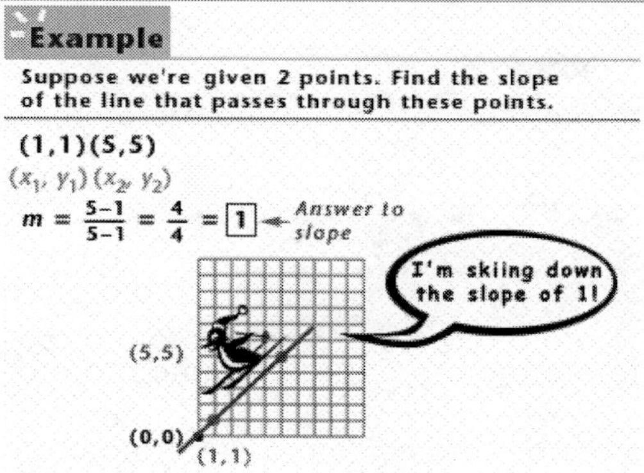

In this example, we find the change between the two points by doing three things:

1. Subtract the two y-values, 5 and 1, and write that as the numerator of our ratio.
2. Subtract the two x-values, 5 and 1, and write that as the denominator of our ratio.
3. Reduce the fraction if possible.

The slope is 1 which tells us that the graph is rising at the same rate it is moving sideways.

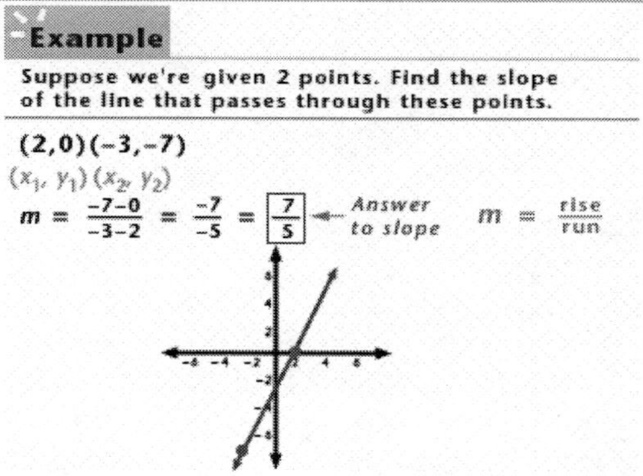

In this example, we follow the same process.

Remember: Decide which point is (x_2, y_2) and be sure to use its coordinates first on both levels. If you don't, your signs will be incorrect.

In this case, we have $-7 - 0 = -7$ over $-3 - 2 = -5$. So, our slope is 7/5. This tells us that the graph is moving up 7 units for each 5 units it moves to the right.

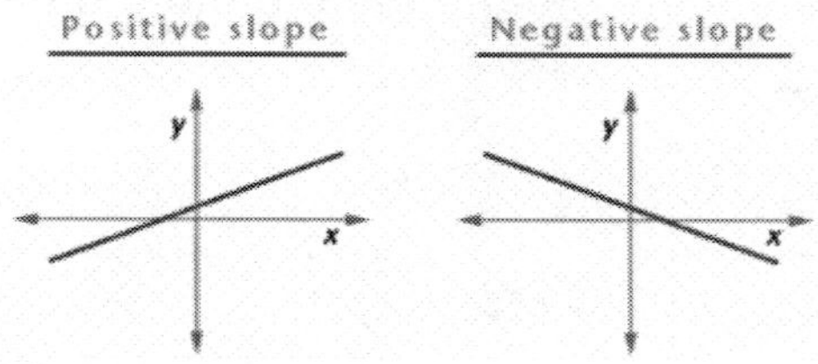

Note: A positive slope indicates a line that is climbing when viewed from left to right.

Note: A negative slope indicates a line that is falling when viewed from left to right.

Sample problems:

1. Find the slope of the line through the two points $(1,-3)$ and $(1,4)$.
   Solution: Undefined
   Explanation: Substitute the x and y values from the 2 points into the formula, (be consistent with the choice for y_2 and x_2): $m = \frac{y_2 - y_1}{x_2 - x_1} = \frac{4-(-3)}{1-1} = \frac{7}{0} =$ undefined.

2. Find the slope of the line through $\left(-\frac{1}{3}, 3\right)$ and $\left(-2, -\frac{1}{3}\right)$.
   Solution: 2
   Explanation: Subsitiute the x & y values into the slope formula:
   $m = \frac{y_2 - y_1}{x_2 - x_1} = \frac{-\frac{1}{3} - 3}{-2 - \left(-\frac{1}{3}\right)} = \frac{-\frac{10}{3}}{-\frac{5}{3}} = -\frac{10}{3} \cdot -\frac{3}{5} = 2.$

3. If the slope of a line that passes through $(5,8)$ and $(9, y)$ is $\frac{3}{2}$, find the value of y.
   Solution: 14
   Explanation: Substitute the values from the points and the slope into the slope formula and solve for y: $m = \frac{y_2 - y_1}{x_2 - x_1} \Rightarrow \frac{3}{2} = \frac{y-8}{9-5}$; $\frac{3}{2} = \frac{y-8}{4}$; $(4)\frac{3}{2} = y - 8$; $6 = y - 8$;
   $y = 14$.

Practice problems: *(Answers on page: 739)*

1. Find the slope of the line through the points $(-1,3)$, $(1,-6)$.
2. Find the slope of the line through the points $(2,2)$, $(0,0)$.
3. If the slope of a line that passes through $(x,-4)$ and $(7,10)$ is $\frac{7}{4}$, find the value of x.

Review questions: *(Answers to odd questions on page: 739)*

1. Find the slope of the line through the points $(2,4)$, $(8,6)$.
2. Find the slope of the line through the points $(9,16)$, $(4,27)$.
3. Find the slope of the line through the points $(22,7)$, $(0,-6)$.
4. Find the slope of the line through the points $(0,2)$, $(-4,-6)$.
5. Find the slope of the line through the points $(-8,-6)$, $(-2,-4)$.

Interpreting Slope from a Graph

- **Slope:** $\frac{rise}{run} = \frac{y_2 - y_1}{x_2 - x_1} = \frac{\Delta y}{\Delta x} = pitch$.
- A **positive slope** indicates that a line rises when viewed from left to right.
- A **negative slope** indicates that a line falls when viewed from left to right.
- The steeper a line rises or falls, the larger the absolute value of the slope will be.
- The **slope of a vertical line** is said to be undefined because the denominator of its fraction equals 0 which is an undefined situation in mathematics.
- The **slope of a horizontal line** is said to be 0 because the numerator of its fraction equals 0.

Example

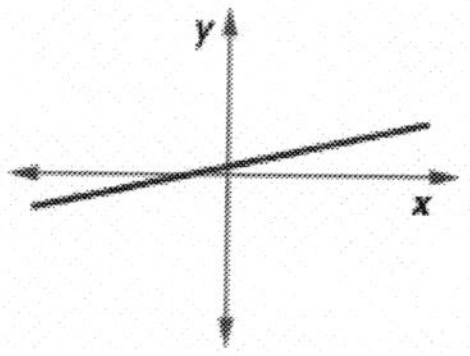

This line has a positive slope because it is tilting upwards when viewed from left to right.

The greater the tilt, the larger the slope value will be.

Example

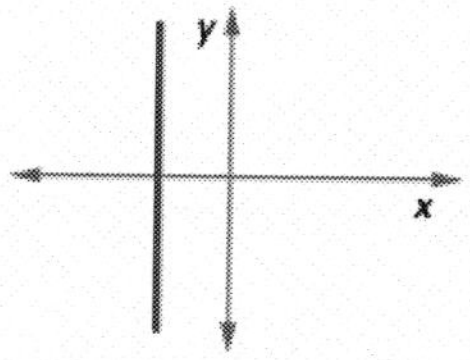

The slope for this line is undefined. There is no change left to right from one point to another on the line. So, when you subtract the x-values in the denominator, your answer is 0.

Example

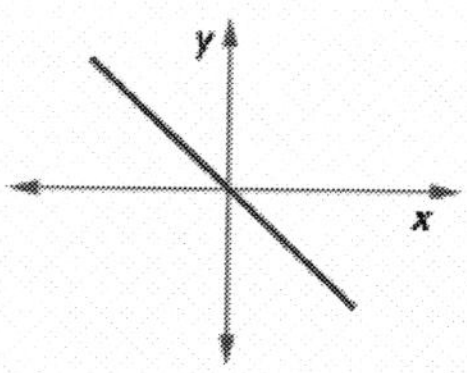

The slope of this line is negative because it tilts down when viewed from left to right. Again, the greater the tilt, the larger the absolute value for the slope.

Example 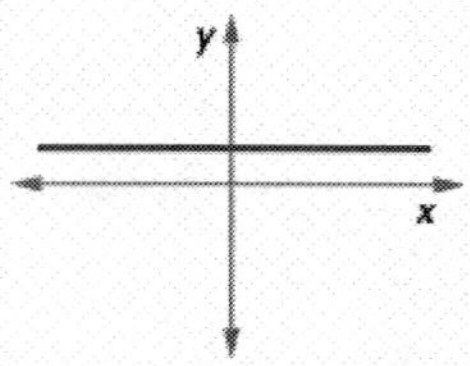	The slope for this line is 0. When you subtract the y-values of any two of its points, you will get 0 because there is no change up and down from one point to another on this line.

Sample problems:

1. If two lines are parallel and the equation of one line is $y = 5$, what is the slope of the other line?
   Solution: 0
   Explanation: The line defined by the equation $y = 5$ is horizontal. Any line parallel to that line will also be horizontal. The slope of any horizontal line is 0.

2. If two lines are perpendicular and the equation of one line is $y = 2x$, does the other line increase or decrease from left to right?
   Solution: Decrease
   Explanation: The line defined by the equation $y = 2x$ has a positive slope (2), so it increases from left to right. A line that is perpendicular to that line will have slope $-\frac{1}{2}$, since perpendicular lines have slopes that are opposite reciprocals. Therefore, the other line will decrease from left to right.

3. If two lines are parallel and the equation of one line is $3x + 2y = 10$, does the other line increase or decrease from left to right?
   Solution: Decrease
   Explanation: Begin by expressing the equation in slope-intercept form so that the slope can be easily identified from the equation. In order to express an equation in slope-intercept form, solve the equation for y:
   $3x + 2y = 10 \Rightarrow 2y = 10 - 3x \Rightarrow y = \frac{10-3x}{2} \Rightarrow y = 5 - \frac{3}{2}x.$
   The line defined by $y = 5 - \frac{3}{2}x$ has a negative slope ($-\frac{3}{2}$), so it decreases from left to right. A line that is parallel to that line will also have slope $-\frac{3}{2}$, since parallel lines have equal slopes. Therefore, both lines will decrease from left to right.

Practice problems: *(Answers on page: 739)*

1. If two lines are parallel and the equation of one line is $x = 5$, what is the slope of the other line?

2. If two lines are perpendicular and the equation of one line is $y = -0.5x$, does the other line increase or decrease from left to right?

3. If two lines are perpendicular and the equation of one line is $x - 5y = 15$, does the other line increase or decrease from left to right?

Review questions: *(Answers to odd questions on page: 739)*

1. If two lines are parallel and the equation of one line is $40x + 5y = 5$ what is the slope of the other line?

2. If two lines are parallel and the equation of one line is $3x - 2y = 18$ does the other line increase or decrease from left to right?

3. If two lines are parallel and the equation of one line is $y = 3x + 1$ does the slope of the other line increase or decrease from left to right?
4. If two lines are perpendicular and the equation of one line is $2x + 3y = 4$ does the slope of the other line increase or decrease from left to right?
5. If two lines are perpendicular and the equation of one line is $3x - 2y = 4$ does the slope of the other line increase or decrease from left to right?

Graphing a Line Using Point and Slope

- **Slope:** $\dfrac{rise}{run} = \dfrac{y_2 - y_1}{x_2 - x_1} = \dfrac{\Delta y}{\Delta x} = pitch$
- A **positive slope** indicates that a line rises when viewed from left to right.
- A **negative slope** indicates that a line falls when viewed from left to right.

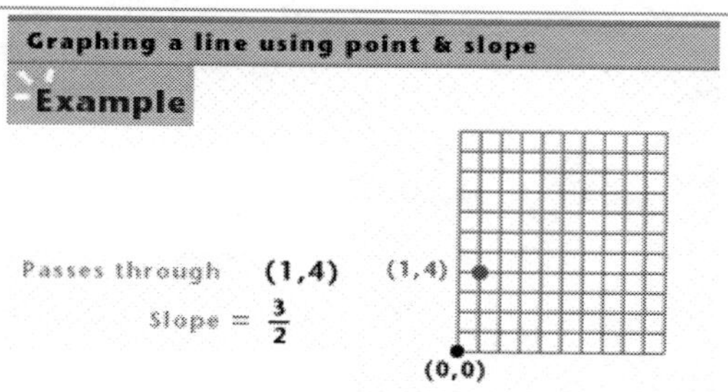

When graphing a line using just one point and the slope, your first step is to locate the point.

Here, the point (1,4) means you move from the origin, (0,0) one space to the right and four spaces up. Then place and label your point.

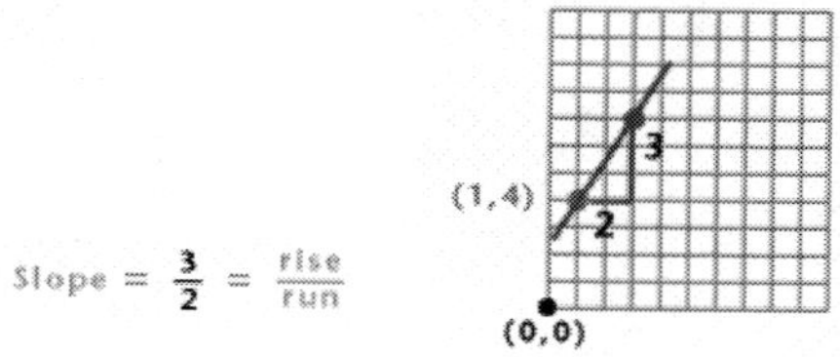

You can use the slope to determine a second point.

In this example, begin at (1,4). From there, count up 3 and to the right 2. Place your second point. By definition, you have enough information now to draw a line. Just as a check you might count again to a third point to extend the line.

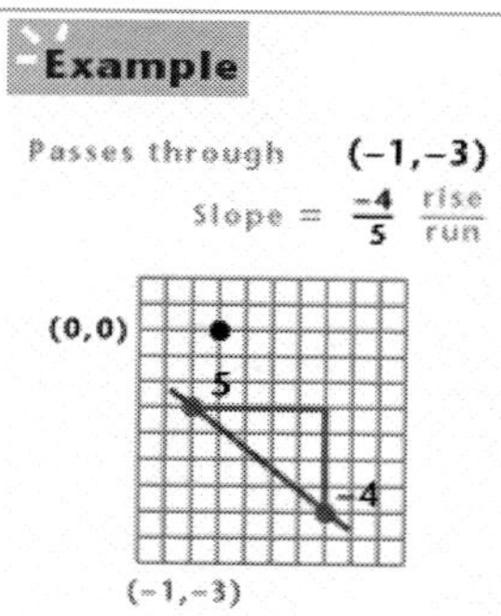

In this example, first locate the point (-1,-3).

The slope is negative, so count down to start instead of up. From (-1,-3), count down 4 and to the right 5 to locate your second point.

Finally, draw your line through the points.

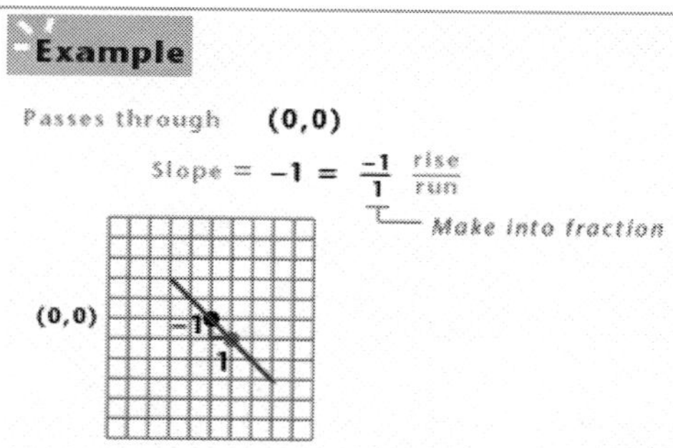

For this line your starting point will be the origin, (0,0). From there, use your slope to count down 1, then to the right 1, and locate your second point.

Finally, draw the line.

Sample problems:

1. Describe the movement indicated when the slope of a line is -3.
   Solution: Move down 3 units, then run to the right 1 unit
   Explanation: The slope of a line is a number that indicates the vertical change and the horizontal change from one point to the next. The numerator of the slope describes the vertical change (the rise) and the denominator describes the horizontal change (the run). The numerator of -3 is -3 and the denominator is 1. Therefore, the movement indicated by the slope is down 3 units, since the number is negative, and over to the right 1 unit.

2. Graph the line with slope $\frac{1}{2}$ that passes through the point $(0,-3)$.
   Solution:

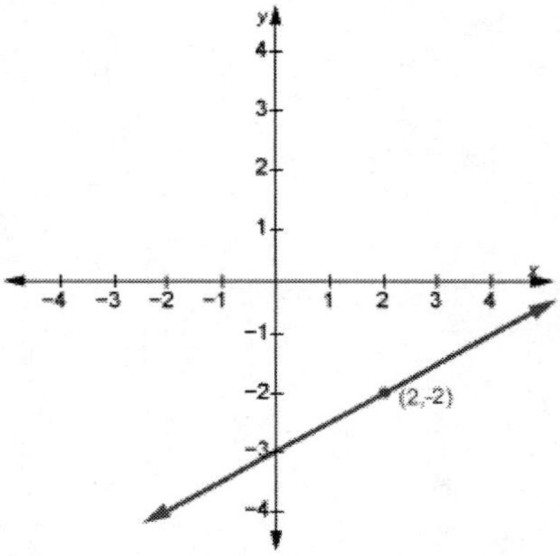

   Explanation: Begin by plotting the given point, $(0,-3)$, on the y-axis. Use the slope to find a second point on the line, $m=\frac{\text{rise}}{\text{run}}=\frac{1}{2}$. From $(0,-3)$, rise 1, then run 2, and then plot a second point at $(2,-2)$. Draw a line through these two points.

3. What is the x-intercept of the line that passes through (4,1) with slope $-\frac{1}{3}$?
   Solution: (7,0)
   Explanation: To solve this problem graphically, first sketch the graph of this line and then determine the x-intercept. Begin by plotting the point (4,1) and then use the slope to determine a second point. The slope is $-\frac{1}{3}$ which indicates that the vertical change (rise) is down 1 unit from (4,1). The horizontal change (run) is to the right 3 units. Thus, the second point is at (7,0) which is located on the x-axis, so it is the x-intercept of the line.

Practice problems: *(Answers on page: 740)*

1. What are the coordinates of the y-intercept of the line that passes through $(-3,5)$ with slope 1?
2. Graph the line with slope -3 that passes through the point $(2,-5)$.
3. Is (4,7) a point on the line that passes through the origin with slope 2?

Review questions: *(Answers to odd questions on page: 740)*

1. Graph the line with slope $\frac{3}{2}$ that passes through the point $(-2,-1)$.
2. Graph the line with slope $-\frac{3}{2}$ that passes through the point $(-2,-1)$.

3. Graph the line with slope -2 that passes through the point $(-2,3)$.

4. Graph the line with slope $\frac{1}{2}$ that passes through the point $(-2,3)$.

5. Graph the line with slope $-\frac{1}{2}$ that passes through the point $(-2,3)$.

Writing an Equation in Slope-Intercept Form

- **Standard equation of a line:** $Ax + By = C$. A linear equation will always have an x to the first power, a y, and some constant.
- **Slope-intercept equation of a line:** $y = mx + b$. The constant, m, represents the slope or rate of change from one point to the next in the line. The constant, b, represents the y-intercept or point where the line crosses the y-axis.
- The ***y*-intercept** is the point where the line crosses the y-axis. The x-value is always 0. The y-value is represented by the variable b. The point's coordinates are $(0,b)$.
- It is often very useful to express an equation that is given in standard form in slope-intercept form.
- To change a standard equation to a slope-intercept equation solve the equation for y.

Example

Find the equation of the line where:
(m) Slope = -2
(b) y-intercept = 5

$$y = mx + b$$

$$\boxed{y = -2x + 5}$$

You can create the equation for a line if you know the y-intercept and its slope.

Start with: $y = mx + b$.
Substitute your slope, -2, in for m.
Substitute your y-intercept, 5,in for b.
You're done.

Example

Find the equation of the line where:
(m) Slope = $\frac{1}{2}$
(b) y-intercept = -6

$$y = mx + b$$

$$\boxed{y = \frac{1}{2}x - 6}$$

Same thing works in this example:

Start with: $y = mx + b$.
Substitute ½ for m: $y = ½\,x + b$.
Substitute –6 for b: $y = ½\,x - 6$.
You're done.

Example Graph this line:

$$y = \frac{-2}{3}x + 1$$

slope *y-intercept*

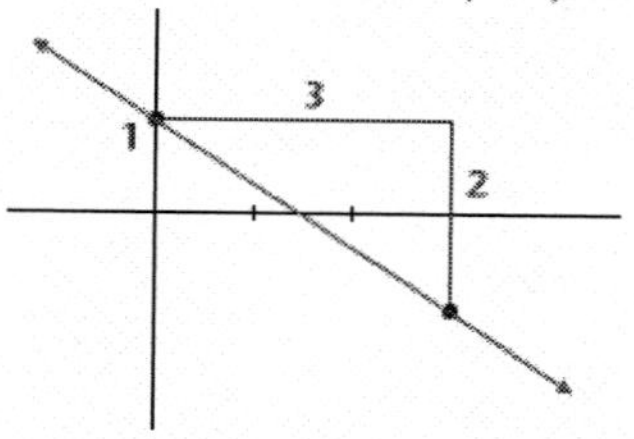

You can also use this form of the equation to create a graph of the line.

Start with the equation: $y = -2/3x + 1$.
Place the y-intercept: $(0,1)$.
Use the slope:
count down –2 and to the right 3.
Place a point at that location.
Draw the line through the two points.

Example Graph this line:

$$y = \frac{1}{2}x - 3$$

slope *y-intercept*

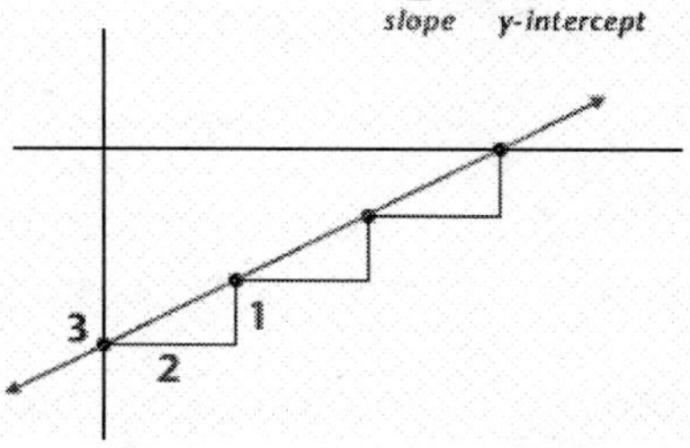

The same process works here.

Start with the equation: $y = ½x - 3$.
Place the y-intercept: (0,-3).
Use the slope:
count up 1 and to the right 2.
Place a point at that location.
Draw the line through the two points. Many people will suggest doing at least three points to reduce the possibility of error.

Sample problems:

1. Write the equation of the line with slope 5 that crosses the y-axis at the origin.
Solution: $y = 5x$
Explanation: Use the slope-intercept form of a linear equation, $y = mx + b$, where m is the slope and b is the y-intercept, to write the equation of this line. Substitute the slope into $y = mx + b$ for m: $y = 5x + b$. Next, substitute the y-intercept into $y = 5x + b$ for b. Since the line crosses the y-axis at the origin, the y-intercept is 0. So, the equation of the line is $y = 5x + 0 \Rightarrow y = 5x$.

2. Find the slope and y-intercept of the line formed by $5x - 2y = 6$.
Solution: $m = \frac{5}{2}$ and $b = -3$
Explanation: Since this equation is in standard form, begin by solving it for y so that it will be expressed in the more useful slope-intercept form: $5x - 2y = 6 \Rightarrow -2y = 6 - 5x \Rightarrow y = \frac{6-5x}{-2} \Rightarrow y = -3 + \frac{5}{2}x = \frac{5}{2}x - 3$. Since the equation is in the form $y = mx + b$, the slope and y-intercept are easily identified. The slope, m, is the coefficient of x and the y-intercept is the constant term. Thus, $m = \frac{5}{2}$ and $b = -3$.

3. Write the equation of the line that passes through the points $(6,-2)$ and $(10,0)$ with y-intercept -5.
Solution: $y = \frac{1}{2}x - 5$
Explanation: The slope and y-intercept must be known to write the equation of a line. The value of b is given, -5, so begin by using the slope formula to find m: $m = \frac{y_2 - y_1}{x_2 - x_1} = \frac{0-(-2)}{10-6} = \frac{2}{4} = \frac{1}{2}$. Now write the equation of the line by substituting m and b into $y = mx + b$: $y = \frac{1}{2}x - 5$.

Practice problems: *(Answers on page: 740)*

1. Write the equation of the line with slope $\frac{4}{3}$ that crosses the y-axis at $(0, -1)$.
2. Find the slope and y-intercept of the line formed by $x + y = 2$.
3. Write the equation of the line that passes through the points $(-1,-3)$ and $(2,6)$ with y-intercept 0.

Review questions: *(Answers to odd questions on page: 740)*

1. Write the equation of the line with slope -3 and y-intercept $(0,4)$.
2. Write the equation of the line with slope 0 and y-intercept $(0, -3)$.
3. Write the equation of the line with slope $\frac{2}{3}$ and y-intercept $(0, -2)$.

4. Find the slope and y-intercept of the line formed by $x - 3y = 12$.
5. Write the equation of the line that passes through the origin and has the same slope as $y = \frac{1}{3}x - 4$.

Writing an Equation Given Two Points

- **Standard equation of a line:** $Ax + By = C$. A linear equation will always have an x to the first power, a y, and some constant.
- **Slope-intercept equation of a line:** $y = mx + b$. The constant, m, represents the slope or rate of change from one point to the next in the line. The constant, b, represents the y-intercept or point where the line crosses the y-axis.
- The ***y*-intercept** is the point where the line crosses the y-axis. The x-value is always 0. The y-value is represented by the variable b. The point's coordinates are $(0,b)$.
- It is often very useful to express an equation that is given in standard form in slope-intercept form.
- To change a standard equation to a slope-intercept equation solve the equation for y.

Example Find the equation of a line in slope-intercept form given these two points: (0, 3) (2, 2) Look! x is 0 → y-intercept $m = \frac{\Delta y}{\Delta x} = \frac{2-3}{2-0} = \frac{-1}{2}$ $y = \frac{-1}{2}x + 3$	You can create the equation of a line given any two points on the line. If you have the point where $x = 0$, that is the y-intercept. So the y-value from that point is b. First calculate the slope: $m = -\frac{1}{2}$. Substitute into the equation: $y = -\frac{1}{2}x + b$. Substitute the intercept: $y = -\frac{1}{2}x + 3$. **Remember:** Keep the coordinates for each point in the same column in the slope formula. In this example, 3 from (0,3) is in the 2nd position, so 0 of (0,3) is also. This habit keeps your signs correct. You're done.
Example Find the equation of a line in slope-intercept form given these two points: (1, 2) (-1, -4) remember to subtract in the same order $m = \frac{\Delta y}{\Delta x} = \frac{2-(-4)}{1-(-1)} = \frac{6}{2} = 3$ $y = 3x + b$ — both points give the same answer $2 = 3(1) + b$ $-4 = 3(-1) + b$ $2 = 3 + b$ $-4 = -3 + b$ $b = -1$ $b = -1$ $y = 3x - 1$	Sometimes you have two points but neither of them is the y-intercept. First calculate your slope. In this case $m = 3$. Substitute 3 for m in the slope-intercept form. Now choose either of your points and substitute its values in for x and y so you can solve for b. In this case you get -1. Substitute the -1 in for b. You're done.

Sample problems:

1. Write the equation of a line in slope intercept form given the points: $(-2,-2)$ and $(3,3)$.

Solution: $y = x$

Explanation: First calculate the slope between the two points: $m = \frac{y_2 - y_1}{x_2 - x_1} = \frac{(-2)-(3)}{(-2)-(3)} = \frac{-5}{-5} = 1$.

Substitute the slope into slope-intercept form: $y = mx + b \Rightarrow y = 1x + b \Rightarrow y = x + b$.

Determine b by substituting one of the points into $y = x + b$ and solve for b: $(3) = (3) + b;\ b = 0$.

Complete the equation by substituting in $b = 0$ into $y = x + b$: $y = x + 0 \Rightarrow y = x$.

2. Write the equation of a line in slope intercept form given the points (7,5) and (0,–2).
   Solution: $y = x - 2$
   Explanation: First calculate the slope between the two points:
   $m = \frac{y_2 - y_1}{x_2 - x_1} = \frac{5-(-2)}{7-(0)} = \frac{7}{7} = 1$. Next, determine b. Notice that the 2nd point is on the y-axis, so -2 is the y-intercept. Now write the equation of the line by substituting the m and b values into $y = mx + b$: $y = 1x + (-2) \Rightarrow y = x - 2$.

3. Write the equation of a line in slope intercept form given the points (2,1) and (–2,–1).
   Solution: $y = \frac{1}{2}x$
   Explanation: First calculate the slope between the two points:
   $m = \frac{y_2 - y_1}{x_2 - x_1} = \frac{1-(-1)}{2-(-2)} = \frac{2}{4} = \frac{1}{2}$. Next, determine b by substituting m and the values from *either* point into $y = mx + b$, then solve for b: $1 = \frac{1}{2}(2) + b;\ b = 0$. Now write the equation of the line by substituting the values for m and b into $y = mx + b$:
   $y = \frac{1}{2}x + 0 \Rightarrow y = \frac{1}{2}x$.

Practice problems: *(Answers on page: 741)*

1. Write the equation of a line in slope intercept form given the points: (1,51) and (0,29).
2. Write the equation of a line in slope intercept form given the points: (–5,5) and (7,– 7).
3. Write the equation of a line in slope intercept form given the points: $\left(1, \frac{-23}{13}\right)$ and $\left(0, \frac{-37}{13}\right)$.

Review questions: *(Answers to odd questions on page: 741)*

1. Write the equation of a line in slope-intercept form given the points (1, 2), (2, 4).
2. Write the equation of a line in slope-intercept form given the points (1.6, 3), (0.3, 1.4).
3. Write the equation of a line in slope-intercept form given the points (0, 0), (–3, 6).
4. Write the equation of a line in slope-intercept form given the points (10, 2), (5, 2).
5. Write the equation of a line in slope-intercept form given the points (3, 6), (–3, 8).

Writing an Equation in Point-Slope Form

- **The point-slope form of an equation: $y - y_1 = m(x - x_1)$.** This equation is created from the slope formula. It allows you to create the equation of a line knowing any one point and the slope.
- **Slope:** $\frac{rise}{run} = \frac{y_2 - y_1}{x_2 - x_1} = \frac{\Delta y}{\Delta x}$

Example Suppose: You are given the slope and a point **Write the equation of the line in point-slope form.** $(-1, 3)\quad m = \frac{-1}{4}$ (x_1, y_1) $y - y_1 = m(x - x_1)$ $y - 3 = \frac{-1}{4}(x + 1)$	Again, you are substituting values into the general equation. Your slope is –1/4. Substitute –1/4 for m. Your point is (-1,3). Substitute its values in for x_1 and y_1. This formula is valuable if you are given the slope and any one point on a line. **Notice:** The signs change as the point values go into the formula. They are subtracting. You've got your equation. You're done.

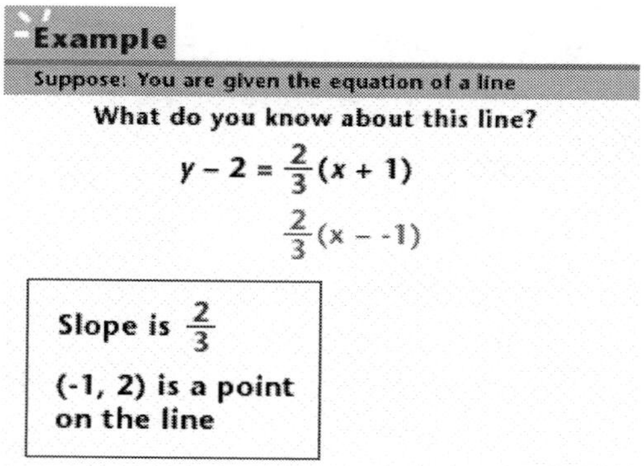	Thinking in reverse, you can look at an equation and discern the details needed to be able to graph a line. Looking at this equation, you know immediately that the slope, m, is 2/3. You also know that one point on the line is located at (-1,2). **Remember:** change the signs on the numbers from the equation to determine the x and y values for the point.
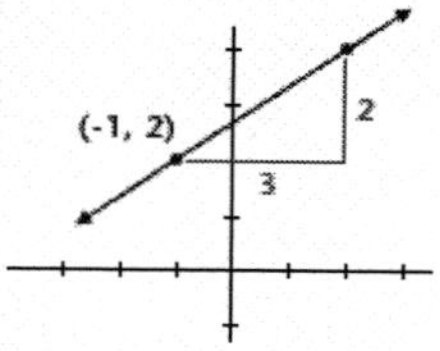	Place the one point you know, (-1,2). From there count down 2 and to the right 3 to locate second point. Draw the line through the two points. You've got your unique line.

Sample problems:

1. Write the equation in point-slope form of the line that passes through $(-4,-1)$ and has a slope of $\frac{2}{3}$.

   Solution: $y+1=\frac{2}{3}(x+4)$

   Explantaion: Substitute $m=\frac{2}{3}$ and the x and y values from the point $(-4,-1)$ into the point-slope formula, $y-y_1=m(x-x_1)$ to write the equation of the line: $y-(-1)=\frac{2}{3}(x-(-4))$; $y+1=\frac{2}{3}(x+4)$.

2. Write the equation in point-slope form of the line that crosses the y-axis at 2 and is parallel to the line described by $3x-5y=20$.

   Solution: $y-2=\frac{3}{5}x$

   Explantaion: Find the slope of $3x-5y=20$ by expressing it in slope-intercept form: $y=\frac{3}{5}x-4$, so the $m=\frac{3}{5}$. The slope of the new line is also $\frac{3}{5}$, since the lines are parallel. Now, using $m=\frac{3}{5}$, (0,2) (the y-intercept), & point-slope formula, write the equation of the line: $y-2=\frac{3}{5}(x-0)$; $y-2=\frac{3}{5}x$.

3. Write the equation in point-slope form of the line passing through $(2,-4)$ that is perpendicular to the line described by $3x+2y=5$.

   Solution: $y+4=\frac{2}{3}(x-2)$

   Explanation: The slope and a point are needed in order to write the equation of a line in point-slope form. A point on the line $(2,-4)$ is given, so begin by finding the slope. The line is perpendicular to $3x+2y=5$, so the lines must have slopes that are negative reciprocals. To find the slope of $3x+2y=5$ express the equation in slope-intercept form, $y=mx+b$: $3x+2y=5 \Rightarrow 2y=5-3x \Rightarrow y=\frac{5-3x}{2} \Rightarrow y=\frac{5}{2}-\frac{3x}{2}$, so the slope is $-\frac{3}{2}$. The slope of a line perpendicular to that line is $\frac{2}{3}$. Now, substitute the slope and the x and y values from the point into point-slope form, $y-y_1=m(x-x_1)$: $y-(-4)=\frac{2}{3}(x-2)$. Simplify: $y+4=\frac{2}{3}(x-2)$.

Practice problems: *(Answers on page: 741)*

1. Write the equation in point-slope form of the line that crosses the x-axis at 3 with a slope of 4.

2. Write the equation of the line in point-slope form that passes through $(-1,5)$ and is perpendicular to the line described by $x-2y=8$.
3. Write the equation of the line in point-slope form that passes through $(-3,2)$ and is parallel to the line that passes through $(5,2)$ and $(7,8)$.

Review questions: *(Answers to odd questions on page: 741)*

1. Write the equation in point-slope form of the line that contains the point $(2,5)$ and has a slope of 4.
2. Write the equation in point-slope form of the line that contains the point $(-1,-6)$ and has a slope of $\frac{1}{4}$.
3. Write the equation in point-slope form of the line that passes through $(4,0)$ and is parallel to the line described by $x+y=3$.
4. Write the equation in point-slope form of the line that passes through $(-3,7)$ and is perpendicular to the line described by $y=5+2x$.
5. Write the equation in point-slope form of the line that passes through $\left(\frac{3}{4},-\frac{2}{3}\right)$ and is perpendicular to $3x+5y=10$.

Matching a Slope-Intercept Equation with Its Graph

- **Slope-intercept equation of a line:** $y = mx + b$. The constant, m, represents the slope or rate of change from one point to the next in the line. The constant, b, represents the y-intercept or point where the line crosses the y-axis.
- **The point-slope form of an equation:** $y - y_1 = m(x - x_1)$. This equation is created from the slope equation. It allows you to create the equation of a line knowing any one point and the slope.
- **Slope:** $\frac{rise}{run} = \frac{y_2 - y_1}{x_2 - x_1} = \frac{\Delta y}{\Delta x}$

<table>
<tr><td>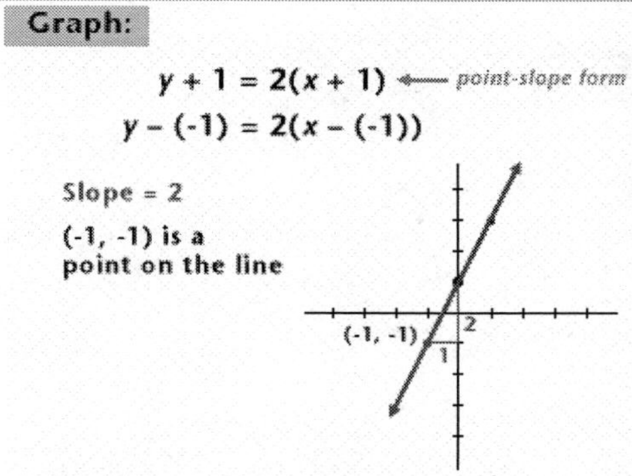
</td><td>This equation is in point-slope form. The slope is 2. The given point is (-1,-1).

Remember: Change the signs for the given point because those coordinates are subtracting in the formula.</td></tr>
<tr><td>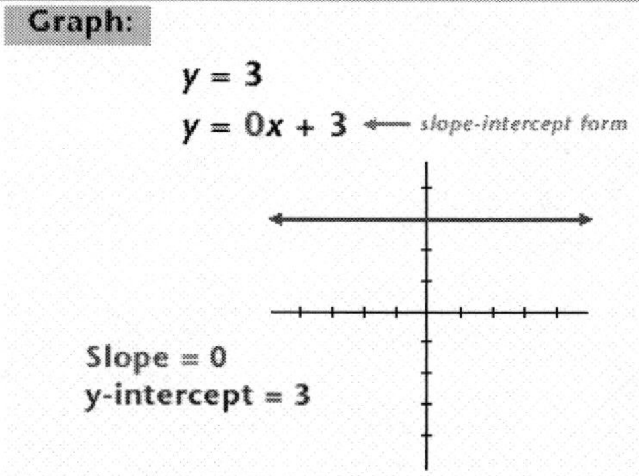
</td><td>This equation does not contain x. Therefore the slope is 0, which makes it a horizontal line. Clearly the y-intercept is at 3.

So, you graph a horizontal line at $y = 3$.</td></tr>
</table>

<table>
<tr>
<td>Graph:
$x = 1$
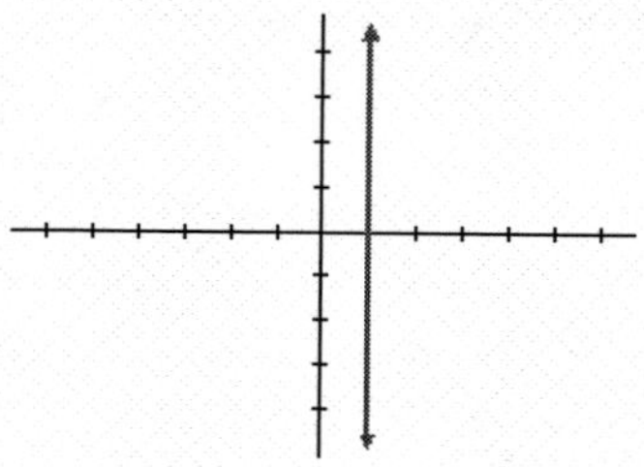</td>
<td>Choose any point on this line. The y can be anything in the real numbers. The $x = 1$.

So, graphing the line shows you it is vertical.</td>
</tr>
<tr>
<td>Graph:
$-2x - 5 = 7$ ⟵ this is not slope-intercept form because there is no y
$-2x = 12$
$x = -6$
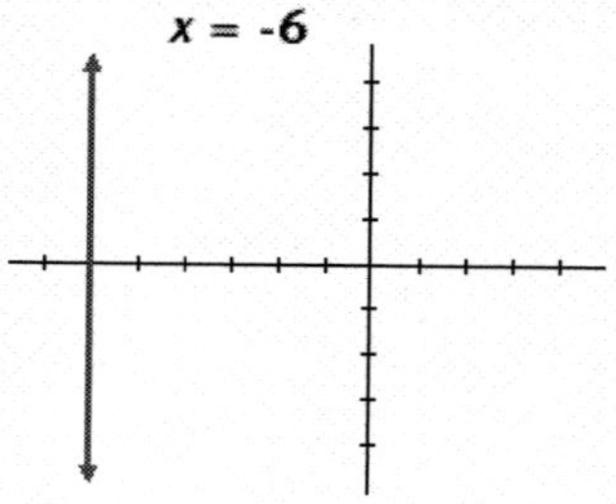</td>
<td>Notice this equation has no y-term.

Solve it for x.
Graph it.

You're done.</td>
</tr>
<tr>
<td>Graph:
$2x - 3y = 1$ ⟵ standard form
$2x = 1 + 3y$ solve for y
$2x - 1 = 3y$
$\frac{2}{3}x - \frac{1}{3} = y$
$y = \frac{2}{3}x - \frac{1}{3}$
y-intercept $= -\frac{1}{3}$
Slope $= \frac{2}{3}$
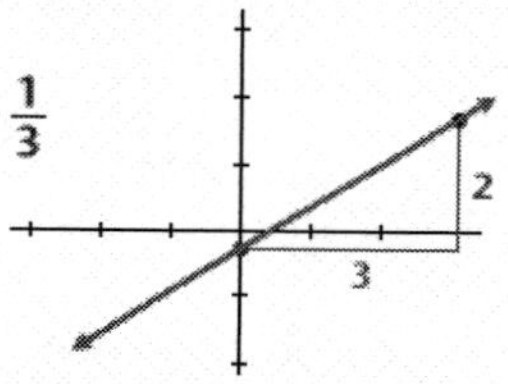
</td>
<td>First, solve this equation for y.

Then you see that your slope is 2/3, and your y-intercept is $-1/3$.

Graph the line. First, locate your y-intercept. Then count up 2 and to the right 3 for the next point. Finally, draw the line.</td>
</tr>
</table>

Sample problems:

1. Does the equation $-4x + 2y = 4$ match the following graph?

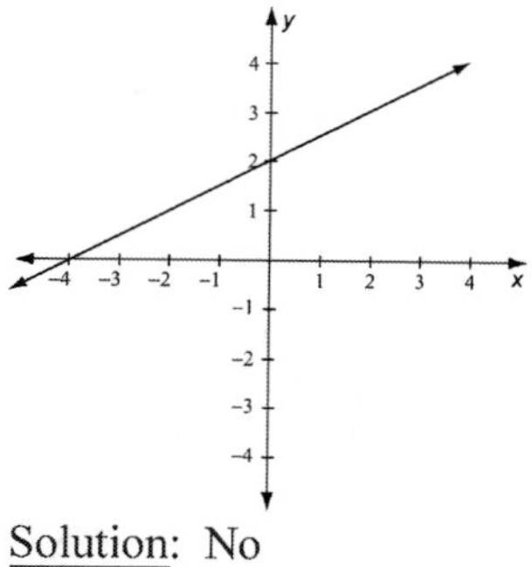

Solution: No

Explanation: Express $-4x + 2y = 4$ in slope-intercept form: $y = 2x + 2$. The slope of this line is 2 and the y-intercept is 2. The y-intercept of the graphed line is also 2. Now determine the slope of the graphed line by counting the $\frac{\Delta y}{\Delta x}$ between any two points. Between the x and y-intercepts the $\Delta y = 2$ and the $\Delta x = 4$, so the slope of the graphed line is $\frac{2}{4} = \frac{1}{2}$, not 2. Therefore, the equation $-4x + 2y = 4$ does not match the graph.

2. Write the equation of a line in slope-intercept form that matches the following graph.

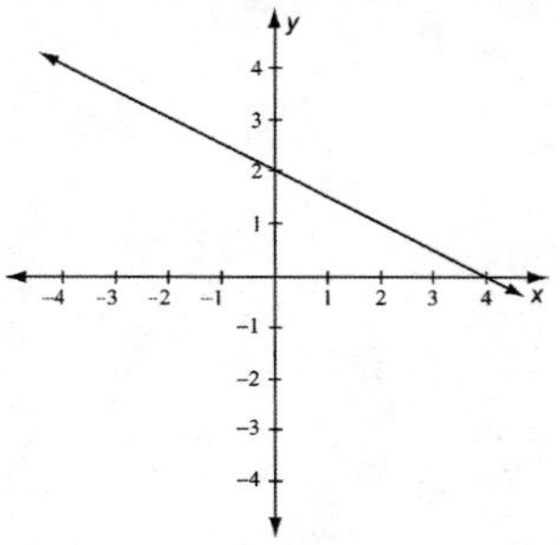

Solution: $y = -\frac{1}{2}x + 2$

Explanation: The y intercept of the graph is 2, so $b = 2$. Next, determine the slope.
Once again, the x and y-intercepts are easy points to use, so $m = \frac{\Delta y}{\Delta x} = \frac{-2}{4} = -\frac{1}{2}$.
Now substitute m and b into slope-intercept form, $y = mx + b$: $y = -\frac{1}{2}x + 2$.

3. Does the equation $3x - 2y = 6$ match the following graph?

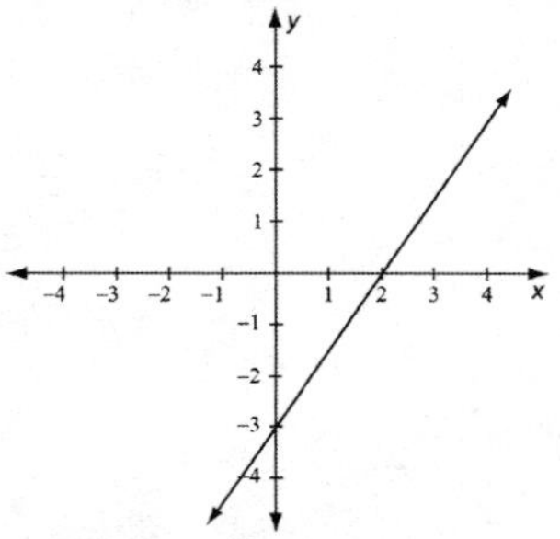

Solution: Yes

Explanation: Express $3x - 2y = 6$ in slope-intercept form: $y = \frac{3}{2}x - 3$. So, $m = \frac{3}{2}$ and $b = -3$. The y-intercept of the graphed line is also -3 & the slope is $\frac{3}{2}$.
Thus, the equation matches the graph.

Practice problems: *(Answers on page: 741)*

1. Does the equation $x - 2y = -3$ match the line graphed below?

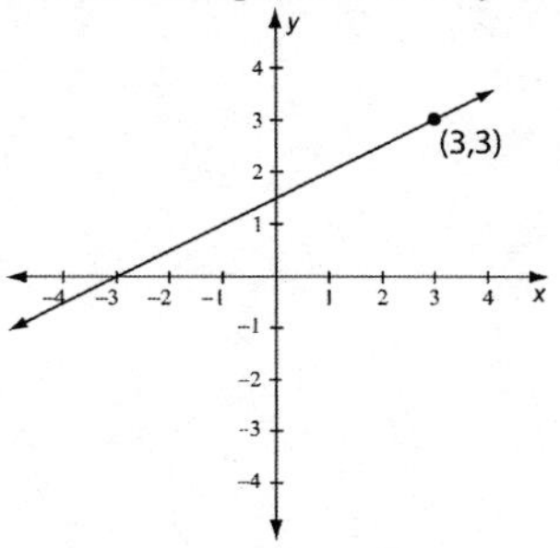

2. Does the equation $x + 2y = 4$ match the following graph?

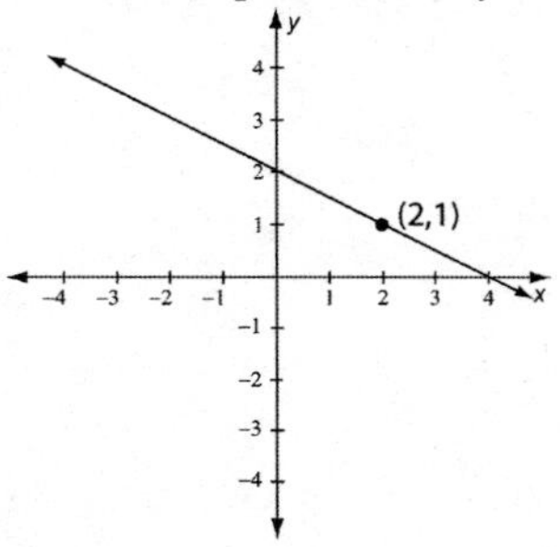

3. Write the equation of a line in slope-intercept form that matches the following graph.

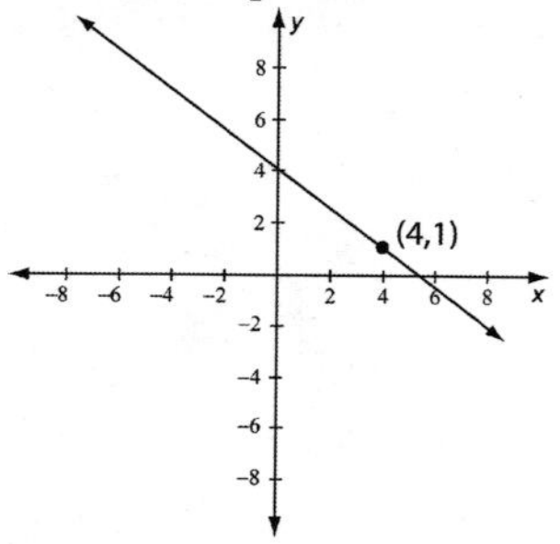

Review questions: *(Answers to odd questions on page: 741)*

1. Does the equation $x + y = 3$ match the following graph?

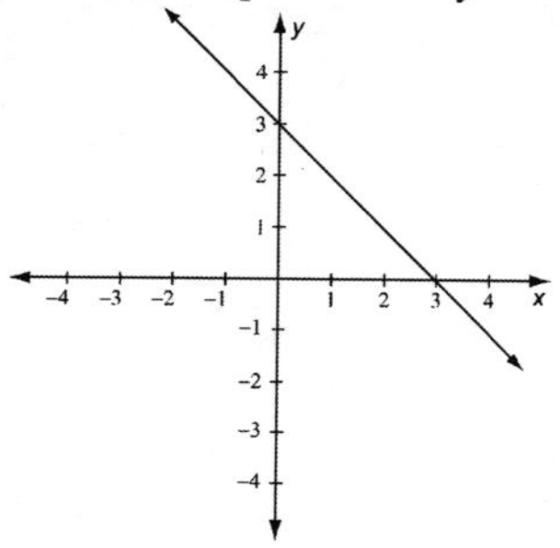

2. Does the equation $x + \frac{1}{3}y$ match the following graph?

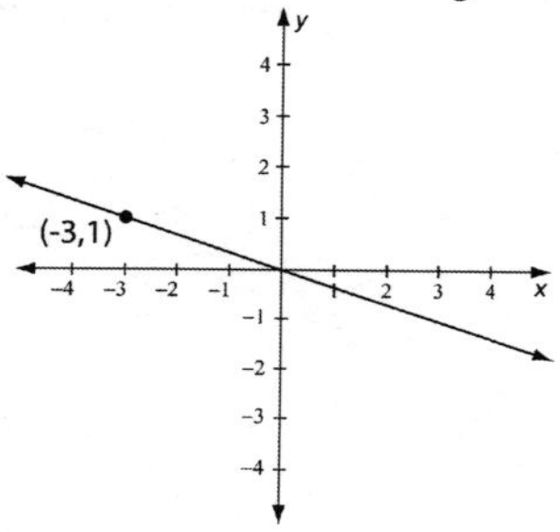

3. Write the equation of a line in slope-intercept form that matches the following graph.

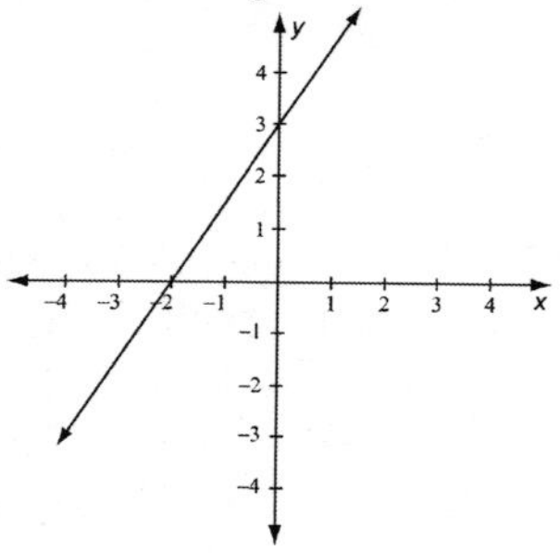

4. Does the equation $x = 4$ match the following graph?

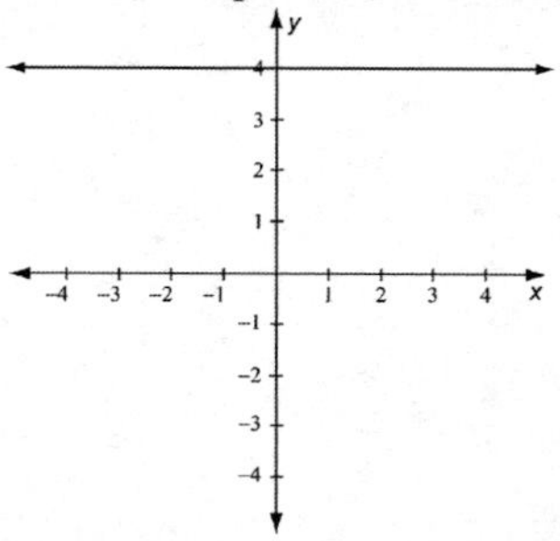

5. Does the equation $3x - 4y = 12$ match the following graph?

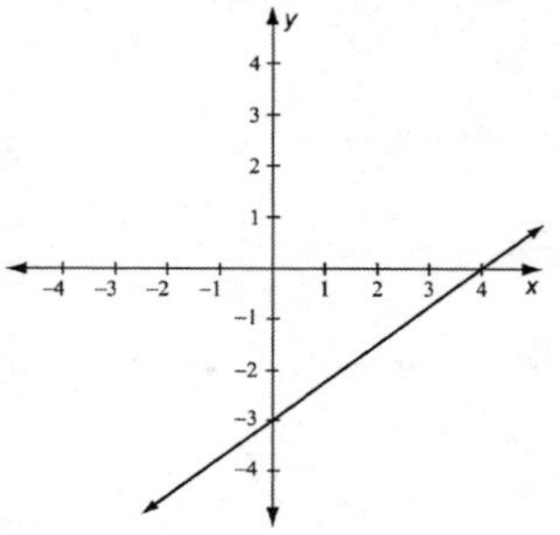

Slope for Parallel and Perpendicular Lines

- Two lines are parallel when they have the same slope and different y-intercepts.
- Two lines are perpendicular when their slopes are the negative reciprocals of each other. Another way to say this is that two lines are perpendicular when the product of their slopes is -1.

Parallel Lines $y = \frac{2}{3}x + 1$ *slope y-intercept* $y = \frac{2}{3}x - 2$ 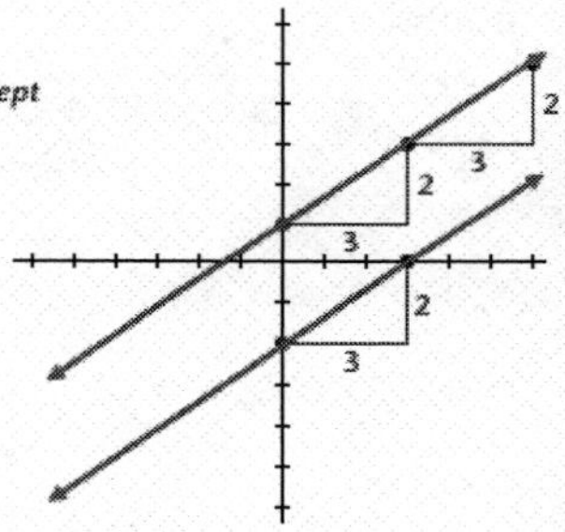	When two lines are parallel, they have exactly the same angle of tilt. They have exactly the same slope with different x- and y-intercepts. All lines parallel to these two lines will have the same slope with unique x- and y-intercepts.
Perpendicular Lines $y = \frac{3}{4}x + 0$ *slope* $y = \frac{-4}{3}x$ *notice the second slope is a negative reciprocal* 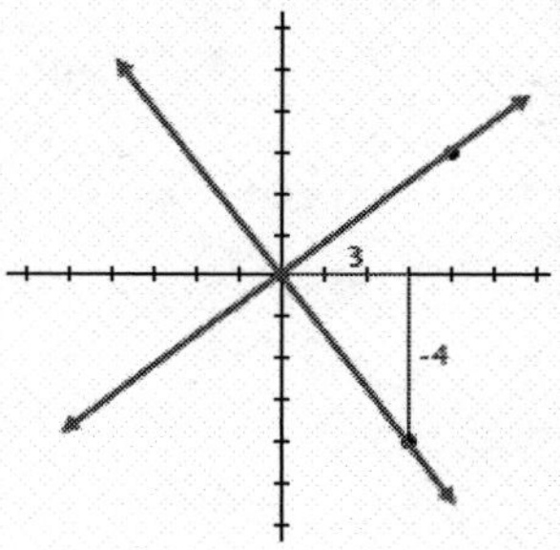	When two lines are perpendicular, they tilt opposite to each other. And, they exactly reverse how their x's and y's change. In this case, every time y changes 3 on the top line, x will change 3 on the second line. And, every time x changes 4 on the top line, y will change 4 on the second line.
Example Find the equation of the line that passes through the point (1, 3) and is parallel to $3x + 4y = -24$	You've just learned that parallel lines have the same slope. And this gives you a point on the second line. That's all you need.

$4y = -3x - 24$ $y = \frac{-3x - 24}{4}$ $y = \underbrace{\frac{-3}{4}}_{\text{slope}}x - \frac{24}{4}$	Your first step is to determine the slope of the parallel line.
point-slope form → $y - y_1 = m(x - x_1)$ $\boxed{y - 3 = \frac{-3}{4}(x - 1)}$	Your second and last step is to substitute the coordinates of the point you were given on the parallel line into the point-slope form of an equation. And, there is your equation!
Example **Find the equation of the line that passes through (1, 2) and is perpendicular to** *find the slope of the original line* $x + y = 4$ $y = -x + 4$ Slope $= \frac{-1}{1}$ So, the slope of the ⊥ line $= -\left(\frac{1}{-1}\right) = 1$ *point-slope form* $y - y_1 = m(x - x_1)$ $y - 2 = 1(x - 1)$ $\boxed{y - 2 = x - 1}$ *slope-intercept form* → $\boxed{y = x + 1}$	Use the same steps here as you did above, only this time the slopes are the negative reciprocals of each other: 1. Find the slope of your equation: $m = -1$. 2. Determine the slope of the perpendicular line: $m = +1$. 3. Substitute into the point-slope form. 4. Do the arithmetic to get to the simpler slope-intercept form of the equation.

Sample problems:

1. What is the slope of a line perpendicular to the line $y = \frac{2}{3}x + 4$?

   Solution: $-\frac{3}{2}$

   Explanation: The slope of the line described by $y = \frac{2}{3}x + 4$ is $\frac{2}{3}$. The slopes of perpendicular lines are always opposite reciprocals. The opposite reciprocal of $\frac{2}{3}$ is $-\frac{3}{2}$.

2. Write the equation of a line through (0,7) that is parallel to the line described by $y = \frac{4}{3}x + \frac{9}{2}$.

   Solution: $y = \frac{4}{3}x + 7$

   Explanation: The slope of the line described by $y = \frac{4}{3}x + \frac{9}{2}$ is $\frac{4}{3}$. Parallel lines have the same slope, so the slope of the new line is also $\frac{4}{3}$. The lines goes through the point (0,7), which is the y-intercept, so $b = 7$. Substitute the m and b values into slope-intercept form: $y = \frac{4}{3}x + 7$.

3. Write the equation in slope-intercept form of a line through $(-1, 2)$ that is perpendicular to the line described by $4x - 3y = 8$.

   Solution: $y = -\frac{3}{4}x + \frac{5}{4}$

   Explanation: Express the equation in slope-intercept form, then identify the slope: $4x - 3y = 8 \Rightarrow y = \frac{4}{3}x - \frac{8}{3}$, so the slope is $\frac{4}{3}$. The slope of a line perpendicular to this given line is $-\frac{3}{4}$. Substitute the slope and the point into the point-slope formula to derive the equation: $y - 2 = -\frac{3}{4}(x - (-1))$. Simplify the equation and solve it for y: $y - 2 = -\frac{3}{4}(x + 1)$; $y = -\frac{3}{4}x - \frac{3}{4} + 2$; $y = -\frac{3}{4}x + \frac{5}{4}$.

Practice problems: *(Answers on page: 741)*

1. What is the slope of the line parallel to the line $2x - y = 5$?
2. What is the slope of the line perpendicular to line $4x - 8y = -24$?
3. Write the equation in slope-intercept form of a line through $(-2, 8)$ that is perpendicular to the line $-4x + 6y = 24$.

Review questions: *(Answers to odd questions on page: 741)*

1. What is the slope of the line parallel to the line $y = \frac{1}{2}x + 3$?
2. Write the equation in slope-intercept form of the line passing through point (4,5) that is parallel to the x-axis.
3. Write the equation in slope-intercept form of the line passing through point $(-1, -2)$ that is perpendicular to the the line $2x + 5y + 8 = 0$.
4. Write the equation in slope-intercept form of the line passing through $(-4, 2)$ that is perpendicular to the line described by $y = \frac{4}{3}x + 7$.
5. Write the equation in slope-intercept form of the line passing through point $(1, -6)$ that is parallel to the the line described by $x + 2y = 6$.

Constructing Linear Function Models of Data

- Slope can be very useful for the examination of data.
- Frequently a straight-line **approximation** of the graph of the data shows the pattern of change involved in the real-world situation.
- It is often possible to write an equation that fits the data, to not only see trends to date but make predictions into the future.

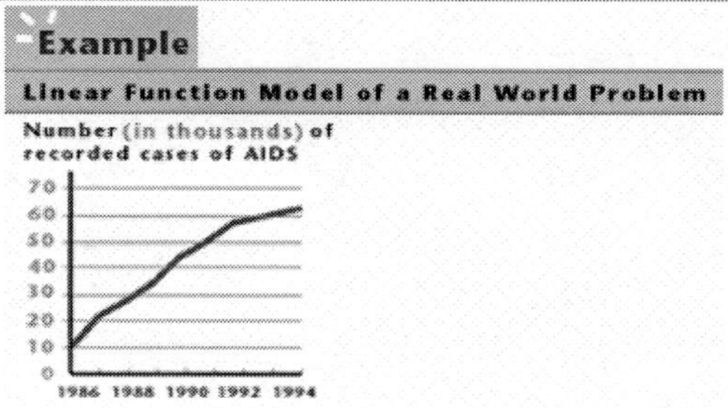	This application shows data related to AIDS. The graph is set up in the typical way with the time changing along the x-axis and the reported data plotted along the y-axis. The number of cases reported in 1986 is the first point of data. The number of cases reported in 1994 is the last point graphed.
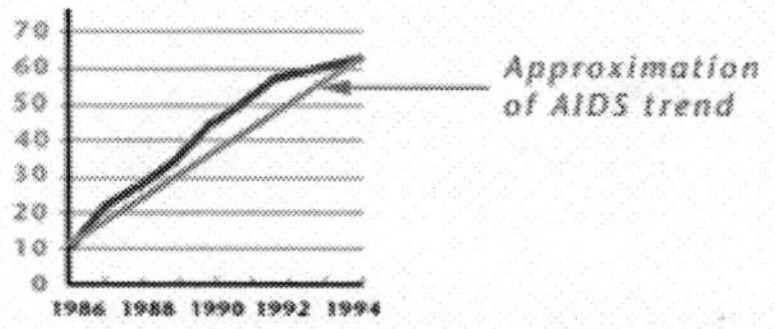	The actual data produces a line graph with a slight curve. You may work with the problem by adding a straight line that **approximates** the curve. Here we mark the line at the starting and ending points of the data curve.
Write the equation for the line. Slope: $m = \frac{\Delta y}{\Delta x}$ (0,11900) -1986 (8,62500) - 1994 $m = \frac{62{,}500 - 11{,}900}{8}$ $= \frac{50600}{8} = 6{,}325$ ← Slope	With a straight line, we can measure constant change from one point in time to another. We can also develop an equation to represent the general pattern of change in the data. **Remember:** slope measures change with vertical change placed over horizontal change. To calculate slope here, the first and last points were used. The slope is the difference between the number of cases reported over the number of years in the study.

$y = 6{,}325x + 11{,}900$ — The equation for AIDS trend	**Remember:** The slope-intercept form for the equation for a line is: $y = mx + b$. Substitute your slope of 6,325 for m. Substitute 11,900 in for the y-intercept, b. You have your equation.
Find the number of cases likely to be reported in 2000 $y = 6{,}325 \bullet 14 + 11{,}900$ $y = \boxed{100{,}400}$ ← Cases for the year 2000	You want to predict the number of cases likely to be reported in the year 2000. That will be 14 years since the first year of reporting. Let $x = 14$ and solve.

Sample problems:

1. At the gas pump, as the price per gallon increases, the number of customers will decrease. A study at Robbie Robin's gas station revealed the data below. A plot and a fitted line is made to the data. Use the data to find the slope that relates the number of customers to the price.

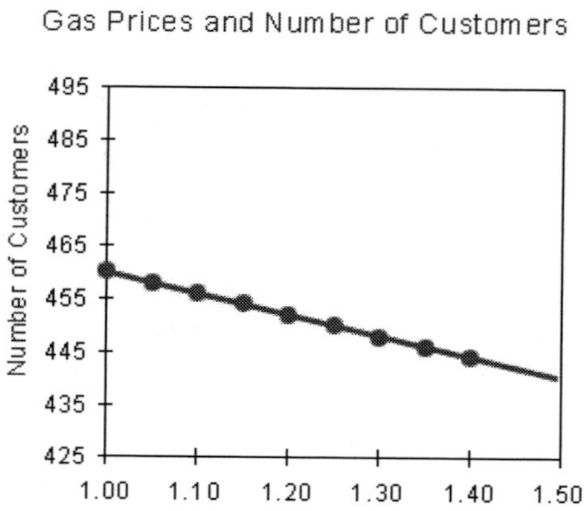

Price/gal

Price/gal (x)	# of Customers (y)
1.00	460
1.05	458
1.10	456
1.15	454
1.20	452
1.25	450
1.30	448
1.35	446
1.40	444

Solution: -40
Explanation: Since the data values all seem to appear on the line, find the slope using any two points. Compute the slope between (1.00,460) and (1.05,458) using the slope formula: $m = \frac{458-460}{1.05-1.00} = \frac{-2}{.05} = -40$.

2. Artificial Technology was studied for the last 12 months and its stock price plotted on the graph. Estimate the price of the stock after 18 months.

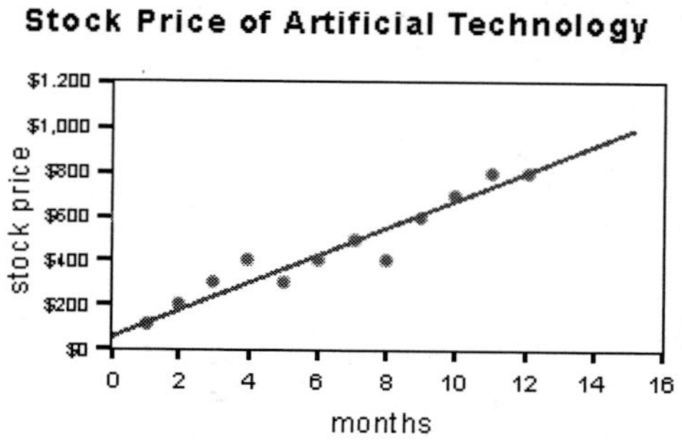

x	y
1	$110
2	$200
3	$300
4	$400
5	$300
6	$400
7	$500
8	$400
9	$600
10	$700
11	$800
12	$800

Solution: \$1,176.41

Explanation: Choose two points on the line: (1,110) and (12,800). Calculate the slope:

$m = \frac{800-110}{12-1} = \frac{690}{11} = 62.73$. Next, use the slope and one of the points to determine the y-intercept. Substitute the m, x, and y values into slope-intercept form, then solve for b: $110 = 62.73(1) + b$; $b = 47.27$. Now, write the equation: $y = 62.73x + 47.27$, where x is the number of months and y is the price of the stock. Substitute 18 into the equation for x to estimate the price of the stock after 18 months: $y = 62.73(18) + 47.27 = 1{,}176.41$.

3. At a loss between being a teacher or being a social worker, a student read that teacher salaries are increasing at a rate of \$3,000 a year. Assuming that the rate of salary increases will determine whether the student becomes a teacher or social worker, should the student become a teacher or a social worker? A table for the salaries of social workers is given for your reference.

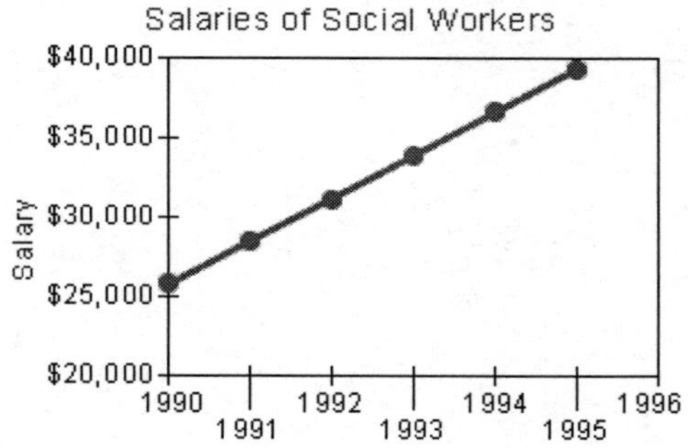

Year

Year (x)	Salary (y)
1990	\$25,700
1991	\$28,400
1992	\$31,100
1993	\$33,800
1994	\$36,500
1995	\$39,200

Solution: teacher

Explanation: To find the rate of salary increases for social workers determine the slope of the line on the graph. To calculate this slope, choose any two points on the line, then substitute them into the slope formula. Since all the points fall on the line, any two points from the table will result in the same slope. The slope is \$2,700, thus the student should be a teacher.

Practice problems: *(Answers on page: 741)*

1. A study of the cost of calculators from 1995-2000 revealed the data below. Find the rate that the cost decreases as defined by the trend line.

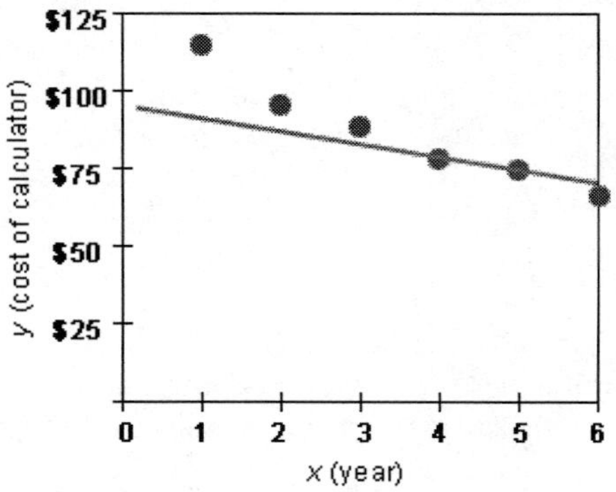

Year		Cost
	x	y
1995	1	\$110
1996	2	\$ 90
1997	3	\$ 84
1998	4	\$ 75
1999	5	\$ 70
2000	6	\$ 60

2. Use the trend line to predict the cost of a calculator in 2002.
Use the graph and table from practice problem #1 to answer this question.

3. According to the trend line, when will the calculator be worthless?
Use the graph and table from practice problem #1 to answer this question.

Review questions: *(Answers to odd questions on page: 741)*

1. A new car was purchased in the 1990 for $21,000. The value of the car over the next six years is shown in the table and graph below. Find the value of the car's rate of decrease.

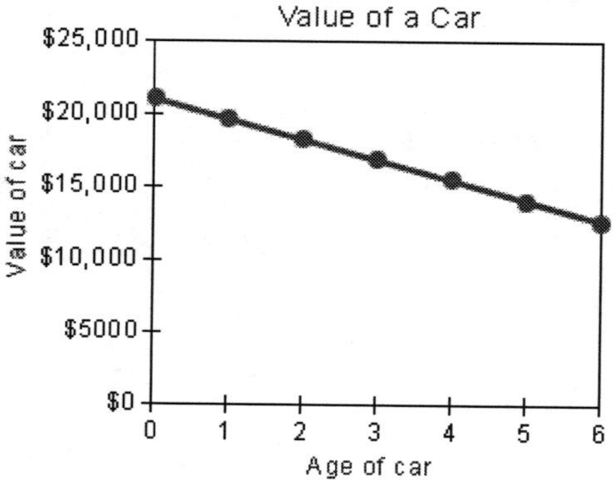

Age of Car (x)	Value of Car (y)
0	$21,000
1	$19,600
2	$18,200
3	$16,800
4	$15,400
5	$14,000
6	$12,600

2. Explain the significance of the graph's y-intercept in the context of the situation. *Use the graph and table from review question #1 to answer this question.*
3. True or false: The car was worth $14,000 in 1995. *Use the graph and table from review question #1 to answer this question.*
4. What was the car worth in 1997? *Use the graph and table from review question #1 to answer this question.*
5. When will the car be worthless? *Use the graph and table from review question #1 to answer this question.*

Linear Cost and Revenue Functions

- **Linear functions** can be used to model many real-world situations, such as the **cost**, **revenue**, and **profit** for a company manufacturing a product.
  - Cost (C) is the amount of money a company must spend to manufacture its product(s).
  - Revenue (R) is the amount of money the company receives from selling its product(s).
  - Profit (P) is the company's net gain: *profit = revenue - cost.*

Example

Making money with linear cost & revenue functions

$R(x) = 259x$

$C(x) = 180x + 10{,}270$

$P(x) = R(x) - C(x)$

$P(x) = 259x - (180x + 10{,}270)$

$P(x) = \boxed{79x - 10{,}270}$ ← The profit function

Linear functions are applicable to many real-world situations.

For example, the **cost**, **revenue**, and **profit** for a company manufacturing a product can be modeled by linear functions.

Given the cost and revenue functions *R(x)* and *C(x)*, the profit function is the difference:
P(x) = R*(x)* - C*(x)*.

Example

What would the profit be if we produced 140 planes?

$P(x) = 79x - 10{,}270$ ← The profit function

$P(140) = 79(140) - 10{,}270$

Profit $= \boxed{\$790}$ ← *Answer*

Applying that profit function to a business problem, you can determine potential profit given a specific number of planes to be produced.

Just plug in the number of planes produced into *P(x).* The result is the profit.

Example **What would the profit be if we produced 20 planes?** $P(20) = 79(20) - 10{,}270$ Profit $= -\$8{,}690$ ← *loss*	What if only 20 planes are produced? Plugging into the profit function results in -\$8,690. A negative profit means the company will experience a loss. The company will probably choose to avoid a loss and produce more than 20 planes.
Example **Where is the break even point? (where profit = 0)** $P(x) = 79x - 10{,}270$ The profit function $79(x) - 10{,}270 = 0$ $x = \frac{10{,}270}{79} \approx \boxed{130}$ ← *Break even point answer*	You can also find the break-even point, or the point where the profit is exactly equal to zero. At the break-even point, the company is not gaining or losing any money. To find where the profit equals zero, set *P(x)* equal to zero and solve for *x*.

Sample problems:

1. A car company has a fixed monthly cost for operating one of its factories of \$1,520,000 for salaries and building operations. Each automobile that it makes has an additional cost of \$18,750. How many cars must the company sell to have at least a monthly profit of \$48,000 if the cars sell for an average price of \$23,500?
   Solution: 331 cars
   Explanation: Set up the equation for cost and revenue, where x is the number of cars produced/sold: $C(x) = 1{,}520{,}000 + 18{,}750x$ and $R(x) = 23{,}500x$. Use $P(x) = R(x) - C(x)$ to set up the profit equation: $P(x) = (23{,}500x) - (1{,}520{,}000 + 18{,}750x)$. Simplify the profit equation: $P(x) = 4750x - 1{,}520{,}000$. To determine the number of cars the company must sell in order to make a monthly profit of at least \$48,000, let $P(x) = 48{,}000$ then solve the equation for x: $48{,}000 = 4{,}750x - 1{,}520{,}000$; $4{,}750x = 1{,}568{,}000$; $x = 330.1$. They can't sell 330.1 cars, so choose between 330 or 331. Since the profit must be "at least" \$4,8000, 330 cars will not produce enough, so they must sell 331 cars per month.

2. A mom-and-pop bookstore has a fixed monthly operating cost of \$6,600 for salaries, their building and taxes. The books they sell cost the company \$7.50 each to produce, with a turnover average of 3,500 volumes each month. How much profit is generated on average if the store sells its books at \$10.50 each?
   Solution: \$3,900
   Explanation: Set up the equation where x is the number of books made/sold: $C(x) = 7.50x + 6{,}600$ and $R(x) = 10.50x$. Use $P(x) = R(x) - C(x)$ to set up the profit equation: $P(x) = 10.50x - (7.50x + 6{,}600)$. Simplify the profit equation: $3x - 6{,}000$. Substitute 3,500 in for x to determine the amount of profit when 3,500 books are sold in a month: $P(3{,}500) = 3(3{,}500) - 6{,}600 = 10{,}500 - 6{,}600 = 3{,}900$. Therefore, the profit will be \$3,900 if they sell 3,500 books for \$10.50 each.

3. A company has a fixed cost of \$27,500/month when it is producing printed tapestries. Each item that it makes has its own cost of \$35. If the tapestries are sold for \$59 each, how many tapestries must be sold each month in order for the company to break even?
   Solution: 1146
   Explanation: Set up the equations for C and R where x is the number of tapestries: $C(x) = 35x + 27{,}500$ and $R(x) = 59x$. Use $P(x) = R(x) - C(x)$ to set up the equation for profit: $P(x) = 59x - (35x + 27{,}500)$. Simplify the profit equation: $P(x) = 24x - 27{,}500$. When a company breaks even the profit is zero. So, to determine the number of tapestries they must produce/sell to break even let $P(x) = 0$ and solve the equation for x: $0 = 24x - 27{,}500$; $-24x = -27{,}500$; $x = 1145.8$. If they sell 1145 they will have a slight loss, but 1146 results in a slight profit. The best answer is 1146.

Practice problems: *(Answers on page: 741)*

1. A temporary agency supplies temporary employees to other companies each workday. They pay an average of \$10/hr and charge an average of \$16/hr. Each temporary worker averages 160 hours per month on a job. For the office and its staff, they have fixed operating costs of \$18,000/month. If they had 22 temps working during April, how much profit did they generate that month?
2. Using the information form question 1, how many temps must they employ in a single month to generate at least \$5,000 in profit?
3. Using the information from question 1, how many temps must they employ in a single month to at least break even?

Review questions: *(Answers to odd questions on page: 741)*

1. A temporary agency supplies temporary employees to other companies each workday. They pay an average of \$10/hr and charge an average of \$16/hr. Each temporary worker averages 160 hours per month on a job. For the office and its staff they have fixed operating costs of \$18,000/month. Assuming that they had 49 temps working during the month of July, what was the total cost to the company of operating during this month?
2. A temporary agency supplies temporary employees to other companies each workday. They pay an average of \$10/hr and charge an average of \$16/hr. Each temporary worker averages 160 hours per month on a job. For the office and its staff they have fixed operating costs of \$18,000/month. Assuming that they had 49 temps working during the month of July, find the total profit for July.
3. Suppose that the fixed operating costs for the agency described in question 2 increased to \$20,000/month. How many employees must they have in order to break even each month?
4. Consider the temporary agency described in question #2. In August the company had a \$10,320 net loss. How many employees did they have in August?
5. Consider the temporary agency described in question 2. In September the company had a \$43,440 net gain. How many employees did they have in September?

Graphing Some Important Functions

- This lecture gathers some basic equations with their graphs so you can have a visual image when you run across each of these examples.

Example

$f(x) = c$

c is a constant

x	$f(x)$ — *y value*
-1	c
0	c
1	c

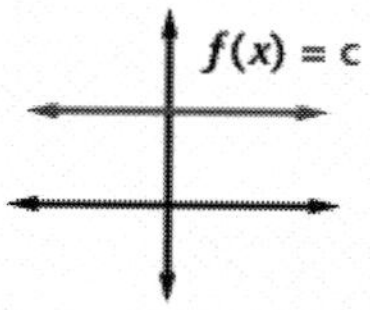

Every point on the line matches some x with the same value for y, c. The line is not moving at all on the vertical scale. Therefore, it is horizontal.

Example

$f(x) = x$

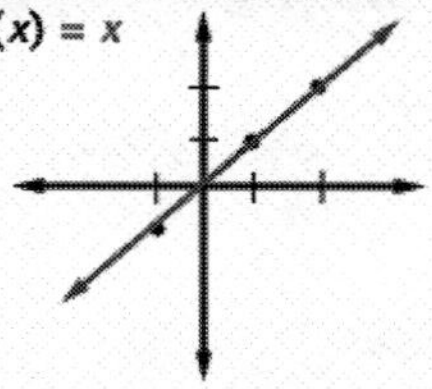

Every point changes x- and y-values exactly the same. So you get a line that divides the matching-signs quadrants exactly in half.

The function of $f(x) = x$ is the linear function.

Example

all parabolas will have this same basic shape

$f(x) = x^2$

x	$f(x)$
-1	1
0	0
1	1
2	4

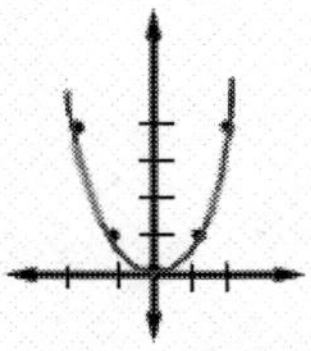

Parabolas are guaranteed symmetry by the x^2 term which neutralizes the signs of the values for x.

The function $f(x) = x^2$ is the quadratic parent function.

Example

x	$f(x)$
-2	-8
-1	-1
0	0
1	1
2	8

$f(x) = x^3$

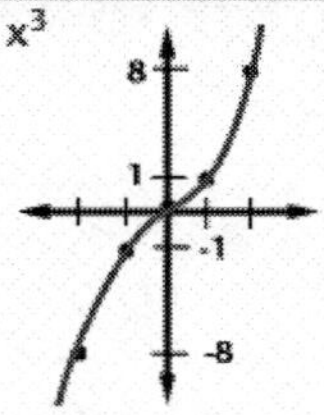

This curve will rise three times faster than it moves sideways thanks to the impact of the x^3 term.

The funtion $f(x) = x^3$ is the cubic parent function.

Example

x	y
-1	undefined
0	0
1	1
4	2
9	3

$f(x) = \sqrt{x}$

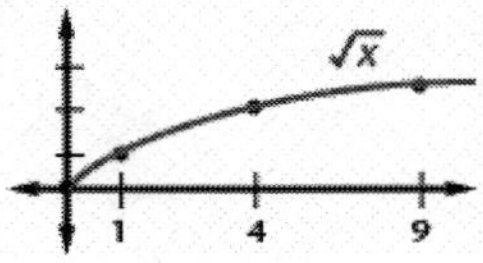

Remember: The value under the radical must be greater than or equal to zero so that a real number root can exist.

The function $f(x) = \sqrt{x}$ is the radical parent function.

Example

x	$f(x)$
-2	2
-1	1
0	0
- 1	1
2	2

$f(x) = |x|$

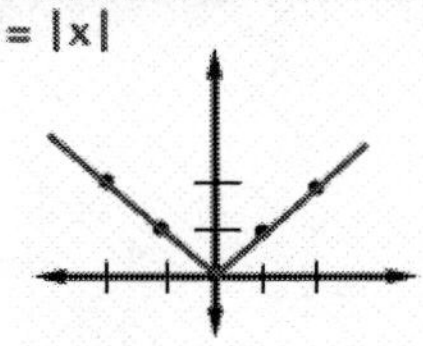

Remember: Absolute value is always positive and graphed along the positive axis regardless of the expression within its notation.

The function $f(x) = |x|$ is the absolute value parent function.

Sample problems:

1. True or false: The graph of $y = 3x^3$ is a parabola.
   Solution: False
   Explanation: The function $y = 3x^3$ is cubic. However, parabolas are formed from quadratic functions where the variable is squared, not cubed.

2. Identify the parent function of $f(x) = |x| + 7$.
   Solution: $f(x) = |x|$
   Explanation: The function $f(x) = |x| + 7$ is an absolute value function, so its parent function is the most basic absolute value function $f(x) = |x|$.

3. All points on the graph of $y = x^2 + 2$ are contained in which quadrants?

   Solution: I and II

   Explanation: The domain of $y = x^2 + 2$ is all real numbers, however the graph is not in all four quadrants. The range is $y \geq 2$ (since any number squared then added to two is greater than or equal to 2), so the y-coordinates are only positive numbers. Thus, the graph is contained in the quadrants where x is negative or positive, but y is only positive, or quadrants I and II.

Practice problems: *(Answers on page: 741)*

1. Identify the parent function of $g(x) = 3\sqrt{x}$.
2. Identify the parent function of $y = x^2 + 4$.
3. In which quadrant do the points of the graph of $x = |y| + 1$ occur?

Review questions: *(Answers to odd questions on page: 741)*

1. True or false: The graph $y = -3$ is a vertical line.
2. True or false: The graph of the parent radical function passes through the origin.
3. Identify the parent function of $y = 6 - x$.
4. Identify the parent function of $f(x) = x^3 - 1$.
5. True or false: The graph of $f(x) = \frac{1}{3}x^2$ is a parabola.

Graphing Piecewise-Defined Functions

- **Piecewise functions** are those that are defined differently on different intervals of the x-axis.

<table>
<tr>
<td>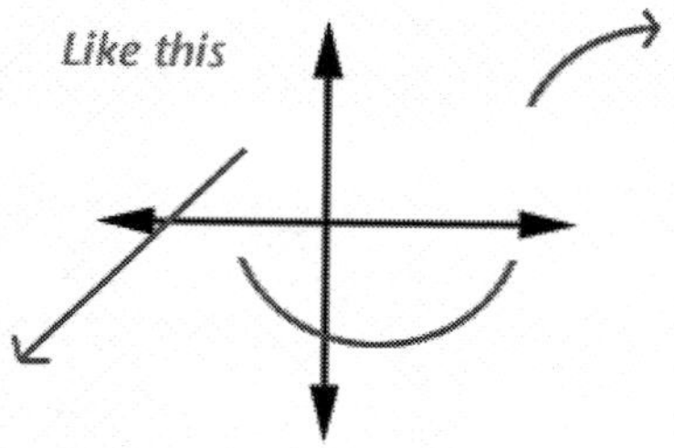
</td>
<td>Piecewise functions can have different shapes from each other in their various parts.

Each part must be graphed separately as you use x-values all along the x-axis.</td>
</tr>
<tr>
<td>$f(x) = \begin{cases} 2x+1 \text{ if } x \geq 0 \\ x \text{ if } x < 0 \end{cases}$
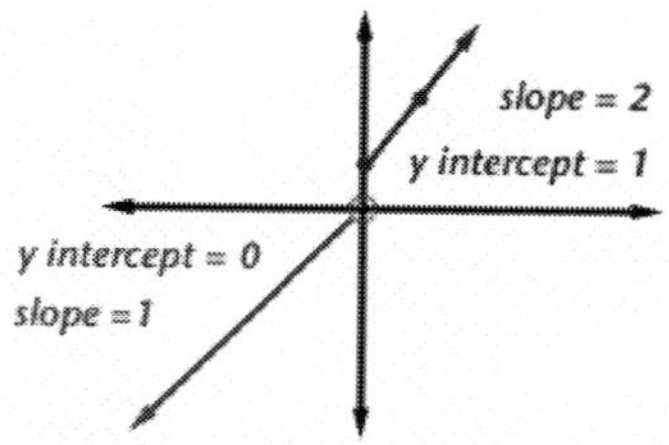
</td>
<td>In this case you will use $2x+1$ every time you are considering an x that is equal to or larger than 0.

You will use x every time you are considering an x that is less than 0.

The result in this case is two unrelated lines, one that includes 0 and moves to the right and one that starts at, but does not include 0, and moves to the left. Notice how the endpoints are represented to show whether 0 is included or excluded on each line.</td>
</tr>
</table>

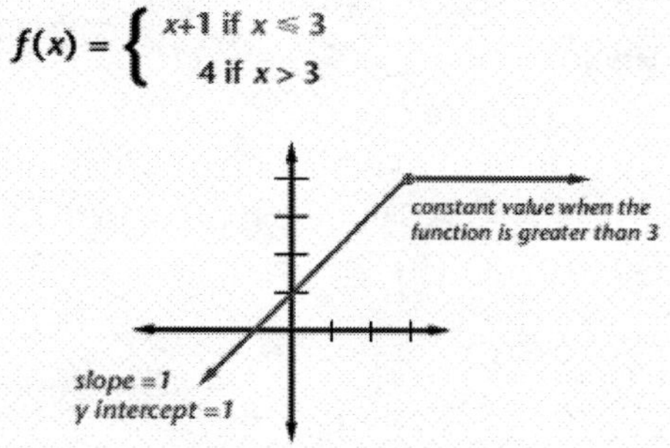	This example graphs $y = 4$ for every x greater than +3. Notice the horizontal line that starts at +3 and moves to the right. The function also includes a graph for x +1 for every x that includes and is less than +3. That graphs a downsloping line that includes +3 and moves to the left. Both lines represent the function.
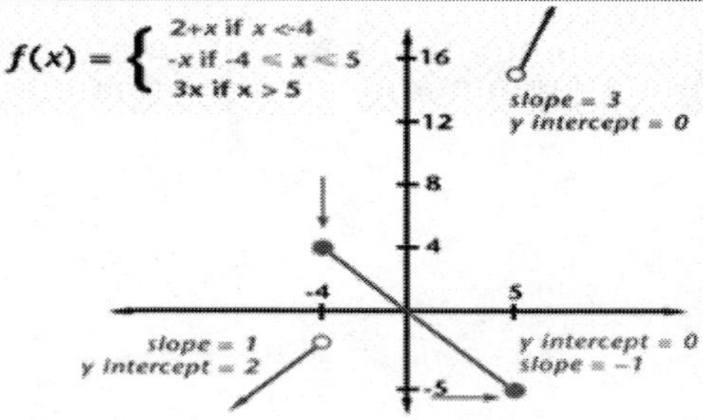	This function uses three different expressions to express itself. The result is three lines each being graphed over its segment of the x-axis. Notice how the endpoints are represented. Notice that the middle line is a line segment with two definite endpoints. The two outer lines each have one definite endpoint but go on infinitely on their segment of the plane.

Sample problems:

1. What is the domain of $f(x)=\begin{cases}3x^2+x & \text{if } x<-2\\ 4-x & \text{if } x\geq -2\end{cases}$?

   Solution: All real numbers

   Explanation: The domain is all possible x values, defined in this function by the two inequalitites $x<-2$ and $x\geq -2$. Together these inequalities include all real numbers.

2. Graph: $f(x)=\begin{cases}x^2 & \text{if } -2\leq x\leq 2\\ 4 & \text{if } x \text{ is any other real number}\end{cases}$

   Solution:

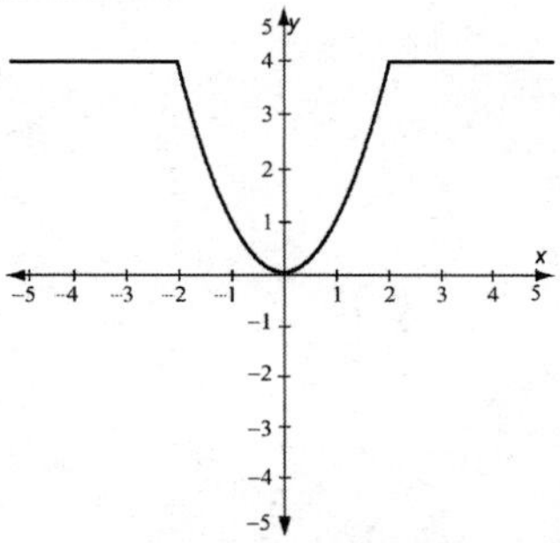

   Explanation: The first case defines the function for $-2<x<2$. Between the points where $x=-2$ and $x=2$, the graph is a parabola with its vertex at the origin. The second case defines the function as a straight line at all other points. For values of x that are less than or equal to -2 or greater than or equal to 2, the function is a straight line at $y=4$. The function is defined at all points. It is represented by the described parabola with specified endpoints and the two rays with specified starting points.

3. Graph: $f(x)=\begin{cases}x+1 & \text{if } x\leq 2\\ x-1 & \text{if } x>2\end{cases}$

   Solution:

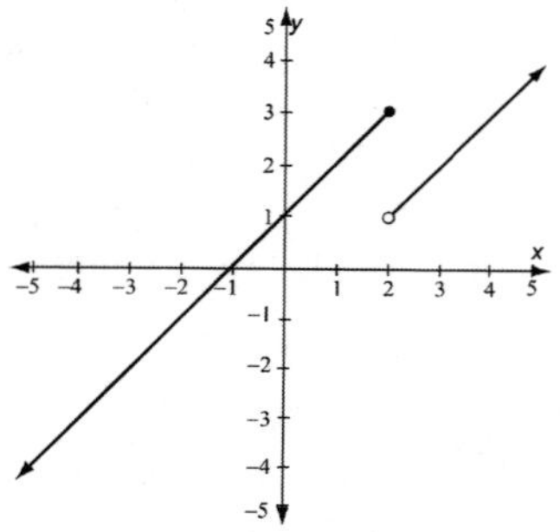

Explanation: The graph of $y = x + 1$ when $x \le 2$ is a line that extends downward from the point $(2,3)$, including $x = 2$. The graph of $y = x - 1$ if $x > 2$ is a line that extends upward from the point $(2,1)$, not including $x = 2$. The solution includes the point $(2,3)$ and shows the correct lines.

Practice problems: *(Answers on page: 741)*

1. What is the domain of $f(x) = \begin{cases} x^2 - 5 & \text{if } 0 \le x < 1 \\ -x & \text{if } x \ge 1 \end{cases}$?

2. Graph: $f(x) = \begin{cases} 3 & \text{if } x \le 0 \\ x^2 & \text{if } x > 0 \end{cases}$

3. Graph: $f(x) = \begin{cases} x & \text{if } x < -1 \\ -x^2 & \text{if } -1 < x < 1 \\ 1 & \text{if } x > 1 \end{cases}$

Review questions: *(Answers to odd questions on page: 742)*

1. For how many integer values of x is $f(x)$ not defined? $f(x) = \begin{cases} x & \text{if } x > 4 \\ -x + 2 & \text{if } 0 \le x < 4 \\ 2x & \text{if } x \le -3 \end{cases}$

2. What is the range of the function represented by the following graph?

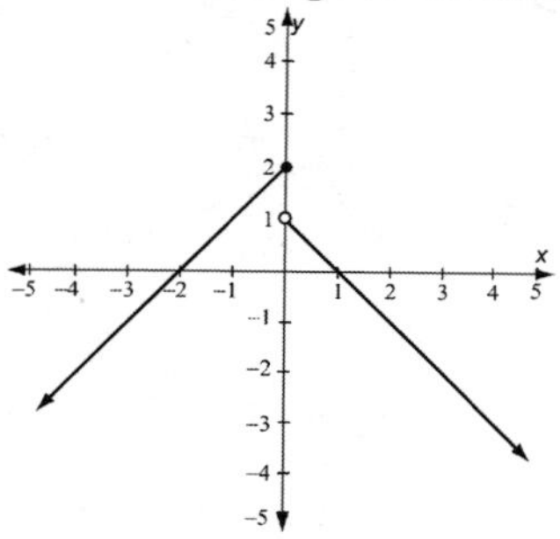

3. What is the domain of $f(x) = \begin{cases} 1 & \text{if } 0 < x < 5 \\ x + 1 & \text{if } x \ge 5 \end{cases}$?

4. Graph: $f(x) = \begin{cases} x^2 + 1 & \text{if } x \ge 0 \\ -3 & \text{if } x < 0 \end{cases}$

5. Graph: $f(x) = \begin{cases} 3 - x & \text{if } x < 1 \\ 4 & \text{if } 1 < x \le 2 \\ x & \text{if } x > 3 \end{cases}$

Matching Equations with Their Graphs

- Each type of equation has its own signature graph. Learn to match graphs with their equations.

<table>
<tr><td>

What is the equation for this graph?

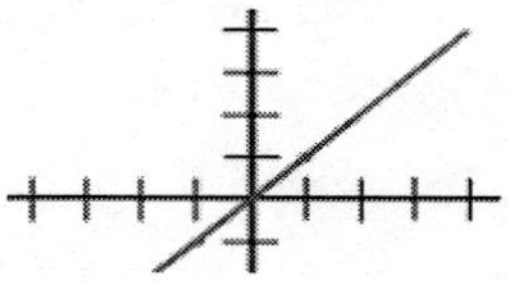

</td><td>

This graph is a straight line with a slope of 1.

$y = x$

If you try some points, you will find (1,1),(-2,-2), (0,0), all on this line.

</td></tr>
<tr><td>

What is the equation for this graph?

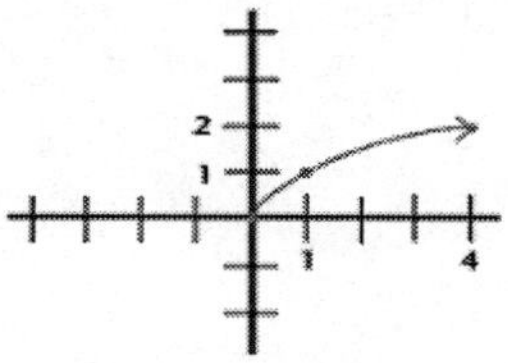

</td><td>

$y = \sqrt{x}$.

Remember: x must be positive or 0 to be under the radical sign. As a result, the graph does not exist to the left of 0 or below the x-axis.

Points you will find on this line include (0,0), (16,4), (25,5) and (4,2).

</td></tr>
<tr><td>

What is the equation for this graph?

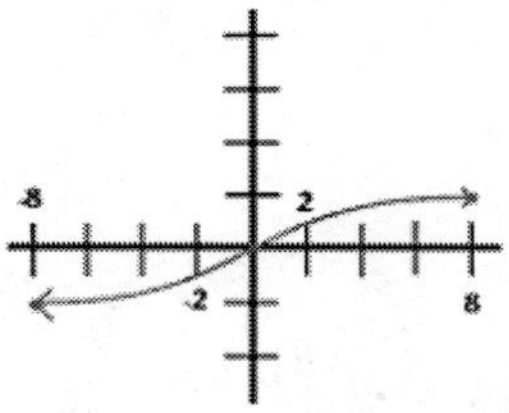

</td><td>

$y = \sqrt[3]{x}$

When you try points with this expression, you will find (1,1), (-1,-1), (-8,-2),(27,3)

On this graph both coordinates always have the same sign and the x-values grow much faster than the y-values. Those two characteristics place this graph in Quadrants I and III following closely along the x-axis.

</td></tr>
<tr><td>

What is the equation for this graph?

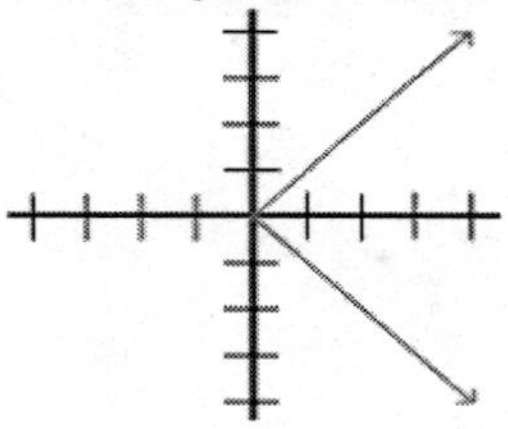

</td><td>

$x = |y|$

Try some points. You will find (0,0), (2,2) and (2,-2), (5,5) and (5,-5) among the points on this line.

There is no way for x to be negative on this graph.

</td></tr>
<tr><td>

What is the equation for this graph?

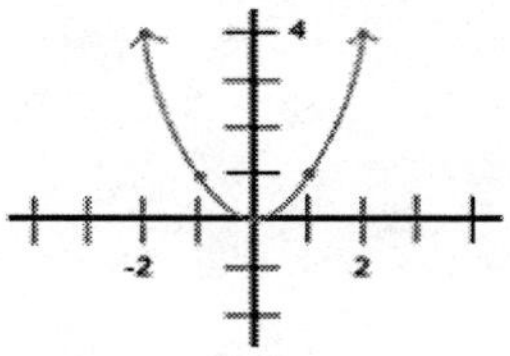

</td><td>

$y = x^2$

Try some points and you will find (0,0), (2,4) and (-2,4), (5,25) and (-5,25).

There is no way for y to be negative and the y-values grow much faster than the x-values.

</td></tr>
</table>

Sample problems:

1. Choose the relation from the following list that best describes the graph below:

$$y = \frac{1}{x};\quad x = y^2;\quad y = \sqrt{x};\quad x = |y|;\quad y = x^2;\quad y = [x];\quad y = x^3;\quad y = |x|;\quad y = \sqrt[3]{x}.$$

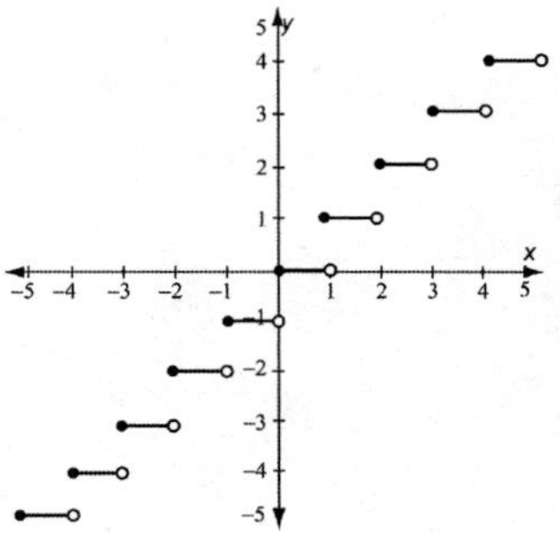

Solution: $y = [x]$

Explanation: The graph shows $y = [x]$. The greatest integer function is a step function, and several values of x give the same value of y, e.g., $[1.1] = [1.5143] = [1.67] = [1.9]$. Each of these pairs with $y = 1$.

2. Choose the relation from the following list that best describes the graph below:
$y = \frac{1}{x}$; $x = y^3$; $y = \sqrt{x}$; $x = |y|$; $y = x^2$; $y = [x]$; $y = x^3$; $y = |x|$; $y = \sqrt[3]{x}$.

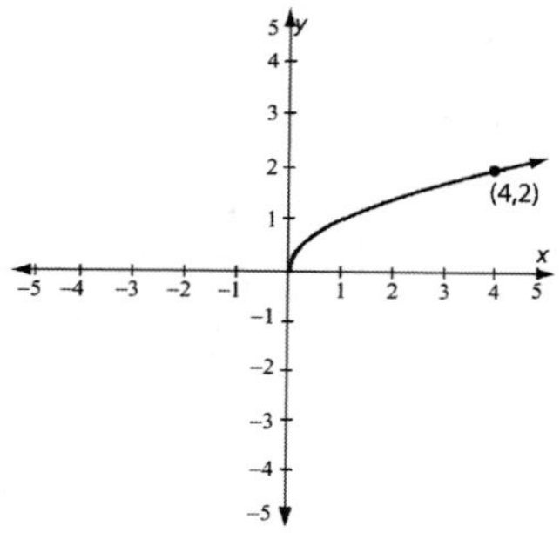

Solution: $y = \sqrt{x}$

Explanation: The domain of the graph shown is $x \geq 0$, which is also the domain of $y = \sqrt{x}$. The point (4,2) is a point on the graph of $y = \sqrt{x}$, since $2 = \sqrt{4}$.

3. Choose the relation from the following list that best describes the graph below:
$y = \frac{1}{x}$; $x = y^2$; $y = \sqrt{x}$; $x = |y|$; $y = x^2$; $y = [x]$; $y = x^3$; $y = |x|$; $y = \sqrt[3]{x}$.

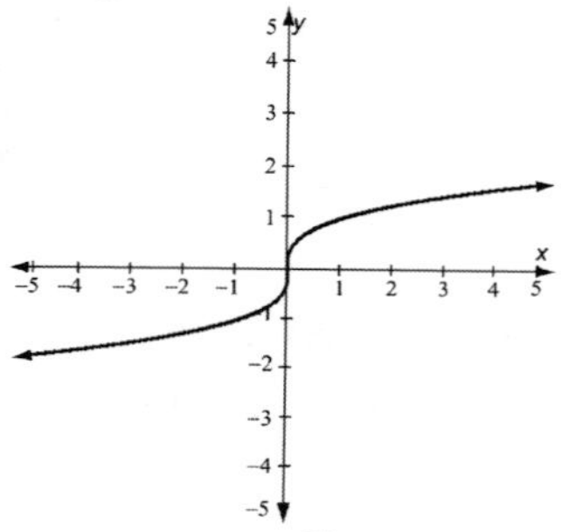

Solution: $y = \sqrt[3]{x}$

Explanation: The graph shows that y equals the cube root of x. This graph passes through the origin, and slowly progresses away from the x-axis in the first and third quadrants.

Practice problems: *(Answers on page: 742)*

1. Choose the relation from the following list that best describes the graph below:
$y = \frac{1}{x}$; $x = y^2$; $y = \sqrt{x}$; $x = |y|$; $y = x^2$; $y = [x]$; $y = x^3$; $y = |x|$; $y = \sqrt[3]{x}$.

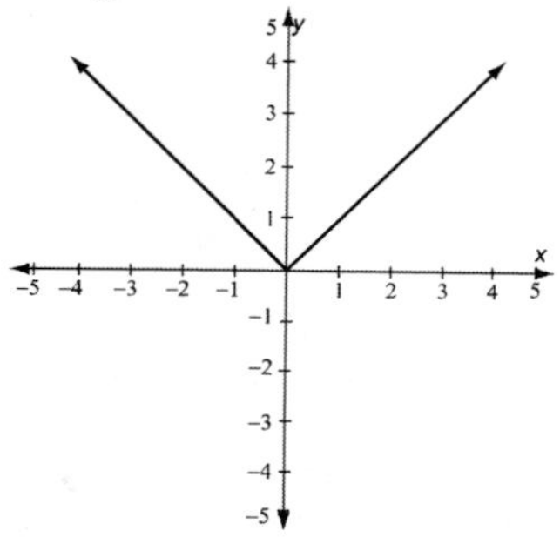

2. Choose the relation from the following list that best describes the graph below:
$y=\frac{1}{x}$; $x=y^2$; $y=\sqrt{x}$; $x=|y|$; $y=x^2$; $y=[x]$; $y=x^3$; $y=|x|$; $y=\sqrt[3]{x}$.

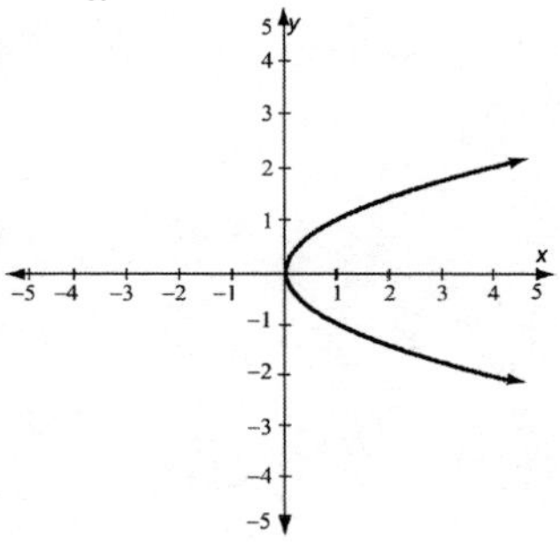

3. Choose the relation from the following list that best describes the graph below:
$y=\frac{1}{x}$; $x=y^2$; $y=\sqrt{x}$; $x=|y|$; $y=x^2$; $y=[x]$; $y=x^3$; $y=|x|$; $y=\sqrt[3]{x}$.

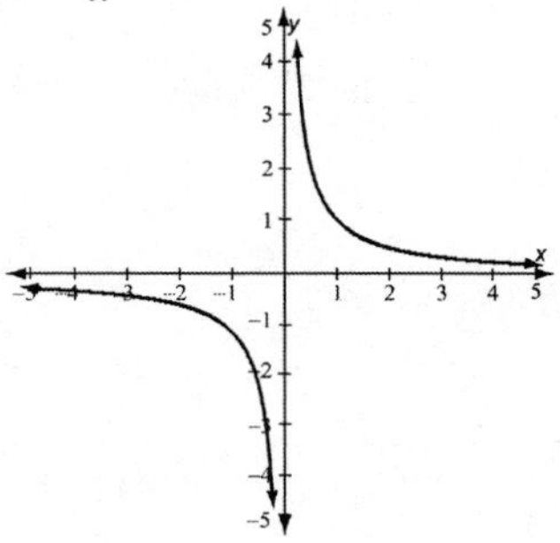

Review questions: *(Answers to odd questions on page: 742)*

1. Choose the relation from the following list that best describes the graph below:
$y=\frac{1}{x}$; $x=y^2$; $y=\sqrt{x}$; $x=|y|$; $y=x^2$; $y=[x]$; $y=x^3$; $y=|x|$; $y=\sqrt[3]{x}$.

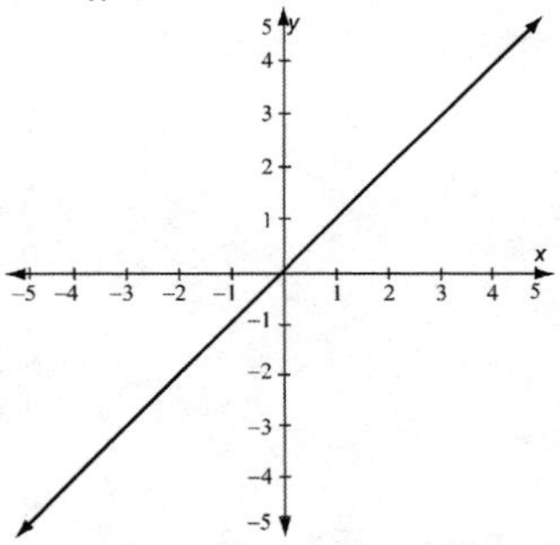

2. Choose the relation from the following list that best describes the graph below:
$y=\frac{1}{x}$; $x=y^2$; $y=\sqrt{x}$; $x=|y|$; $y=x^2$; $y=[x]$; $y=x^3$; $y=|x|$; $y=\sqrt[3]{x}$.

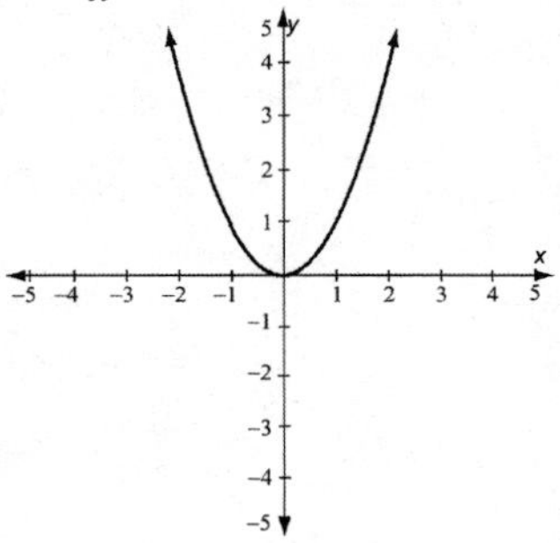

3. Choose the relation from the following list that best describes the graph below:
$y=\frac{1}{x}$; $x=y^2$; $y=\sqrt{x}$; $x=|y|$; $y=x^2$; $y=[x]$; $y=x^3$; $y=|x|$; $y=\sqrt[3]{x}$.

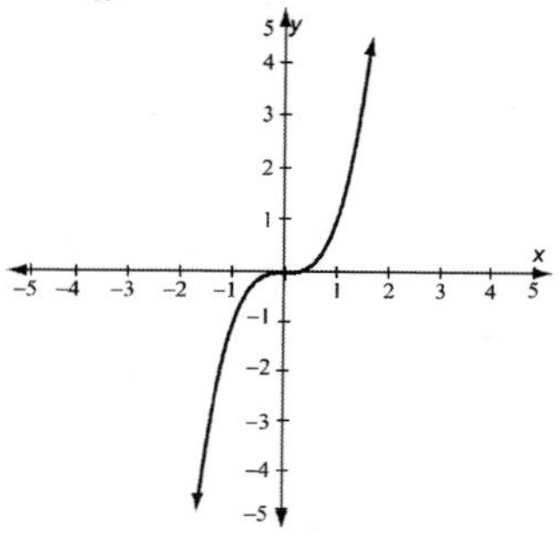

4. Choose the relation from the following list that best describes the graph below:
$y=2^x$; $x=y^3$; $y=\sqrt{x}$; $x=|y|$; $y=x^2$; $y=[x]$; $y=x^3$; $y=|x|$; $y=\sqrt[3]{x}$.

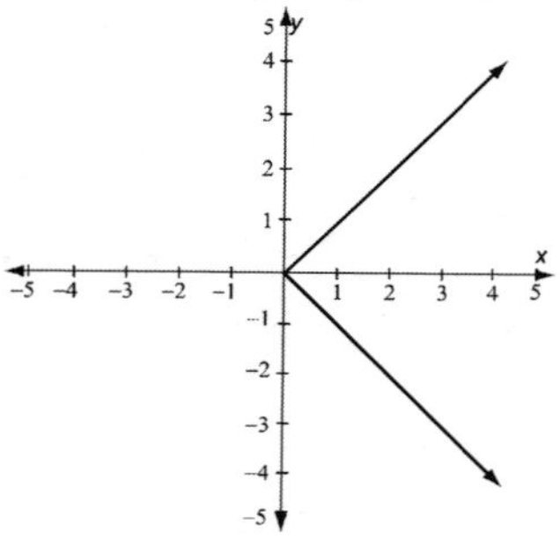

5. Choose the relation from the following list that best describes the graph below:
$y=2^x$; $x=y^3$; $y=\sqrt{x}$; $x=|y|$; $y=x^2$; $y=[x]$; $y=x^3$; $y=|x|$; $y=\sqrt[3]{x}$.

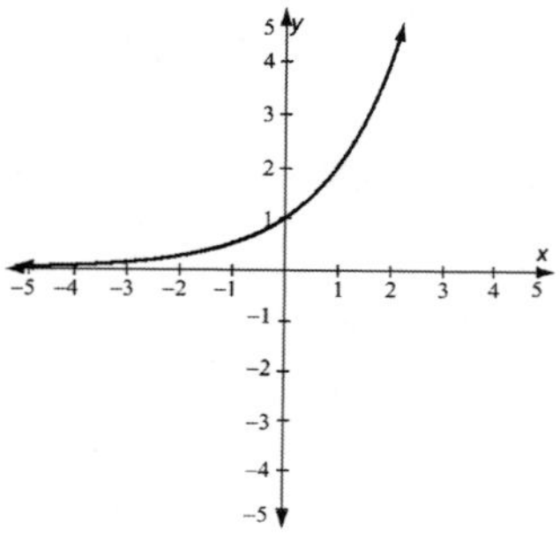

The Greatest Integer Function

- The **greatest integer function** looks for the greatest integer that is less than or equal to x in the notation $[x]$.
- The graph of this function is sometimes referred to as a "step-function" because of its appearance.

$[3.8]=3$ $[17.139]=17$ $[49]=49$ $[1.3]=1$ $[-1.4]=-2$ $[-\frac{1}{2}]=-1$	Here are some examples that satisfy the **greatest integer function**. **Note:** The greatest integer for a negative value will be the integer closer to zero. Visualize the positions on a number line to help you make your choice.

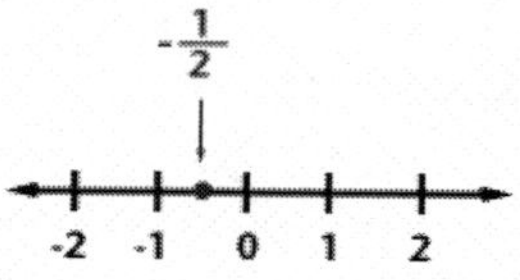

[x] - the greatest integer function

– the biggest integer that is less than or equal to x

$f(x) = [x]$

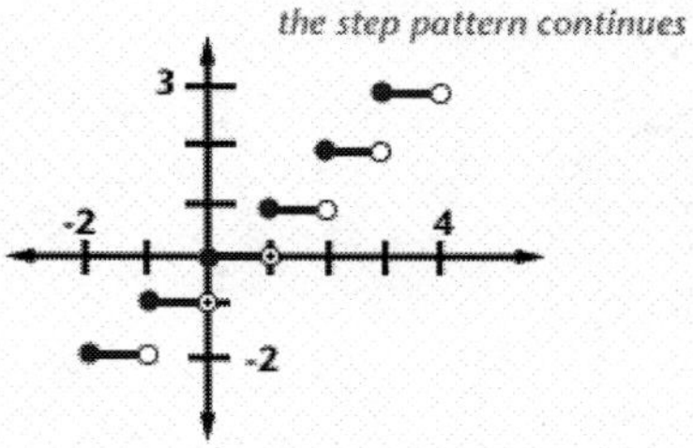

Because the fraction values of x result in integer values for y, the graph looks like a stairstep of short horizontal lines.

For example, for all the xs between 1.0 and 2.0, the y-values equal 1.

Likewise for all the xs between –2 and –1, the y-values equal –1. You can see these in the graph in this example.

Sample problems:

1. Evaluate: $[4.6]+[5.6]-[4.6+5.6]$
   Solution: -1
   Explanation: $[4.6]+[5.6]-[4.6+5.6]=4+5-[10.2]=4+5-10=-1$

2. Evaluate: $[-\pi]+[\sqrt{3}]$
   Solution: -3
   Explanation: $[-\pi]+[\sqrt{3}]\approx[-3.14159]+[1.73]=-4+1=-3$

3. Evaluate: $\left[\frac{10}{3}\right]-[-12.9-1.05]+[16.008]$
   Solution: 33
   Explanation: $\left[\frac{10}{3}\right]-[-12.9-1.05]+[16.008]=[3.33]-[-13.95]+[16.008]=3--14+16=33$

Practice problems: *(Answers on page: 742)*

1. Evaluate: $[-8.5]+[7.1]$
2. Evaluate: $\frac{[-5.2]}{[3.77]}+[19.5]-[-2]$
3. Evaluate: $[-0.05]+[1.7+22.1]-[\pi]$

Review questions: *(Answers to odd questions on page: 742)*

1. Evaluate: $\left[-\frac{19}{3}\right]$
2. Evaluate: $[5.7]+[1.3]+[-22.9]-[1.7]$
3. Evaluate: $[1]+\left[\frac{11}{3}\right]+[-\pi+1]-\left[-\frac{2}{5}\right]$
4. Evaluate: $[-2]-[1.0009]+[\pi+1]-[-\pi]$
5. Evaluate: $[-0.2-9.1]+[5.4-8.3+1]-[-5]$

Graphing the Greatest Integer Function

- The greatest integer function looks for the greatest integer that is less than or equal to x in the notation $[x]$.
- The graph of this function is sometimes referred to as a "step-function" because of its appearance.

$f(x) = [2x-1]$

The greatest integer brackets should be a tip off that some sort of step function graph is appropriate.

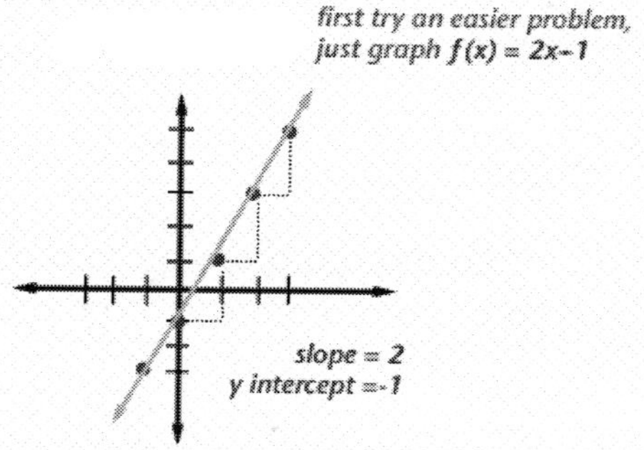

If you graph the expression inside the brackets you can visually see the general path that will be involved.

In this example, the expression graphs a line.

Notice the specific points that were located based on the y-intercept and the slope of the expression. Each one is a point where x has an integer value.

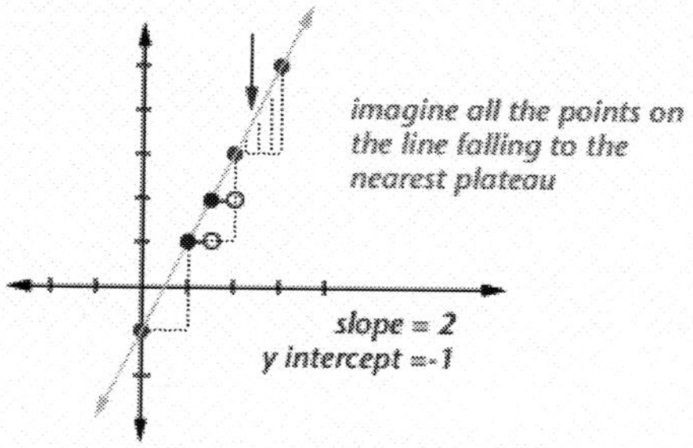

Now, think about all the values between the points shown. The y for every point will be the largest integer than does not exceed the $f(x)$ at that point. For example, when $x = 2\frac{1}{4}$, $2x - 1 = 3\frac{1}{2}$ and $[2x - 1] = 3$, the largest integer not exceeding $3\frac{1}{2}$. If you look on the graph, you will see this point $(2\frac{1}{4},3)$ is graphed on the short blue line that begins at (2,2).

$f(x) = [2x-1]$

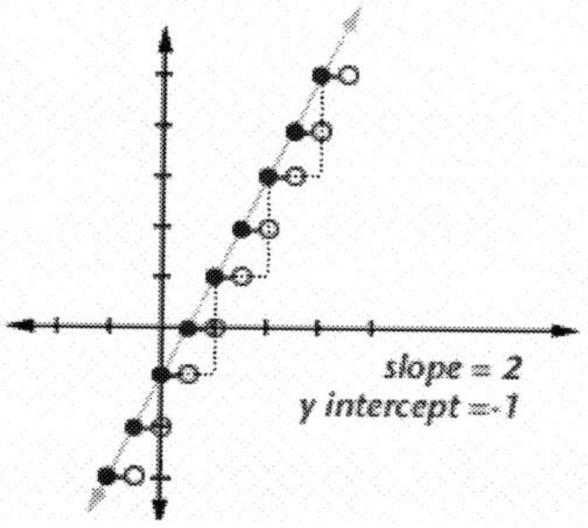

For this particular example, a new blue "step" will start whenever x is an integer or attached to the fraction ½. That is because all the xs multiply with 2 and produce integers. Think about the point where $x = 2\frac{1}{2}$. At this point $2x - 1 = 4$ and $[2x - 1] = 4$. So, at the point $(2\frac{1}{2},4)$ expect a new blue line to start. And sure enough one does. The result is a graph composed of an ascending set of short "steps" each one covering half its integer space on the y-axis.

Sample problems:

1. Graph: $y = [x - 2]$
   Solution:

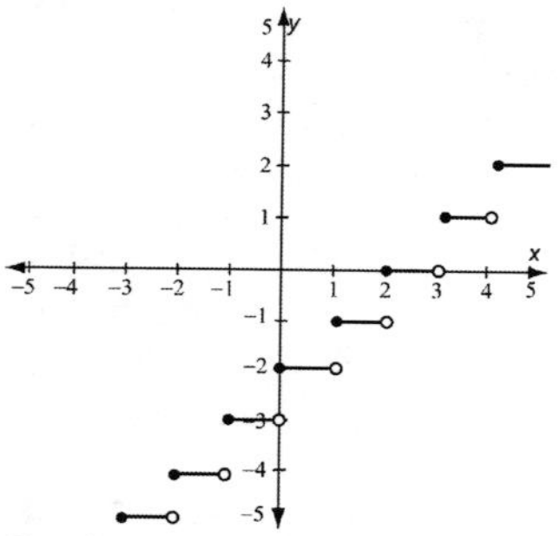

Explanation: Begin to sketch the graph of $y = x - 2$: plot the y-intercept $(0, -2)$ and a few points using the slope $(1, -1)$, $(2,0)$, and $(3,1)$. Instead of drawing a line through the points, draw a horizontal line segment from each point extending one unit to the right. The line segment should have a closed point at the left side and an open point at the right. Repeat the pattern.

2. Graph: $y=[2x+3]$
Solution:

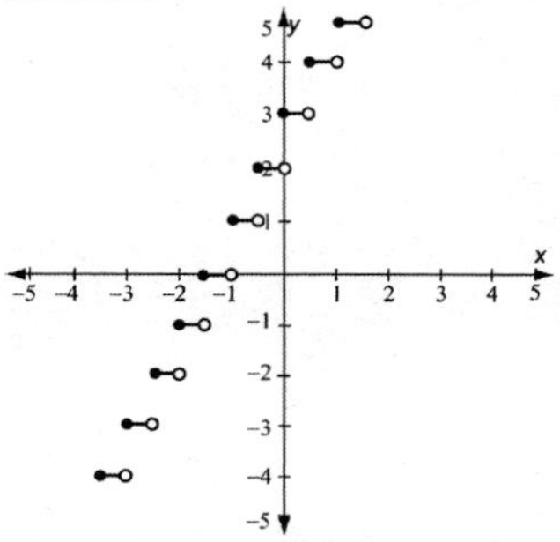

Explanation: Begin to sketch the graph of $y = 2x+3$: plot the y-intercept (0,3) and a few points using the slope (1,5), (2,7), and (3,9). Instead of drawing a line through the points, draw a horizontal line segment from each point extending one-half unit to the right. The line segment should have a closed point at the left side and an open point at the right. Repeat the pattern.

3. How are the graphs of $f(x)=[x+5]$ and $g(x)=[x]+5$ related?
Solution: The graphs are identical.
Explanation: $[5]=5$. The greatest integer less than or equal to 5 is 5. $[x+5]=[x]+[5]$. Because 5 is an integer, it doesn't matter whether 5 is added before or after the greatest of x is determined. Thus, for any number, $[x+5]=[x]+5$. Putting these ideas together you can see that the two functions are identical as are their graphs.

Practice problems: *(Answers on page: 742)*

1. Graph: $y=[x+3]$
2. Graph: $y=[\frac{1}{2}x-1]$
3. How are the graphs of $y=[x]$ and $y=[-x]$ related?

Review questions: *(Answers to odd questions on page: 742)*

1. Graph: $y=[x]-1$
2. Graph: $y=[2x]$
3. Graph: $y=[\frac{1}{3}x-5]$
4. How are the graphs of $y=[x]$ and $y=[x-1]$ related?
5. True or false: Each step in the graph of $y=[\frac{1}{2}x]$ is twice the length of each step in the graph of $y=[x]$.

Deconstructing the Graph of a Quadratic Function

- Quadratic functions:
  1) represent parabolas;
  2) have symmetry;
  3) have a turning point, either a maximum or a minimum.
- The domain is the set of all real numbers.

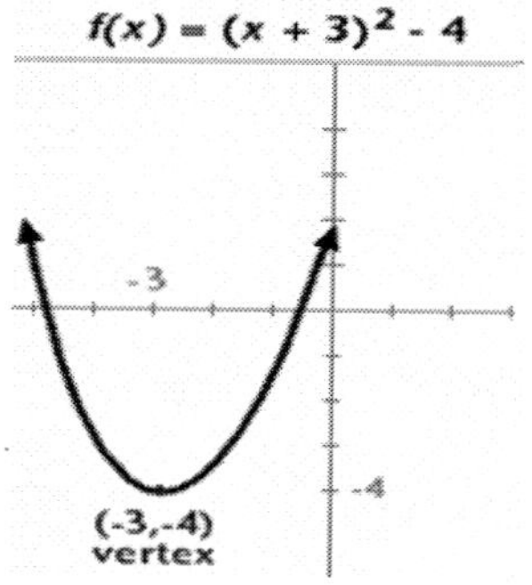

Your function is $f(x) = (x + 3)^2 - 4$, so you know that your vertex is not going to be at the origin.

One way to graph a parabola is to randomly choose values for x, substitute them into the expression, calculate the resulting y-value, and plot each point.

If you do that for this example, you will get this graph.

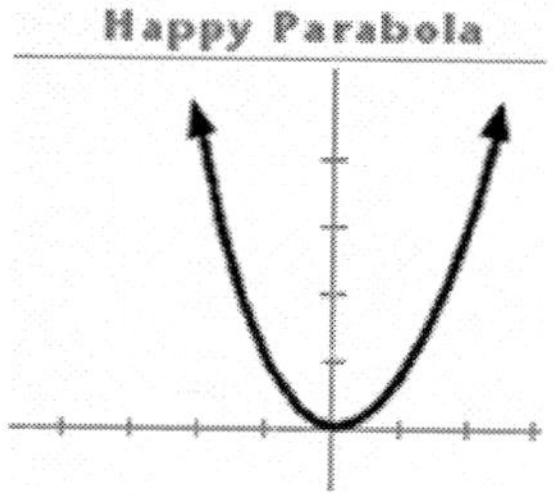

Here's another approach you can use either to create your graph or to check your arithmetic.

Step One: You know that all quadratics graph a parabola. Here is the standard "happy" parabola with its vertex at the origin.

Step Two: Check for any shift away from the origin.
Be careful about shifting from the origin that you shift both sideways and vertically in the correct direction.

Here's Dr. Burger's rule for shifting. Learn this little rule to be sure you always shift in the correct direction.

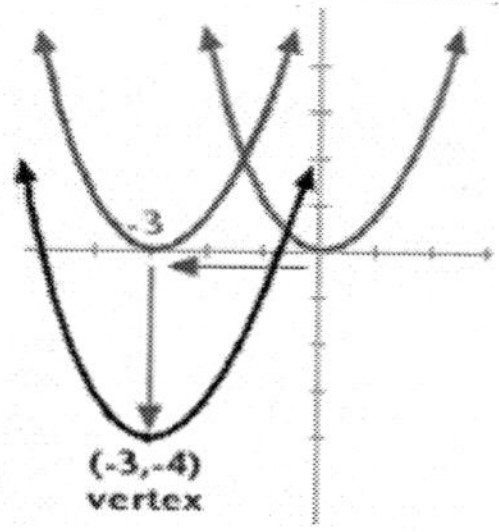

Checking your function, $f(x) = (x + 3)^2 - 4$, you see that you are directed to shift to the left 3 units and down 4 units from the origin.

You can do that and locate your graph.

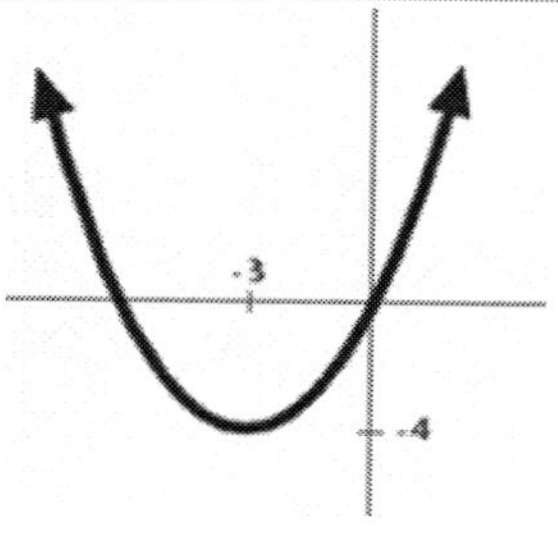

In this example, your domain is the set of all real numbers.

Your range is more limited. The smallest y-value that you will have is the one at the vertex, which is -4. As a result, your range is limited to all the numbers between -4 and $+\infty$.

Sample problems:

1. Describe the shifts made to the graph of $y = x^2$ when $y = (x-5)^2 + 1$ is graphed.
   Solution: 5 units to the right and one unit up
   Explanation: In the function $y = (x-5)^2 + 1$, 5 is subtracted from x which indicates a shift of 5 units to the right and 1 is added which indicates a shift of one unit up. The vertex of this parabola is located at (5,1) which is 5 units to the right and one unit up from the vertex of $y = x^2$, (0,0).

2. Identify the vertex of the parabola described by $y=(x+2)^2-3$.
   Is the vertex the maximum or minimum of the parabola?
   Solution: $(-2,-3)$, minimum
   Explanation: The vertex of $y=(x+2)^2-3$ is 2 units to the left and 3 units down from (0,0), or at (–2,–3). The parabola opens up, so the vertex is the minimum.

3. Determine the range of $y=-(x+1)^2+4$.
   Solution: $y\le 4$
   Explanation: The vertex of $y=-(x+1)^2+4$ is at (–1,4). The parabola opens down, so the maximum y-value is 4. Thus, the range is $y \le 4$.

Practice problems: *(Answers on page: 742)*

1. Describe the shifts made to the graph of $y=x^2$ when $y=(x+2)^2-1$ is graphed.
2. Identify the vertex of the parabola described by $y=-(x+5)^2$.
   Is the vertex the maximum or minimum of the parabola?
3. Determine the range of $y=(x-6)^2-3$.

Review questions: *(Answers to odd questions on page: 743)*

1. Describe the shifts made to the graph of $y=x^2$ when $y=\left(x-\frac{1}{2}\right)^2+3$ is graphed.
2. Describe the shifts made to the graph of $y=x^2$ when $y=(x+5)^2-2$ is graphed.
3. Identify the vertex of the parabola described by $y=-(x-7)^2+1$.
   Is the vertex the maximum or minimum of the parabola?
4. Determine the range of $y=(x-1)^2$.
5. Determine the range of $y=-(x-4)^2+2$.

Nice-Looking Parabolas

- **Standard form of a parabola:** $f(x) = ax^2 + bx + c$.
- **Vertex of a parabola:** (h,k).
  - $h = -b/2a$.
  - $k = f(h)$.
- **Standard form for parabola showing vertex:** $f(x) = a(x - h)^2 + k$.

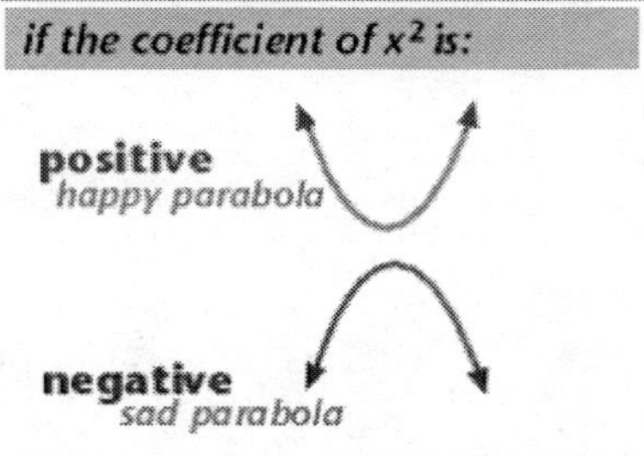	The direction a parabola opens is easy to determine. Look at the coefficient of the squared term in the function. If the coefficient is positive, the curve opens in the positive direction. If the coefficient is negative, the curve opens in the negative direction.

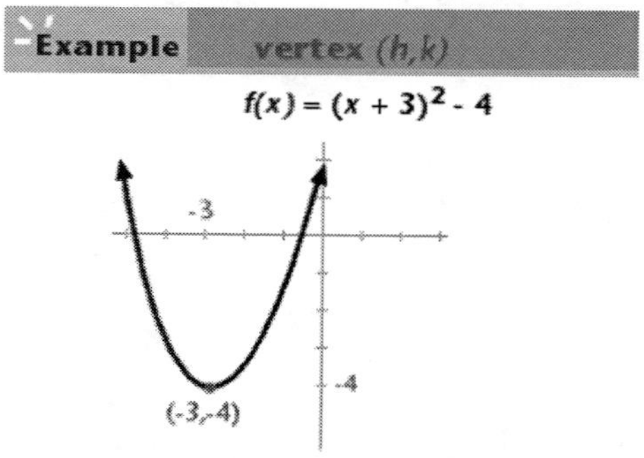

First, consider the standard form of a parabola:
$f(x) = a(x - h)^2 + k$

Then look at this example. The vertex (h, k) is easily determined to be (-3, -4).

Remember: h is subtracting so change the sign of the x-value before using it in the vertex.

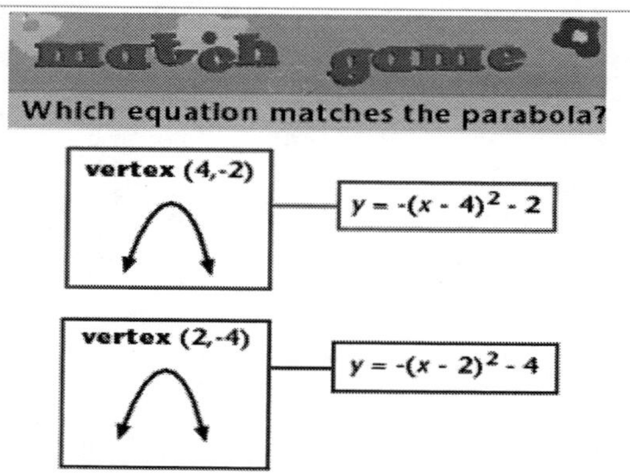

Notice: Downturning parabolas have negative coefficients on the squared term in their equations.

Notice: The x-value changes sign as a coordinate from what is used in the equation.

Sample problems:

1. Determine the direction and vertex of the parabola described by $y = -2(x-1)^2 + 4$.
   Solution: opens down, vertex: (1,4)
   Explanation: This equation is in vertex form: $y = a(x-h)^2 + k \Rightarrow y = -2(x-1)^2 + 4$, so $a = -2$, $h = 1$, and $k = 4$. Since a is negative, the parabola must open down. The vertex is located at the point (h,k), so the vertex of this parabola is at (1,4).

2. Determine the direction and vertex of the parabola described by $y = 3(x+2)^2 - 4$.
   Solution: opens up, vertex: $(-2,-4)$
   Explanation: This equation is in vertex form: $y = a(x-h)^2 + k \Rightarrow y = 3(x+2)^2 - 4 = 3(x-(-2))^2 + (-4)$, so $a = 3$, $h = -2$, and $k = -4$. Since a is positive, the parabola must open up. The vertex is located at the point (h,k), so the vertex is at $(-2,-4)$.

3. True or false: The vetex of the parabola described by $y = (x+5)^2$ is at $(-5,0)$.
   Solution: True
   Explanation: This equation is in vertex form:
   $y = a(x-h)^2 + k \Rightarrow y = (x+5)^2 = 1(x-(-5))^2 + 0$, $h = -5$, and $k = 0$.
   The vertex is located at the point (h,k), so it is at $(-5,0)$.

Practice problems: *(Answers on page: 743)*

1. Determine the direction and vertex of the parabola described by $y = 5 - x^2$.
2. Determine the direction and vertex of the parabola described by $y = (x-2)^2$.
3. Determine the direction and vertex of the parabola described by $f(x) = \frac{1}{2}(x+3)^2 - 7$.

Review questions: *(Answers to odd questions on page: 743)*

1. Determine the direction and vertex of the parabola described by $y = x^2 - 8$.
2. Determine the direction and vertex of the parabola described by $y = -x^2 - 2$.
3. Determine the direction and vertex of the parabola described by $y = -(x-3)^2 - 2$.
4. Determine the direction and vertex of the parabola described by $y = (x+3)^2 - 1$.
5. Determine the direction and vertex of the parabola described by $y = 5(x+1)^2 + 1$.

Using Discriminants to Graph Parabolas

- **Quadratic equation:** $ax^2 + bx + c = 0$.
- **Quadratic formula:** $x = \dfrac{-b \pm \sqrt{b^2 - 4ac}}{2a}$.
- **Discriminant:** $b^2 - 4ac$. Checking the value of the discriminant tells about the solutions:
  - $b^2 - 4ac > 0$ indicates there are two real solutions.
  - $b^2 - 4ac = 0$ indicates there is only one solution.
  - $b^2 - 4ac < 0$ indicates there are no real solutions.

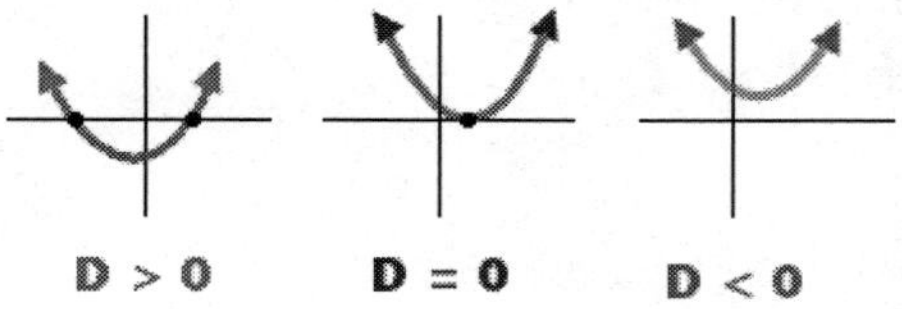	Analyzing the discriminant gives you an idea where to graph the curve of a quadratic function.
Example 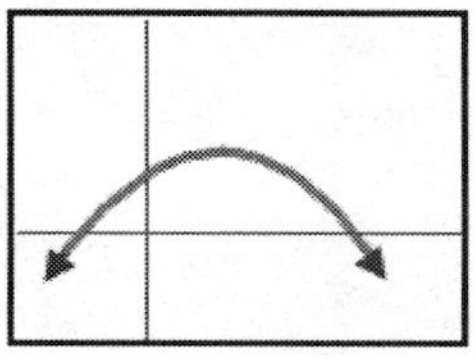	Matching the graph with the elements of its function, this parabola has: -a value of a that is less than 0, because it turns down, -a discriminant greater than 0 because it crosses the x-axis twice and must have two real-number solutions.
Example 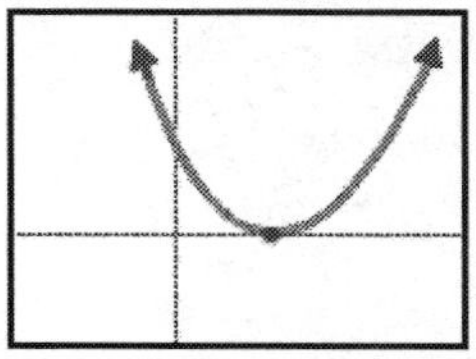	This is a positive parabola with one real solution: its $a > 0$, and its discriminant = 0.
Example 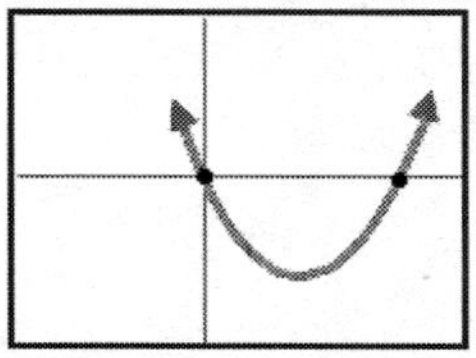	This is a positive parabola with two real solutions: its $a > 0$, and its discriminant > 0.

Example 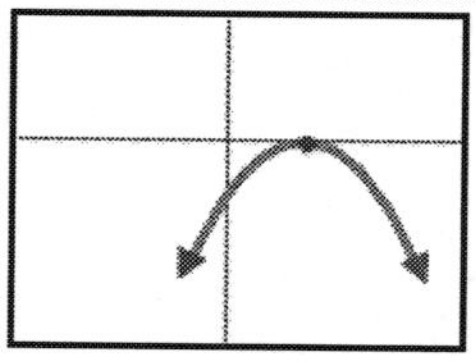	This is a negative parabola with one real solution: its $a < 0$, because it turns down, and its discriminant $= 0$.
Example 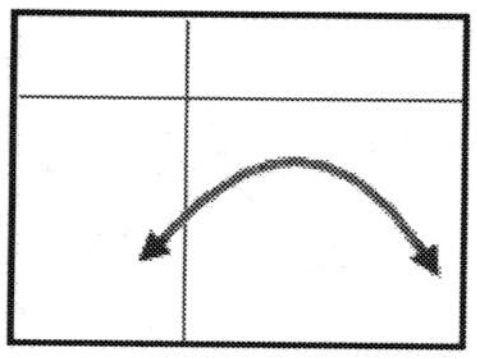	This is a negative parabola with no real solutions: it's $a < 0$, and its discriminant < 0.

Sample problems:

1. Suppose the vertex of a parabola is at (0, 3) and the parabola opens down. What can you determine about the value of the discriminant?
   Solution: the discriminant is > 0
   Explanation: The vertex of the parabola is above the x-axis and the parabola opens down. Thus, the parabola must cross the x-axis twice. Therefore, the discriminant must be a positive number.

2. Suppose a parabola opens up and the vertex is on the x-axis. What can you determine about the value of a and the discriminant?
   Solution: a is positive and the discriminant is 0.
   Explanation: Two aspects of the parabola are given: 1) the parabola opens up and 2) the vertex is on the x-axis. Since the parabola opens up, the value of a is positive. Since the vertex is on the x-axis, the parabola crosses the x-axis only once. Therefore, the discriminant must be 0.

3. Suppose the vertex of a parabola is in the 1st quadrant and the y-value of the y-intercept is greater than the y-value of the vertex. What can you determine about the values of a, c, and the discriminant?
   Solution: a is positive, c is positive, and the discriminant is negative
   Explanation: Visualize the parabola. The y-intercept must be higher than the vertex since the y-value of the y-intercept is greater than the y-value of the vertex. Since the y-intercept is higher than the vertex the parabola must open up, so a is positive. Additionally, c must be positive. A parabola with the vertex in the 1st quadrant that opens up does not cross the x-axis, so the discriminant must be negative.

Practice problems: *(Answers on page: 743)*

1. True or false: The equation of the following parabola has a negative discriminant.

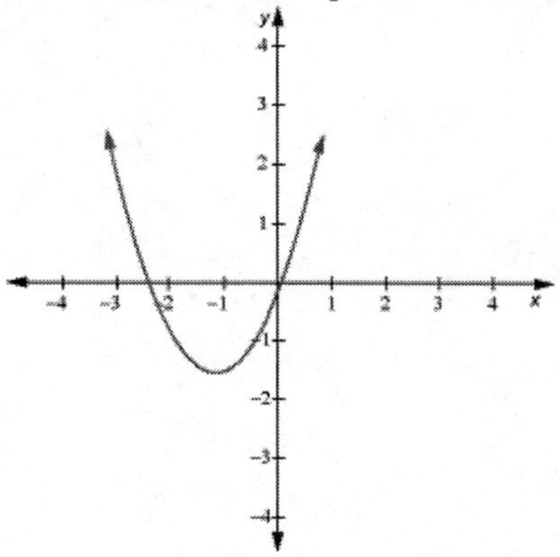

2. Suppose the discriminant of a quadratic equation is 0 and the value of a is less than 0. What can you determine about the parabola defined by this equation?

3. Suppose the vertex of a parabola is in the 4th quadrant and the parabola opens up. What can you determine about the discriminant?

Review questions: *(Answers to odd questions on page: 743)*

1. True or false: The equation of the parabola below has a positive discriminant.

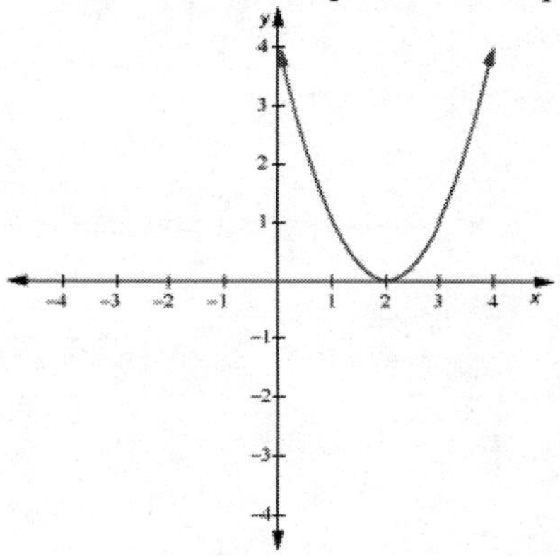

2. True or false: The equation of the parabola below has a negative discriminant.

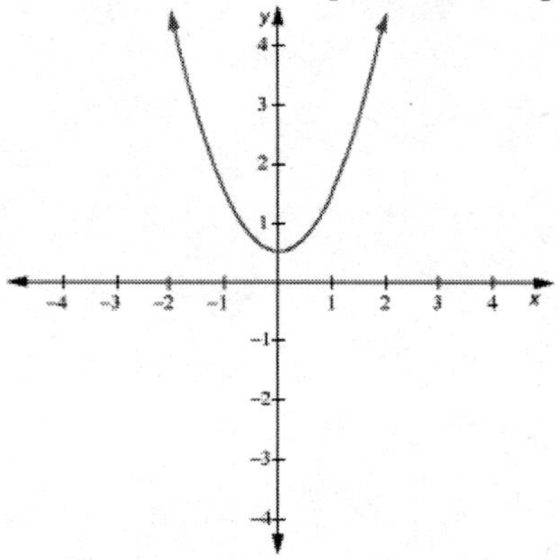

3. True or false: The equation of the parabola below has a positive discriminant.

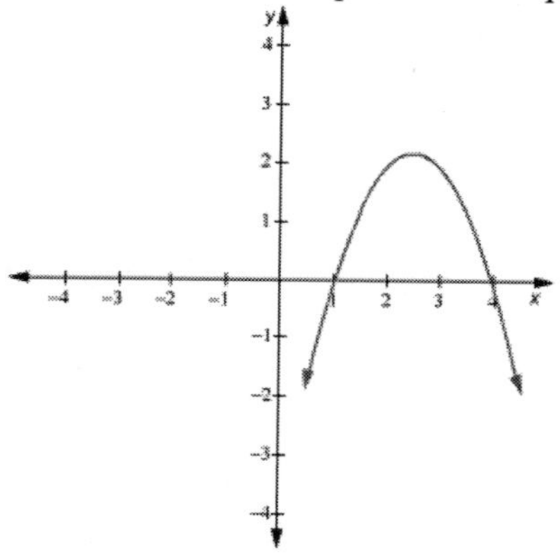

4. Suppose the discriminant of a quadratic equation is 4 and the vertex of the parabola described by this equation is in the 2nd quadrant. What can you determine about the value of the a in the equation?

5. Suppose the vertex of a parabola is on the x-axis and the y-intercept is less than 0. What can you determine about the discriminant and the value of the a?

Maximum Height in the Real World

- **Standard form of a parabola:** $f(x) = ax^2 + bx + c$.
- **Vertex of a parabola:** (h,k), where $h = \dfrac{-b}{2a}$ and $k = f(h)$.
- **Standard form for parabola showing vertex:** $f(x) = a(x - h)^2 + k$.

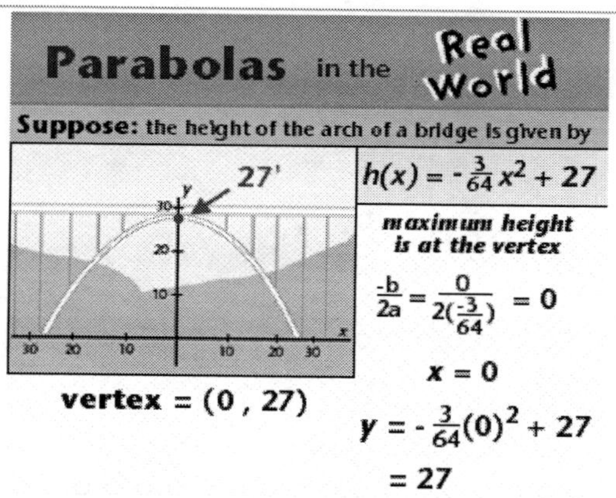

In this example, your x-axis represents the distance in feet that the bridge spans.

The graph is set so that $x = 0$ where the bridge's curve is at its highest; i.e., at the vertex.

So, $h = 0$.

Solve for k, which turns out to be 27 feet.

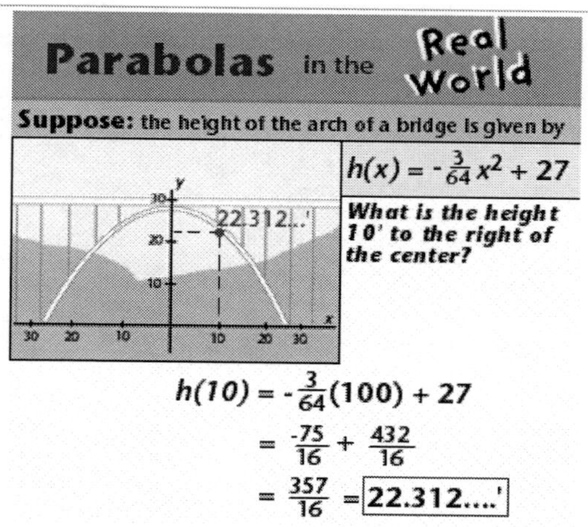

Now you want to find the height of the span 10 feet on either side of center.

This means $x = 10$.

Substitute 10 into the function for x and solve for the y, or height.

That height is 22.312 feet.

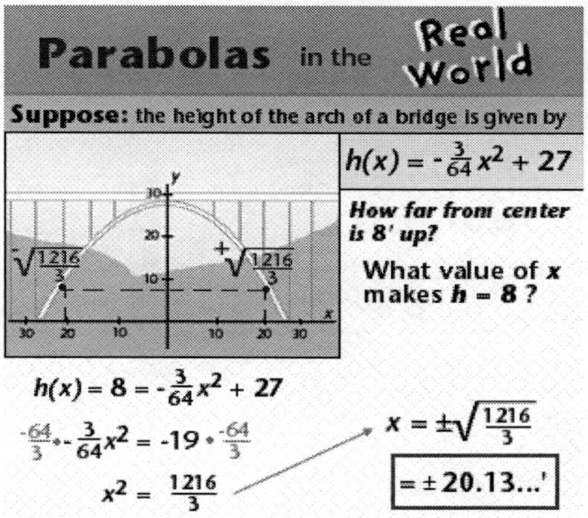

Now you want to find the location of a specific height of the span of the bridge.

Set the height to 8 feet; i.e., $h(x) = 8$. That means that the function, $h(x)$, equals 8. Now solve for x.

The edge of the bridge is 8 feet above its base on either side at 20.13 feet from the height of the arch.

Sample problems:

1. A model rocket is shot into the air. Its height in feet, y, after x seconds is given by the function $y = -16x^2 + 128x$. Find the maximum height of the rocket.
   Solution: 256 feet
   Explanation: The maximum height is the y-coordinate of the vertex, (h, k). Find h:
   $h = \dfrac{-b}{2a} = \dfrac{-128}{2(-16)} = 4$. The maximum height of the rocket is 256 feet.

2. Using the situation from sample problem #1, determine how long the rocket stays in the air.
   Solution: 8 seconds
   Explanation: The rocket will stay in the air until the height is 0, so substitute 0 into the equation for y and solve for x: $0 = -16x^2 + 128x$. Divide the equation by -16: $0 = x^2 - 8x$. Factor and solve: $0 = x(x-8)$; $x = 0$ or $x - 8 = 0$; $x = 0$ or $x = 8$. The height of the rocket is 0 after 0 seconds and after 8 seconds. So the rocket stays in the air for 8 seconds.

3. A batter hits a baseball and the ball, y, after x seconds is given by the function $y = -16x^2 + 58x + 3$. How long does it take for the ball to reach its maximum height?
   Solution: 1.8 seconds
   Explanation: The maximum height of the ball is the y-coordinate of the vertex. But, the time it takes the ball to reach that maximum height is the x-coordinate of the vertex. Find the x-coordinate of the vertex: $h = \dfrac{-b}{2a} = \dfrac{-58}{2(-16)} = 1.8125$. So the ball reaches its maximum height after 1.8 seconds.

Practice problems: *(Answers on page: 743)*

1. In a baseball game, a batter pops a ball straight up in the air as given by the function: $f(x) = -16t^2 + 160t$, where t is in seconds. A seagull is witnessed swooping down and swallowing the ball at an altitude of 300 feet. Find the time, t, when the seagull ate the ball.
2. The ball described in problem #1 will reach its maximum height before being eaten by the seagull. After how many seconds will the ball reach its maximum height and what will that height be?
3. Suppose the ball described in problem #1 was not eaten by the seagull. After how many seconds will the ball hit the ground?

Review questions: *(Answers to odd questions on page: 743)*

1. An electronics company found that for a particular model of television they manufacture the revenue is given by the function $f(x) = 4000p - 4p^2$, where the unit price of the television is p dollars. What unit price should be established for the television to maximize revenue?
2. If a stone is thrown directly upwards from the ground with an initial velocity of 80 feet per second, the height of the stone is $s(t) = -16t^2 + 80t$. Find the maximum height of the stone before it falls back to the ground .
3. If a stone is thrown directly upwards from the ground with an initial velocity of 60 feet per second, the height of the stone is $s(t) = -16t^2 + 60t$. Find how long it would take before the stone reaches maximum height.
4. A one-way tunnel is in the shape of a parabola, $f(x) = -\frac{1}{4}x^2 + 9$, where $-6 \le x \le 6$. Find the height of the tallest truck of width 8 feet that can pass through this tunnel.
5. An object is dropped from a height of 100 feet. At any time $t > 0$, the height of the object is given by $f(t) = -16t^2 + 100$. How many seconds will it take for the object to hit the ground?

Finding the Vertex by Completing the Square

- **Standard form of a parabola:** $f(x) = ax^2 + bx + c$.
- **Vertex of a parabola:** (h,k).
  - $h = -b/2a$.
  - $k = f(h)$.
- **Vertex form for parabola :** $f(x) = a(x - h)^2 + k$.
- Completing the square is one method for changing a function into the vertex form in order to be able to graph it easier.

Example find the vertex

$f(x) = x^2 + 4x + 1$

complete the square

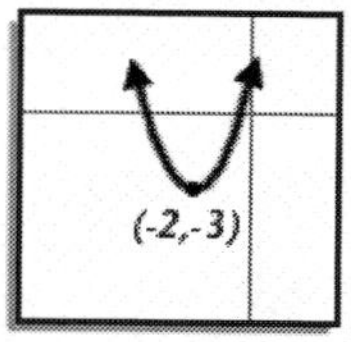

$= (x^2 + 4x + \underline{4}) + 1 - \underline{4}$

take $\frac{1}{2}$ and square

what is added must be subtracted

$= (x + 2)^2 - 3$

vertex = (-2,-3)

In this example the x-terms are $(x^2 + 4x)$.

To complete that square, divide the 4 in half, square it, and add it inside the x-term expression so that you have $(x^2 + 4x + 4)$. To maintain the balance of the function, add a -4 outside the x-term expression.

Combine like terms and contract the square.

The vertex is at (-2,-3).

In addition you know this will be a positive parabola.

Your graphing job is easy.

Example

$f(x) = x^2 - 8x + 5$

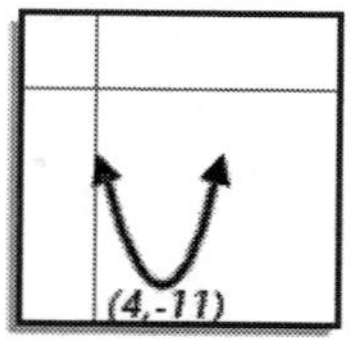

$= (x^2 - 8x + \underline{16}) + 5 - \underline{16}$

take $\frac{1}{2}$ and square

what is added must be subtracted

$= (x - 4)^2 - 11$

vertex = (4, -11)

Follow the same process for this example as above.

Within the x-expression, you'll add 16.
Outside that expression, add -16 for balance.

Factor into squared form and your vertex is (4,-11).

It's a positive parabola.

Example

$f(x) = -x^2 + 4x + 2$

$= -(x^2 - 4x - 2)$ *factor out (-)*

$= -((x^2 - 4x + 4) - 2 - 4)$

take $\frac{1}{2}$ and square

what is added must be subtracted

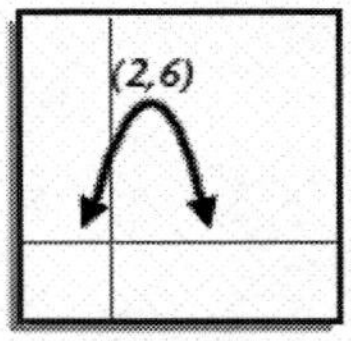

$= -((x - 2)^2 - 6)$

$= -(x - 2)^2 + 6$ *distribute (-)*

vertex $= (2,6)$

Again, follow the same process as above.

Calculate the value to add and subtract.
Factor into squared form.
Graph the vertex.

Note that this is a negative parabola and graph the curve.

Sample problems:

1. Use the completing the square method to find the vertex of the parabola defined by $y = x^2 + 6x - 5$.
   Solution: $(-3,-14)$
   Explanation: Express the equation in vertex form, $y = a(x-h)^2 + k$, by completing the square. First, square $\frac{1}{2}$ of the linear coefficient, then add that number and subtract it to balance the equation: $y = x^2 + 6x - 5 = (x^2 + 6x) - 5 = (x^2 + 6x + 9) - 5 - 9$. Next, factor the trinomial and simplify: $y = (x+3)^2 - 14$, so the vertex is at $(-3,-14)$.

2. Use the completing the square method to find the vertex of $f(x) = -x^2 + 10x - 7$.
   Solution: $(5,18)$
   Explanation: The coefficient of the quadratic term is not 1, so factor -1 from the expression: $f(x) = -(x^2 + 10x - 7)$. Next, add and subtract 25 to complete the square inside the parentheses: $f(x) = -((x^2 + 10x + 25) + 7 - 25)$. Next, factor and simplify: $f(x) = -((x-5)^2 - 18)$. Now distribute the negative: $f(x) = -(x-5)^2 + 18$. Thus, the vertex is at $(5,18)$.

3. Find the vertex of the parabola defined by $y = 2x^2 - 8x + 1$ by completing the square.
   Solution: $(2,-7)$
   Explanation: Factor 2 from the expression: $y = 2(x^2 - 4x + \frac{1}{2})$. Complete the square: $y = 2((x^2 - 4x + 4) + \frac{1}{2} - 4)$. Factor, simplify, and then distribute the 2: $y = 2((x-2)^2 - \frac{7}{2})$; $y = 2(x-2)^2 - 7$. So the vertex is at $(2,-7)$.

Practice problems: *(Answers on page: 743)*

1. Use the completing the square method to find the vertex of $y = -x^2 + \frac{1}{2}x - 1$.
2. Use the completing the square method to find the vertex of $y = -2x^2 - 8x + 1$.
3. Use the completing the square method to find the vertex of $y = -4x^2 + 2x - 3$.

Review questions: *(Answers to odd questions on page: 743)*

1. Use the completing the square method to find the vertex of $y = x^2 - 2x + 6$.
2. Use the completing the square method to find the vertex of $y = 2x^2 - 4x + 8$.
3. Use the completing the square method to find the vertex of $f(x) = -x^2 - 2x - 2$.
4. Use the completing the square method to find the vertex of $y = 3x^2 + 3x + \frac{3}{4}$.

5. Use the completing the square method to find the vertex of $f(x) = -5x^2 + 5x - \frac{1}{4}$.

Using the Vertex to Write the Quadratic Equation

- **Standard form of a parabola:** $f(x) = ax^2 + bx + c$.
- **Vertex of a parabola:** (h,k).
    - $h = -b/2a$.
    - $k = f(h)$.
- **Vertex form for parabola:** $f(x) = a(x - h)^2 + k$.
- To rewrite an equation in the vertex form:
    - Find the value of h.
    - Find the value of k.
    - Substitute these values into the vertex form.

$h = \frac{-b}{2a}$ $k = f(h)$ **Example** *write equation in standard form* $f(x) = x^2 + 4x + 1$ $a=1 \quad b=4 \quad c=1$ $h = \frac{-4}{2} = -2$ $k = f(-2) = (-2)^2 + 4(-2) + 1$ $= -3$ vertex $= (-2,-3)$ $= (x+2)^2 - 3$	One way to determine the vertex (h,k) of a parabola is to use these formulas for h and k. In this example, $a = 1$ and $b = 4$. So, $h = -(4)/2(1) = -2$. $k = f(-2) = (-2)2 + 4(-2) + 1 = -3$ The vertex is (h,k) and now known. Substitute these coordinates in to write the equation in standard form.
Example *write equation in standard form* $f(x) = x^2 - 8x + 5$ $a=1 \quad b=-8 \quad c=5$ $h = \frac{\not{16}\,8}{2} = \not{8}\,4$ $k = f(h) = \not{8}^2\,(4) - 8(\not{8}\,(4)) + 5$ $= \not{5}\,-11$ vertex $= \not{(8,5)}\,(4,-11)$ $= \not{(x-8)^2+5}$ $= (x-4)^2 - 11$	This example points out the value of being accurate and careful in what you are doing. You are following the same process: 1. Determine h and k. (Please use the correct numbers, or .....oops.) 2. Write the vertex. 3. Write the function in standard form showing the vertex.
Example *write equation in standard form* $f(x) = -x^2 + 4x + 2$ $a=-1 \quad b=4 \quad c=2$ $h = \frac{-4}{-2} = 2$ $k = f(h) = -2^2 + 4(2) + 2$ $= 6$ vertex $= (2,6)$ $= -(x-2)^2 + 6$	You know that this is a down-turned parabola because x^2 has a negative coefficient. Find h and k. Write the equation in standard form. Be sure to substitute the a value back into vertex form.

Sample problems:

1. Use the vertex to express the equation $f(x) = x^2 + 10x - 12$ in vertex form.
   Solution: $y = (x+5)^2 - 37$
   Explanation: Begin by using the formulas for h and k to find the vertex: $h = \frac{-b}{2a} = \frac{-10}{2(1)} = -5$ and $k = f(h) = f(-5) = (-5)^2 + 10(-5) - 12 = -37$. Next, substitute the a, h, and k values into the vertex form, $y = a(x-h)^2 + k$: $y = 1(x-(-5))^2 + (-37)$. Simplify: $y = (x+5)^2 - 37$.

2. Use the vertex to express the equation $y = -2x^2 - 8x + 1$ in vertex form.
   Solution: $y = -2(x+2)^2 + 9$
   Explanation: Find h and k: $h = \frac{-(-8)}{2(-2)} = -2$ and $k = -2(-2)^2 - 8(-2) + 1 = 9$.
   Now substitute the a, h, and k values into the vertex form: $y = -2(x+2)^2 + 9$.

3. Suppose there is a parabola with the vertex at $(3,4)$ and $(1,-4)$ is a point on that parabola. Use vertex form to find the value of a, then write the equation that describes this parabola in standard form.
   Solution: $y = -2x^2 + 12x - 14$
   Explanation: First find the value of a by substituting the values from the vertex and the point into the vertex form: $y = a(x-h)^2 + k \Rightarrow -4 = a(1-3)^2 + 4$ since $(3,4)$ is (h,k) and $(1,-4)$ is (x,y). Simplify and solve the equation: $-4 = a(1-3)^2 + 4$; $-4 = 4a + 4$; $-8 = 4a$; $a = -2$. Next, substitute the a, h, and k values into the vertex form: $y = a(x-h)^2 + k \Rightarrow y = -2(x-3)^2 + 4$.
   Simplify this equation to express it in standard form: $y = -2(x^2 - 6x + 9) + 4$; $y = (-2x^2 + 12x - 18) + 4$; $y = -2x^2 + 12x - 14$.

Practice problems: *(Answers on page: 743)*

1. Use the vertex to express $y = x^2 - 6x + 10$ in vertex form.
2. Use the vertex to express $f(x) = 2x^2 + 12x + 13$ in vertex form.
3. Write the equation of a parabola that passes through the point (3,10) and has the same vertex as $y = 5(x-1)^2 - 2$.

Review questions: *(Answers to odd questions on page: 743)*

1. Use the vertex to express $y = x^2 - 8x + 17$ in vertex form.
2. Use the vertex to express $f(x) = -x^2 + 10x - 22$ in vertex form.
3. Use the vertex to express $y = 5x^2 + 10x + 7$ in vertex form.
4. Write the equation of a parabola that passes through the point $(-2, 61)$ and has the same vertex as $y = \frac{1}{2}(x-1)^2 - 2$.
5. Write the equation of a parabola that passes through the point $(5, -14)$ and has the same vertex as $f(x) = -x^2 + 6x - 35$.

Finding the Maximum or Minimum of a Quadratic

- Every parabola has a turning point, or vertex. This point is the **minimum point** on a positive parabola. It is the **maximum point** on a negative parabola.
- On a parabola opening along the y-axis, the maximum or minimum value relates to the height of the curve. Therefore, it is the k-value of the vertex. This maximum or minimum occurs at the point on the curve when x has the h-value of the vertex.

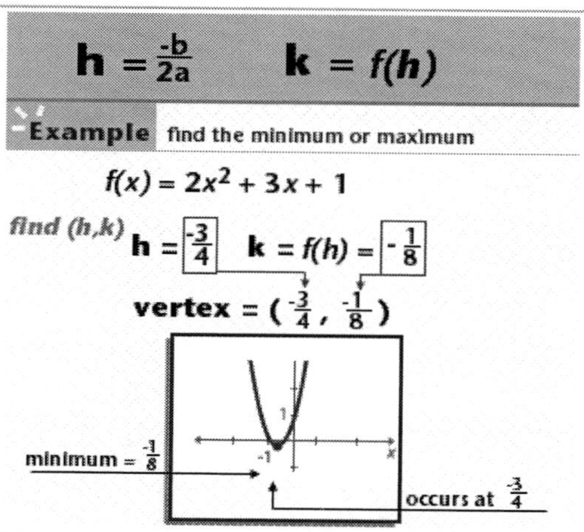

This parabola is positive; it will have a minimum.

The minimum value is –1/8 (k). This value occurs at –3/4 (h).

Graphing the curve gives us a visual relationship to the changes occurring for various x- and y-values related to this function.

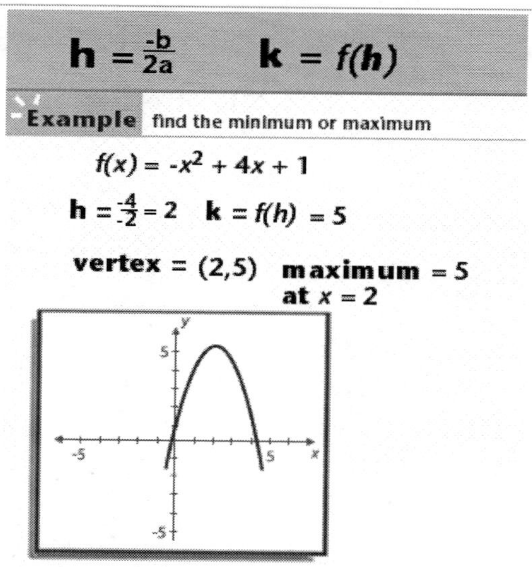

This parabola is a negative curve. So, you know that it will have a maximum point.

Doing the arithmetic, you find that the curve's maximum is 5(k), reached at the point 2(h).

Again, a quick sketch of the curve gives you a visual concept of how values change across the span of this curve.

Sample problems:

1. Find the maximum value of $f(x) = -x^2 - 5x$.

   Solution: $\dfrac{25}{4}$

   Explanation: Find the vertex, (h,k), using $h = -\frac{b}{2a}$ and $k = f(h)$. Find h: $h = -\frac{b}{2a} = -\frac{-5}{2(-1)} = -\frac{5}{2}$. Next, find k: $k = f\left(-\frac{5}{2}\right) = -\left(-\frac{5}{2}\right)^2 - 5\left(-\frac{5}{2}\right) = \frac{25}{4}$. So, the vertex is $\left(-\frac{5}{2}, \frac{25}{4}\right)$. Since the maximum value is the y-coordinate of the vertex, the maximum is $\frac{25}{4}$.

2. True or false: The maximum value of the function $f(x) = 2x^2 - 3x - 1$ is $-\dfrac{17}{8}$.

   Solution: False

   Explanation: Since $a > 0$, the parabola opens up and extends infinitely in the positive direction. Therefore, there is no maximum value. (However, the minimum value is $-\dfrac{17}{8}$.)

3. True or false: The maximum value of the function $f(x) = -\frac{1}{4}x^2 + \frac{1}{3}x + \frac{1}{2}$ is $\frac{11}{18}$.

<u>Solution:</u> True

<u>Explanation:</u> Since $a < 0$ the parabola opens down, and there is a maximum.

Find h: $h = -\frac{b}{2a} = -\frac{\frac{1}{3}}{2\left(-\frac{1}{4}\right)} = -\frac{\frac{1}{3}}{-\frac{1}{2}} = \frac{2}{3}$. Since the maximum is the y-coordinate of the vertex, the maximum value is found by computing $f\left(\frac{2}{3}\right)$: $f\left(\frac{2}{3}\right) = -\frac{1}{4}\left(\frac{2}{3}\right)^2 + \frac{1}{3}\left(\frac{2}{3}\right) + \frac{1}{2} = \frac{11}{18}$.

Practice problems: *(Answers on page: 743)*

1. Find the maximum or minimum value of the function $f(x) = 4x^2 + 1$.
2. Find the maximum or minimum value of the function $f(x) = \frac{1}{3}x^2 - \frac{1}{4}x - \frac{1}{2}$.
3. True or false: The minimum value of the function $y = x^2 + 6x + 1$ is -8.

Review questions: *(Answers to odd questions on page: 743)*

1. Find the maximum or minimum value of the function $f(x) = -3x^2 + 2$.
2. Find the minimum value of $f(x)$ where $f(x) = 2x^2 - 4x + 1$.
3. Find the minimum value of y where $y = 5x^2 + 11x$.
4. Find the maximum value of y, where $y = -2x^2 + 4x - 1$.
5. Find the maximum or minimum value of the function $f(x) = -\frac{3}{4}x^2 + \frac{1}{2}x + 2$.

Graphing Parabolas

- **Vertex form for a parabola:** $f(x) = a(x - h)^2 + k$.
- To graph a parabola from a quadratic equation find several useful points (the vertex, x-intercept(s), and y-intercept) then sketch the parabola through these points.
  - First, identify the vertex: *(h, k).*
  - Second, determine whether the curve is a positive or negative parabola.
  - Finally, set the expression equal to 0 and solve for the x-values. These are the points where the curve crosses the x-axis.
- The **axis of symmetry** is the imaginary line that passes through the vertex and is parallel to the axis along which the curve is opening.

Example graph the equation

$f(x) = -2(x + 3)^2 + 2$

vertex = (-3,2)

find x-intercept; set equal to 0

$-2(x + 3)^2 + 2 = 0$

factor out -2

$2(1 - (x + 3)^2) = 0$

divide by 2

$1 - (x + 3)^2 = 0$

factor difference of 2 squares

$(1 + (x + 3))(1 - (x + 3)) = 0$

$x + 4 = 0 \quad 1 - x - 3 = 0$

$x = -4 \quad x = -2$

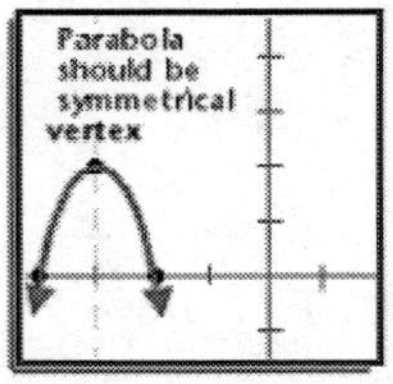

This example is for a negative parabola – because a coefficient is negative.

The vertex is shown in the expression: (-3,2).
Remember: the x-value changes sign.

To find the x-intercepts, set everything equal to 0 and solve for x.

These are the points where the curve crosses the x-axis.

Graph everything and you are done.

Example graph the equation $f(x)= x^2 - 2x + 3$ *find vertex by using formula* $x = \frac{2}{2} = 1$ $y = f(1) = 1^2 - 2(1) + 3$ **vertex (1 , 2)** *find y intercept* $f(0) = 0^2 - 2(0) + 3$ $= 3$	Since this equation is in standard form, find the vertex using the formuls for h and k: $h = -b/2a = -(-2)/2(1) = 1$ $k = f(h) = f(1) = 1^2\text{-}2(1) = 3 = 2$ So the vertex is at (1, 2). The parabola opens up since a is positive.
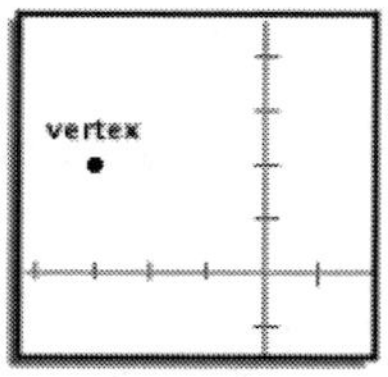	With the vertex above the x-axis and the curve opening upward, you know the curve will never cross the x-axis.
find y intercept $f(0) = 0^2 - 2(0) + 3$ $= 3$	So look for the y-intercept. Solve $f(x)$ for $x = 0$. This y-value is where the curve will cross the y-axis. In this case, that is the point (0,3). The y-intecept is always at c.
Hint: If you find one point, the axis of symmetry will tell you where another point is 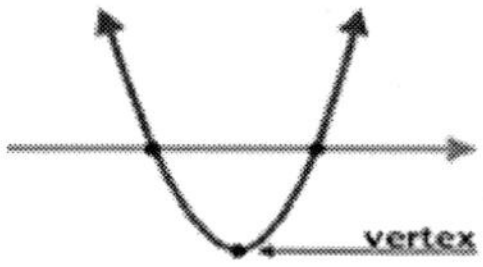	Now, use the fact that a parabola has symmetry to help locate a second point. In this example, the y-intercept is to the left 1 unit and up 1 unit from the vertex. So, to graph your matching point, locate the point that is to the right 1 unit and up 1 unit from the vertex.
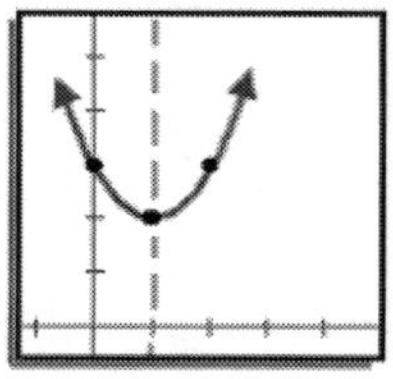	Now your curve is noted and you can draw it.

Sample problems:

1. Find the vertex, direction, x-intercepts (if they exist), and y-intercept for the parabola defined by the function: $f(x) = -3(x-2)^2 - 6$.
   Solution: vertex: $(2, -6)$; direction: down; x-intercept: none exist; y-intercept: $(0, -18)$
   Explanation: Since the equation is in vertex form, $y = a(x-h)^2 + k$, determine the vertex by identifying h and k from the equation: $f(x) = -3(x-2)^2 - 6 \Rightarrow h = 2$ and $k = -6$, so the vertex is at $(2, -6)$. The direction is determined by identifying the value of a. In this equation a is -3, so the parabola opens down. The x-intercepts do not always exist on a parabola. In this case the vertex is below the x-axis and the parabola opens down, so by visualizing the graph it may be determined that there are no x-intercepts. The y-intercept is found by substituting $x = 0$ into the equation, then solving for y:
   $f(x) = -3(0-2)^2 - 6 = -3(-2)^2 - 6 = -3(4) - 6 = -18$. Therefore, the y-intercept is $(0, -18)$.

2. Find the vertex, direction, x-intercepts (if they exist), and y-intercept for the parabola defined by the function $y=(x+5)^2$.
   Solution: vertex: $(-5,0)$; direction: up; x-intercept: $(-5,0)$
   y-intercept: $(0,25)$
   Explanation: Since the equation is in vertex form, $y=a(x-h)^2+k$, determine the vertex by identifying h and k from the equation: $f(x)=(x+5)^2=1(x-(-5))^2+0 \Rightarrow$ $h=-5$ and $k=0$, so the vertex is at $(-5,0)$. In this equation a is 1, so the parabola opens up. The vertex is on the x-axis, so the parabola must have only one x-intercept and it is the vertex, so the x-intercept is also at $(-5,0)$. The y-intercept is found by substituting $x=0$ into the equation, then solving for y: $y=(0+5)^2=(5)^2=25$. Therefore, the y-intercept is $(0,25)$.

3. Find the vertex, direction, x-intercepts (if they exist), and y-intercept for the parabola defined by the function $f(x)=x^2+6x+8$.
   Solution: vertex: $(-3,-1)$; direction: up; x-intercept: $(-4,0)$ and $(-2,0)$;
   y-intercept: $(0,8)$
   Explanation: Since the equation is in standard form, determine the vertex by using the formulas for h and k: $h=\frac{-b}{2a}=\frac{-6}{2(1)}=-3$ and
   $k=f(h)=f(-3)=(-3^2)+6(-3)+8=9-18+8=-1$, so the vertex is $(-3,-1)$.
   Since a is positive, the parabola opens up. The vertex is below the x-axis and the parabola opens up, so the parabola must have two x-intercepts. Find the x-intercepts by substituting $y=0$ into the equation, then solve for x: $0=x^2+6x+8$;
   $0=(x+4)(x+2)$; $x+4=0$ or $x+2=0$; $x=-4$ or $x=-2$. So the x-intercept are at $(-4,0)$ and $(-2,0)$. Determine the y-intercept by substituting $x=0$ into the equation: $0^2+6(0)+8=8$, so the y-intercept is at $(0,8)$. (Note: the y-intercept is always c.)

Practice problems: *(Answers on page: 743)*

1. Find the vertex, direction, x-intercepts (if they exist), and y-intercepts for the parabola defined by the function $f(x)=3x^2$.
2. Find the vertex, direction, x-intercepts (if they exist), and y-intercepts for the parabola defined by the function $y=\frac{1}{2}(x-4)^2$
3. Find the vertex, direction, x-intercepts (if they exist) and y-intercept for the parabola defined by the function $g(x)=5-2x-3x^2$

Review questions: *(Answers to odd questions on page: 743)*

1. Find the vertex, direction, x-intercepts (if they exist) and y-intercept for the parabola defined by the function $f(x)=\dfrac{3x^2}{4}$
2. Find the vertex, direction, x-intercepts (if they exist) and y-intercept for the parabola defined by the function $f(x)=-(x+3)^2$
3. Find the vertex, direction, x-intercepts (if they exist) and y-intercept for the parabola defined by the function $y=x^2+2x-6$
4. Find the vertex, direction, x-intercepts (if they exist) and y-intercept for the parabola defined by the function $f(x)=4x^2-4x+3$

5. Find the vertex, direction, x-intercepts (if they exist) and y-intercept for the parabola defined by the function $f(x) = -2x^2 + 6x - 3$

Shifting Curves along Axes

- Shifting a graph up is a matter of adding a value to the expression that produces the y-values. Likewise, shifting a graph down is a matter of subtracting a value from the same expression.
- Shifting a graph to the right on the axes is a matter of adding a value so that the x-values increase. Likewise, shifting a graph to the left is a matter of subtracting a value so that the x-values decrease.
- **Symmetry** means that half the graph is the exact mirror image of the other half.

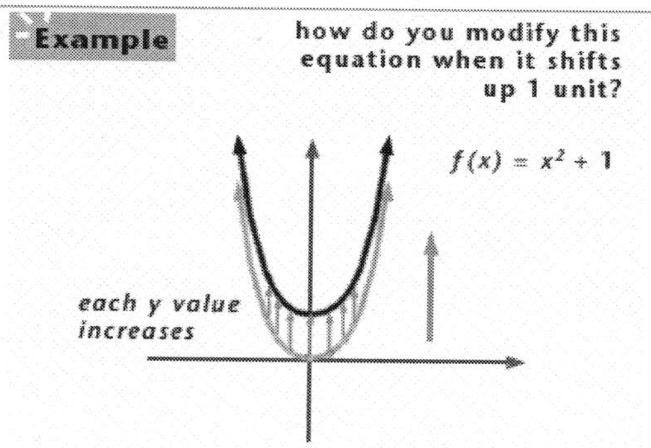

Moving a graph up on the axes involves adding a value to the expression that produces the y-values.

In this example, $f(x) = x^2$ is shown graphed with its vertex at the origin. Then, +1 is added to the expression for $f(x)$, or y. As a result, the entire curve lifts up one unit on the axes. This change is shown by the upper curve on the graph.

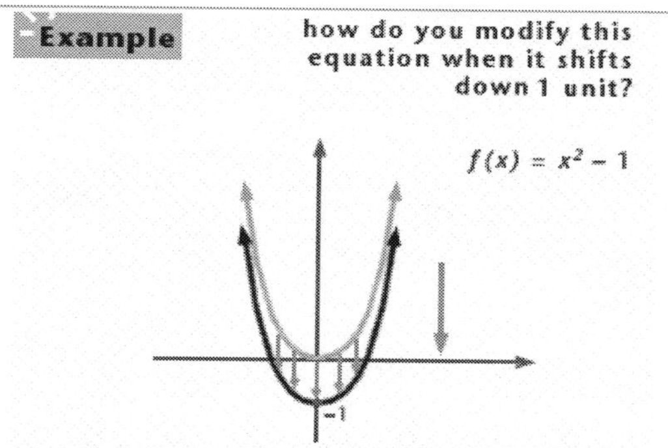

Moving a graph down on the axes involves subtracting a value from the expression that produces the y-values.

In this example, $f(x) = x^2$ is shown graphed with its vertex at the origin. Then, -1 is added to the expression for $f(x)$ so that the entire curve shifts down one unit on the axes. This change is shown by the lower curve on the graph.

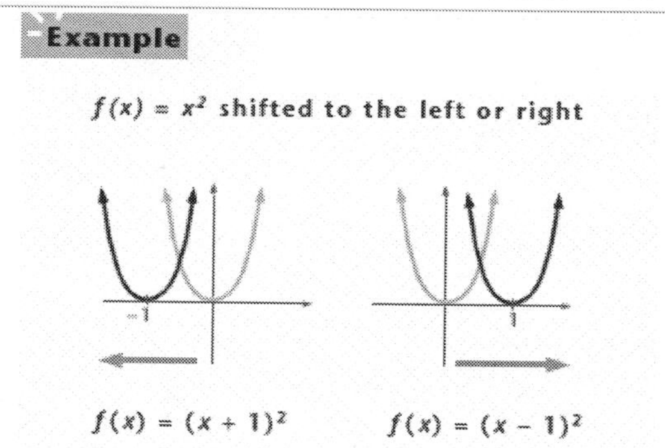

Movement sideways on a graph involves changing x-values without changing y-values.

You generally do it by adding or subtracting some value to the x within parentheses so that the manipulations of the equation include it with the x-values.

NOTE: The curve moves sideways opposite to the sign of the number added to the x expression.

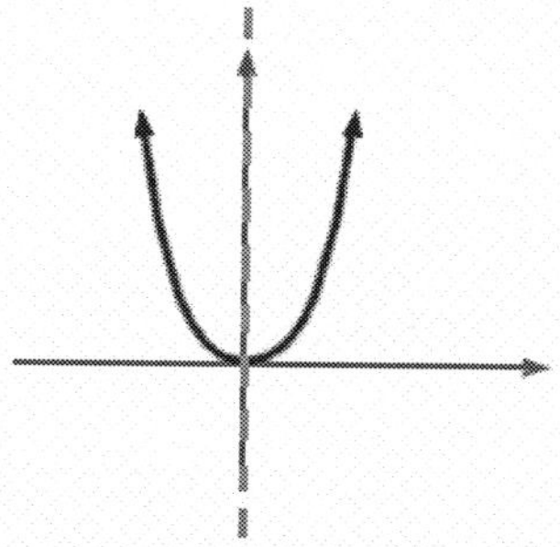

Symmetry means that you can cut a curve in half, flip one half over on top of the other one, and they will exactly match.

Symmetry also means that if you put a mirror at the vertex of a curve, the curve that appears in the mirror will exactly match the portion of the graph that the mirror is covering up.

Sample problems:

1. True or false: The equation $y=(x-4)^2-1$ will shift the graph of $y=x^2$ to the left 4 units and down 1 unit.
   Solution: False
   Explanation: Subtracting 1 from the expression shifts the parabola down 1 unit. Subtracting 4 from the x value within the parentheses shifts the parabola to the right 4 units. Remember, the curve moves sideways opposite to the sign of the number added to the x within the parentheses.

2. Write the equation that would move $y=(x+1)^2+5$ to the left 3 units and down 7 units.
   Solution: $y=(x+4)^2-2$
   Explanation: To move a curve to the left 3 units, add 3 within the parentheses. To move a curve down 7 units subtract 7 outside the parentheses. So, $y=(x+1)^2+5$ becomes $y=(x+1+3)^2+5-7 \Rightarrow y=(x+4)^2-2$.

3. Write the equation that would move $y=x^2-4$ up 5 units and to the right 3 units.
   Solution: $y=(x-3)^2+1$
   Explanation: To shift up 5 units, add 5 outside the parentheses. To shift right 3 units, subtract 3 within the parentheses. Thus, $y=(x-3)^2-4+5 \Rightarrow y=(x-3)^2+1$.

Practice problems: *(Answers on page: 743)*

1. How could you change the function $f(x)=x^2-2$ so that its graph will shift up two units?
2. How would you change the function, $f(x)=x^2$, so that its graph would shift 3 units higher?
3. Write the equation that will shift $y=(x-2)^2-1$ to the left 2 units and up 1 unit.

Review questions: *(Answers to odd questions on page: 744)*

1. What would you do to $f(x)=3x^2-7$ so that its graph will pass through $(0,0)$?
2. What would you do to the function $f(x)=2x^3+2$ so that its graph will pass through $(0,0)$?
3. True or false: The equation $y=(x+3)^2+5$ will shift the graph of $y=x^2$ to the left 3 units and up 5 units.
4. True or false: The equation $y=(x-1)^2-7$ will shift the graph of $y=x^2$ to the left 1 unit and down 7 units.
5. Write the equation that will shift the graph of $y=(x-1)^2$ to the right 5 units and down 2 units.

Shifting or Translating Curves along Axes

- Shifting up or down on a graph is a matter of adding or subtracting a value to the expression that gives you the y-values.
- Shifting sideways on a graph is a matter of adding or subtracting within parentheses with the x. Remember shifts move opposite to the signs added in these x-expressions.
- Shift carefully. When you add to y, go high. When you add to x, go west.

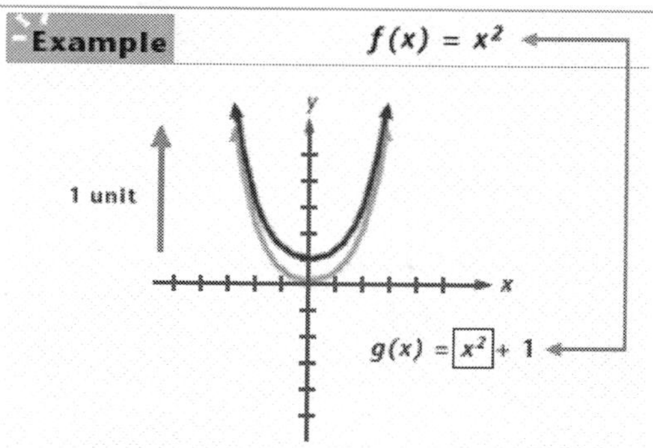

In this case, +1 was added to the expression used to derive the y-values.

Sure enough, the entire curve shifted up one unit on the axes.

This happens because for every point (x,y) on the original curve there exists a point $(x,y+1)$ on the new curve.

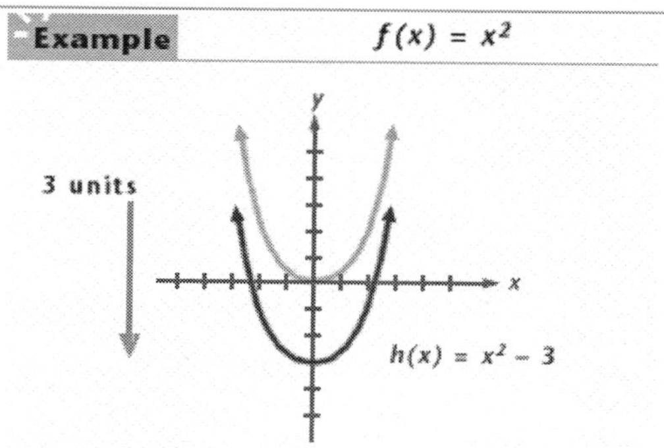

In this example, -3 is added to the expression used to derive the y-values.

The result is that every y is reduced by 3 and the entire curve drops three units on the axes.

In generic terms, for every point (x,y) on the original curve there exists a point $(x,y - 3)$ on the new curve.

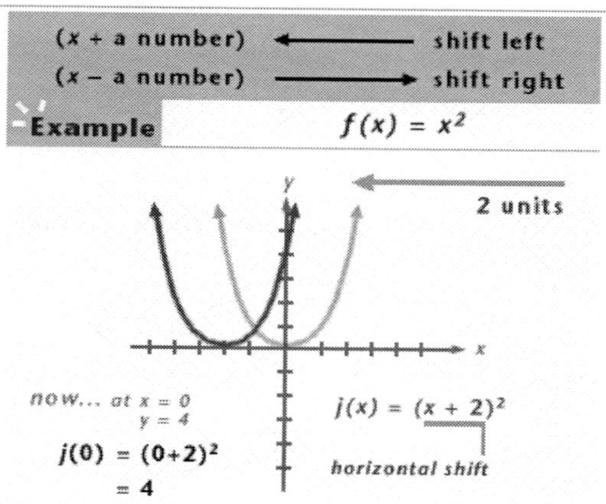

Shifting sideways is a little more complicated. The value to shift must accompany the x within the parentheses. By doing this, you are really changing the value of x.

Notice that when you add a positive number to x, the graph shifts to the negative, i.e., to the left.

In this example, $(x + 2)^2$ shifts the curve 2 units to the left.

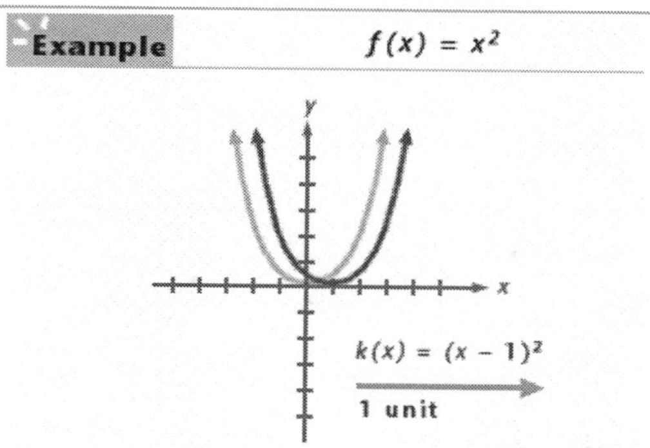

Once again, here is the basic parabola with its vertex at the origin.

In this example, $(x - 1)^2$ shifts the curve 1 unit to the right.

When you add a negative number to x, the graph shifts to the positive, i.e., to the right.

Sample problems:

1. Modify the equation $f(x) = 3(x+2)^2 - \frac{4}{5}$ to shift the parabola up $3\frac{1}{2}$ units and to the left 7 units.

   Solution: $f(x) = 3(x+9)^2 + 2\frac{7}{10}$

   Explanation: Add $3\frac{1}{2}$ to $-\frac{4}{5}$ to shift the parabola up $3\frac{1}{2}$ units, and add 7 to 2 to shift the parabola 7 units to the left: $f(x) = 3(x+2+7) - \frac{4}{5} + 3\frac{1}{2} \Rightarrow f(x) = 3(x+9) + 2\frac{7}{10}$.

2. Modify the equation $y = -x^2 + \frac{2}{3}$ to shift the parabola to the right 5 units and down 2 units.

   Solution: $y = -(x-5)^2 - 1\frac{1}{3}$

   Explanation: Subtract 5 from x to shift the parabola to the right 5 units and subtract 2 from $\frac{2}{3}$ to shift the parabola down 2 units: $y = -(x-5)^2 + \frac{2}{3} - 2 \Rightarrow y = -(x-5)^2 - 1\frac{1}{3}$.

3. What are the new values of b and c when the graph of $y = x^2 + 4x + 3$ is shifted up 2 units and to the left 3 units? (Recall the standard form of a quadratic: $ax^2 + bx + c$)
   Solution: $b = 10$ and $c = 26$
   Explanation: Express the equation in vertex form by completing the square: $y = (x^2 + 4x + 4) + 3 - 4$;
   $y = (x+2)^2 - 1$. Now add 2 to -1 and add 3 to 2 to do the shifting:
   $y = (x+2+3)^2 - 1 + 2 \Rightarrow y = (x+5)^2 + 1$.
   Next, express the equation in standard form by simplifying:
   $y = (x+5)^2 + 1$; $y = (x^2 + 10x + 25) + 1$; $y = x^2 + 10x + 26$.

Practice problems: *(Answers on page: 744)*

1. Modify the following equation to shift this parabola $2\frac{1}{2}$ units down: $f(x) = \frac{5}{4}\left(x - \frac{9}{2}\right)^2 + \frac{17}{4}$
2. Modify the following equation to shift this curve 3 units to the left: $f(x) = 2x^2 - 5$
3. What are the new values of b and c when the graph of $y = x^2 + 6x - 5$ is shifted down 4 units and to the right 1 unit?

Review questions: *(Answers to odd questions on page: 744)*

1. Modify the equation $f(x) = 5(x+3)^2 - 1$ to shift the parabola $5\frac{1}{2}$ units to the right.
2. Modify the equation $f(x) = -4.75(x - 0.25)^2 - 2$ to shift the parabola up 3.45 units and to the left 11.8 units.
3. Modify the equation $f(x) = -x^2 + 3$ to shift the parabola $3\frac{2}{5}$ units to the left.
4. Modify the equation $f(x) = -x^2 - 5$ to shift the parabola 4 units to the right and 1 unit down.
5. What are the new values of b and c when the graph of $y = x^2 + 8x - 7$ is shifted down 3 units and to the right 4 units.

Stretching a Graph

- Multiplying the equation of a quadratic function by a coefficient greater than 1 makes the parabola narrower.
- Multiplying the equation of a quadratic function by a coefficient between 0 and 1 makes the parabola wider.

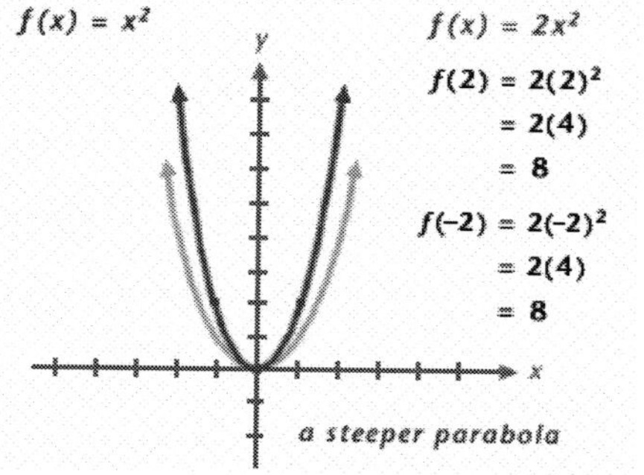

Here the function $f(x) = x^2$ was graphed first.

Then, $f(x) = 2x^2$ was graphed. It is steeper and therefore narrower than the original parabola.

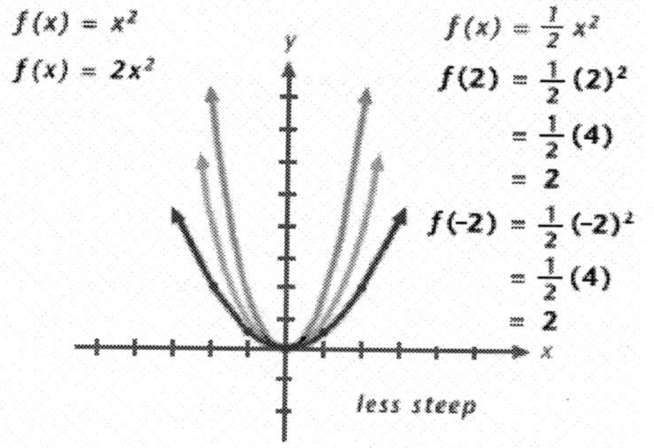

Using the same axes, the curve of $f(x) = \frac{1}{2}x^2$ was added. This curve is the least steep of the three curves.

Another way of describing this curve is to say that it is the widest and most open.

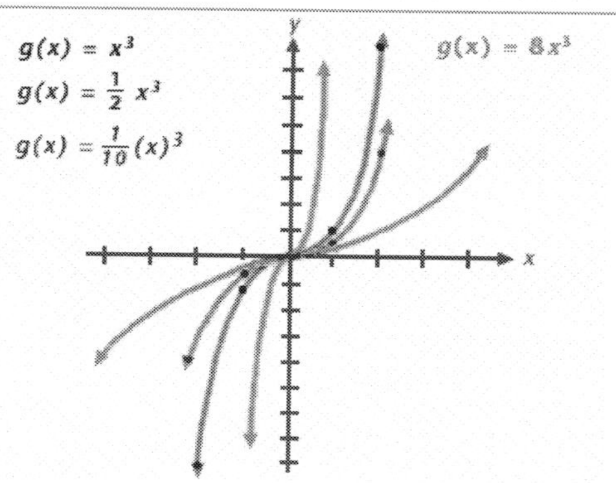

The same pattern holds for curves other than parabolas. On these axes, you have the graph of $g(x) = x^3$.

The steepest graph is that of $g(x) = 8x^3$. The two wider curves on the axes are for $g(x) = \frac{1}{2}x^3$ and $g(x) = \frac{1}{10}x^3$.

Sample problems:

1. True or false: The graph of $f(x) = \frac{1}{4}x^2$ is wider than the graph of $f(x) = x^2$.
   Solution: True
   Explanation: The width of the parabola is described by the value of the coefficient, a. If $|a| > 1$, then the parabola is narrower than $f(x) = x^2$. If $|a| < 1$, then the parabola is wider than $f(x) = x^2$. In the function $f(x) = \frac{1}{4}x^2$, $a = \frac{1}{4}$, so the parabola is wider than $f(x) = x^2$ since $|a| < 1$.

2. True or false: The graph of $f(x) = -\frac{8}{3}x^2$ is wider than the graph of $f(x) = x^2$ and it opens in the opposite direction.
   Solution: False
   Explanation: Since $|a| = \left|-\frac{8}{3}\right| = \frac{8}{3} > 1$, the parabola is narrower than the graph of $f(x) = x^2$. However, the parabolas do open in opposite directions since the a values have opposite signs.

3. Write the function that results in the following changes to the graph of $f(x) = x^2$: shifts 2 units to the right, shifts 5 units up, and is 3 times wider.

 Solution: $f(x) = \frac{1}{3}(x-2)^2 + 5$

 Explanation: Shifting the parabola formed by $f(x) = x^2$ to the right 2 units and up 5 units results in a move of the vertex from (0,0) to (2,5). Thus, $h = 2$ and $k = 5$, so the new function is $f(x) = a(x-2)^2 + 5$. The new graph is also 3 times wider, so divide the a value in $f(x) = x^2$ by 3. Thus, $a = \frac{1}{3}$ and the complete function is $f(x) = \frac{1}{3}(x-2)^2 + 5$.

Practice problems: *(Answers on page: 744)*

1. True or false: The graph of $f(x) = 4x^2$ is wider than the graph of $f(x) = 7x^2$.
2. True of false: If $y = ax^2$ opens up and is wider than $y = x^2$, then $a > 1$.
3. True of false: If $y = ax^2$ opens down and is narrower than $y = 5x^2$, then $a < -5$.

Review questions: *(Answers to odd questions on page: 744)*

1. True or false: The graph of $f(x) = -5x^2$ is narrower than the graph of $f(x) = -3x^2$.
2. Write the function that results in the following changes to the graph of $f(x) = -x^2$: shifts up 2 units, to the left 5 units, and is 3 times as narrow.
3. True or false: The parabola formed by $f(x) = 4x^2$ is 4 times as wide as the parabola formed by $f(x) = x^2$.
4. Write the function that results in the following changes to the graph of $f(x) = -x^2$: flips over and is 3 times wider.
5. If the a value of $f(x) = x^2$ is multiplied by a negative integer other than -1, how is the graph affected?

Graphing Quadratics Using Patterns

- To graph any function, follow these steps:
  1. Determine its basic shape centered at the origin.
  2. Determine its sign so you can sketch how it opens.
  3. Determine its steepness so you can sketch its shape.
  4. Determine its location according to any shift indicated.
- Remember that when you add within the x^2 term, the curve shifts to the left; when you add onto the expression, the curve shifts higher. Dr. Burger says: when you add to the x, go west; when you add to the y, go high.

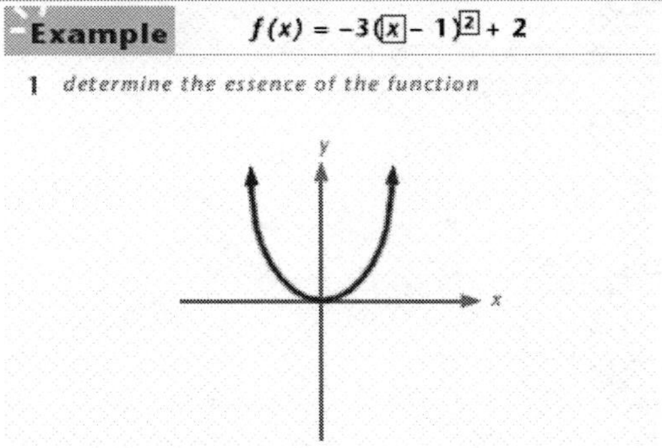	Your first step is to graph the general shape of the curve centered at the origin. In this example, only the x is squared, so you will have a parabola as shown.

2 *determine the sign* 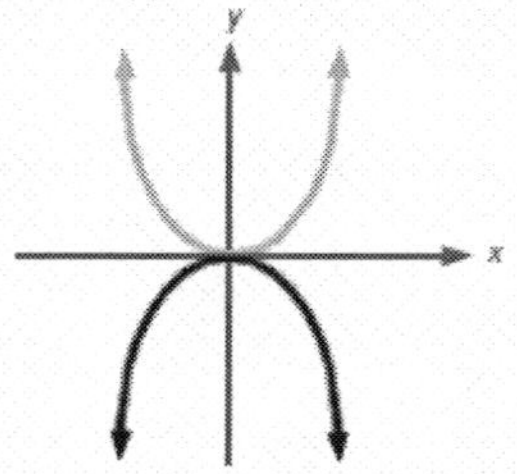	Your next step is to determine which direction the parabola will open. If the coefficient of the x-term is negative, the curve will open downward. Otherwise, it opens upward. In this example, the coefficient is negative, so the curve opens downward, as shown.
3 *determine steepness of the curve* 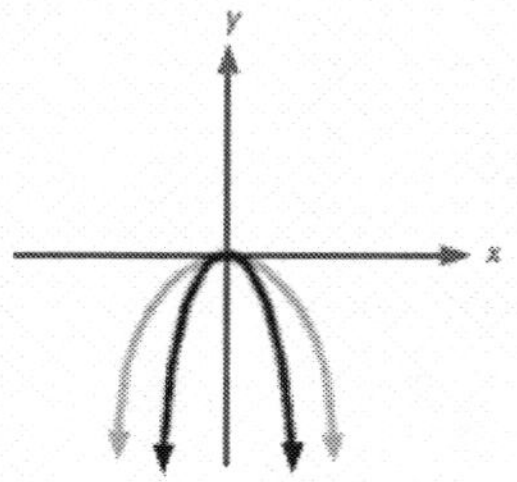	The third step is to determine how wide or narrow the curve is; i.e., the curve's steepness or pitch. In this case, the x-term is multiplied by 3 which will make the curve noticeably narrower than the generic parabola, as shown here.
4 *determine any shift* 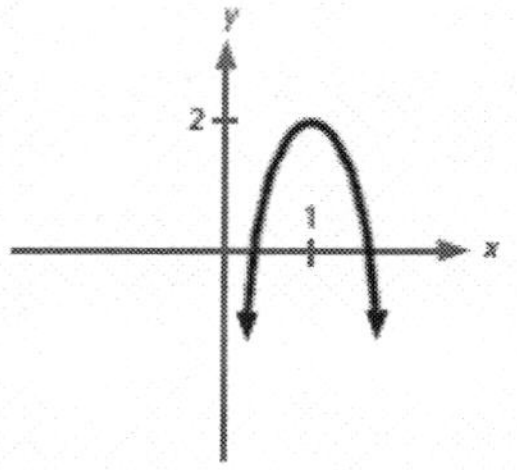	Your final step is to check for any shifts of the vertex away from the origin. In this example, the $(x - 1)$ indicates a move to the right 1 unit. The +2 indicates a move up 2 units. You can see on the graph that the curve has moved its vertex to the right 1 and up 2.

Sample problems:

1. Write the equation of a parabola that has the vertex at (5,4), is 3 times narrower than $y = x^2$, and opens down along the y-axis.

   Solution: $y = -3(x-5)^2 + 4$

   Explanation: Substitute the (h, k) values from the vertex into vertex form: $y = a(x-5)^2 + 4$.

   To make the parabola 3 times narrower than $y = x^2$, multiply a in $y = x^2$ by 3: $y = 3(x-7)^2 - 1$.

   To produce a parabola that opens down, the sign of a must be negative: $y = -3(x-7)^2 - 1$.

2. Write a function that produces the following changes to $y = x^2$: shifts to the right 7 units, shifts down 1 unit, 4 times wider, and opens in the opposite direction.

   Solution: $y = -\frac{1}{4}(x-7)^2 - 1$

   Explanation: Subtract 7 from x to shift to the right: $y = (x-7)^2$. Subtract 1 to shift down: $y = (x-7)^2 - 1$. To make the parabola 4 times wider, divide a by 4: $y = \frac{1}{4}(x-7)^2 - 1$. Change the sign of a to open the parabola in the opposite direction: $y = -\frac{1}{4}(x-7)^2 - 1$.

3. Write a function that produces the following changes to $y = -5x^2$: shifts to the left 2 units, shifts up 3 units, 2 times wider, and opens in the opposite direction.

   Solution: $y = \frac{5}{2}(x+2)^2 + 3$

   Explanation: Add 2 to x to shift to the left: $y = -5(x+2)^2$. Add 3 to shift up: $y = -5(x+2)^2 + 3$.

   To make the parabola 2 times wider, divide a by 2: $y = -\frac{5}{2}(x+2)^2 + 3$. Change the sign of a to open the parabola in the opposite direction: $y = \frac{5}{2}(x+2)^2 + 3$.

Practice problems: *(Answers on page: 744)*

1. Write the equation of a parabola with vertex at $(-7,0)$ that is 4 times narrower than $y = \frac{5}{6}x^2$.

2. Write a function that produces the following changes to $y = x^2$: shifts to the right 3.25 units and shifts up 1.5 units.

3. Write a function that produces the following changes to $y = 3(x+5)^2 + 1$: shifts to the left 3 units, shifts down 4 units, and is 3 times wider.

Review questions: *(Answers to odd questions on page: 744)*

1. Write the equation of a parabola with vertex at $(-2,5)$ with width that is $\frac{1}{4}$ of the width of $y = x^2$.
2. Write a function that produces the following changes to $y = x^2$: shifts to the right 2 and up 5 units.
3. Write a function that produces the following changes to $y = x^2 + 4$: shifts to the left 3 units and opens in the opposite direction.
4. Write a function that produces the following changes to $y = -2x^2 - 1$: shifts to the right 3 units, shifts up 5 units, opens in the opposite direction, and is 4 times wider.

5. Write a function that produces the following changes to $y = -(x-3)^2 + 1$: shifts down 4 units, to the left 11 units, and opens in a positive direction.

Determining Symmetry

- **Symmetry** indicates that half the graph of a curve is an exact mirror image of the other half of the graph. You can take the right half of the curve and flip it over the y-axis to see the left half of the curve.
- An **even function** is one which exactly maps one half of itself on the right side of the its axis and exactly reflects that half on the left side of its axis; i.e., an even function is one which is symmetrical about its axis.
- An even function will pair each y-value used with both x and $-x$ for every value used for x. This means that $f(x) = f(-x)$ for these equations.
- An **odd function** will be symmetrical but in respect to the origin, (0,0). For an odd function, every point (x,y) will be match with $(-x,-y)$. You can take the right half of the curve and flip it over the y-axis, then flip it again over the x-axis to see the left half of the curve.
- For an odd function, every $f(-x) = -f(x)$. Every $-x$-value is matched with its $-y$-value.
- A circle is symmetrical with respect to the x-axis, the y-axis and also with the origin. Remember that a circle is not a function because it cannot pass the vertical line test.

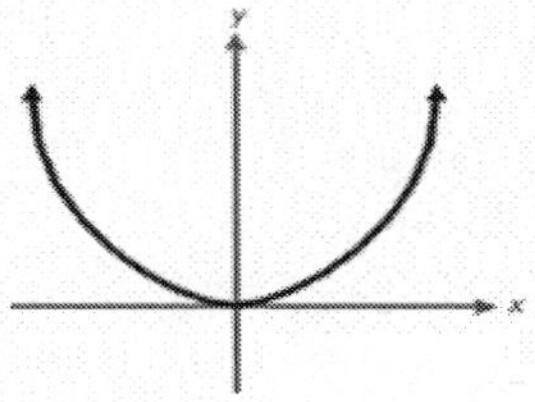

You can graph one side of an even function, and flip that curve over the y-axis to get the rest of the graph. You know that every point (x,y) matches with its own $(-x,y)$.

<table>
<tr>
<td>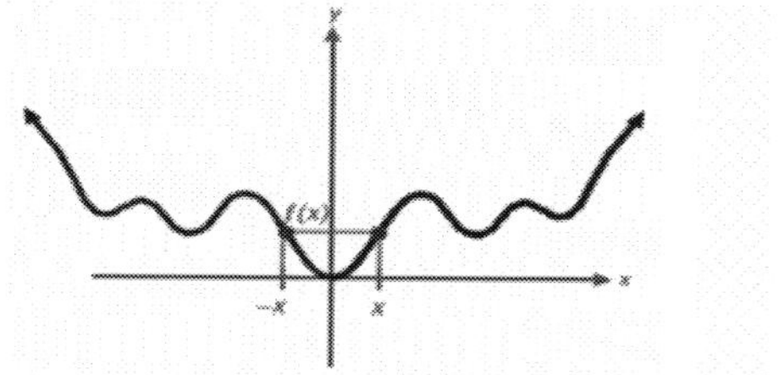
</td>
<td>If you work out the curve from (0,0) to the right of the y-axis, you can sketch the left side in mirror image and be done. What you will notice if you actually work out the points is that for every point (x,y) that you have, you will also have the point $(-x,y)$.</td>
</tr>
<tr>
<td>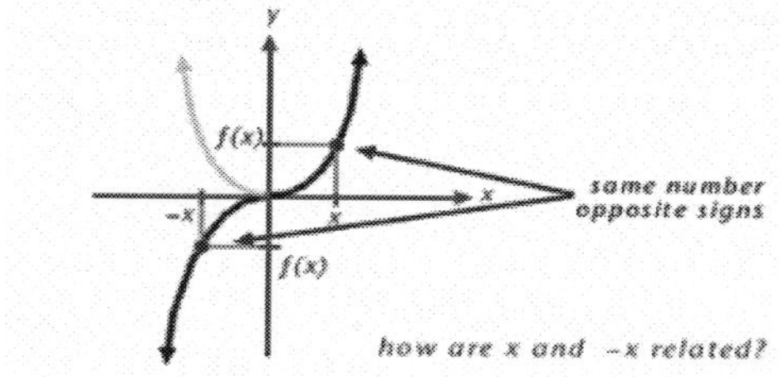
</td>
<td>Odd functions flip from one quadrant to the opposite quadrant skipping the one in between.

As you can see in this example, $f(x)$ will pair with $-f(x)$.</td>
</tr>
<tr>
<td>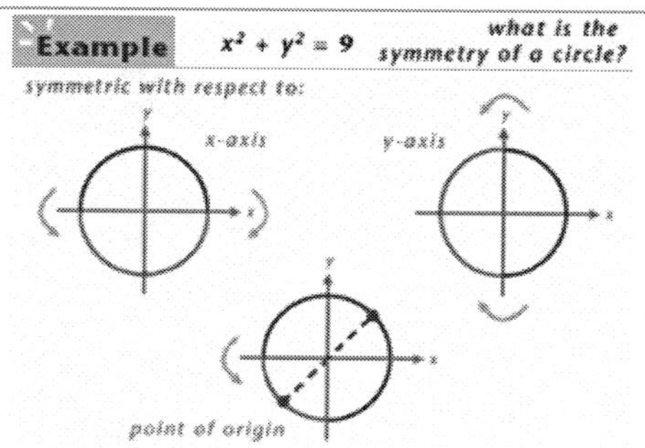
</td>
<td>In this example, the circle is centered at the origin and has a radius of 3.

It is not a function because the xs are paired with more than one y.

It is symmetrical several ways. You can flip it over the y-axis; you can flip it over the x-axis; you can flip it around the origin.</td>
</tr>
</table>

Sample problems:

1. If $f(x)$ is an even function and the points $(1,2)$, $(3,10)$, and $(4,17)$ lie on the graph of $f(x)$, identify three additional points on the graph.
   Solution: $(-1,2)$, $(-3,10)$, and $(-4,17)$
   Explanation: Since $f(x)$ is an even function the graph is symmetrical around the y-axis. Reflect each given point over the y-axis: $(1,2)$, $(3,10)$, and $(4,17)$ $\rightarrow$ $(-1,2)$, $(-3,10)$, and $(-4,17)$.

2. If $f(x)$ is an odd function and the points $(-1,5)$ and $(0,-1)$ lie on the graph of $f(x)$, identify two additional points on the graph.
   Solution: $(1,-5)$ and $(0,1)$
   Explanation: Since $f(x)$ is an add function the graph is symmetrical around the origin. To reflect the given points over the origin, switch the sign of each coordinate: $(-1,5)$ and $(0,-1) \rightarrow (1,-5)$ and $(0,1)$.

3. Determine if the function is even, odd, or neither: $f(x) = x^2 + 1$
   Solution: Even
   Explanation: If $f(x)$ is an even function, then $f(-x) = f(x)$. If $f(x)$ is an odd function, then $f(-x) = -f(x)$. If $f(-x) \neq f(x)$ and $f(-x) \neq -f(x)$, then the function is neither even nor odd.
   Find $f(-x)$: $f(-x) = (-x)^2 + 1 = x^2 + 1 = f(x)$. Thus, $f(x)$ is an even function since $f(-x) = f(x)$.

Practice problems: *(Answers on page: 744)*

1. If $f(x)$ is an even function and the points $(-4,-1)$ and $(5,0)$ lie on the graph of $f(x)$, identify two additional points on the graph.
2. If $f(x)$ is an odd function and the points $(2,0)$ and $(-5,-1)$ lie on the graph of $f(x)$, identify two additional points on the graph.

3. Determine if the function is even, odd, or neither: $f(x)=\dfrac{2x+x^3}{3}$

Review questions: *(Answers to odd questions on page: 744)*

1. If $f(x)$ is an even function and the points $(3,-2)$ and $(0,-1)$ lie on the graph of $f(x)$, identify two additional points on the graph.
2. If $f(x)$ is an even function and the points (a,b) and (c,d) lie on the graph of $f(x)$, identify two additional points on the graph.
3. If $f(x)$ is an odd function and the points $(13,-4)$ and $(-7,-1)$ lie on the graph of $f(x)$, identify two additional points on the graph.
4. If $f(x)$ is an odd function and the points $(a,-b)$ and $(-c,d)$ lie on the graph of $f(x)$, identify two additional points on the graph.
5. Determine if the function is even, odd, or neither: $f(x)=x^2-x^3$

Reflections

- **Reflecting a curve** over the x-axis matches every original (x,y) with its own $(x,-y)$.
- Reflecting a curve over the y-axis matches every (x,y) with its own $(-x,y)$.

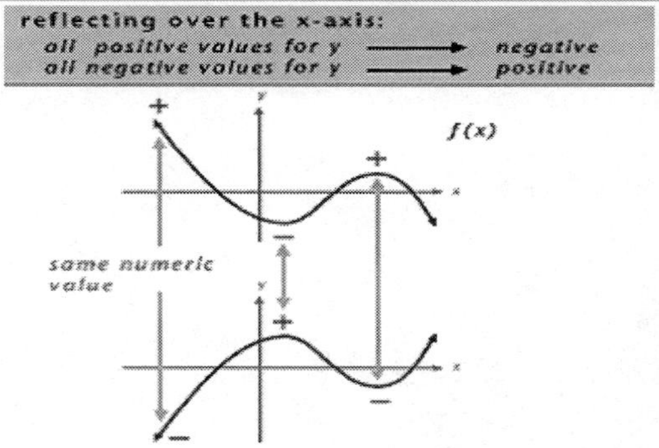

This curve is **reflecting** over the x-axis. You can see visually how every point that was above the x-axis is now the exact same distance below the x-axis and the same distance from the origin.

So, every (x,y) is matched with its $(x,-y)$.

You reflect any curve over the x-axis by changing the sign of the y-value in every point.

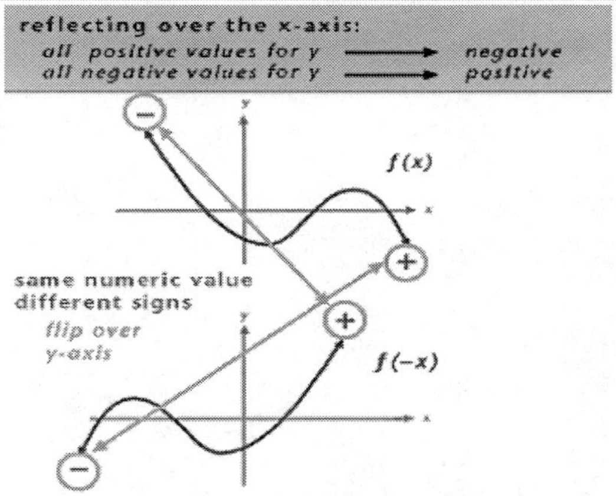

You can see that reflecting over the y-axis works the same way, only now it is the x-values that are affected.

From this graph you can see that every point on the curve has moved at the same height from x units from the origin to $-x$ units from the origin.

So, every (x,y) is now matched with its own $(-x,y)$.

You can achieve a reflection around the y-axis by changing the sign of the x-value for every (x,y) in the curve.

Example

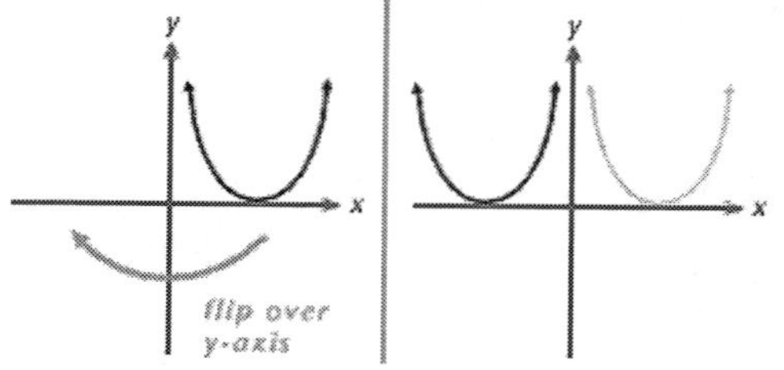

This graph shows an example where the entire curve has shifted around the y-axis. Even though the curve looks like it has merely moved, it really has flipped over as every x-value became a $-x$.

Sample problems:

1. If the points $(1,-3)$, $(0,5)$, and $(-4,-2)$ lie on the graph of $f(x)$, identify three points on the graph when $f(x)$ is reflected across the x-axis.
   Solution: $(1,3)$, $(0,-5)$, and $(-4,2)$
   Explanation: When $f(x)$ is reflected across the x-axis, the sign of each y-coordinate is switched: $(1,-3)$, $(0,5)$, and $(-4,-2)$ $\rightarrow$ $(1,3)$, $(0,-5)$, and $(-4,2)$.

2. If the points $(-a,b)$ and $(c+d,-e)$ lie on the graph of $f(x)$, identify two points on the graph when $f(x)$ is reflected across the y-axis.
   Solution: (a,b) and $(-c-d,-e)$
   Explanation: When $f(x)$ is reflected across the y-axis, the sign of each x-coordinate is switched: $(-a,b)$ and $(c+d,-e)$ $\rightarrow$ (a,b) and $(-c-d,-e)$.

3. Sketch a reflection of the graph below across the y-axis.

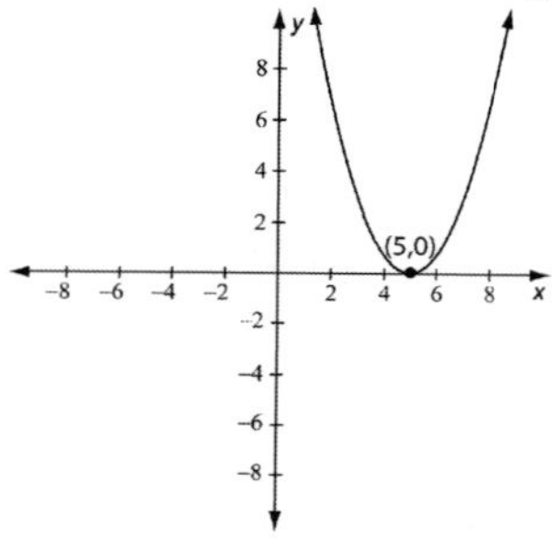

   Solution:

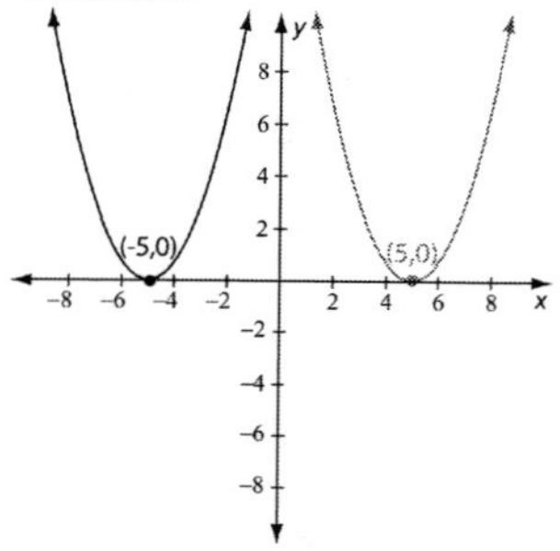

   Explanation: To reflect $f(x)$ across the y-axis, switch the sign of each x-coordinate. Choose any point on the graph. Plot the reflection point: do not shift vertically, shift horizontally an equal distance from the y-axis, but in the opposite direction. Repeat the pattern for several points.

Practice problems: *(Answers on page: 744)*

1. If the points $(-5,-2)$, $(1,-7)$, and $(0,-2)$ lie on the graph of $f(x)$, identify three points on the graph when $f(x)$ is reflected across the x-axis.

2. If the points $(1-a, b-d)$ and $(c-d, e)$ lie on the graph of $f(x)$, identify two points on the graph when $f(x)$ is reflected across the y-axis.
3. Sketch a reflection of the graph below across the x-axis.

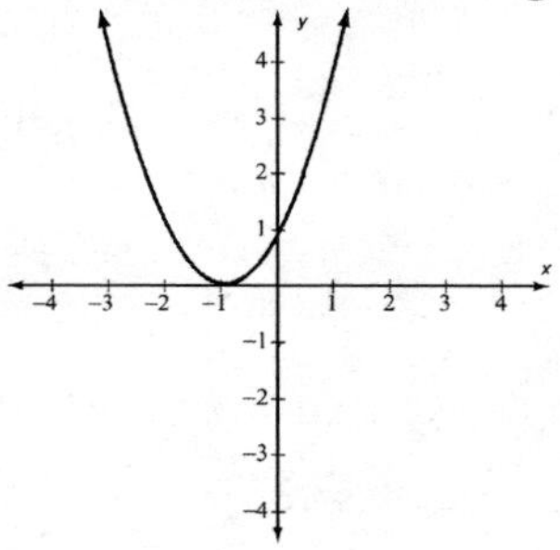

Review questions: *(Answers to odd questions on page: 744)*

1. If the points $(10,-2)$, $(-1,3)$, and $(0,0)$ lie on the graph of $f(x)$, identify three points on the graph when $f(x)$ is reflected across the y-axis.
2. If the points (x,y) and $(-w,-z)$ lie on the graph of $f(x)$, identify two points on the graph when $f(x)$ is reflected across the y-axis.
3. If the points $(2a+x, 1-y)$ and $(z-w, 1+z)$ lie on the graph of $f(x)$, identify two points on the graph when $f(x)$ is reflected across the x-axis.
4. Sketch a reflection of the graph below across the x-axis.

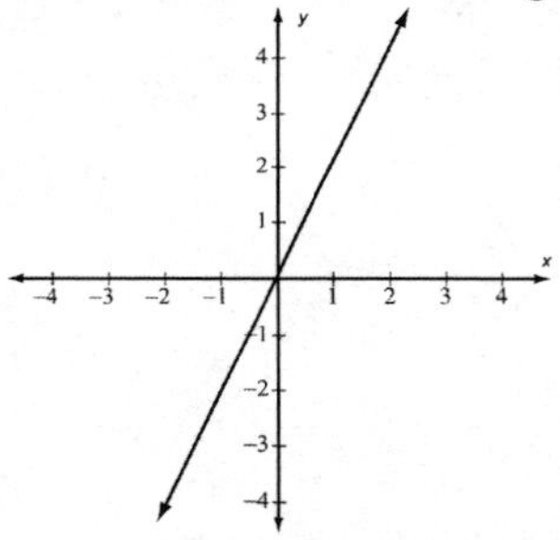

5. Sketch a reflection of the graph below across the y-axis.

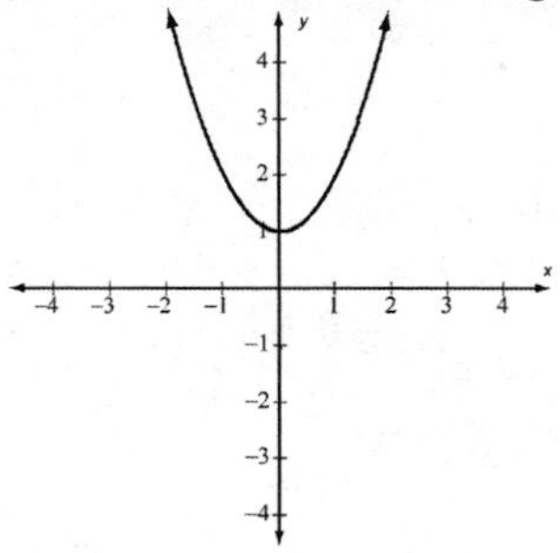

Reflecting Specific Functions

- Reflecting over the x-axis means that the y values will change signs. Any $+y$ will become $-y$ while any $-y$ will become $+y$.
- Reflecting over the y-axis means that the x values will change signs. Any $+x$ will become $-x$ while any $-x$ will become $+x$.
- When reflecting a function across the x-axis, change the sign of every term in the expression because they all are part of finding the y-value.
- When reflecting a function across the y-axis, change only the sign of every x-term because each x is becoming $-x$.

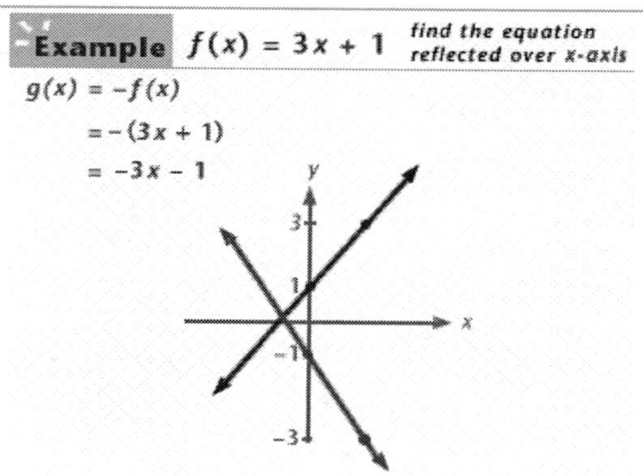

This example shows a reflection across the x-axis. When you compare the original and the reflected lines, you can see that the reflected line has changed all signs for y-values.

This can be easily achieved by changing signs over the entire expression and then finding values in the new expression. In this example, the $(3x + 1)$ changes to be $-(3x + 1)$, or $-3x - 1$.

You do this because it is the entire expression that gives you each value for y.

This method also gives you the equation of the reflection.

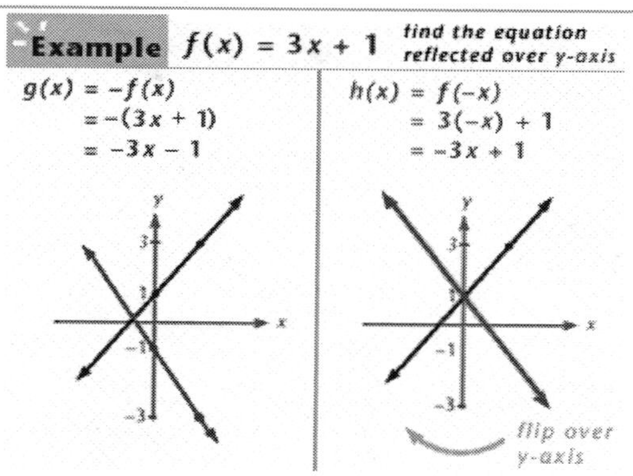

Any reflection over the y-axis involves changing the signs for all the x-values.

For every x in the expression, substitute in a $-x$. Then figure the final expression.

Note: To reflect across the y-axis, change the sign of every x in the expression.

Note: To reflect across the x-axis, change the entire expression.

Sample problems:

1. For the function, $y = -\frac{3}{4}x + 1$, find the original and reflected points about the x-axis for the value $x = 8$.
   Solution: $(8, -5)$ and $(8, 5)$
   Explanation: Substituting $x = 8$ into the function and solving for y:
   $y = -\frac{3}{4}(8) + 1 = -6 + 1 = -5$. The original point is $(8, -5)$. To reflect the point about the x-axis switch the sign of the y-coordinate: $(8, -5) \rightarrow (8, 5)$.

2. Let $g(x)$ be the result when $f(x) = 2x - 5$ is reflected across the x-axis. Find $g(x)$.
   Solution: $g(x) = 5 - 2x$
   Explanation: The reflection of $f(x)$ across the x-axis is $-f(x)$:
   $g(x) = -f(x) = -(2x - 5) = -2x + 5 = 5 - 2x$.

3. Let $g(x)$ be the result when $f(x) = x^2 + x$ is reflected across the y-axis. Find $g(x)$.
   Solution: $g(x) = x^2 - x$
   Explanation: The reflection of $f(x)$ across the y-axis is $f(-x)$:
   $g(x) = f(-x) = (-x)^2 + (-x) = x^2 - x$.

Practice problems: *(Answers on page: 744)*

1. For the function, $y = 4 - x^2$, find the original and reflected points about the y-axis for the value $x = -1$.
2. Let $g(x)$ be the result when $f(x) = 2x^2 - x + 1$ is reflected across the x-axis. Find $g(x)$.
3. Let $g(x)$ be the result when $f(x) = \dfrac{1 - x^3}{x^2}$ is reflected across the y-axis. Find $g(x)$.

Review questions: *(Answers to odd questions on page: 744)*

1. For the function, $y = x - x^3$, find the original and reflected points about the y-axis for the value $x = 2$.
2. For the function, $y = 3x - 2$, find the original and reflected points about the x-axis for the value $x = a + 1$.
3. Let $g(x)$ be the result when $f(x) = -x^3 - x^2 + x$ is reflected across the x-axis. Find $g(x)$.
4. Let $g(x)$ be the result when $f(x) = -5x^3 + 2x^2$ is reflected across the y-axis. Find $g(x)$.
5. Let $g(x)$ be the result when $f(x) = 1 - x + x^3$ is reflected across the y-axis. Find $g(x)$.

Using Operations on Functions

- Using operations with functions is a useful way to create new functions for new purposes.
- All four of the basic operations can be used to combine two or more functions into a new function.
- Remember to watch signs carefully.
- Remember to change your domains appropriately when functions become denominators.

Example $(f+g)(x)$ $f(x) = 2x+3$ $g(x) = 4x+8$ $(f+g)(x) = 6x+11$ *By combining these two functions we created another*	Adding two functions is just a matter of combining like terms. Here you add $2x$ and $4x$ to get $6x$. You add 3 and 8 to get 11. And there you have your $(f+g)(x)$, a whole new function. Subtracting works the same way if you remember to change the signs appropriately before you combine the like terms.
Example $(fg)(x)$ $f(x) = 2x+3$ $g(x) = 4x+8$ $(f+g)(x) = 6x+11$ $(fg)(x) = (4x+8)(2x+3)$ $= 8x^2+28x+24$	Multiplying two functions is just a matter of combining two expressions. Write your multiplication problem out, then FOIL carefully to get your new function.
Example $\left(\frac{f}{g}\right)(x)$ $f(x) = 2x+3$ $g(x) = 4x+8$ $\left(\frac{f}{g}\right)(x) = \frac{2x+3}{4x+8}$ *Must be careful to not have a value that would make the denominator zero* *Ex: $x = -2$ (not allowed)*	We can take the same two functions and set up a division problem. Notice how it looks just like a fraction. If anything can be factored out to "reduce" the fraction, do that too. **Note:** The denominator can never equal 0, so the domain must be defined to exclude any values for x that would set the denominator equal to 0.
Example $\left(\frac{g}{f}\right)(x)$ $f(x) = x^2-1$ $g(x) = (x+2)^2$ $\left(\frac{g}{f}\right)(x) = \frac{(x+2)^2}{x^2-1}$ Domain $= \mathbb{R} \setminus \{\pm 1\}$ *Except*	Each of these curves taken separately is a parabola. Each parabola is defined at every point and its domain is the set of all real numbers. **Note:** two values must be excluded because they cause the denominator to equal 0. Those two values, in this example, are +1 and –1.

Sample problems:

1. If $j(x)=2x^5-6x^3+7x-11$ and $k(x)=x^5+3x^4+3x^3+4$, what is $(j-k)(x)$?
   Solution: $x^5-3x^4-9x^3+7x-15$
   Explanation: The notation $(j-k)(x)$ means to subtract the two functions in terms of x. Distribute the negative throught the 2nd function then combine like terms: $(j-k)(x)=j(x)-k(x)=$ $(2x^5-6x^3+7x-11)-(x^5+3x^4+3x^3+4)=2x^5-6x^3+7x-11-x^5-3x^4-3x^3-4=$ $x^5-3x^4-9x^3+7x-15$.

2. If $m(x)=(x+1)$ and $n(x)=(x^2-1)$, what is $\dfrac{m(x)}{n(x)}$?
   Solution: $\dfrac{1}{x-1}$, $x\neq\pm1$
   Explanation: The notation $\frac{m(x)}{n(x)}$ means to divide the two functions in terms of x. Write the two functions as a fraction: $\frac{m(x)}{n(x)}=\frac{x+1}{x^2-1}$. To simplify, factor then cancel: $\frac{x+1}{x^2-1}=\frac{x+1}{(x+1)(x-1)}=\frac{1}{x-1}$. Determine the domain by setting the denominator equal to 0 and solve for x: $(x+1)(x-1)=0$; $x+1=0$ or $x-1=0$; $x=-1$ or $x=1$. So the domain is all real numbers except ±1.

3. If $f(x)=x^2-x$ and $g(x)=7-2x$, what is $(g+f)(x-h)$?
   Solution: $x^2-3x-2xh+3h+h^2+7$
   Explanation: $(g+f)(x-h)=g(x-h)+f(x-h)=7-2(x-h)+(x-h)^2-(x-h)$ $=7-2x+2h+x^2-2xh+h^2-x+h=x^2-3x-2xh+3h+h^2+7$.

Practice problems: *(Answers on page: 744)*

1. If $g(x)=7x^2$ and $h(x)=(4x-1)$, what is $(gh)(x)$?
2. If $f(x)=3x-2$ and $g(x)=7x+12$, what is the sum of the two functions?
3. If $f(x)=3x^2-5x$ and $g(x)=2x+3$, what is $(f-g)(x+h)$?

Review questions: *(Answers to odd questions on page: 745)*

1. True or false: Given two functions $f(x)$ and $g(x)$, $(f+g)(x)=f(x)+g(x)$.
2. Given $r(x)=7x-22$ and $t(x)=x^2+3$, express the sum $(r+t)(x)$.
3. If $m(x)=x+5$ and $n(x)=x^2-25$, what is $\dfrac{m(x)}{n(x)}$?
4. If $p(x)=3x-1$ and $q(x)=2x+5$, what is $(pq)(x)$?
5. If $f(x)=5x^3-6x+4$ and $g(x)=x^3+x^2+x+1$, what is $(f-g)(x)$?

Composite Functions

- A **composite function** is made up of multiple functions acting on each other in a specified order.
- The benefit of composing functions with each other is that you can follow one input through several processes to reach a final output.
- **Composition notation:** $f\circ g$ indicates that *f (x)* will be evaluated with the output from *g (x)*.
- Note carefully which function is going to be used first. Make sure that the first function's output is used in the second function.

Example $f(x) = 3x-1$ $g(x) = 2x^2+x+1$	$(g \circ f)(3) = g(f(3))$ $= g(3 \cdot 3-1)$ $= g(8)$ $= 2(8)^2+8+1$ $= 128+8+1$ $= \boxed{137}$ ← Answer	The composition, g of f, is being evaluated here at $x = 3$. First $f(x)$ is evaluated for $x = 3$. The answer is 8. Next, $g(x)$ is evaluated for $x = 8$. The answer is 137. So, $g \circ f(3) = 137$.
Example $f(x) = 3x-1$ $g(x) = 2x^2+x+1$	$(f \circ g)(3) = f(g(3))$ $= f(2(3)^2+3+1)$ $= f(22)$ $= 3 \cdot 22-1$ $= \boxed{65}$ ← Answer	In this example, the composition is f of g. So, first evaluate $g(x)$ for $x = 3$. The answer is 22. Next evaluate $f(x)$ for $x = 22$. The answer is 65. Therefore, $f \circ g(3) = 65$.

Sample problems:

1. Find $(f \circ g)(3)$ for $f(x) = 4x^2 - 5x$ and $g(x) = x^3 - 2x + 4$.
   Solution: 2375
   Explanation: The notation $(f \circ g)(3)$ means to evaluate the function g for 3, then use that result to evaluate f: $(f \circ g)(3) = f(g(3)) = f\left((3)^3 - 2(3) + 4\right) = f(25) = 4(25)^2 - 5(25) = 2375$.

2. Find $(g \circ f)(-1)$ for $f(x) = 2x^7 + x^3$ and $g(x) = x^4 + 2$.
   Solution: 83
   Explanation: The notation $(g \circ f)(-1)$ means to evaluate the function f for -1, then use that result to evaluate g: $(g \circ f)(-1) = g(f(-1)) = g\left(2(-1)^7 + (-1)^3\right) = g(-3) = (-3)^4 + 2 = 83$.

3. Find $(f \circ g)(2)$ for $f(x) = \dfrac{x^3+5}{x}$ and $g(x) = \sqrt{2x^4+4}$.
   Solution: $36\frac{5}{6}$
   Explanation: The notation $(f \circ g)(2)$ means to evaluate the function g for 2, then use that result to evaluate f: $(f \circ g)(2) = f(g(2)) = f\left(\sqrt{2(2)^4+4}\right) = f(6) = \frac{(6)^3+5}{6} = \frac{221}{6} = 36\frac{5}{6}$.

Practice problems: *(Answers on page: 745)*

1. Find $(f \circ g)(4)$ for $f(x) = x + 4$ and $g(x) = x^2 - 4$.
2. Find $(g \circ f)(2)$ for $f(x) = 2x$ and $g(x) = 2x + 1$?
3. Find $(g \circ f)\left(\frac{1}{2}\right)$ for $f(x) = 8x^2$ and $g(x) = \dfrac{\sqrt{3x^3+1}}{2x}$.

Review questions: *(Answers to odd questions on page: 745)*

1. What is $(f \circ g)(5)$ if $f(x) = x^2$ and $g(x) = x - 3$?
2. What is $(f \circ g)(7)$ if $f(x) = x^2$ and $g(x) = x - 3$?
3. Find $(f \circ g)(x)$ if $f(x) = 2x + 1$ and $g(x) = x^2 + 5$

4. Let $f(x)=\dfrac{1}{x^2}$ and $g(x)=x+2$. Find $(g\circ f)(1)$.

5. Given $p(x)=x^2-x-5$ and $r(x)=2x-1$, evaluate $(p\circ r)(3)$.

Components of Composite Functions

- The benefit of composing functions with each other is that you can follow one input through several processes to reach a final output.
- **Composition notation:** $f\circ g$ indicates that $f(x)$ will be evaluated with the output from $g(x)$.
- Note carefully which function is going to be used first. Make sure that function's output is used in the second function.

Example $f(x)=3x-1$ $(f\circ f)(2)=f(f(2))$ $=f(5)$ $3(5)-1=14$ $=\boxed{14}$ ← *Answer*	You can even create a composition of a function with itself. In this example, you are asked for $f\circ f$ at $x=2$. First evaluate $f(x)$ at $x=2$. The answer is 5. Then evaluate $f(x)$ at $x=5$. The answer is 14. 14 is the value of $f\circ f$.
Example $g(x)=2x^2+x+1$ $(g\circ g)(2)=g(g(2))$ $=g(11)$ $2(11)^2+11+1=$ $=\boxed{254}$ $242+11+1=254$ *Answer*	In this case, you are to evaluate $g\circ g$ when $x=2$. Evaluate $g(x)$ at $x=2$. The answer is 11. Then, evaluate $g(x)$ again at $x=11$. The answer is 254. 254 is the value of $g\circ g$ when $x=2$.
Example $f(x)=3x-1$ $g(x)=2x^2+x+1$ In General: $(f\circ g)(x)=f(g(x))$ $=f(2x^2+x+1)$ $=3(2x^2+x+1)-1$ *Plug in stuff to x* $=\boxed{6x^2+3x+2}$ ← *Answer*	In this example, you are to evaluate $f\circ g$ when $x=x$. Following your process, evaluate $g(x)$ is when $x=x$. It's $2x^2+x+1$. There's no change because it was already stated in terms of x. Now, substitute all of that into $f(x)$ in place of every x you see. Do any multiplying and combine like terms. You get $6x^2+3x+2$, which is the value of $f\circ g$ when $x=x$.
Example $f(x)=3x-1$ $g(x)=2x^2+x+1$ $(g\circ f)(x)=g(f(x))$ $=g(3x-1)$ *Plug in stuff* $=2(3x-1)^2+(3x-1)+1$ $=2(9x^2-6x+1)+3x$ $(g\circ f)(x)=\boxed{18x^2-9x+2}$ ← *Answer*	Now, let's reverse the composition. This time evaluate $g\circ f$ when $x=x$. Starting with $f(x)$ when $x=x$, there is no change. Substitute the entire $f(x)$ expression for every x in $g(x)$ and evaluate. The answer is very different from the answer you found for the composition $f\circ g$.

Sample problems:

1. What is $(f\circ g)(x)$ when $f(x)=3x^2$ and $g(x)=\dfrac{x}{2}$?

   Solution: $\dfrac{3x^2}{4}$

   Explanation: Evaluate the function g for x, then use that result to evalute f:

   $(f\circ g)(x)=f(g(x))=f\left(\frac{x}{2}\right)=3\left(\frac{x}{2}\right)^2=\frac{3x^2}{4}$.

2. What is $(g \circ f)(2x+1)$ when $f(x) = 3x+4$ and $g(x) = x^2 - 1$?
   Solution: $36x^2 + 84x + 48$
   Explanation: Evaluate the function f for $2x+1$, then use that result to evalute g:
   $(g \circ f)(2x+1) = g\left(f(2x+1)\right) = g\left(3(2x+1)+4\right) = g(6x+7) = (6x+7)^2 - 1 =$
   $36x^2 + 84x + 48$.

3. Let $f(x) = x^2 + 5$ and $g(x) = x - 1$. Find $(f \circ g)(2a+2)$.
   Solution: $4a^2 + 4a + 6$
   Explanation: Evaluate $g(x)$ for $2a+2$, then use the result to evaluate
   then use $g(x)$ to evaluate $f(x)$: $(f \circ g)(2a+2) = f\left(g(2a+2)\right) = f\left((2a+2)-1\right) =$
   $f(2a+1) = (2a+1)^2 + 5 = 4a^2 + 4a + 1 + 5 = 4a^2 + 4a + 6$.

Practice problems: *(Answers on page: 745)*

1. Let $f(x) = 5x^2$ and $g(x) = 6x+4$. Find $(f \circ g)(x)$.
2. What is $(f \circ g)(x+1)$ when $f(x) = x^2 + 5$ and $g(x) = 6 - x$?
3. Let $f(x) = 3x^2 - 4$ and $g(x) = 5 - x$. Find $(g \circ f)(x+1)$.

Review questions: *(Answers to odd questions on page: 745)*

1. Find $(g \circ f)(2)$ for $f(x) = -4x^2 + 2x - 3$ and $g(x) = 3x - 5$.
2. What is $(f \circ g)(x)$ when $f(x) = x^2$ and $g(x) = \dfrac{3x}{2}$.
3. Let $f(x) = 2x^2 + 3$ and $g(x) = 3x - 4$. Find $(f \circ g)(x)$.
4. Given $h(x) = 3x^2 + 5x + 7$ and $j(x) = 2x + 1$, express $(j \circ h)(x)$.
5. What is $(g \circ f)(2x)$ when $f(x) = (x+1)^2$ and $g(x) = 3x + 5$?

Finding Functions That Form a Given Composite

- The benefit of composing functions with each other is that you can follow one input through several processes to reach a final output.
- **Composition notation:** $f \circ g$ indicates that $f(x)$ will be evaluated with the output from $g(x)$.
- Note carefully which function is going to be used first. Make sure that function's output is used in the second function.

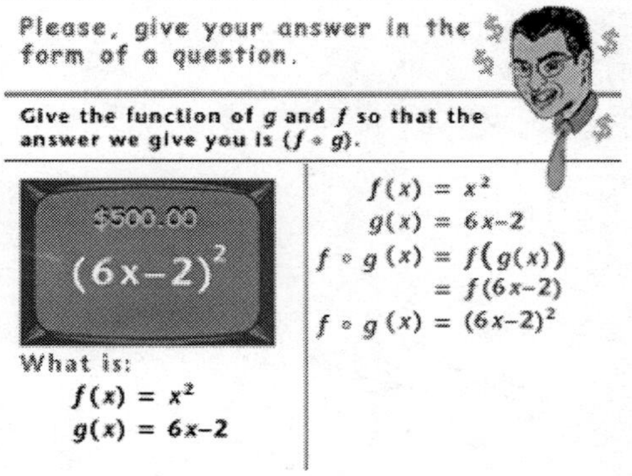

In this example, you are given the composition $f \circ g$ and asked to name the two functions that could have been used to create this composition.

You know that $f \circ g\,(x) = f[g\,(x)]$.
In this case the only thing that $g\,(x)$ could be is the expression $(6x - 2)$.
So, set $g\,(x) = 6x - 2$.
That leaves $f(x) = x^2$.

And that agrees with what the screen shows.

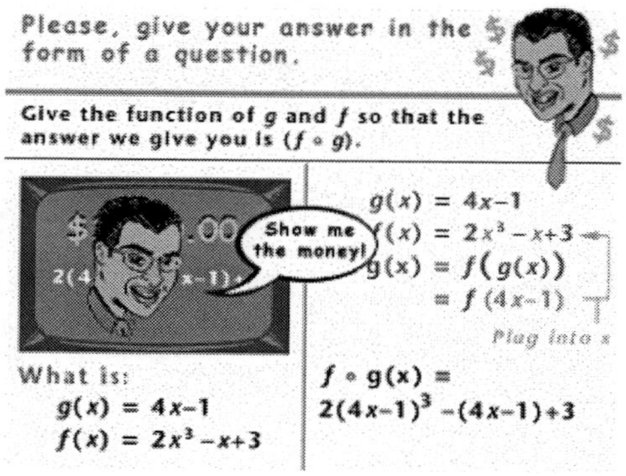

In this case, you are given that the composition $f \circ g = 2(4x-1)3 - (4x-1) + 3$.

It would appear that the equivalent of an x-term here is $(4x-1)$.
So, $g(x)$ must equal $(4x-1)$.
If so, replacing every $(4x-1)$ with x, we get $f(x)$ equals $2x^3 - x + 3$.

Sample problems:

1. Find the functions $f(x)$ and $g(x)$ such that $(f \circ g)(x) = (x^2-3)^4 + 1$.
   Solution: $f(x) = x^4 + 1,\ g(x) = x^2 - 3$
   Explanation: Let the expression inside the parentheses be $g(x)$, so $g(x) = x^2 - 3$.
   To find $f(x)$, substitute x into the composite function for $g(x)$:
   $(x^2-3)^4 + 1 \rightarrow (x)^4 + 1$, so $f(x) = x^4 + 1$.

2. Find the functions $f(x)$ and $g(x)$ such that $(f \circ g)(x) = 6(x^2)^2 - 2(x^2)$.
   Solution: $g(x) = x^2,\ f(x) = 6x^2 - 2x$
   Explanation: Let the expression inside the parentheses be $g(x)$, so $g(x) = x^2$.
   To find $f(x)$, substitute x into the composite function for $g(x)$:
   $6(x^2)^2 - 2(x^2) \rightarrow 6x^2 - 2x$, so $f(x) = 6x^2 - 2x$.

3. Find the functions $f(x)$ and $g(x)$ such that $(f \circ g)(x) = 3x^2 - x^4$.
   Solution: $g(x) = x^2,\ f(x) = 3x - x^2$
   Explanation: Express the composite function as a function with a common expression inside more than one set of parentheses (if possible):
   $x^2 - x^4 = 3(x^2) - (x^2)^2$. Let the common expression inside the parentheses be $g(x)$, so $g(x) = x^2$. To find $f(x)$, substitute x into the composite function for $g(x)$: $3(x^2) - (x^2)^2 \rightarrow 3(x) - (x)^2$, so $f(x) = 3x - x^2$.

Practice problems: *(Answers on page: 745)*

1. Find the functions $f(x)$ and $g(x)$ such that $(f \circ g)(x) = 2(3x-1)^2$
2. Find the functions $f(x)$ and $g(x)$ such that $(f \circ g)(x) = -(x^2)^2 + 5(x^2)$.
3. Find the functions $f(x)$ and $g(x)$ such that $(f \circ g)(x) = \frac{1}{2}x^6 - 3x^3 + 1$.

Review questions: *(Answers to odd questions on page: 745)*

1. Find the functions $f(x)$ and $g(x)$ such that $(f \circ g)(x) = 3(1-x)^5$.
2. Find the functions $f(x)$ and $g(x)$ such that $(f \circ g)(x) = -2(x^2+1)^3 - 5(x^2+1)^2$.

3. Find the functions $f(x)$ and $g(x)$ such that $(f \circ g)(x) = 3(2x)^6 + 3(2x)^3 - (2x)$.
4. Find the functions $f(x)$ and $g(x)$ such that $(f \circ g)(x) = 2x^2 + 4x^4 - 8x^6$.
5. Find the functions $f(x)$ and $g(x)$ such that $(f \circ g)(x) = x^8 - x^4$.

Finding the Difference Quotient of a Function

- Difference quotient:

$$D(x) = \frac{f(x+h) - f(x)}{h}$$

- This concept and formula are extremely useful in calculus when you are trying to solve for instantaneous rates of change.
- This formula is one way that composition of functions is used. In a problem, you are given a function and you substitute it into this formula for the values $x = x + h$, and $x = x$.

Example $D(x) = \frac{f(x+h)-f(x)}{h}$ (Substitute) $f(x) = 3x-5$ $D(x) = \frac{3(x+h)-5-(3x-5)}{h}$	This example shows how the difference quotient formula is used to solve problems. You are given the function ($3x - 5$). In the formula, replace $f(x + h)$ with $3(x + h) - 5$. Replace $-f(x)$ with $-(3x - 5)$. **Remember:** In the second substitution all the signs will change because you are subtracting.
$= \frac{3x+3h-5-3x+5}{h}$ $= \boxed{3}$ ← Answer if $h \neq 0$	Then remove your parentheses, combine like terms, and you have your answer. **Note:** Your answer MUST presume that h is not equal to 0.
The difference quotient is just another example of composition that you will see later in calculus.  **Example** $D(x) = \frac{f(x+h)-f(x)}{h}$ (Substitute) $f(x) = 1-x^2$ $D(x) = \frac{1-(x+h)^2-(1-x^2)}{h}$ $= \frac{1-(x^2+2hx+h^2)-1+x^2}{h}$ $= \frac{-2hx-h^2}{h} = \frac{h(-2x-h)}{h} = \boxed{-2x-h}$ ← Answer if $h \neq 0$	Here is another example. You are given the function $f(x) = 1 - x^2$. Find the difference quotient. Substitute $(x + h)$ for x. Remove parentheses with a careful regard for signs. Combine like terms and reduce where possible to find your answer. In this case, the difference quotient for the function $f(x) = 1 - x^2$ is $-2x - h$. Assume as a requirement that h cannot equal 0.

Sample problems:

1. Given $f(x) = x^2 - x + 1$, find $f(x+h) - f(x)$.
   Solution: $h^2 - h + 2xh$
   Explanation: $f(x+h) - f(x) = \left[(x+h)^2 - (x+h) + 1\right] - \left[x^2 - x + 1\right] =$
   $\left[(x^2 + 2xh + h^2) - (x+h) + 1\right] - \left[x^2 - x + 1\right] = x^2 + 2xh + h^2 - x - h + 1 - x^2 + x - 1 =$
   $h^2 - h + 2xh$

2. Calculate the difference quotient for the function $f(x)=x^2$.
   Solution: $2x+h,\ h\neq 0$

   Explanation: $D(x)=\dfrac{f(x+h)-f(x)}{h}=\dfrac{\left[(x+h)^2\right]-\left(x^2\right)}{h}=$
   $\dfrac{\left[x^2+2hx+h^2\right]-\left(x^2\right)}{h}=\dfrac{2hx+h^2}{h}=\dfrac{h(2x+h)}{h}=2x+h,\ \ h\neq 0.$

3. Calculate the difference quotient for the function $f(x)=x^2-3x+2$.
   Solution: $2x+h-3,\ h\neq 0$

   Explanation: $D(x)=\dfrac{f(x+h)-f(x)}{h}=\dfrac{\left[(x+h)^2-3(x+h)+2\right]-\left(x^2-3x+2\right)}{h}=$
   $\dfrac{\left[x^2+2hx+h^2-3x-3h+2\right]-\left(x^2-3x+2\right)}{h}=\dfrac{x^2+2hx+h^2-3x-3h+2-x^2+3x-2}{h}=$
   $\dfrac{2hx+h^2-3h}{h}=\dfrac{h(2x+h-3)}{h}=2x+h-3,\ \ h\neq 0.$

Practice problems: *(Answers on page: 745)*

1. Given $f(x)=5x^2+2x-1$, find $f(x+h)-f(x)$.
2. Calculate the difference quotient for the function $f(x)=(x+1)^2$.
3. Calculate the difference quotient for the function $f(x)=2x^2-3x$.

Review questions: *(Answers to odd questions on page: 745)*

1. Given $f(x)=x^2+1$, find $f(x+h)-f(x)$.
2. Given $f(x)=x-x^2$, find $f(x+h)-f(x)$.
3. Calculate the difference quotient for the function $f(x)=(x-3)^2$.
4. Calculate the difference quotient for the function $f(x)=x^2-x+4$.
5. Calculate the difference quotient for the function $f(x)=5x-x^3$.

4

Polynomial and Rational Functions

Using Long Division with Polynomials

- Division for polynomials follows the same procedures as long division with numbers. To divide polynomials, follow the same steps you used for elementary school long division.
- When setting up your polynomial division problems, be sure to arrange the dividend (the divided number) with the powers of the terms in descending order. If any power is missing, insert its term with a 0 coefficient.
- Your remainder is always less than your divisor, or you could keep dividing.

$\frac{f(x)}{g(x)}$ $\begin{array}{r} q(x) \\ g(x)\overline{)f(x)} \\ \overline{r(x)} \end{array}$ $\frac{103}{3}$ $\begin{array}{r} 34 \\ 3\overline{)103} \\ -9\downarrow \\ 13 \\ -12 \\ 1 \end{array}$ *remainder*	Any fraction is a division problem with the divided number, **dividend**, as the numerator, and the dividing number, **divisor**, as the denominator. In this case, the $f(x)$ matches the 103 in the fraction, and it gets divided into. The $g(x)$ matches the 3 in the fraction, and it does the dividing. The $q(x)$ matches the 34 in the fraction problem, and is the answer (quotient).
dividend *quotient* $f(x) = g(x)q(x) + r(x)$ *divisor* *remainder* *dividend* *quotient* $103 = 3\,(34) + 1$	**Note:** The original dividend can be recreated by multiplying the quotient with the divisor and adding the remainder to that product. This is your way to check your division answer for accuracy.
$\frac{f(x)}{g(x)} \longrightarrow \begin{array}{r} q(x) \\ g(x)\overline{)f(x)} \\ \overline{r(x)} \end{array}$ $\frac{f(x)}{g(x)} \longrightarrow q(x) + \frac{r(x)}{g(x)}$	Another way to express the quotient and remainder is as the sum of the quotient and the remainder divided by the divisor.
Example **Long Division of Polynomials** $\frac{x^4 + 3x^2 - 6x - 10}{x^2 + 3x - 5}$ $x^2 + 3x - 5\overline{)x^4 + 0x^3 + 3x^2 - 6x - 10}$ ↑ *write out every power of x, even if you have to use a coefficient of zero*	In this example, first set up the long division problem and include $0x^3$ as a place.
$\begin{array}{r} x^2 \\ x^2 + 3x - 5\overline{)x^4 + 0x^3 + 3x^2 - 6x - 10} \\ -\underline{(x^4 + 3x^3 - 5x^2)} \end{array}$	Next, figure what multiplies with x^2 to produce x^4. Since x^2 is the answer, write x^2 on the answer line then multiply x^2 by the divisor.
$\begin{array}{r} x^2 \\ x^2 + 3x - 5\overline{)x^4 + 0x^3 + 3x^2 - 6x - 10} \\ -\underline{(x^4 + 3x^3 - 5x^2)} \downarrow \\ -3x^3 + 8x^2 - 6x \end{array}$	Subtract $x^4+3x^3-5x^2$ from the dividend and bring down the next term to be divided.
$\begin{array}{r} x^2 - 3x \\ x^2 + 3x - 5\overline{)x^4 + 0x^3 + 3x^2 - 6x - 10} \\ -\underline{(x^4 + 3x^3 - 5x^2)} \\ -3x^3 + 8x^2 - 6x \\ -\underline{(-3x^3 - 9x^2 + 15x)} \downarrow \\ 17x^2 - 21x - 10 \end{array}$	Repeat the process: · What term multiplies with x^2 to give $-3x^3$? · Multiply $-3x$ by the divisor. · Subtract and bring down the last term in the dividend

$x^2 - 3x + 17$ $x^2 + 3x - 5\,\overline{)\,x^4 + 0x^3 + 3x^2 - 6x - 10}$ $-\underline{(x^4 + 3x^3 - 5x^2)}$ $-3x^3 + 8x^2 - 6x$ $-\underline{(-3x^3 - 9x^2 + 15x)}$ $17x^2 - 21x - 10$ $-\underline{(17x^2 + 51x - 85)}$ $-72x + 75$	Again, repeat the process: · What term multiplies with x^2 to give $17x^2$? · Multiply 17 by the divisor.There are no more terms in the dividend, so the process is complete
Quotient = $x^2 - 3x + 17$ $x^2 + 3x - 5\,\overline{)\,x^4 + 0x^3 + 3x^2 - 6x - 10}$ $-\underline{(x^4 + 3x^3 - 5x^2)}$ $-3x^3 + 8x^2 - 6x$ $-\underline{(-3x^3 - 9x^2 + 15x)}$ $17x^2 - 21x - 10$ $-\underline{(17x^2 + 51x - 85)}$ Remainder = $-72x + 75$	The leftover expression, $-72x + 75$, is the remainder.

Sample problems:

1. Divide: $\dfrac{5x^2 - 6x - 8}{x - 2}$

   Solution: $5x + 4$

   Explanation: Set up like regular long division:

$$\begin{array}{r} 5x + 4 \\ x-2\,\overline{)\,5x^2 - 6x - 8} \\ -\underline{(5x^2 - 10x)} \\ 4x - 8 \\ -\underline{(4x - 8)} \\ 0 \end{array}$$

   Thus, the quotient is $5x + 4$.

2. Divide: $\dfrac{x^4 + x^2 + x + 1}{x - 2}$

   Solution: $x^3 + 2x^2 + 5x + 11$, R(23)

   Explanation: Set up the problem, include the $0x^3$:

$$\begin{array}{r} x^3 + 2x^2 + 5x + 11 \\ x-2\,\overline{)\,x^4 + 0x^3 + x^2 + x + 1} \\ -\underline{(x^4 - 2x^3)} \\ 2x^3 + x^2 \\ -\underline{(2x^3 - 4x^2)} \\ 5x^2 + x \\ -\underline{(5x^2 - 10x)} \\ 11x + 1 \\ -\underline{(11x - 22)} \\ 23 \end{array}$$

   Thus, the quotient is $x^3 + 2x^2 + 5x + 11$, R(23).

3. Divide: $\dfrac{x^6 - 6x^5 + 12x^3 - 12x^2 + 20}{x^3 - 6x^2 + 10}$

<u>Solution</u>: $x^3 + 2$

<u>Explanation</u>: Set up the division problem and insert placeholders as needed in the divisor and dividend:

$$\begin{array}{r} x^3 + 0x^2 + 0x + 2 \\ x^3 - 6x^2 + 0x + 10 \overline{\big) x^6 - 6x^5 + 0x^4 + 12x^3 - 12x^2 + 0x + 20} \\ -\left(x^6 - 6x^5 + 0x^4 \;\; + 10x^3\right) \\ \hline 2x^3 - 12x^2 + 0x + 20 \\ -\left(2x^3 - 12x^2 + 0x + 20\right) \\ \hline 0 \end{array}$$

Thus, the quotient is $x^3 + 2$.

Practice problems: *(Answers on page: 745)*

1. Divide: $\dfrac{-x^3 + 2x - 7}{x + 4}$
2. Divide: $\dfrac{5x^2 - 3x + 2}{x^2 - 3x}$
3. Divide: $\dfrac{2x^6 + 10x^4 + 13x^3 - 5x - 7}{x^3 + 5x + 7}$

Review questions: *(Answers to odd questions on page: 745)*

1. Divide: $\dfrac{x^2 - 5x + 4}{x - 3}$
2. Divide: $\dfrac{x^3 + 2x^2 + 2x + 1}{x + 2}$
3. Divide: $\dfrac{x^3 - 8x + 2}{x + 3}$
4. Divide: $\dfrac{7x^3 + 4x^2 - 3x - 3}{x^2 + 3x}$
5. Divide: $\dfrac{x^3 + 6x + 3}{x^2 - 2x + 2}$

Long Division: Another Example

- When you see a rational expression composed of polynomials, you can divide the numerator by the denominator.
- Division with polynomials is very similar to division with real numbers. Use the same steps you used in elementary school.
- Be careful to match like terms when you are adding and subtracting. The area for focus is to be sure that all the exponents match.

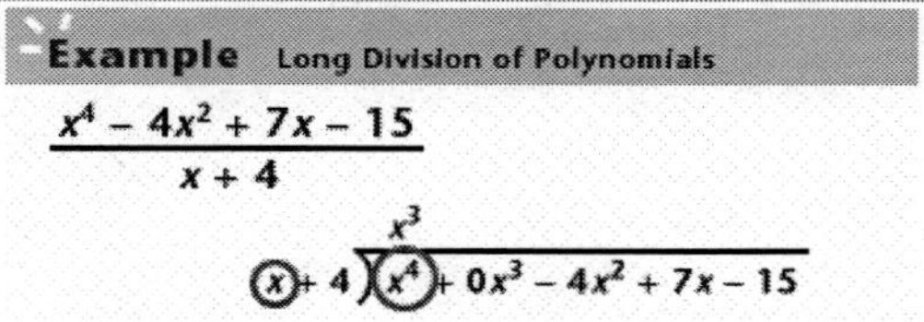

In this example, $(x + 4)$ can divide into the numerator, $(x^4 - 4x^2 + 7x - 15)$.

Once the problem is set up, ask yourself "What can I multiply with x to have an answer of x^4?"

x^3, of course.

x^3 $x+4\overline{)\,x^4+0x^3-4x^2+7x-15}$ $-(x^4+4x^3)$ $-4x^3-4x^2$	x^3 is the first term of your answer. Multiply it with both x and 4, and write the answers under their matching terms. Next, subtract your products from the terms in the polynomial being divided. **Note:** Arrange the terms in descending order with any missing exponents written in with coefficients of 0. This greatly helps you line up your terms and subtract properly.
Quotient $= x^3-4x^2+12x-41$ $x+4\overline{)\,x^4+0x^3-4x^2+7x-15}$ $-(x^4+4x^3)$ $-4x^3-4x^2$ $-(-4x^3-16x^2)$ $12x^2+7x$ $-(12x^2+48x)$ $-41x-15$ $-(-41x-164)$ Remainder $= 149$	Now, repeat the process using the terms derived from your first cycle of multiplying and subtracting. Repeat this until all terms have been used. Note any remainder. Sometimes remainders are written in a fraction with the dividing number as the denominator. All of these steps are the same ones used for dividing with real numbers.

Sample problems:

1. Divide: $\dfrac{-x^3+2x+6}{x-4}$

   Solution: $-x^2-4x-14, \text{R}(-50)$

   Explanation: Express the problem including all terms:

$$\begin{array}{r} -x^2-4x-14 \\ x-4\overline{)\,-x^3+0x^2+2x+6} \\ -(-x^3+4x^2) \\ -4x^2+2x \\ -(-4x^2+16x) \\ -14x+6 \\ -(-14x+56) \\ -50 \end{array}$$

2. Divide: $\dfrac{2x^4+3x^3+2x^2+1}{x^2+4x}$

   Solution: $2x^2-5x+22,\ \text{R}(-88x+1)$

   Explanation: Express the problem including all terms:

$$\begin{array}{r} 2x^2-5x+22 \\ x^2+4x\overline{)\,2x^4+3x^3+2x^2+0x+1} \\ -(2x^4+8x^3) \\ -5x^3+2x^2 \\ -(-5x^3-20x^2) \\ 22x^2+0x \\ -(22x^2+88x) \\ -88x+1 \end{array}$$

3. Divide: $\dfrac{-4x^3+x^2+3x}{2x+1}$

Solution: $-2x^2+\dfrac{3}{2}x+\dfrac{3}{4},\ \text{R}\left(-\dfrac{3}{4}\right)$

Explanation:
$$\begin{array}{r}
-2x^2+\tfrac{3}{2}x+\tfrac{3}{4} \\
2x+1\overline{)-4x^3+x^2+3x+0} \\
\underline{-(-4x^3-2x^2)} \\
3x^2+3x \\
\underline{-(3x^2+\tfrac{3}{2}x)} \\
\tfrac{3}{2}x+0 \\
\underline{-(\tfrac{3}{2}x+\tfrac{3}{4})} \\
-\tfrac{3}{4}
\end{array}$$

Practice problems: *(Answers on page: 745)*

1. Divide: $\dfrac{4x^4+3x^2-1}{x^2+2x}$
2. Divide: $\dfrac{-3x^4}{x-2}$
3. Divide: $\dfrac{5x^4-\frac{1}{4}x^2+x}{2x+1}$

Review questions: *(Answers to odd questions on page: 745)*

1. Divide: $\dfrac{x^4+x^2+x+1}{x+2}$
2. Divide: $\dfrac{4x^2-2x-2}{x-1}$
3. Divide: $\dfrac{5x^4-6x-8}{x+2}$
4. Divide: $\dfrac{10x^3+4x^2-3x-3}{x^2-x}$
5. Divide: $\dfrac{-x^4-2x^3-3x^2-4x+5}{x^2-2x}$

Using Synthetic Division with Polynomials

- **Synthetic division** is a shorthand method for dividing polynomials when the divisor is in the form $(x+c)$.
- Synthetic division only works when the coefficient for x in the dividing polynomial is $+1$. If there is any other coefficient on the term of highest degree, divide the dividing polynomial by that coefficient to eliminate it.
- To set up the problem, change the sign of the constant in the divisor and set it up to divide with all the coefficients of the problem.
- Be sure that the coefficients match terms in descending degree and that you include coefficients of 0 for any exponents that are missing.

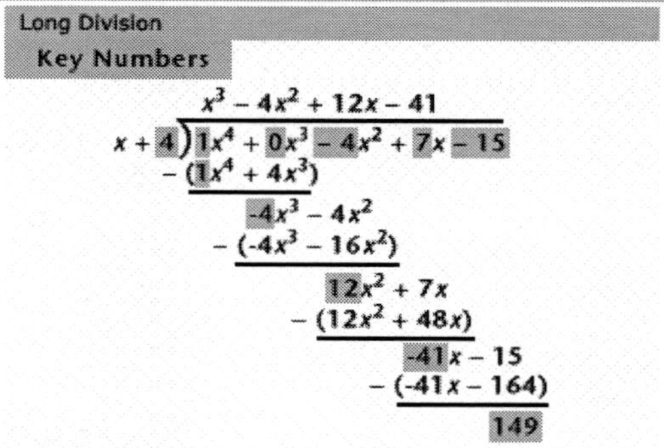

Synthetic division depends on using the key numbers in a division problem.

The key numbers are all the coefficients and constants.

Notice: this includes coefficients of 0 for terms that would otherwise not be stated.

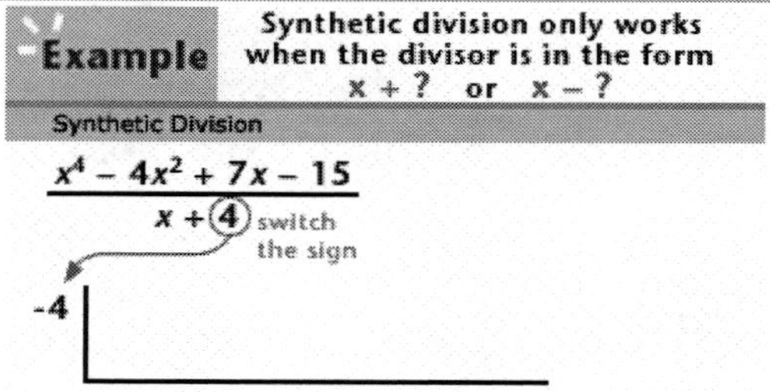

Set up your dividing problem.

Change the sign on the +4 and place the –4 as the divisor.

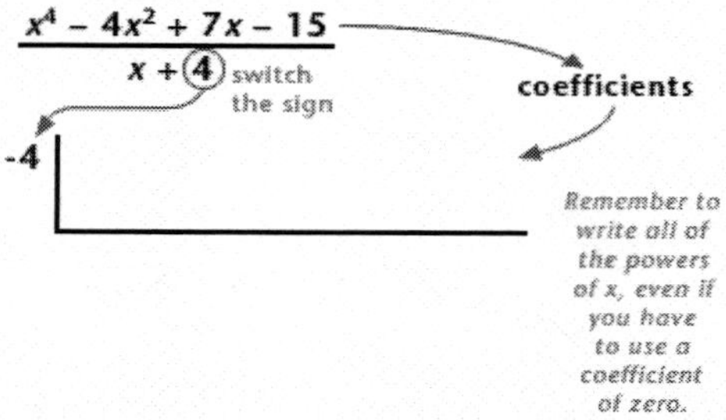

Write the coefficient for every term in the divided polynomial after you have arranged all the terms in descending order with the highest degree first.

Note: Include a 0 as the coefficient whenever a degree is skipped in the descending order. In this example, there is no x^3 term. So a 0 is placed in the line as the coefficient for the $0x^3$s.

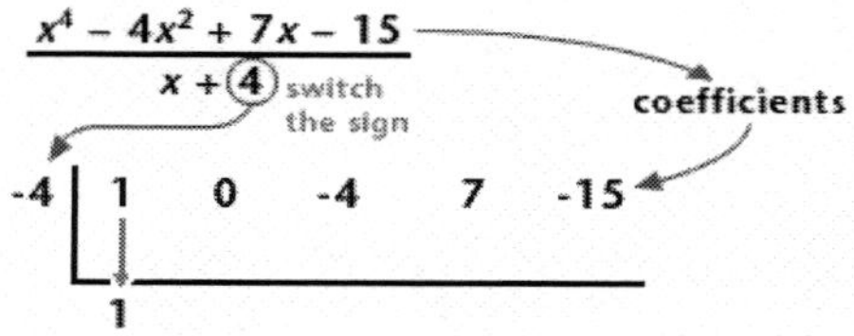

Then you follow the process:

Step One:
Bring down the first number in the list being divided, 1.

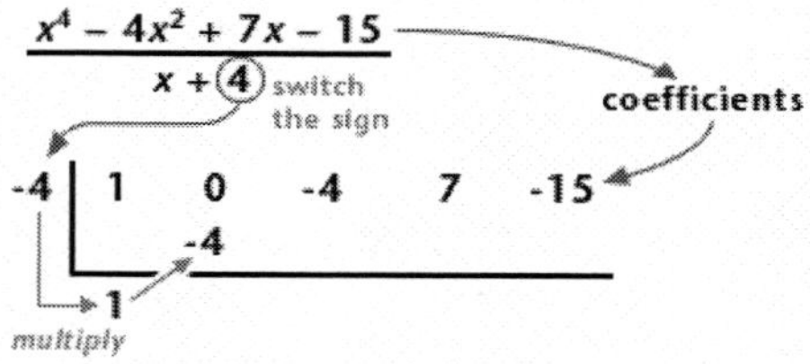

Step Two:
Multiply that number, 1, with the dividing number, -4.

Step Three:
Write the product, -4, under the second number being divided, 0.

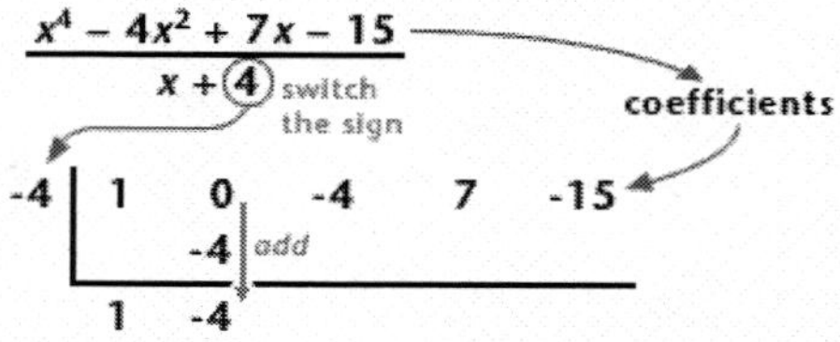

Step Four:
Add 0 + -4 = -4. Write the sum under its adding numbers.

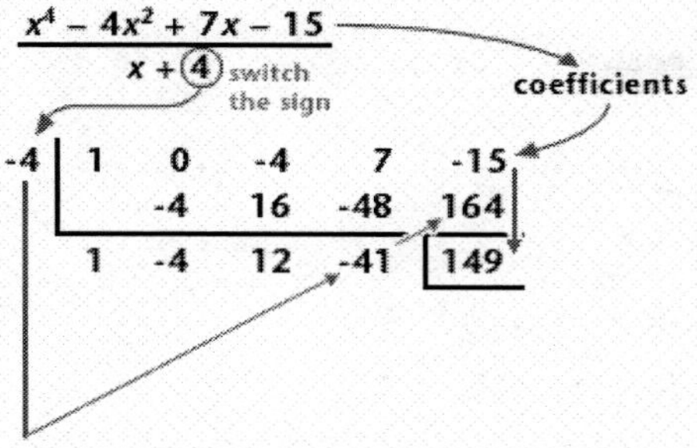

Step Five:
Repeat the process to divide all numbers:
Multiply the sum with the –4;
Write the product under the next number being divided.
Add the product to the number it is under.
Write the total under the product.

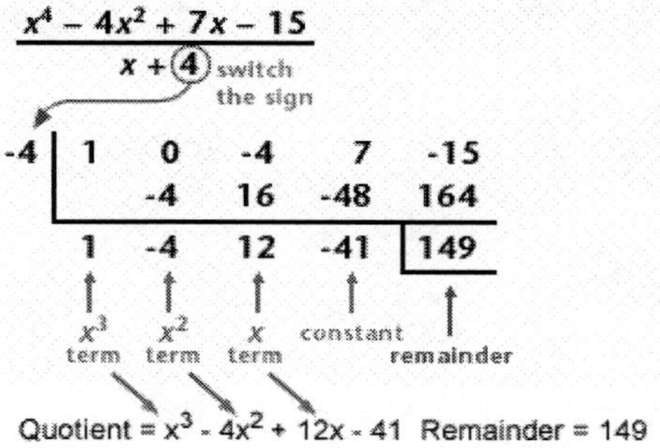

Step Seven:
Use each number in your answer as the coefficient for its x. Begin your xs at one degree less than the divided polynomial had. End with the remainder, if any.

This process gives you the same answer you get if you work the problem using long division.

Sample problems:

1. Divide: $\dfrac{x^3+3x^2-x+1}{x-2}$

   Solution: $x^2+5x+9,\ \mathrm{R}(19)$

   Explanation: Set up the problem for synthetic division: $2\,\begin{array}{|rrrr} 1 & 3 & -1 & 1 \\ \hline \end{array}$

   Next, bring down the 1, then begin the process of multiplying and adding: $2\,\begin{array}{|rrrr} 1 & 3 & -1 & 1 \\ & 2 & 10 & 18 \\ \hline 1 & 5 & 9 & \boxed{19} \end{array}$

   So, the quotient is x^2+5x+9 and the remainder is 19.

2. Divide: $\dfrac{2x^3-3x^2+4x+3}{x+\frac{1}{2}}$

   Solution: $2x^2-4x+6$

   Explanation: Set up the problem for synthetic division: $-\frac{1}{2}\,\begin{array}{|rrrr} 2 & -3 & 4 & 3 \\ \hline \end{array}$

   Next, bring down the 2, then begin the process of multiplying and adding:

   $$-\frac{1}{2}\,\begin{array}{|rrrr} 2 & -3 & 4 & 3 \\ & -1 & 2 & -3 \\ \hline 2 & -4 & 6 & \boxed{0} \end{array}$$

   So, the quotient is $2x^2-4x+6$ and there is no remainder.

3. Divide: $\dfrac{4x^3+16x^2-23x-15}{x+\frac{1}{2}}$

<u>Solution</u>: $4x^2+14x-30$

<u>Explanation</u>: Set up the problem for synthetic division:

$$-\tfrac{1}{2}\;\begin{array}{|rrrr} 4 & 16 & -23 & -15 \\ & & & \\ \hline \end{array}$$

Bring down the 4 and begin the process of multiplying and adding:

$$\begin{array}{r|rrrr} -\tfrac{1}{2} & 4 & 16 & -23 & -15 \\ & & -2 & -7 & 15 \\ \hline & 4 & 14 & -30 & 0. \end{array}$$

So, the quotient is $4x^2+14x-30$.

Practice problems: *(Answers on page: 745)*

1. Divide: $\dfrac{x^4+6x^2-7x+12}{x-2}$
2. Divide: $\dfrac{y^3+y^2-20}{y+2}$
3. Divide: $\dfrac{8x^2+1}{x+\frac{1}{4}}$

Review questions: *(Answers to odd questions on page: 745)*

1. Divide: $\dfrac{x^3+5x^2+6x}{x+2}$
2. Divide: $\dfrac{x^4+5x^3-4x^2-x}{x-1}$
3. Divide: $\dfrac{x^4+x^3+x}{x+2}$
4. Divide: $\dfrac{x^5+5x^4-3x^3+2}{x-3}$
5. Divide: $\dfrac{6x^6+5x^5+4x^4+3x^3+2x^2+x+1}{x+1}$

More Synthetic Division

- Synthetic division only works when divisor is $(x \pm c)$. x must be a first-degree term.
- To set up the problem, change the sign of the constant in the divisor and set it up to divide with all the coefficients of the problem.
- Be sure that the coefficients match terms in descending degree and that you include coefficients of 0 for any exponents that are missing.

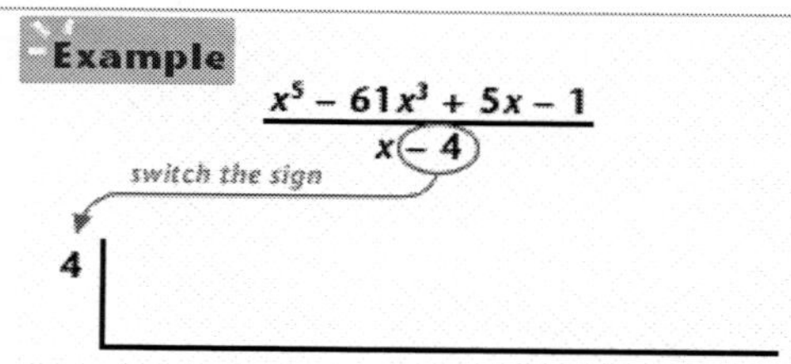	Switch the sign of the dividing constant and write it as the divisor.

Example $\dfrac{x^5 - 61x^3 + 5x - 1}{x - 4}$ (switch the sign; coefficients) $4 \,\vert\, 1 \quad 0 \quad -61 \quad 0 \quad 5 \quad -1$	Write the coefficients of the terms being dividing in descending order and including a coefficient of 0 for any missing term.
1	Bring down into the answer the first number from the string being divided.
$4 \,\vert\, 1 \quad 0$ $\quad\quad 4$ $\quad 1 \quad 4$ (multiply)	Multiply the dividing number, 4, with the number brought down, 1, and write the answer, 4, under the next term in the divided string.
$4 \,\vert\, 1 \quad 0 \quad -61 \quad 0 \quad 5 \quad -1$ $\quad\quad 4$ (add) $\quad 1 \quad 4$ (multiply)	Add the product to the number you wrote it under. Write the total under the product.
$4 \,\vert\, 1 \quad 0 \quad -61 \quad 0 \quad 5 \quad -1$ $\quad\quad 4 \quad 16 \quad -180 \quad -720 \quad -2860$ $\quad 1 \quad 4 \quad -45 \quad -180 \quad -715 \quad -2861$	Repeat that cycle across the divided string of terms.
$x^4 + 4x^3 - 45x^2 - 180x - 715$ Remainder = -2861	Match each number as the coefficient for its term, beginning the first term at one degree less than the original polynomial being divided.

Sample problems:

1. Divide: $\dfrac{3x^4 + 2x^2 - 9x - 7}{x - 4}$

   Solution: $3x^3 + 12x^2 + 50x + 191, \text{ R}(757)$

   Explanation:

   $$\begin{array}{r|rrrrr} 4 & 3 & 0 & 2 & -9 & -7 \\ & & 12 & 48 & 200 & 764 \\ \hline & 3 & 12 & 50 & 191 & \boxed{757} \end{array} \Rightarrow 3x^3 + 12x^2 + 50x + 191, \text{ R}(757)$$

2. Divide: $\dfrac{4x^4 - 15x^2 - 4}{x - 2}$

   Solution: $4x^3 + 8x^2 + x + 2$

   Explanation:

   $$\begin{array}{r|rrrrr} 2 & 4 & 0 & -15 & 0 & -4 \\ & & 8 & 16 & 2 & 4 \\ \hline & 4 & 8 & 1 & 2 & 0 \end{array} \Rightarrow 4x^3 + 8x^2 + x + 2$$

3. Divide: $\dfrac{3x^3 - 4x^2 + 5}{x - \frac{3}{2}}$

   Solution: $3x^2 + \dfrac{1}{2}x + \dfrac{3}{4}, \text{ R}\left(\dfrac{49}{8}\right)$

   Explanation:
   $$\begin{array}{r|rrrr} \frac{3}{2} & 3 & -4 & 0 & 5 \\ & & \frac{9}{2} & \frac{3}{4} & \frac{9}{8} \\ \hline & 3 & \frac{1}{2} & \frac{3}{4} & \frac{49}{8} \end{array} \Rightarrow 3x^2 + \tfrac{1}{2}x + \tfrac{3}{4}, \text{ R}(\tfrac{49}{8})$$

Practice problems: *(Answers on page: 745)*

1. Divide: $\dfrac{x^4 - 10x^2 - 2x + 4}{x+3}$

2. Divide: $\dfrac{x^3 + 512}{x+8}$

3. Divide: $\dfrac{x^3}{x+\frac{1}{2}}$

Review questions: *(Answers to odd questions on page: 745)*

1. Divide: $\dfrac{x^3 + 2x^2 - 8x - 17}{x-3}$

2. Divide: $\dfrac{3x^4 + 2x^3 + 4x^2 + 5x}{x+2}$

3. Divide: $\dfrac{x^3 - 5x^2 + 4x - 3}{x-3}$

4. Divide: $\dfrac{2x^3 + 3x^2 - 16x + 10}{x+4}$

5. Divide: $\dfrac{6x^4 + 9x^3 - 14x^2 + 6x - 1}{x-\frac{1}{2}}$

The Remainder Theorem

- The **remainder theorem**: If a polynomial $p(x)$ is divided by $(x - c)$, then its remainder is $p(c)$. Note in $(x - c)$, the c is subtracting; as a result, any constant must change its sign before being substituted into the polynomial.
- This theorem and synthetic division allow the evaluation of some really big and complicated polynomials that might otherwise just baffle everybody.
- The remainder will always have less value than the dividing expression.
- The remainder will not have any x-terms, or you would be able to continue dividing.

Example

$p(x) = 2x^3 - x + 1$

What is the remainder if you divide by $x - 2$?

Remainder $= p(2) = 15$

$p(2) = 2(2^3) - 2 + 1$
$p(2) = 2(8) - 2 + 1$
$p(2) = 16 - 2 + 1$
$p(2) = 15$

The **remainder theorem** says to substitute the dividing constant into the polynomial, and evaluate. The answer equals the remainder derived by dividing the polynomial.

In this case, the relevant constant is 2.

Note: In the standard form of $(x - c)$, the c is subtracting. So, any c must reverse its sign before you substitute it into the polynomial.

Substitute 2 into the polynomial. The answer is 15.

Check with Synthetic Division

$\dfrac{2x^3 - x + 1}{x - 2}$

2	2	0	-1	1
		4	8	14
	2	4	7	15

Remainder

Now, do the actual division. We chose to use synthetic division because it's faster.

The remainder is 15.
The remainder theorem works.

Example $p(x) = -x^2 + 10x - 3$ **What is the remainder if you divide by $x + 4$?** $x - (-4)$ $p(-4) = -(-4^2) + 10(-4) - 3$ $= -16 - 40 - 3$ $= -59 =$ Remainder	Here's another example. The remainder theorem instructs us to substitute –4 into the polynomial. The result is –59.
Check with Synthetic Division $\frac{-x^2 + 10x - 3}{x + 4}$ -4 | -1 10 -3 4 -56 -1 14 | -59 Remainder	Check again by doing the division itself. Sure enough, the remainder is –59.

Sample problems:

1. Find the remainder when $7x^4 + 4x^3 - 2x^2 - 1$ is divided by $x - 3$.
   Solution: 656
   Explanation: For $\frac{f(x)}{x-c}$, the remainder is $f(c)$. The divisor is $x-3$, so $c = 3$. Evaluate $f(c)$:
   $f(3) = 7(3)^4 + 4(3)^3 - 2(3)^2 - 1$
   $= 7(81) + 4(27) - 2(9) - 1$
   $= 567 + 108 - 18 - 1$
   $= 656.$

2. Find the remainder when $16x^4 + 25x^3 - 32x + 15$ is divided by $x - 10$.
   Solution: 184,695
   Explanation: Evaluate $f(c)$: $f(10) = 16(10)^4 + 25(10)^3 - 32(10) + 15 = 184{,}695.$

3. Find the remainder when $1 - x + \frac{3}{4}x^2 - x^3$ is divided by $x + \frac{1}{2}$.
   Solution: $\frac{29}{16}$
   Explanation: Evaluate $f(c)$:
   $f(-\frac{1}{2}) = 1 - (-\frac{1}{2}) + \frac{3}{4}(-\frac{1}{2})^2 - (-\frac{1}{2})^3$
   $= 1 + \frac{1}{2} + \frac{3}{4}(\frac{1}{4}) - (-\frac{1}{8})$
   $= 1 + \frac{1}{2} + \frac{3}{16} + \frac{1}{8}$
   $= \frac{3}{2} + \frac{3}{16} + \frac{1}{8}$
   $= \frac{27}{16} + \frac{1}{8}$
   $= \frac{29}{16}.$

Practice problems: *(Answers on page: 745)*

1. Find the remainder when $-5x^3 + 10x^2 - 15x + 20$ is divided by $x + 5$.
2. Find the remainder when $-x^4 + 8x^3 + 2x + 1$ is divided by $x - \frac{1}{2}$.
3. Find the remainder when $\frac{1}{2}x^3 - \frac{2}{3}x^2 + 1$ is divided by $x - \frac{1}{3}$.

Review questions: *(Answers to odd questions on page: 745)*

1. Find the remainder when $4x^2 + 12x + 5$ is divided by $x + 1$.

2. Find the remainder when $x^3 + 3x^2 - 7x + 6$ is divided by $x - 2$.
3. Find the remainder when $x^3 + 2x^2 - 7$ is divided by $x + 2$.
4. Find the remainder when $5x^4 + 30x^3 - 40x^2 + 36x + 14$ is divided by $x + 7$.
5. Find the remainder when $x^7 - 3x^2 - 1$ is divided by $x - 3$.

More on the Remainder Theorem

- The **remainder theorem**: If a polynomial $p(x)$ is divided by $(x - c)$, then its remainder is $p(c)$. Note in $(x - c)$, the c is subtracting; as a result, any constant must change its sign before being substituted into the polynomial.
- This theorem and synthetic division allow the evaluation of some really big and complicated polynomials that might otherwise just baffle everybody.
- The remainder will always have less value than the dividing expression.
- The remainder will not have any x-terms, or you would be able to continue dividing.

$$p(x) = q(x)(x - c) + p(c)$$

↑ *remainder*

Suppose that you are asked to evaluate a polynomial for number *c*.

You could plug *c* in for every *x* and evaluate,

or...

You could divide the polynomial by $x - c$ using synthetic division, and see what the remainder is.

The remainder = $p(c)$.

The remainder theorem is a shortcut method to determine the remainder of a polynomial division problem. In some cases, the polynomial may be very complicated or the remainder is all you need, and using this theorem is the best choice.

Your other choice is to divide the polynomials and get the entire answer with the remainder.

Example $p(x) = 5x^3 - 6x^2 - 28x - 2$

$p(-2) = ?$

You could plug -2 in for every *x*...

$$p(-2) = 5(-2)^3 - 6(-2)^2 - 28(-2) - 2$$

This will equal -10

In this example, suppose you are asked to evaluate $p(x)$ for $x = -2$.

If you substitute into the polynomial, the result is -10.

Or, you could divide by $x - (-2)$, because the remainder = $p(-2)$. $x + 2$

$$\begin{array}{r|rrrr} -2 & 5 & -6 & -28 & -2 \\ & & -10 & 32 & -8 \\ \hline & 5 & -16 & 4 & \boxed{-10} = p(-2) \end{array}$$

remainder

Another choice is to divide the polynomial by $(x + 2)$. If you divide this out you arrive at an answer with the remainder being -10, the same as you got above by evaluating $p(x)$ for $x = -2$.

Example $p(x) = 3x^2 - 1$

$p(2) = ?$

You could plug 2 in for every *x*...

$$\begin{aligned} p(2) &= 3(2^2) - 1 \\ &= 3(4) - 1 \\ &= 12 - 1 \\ &\boxed{= 11} \end{aligned}$$

Here's a second example. If someone asked you to evaluate the expression for $x = 2$, you would substitute 2 in for every x and evaluate. The result would be 11.

Or, you could divide by $x - 2$, because the remainder = $p(2)$.

$$\begin{array}{r|rrr} 2 & 3 & 0 & -1 \\ & & 6 & 12 \\ \hline & 3 & 6 & \boxed{11} = p(2) \end{array}$$

remainder

Again, in the same situation, if you divide by $(x - 2)$ (remember to change signs), you find a division answer with a remainder of 11.

Sample problems:

1. Find the remainder when $2x^3+4x^2-4x+2$ is divided by $x+4$.

   Solution: -46

   Explanation: For $\dfrac{f(x)}{x-c}$, the remainder is $f(c)$.

   Evaluate $f(c)$: $f(-4)=2(-4)^3+4(-4)^2-4(-4)+2=-46$.

2. Given the function $f(x)=x^6+4x^3-2x-1$, find $f(-2)$ using synthetic division.

   Solution: 35

   Explanation: For $\dfrac{f(x)}{x-c}$, the remainder is $f(c)$. Therefore, the value of $f(-2)$ is the remainder of $\dfrac{f(x)}{x+2}$. Set up the problem for synthetic division and solve:

$$\begin{array}{r|rrrrrrr} -2 & 1 & 0 & 0 & 4 & 0 & -2 & -1 \\ & & -2 & 4 & -8 & 8 & -16 & 36 \\ \hline & 1 & -2 & 4 & -4 & 8 & -18 & 35 \end{array}$$

   The remainder is 35, so $f(-2)=35$.

3. Use synthetic division to find $f\left(\dfrac{1}{2}\right)$ when $f(x)=4x^2-3x+\dfrac{1}{2}$.

   Solution: 0

   Explanation:

$$\begin{array}{r|rrr} \frac{1}{2} & 4 & -3 & \frac{1}{2} \\ & & 2 & -\frac{1}{2} \\ \hline & 4 & -1 & 0 \end{array}$$

   The remainder is 0, so $f(\tfrac{1}{2})=0$.

Practice problems: *(Answers on page: 745)*

1. Use synthetic division to find $f(-2)$ when $f(x)=-x^5-x^4-x^3-x^2-x-1$.
2. Use synthetic division to find $f(-1)$ when $f(x)=-x^3-2x^2+10x-24$.
3. Use synthetic division to find $f\left(-\dfrac{3}{4}\right)$ when $f(x)=4x^3-3x^2+5$.

Review questions: *(Answers to odd questions on page: 746)*

1. Use synthetic division to find $f(3)$ when $f(x)=x^2-5x+4$.
2. Use synthetic division to find $f(6)$ when $f(x)=3x^2+5x$.
3. Use synthetic division to find $f(-2)$ when $f(x)=x^3+2x^2+2x+1$.
4. Use synthetic division to find $f\left(\dfrac{2}{3}\right)$ when $f(x)=3x^3+4x^2-2x+1$.
5. Use synthetic division to find $f(0.1)$ when $f(x)=x^3+2x^2-3x-8$.

The Factor Theorem and Its Uses

- The **factor theorem** says $(x - c)$ must be a factor of the polynomial if it divides into the polynomial with a remainder of 0. Also, if you substitute c into $f(x)$, $f(c) = 0$.
- The remainder theorem says that for $\frac{f(x)}{x-c}$, the remainder is $f(c)$.
- Synthetic division only works when the divisor is in the form, $x - c$. Also, remember before you divide to arrange the powers in the dividend in descending order and have a term for every power even if the term must have a coefficient of 0.

Example $\frac{x^2+x-6}{x+3}$

$$\begin{array}{r|rrr} -3 & 1 & 1 & -6 \\ & & -3 & 6 \\ \hline & 1 & -2 & \boxed{0} \end{array}$$

$$\frac{x^2+x-6}{x+3} = x - 2$$

Set up your synthetic division by writing the coefficients in the order of the descending terms, $1 - 1 - 6$. Now you will divide by the "c" of $(x - c)$. In this case that is -3.

To divide, bring down the first 1. Multiply it with the dividing -3 and write it under the second 1. Add that column. Multiply the answer, -2 with the dividing -3 and write that answer in the next column. Add that column.

Note: $x - c$ means the sign will change on the constant in the divisor.

potential factor

$2x^3+x^2+2 \longleftarrow x+1$

plug in -1, if it =0, it's a factor.
if it ≠0, it's not a factor.

$2(-1)^3+(-1)^2+2 = 1 \neq 0$

not a factor

Any time the remainder equals 0 the dividing number, in this case $x + 1$, is a factor of the number being divided.

If $x + 1$ is a factor, substitute -1 into the expression and your answer is 0.

In this case, the expression equals 1, which is not 0. Therefore, $x + 1$ is not a factor.

potential factor

x^3+2x^2-3 $x-1$

plug in 1, if it =0, it's a factor.
if it ≠0, it's not a factor.

$1 + 2 - 3 = 0$ it's a factor!

Try again. If $x - 1$ is a factor, substituting $+1$ into the expression will produce 0.

It does. This means that $x - 1$ is a factor of $x^3 + 2x^2 - 3$.

Sample problems:

1. Use synthetic division to determine if $x-3$ is a factor of $x^3+4x^2-23x+6$.
   Solution: $x-3$ is a factor of $x^3+4x^2-23x+6$
   Explanation: Divide $x-3$ into the expression $x^3+4x^2-23x+6$:

$$\begin{array}{r|rrrr} 3 & 1 & 4 & -23 & 6 \\ & & 3 & 21 & -6 \\ \hline & 1 & 7 & -2 & 0 \end{array}$$

   The last number indicates that the remainder is 0, thus the divisor is a factor.

2. Use the factor theorem to determine if $x+1$ is a factor of $2x^3-5x-7$.
   Solution: $x+1$ is not a factor of $2x^3-5x-7$
   Explanation: The factor theorem states that if $x-c$ is a factor of $f(x)$, then $f(c)=0$. Evaluate $f(c)$: $f(-1)=2(-1)^3-5(-1)-7=-2+5-7=-4$.
   Since $f(c)\neq 0$, the divisor is not a factor.

3. Use the factor theorem to determine if $x-4$ is a factor of $x^6-4x^5-5x^2+22x-8$.
   Solution: $x-4$ is a factor of $x^6-4x^5-5x^2+22x-8$
   Explanation: Evaluate $f(c)$: $f(4)=(4)^6-4(4)^5-5(4)^2+22(4)-8=0$.
   Since $f(c)=0$, the divisor is a factor.

Practice problems: *(Answers on page: 746)*

1. Use synthetic division to determine if $x-5$ is a factor of $5x^4+x^2-3x+18$.
2. Use the factor theorem to determine if $x-1$ is a factor of $2x^5-2x^4-5x^2+6x-1$.
3. Use the factor theorem to determine if $x+7$ is a factor of $x^6-x^2+2x-10$.

Review questions: *(Answers to odd questions on page: 746)*

1. Use synthetic division to determine if $x+1$ is a factor of $2x^4+2x^3-x^2+7x+8$.
2. Use synthetic division to determine if $x-2$ is a factor of $7x^3-x^2+5x-14$.
3. Use the factor theorem to determine if $x+5$ is a factor of $4x^5-7x^2+20x-13$.
4. Use the factor theorem to determine if $x-1$ is a factor of x^6-1.
5. Use the factor theorem to determine if $x+4$ is a factor of $7x^6-2x^5-3x^2-x-7$.

Factoring a Polynomial Given a Zero

- A **zero** of a polynomial is a point where the graph crosses the x-axis. Also, if you substitute that point into the polynomial, its value equals 0; i.e., $f(x)=0$ for $(x-c)$.
- The factor theorem states that $(x-c)$ is a factor of $f(x)$ if $f(c)=0$.

Example $f(x)=x^3-x^2-4x-6$ given: $x=3$ is zero $(3)^3-(3)^2-4(3)-6=0$	In this case, since $f(3)=0$, then x - 3 is a factor of $f(x)$. **Note:** +3 must change so the factor is $x-3$.
$\begin{array}{r\|rrrr} 3 & 1 & -1 & -4 & -6 \\ & & 3 & 6 & 6 \\ \hline & 1 & 2 & 2 & \boxed{0} \end{array}$ $f(x)=(x^2+2x+2)(x-3)$ x^2 term, x term, constant	Divide $(x$ - 3) into $f(x)$. Synthetic division gives you coefficients of 1, 2, and 2. The new trinomial shows (x^2+2x+2) and the factor $(x$ - 3). A good check on your process is to remember that the remainder must be 0.
$0=(x^2+2x+2)$ $x=\frac{-2\pm\sqrt{4-8}}{2}$ $x=\frac{-2\pm\sqrt{-4}}{2}$ $x=\frac{-2\pm 2i}{2}=-1\pm i$ the roots: 3, $-1+i$, $-1-i$	At this point, we know one root, 3, and the trinomial, x^2+2x+2. To find the other roots factor or use the quadratic formula. The formula gives us two more roots, $-1+i$ and $-1-i$. So, we have three roots, which we would expect for a polynomial of three degrees.

Example $f(x)=x^3-2x^2-5x+6$ $x=1$ is a zero $f(1)=0$ find all other zeros 1 | 1 -2 -5 6 1 -1 -6 1 -1 -6 | 0 $f(x)=(x-1)(x^2-x-6)$	In this problem, you know that $x=1$ is a zero, which means that $(x-1)$ is a factor. Do synthetic division to find the polynomial after factoring. $f(x)$ now equals the two factors multiplying.
$=(x-1)(x+2)(x-3)=0$ zeros of $f(x)$ are $x=1, -2, 3$	In this example, the trinomial easily factors and now $f(x)$ has three factors, which means three zeros: 1, -2, and 3.
$f(x)=(x-1)(x^2-x-6)$ $=(x-1)(x+2)(x-3)=0$ zeros of $f(x)$ are $x=1, -2, 3$ 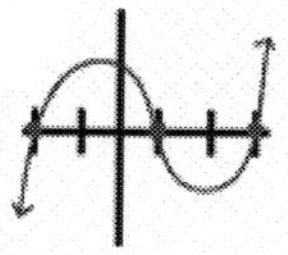	Having three real number zeros means that the curve crosses the x-axis three times. This graph shows how that looks.

Sample problems:

1. Given that $f(x)=x^2-4x-21$ and that $f(-3)=0$, find all zeros of $f(x)$.
   Solution: $x=-3$, $x=7$
   Explanation: If $f(-3)=0$, then -3 is a zero of $f(x)$ and $x+3$ is a factor of $f(x)$.
   Factor $f(x)$ into $x+3$ and a second binomial: $f(x)=x^2-4x-21=(x+3)(x-7)$.
   Set the second factor equal to 0 and solve for x: $x-7=0$; $x=7$.
   The zeros are $x=-3$ and $x=7$.

2. Given that $f(x)=6x^2-126x+540$ and that $f(15)=0$, find all zeros of $f(x)$.
   Solution: $x=15$, $x=6$
   Explanation: If $f(15)=0$, then 15 is a zero of $f(x)$ and $x-15$ is a factor of $f(x)$.
   Divide $f(x)$ by $x-15$ to find a second factor:
   $$\begin{array}{r|rrr} 15 & 6 & -126 & 540 \\ & & 90 & -540 \\ \hline & 6 & -36 & 0 \end{array}$$
   Therefore, $6x-36$ is a second factor of $f(x)$ and $f(x)=(x-15)(6x-36)$.
   Set the second factor equal to 0 and solve for x: $6x-36=0$; $x=\frac{36}{6}=6$.
   The second zero is 6. The zeros are $x=15$ and $x=6$.

3. Given that $f(x)=2x^3-5x^2-22x-15$ and that $f(-1)=0$, find all zeros of $f(x)$.
   Solution: $x=-1$, $x=5$, $x=-\frac{3}{2}$
   Explanation: If $f(-1)=0$, then -1 is a zero of $f(x)$ and $x+1$ is a factor of $f(x)$.
   Divide $f(x)$ by $x+1$ to find a second factor:
   $$\begin{array}{r|rrrr} -1 & 2 & -5 & -22 & -15 \\ & & -2 & 7 & 15 \\ \hline & 2 & -7 & -15 & 0 \end{array}$$
   Therefore, $2x^2-7x-15$ is a second factor of $f(x)$ and $f(x)=(x+1)(2x^2-7x-15)$.
   Set the second factor equal to 0 and solve for x: $2x^2-7x-15=0$; $(2x+3)(x-5)=0$;
   $2x+3=0$ or $x-5=0$; $x=-\frac{3}{2}$ or $x=5$. The zeros are $x=-1$, $x=5$, and $x=-\frac{3}{2}$.

Practice problems: *(Answers on page: 746)*

1. Given that $f(x)=x^2-12x-20$ and that $f(10)=0$, find all zeros of $f(x)$.
2. Given that $f(x)=x^3+3x^2-x-3$ and that $f(-3)=0$, find all zeros of $f(x)$.

3. Given that $f(x) = 2x^3 - 3x^2 - 39x + 20$ and that $f(5) = 0$, find all zeros of $f(x)$.

Review questions: *(Answers to odd questions on page: 746)*

1. Given that $f(x) = x^2 + 7x - 60$ and that $f(-12) = 0$, find all zeros of $f(x)$.
2. Given that $f(x) = x^2 - 20x - 800$ and that $f(40) = 0$, find all zeros of $f(x)$.
3. Given that $f(x) = x^3 + x^2 - 4x - 4$ and that $f(-1) = 0$, find all zeros of $f(x)$.
4. Given that $f(x) = 3x^3 - 31x^2 + 96x - 80$ and that $f(4) = 0$, find all zeros of $f(x)$.
5. Given that $f(x) = 6x^3 - 35x^2 - 8x + 12$ and that $f(6) = 0$, find all zeros of $f(x)$.

Presenting the Rational Zero Theorem

- A rational number is a fraction. An irrational number is a radical or imaginary number that cannot be written as a fraction.
- If the polynomial $f(x) = a_n x^n + a_{n-1} x^{x-1} + \ldots a_1 x + a_0$ has integer coefficients, then every rational zero of f has the form $\frac{p}{q}$ where p and q have no common factors other than 1, p is a factor of a_0, and q is a factor of a_n. (The factors of a_0 and a_n include all positive and negative factors.)
- The **rational zero theorem** says that every rational zero for a function takes the form of a fraction with the numerator being a factor of the constant that ends the function and the denominator being a factor of the coefficient of the highest power in the function.
- To find all rational zeros, make a list of the factors of the final constant and the beginning coefficient. Combine these factors in all unique possibilities with the constant's factors in the numerator and the coefficient's factors in the denominator. Substitute each of these into the function, and each one that yields f (x) = 0 is a rational zero.

$f(x)=(3x-1)(x+2)(2x-5)=0$ $3x=1$ $\quad 2x=5$ zeros: $x=\frac{1}{3}$ $\quad x=-2$ $\quad x=\frac{5}{2}$	Because this function is already factored, its zeros are easy to find.
$f(x)=(3x-1)(x+2)(2x-5)=0$ $=6x^3$ + blah blah + junk $+10$	To see how the **rational zero theorem** works, multiply the factors together and focus your attention on the 6, which is the coefficient of the highest power, and the 10, which is the final constant.
all possible factors of the coefficient of the highest power: ±1, ±2, ±3, ±6 all possible factors of the constant term: ±1, ±2, ±5, ±10	Make a list of all the factors of 6. Also make a list of all the factors of 10. The theorem says that every rational zero must be a fraction with a factor of 10 in the numerator, and a factor of 6 in the denominator.
$f(x)=(3x-1)(x+2)(2x-5)=0$ $=6x^3$ + blah blah + junk $+10$ $3x=1$ $\quad 2x=5$ zeros: $x=\frac{1}{3}$ $\quad x=-2$ (circled) $\quad x=\frac{5}{2}$	One zero is 2. It fits the rule that every possible zero is on the list of *p*/*q* values. "*p*" is all the factors of 10. "*q*" is all the factors of 6. Your zero, 2, has a numerator of 2, which is a factor of 10. Its denominator is 1, which is a factor of 6.
$3x=1$ $\quad 2x=5$ zeros: $x=\frac{1}{3}$ $\quad x=-2$ $\quad x=\frac{5}{2}$ (circled)	Another zero is 5/2. It also has a factor of 10 in the numerator, and a factor of 6 in the denominator. You can check every rational zero and find that the theorem applies.

Sample problems:

1. List all the possible rational zeros of $f(x)=x^3+5x^2+x-3$, using the rational zero theorem.
   Solution: $x=\pm 1,\ \pm 3$
   Explanation: From the rational zero theorem, if p is a factor of -3 and q is a factor of 1, then $\frac{p}{q}$ is a possible rational zero of $f(x)$. Factor p and q: $p=\pm 1,\ \pm 3$ and $q=\pm 1$.
   So the possible rational zeros are $\frac{p}{q}$: $\pm 1,\ \pm 3$.

2. List all the possible rational zeros of $f(x)=21x^3+18x^2+9x-12$, using the rational zero theorem.
   Solution: $x=\pm 1,\ \pm 2,\ \pm 3,\ \pm 4,\ \pm 6,\ \pm 12,\ \pm\frac{1}{3},\ \pm\frac{2}{3},\ \pm\frac{4}{3},\ \pm\frac{1}{7},\ \pm\frac{2}{7},\ \pm\frac{3}{7},$ $\pm\frac{4}{7},\ \pm\frac{6}{7},\ \pm\frac{12}{7},\ \pm\frac{1}{21},\pm\frac{2}{21},\ \pm\frac{4}{21}$
   Explanation: From the rational zero theorem, if p is a factor of -12 and q is a factor of 21, then $\frac{p}{q}$ is a possible rational zero of $f(x)$.
   Factor p and q: $p=\pm 1,\ \pm 2,\ \pm 3,\ \pm 4,\ \pm 6,\ \pm 12$, and $q=\pm 1,\ \pm 3,\ \pm 7,\ \pm 21$.
   So the possible rational zeros are $\frac{p}{q}$: $\pm 1,\ \pm 2,\ \pm 3,\ \pm 4,\ \pm 6,\ \pm 12,\ \pm\frac{1}{3},\ \pm\frac{2}{3},$ $\pm\frac{4}{3},\ \pm\frac{1}{7},\ \pm\frac{2}{7},\ \pm\frac{3}{7},\ \pm\frac{4}{7},\ \pm\frac{6}{7},\ \pm\frac{12}{7},\ \pm\frac{1}{21},\ \pm\frac{2}{21},\ \pm\frac{4}{21}$.

3. List all the possible rational zeros of $f(x)=20x^3-5x^2-9x-18$, using the rational zero theorem.
   Solution: $x=\pm 1,\ \pm 2,\ \pm 3,\ \pm 6,\ \pm 9,\ \pm 18,\ \pm\frac{1}{2},\ \pm\frac{3}{2},\ \pm\frac{9}{2},\ \pm\frac{1}{4},\ \pm\frac{3}{4},\ \pm\frac{9}{4},\ \pm\frac{1}{5},$ $\pm\frac{2}{5},\ \pm\frac{3}{5},\ \pm\frac{6}{5},\pm\frac{9}{5},\ \pm\frac{18}{5},\ \pm\frac{1}{10},\ \pm\frac{3}{10},\ \pm\frac{9}{10},\ \pm\frac{1}{20},\ \pm\frac{3}{20},\ \pm\frac{9}{20}$
   Explanation: From the rational zero theorem, p is a factor of -18: $\pm 1,\ \pm 2,\ \pm 3,$ $\pm 6,\ \pm 9,\ \pm 18$ and q is a factor of 20: $\pm 1,\ \pm 2,\ \pm 4,\ \pm 5,\ \pm 10,\ \pm 20$. The possible rational zeros are $\frac{p}{q}$ or $\pm 1,\ \pm 2,\ \pm 3,\ \pm 6,\ \pm 9,\ \pm 18,\ \pm\frac{1}{2},\ \pm\frac{3}{2},\ \pm\frac{9}{2},\ \pm\frac{1}{4},\ \pm\frac{3}{4},$ $\pm\frac{9}{4},\ \pm\frac{1}{5},\ \pm\frac{2}{5},\ \pm\frac{3}{5},\ \pm\frac{6}{5},\ \pm\frac{9}{5},\ \pm\frac{18}{5},\ \pm\frac{1}{10},\ \pm\frac{3}{10},\ \pm\frac{9}{10},\ \pm\frac{1}{20},\ \pm\frac{3}{20},\ \pm\frac{9}{20}$.

Practice problems: *(Answers on page: 746)*

1. List all the possible rational zeros of $f(x)=x^3+3x^2+x+6$, using the rational zero theorem.
2. List all the possible rational zeros of $f(x)=5x^4+13x^2-5$, using the rational zero theorem.
3. List all the possible rational zeros of $f(x)=2x^3+6x^2+6x+14$, using the rational zero theorem.

Review questions: *(Answers to odd questions on page: 746)*

1. List all the possible rational zeros of $f(x)=x^3+7x^2+x-10$, using the rational zero theorem.
2. List all the possible rational zeros of $f(x)=3x^3+8x^2-2x-6$, using the rational zero theorem.
3. List all the possible rational zeros of $f(x)=3x^4+x^2-9$, using the rational zero theorem.
4. List all the possible rational zeros of $f(x)=5x^3+2x^2-7x+15$, using the rational zero theorem.
5. List all the possible rational zeros of $f(x)=5x^3-8x^2+5x-10$, using the rational zero theorem.

Considering Possible Solutions

- If the polynomial $f(x)=a_n x^n + a_{n-1}x^{x-1} + \ldots a_1 x + a_0$ has integer coefficients, then every rational zero of f has the form $\frac{p}{q}$ where p and q have no common factors other than 1, p is a factor of a_0, and q is a factor of a_n. (The factors of a_0 and a_n include all positive and negative factors.)
- Any function of degree n will have n roots, or zeroes, in some mixture of real and imaginary numbers.

The Rational Zero Theorem $f(x)=a_N x^N + a_{N-1}x^{N-1}+\ldots+a_1x+a_0$ *If $\frac{P}{Q}$ is a 0 of f(x) then P is a factor of a_0 and Q is a factor of a_N* $f(x)=2x^2+7x+3$ *eight possible candidates* candidates: ±1, ±1/2, ±3, ±3/2 all possible factors of 3: ±1, ±3 — all possible factors of 2: ±1, ±2 *Take all possible P's over all possible Q's and you have a list of all possible candidates for zeros.*	To create your list of possible zeros for this $f(x)$: Look at the constant ending the function: 3. Look at the coefficient of the highest-degree term in the function x^2: 2. 1. List all the factors of 3 2. List all the factors of 2 3. Make all the possible numbers with the factors of 3 as the numerators and the factors of 2 as the denominators. **Note:** Remember to consider that every factor can be both + and –.
$=(2x+1)(x+3)$ candidates: ~~±1~~, ±1/2, ±3, ±3/2 all possible factors of 3: ±1, ±3 — all possible factors of 2: ±1, ±2 *Take all possible P's over all possible Q's and you have a list of all possible candidates for zeros.*	Now substitute each possibility into the function in place of x. Any value for which $f(x) = 0$ is a root of the function. From our list of eight possibilities, two created $f(x) = 0$. So, we know that our zeroes are –1/2 and –3.
or we could have factored it into: $=(2x+1)(x+3)$ and found our zeros from there zeros: -1/2, -3	If the function factors, you can do that process and derive the same answers.

Sample problems:

1. According to the rational zero theorem, which of the following choices is NOT a candidate to be a zero of $f(x)=4x^2+7x^2-12$: 4, 3, 7, or 6?
   Solution: 7
   Explanation: According to the rational zero theorem, all the possible real number zeros of a polynomial will be found in the list composed of fractions made up of the factors of the constant in the numerator and factors of the coefficient of the term with highest degree in the denominator. In this case, that means fractions made up of all the factors of 12 over all the factors of 4. The factors of 12 are $\pm 1,\ \pm 2,\ \pm 3,\ \pm 4,\ \pm 6$ and ± 12. The factors of 4 are $\pm 1,\ \pm 2$ and ± 4. The pool of possible zeros for the polynomial is: $\pm 1,\ \pm 2,\ \pm 3,\ \pm 4,\ \pm 6,\ \pm 12,\ \pm\frac{1}{2},\ \pm\frac{3}{2},\ \pm\frac{1}{4},\ \pm\frac{3}{4}$. Thus, 7 is not a possible zero.

2. According to the rational zero theorem, which of the following choices is NOT a candidate to be a zero of $f(x) = 38x^3 + 43x - 10$: $\frac{5}{19}$, $-\frac{5}{19}$, 3, or -2?

Solution: 3

Explanation: According to the rational zero theorem, all the possible real number zeros of a polynomial will be found in the list composed of fractions made up of the factors of the constant in the numerator and factors of the coefficient of the term with highest degree in the denominator. In this case, that means fractions made up of all the factors of 10 over all the factors of 38. The factors of 10 are ± 1, ± 2, ± 5, and ± 10. The factors of 38 are ± 1, ± 2, ± 19 and ± 38. The pool of possible zeros for the polynomial is: ± 1, ± 2, ± 5, ± 10, $\pm\frac{1}{2}$, $\pm\frac{5}{2}$, $\pm\frac{1}{19}$, $\pm\frac{1}{38}$, $\pm\frac{2}{19}$, $\pm\frac{5}{19}$, $\pm\frac{5}{38}$, $\pm\frac{10}{19}$. Thus, 3 is not a possible zero.

3. According to the rational zero theorem, which of the following choices is NOT a candidate to be a zero of $f(x) = 33x^3 - 19x - 12$: 17, $\frac{4}{11}$, $-\frac{4}{11}$, or -4?

Solution: 17

Explanation: According to the rational zero theorem, all the possible real number zeros of a polynomial will be found in the list composed of fractions made up of the factors of the constant in the numerator and factors of the coefficient of the term with highest degree in the denominator. In this case, that means fractions made up of all the factors of 12 over all the factors of 33. The factors of 12 are ± 1, ± 2, ± 3, ± 4, ± 6 and ± 12. The factors of 33 are ± 1, ± 3, ± 11 and ± 33. The pool of possible zeros for the polynomial does not include 17. Thus, 17 is not a possible zero.

Practice problems: *(Answers on page: 746)*

1. According to the rational zero theorem, which of the following choices is NOT a candidate to be a zero of $f(x) = 18x^3 + 30x + 20$: 21, -2, $-\frac{10}{9}$, or $\frac{10}{9}$?
2. According to the rational zero theorem, which of the following choices is NOT a candidate to be a zero of $f(x) = 22x^3 + 34x + 24$: $\frac{12}{11}$, $-\frac{12}{11}$, 11, or -4?
3. According to the rational zero theorem, which of the following choices is NOT a candidate to be a zero of $f(x) = 36x^3 - 47x + 44$: -2, $-\frac{11}{9}$, $\frac{11}{9}$, or 25?

Review questions: *(Answers to odd questions on page: 746)*

1. According to the rational zero theorem, which of the following choices is NOT a candidate to be a zero of $f(x) = 39x^3 - 11x - 18$: -3, $-\frac{6}{13}$, 12, or $\frac{6}{13}$?
2. According to the rational zero theorem, which of the following choices is NOT a candidate to be a zero of $f(x) = 20x^3 + 21x - 36$: $-\frac{9}{5}$, $\frac{9}{5}$, -4, or 8?
3. According to the rational zero theorem, which of the following choices is NOT a candidate to be a zero of $f(x) = 32x^3 + 25x - 34$: -2, $\frac{17}{16}$, $-\frac{17}{16}$, or 4?
4. According to the rational zero theorem, which of the following choices is NOT a candidate to be a zero of $f(x) = 48x^3 - 38x + 16$: $\frac{1}{3}$, $-\frac{1}{3}$, -2, or 13?

5. According to the rational zero theorem, which of the following choices is NOT a candidate to be a zero of $f(x) = 26x^3 - 50x - 44$: 24, $-\frac{22}{13}$, -2, or $\frac{22}{13}$?

Finding Polynomials Given Zeros, Degree, and One Point

- The **factor theorem** states that $(x - c)$ is a factor of $f(x)$ if $f(c) = 0$.
- A real **zero** of a polynomial is a point where the graph intersects the x-axis. Also, if you substitute that point into the polynomial, its value equals 0; i.e., $f(x) = 0$ for $(x - c)$.
- Given three zeroes and one point on the curve, the third degree polynomial function can be determined because only one function will have all four elements in common.

Example Find the cubic polynomial whose zeros (roots) are at $x=-3$, $x=1$, and $x=4$. Given $f(2)=30$ $f(x)=(x-{-3})(x-1)(x-4)$ *by the factor theorem, these are all factors*	Given this information, you can easily show all three factors multiplying together.
$f(x)= a(x-{-3})(x-1)(x-4)$ $f(2)= a(2-{-3})(2-1)(2-4)$ $f(2)= a(5)(1)(-2)=30$ $-10a=30$ $a=-3$	But there may be some constant other than 1 multiplying with these factors. You know that when $x = 2, f(x) = 30$. Set up the factors and solve for a.
$f(x)=-3(x+3)(x-1)(x-4)$	Substitute your –3 in place of a in $f(x)$.
$f(x)=-3(x^2+2x-3)(x-4)$ $f(x)=-3(x^3+2x^2-3x-4x^2-8x+12)$ $f(x)=-3(x^3-2x^2-11x+12)$	Multiply the factors together to get $f(x)$.
Example Find the cubic whose roots (zeros) are $x=-1$, 2, and 4. Given $f(1)=3$ $f(x)= a(x-{-1})(x-2)(x-4)$	In this example, you quickly write all the factors and note that you must find a.
$f(1)= a(2)(-1)(-3)=3$ $6a=3$ $a=\frac{1}{2}$ $f(x)=\frac{1}{2}(x+1)(x-2)(x-4)$	Since you know that $f(x) = 3$ when $x = 1$, you substitute in for x and solve for a. Next you substitute your ½ in for a.
$f(x)=\frac{1}{2}(x^2-x-2)(x-4)$ $=\frac{1}{2}(x^3-5x^2+2x+8)$ $\boxed{=\frac{1}{2}x^3-\frac{5}{2}x^2+x+4}$	Finally, you multiply all the factors together and you have your function.

Sample problems:

1. Find a third degree polynomial, $f(x)$, such that $f(x)$ has roots $x = 2$, $x = 3$, and $x = 4$, and $f(1) = -6$.
   Solution: $f(x) = x^3 - 9x^2 + 26x - 24$
   Explanation: Express each root (or zero) as a factor: $x = 2 \Rightarrow (x-2)$; $x = 3 \Rightarrow (x-3)$; $x = 4 \Rightarrow (x-4)$, so $f(x) = a(x-2)(x-3)(x-4)$. Use the given point, $f(1) = -6$, to determine a: $-6 = a(1-2)(1-3)(1-4)$; $-6 = a(-1)(-2)(-3)$; $-6 = -6a$; $a = 1$.
   Substitute $a = 1$ into the polynomial and simplify:
   $f(x) = 1(x-2)(x-3)(x-4) = x^3 - 9x^2 + 26x - 24$.

2. Find a third degree polynomial, $f(x)$, such that $f(x)$ has roots $x=-2$, $x=1$, and $x=5$, and $f(0)=2$.
   Solution: $f(x)=\frac{1}{5}x^3-\frac{4}{5}x^2-\frac{7}{5}x+2$
   Explanation: Express each zero as a factor: $x=-2 \Rightarrow (x+2)$; $x=1 \Rightarrow (x-1)$; $x=5 \Rightarrow (x-5)$, so $f(x)=a(x+2)(x-1)(x-5)$. Use the given point, $f(0)=2$, to determine a: $2=a(0+2)(0-1)(0-5)$; $2=a(2)(-1)(-5)$; $2=10a$; $a=\frac{1}{5}$.
   Substitute $a=\frac{1}{5}$ into the polynomial and simplify: $f(x)=\frac{1}{5}(x+2)(x-1)(x-5)=$ $\frac{1}{5}(x^3-4x^2-7x+10)=\frac{1}{5}x^3-\frac{4}{5}x^2-\frac{7}{5}x+2.$

3. Find a polynomial, $f(x)$, such that $f(x)$ has three roots, two of the roots are $x=3$ and $x=5$, the leading coefficient is 1, and $f(2)=-3$.
   Solution: $f(x)=x^3-11x^2+39x-45$
   Explanation: Since $f(x)$ has three roots, let the third root be c.
   Express each root as a factor: $x=3 \Rightarrow (x-3)$; $x=5 \Rightarrow (x-5)$; $x=c \Rightarrow (x-c)$, so $f(x)=1(x-3)(x-5)(x-c)$. Use the given point, $f(2)=-3$, to find c:
   $-3=1(2-3)(2-5)(2-c)$; $-3=1(-1)(-3)(2-c)$; $-3=3(2-c)$; $-1=2-c$; $c=3$
   Substitute $c=3$ into the polynomial and simplify:
   $f(x)=1(x-3)(x-5)(x-3)=x^3-11x^2-8x^2+39x-45.$

Practice problems: *(Answers on page: 746)*

1. Find a third degree polynomial, $f(x)$, such that $f(x)$ has roots $x=-1$, $x=1$, and $x=5$, and $f(0)=15$.
2. Find a third degree polynomial, $f(x)$, such that $f(x)$ has roots $x=-3$, $x=-2$, and $x=1$, and $f(2)=10$.
3. Find a polynomial, $f(x)$, such that $f(x)$ has three roots, two of the roots are $x=-5$ and $x=2$, the leading coefficient is -3, and $f(-2)=-36$.

Review questions: *(Answers to odd questions on page: 746)*

1. Find a third degree polynomial, $f(x)$, such that $f(x)$ has roots $x=0$, $x=2$, and $x=5$, and $f(3)=-12$.
2. Find a third degree polynomial, $f(x)$, such that $f(x)$ has roots $x=-3$, $x=-1$, and $x=2$, and $f(0)=6$.
3. Find a third degree polynomial, $f(x)$, such that $f(x)$ has roots $x=-5$, $x=-2$, and $x=5$, and $f(10)=540$.
4. Find a polynomial, $f(x)$, such that $f(x)$ has three roots, two of the roots are $x=-4$ and $x=1$, the leading coefficient is 2, and $f(-3)=8$.
5. Find a polynomial, $f(x)$, such that $f(x)$ has three roots, two of the roots are $x=-3$ and $x=6$, the leading coefficient is $\frac{2}{3}$, and $f(0)=-12$.

Finding all Zeros and Multiplicities of a Polynomial

- A real **zero**, or root, is a point where a curve crosses or touches the x-axis.
- **Multiplicity** of a zero is the number of times the value is a solution for the polynomial.
- A curve which just touches the x-axis, but doesn't cross it, is said to have a zero at that point with multiplicity of two.

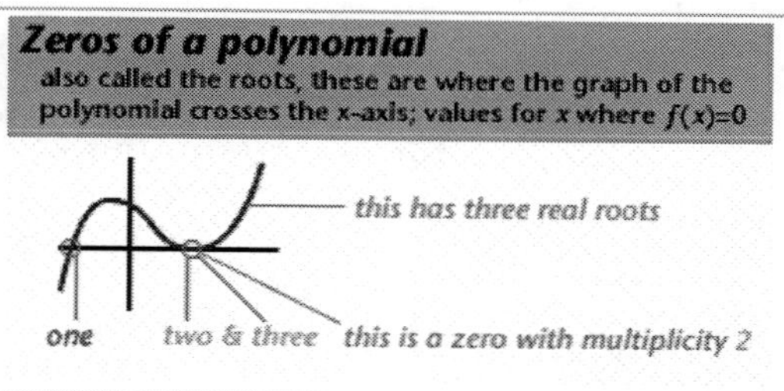

This curve has roots with several types of multiplicity.

There is one root with multiplicity one because it crosses the x-axis. A second root has multiplicity two where it touches, but does not cross, the x-axis.

Example What are the zeros and their multiplicity for x^2-4x+4?

$$x^2-4x+4=0$$
$$(x-2)(x-2)=0$$
$$(x-2)^2=0$$

This function has one zero, $x=2$, which has multiplicity two because it takes two of them to complete the function.

Example Find all zeros and their multiplicity for $7x^3+x$.

$$7x^3+x=0$$
$$x(7x^2+1)=0$$
$$x=0 \text{ and } 7x^2+1=0$$
$$7x^2=-1$$
$$x^2=-\frac{1}{7}$$
$$x=\pm\sqrt{-\frac{1}{7}}$$
$$x=\pm\sqrt{\frac{1}{7}}\,i$$

the three roots

This function has three roots. They are the real root, 0, and the two imaginary roots,

$+\sqrt{\frac{1}{7}}i$ and $-\sqrt{\frac{1}{7}}i$.

Each root is used only once, so each one has a multiplicity of one.

Example Find the zeros and multiplicity for $f(x)=(x+1)^2(x-1)^3(x^2-10)$.

$$f(x)=(x+1)^2(x-1)^3(x^2-10)$$
$$0=(x+1)^2(x-1)^3(x^2-10)$$

This function has roots of -1, 1, $\sqrt{10}$, and $-\sqrt{10}$.

The root -1 has multiplicity two because it is used twice in $(x+1)$.
The root 1 has multiplicity three because it is used three times in $(x-1)$.
The root has multiplicity one because it is used only once.
The root - likewise has multiplicity one.

Sample problems:

1. Given that $f(x)=(x-1)(x+5)^3$, find each zero of $f(x)$ and state its multiplicity.
   Solution: $x=1$, multiplicity 1; $x=-5$, multiplicity 3
   Explanation: The zeros of $f(x)$ are located at c for each factor $x-c$ and the multiplicity is determined by the number of times that factor occurs in the polynomial, or the exponent of the factor. The first factor of $f(x)$ is $x-1$, thus $f(x)$ has a zero at $x=1$ with multiplicity 1. The second factor of $f(x)$ is $(x+5)^3$, thus $f(x)$ has a second zero at $x=-5$. This factor occurs three times in $f(x)$, so the multiplicity of $x=-5$ is three.

2. Given that $f(x)=(2x+1)^2(x^2-9)$, find each zero of $f(x)$ and state its multiplicity.
   Solution: $x=-\frac{1}{2}$, multiplicity 2; $x=-3$, multiplicity 1; $x=3$, multiplicity 1
   Explanation: Set the first factor equal to zero and solve for x: $2x+1=0$; $x=-\frac{1}{2}$.
   Thus, $x=-\frac{1}{2}$ is a zero and its multiplicity is 2 (since the exponent of $(2x+1)$ is 2).
   Set the second factor equal to zero and solve x: $x^2-9=0$; $x^2=9$; $x=\pm\sqrt{9}=\pm3$.
   Thus, $f(x)$ also has zeros at 3 and -3, each with multiplicity 1.

3. Given that $f(x)=x(x+3)^5(x^2+4)$, find each zero of $f(x)$ and state its multiplicity.
   Solution: $x=0$, multiplicity 1; $x=-3$, multiplicity 5; $x=2i$, multiplicity 1; $x=-2i$, multiplicity 1
   Explanation: Set each factor equal to zero and solve for x:
   $x \to x=0$, multiplicity 1
   $(x+3)^5 \to x+3=0$; $x=-3$, multiplicity 5
   $(x^2+4) \to x^2+4=0$; $x^2=-4$; $x=\sqrt{-4}=\pm2i$, multiplicity 1

Practice problems: *(Answers on page: 746)*

1. Given that $f(x)=(x+2)^3(x-1)^2$, find each zero of $f(x)$ and state its multiplicity.

2. Given that $f(x) = x^2(x+1)^5(x^2+8x+16)$, find each zero of $f(x)$ and state its multiplicity.

3. Given that $f(x) = (3x-1)^2(x^2+1)^3$, find each zero of $f(x)$ and state its multiplicity.

Review questions: *(Answers to odd questions on page: 746)*

1. Given that $f(x) = x^5$, find each zero of $f(x)$ and state its multiplicity.
2. Given that $f(x) = x^2 + 5x + 6$, find each zero of $f(x)$ and state its multiplicity.
3. Given that $f(x) = x(x-2)(x+1)^3$, find each zero of $f(x)$ and state its multiplicity.
4. Given that $f(x) = (x^3+8x^2+7x)(x^2-25)^4$, find each zero of $f(x)$ and state its multiplicity.
5. Given that $f(x) = x^2(2x-5)^4(x^2+9x)$, find each zero of $f(x)$ and state its multiplicity.

Finding the Real Zeros for a Polynomial

- The **factor theorem** says $(x - c)$ must be a factor of the polynomial if it divides into the polynomial with a remainder of 0.
- A real **zero**, or root, is a point where a curve crosses or touches the x-axis.
- Difference of two cubes: $x^3 - y^3 = (x-y)(x^2+xy+y^2)$.

SUPPOSE: $f(x)=x(x-4)(x-1)(x+7)$ $x(x-4)(x-1)(x+7)=0$ *After you set it equal to zero, one of these terms must equal zero.*	Set this function equal to 0. Then solving for the roots is easy. Since it's already factored, set each factor equal to 0. One of the factors must equal 0 for the product to be 0. Now, solve each factor for x. This example has 4 real roots. They are 0, 4, 1, and –7.
SUPPOSE: $f(x)=2x^3-7x^2-15x$ $=x(2x^2-7x-15)=0$ $x(2x+3)(x-5)=0$	This example also factors. You can see that there are three real roots. They are 0, -3/2, and 5.
SUPPOSE: $f(x)=x^3-1$ $=x^3-1=0$ $=x^3-1=(x-1)(x^2+x+1)=0$	For this function, one factor can easily be done leaving a trinomial.
Quadratic Formula: $x = \frac{-b \pm \sqrt{b^2 - 4ac}}{2a}$ **Discriminant:** $b^2 - 4ac$ $(x^2+x+1)=0$ $1-4=-3$	The trinomial cannot be factored. Because the discriminant from the quadratic formula has a negative value for this function, you quickly learn that the remaining two roots will be imaginary numbers.
x=1 is the only real zero 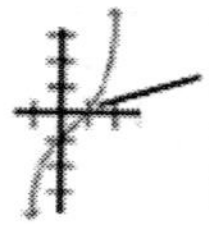 cubic only crosses the x-axis once, at x=1	The graph of the curve supports your finding that there is only one real root. The curve crosses the x-axis in only one location. The other roots must be imaginary.

Sample problems:

1. Given $f(x) = (3x-9)(2x^2+8)(5x-12)^2$, find all real zeros of $f(x)$.
   Solution: $x = 3$, $x = \frac{12}{5}$
   Explanation: Set each factor equal to 0 and solve for x. $3x-9=0;\ \ x=3$, $2x^2+8=0;\ \ 2x^2=-8;\ \ x^2=-4;\ \ x=\pm\sqrt{-4},\ \ 5x-12=0;\ \ x=\frac{12}{5}$.
   The real zeros are $x=3$ and $x=\frac{12}{5}$, $x=\pm\sqrt{-4}$ is imaginary and not real.

2. Given $f(x)=(4x^2-9)(x-1)^2(x^2+1)$, find all real zeros of $f(x)$.
   Solution: $x=\pm\frac{3}{2}$, $x=1$
   Explanation: Set each factor equal to 0 and solve for x. $4x^2-9=0;\ \ x^2=\frac{9}{4};$ $x=\pm\sqrt{\frac{9}{4}}=\pm\frac{3}{2},\ \ x-1=0;\ \ x=1,\ \ x^2+1=0;\ \ x^2=-1;\ \ x=\sqrt{-1}.$
   The real zeros are $x=\pm\frac{3}{2}$ and $x=1$.

3. Given $f(x)=x^3+2x^2+8x$, find all real zeros of $f(x)$.
   Solution: $x=0$
   Explanation: Set the equation equal to 0 and solve for x.
   $x^3+2x^2+8x=0;\ \ x\left(x^2+2x+8\right)=0;\ \ x=0 \text{ or } x^2+2x+8=0.$
   Use the quadratic formular to solve $x^2+2x+8=0$:
   $$x=\frac{-2\pm\sqrt{2^2-4(1)(8)}}{2(1)}=\frac{-2\pm\sqrt{4-32}}{2}=\frac{-2\pm\sqrt{-28}}{2},$$
   the discriminant is less than 0, so this is not a real zero.
   Thus, the only real zero of $f(x)$ is $x=0$.

Practice problems: *(Answers on page: 746)*

1. Given $f(x)=x\left(x^2+1\right)^3\left(x^2-100\right)^2$, find all real zeros of $f(x)$.
2. Given $f(x)=\left(x^3-x^2\right)\left(x^2+5x+3\right)$, find all real zeros of $f(x)$.
3. Given $f(x)=\left(x^2-9x\right)\left(x^2+5x+7\right)$, find all real zeros of $f(x)$.

Review questions: *(Answers to odd questions on page: 746)*

1. Given $f(x)=\left(4x^2-1\right)^3$, find all real zeros of $f(x)$.
2. Given $f(x)=\left(x^3+x^2\right)$, find all real zeros of $f(x)$.
3. Given $f(x)=\left(x^2-x\right)\left(x^2-3x+1\right)$, find all real zeros of $f(x)$.
4. Given $f(x)=x^3+x^2+2x$, find all real zeros of $f(x)$.
5. Given $f(x)=\left(x^2+15\right)\left(x^2-4x+9\right)$, find all real zeros of $f(x)$.

Using Descartes' Rule of Signs

- **Rene Descartes** (1596 -1650) was significant both to mathematics and to philosophy.
  - He developed the Cartesian system with the x and y axes used for graphing.
  - He developed the rule about possible solutions to functions that is presented here.
  - He posed the still quoted "I think, therefore I am" proof of existence for philosophers.
- **Descartes' rule of signs** informs us about potential roots:
  1. Write the polynomial with highest degree term first and the others following in descending order
  2. Then examine the function when $+x$ is substituted. The number of sign changes from one term to the next tells you the number of positive real roots or that number less some real even number.
  3. Finally look at the function when $-x$ is substituted. The number of sign changes from one term to the next now tells you the number of negative real roots or that number less some real even number.
- The number of real number zeros that exist is never a negative number.

Descartes Rule of Sign • write poly. in descending order with highest exp. first • then look at the # of sign changes of the coefficients $f(x)=x^4-6x^3+4x^2+x-5$ 1 1 1 *three changes in sign*	In this example, there are three sign changes when x is used in the function.
This means there are EITHER three real positive roots OR three minus an even number real positive roots. 	The fact that there are three sign changes tells you that the function has either 3 or 1 positive real roots. The reason for decreasing by 2 is that some of your roots might be complex numbers. Complex roots always come in pairs because if one complex number is a root, its conjugate will also be a root.
to find the number of negative real roots, plug in -x $f(-x)=x^4+6x^3+4x^2-x-5$ *only one change in sign*	To find the number of negative real roots, substitute $-x$ into the function.
the number of negative real roots is either equal to the number of sign changes or the number of sign changes minus an even number. 	There is only one sign change for $-x$. This tells you that there is only one negative real root for the function.

Sample problems:

1. Given $f(x)=4x^4-x^3+4x^2-x-4$, use Descartes' rule of signs to determine the possible number of positive and negative real zeros.
   Solution: 3 or 1 positive; 1 negative
   Explanation: To determine the possible number of positive real zeros for $f(x)$ count the sign changes in $f(x)$ and $f(-x)$: $f(x)=4x^4-x^3+4x^2-x-4$ changes signs 3 times and $f(-x)=4x^4+x^3+4x^2+x-4$ changes signs 1 time.
   Therefore, there are 3 or 1 positive real zeros and 1 negative real zero.

2. Given $f(x)=4x^4+3x^3+2x^2+x+54$, use Descartes' rule of signs to determine the possible number of positive and negative real zeros.
   Solution: 0 positive; 4, 2, or 0 negative
   Explanation: To use Descarte's rule of signs, you must count the sign changes for $f(x)=4x^4+3x^3+2x+x+5$ and $f(-x)=4x^4-3x^3+2x^2-x+5$.
   There are no sign changes for $f(x)$ and 4 sign changes for $f(-x)$. Therefore, there are no positive real zeros for $f(x)$ and 4, 2, or no negative real zeros for $f(x)$.

3. Given $h(x) = -5x^5 + 6x^4 + 3x^3 - 4x^2 + 5x + 94$, use Descartes' rule of signs to determine the possible number of positive and negative real zeros.
   Solution: 3 or 1 positive; 2 or 0 negative
   Explanation: To use Descartes' rule of signs, find the number of sign changes for
   $h(x) = -5x^5 + 6x^4 + 3x^3 - 4x^2 + 5x + 9$ and $h(-x) = 5x^5 + 6x^4 - 3x^3 - 4x^2 - 5x + 9$.
   $h(x)$ changes sign 3 times and $h(-x)$ changes sign 2 times. So there are 3 or 1 positive real zeros and 2 or 0 negative real zeros.

Practice problems: *(Answers on page: 746)*

1. Given $f(x) = x^4 - x^2$, use Descartes' rule of signs to determine the possible number of positive and negative real zeros.
2. Given $f(x) = -3x^7 + 4x^4 + 3x^2 - 2x - 1$, use Descartes' rule of signs to determine the possible number of positive and negative real zeros.
3. Given $f(x) = 3x^6 - 4x^4 + 3x^3 + 2x^2 - x - 3$, use Descartes' rule of signs to determine the possible number of positive and negative real zeros.

Review questions: *(Answers to odd questions on page: 746)*

1. Given $f(x) = -4x^7 + x^3 - x^2 + 2$, use Descartes' rule of signs to determine the possible number of positive and negative real zeros.
2. Given $f(x) = 2x^6 - 3x^2 - x + 1$, use Descartes' rule of signs to determine the possible number of positive and negative real zeros.number
3. Given $f(x) = 3x^3 - 2x^2 + x + 2$, use Descartes' rule of signs to determine the possible number of positive and negative real zeros.
4. Given $f(x) = -x^4 + x^2 - 1$, use Descartes' rule of signs to determine the possible number of positive and negative real zeros.
5. Given $f(x) = x^5 + x^4 + x^2 + x + 1$, use Descartes' rule of signs to determine the possible number of positive and negative real zeros.

Finding the Zeros of a Polynomial from Start to Finish

- The **factor theorem** says that $(x - c)$ is a factor when $f(c) = 0$.
- Finding all the zeros of a polynomial involves:
  1. Listing all the possible real number candidates.
  2. Testing the candidates to see which ones work.
  3. Using division to factor out the $(x - c)$ when you find a zero, or root.
- Every rational integral function of n degree has exactly n roots.
  - Some may be repeated.
  - Some may be complex numbers, which always come in conjugate pairs.
- The rational root theorem says that every possible real number root is in the form of p/q:
  - p is a factor of the constant at the end of the function, and
  - q is a factor of the coefficient of the highest power.

Find the rational roots for $f(x)=x^3+3x^2-6x-8$ *to find all the zeros (roots) set equal to zero and solve for x* **candidates:** $\pm1, \pm2, \pm4, \pm8 \,\|\, \pm1$	In this example, p is the factors of -8: $\pm1, \pm2, \pm4, \pm8$. The values for q are: ±1. All possible p/q values are $\pm1, \pm2, \pm4, \pm8$.

test the candidates: $f(1) = (1)^3+3(1)^2-6(1)-8=-10 \quad f(1) \neq 0$ not a root $f(-1) = (-1)^3+3(-1)^2-6(-1)-8=-1+3+6-8=0$ it's a root! $f(2) = (2)^3+3(2)^2-6(2)-8=8+12-12-8=0$ it's a root!	The next step is to substitute p/q values into $f(x)$ searching for any $f(c) = 0$. Both -1 and 2 create $f(c) = 0$. That indicates that both $(x+1)$ and $(x-2)$ are factors of $f(x)$.
if 2 is a zero, then x-2 is a factor $2 \,\|\, 1 \quad 3 \quad -6 \quad -8$ *flip the sign and bring down the coefficients from f(x)*	**Note:** The c -value changes signs as a factor because the formula is $(x-c)$.
$\begin{array}{r\|rrrr} 2 & 1 & 3 & -6 & -8 \\ & & 2 & 10 & 8 \\ \hline & 1 & 5 & 4 & \boxed{0} \end{array}$	Once your c is set, you are ready to divide. Your division answer gives you the coefficients for the terms with $(x-c)$ factored out.
$f(x)=(x-2)(x^2+5x+4)$ $=(x-2)(x+4)(x+1)$	Once you divide down to a quadratic, just factor it if possible. That puts all your zeros in clear view.
zeros: $x=2,\ x=-4,\ x=-1$	When you are totally factored, state your list of zeros.

Sample problems:

1. Given $f(x) = x^3 - 3x^2 - 10x + 24$, find all real zeros of $f(x)$.
   Solution: $x = -3, 2, 4$
   Explanation: Use the rational zero theorem to list all possible zeros, $\frac{p}{q}$, where p = factor of 24 and q = factor of 1: $\pm 1,\ \pm 2,\ \pm 3,\ \pm 4,\ \pm 6,$ $\pm 8,\ \pm 12,\ \pm 24$.
   If c is a zero of $f(x)$ then $f(c) = 0$, so test the possible zeros:
   $f(1) = (1)^3 - 3(1)^2 - 10(1) + 24 = 12$, so 1 is not a zero,
   $f(-1) = (-1)^3 - 3(-1)^2 - 10(-1) + 24 = 30$, so -1 is not a zero,
   $f(2) = (2)^3 - 3(2)^2 - 10(2) + 24 = 0$, so 2 is a zero and thus $x - 2$ is a factor of $f(x)$.
   Use synthetic division to divide $f(x)$ by $x - 2$ to find the additional factor:
   $$\begin{array}{r|rrrr} 2 & 1 & -3 & -10 & 24 \\ & & 2 & -2 & -24 \\ \hline & 1 & -1 & -12 & 0 \end{array}$$
   The remaining polynomial is $x^2 - x - 12$, so $f(x) = (x-2)(x^2 - x - 12)$.
   Factor: $f(x) = (x-2)(x^2 - x - 12) = (x-2)(x+3)(x-4)$.
   Set each factor equal to 0 and solve for x. Therefore, the zeros are $x = 2,\ -3$, and 4.

2. Given $f(x)=2x^3+7x^2-17x-10$, find all real zeros of $f(x)$.
   Solution: $x=-5,-\frac{1}{2},2$
   Explanation: Use the rational zero theorem to list possible zeros: $\pm1,\ \pm2,\ \pm5,\ \pm10....$
   Test the possible zeros:
   $f(1)=2(1)^3+7(1)^2-17(1)-10=-18$, so 1 is not a zero,
   $f(2)=2(2)^3+7(2)^2-17(2)-10=0$, so 2 is a zero and thus $x-2$ is a factor of $f(x)$.
   Use synthetic division to divide $f(x)$ by $x-2$ to find the additional factor:
   $$\begin{array}{r|rrrr} 2 & 2 & 7 & -17 & -10 \\ & & 4 & 22 & 10 \\ \hline & 2 & 11 & 5 & 0 \end{array}$$
   The remaining polynomial is $2x^2+11x+5$, so $f(x)=(x-2)(2x^2+11x+5)$.
   Factor: $f(x)=(x-2)(2x^2+11x+5)=(x-2)(2x+1)(x+5)$.
   Set each factor equal to 0 and solve for x. Therefore, the zeros are $x=2,\ -\frac{1}{2}$, and -5.

3. Given $f(x)=x^4+16x^3+89x^2+194x+120$, find all real zeros of $f(x)$.
   Solution: $x=-1,-4,\ -5,\ -6$
   Explanation: Use the rational zero theorem to list possible zeros: $\pm1,\ \pm2,\ \pm3,\ \pm4....$
   According to Descartes sign rule, there can be no positive zeros.
   Test the possible negative zeros:
   $f(-1)=(-1)^4+16(-1)^3+89(-1)^2+194(-1)+120=0$, so -1 is a zero and thus $x+1$ is a factor of $f(x)$.
   Use synthetic division to divide $f(x)$ by $x+1$ to find the additional factor:
   $$\begin{array}{r|rrrrr} -1 & 1 & 16 & 89 & 194 & 120 \\ & & -1 & -15 & -74 & -120 \\ \hline & 1 & 15 & 74 & 120 & 0 \end{array}$$
   The remaining polynomial is $x^3+15x^2+74x+120$, so $f(x)=(x+1)(x^3+15x^2+74x+120)$.
   Test more possible negative zeros to find an addtional root:
   $f(-2)=(-2)^4+16(-2)^3+89(-2)^2+194(-2)+120=-24$, so -2 is not a zero,
   $f(-3)=(-3)^4+16(-3)^3+89(-3)^2+194(-3)+120=-12$, so -3 is not a zero,
   $f(-4)=(-4)^4+16(-4)^3+89(-4)^2+194(-4)+120=0$, so -4 is a zero.
   Use synthetic division again to divide $x^3+15x^2+74x+120$ by $x+4$ to find the additional factor:
   $$\begin{array}{r|rrrr} -4 & 1 & 15 & 74 & 120 \\ & & -4 & -44 & -120 \\ \hline & 1 & 11 & 30 & 0 \end{array}$$
   The remaining polynomial is $x^2+11x+30$, so $f(x)=(x+1)(x+4)(x^2+11x+30)$.
   Factor: $f(x)=(x+1)(x+4)(x^2+11x+30)=(x+1)(x+4)(x+5)(x+6)$.
   Set each factor equal to 0 and solve for x. Therefore, the zeros are $x=-1,\ -4,\ -5$, and -6.

Practice problems: *(Answers on page: 747)*

1. Given $f(x)=x^3+5x^2-17x-21$, find all real zeros of $f(x)$.
2. Given $f(x)=2x^3-15x^2+34x-24$, find all real zeros of $f(x)$.
3. Given $f(x)=2x^4+23x^3+97x^2+178x+120$, find all real zeros of $f(x)$.

Review questions: *(Answers to odd questions on page: 747)*

1. Given $f(x)=x^3+3x^2-x-3$, find all real zeros of $f(x)$.
2. Given $f(x)=x^3+7x^2+4x-12$, find all real zeros of $f(x)$.

3. Given $f(x) = 5x^3 + 24x^2 + 31x + 12$, find all real zeros of $f(x)$.
4. Given $f(x) = 6x^3 - x^2 - 21x + 10$, find all real zeros of $f(x)$.
5. Given $f(x) = 3x^4 + 5x^3 - 77x^2 - 125x + 50$, find all real zeros of $f(x)$.

Matching Graphs to Polynomial Functions

- **Rational root theorem**: Given $f(x) = a_n x^n + a_{n-1} x^{n-1} + \ldots + a_1 x + a_o$, if p/q is a root of $f(x)$, then p is a factor of a_o and q is a factor of a_n.
- The rational root theorem is very important in locating possible roots for complicated polynomials. It greatly limits the number of possible roots you have to check and makes finding all the roots actually possible.
- When graphing polynomials, every maximum and minimum point marks a boundary separating two regions. A curve will tend to have as many regions as its degree.
- **Multiplicity**: the number of times a specific value is a root for a polynomial.

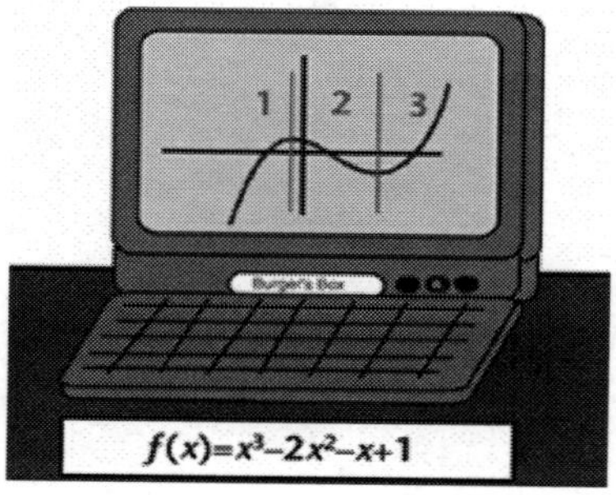	A cubic function is a third-degree function, which means that its highest term has 3 for its exponent. Notice that its graph divides into three regions. Each region has one root.
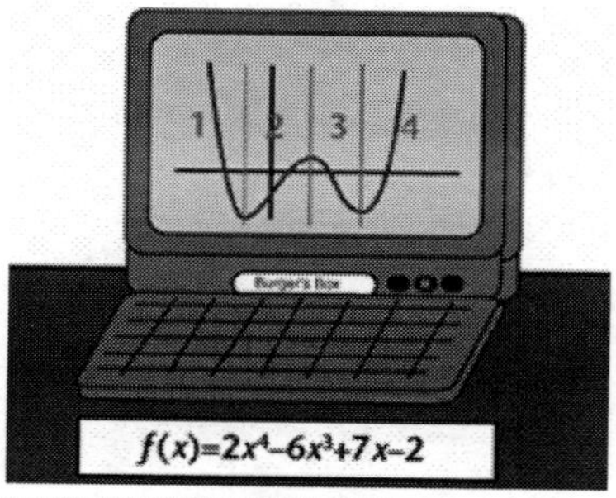	Fourth degree polynomials tend to have four regions with a root in each one.
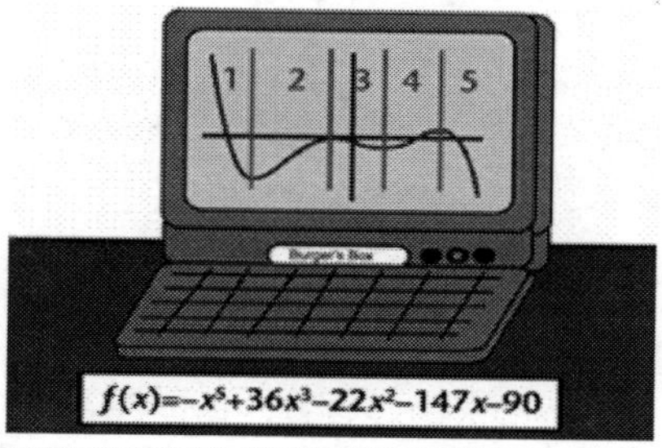	Fifth degree functions tend to have five regions, and you see the pattern.
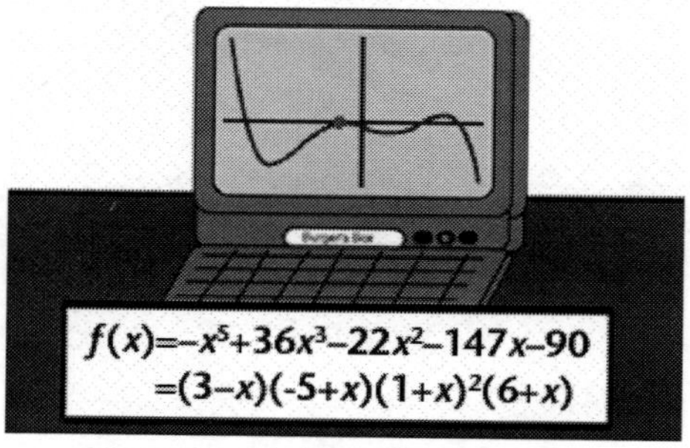 zeros: $x=-6$, $x=-1$, $x=5$, $x=3$	In this example, the only possibilities for the **numerator of any rational root** are the factors of 90. So, your first step is to make a list of all the factors of 90. The only possibilities for the denominator of any rational root are the factors of the coefficient of x^5; i.e., the factors of 1. Now try all the possibilities for p/q with these factors and see which numbers are roots for $p(x)$.

Sample problems:

1. How many positive real roots does this function have?

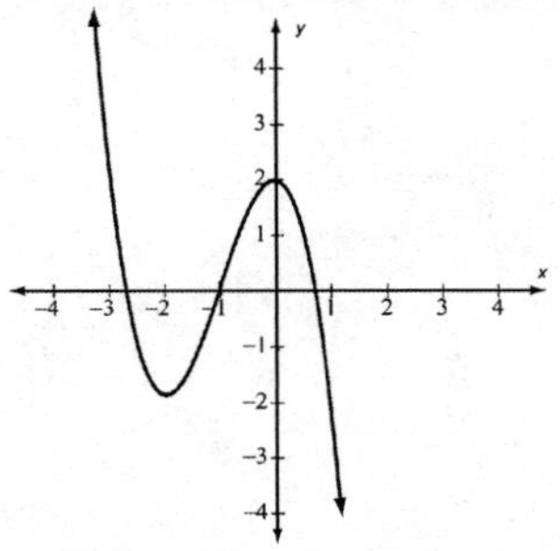

Solution: 1
Explanation: The graph crosses the positive x-axis in one place, so there is one positive real root.

2. True or false: The following graph represents a polynomial function with 2 real zeros.

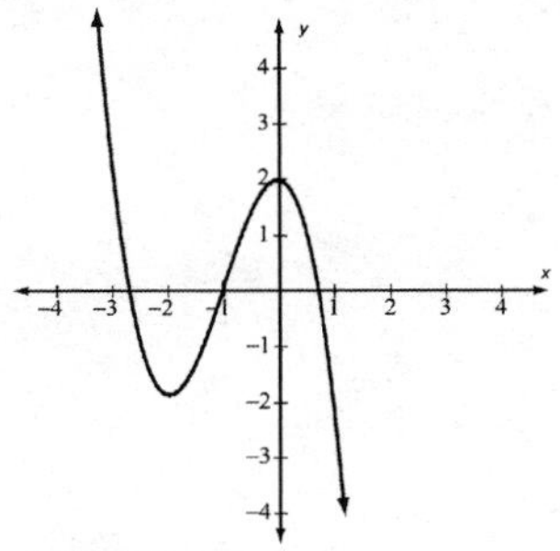

Solution: False
Explanation: The given graph intersects the x-axis 3 times. Therefore, the polynomial function that describes the graph must have 3 real roots.

3. True or false: The following graph is defined by a polynomial function of even degree.

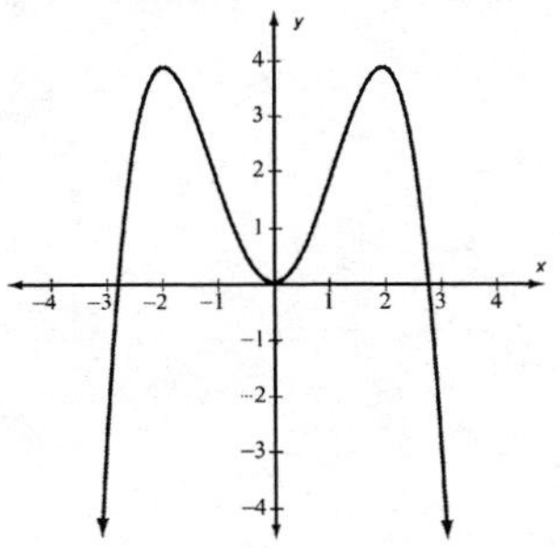

Solution: True
Explanation Since both ends of the graph extend in the same direction the degree of the polynomial must be even.

Practice problems: *(Answers on page: 747)*

1. How many negative real roots does this function have?

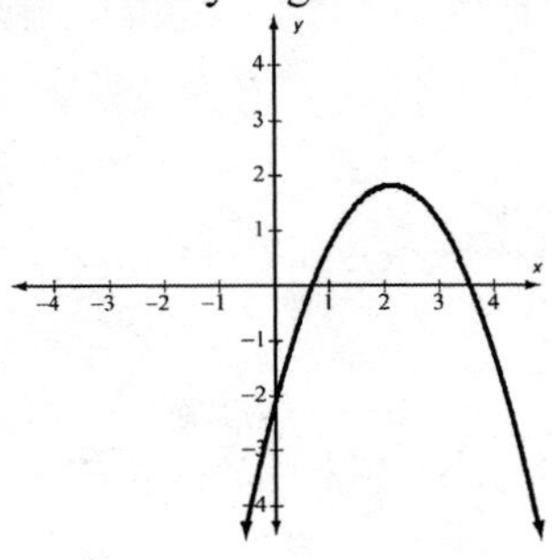

2. True or false: The following function has a positive roots with multiplicity greater than 1.

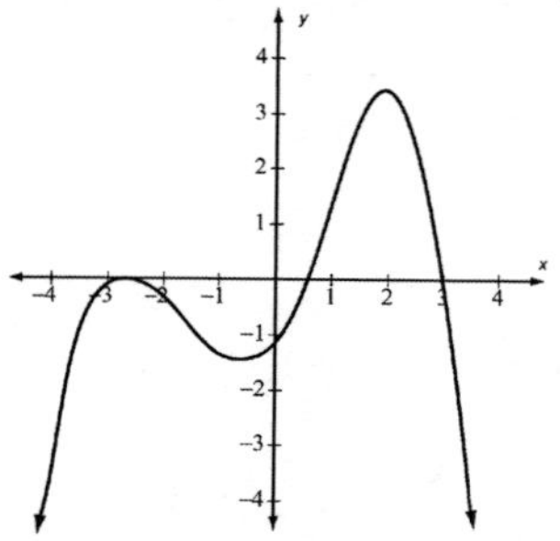

3. True or false: The following function is defined by a function of degree 2.

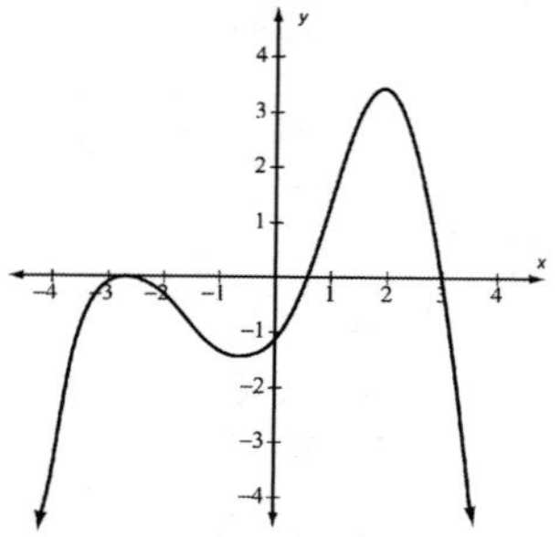

Review questions: *(Answers to odd questions on page: 747)*

1. How many real roots does this function have?

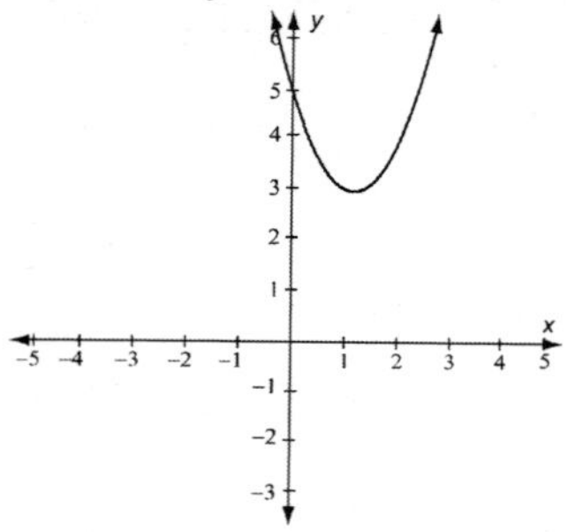

2. True or false: The following graph represents a function of odd degree.

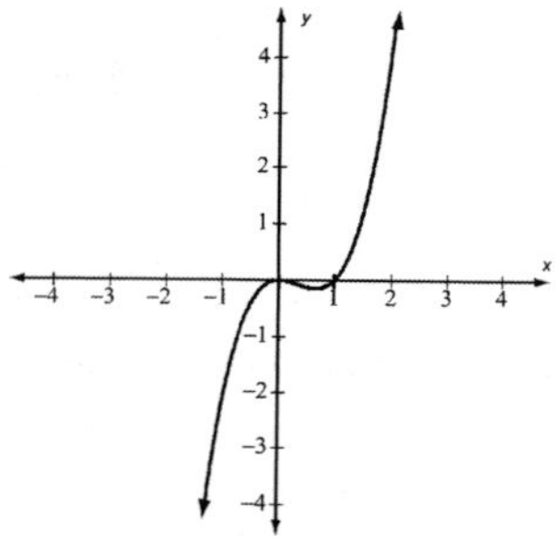

3. True or false: The following graph represents a function of even degree.

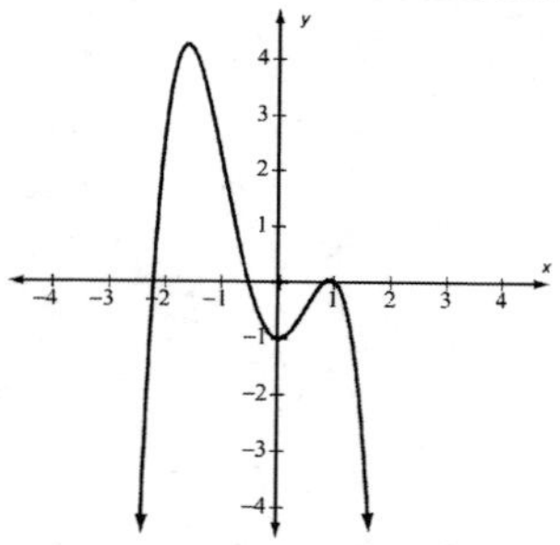

4. True or false: The following graph may represent a function of degree 2.

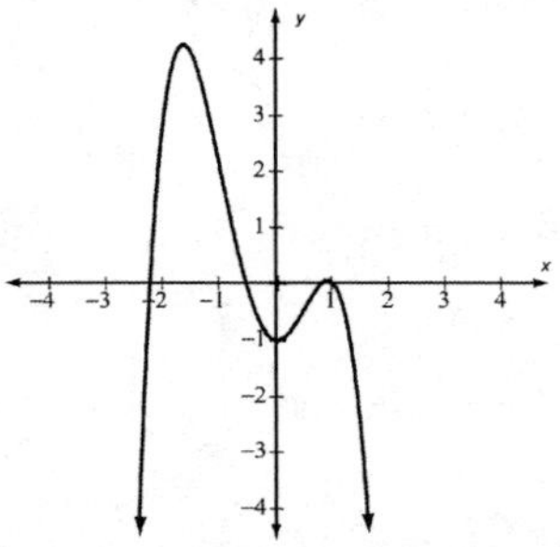

5. List 3 attributes of the polynomial function defined by the following graph.

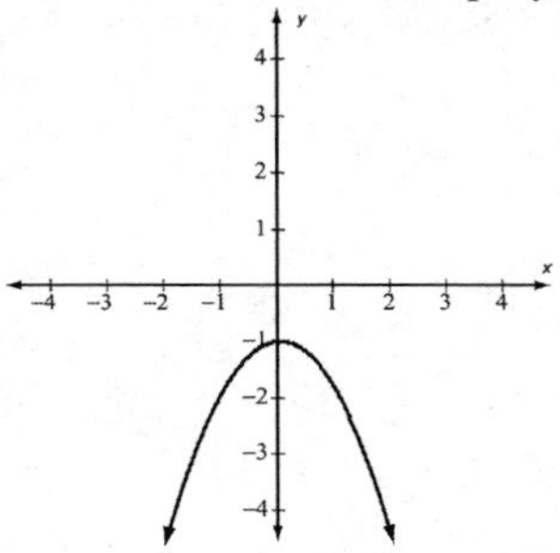

Sketching the Graphs of Basic Polynomial Functions

- Graphs of polynomials with even degree have end behavior that is U-shaped. If the leading coefficient of the polynomial is positive, the U-shape is right side up. If the leading coefficient is negative, the U-shape is upside-down.
- Graphs of polynomials with odd degree are S-shaped. If the leading coefficient of the polynomial is positive, the graph increases as x increases. If the leading coefficient is negative, then the graph decreases as x increases.
- For the graphs of $y = x^2$, $y = x^4$, $y = x^6$, and so on, the higher the degree, the sharper the turns in the U-shape of the graph.
- For the graphs of $y = x$, $y = x^3$, $y = x^5$ and so on, the higher the degree, the sharper the turns in the S-shape of the graph.

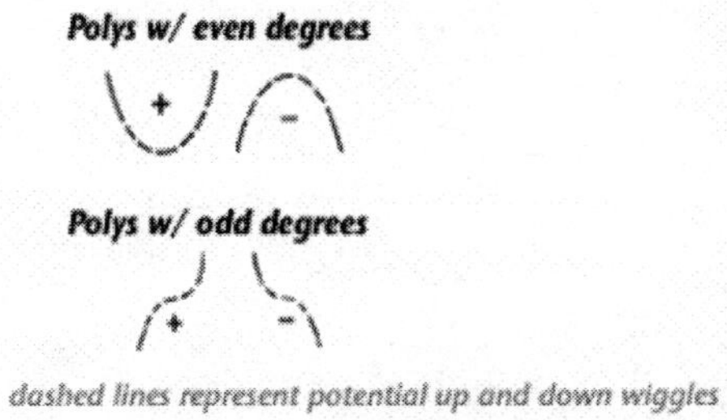	Previously, you saw that the graphs of polynomials with even degree have the same basic U-shape. Similarly, the graphs of polynomials with odd degree have the same basic S-shape.
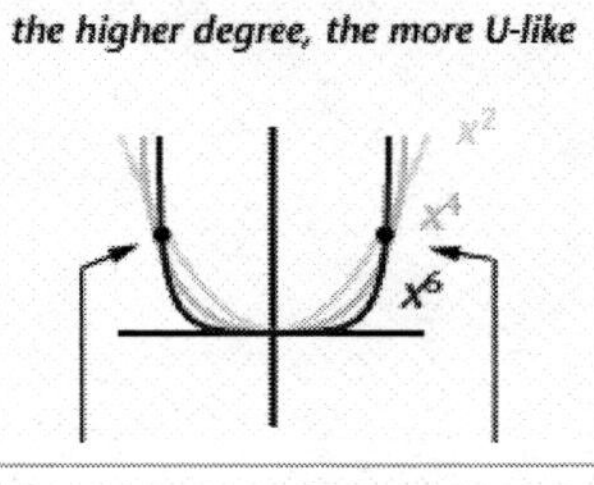	For the graphs of $y = x^2$, $y = x^4$, $y = x^6$, and so on, the higher the degree, the sharper the turns in the U-shape of the graph. Remember, though, that no matter how high the degree, the graph is always a smooth curve with no corners.
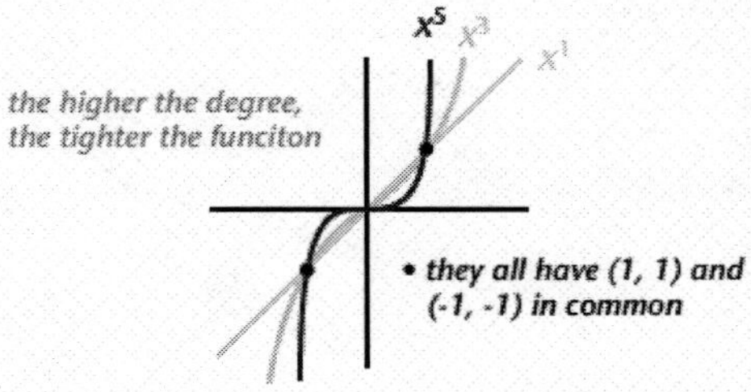	For the graphs of $y = x$, $y = x^3$, $y = x^5$, and so on, the higher the degree, the sharper the turns in the S-shape of the graph. Notice, too, the two points common to every graph of this type. Like before, though, no matter how high the degree, the graph is always a smooth curve with no corners.

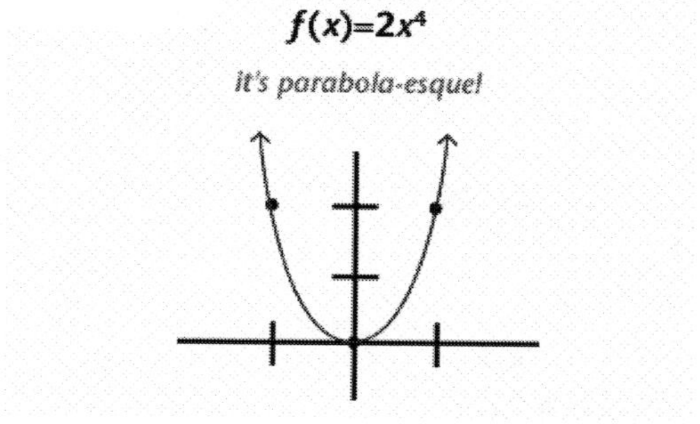

Let's graph the function $f(x) = 2x^4$.

The polynomial is even, so the graph will be U-shaped.

The leading coefficient is positive (in this case, it is 2), so the U-shape will be right side up.

The biggest power of x is x^4, so the U-shape will be "tighter" than the parabola $y = x^2$.

Finally, the coefficient of 2 in front stretches the U-shape in the vertical direction. Plot a few points and sketch the graph!

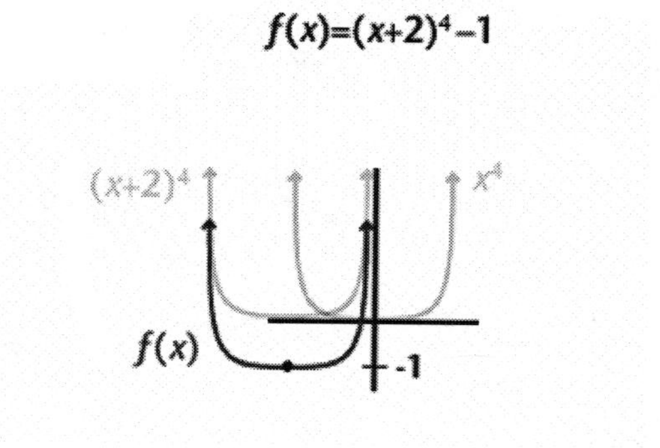

How about $f(x) = (x + 2)^4 - 1$?

One good way to graph this complicated function is to take several steps.

First, graph $y = x^4$.

Then, graph $y = (x+2)^4$, which is the same graph shifted 2 units to the left.

Finally, shift this new graph 1 unit downwards.

The result is the desired graph!

Sample problems:

1. Sketch the graph of $f(x) = -x^4$.
   Solution:

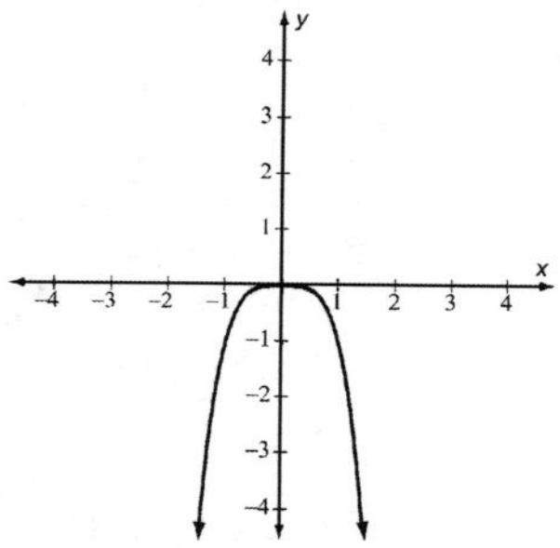

Explanation: Start with the graph of $f(x) = x^4$ and then reflect it across the x-axis, since the coefficient is -1.

2. Sketch the graph of the following polynomial function: $f(x) = \frac{1}{3}(x-2)^5$.
   Solution:

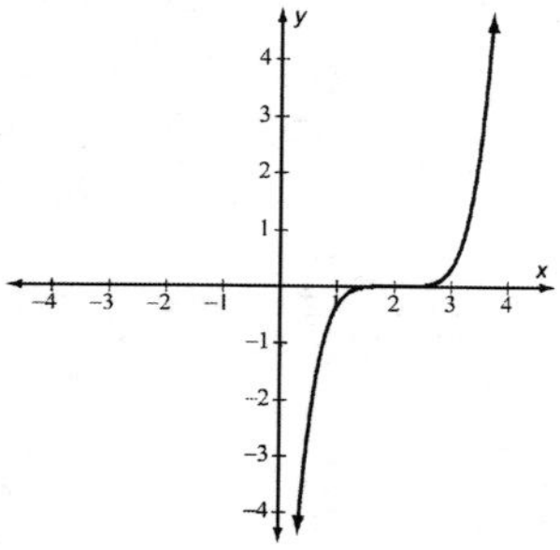

Explanation: Start with the graph of $f(x) = x^5$, then scale the graph by a factor of $\frac{1}{3}$ and shift to the right 2 units.

3. What general shape would you expect the graph of $f(x) = 3x^6 - 5x^3 + 2$ to have?
Solution: U-shaped opening up
Explanation: The function $f(x)$ has degree 6, so the graph must be U-shaped. The leading coefficient is positive, so the parabola-like shape must open upwards.

Practice problems: *(Answers on page: 747)*

1. Sketch the graph of $y = x^3 - 2$.
2. Sketch the graph of $y = x^4 + 1$.
3. What general shape would you expect the graph of $y = -\frac{1}{3}x^4 + 2x^2 - x$ to have?

Review questions: *(Answers to odd questions on page: 747)*

1. Sketch the graph of $y = 2x^4$.
2. Sketch the graph of $y = (x-3)^3$.
3. Sketch the graph of $f(x) = (x-1)^4 + 2$.
4. Sketch the graph of $f(x) = \frac{1}{2}(x+3)^4$.
5. Sketch the graph of $f(x) = x^5 - 1$.

Understanding Rational Functions

- **Rational functions** are quotients of polynomials.
- An **asymptote** is a line that the graph of a function approaches but never touches. Asymptotes can be either vertical or horizontal.

What is a Rational Function? $\frac{\text{polynomial}}{\text{polynomial}}$

Previously, you studied polynomials and their graphs. **Rational functions** are natural extensions of polynomials. They are functions in the form of a fraction where the numerator and denominator are polynomials.

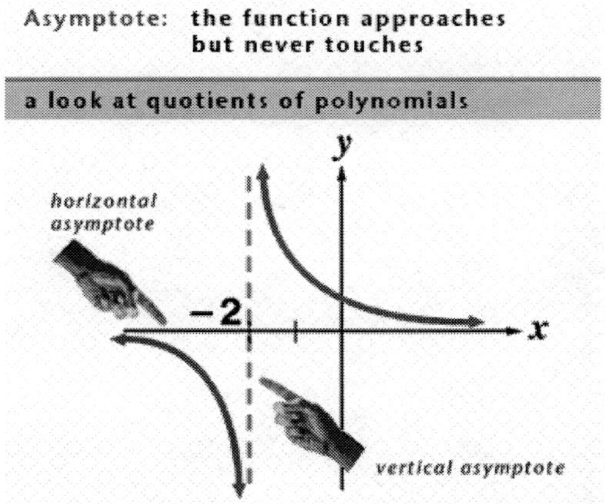

The graphs of rational functions often have asymptotes, or lines that a function gets closer and closer to but never touches. Horizontal asymptotes are horizontal lines, and vertical asymptotes are vertical lines.

This is the graph of a typical rational function. Notice the vertical asymptote at $x = -2$ and the horizontal asymptote at $y = 0$ (the x-axis). The function gets closer and closer to these asymptotes, but it never touches them.

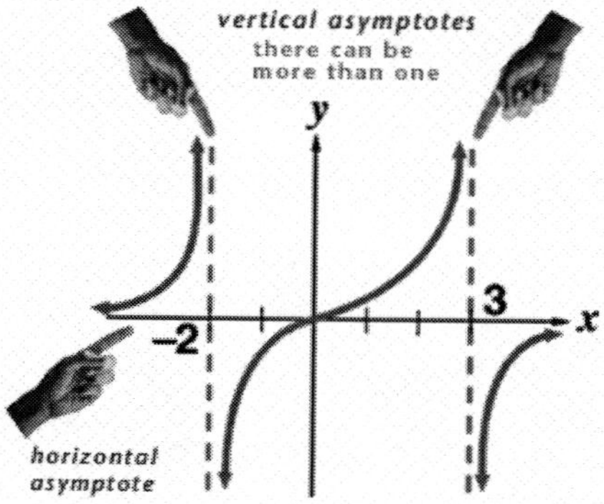	The graph of this rational function has two vertical asymptotes (one at $x = -2$ and one at $x = 3$) and one horizontal asymptote (at $y = 0$, or the x-axis). There is no limit to the number of asymptotes a graph can have. **NOTICE:** The function is undefined at the x-values where the vertical asymptotes are located. This happens because the denominator of the function equals zero at these points.
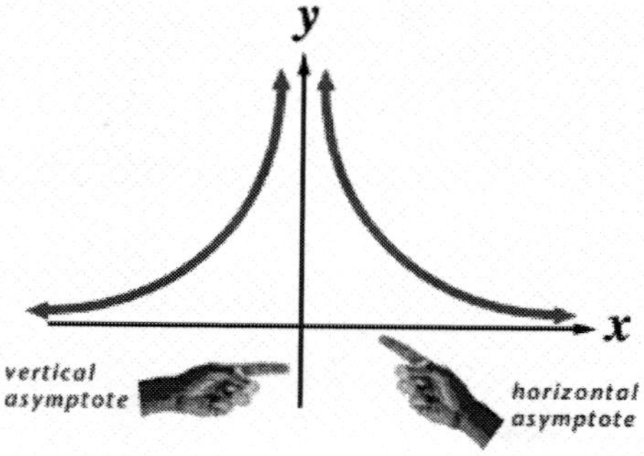	This is another example of the graph of a rational function. It has a vertical asymptote at $x = 0$ (the y-axis) and a horizontal asymptote at $y = 0$ (the x-axis).

Sample problems:

1. What is the domain of this graph?

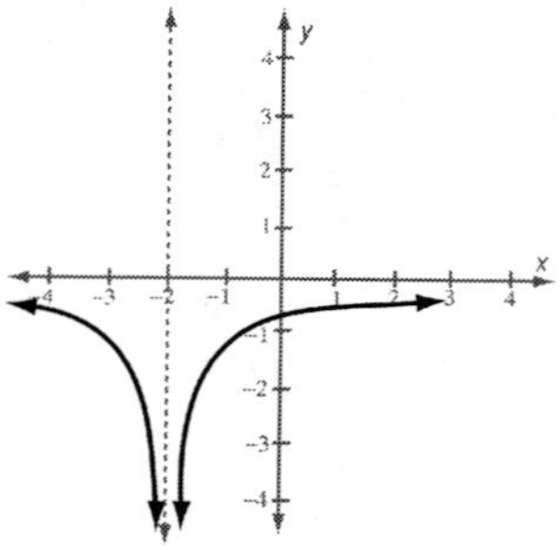

Solution: all real numbers such that $x \neq -2$
Explanation: There is only one vertical asymptote at $x = -2$. Since the curve has no other breaks in it, the domain is all real numbers except -2. In interval notation, this is $(-\infty, -2) \cup (-2, \infty)$.

2. What is the range of this graph?

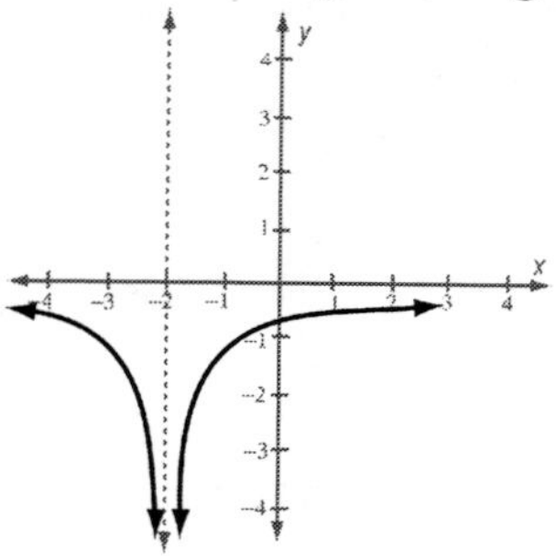

Solution: all real numbers less than 0
Explanation: There is only one horizontal asymptote at the x-axis $(y = 0)$. Since the graph stays below the x-axis, the range is all negative real numbers. In interval notation this is $(-\infty, 0)$.

3. State the horizontal and vertical asymptotes of the graph below.

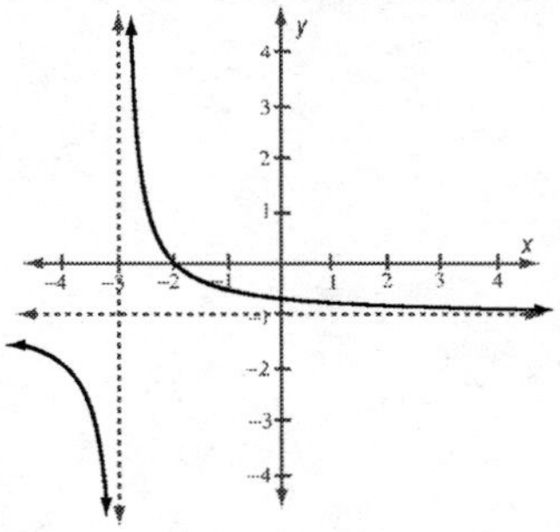

Solution: $y = -1$ and $x = -3$

Explanation: The asymptotes of a graph of a rational funtion are the values outside of the domain and range. The domain is all real numbers such that $x \neq -3$, so the vertical asymptote is $x = -3$ and the range is all real numbers such that $y \neq -1$, so the horizontal asymptote is $y = -1$

Practice problems: *(Answers on page: 747)*

1. What is the domain and range of this graph?

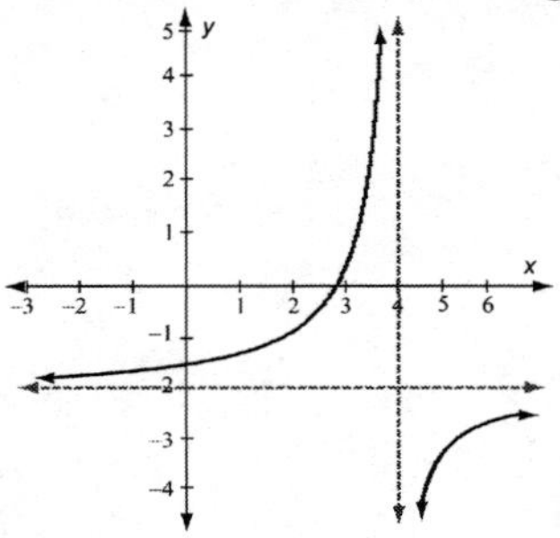

2. What is the domain and range of this graph?

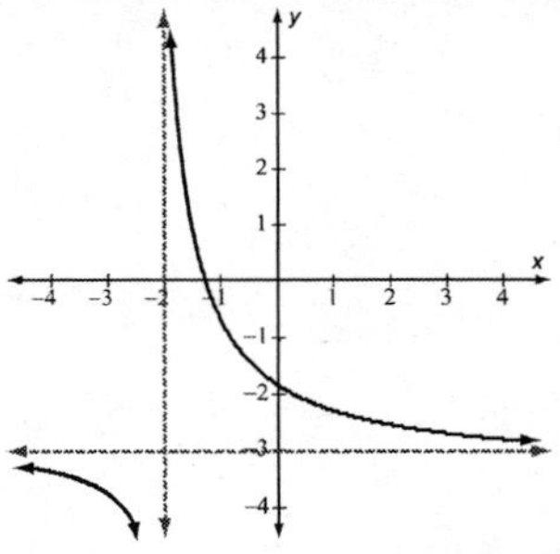

3. State the horizontal and vertical asymptotes of the graph below.

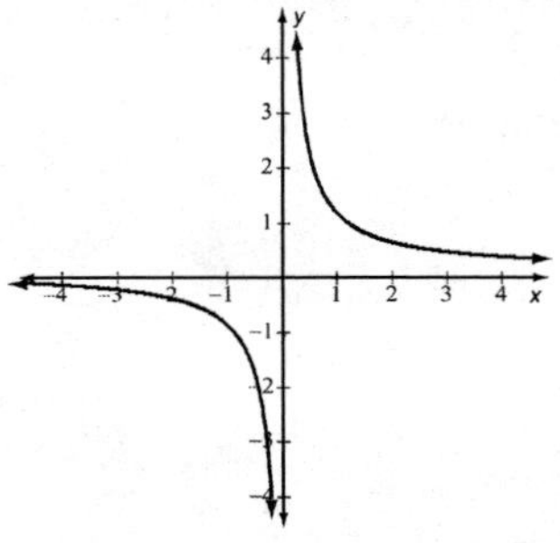

Review questions: *(Answers to odd questions on page: 747)*

1. What is the domain and range of this graph?

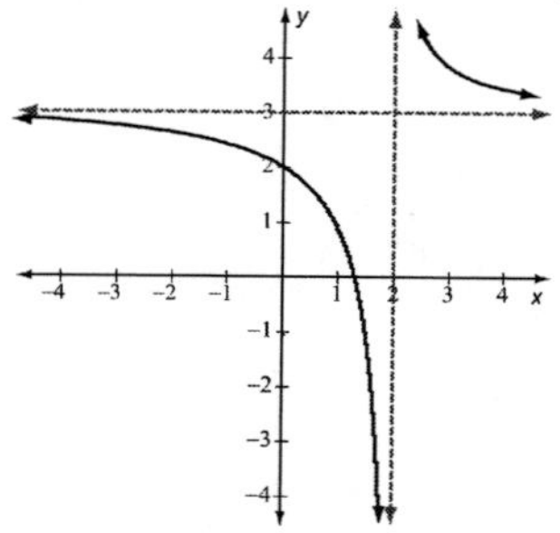

2. What is the domain and range of this graph?

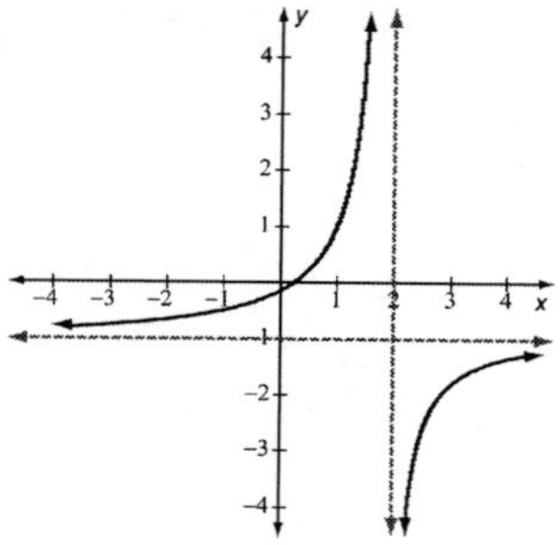

3. What is the domain and range of this graph?

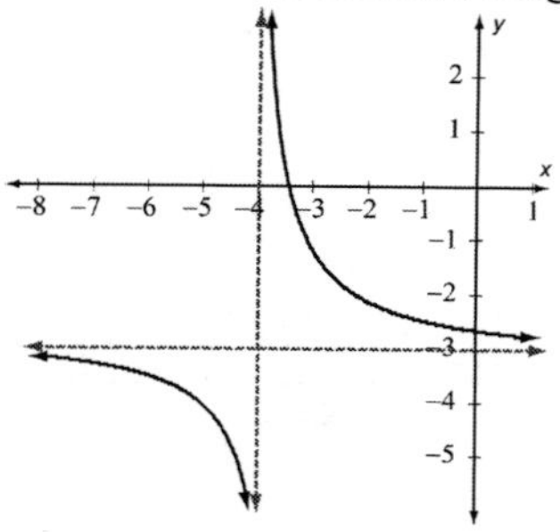

4. State the horizontal and vertical asymptotes of the graph below.

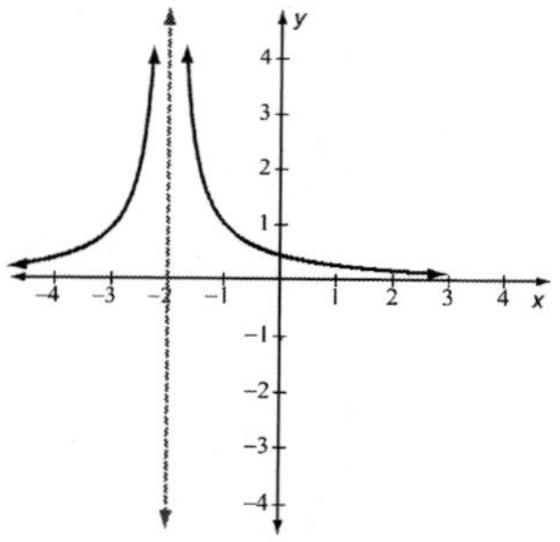

5. State the horizontal and vertical asymptotes of the graph below.

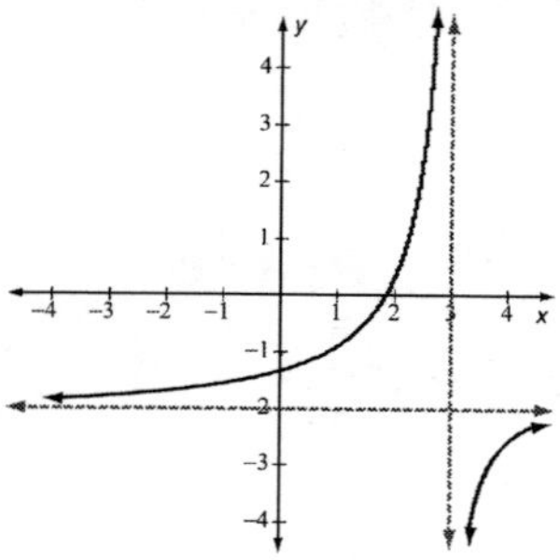

Basic Rational Functions

- **Rational functions** are quotients of polynomials.
- An asymptote is a line that the graph of a function approaches but never touches. Asymptotes can be either vertical or horizontal.

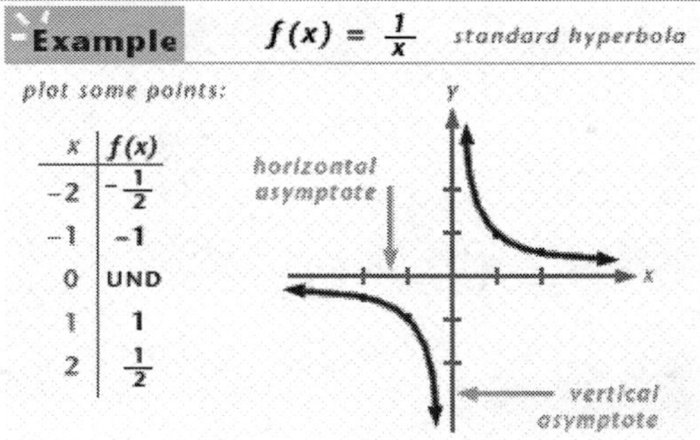

Let's take a look at the graphs of some basic rational functions.

The function $f(x)=1/x$ is one of the most basic rational functions. Its graph has a vertical asymptote at $x = 0$ (the y-axis) and a horizontal asymptote at $y = 0$ (the x-axis). Notice that $f(x)=1/x$ is undefined at $x = 0$, where the vertical asymptote is located, because the denominator of the fraction is equal to zero there.

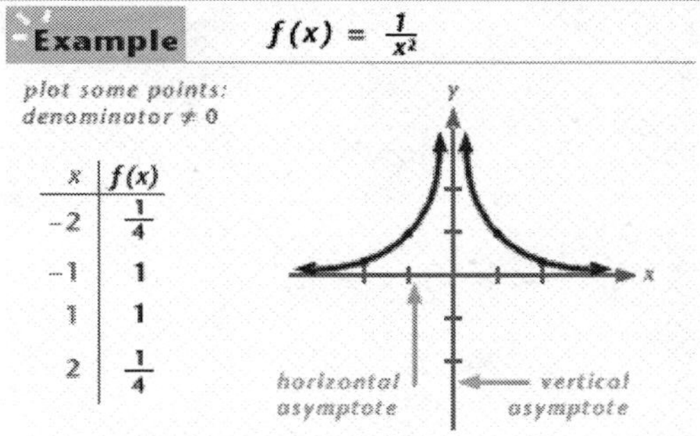

This is the graph of $f(x)=1/x$ 2. It also has a vertical asymptote at $x = 0$ (the y-axis) and a horizontal asymptote at $y = 0$ (the x-axis). Notice, though, that this graph never takes negative y-values.

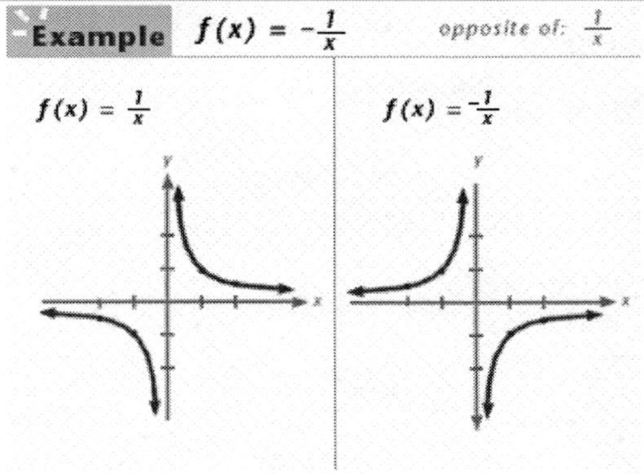

What about the graph of $f(x) = -1/x$? We can graph this rational function by reflecting the graph of $y = 1/x$ over the x-axis.

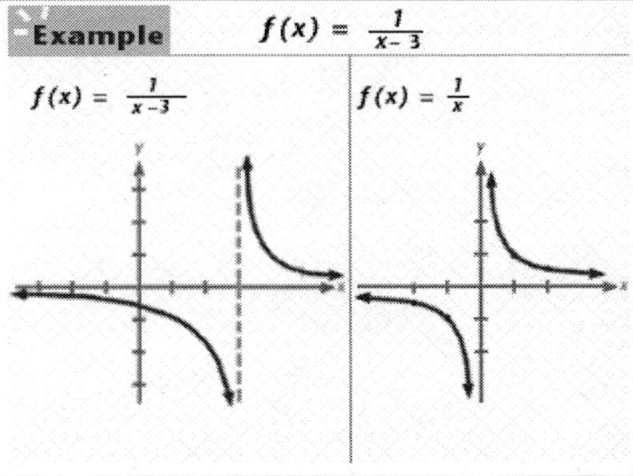

One more example. How can we graph this function? The first step is to graph the function $y = 1/x$. Then, since 3 is subtracted from x in $f(x)$, shift this graph 3 units to the right to find the graph of $f(x)$. Notice that $f(x)$ has a vertical asymptote at $x = 3$, where its denominator is undefined.

REMEMBER: When shifting graphs of functions: "Add to y, go high. Add to x, go west."

Sample problems:

1. Sketch the graph of $f(x)=\frac{1}{x}-2$

Solution:

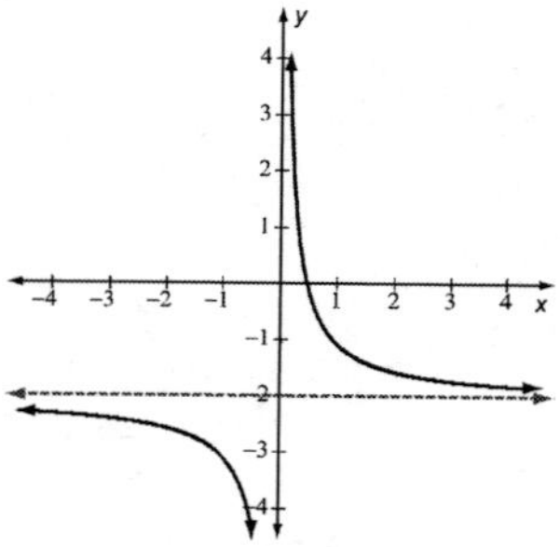

Explanation: Sketch the graph of $y=\frac{1}{x}$. Shift the entire graph down 2 units. The horizontal asymptote is now $y=-2$ and the vertical asymptote is still the y-axis.

2. Sketch the graph of $f(x)=\frac{1}{x-2}+1$

Solution:

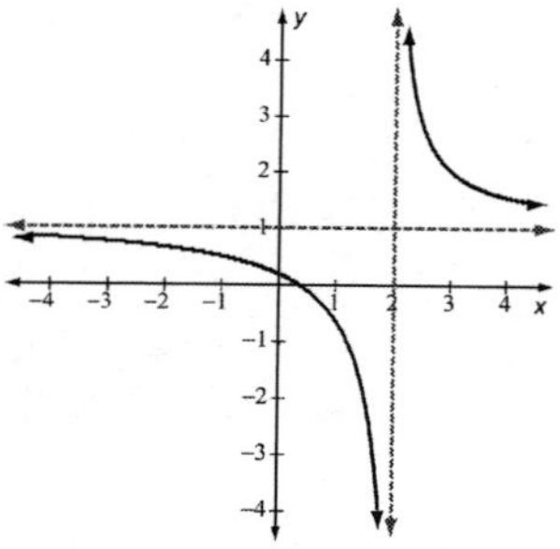

Explanation: Sketch the graph of $y=\frac{1}{x}$. Shift the entire graph to the right 2 units and up one unit. The vertical asymptote is now $x=2$ and the horizontal asymptote is now $y=1$.

3. Sketch the graph of $f(x)=-\frac{1}{x+3}$

Solution:

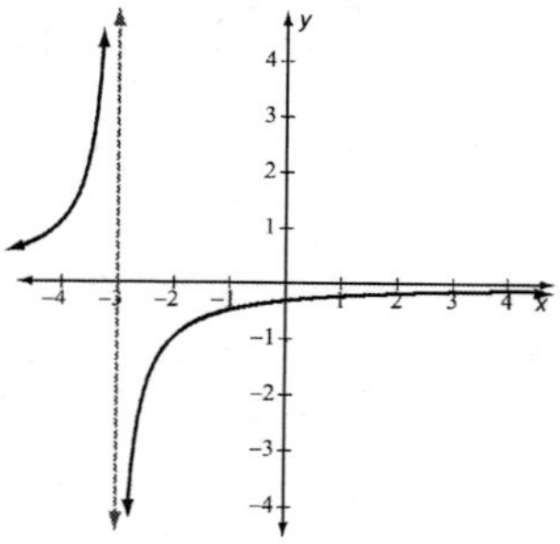

Explanation: Sketch the graph of $y=\frac{1}{x}$. Reflect the graph over the x-axis, since the function is $-\frac{1}{x+3}$, and shift the graph 3 units to the left.

Practice problems: *(Answers on page: 747)*

1. Sketch the graph of $f(x)=\frac{1}{x}+3$.

2. Sketch the graph of $f(x)=-\frac{1}{x-2}$.

3. Sketch the graph of $f(x)=\dfrac{1}{x+1}-4$.

Review questions: *(Answers to odd questions on page: 748)*

1. Sketch the graph of $f(x)=\dfrac{1}{x}-5$.
2. Sketch the graph of $f(x)=-\dfrac{1}{x}$.
3. Sketch the graph of $f(x)=-\dfrac{1}{x+2}$.
4. Sketch the graph of $f(x)=\dfrac{1}{x+2}-1$.
5. Sketch the graph of $f(x)=\dfrac{1}{x^2}$.

Vertical Asymptotes

- A vertical asymptote is a vertical line that the graph of a function approaches but never touches.
- To find the vertical asymptotes of a rational function:
  1. Cancel any common factors in the numerator and denominator to put the fraction in lowest terms.
  2. Set the denominator equal to 0 and solve for *x*.

Example $p(x)=\dfrac{3}{2x-4}$ *find the vertical asymptote* ✔ *lowest terms?* ✔ *set denominator = 0* $2x-4=0$ $2x=4$ $\boxed{x=2}$ vertical asymptote (VA)	Previously, you saw how rational functions often have vertical asymptotes in their graphs. Now you will learn how to find those vertical asymptotes algebraically. The first step is to reduce the fraction to lowest terms. In this case, this step is not necessary because the fraction is already in lowest terms. The second step is to set the denominator equal to zero and solve for *x*. The result is the vertical asymptote.
Example $p(x)=\dfrac{5+3x}{x^2+4x-5}$ *find the vertical asymptote* $\dfrac{5+3x}{(x-1)(x+5)}$ ✔ *lowest terms?* ✔ *factor denominator* $\boxed{x=1,\ x=-5}$ ✔ *set denominator = 0*	Let's try another problem. After factoring the denominator, you can see that there are no terms to cancel, so the fraction is already in lowest terms. Set the denominator equal to zero, solve for *x*, and you're done.
Example $f(x)=\dfrac{x^2-1}{x+1}$ *find the vertical asymptote* ✔ *lowest terms?* $\dfrac{(x+1)(x-1)}{(x+1)}$ ✔ *set denominator = 0* remember: *only if* $x\neq -1$ $f(x)=x-1$ ⟵ straight line no VA !	After factoring the numerator in this problem, you find that the fraction is not in lowest terms because the $(x+1)$ terms can be cancelled away. **REMEMBER:** If you cancel a term from the numerator and denominator of a fraction, you have to promise that the old denominator will never equal zero. After you cancel the $(x+1)$ terms, there is no denominator, so there are no vertical asymptotes! The graph of this function is a straight line with a hole in it at $x=-1$.

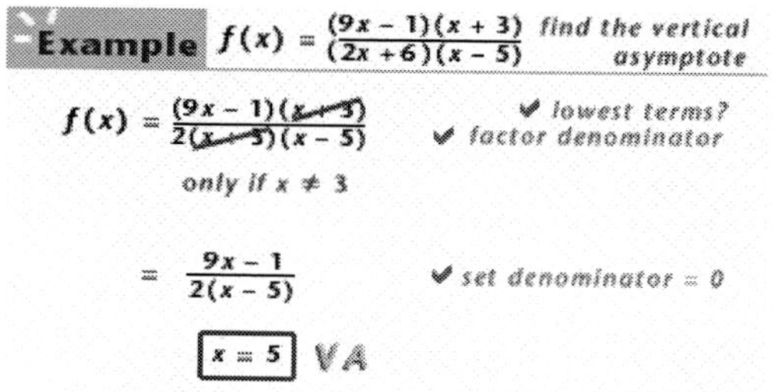

One last example. Can you find the vertical asymptotes of this function?

Factor the denominator and cancel the $(x + 3)$ terms. After you have cancelled the terms, the fraction is in lowest terms. Set the denominator equal to zero and solve for x.

Sample problems:

1. Given $f(x) = \frac{2}{x-4}$, find the vertical asymptote(s).
   Solution: $x = 4$
   Explanation: The expression cannot be simplified, so set the denominator equal to 0 and solve for x: $x - 4 = 0;\ x = 4$. Thus, the vertical asymptote is $x = 4$.

2. Given $f(x) = \frac{x}{x^2 - 5x - 6}$, find the vertical asymptote(s).
   Solution: $x = 6$ and $x = -1$
   Explanation: The expression cannot be simplified, so set the denominator equal to 0 and solve for x: $x^2 - 5x - 6 = 0;\ (x-6)(x+1) = 0$. Thus, the graph must have two vertical asymptotes: $x = 6$ and $x = -1$.

3. Given $f(x) = \frac{x+2}{x^2 - 3x - 10}$, find the vertical asymptote(s).
   Solution: $x = 5$
   Explanation: Simplify the expression: $\frac{x+2}{x^2-3x-10} = \frac{x+2}{(x+2)(x-5)} = \frac{1}{x-5}$.
   Set the denominator equal to 0 and solve for x: $x - 5 = 0;\ x = 5$. Thus, the vertical asymptote is $x = 5$.

Practice problems: *(Answers on page: 748)*

1. Given $f(x) = \frac{1}{x+7}$, find the vertical asymptote(s).
2. Given $f(x) = \frac{x}{x^2 - 9}$, find the vertical asymptote(s).
3. Given $f(x) = \frac{x^2 + 5x + 6}{x+3}$, find the vertical asymptote(s).

Review questions: *(Answers to odd questions on page: 748)*

1. Given $f(x) = \frac{6}{x}$, find the vertical asymptote(s).
2. Given $f(x) = \frac{3-x}{x+5}$, find the vertical asymptote(s).
3. Given $f(x) = \frac{1}{x^2 - 25}$, find the vertical asymptote(s).
4. Given $f(x) = \frac{x+7}{x^2 + 9x + 14}$, find the vertical asymptote(s).

5. Given $f(x) = \dfrac{x^2 - 16}{x + 4}$, find the vertical asymptote(s).

Horizontal Asymptotes

- A **horizontal asymptote** is a horizontal line that the graph of a function approaches but never touches.
- To find the horizontal asymptotes of a rational function, consider the largest powers of x in the numerator and denominator:

1. If the largest power of x is in the denominator, the function has a horizontal asymptote at $y = 0$ (the x -axis).
2. If the largest power of x is in the numerator, the function has no horizontal asymptote.
3. If the powers of x are equal in the numerator and denominator, the function has a horizontal asymptote. Divide the coefficients of the largest powers of x to find out where the asymptote is located.

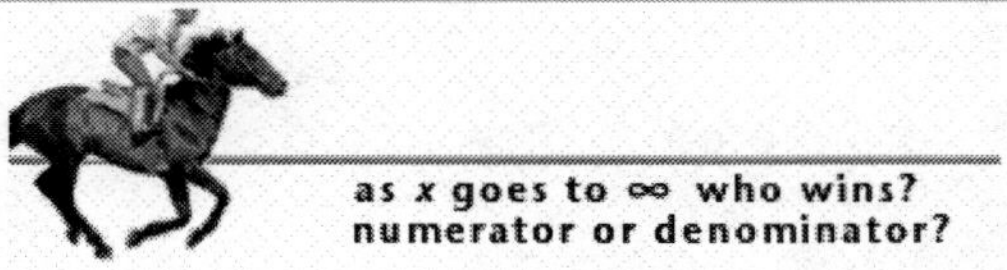	When finding the **horizontal asymptotes** of a function, you want to examine what happens to the function as x becomes very large. You can view this as a race between the numerator and the denominator—which one will get to infinity first?
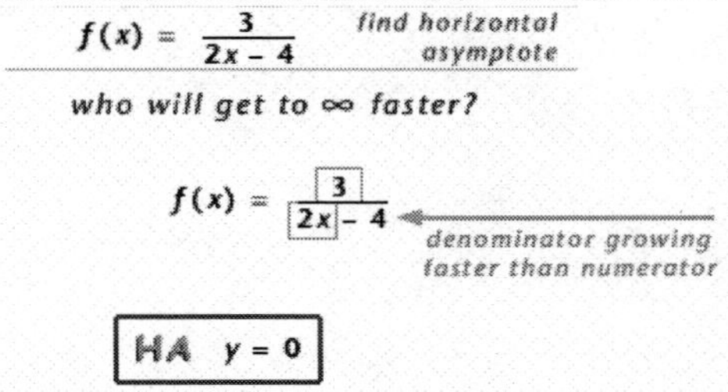	Let's try an example. In this problem, the largest power of x in the denominator, 1, is greater than the largest power of x in the numerator, 0. This means that the denominator goes to infinity faster than the numerator as x gets large. The denominator wins the race! $f(x)$ has a horizontal asymptote at $y = 0$.
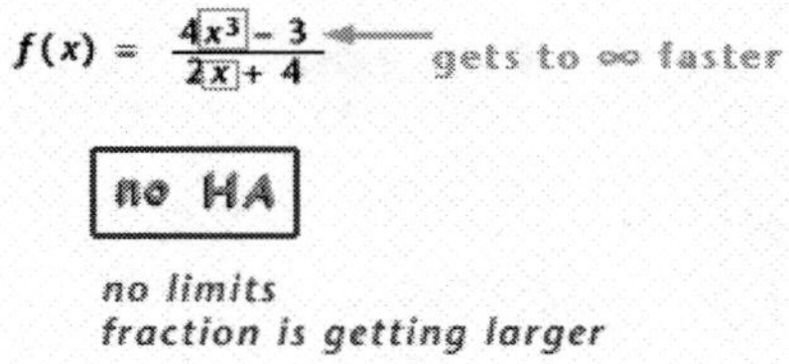	In this example, the largest power of x in the numerator, 3, is greater than the largest power of x in the denominator, 1. The numerator goes to infinity faster than the denominator as x gets large. So, as x gets large, $f(x)$ doesn't approach any value. There is no horizontal asymptote.
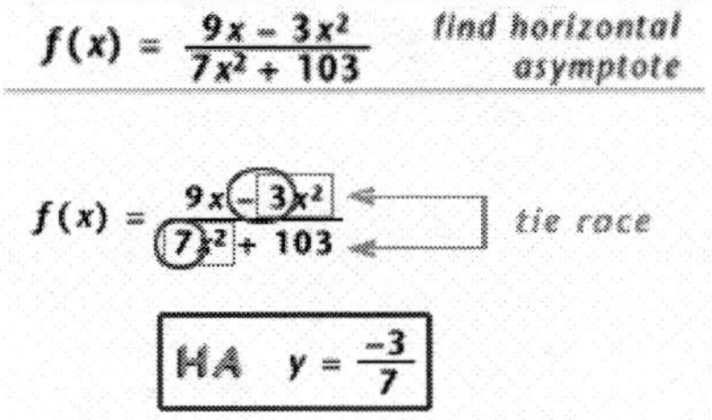	In this problem, the largest power of x in the numerator is equal to the largest power of x in the denominator. This tells you that there is a horizontal asymptote. To find the asymptote, divide the coefficients of the largest powers of x. The horizontal asymptote in this example is $y = -3/7$.

Sample problems:

1. Give the equation of the horizontal asymptote of the following function: $f(x) = \frac{x-5}{7}$.
   Solution: No horizontal asymptote
   Explanation: The numerator has a degree of 1 and the denominator has a degree of 0. Therefore there is no horizontal asymptote.

2. Given $f(x)=\dfrac{4x^3-7x}{5x^6+1}$, find the horizontal asymptote if it exists.
Solution: $y=0$
Explanation: The numerator has a degree of 3 and the denominator has a degree of 6. Therefore, since the degree is greater in the denominator, the equation of the horizontal asymptote is $y=0$.

3. Given $f(x)=\dfrac{3-2x^3}{5x^3}$, find the horizontal asymptote if it exists.
Solution: $y=-\dfrac{2}{5}$
Explanation: Since the degrees of the numerator and the denominator are equal, the equation of the horizontal asymptote is $y=\dfrac{a}{b}$, where a and b are the coefficients of the terms with the highest degrees in the numerator and denominator respectively. The coefficient of the highest degree term in the numerator is -2 and the coefficient of the highest degree term in the denominator is 5, so the equation of the horizontal asymptote is $y=-\dfrac{2}{5}$.

Practice problems: *(Answers on page: 748)*

1. Given $f(x)=\dfrac{9}{x-3}$, find the horizontal asymptote if it exists.
2. Given $f(x)=\dfrac{2x^3+x-7}{2x^4+1}$, find the horizontal asymptote if it exists.
3. Given $f(x)=\dfrac{x^4+5x+9}{4x^4+3x-5}$, find the horizontal asymptote if it exists.

Review questions: *(Answers to odd questions on page: 748)*

1. Given $f(x)=\dfrac{8}{x-4}$, find the horizontal asymptote if it exists.
2. Given $f(x)=\dfrac{4x^2+5}{5x^5-9}$, find the horizontal asymptote if it exists.
3. Given $f(x)=\dfrac{4x^5+5}{4x^5+2x-6}$, find the horizontal asymptote if it exists.
4. Given $f(x)=\dfrac{5x^5-5}{5x^4+x+6}$, find the horizontal asymptote if it exists.
5. Given $f(x)=\dfrac{2x^3+7}{5x^2+4x+7}$, find the horizontal asymptote if it exists.

Graphing Rational Functions

- An asymptote is a line that the graph of a function approaches but never touches. Asymptotes can be either vertical or horizontal.
- You can use the horizontal and vertical asymptotes of a rational function to help you sketch its graph.

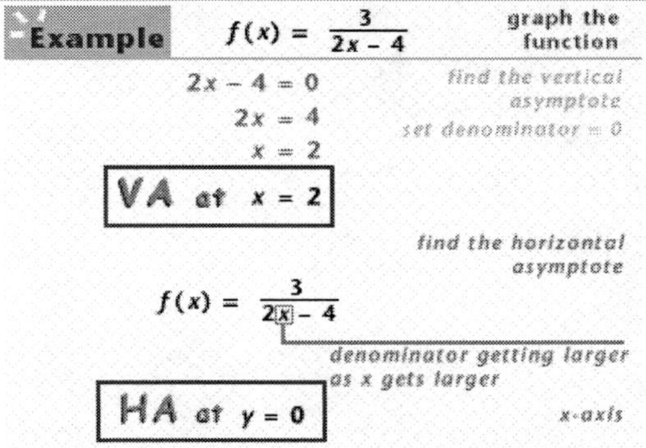

You can use what you have learned about horizontal and vertical asymptotes to graph rational functions.

This question asks you to graph the function $f(x)$.

The first step is to find the vertical asymptotes. The fraction is already in lowest terms, so just set the denominator equal to zero and solve for x.

Now find the horizontal asymptotes. The largest power of x in the denominator is greater than the largest power of x in the numerator, so there is a horizontal asymptote at $y = 0$.

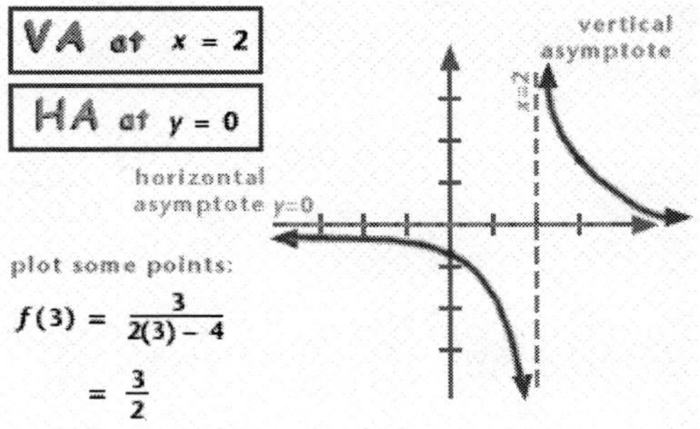

The asymptotes split the plane up into separate regions.

Plot a few points so you know which regions the graph is in and to give you a rough idea of the shape of the curve. Draw a curve that goes through those points and approaches the asymptotes. This curve is the graph of $f(x)$!

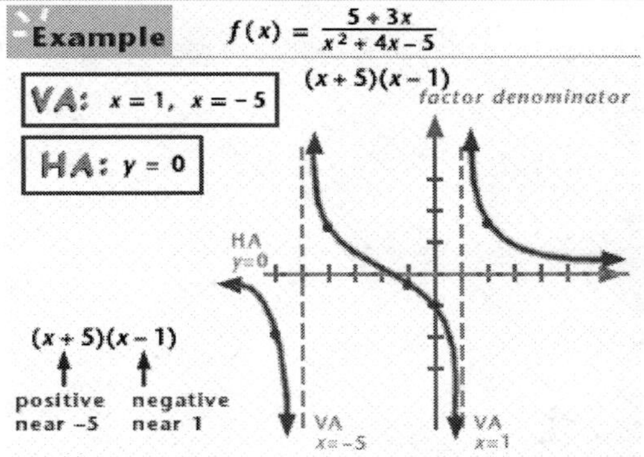

Let's try another example.

The first step is to find the vertical asymptotes. In this case, there are two. Next, find the horizontal asymptotes. Here, there is one at $y = 0$.

Sketch the asymptotes on a graph. They split the plane up into different regions. Plot some points so you know which regions the graph of $f(x)$ is in. Draw a curve that goes through those points and approaches the asymptotes and you're done.

NOTICE: You can also find and plot the x and y-intercepts to help you draw the graph.

Sample problems:

1. Graph: $f(x) = \frac{x^2-4}{x^2-1}$.

   Solution:

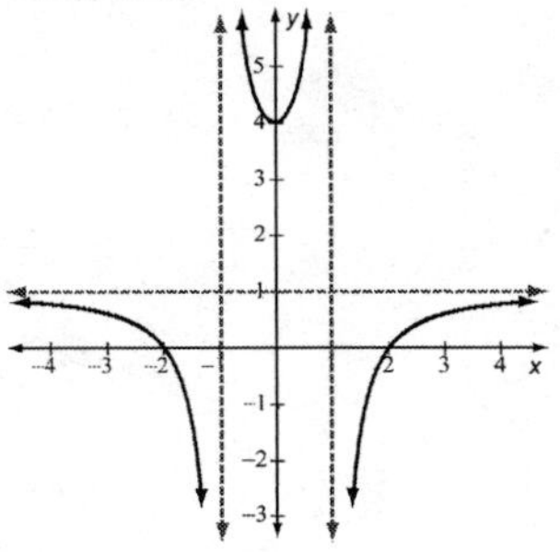

Explanation: Setting the denominator equal to 0 and factoring, we determine that the function has vertical asymptotes at $x=1$ and $x=-1$. Since the degree of the numerator is equal to the degree of the denominator, the equation of the horizontal asymptote is $y=\frac{1}{1}=1$. Some points in a table of values for $y=\frac{x^2-4}{x^2-1}$ are $(-2,0)$, $(0,4)$ and $(2,0)$. Plot these points and watch for symmetry.

2. Graph: $f(x)=\dfrac{x+10}{x^2-2x-3}$

Solution:

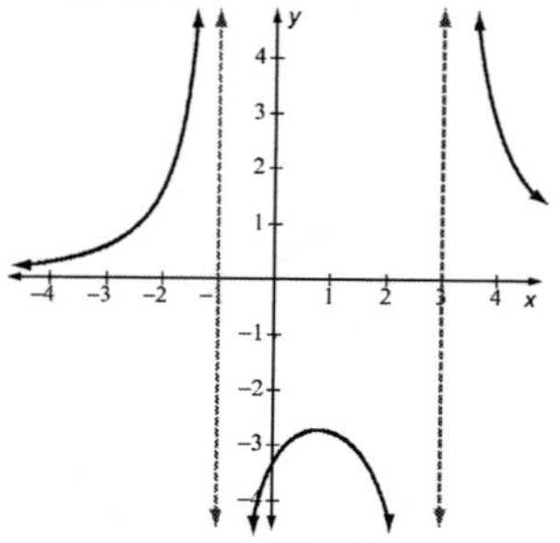

Explanation: Setting the denominator equal to 0 and factoring, we determine that the function has vertical asymptotes at $x=-1$ and $x=3$. Since the degree of the numerator is less than the degree of the denominator, the equation of the horizontal asymptotes is $y=0$. Some points in a table of values for $y=\frac{(x+10)}{(x^2-2x-3)}$ are $\left(-2,\frac{8}{5}\right)$, $\left(0,-\frac{10}{3}\right)$ and $(2,-4)$. Plot these points and watch for symmetry.

3. Graph: $f(x)=\dfrac{x}{x^2-4}$.

Solution:

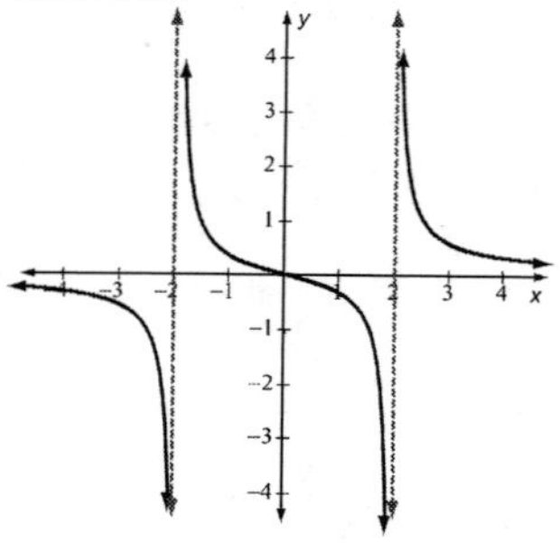

Explanation: Setting the denominator equal to 0 and factoring, we determine that the function has vertical asymptotes at $x=2$ and $x=-2$. Since the degree of the numerator is less than the degree of the denominator, the equation of the horizontal asymptote is $y=0$. Some points in a table of values for $y=\frac{x}{x^2-4}$ are $\left(-3,-\frac{3}{5}\right)$, $(0,0)$ and $\left(3,\frac{3}{5}\right)$. Plot these points and watch for symmetry.

Practice problems: *(Answers on page: 748)*

1. Graph: $f(x)=\dfrac{3}{x-2}$

2. Graph: $f(x)=\dfrac{5x}{x-1}$

3. Graph: $f(x)=\dfrac{3x}{x^2-4}$

Review questions: *(Answers to odd questions on page: 748)*

1. Graph: $f(x)=\dfrac{-3}{x+1}$
2. Graph: $f(x)=\dfrac{x-2}{x-5}$
3. Graph: $f(x)=\dfrac{x-1}{x-3}$
4. Graph: $f(x)=\dfrac{2x}{x^2-1}$
5. Graph: $f(x)=\dfrac{-3x}{x^2-25}$

Examples with Quadratics

- An asymptote is a line that the graph of a function approaches but never touches. Asymptotes can be either vertical or horizontal.
- You can use the horizontal and vertical asymptotes of a rational function to help you sketch its graph.

Example $f(x)=\dfrac{x^2-1}{x+1}$ graph the function ✔ lowest terms? $f(x)=\dfrac{(x+1)(x-1)}{(x+1)}$ (with $(x+1)$ crossed out) $x\neq -1$ promise: denominator $\neq 0$ $f(x)=x-1$	This problem asks you to graph the rational function $f(x)$. First, find the vertical asymptotes. The $(x+1)$ terms in the numerator and denominator cancel, so there are none. There are no horizontal asymptotes either.
$f(-1)=(-1)-1$ $=-2$ 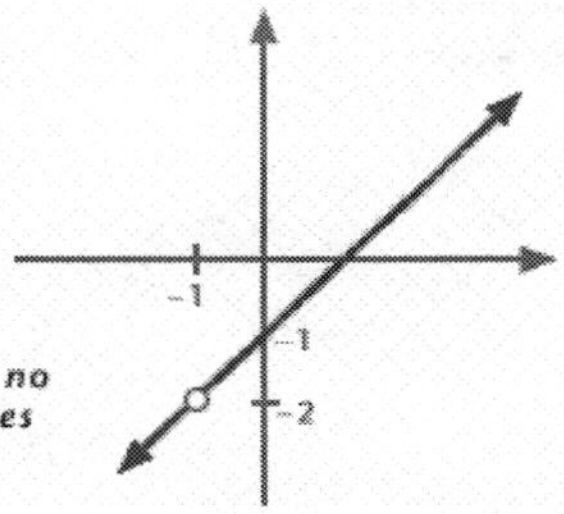 note: *there are no asymptotes*	This is an easy one! The function is just a line with a hole in it at $x=-1$.
Example $f(x)=\dfrac{(9x-1)(x+3)}{(2x+6)(x-5)}$ graph the function ✔ lowest terms? factor $f(x)=\dfrac{(9x-1)(x+3)}{2(x+3)(x-5)}$ (with $(x+3)$ crossed out) $=\dfrac{(9x-1)}{2(x-5)}$ promise: *denominator* $\neq 0$ $x\neq -3$ VA: $x=5$ *find vertical asymptote set denominator = 0*	What about this problem? The first step is to find the vertical asymptotes. Factor and cancel some terms to put the fraction in lowest terms. Set the denominator equal to zero and solve for x. **REMEMBER:** When you cancel terms in a rational function, you have to promise that the old denominator will never equal zero.
$=\dfrac{(9x-1)}{(2x-5)}$ HA: $y=\dfrac{9}{2}$	Now find the horizontal asymptotes. The largest power of x in the numerator is equal to the largest power of x in the denominator, so there is a horizontal asymptote located at the quotient of the coefficients.

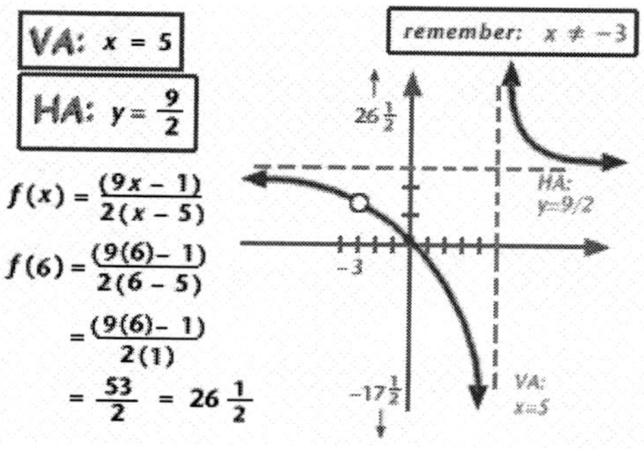

Time to draw the graph. Sketch in the asymptotes, plot a few points, and draw in the curve.

Don't forget about your promise! There is a hole in the graph at
$x = -3$.

Sample problems:

1. Graph the following rational function $f(x) = \dfrac{x^2 - 9}{x - 3}$.

   Solution:

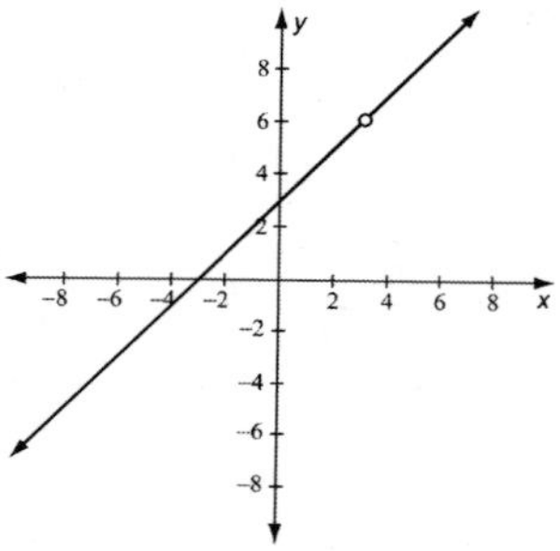

   Explanation: Factoring the numerator yields $x - 3$ as a factor common to both the numerator and denominator. Therefore, the graph will have a hole at $x = 3$. The function can be described as $f(x) = x + 3$, for x not equal to 3. Substitute $x = 3$ into the expression $x + 3$ to find the coordinates of the hole, $(3, 6)$. Since the degree of the numerator is greater than the degree of the denominator, there is no horizontal asymptote. Notice that, except for the hole, the graph is a line.

2. Graph the following rational function: $f(x) = \dfrac{(2x+4)(x-1)}{(x+3)(x+2)}$.

   Solution:

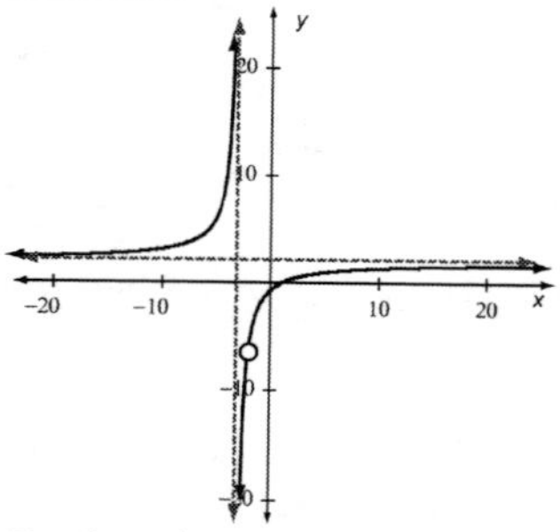

   Explanation: According to the numerator, we find that $x + 2$ is a common factor between the numerator and denominator. Therefore we have a hole at $x = -2$. Substituting into $\dfrac{2(x-1)}{(x+3)}$, we find that the hole has coordinates $(-2, -6)$. Setting the other factor in the denominator equal to 0, we determine that the function has a vertical asymptote at $x = -3$. Since the degree of the numerator is the same as the degree of the denominator, the equation of the horizontal asymptote is $y = 2$. Graph the function using symmetry.

3. Graph the following rational function: $f(x)=\frac{x+1}{x^2+1}$.

Solution:

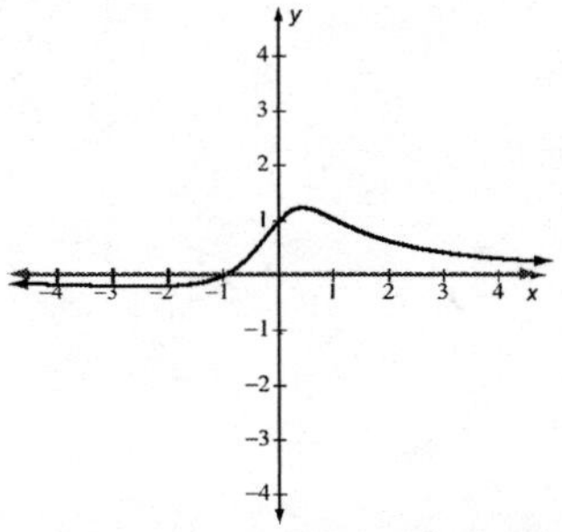

Explanation: The numerator and denominator have no factors in common. Therefore, there are no holes in the graph. Since the denominator never equals 0, the function has no vertical asymptotes. The degree of the numerator is less than the degree of the denominator, so the equation of the horizontal asymptote is $y = 0$. Plot some points and sketch the graph.

Practice problems: *(Answers on page: 748)*

1. Graph: $f(x)=\frac{x-5}{x^2-6x+5}$
2. Graph: $f(x)=\frac{(-2x-4)(x+4)}{(x+5)(x-2)}$
3. Graph: $f(x)=\frac{x^2}{x^2-16}$

Review questions: *(Answers to odd questions on page: 749)*

1. Graph: $f(x)=\frac{x-4}{x^2-2x-8}$
2. Graph: $f(x)=\frac{(-5x-15)(x-2)}{(x+4)(x-5)}$
3. Graph: $f(x)=\frac{(4x+12)(x-2)}{(x-5)(x+4)}$
4. Graph: $f(x)=\frac{x^2}{x^2-9}$
5. Graph: $f(x)=\frac{1}{x^2+3}$

5

Exponential and Logarithmic Functions

Understanding Inverse Functions

- An **inverse function** "undoes" another function.
  If $g(x)$ is the inverse function of $f(x)$, then $g\left[\left(f(x)\right)\right]=x$ and $f\left[\left(g(x)\right)\right]=x$.
- Not all functions have inverse functions.

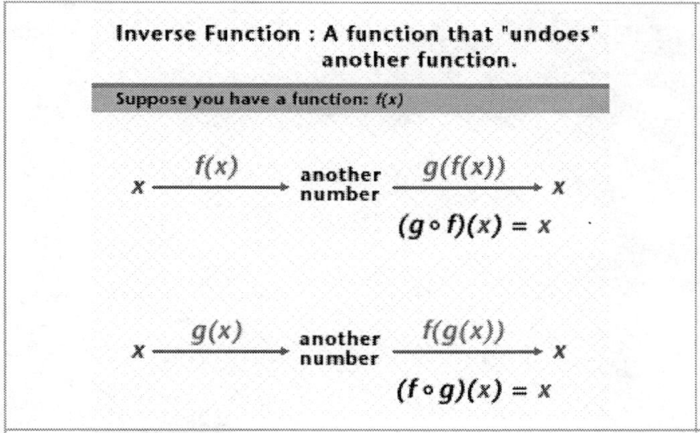

We are going to explore the concept of inverse functions.

A function $f(x)$ takes an input, x, and produces an output, $f(x)$. Its inverse function $g(x)$ takes $f(x)$ as its input and outputs x. It "undoes" the action of $f(x)$.

If $g(x)$ is the inverse function of $f(x)$, then $f(x)$ is also the inverse function of $g(x)$. So $f(x)$ undoes the action of $g(x)$, too.

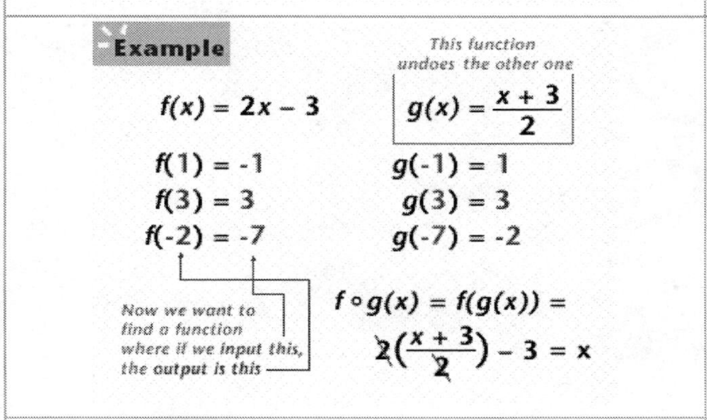

That was pretty abstract. Let's try a concrete example.

Consider this function $f(x)$. If you plug in $x=1$, $f(x)$ outputs -1. If you plug in $x=-2$, $f(x)$ outputs -7, and so on. In order to find the inverse function, you need a function that will "undo" $f(x)$. You need a function that will output 1 when you plug in $x=-1$ and output -2 when you plug in $x=-7$, and so on. Notice that the function $g(x)$ does exactly this.

In fact, if you compute the value of $f[g(x)]$, you find that it is equal to x. The functions really are inverses!

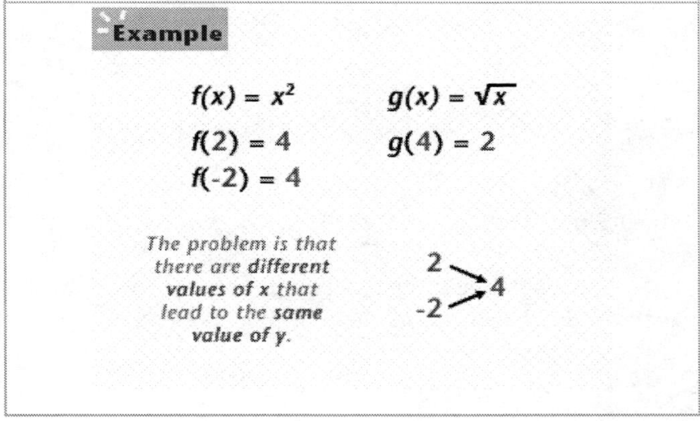

Does the function $f(x)=x^2$ have an inverse?

$g(x)=\sqrt{x}$ looks like a good possibility for the inverse, but notice that $f(-2)=4$, whereas $g(4)\neq-2$.

The problem is that for $f(x)=x^2$, two different input values lead to the same output value. So given the output value, a hypothetical inverse function wouldn't know which of the two inputs to return! The function $f(x)=x^2$ has no inverse.

REMEMBER: Not all functions have inverses.

Sample problems:

1. Given that $f(5)=15$, find $f^{-1}(15)$.
   Solution: 5
   Explanation: The inverse function reverses the input and output. So, $f^{-1}(15)=5$, since $f(5)=15$.

2. True or false: If (2,19) is a member of f, and f^{-1} exists, then the point (19,2) is a member of f^{-1}.
   Solution: True
   Explanation: If (2,19) is a member of f that means that $f(2)=19$. The inverse reverses the input and output, so $f^{-1}(19)=2$. Therefore, (19,2) is a member of f^{-1}.

3. Given that $g^{-1}(-4) = 3$, find $g(3)$.
   Solution: -4
   Explanation: The inverse function reverses the input and output. So, $g(3) = -4$, since $g^{-1}(-4) = 3$.

Practice problems: *(Answers on page: 749)*

1. Given that $g^{-1}(x)$ is the inverse of $g(x)$ and that $g^{-1}(-4) = 3$, find $g(3)$.

2. If $(-3, \frac{1}{2})$ is a member of f, and f^{-1} exists, find $f^{-1}(\frac{1}{2})$.

3. Given that $g^{-1}(5) = 2$, find $g(2)$.

Review questions: *(Answers to odd questions on page: 749)*

1. Given that $f(12) = 6$, find $f^{-1}(6)$.
2. Given that $g^{-1}(-3) = 8$, find $g(8)$.
3. Given that $g^{-1}(x)$ is the inverse of $g(x)$ and that $g^{-1}(5) = 2$, find $g(2)$.
4. If $(6.3, 3.2)$ is a member of f, and f^{-1} exists, find $f^{-1}(3.2)$.
5. If $(17.5, -0.2)$ is a member of f, and f^{-1} exists, find $f^{-1}(-0.2)$.

The Horizontal Line Test

- The **horizontal line test**: If the graph of a function intersects every horizontal line at most once, then the function has an inverse.
- A **one-to-one function** is a function that satisfies the horizontal line test. For a one-to-one function, every output y-value comes from exactly one input x-value.

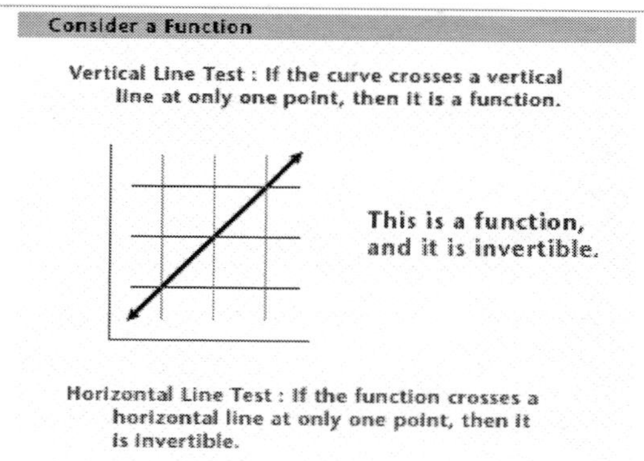

Previously you learned that you could find out whether a graph described a function using the vertical line test.

Now, you can use the **horizontal line test** to determine whether a function has an inverse. If the graph of a function intersects every horizontal line at most once, the function has an inverse. Otherwise, the function has no inverse, because some y-values (outputs) might have more than one corresponding x-value (input).

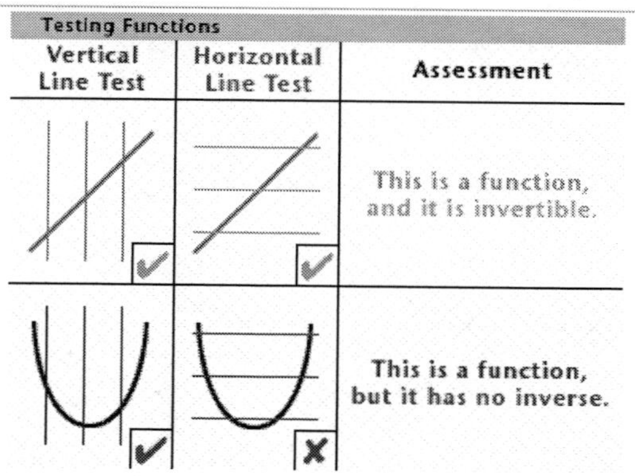

The horizontal line test tells you that a linear function has an inverse.

A parabola, though, has no inverse because it fails the horizontal line test. Sometimes, two different x-values lead to the same y-value.

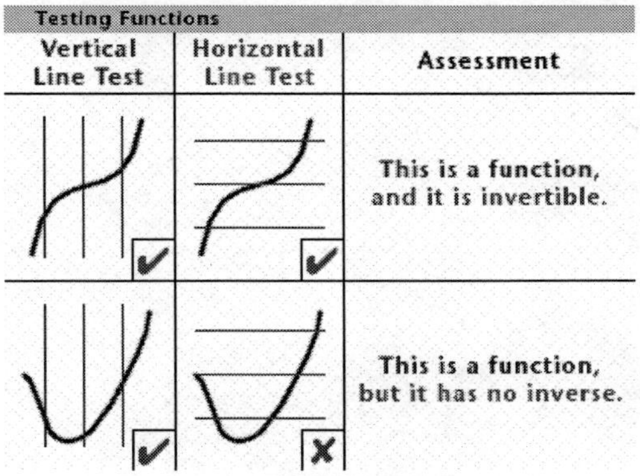

Let's try some more examples.

This cubic function has an inverse. It intersects any horizontal line at exactly one point.

This exotic function fails the horizontal line test and has no inverse.

One-to-One Functions : Functions where every *x* goes to only one *y*, and every *y* came from only one *x*.

Functions that pass the horizontal line test are also known as **one-to-one functions**. For a one-to-one function, every x-value goes to only one y-value, and every y-value corresponds to only one x-value. A function has an inverse if it is one-to-one, and a function is one-to-one if it has an inverse.

Sample problems:

1. Does the inverse function of $y = \dfrac{x}{3} + 2$ exist?

   Solution: Yes

   Explanation: An inverse function exists if the graph passes the horizontal line test. To pass the horizontal line test, any horizontal line can intersect the graph no more than one time. The graph of $y = \frac{x}{3} + 2$ is a line since the equation is linear (no exponents), and the line is slanted up since the slope is $\frac{1}{3}$. This graph passes the horizontal line test, so the inverse function of $y = \frac{x}{3} + 2$ exists.

2. True or false: The following graph is a one-to-one function.

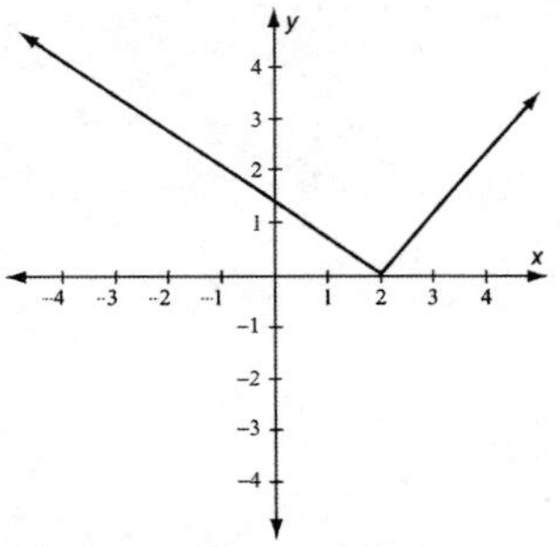

   Solution: False

   Explanation: The graph fails the horizontal line test, therefore it is not one-to-one.

3. True or false: $f(x) = 3 - x^2$ is a one-to-one function.

   Solution: False

   Explanation: The graph of $f(x) = 3 - x^2$ is a parabola since the equation is quadratic (x is squared) and the parabola opens down since the coefficient of x^2 is negative. This graph fails the horizontal line test since many horizontal lines will intersect the parabola twice. Therefore, it is not a one-to-one function.

Practice problems: *(Answers on page: 749)*

1. Does the inverse of $f(x) = 2x + 5$ exist?

2. True or false: The following graph is a one-to-one function.

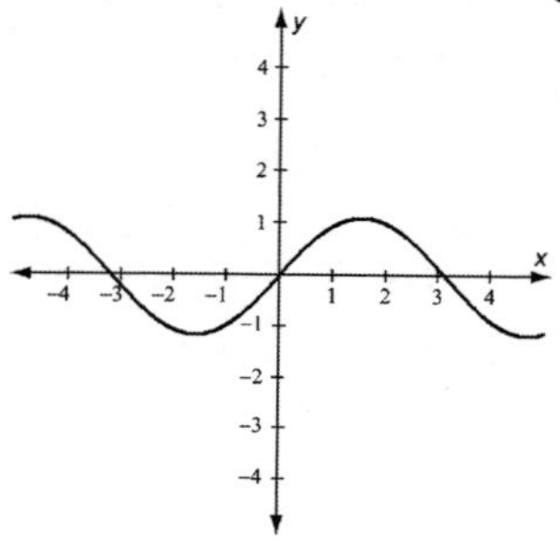

3. True or false: $g(x)=x^3+5x-1$ is a one-to-one function.

Review questions: *(Answers to odd questions on page: 749)*

1. Does the inverse of $h(x)=x^3-x+1$ exist?
2. True or false: The following graph is a one-to-one function.

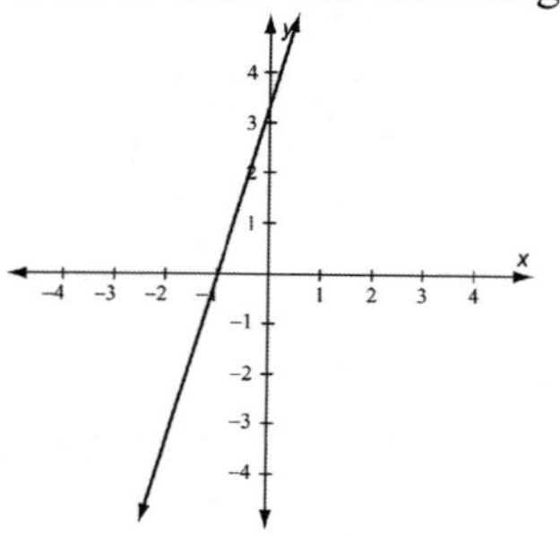

3. True or false: The following graph is a one-to-one function.

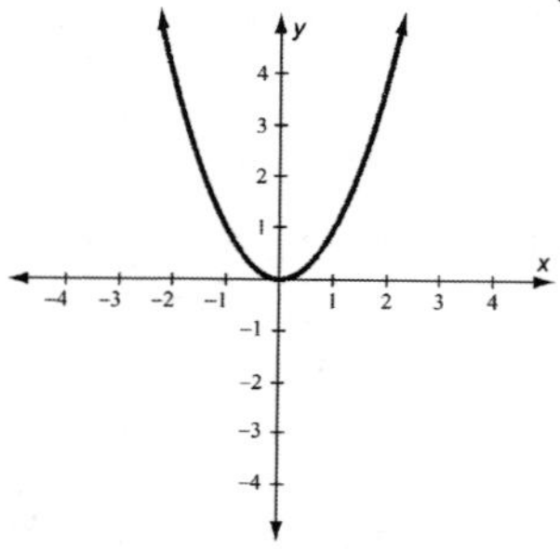

4. True or false: The following graph is a one-to-one function.

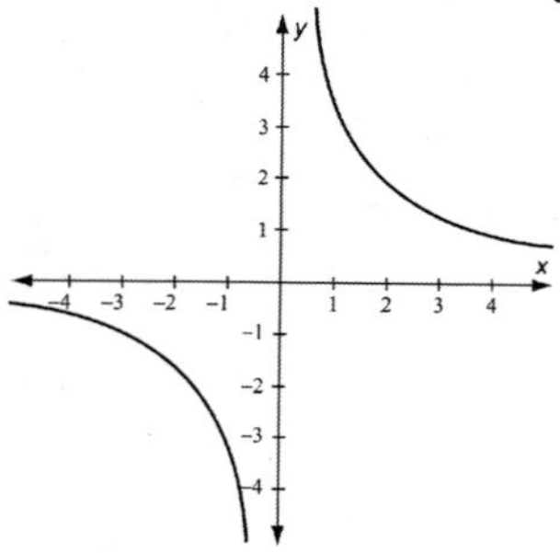

5. True or false: $g(x)=x^3+3x-7$ is a one-to-one function.

Are Two Functions Inverses of Each Other?

- The graphs of inverse functions are reflections of each other across the line $y=x$.
- The notation $f^{-1}(x)$ means "the inverse of the function $f(x)$".
- Inverse functions satisfy the two equations $f\circ f^{-1}(x)=x$ and $f^{-1}\circ f(x)=x$.

Identifying Inverses Visually

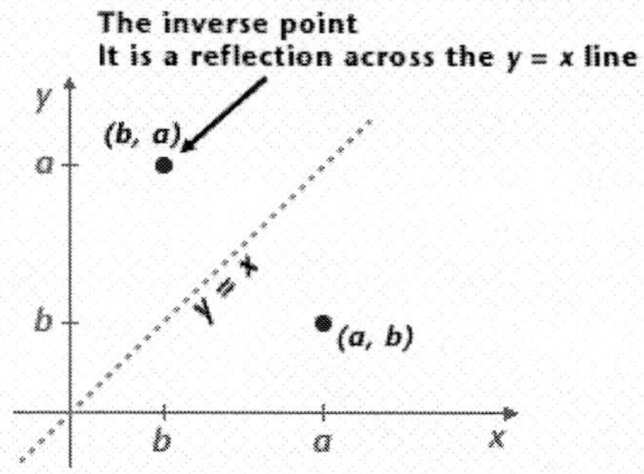

There is an easy way to determine whether two functions are inverses from their graphs.

Suppose that the point (a, b) is on the graph of a function. Then the input a results in the output b for that function. The inverse function will take the value b and output the value a. In other words, the point (b, a) will be on the graph of the inverse function. So, the inverse function will be the reflection of the original function across the line $y = x$.

To denote an inverse function of $f(x)$, write $f^{-1}(x)$

You will see this notation for inverse functions in the future. Notice that $f^{-1}(x) \neq \frac{1}{f(x)}$.

Example – Identifying Inverses Graphically –

$f(x) = 2x - 3$

$f^{-1}(x) = \frac{x+3}{2} = \frac{1}{2}x + \frac{3}{2}$

The two lines are reflections of each other. So, they are inverses.

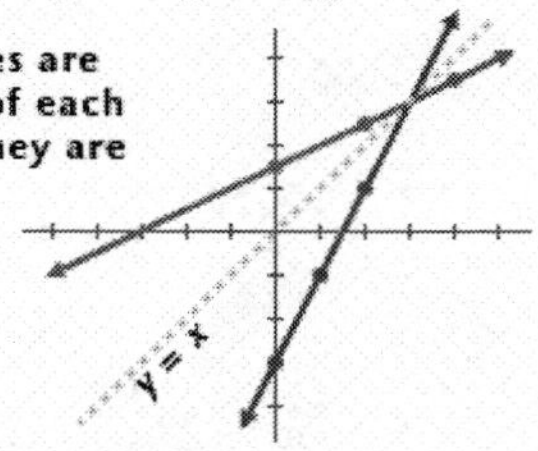

✓ $f \circ f^{-1}(x) = f(f^{-1}(x)) = 2\left(\frac{x+3}{2}\right) - 3 = \boxed{x}$

✓ $f^{-1} \circ f(x) = f^{-1}(f(x)) = \frac{2x - 3 + 3}{2} = \frac{2x}{2} = \boxed{x}$

How can you check to see if these two functions are inverses? One method is to examine the graphs of the functions.

The graphs of the two functions are reflections of each other across the line $y = x$. You can conclude that the functions are indeed inverses.

You can also check that two functions are inverses algebraically. Just evaluate $f \circ f^{-1}(x)$ and $f^{-1} \circ f(x)$. If they are both equal to x, then the functions are inverses.

Example – Identifying Inverses Algebraically –

$f(x) = \frac{2}{x+6}$

$f^{-1}(x) = \frac{6x+2}{x}$

☐ $f \circ f^{-1}(x) = f(f^{-1}(x)) = \dfrac{2}{\frac{6x+2}{x} + 6} = \dfrac{2}{\frac{6x+2}{x} + \frac{6x}{x}} = \dfrac{2}{\frac{12x+2}{x}} = \dfrac{2x}{12x+2}$

Here is another example. One way to check whether these two functions are inverses would be to see if their graphs were reflections of each other across the line $y = x$.

Another way is to compute $f \circ f^{-1}(x)$ and $f^{-1} \circ f(x)$. In this case, $f \circ f^{-1}(x) \neq x$, so the two functions are not inverses.

Sample problems:

1. True or false: Given $f(x) = -\frac{2}{x}$ and $g(x) = \frac{2}{x}$, f and g are inverses of one another.

   Solution: False

   Explanation: Evaluate: $f \circ g = f(g(x)) = -\frac{2}{\frac{2}{x}} = -2 \div \frac{2}{x} = -2 \cdot \frac{x}{2} = -x$. Since $f(g(x)) \neq x$, f and g are not inverse functions.

2. True or false: Given $f(x) = 2 + x^3$ and $g(x) = \sqrt[3]{x-2}$, f and g are inverses of one another.
Solution: True

Explanation: Evaluate: $f \circ g = f(g(x)) = 2 + \left(\sqrt[3]{x-2}\right)^3 = 2 + (x-2) = 2 + x - 2 = x$.

Evaluate: $g \circ f = g(f(x)) = \sqrt[3]{(2+x^3)-2} = \sqrt[3]{2+x^3-2} = \sqrt[3]{x^3} = x$. Since $f(g(x)) = x$ and $g(f(x)) = x$, f and g are inverses of one another.

3. Determine whether the functions below are inverses of each other by comparing their graphs with the line $y = x$.

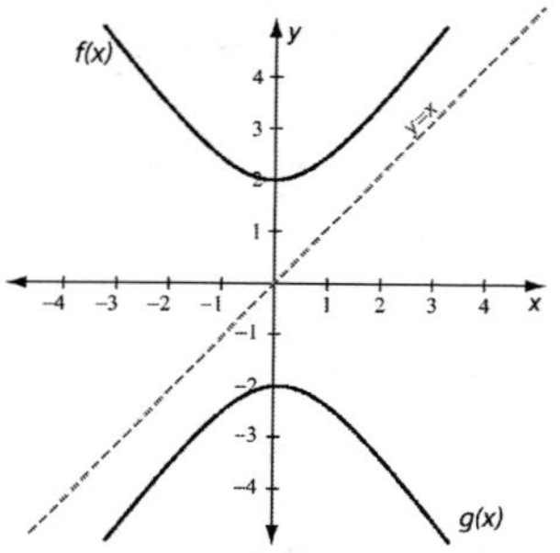

Solution: They are not inverses
Explanation: The two functions are not reflections of each other across the line $y = x$; therefore they are not inverses.

Practice problems: *(Answers on page: 749)*

1. Determine whether the functions below are inverses of each other by comparing their graphs with the line $y = x$.

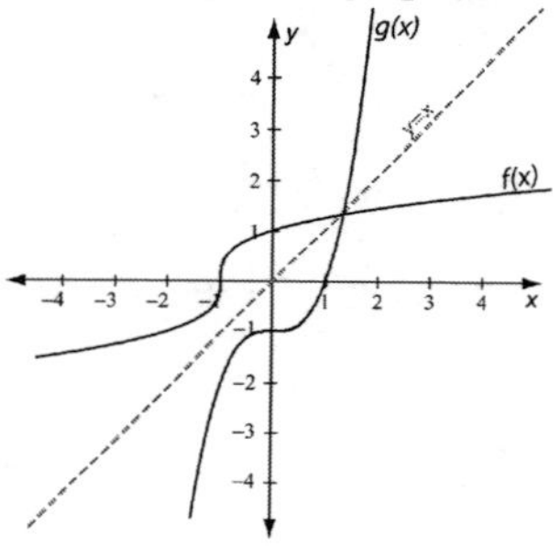

2. True or false: Given $f(x) = \sqrt{4-x}$, $x \le 4$ and $g(x) = 4 - x^2, x > 0$, f and g are inverses of one another.
3. True or false: Given $f(x) = \dfrac{(4x-2)}{5}$ and $g(x) = \dfrac{(5x+2)}{4}$, f and g are inverses of one another.

Review questions: *(Answers to odd questions on page: 749)*

1. Given that $f(x) = \dfrac{8x+3}{7}$ and $g(x) = \dfrac{7x-3}{8}$, are f and g inverses of one another?
2. Given that $f(x) = \sqrt{4-x}$, with domain $(-\infty, 4]$ and $g(x) = 4 - x^2$, with domain $(0, \infty)$, are f and g inverses of one another?
3. Given that $f(x) = \dfrac{3}{2-x}$ and $g(x) = 2 + \dfrac{3}{x}$, are f and g inverses of one another?

4. Determine whether each pair of functions are inverses of each other or not by comparing their graphs with the line $y = x$.

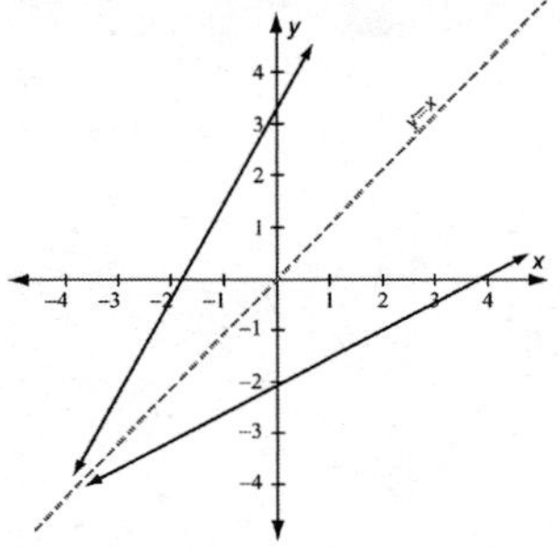

5. True or false: Given $f(x) = 2 + x^3$ and $g(x) = \sqrt[3]{x-2}$, f and g are inverses of one another.

Graphing the Inverse

- The horizontal line test says that if the graph of a function intersects every horizontal line at most once, then the function has an inverse.
- The graphs of inverse functions are reflections of each other across the line $y = x$.

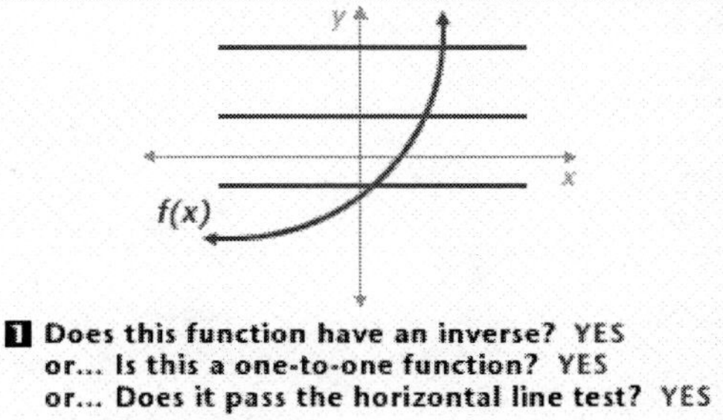	Take a look at the graph of this function. Does this function have an inverse? You can answer this question using the horizontal line test. $f(x)$ is one-to-one because it passes the horizontal line test. It has an inverse for the same reason.
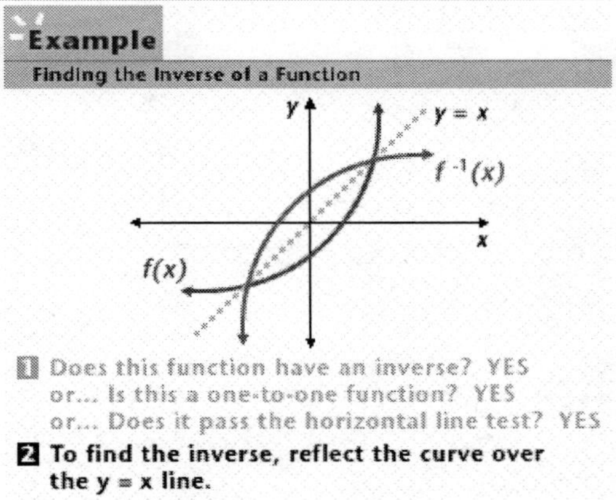	To actually find the inverse function, just reflect the graph of $f(x)$ over the line $y = x$. The result is the graph of $f^{-1}(x)$.
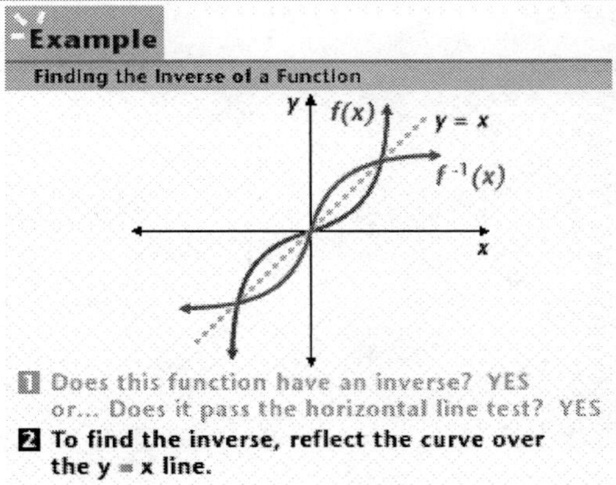	In this example, the inverse of the function $f(x)$ has been sketched in along with the graph of $f(x)$. The two graphs are reflections of each other across the line $y = x$.

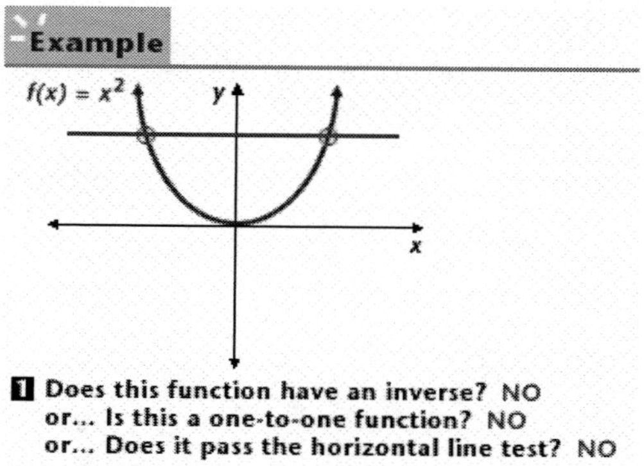

What about this function? Can you sketch its inverse?

This function fails the horizontal line test! It has no inverse.

Sample problems:

1. Graph the inverse f^{-1} (if it exists) of the function f.

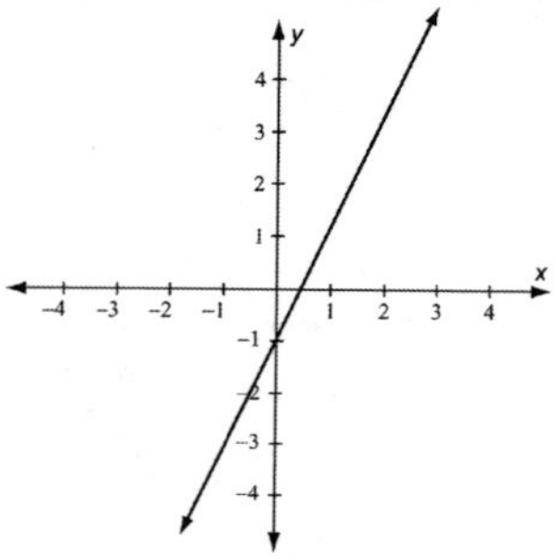

Solution:

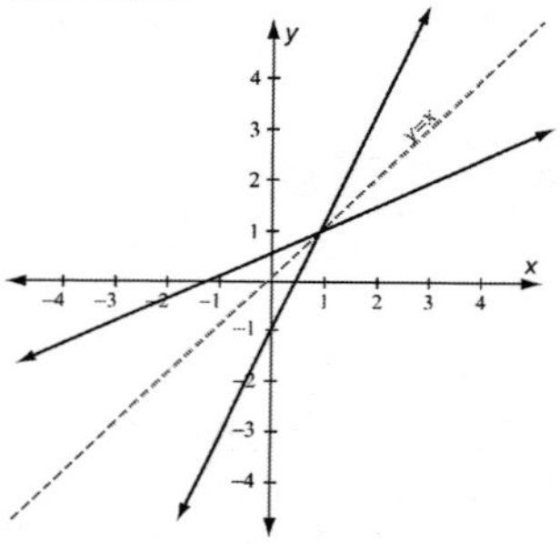

Explanation: The function is one-to-one since it passes the vertical and horizontal line tests. Therefore the inverse function does exist. To graph the inverse, sketch the line $y = x$ then reflect the given line over the line $y = x$.

2. Graph the inverse f^{-1} (if it exists) of the function f.

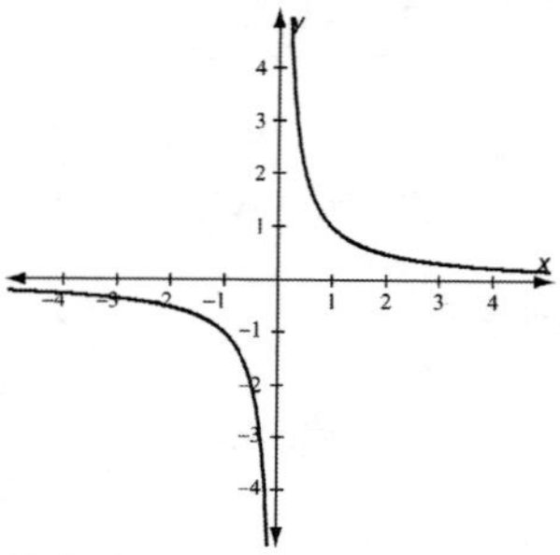

Solution:

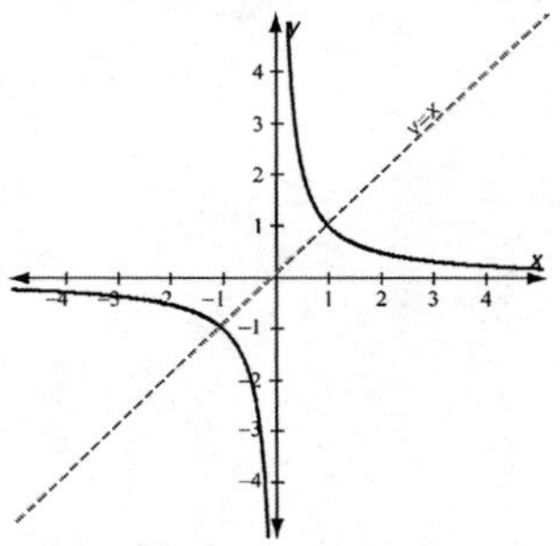

Explanation: The sketched reflection creates a duplicate of the graph. So, the function is its own inverse, $f = f^{-1}$.

3. Graph the inverse f^{-1} (if it exists) of the function f, and find $f^{-1}(1)$.

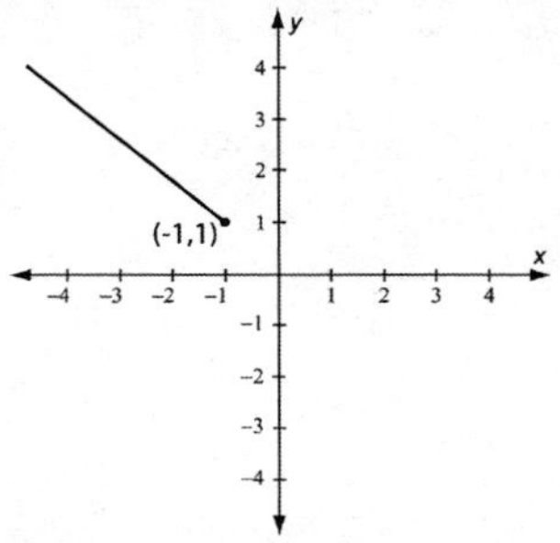

Solution: $f^{-1}(1)$ is -1.

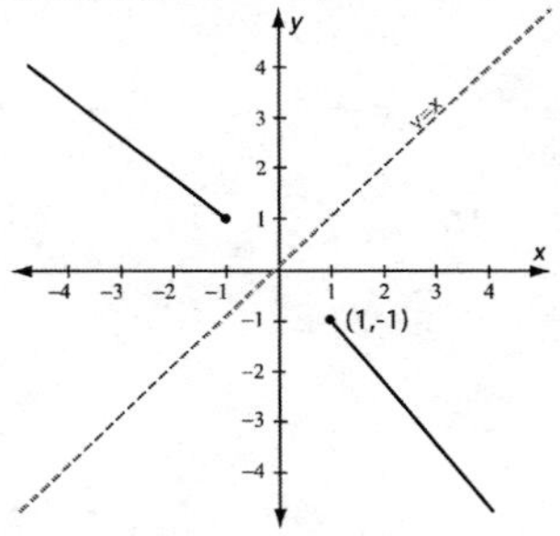

Explanation: Sketch the graph by reflecting the given graph across the line $y = x$. Use the new graph, f^{-1}, to determine $f^{-1}(1)$, the y-value that corresponds with $x = 1$, so $f^{-1}(1) = -1$.

Practice problems: *(Answers on page: 749)*

1. Graph the inverse f^{-1} (if it exists) of the function f.

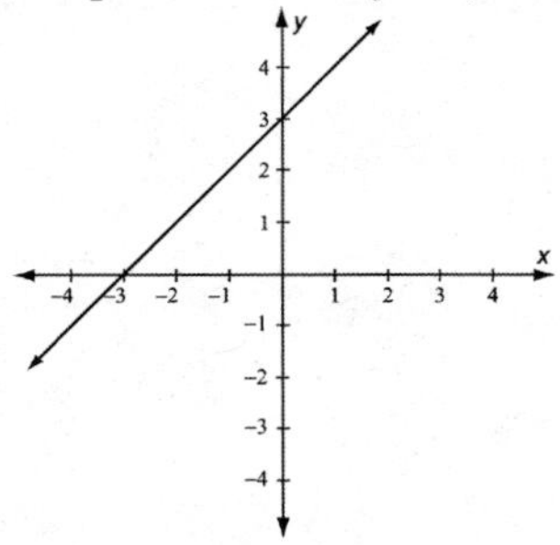

2. Graph the inverse f^{-1} (if it exists) of the function f.

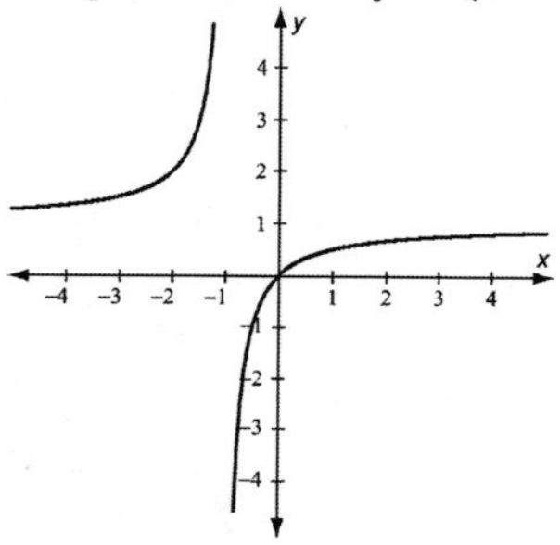

3. Graph the inverse f^{-1} (if it exists) of the function f, and find $f^{-1}(0)$.

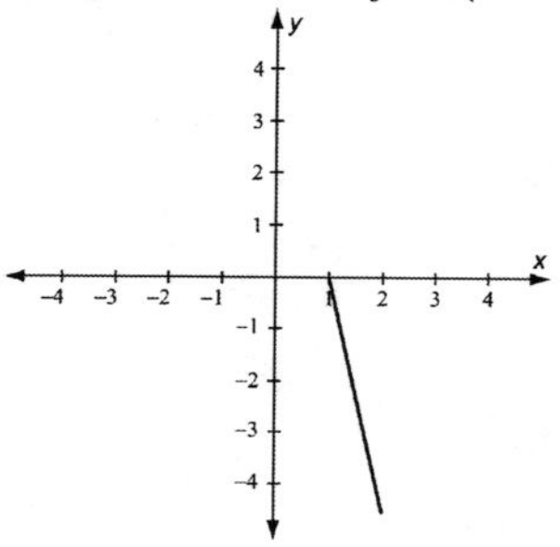

Review questions: *(Answers to odd questions on page: 749)*

1. Graph the inverse f^{-1} (if it exists) of the function f.

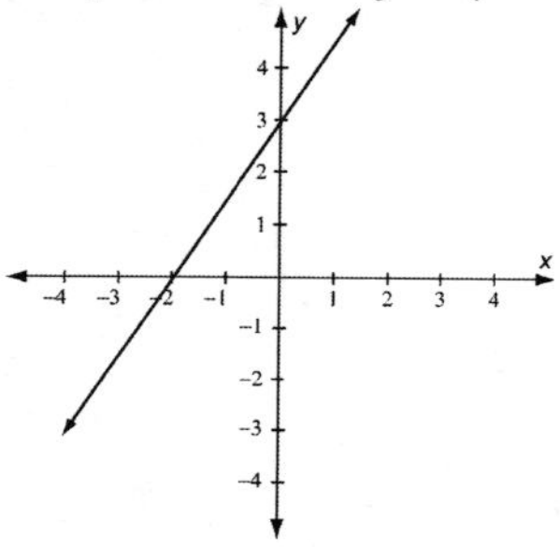

2. Graph the inverse f^{-1} (if it exists) of the function f.

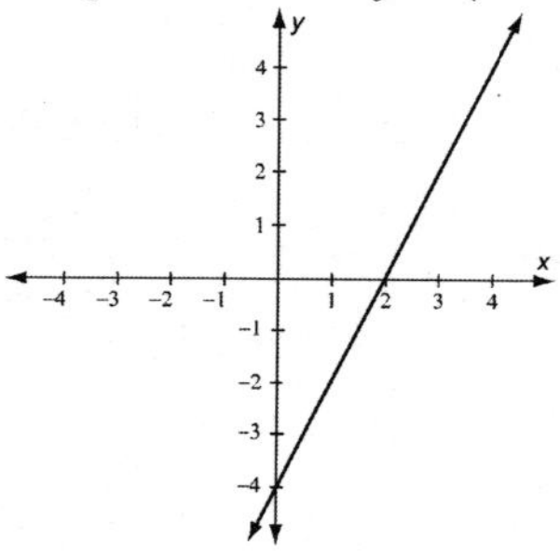

3. Graph the inverse f^{-1} (if it exists) of the function f.

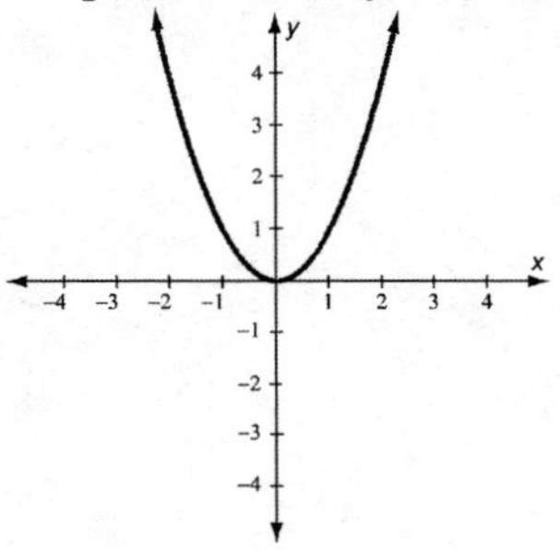

4. Graph the inverse f^{-1} (if it exists) of the function f.

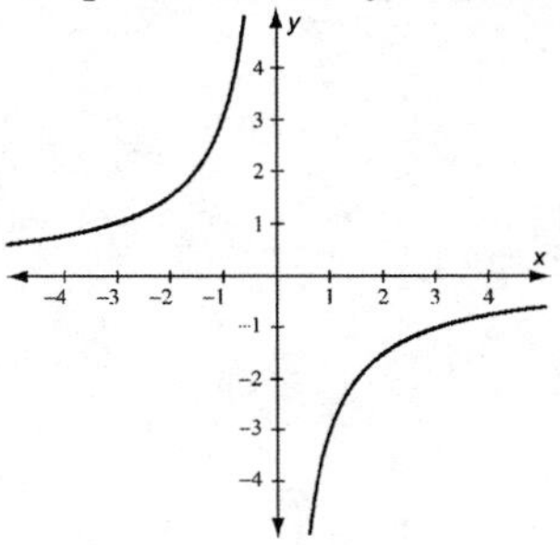

5. Graph the inverse f^{-1} of the function f, and find $f^{-1}(2)$.

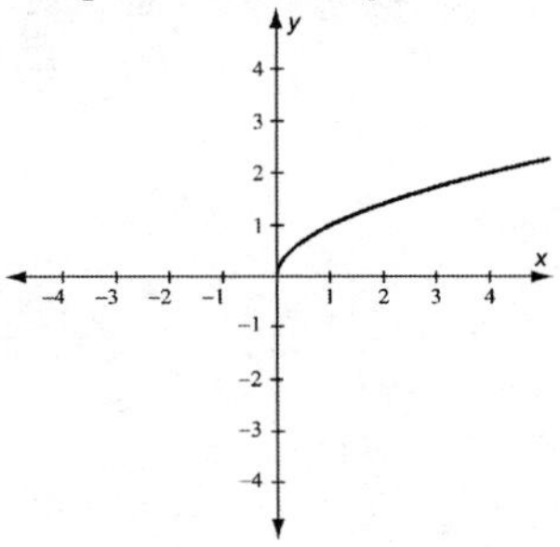

Finding the Inverse of a Function

- To find the inverse of a function algebraically:
  1. Swap the x variables with the y variables.
  2. Solve the new equation for y. If this new equation cannot be solved for y as a function of x, the original function does not have an inverse

Example	
Example **Finding the Inverse of a Function** *f(x) is the same thing as y* $y = 4x - 3 = f(x)$ $x = 4y - 3$ *Swap the x and y, then solve for y.* $4y = x + 3$ *If you can't solve for y, then the function has no inverse.* $y = \frac{x+3}{4} = f^{-1}(x)$	Previously, you learned how to find the inverse of a function graphically. Now you will learn how to find the inverse of a function algebraically. To find the inverse of this function, first swap the variable x with the variable y. Now solve the new equation for y. The result is the inverse function!

Example Find the inverse of $y = \frac{-6}{x}$ $x = \frac{-6}{y}$ *Swap the x and y* $y\left(x = \frac{-6}{y}\right)$ $yx = -6$ $y = \frac{-6}{x} = f^{-1}(x)$	Let's try another one. Can you find the inverse of this function? First, swap the x with the y. Now solve for y. You've found the inverse function $f^{-1}(x)$.
Example Find the inverse of $f(x) = y = x^2$ $x = y^2$ *Swap the x and y* $y = \pm\sqrt{x}$ This is not a function, because there are two values for y.	Let's try out our method on this function. Swap the x with the y. Then solve for y. Whoops! We don't get a function when we solve for y. This means that the original function does not have an inverse. **REMEMBER:** Not all functions have inverses!

Sample problems:

1. Find the inverse of $f(x) = \dfrac{2x-1}{3}$, if it exists.

   Solution: $f^{-1}(x) = \dfrac{3x+1}{2}$

   Explanation: Replace $f(x)$ with y: $y = \frac{2x-1}{3}$. Interchange the x and y variables: $x = \frac{2y-1}{3}$.
   Solve for y: $3x = 2y-1$; $2y = 3x+1$; $y = \frac{3x+1}{2}$. Replace y with $f^{-1}(x)$: $f^{-1}(x) = \frac{3x+1}{2}$.
   Check the inverse by evaluating $f^{-1}\left(f(x)\right)$ and $f\left(f^{-1}(x)\right)$,
   which should both equal x if they are indeed inverses.

2. Find the inverse of $u(x) = -3\sqrt{\dfrac{x}{3}}$, $x \ge 0$, if it exists, then find $u^{-1}(0)$.

   Solution: $u^{-1}(x) = \dfrac{x^2}{3}$; $u^{-1}(0) = 0$

   Explanation: Since the function is restricted to where $x \ge 0$, it is one-to-one. Replace $u(x)$ with y and swap the variables: $y = -3\sqrt{\frac{x}{3}} \Rightarrow x = -3\sqrt{\frac{y}{3}}$. Solve for y: $x^2 = (-3\sqrt{\frac{y}{3}})^2$; $x^2 = (-3)^2(\sqrt{\frac{y}{3}})^2$; $x^2 = 9\left(\frac{y}{3}\right)$; $x^2 = 3y$; $y = \frac{x^2}{3}$. So, $u^{-1}(x) = \frac{x^2}{3}$, $x \ge 0$. Find $u^{-1}(0)$ by substituting 0 into the inverse function for x: $u^{-1}(0) = \frac{(0)}{3} = 0$.

3. The apparent brightness b (in lumens) of a light source is a function of your distance x (in km) from the source and is given by $b(x) = \dfrac{32}{x^2}$. Find $b^{-1}(x)$, evaluate $b^{-1}(8)$, and explain the meaning of $b^{-1}(8)$ in the context of this problem.

   Solution: $b^{-1}(x) = \sqrt{\dfrac{32}{x}}$; $x \ge 0$; $b^{-1}(8) = 2$; at 2km the brightness of the light is 8 lumens.

   Explanation: Since x represents distance, assume $x \ge 0$, so $b(x)$ is one-to-one. Swap variables and solve for y: $b(x) = \frac{32}{x^2}$; $y = \frac{32}{x^2} \Rightarrow x = \frac{32}{y^2}$; $y^2x = 32$; $y^2 = \frac{32}{x}$; $y = \sqrt{\frac{32}{x}}$. So, $b^{-1} = \sqrt{\frac{32}{x}}$. Evaluate: $b^{-1}(8) = \sqrt{\frac{32}{8}} = \sqrt{4} = 2$km, which means that 8 lumens of light are experienced from 2km.

Practice problems: *(Answers on page: 749)*

1. Find the inverse of $g(x) = \dfrac{3(5-2x)}{7}$, and evaluate $g^{-1}(3)$.

2. Algebraically find the equation of the inverse function. If the function is not invertible, state why. $y = \dfrac{4-x^2}{2}$.

3. If x represents the length (in feet) of a pendulum, the period of swing (in seconds) of the pendulum is given by $p(x) = \sqrt{\dfrac{x}{5}}$. Find the equation for p^{-1} and compute $p^{-1}(3)$. What does $p^{-1}(3)$ represent?

Review questions: *(Answers to odd questions on page: 750)*

1. Find the inverse of $f(x) = 2x+1$, if it exists, then find $f^{-1}(5)$.

2. Find the inverse of $f(x) = \dfrac{-5x}{3}$; if it exists, then find $f^{-1}(4)$.

3. Algebraically find the equation of the inverse function. If the function is not invertible, state why. $y = 2x^2 - 5,\ x \geq 0$

4. Find the inverse of $u(x) = -3\sqrt{\dfrac{x}{3}},\ x \geq 0$; if it exists, then find $u^{-1}(-2)$.

5. The time (in hours) required by a team of rescuers to find a lost hiker depends on the number of rescuers x and is given by $t(x) = \dfrac{80}{x}$. What does $t^{-1}(5)$ represent? Now find the equation for $t^{-1}(x)$ and compute $t^{-1}(5)$.

Finding the Inverse of a Function with Higher Powers

- To find the inverse of a function algebraically:
  1. Swap the x variables with the y variables.
  2. Solve the new equation for y. If this new equation cannot be solved for y as a function of x, the original function does not have an inverse.

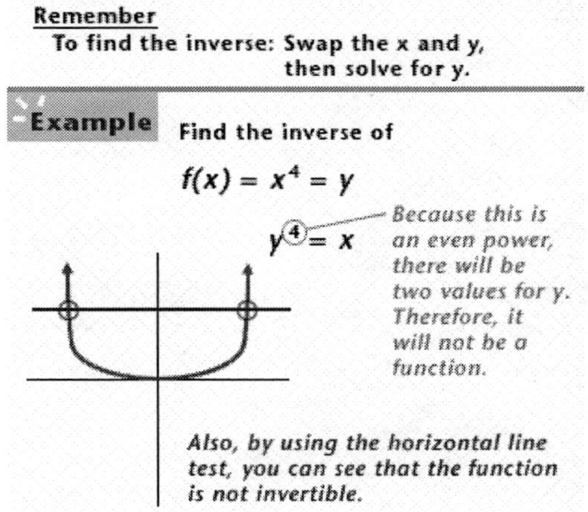

Let's do some practice problems finding the inverses of functions.

To find the inverse of this function, just swap the *x*s and *y*s and solve for *y*. In this case, when you solve for *y*, you do not get a function. This means that *f (x)* has no inverse.

Another way to see why *f (x)* has no inverse is to graph the original function *f (x)* and notice that it fails the horizontal line test. *f (x)* is not one-to-one, so it is not invertible.

<table>
<tr>
<td>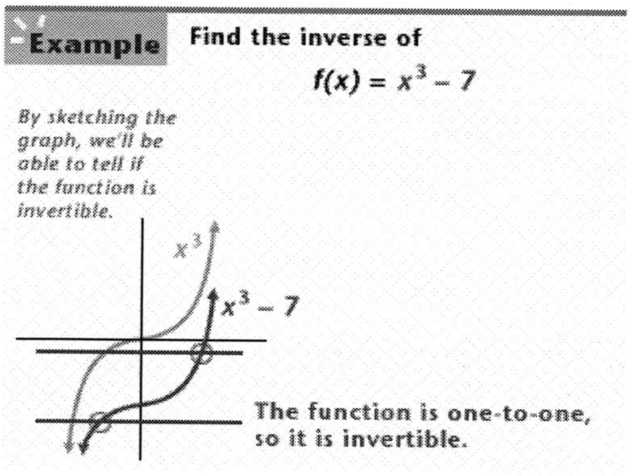
</td>
<td>Take a look at this problem.

If you want to, you can sketch the graph of $f(x)$ first to make sure that it has an inverse. In this case, the graph of $f(x)$ passes the horizontal line test. It therefore has an inverse function.</td>
</tr>
<tr>
<td>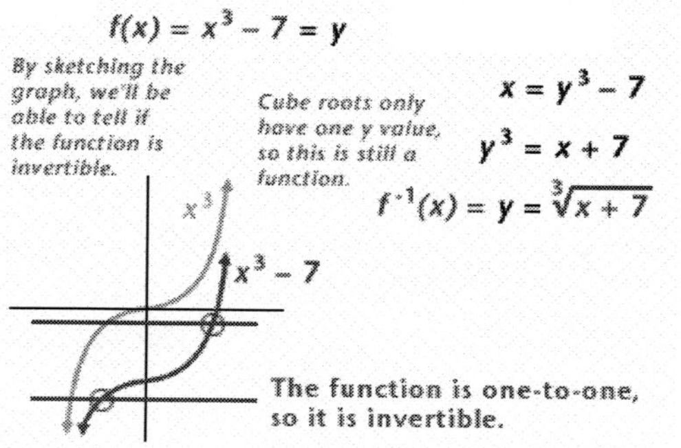
</td>
<td>To find the inverse function, swap the x with the y and solve for y. You can do this by using a cube root.

The result is a function, so there are no problems. You've found the inverse function $f^{-1}(x)$.</td>
</tr>
</table>

Sample problems:

1. Given $m(x)=2\sqrt[3]{4x-8}$, write the equation of the inverse of $m(x)$ and find $m^{-1}(2)$.
   Solution: $m^{-1}(x)=\frac{x^3}{32}+2$ and $m^{-1}(2)=\frac{9}{4}$
   Explanation: Since the function *is* one-to-one, interchange "x" and "y"
   and solve for (the new) y: $y=2\sqrt[3]{4x-8}\ \rightarrow\ x=2\sqrt[3]{4y-8}$;
   $(x)^3=\left(2\sqrt[3]{4y-8}\right)^3$; $x^3=8(4y-8)$; $x^3=32y-64$; $32y=x^3+64$; $y=\frac{x^3}{32}+2$.
   Relabel "y" as $m^{-1}(x)$: $m^{-1}(x)=\frac{x^3}{32}+2$.
   Evaluate the inverse function: $m^{-1}(2)=\frac{(2)^3}{32}+2=\frac{9}{4}$.

2. Given $f(x)=32(x-1)^5+17$, find the equation of the inverse function.
   If the function is not invertible, state why.
   Solution: $f^{-1}(x)=1+\frac{\sqrt[5]{(y-17)}}{2}$
   Explanation: Since the function *is* one-to-one, interchange "x" and "y" and solve for y:
   $y=32(x-1)^5+17\rightarrow x=32(y-1)^5+17$; $x-17=32(y-1)^5$; $\frac{x-17}{32}=(y-1)^5$;
   $\sqrt[5]{\frac{x-17}{32}}=\sqrt[5]{(y-1)^5}$; $\frac{\sqrt[5]{x-17}}{2}=y-1$; $1+\frac{\sqrt[5]{x-17}}{2}=y$.
   Thus, the inverse is $f^{-1}(x)=1+\frac{\sqrt[5]{x-17}}{2}$.

3. Afternoon "monsoon" thunderstorms in the Sonoran desert dramatically cool the atmosphere. The air temperature A (in degrees F) as a function of the time elapsed since the first raindrop fell, t (in hours) is given by $A = \frac{10}{\left(t+\frac{1}{2}\right)^2} + 65$.

   Write an equation that expresses t as a function of A.

   Solution: $t = \sqrt{\frac{10}{(A-65)}} - \frac{1}{2}$

   Explanation: Solve for t: $A = \frac{10}{\left(t+\frac{1}{2}\right)^2} + 65$; $A - 65 = \frac{10}{\left(t+\frac{1}{2}\right)^2}$; $\left(t+\frac{1}{2}\right)^2 = \frac{10}{A-65}$;

   $\sqrt{\left(t+\frac{1}{2}\right)^2} = \sqrt{\frac{10}{A-65}}$; $t + \frac{1}{2} = \sqrt{\frac{10}{A-65}}$; $t = \sqrt{\frac{10}{A-65}} - \frac{1}{2}$.

Practice problems: *(Answers on page: 750)*

1. Given $f(x) = 27(x+5)^3$, write the equation of the inverse of $f(x)$ and find $f^{-1}(-8)$.

2. Given $f(x) = 32(x-1)^2 + 17$, find the equation of the inverse function.
   If the function is not invertible, state why.

3. A forensic scientist finds that the time T (in hours) since ingestion of a poison relates to the amount x (in grams) of the poison still in the bloodstream and is given by $T(x) = \sqrt[4]{1000 - 500x}$. What does $T^{-1}(1)$ represent? Now find the equation for $T^{-1}(x)$ and compute $T^{-1}(1)$.

Review questions: *(Answers to odd questions on page: 750)*

1. Given $f(x) = \frac{(x-1)^3}{2}$, write the equation of the inverse of $f(x)$ and find $f^{-1}(4)$.

2. Given $f(x) = (x+3)^2 - 5$ for $x \geq -3$, find the equation of the inverse function.
   If the function is not invertible, state why.

3. Given $f(x) = \frac{2}{3}(x+7)^6$, find the equation of the inverse function.
   If the function is not invertible, state why.

4. Given $f(x) = 7 - \frac{1}{125}(x-3)^3$, find the equation of the inverse function.
   If the function is not invertible, state why.

5. The wind speed S (in mph) needed to produce electric power p (in watts) by a high-tech windmill is given by $S(p) = \sqrt[3]{20p}$. What does $S^{-1}(10)$ represent? Now find the equation for $S^{-1}(p)$ and compute $S^{-1}(10)$.

An Introduction to Exponential Functions

- **Exponential functions** are functions where the variable is in the exponent or power.

Exponential functions Recall: A polynomial has the basic shape: x^3 An exponential function has the basic shape: 3^x Compare by plugging in: x^3: $(2)^3 = 8$, $(3)^3 = 27$, $(4)^3 = 64$ 3^x: $3^{(2)} = 9$, $3^{(3)} = 27$, $3^{(4)} = 81$ $x^3 < 3^x$	By now you are pretty familiar with polynomials and polynomial functions. When dealing with polynomials, a variable like x is raised to some power. What if the variable is in the exponent? These functions are called exponential functions. The polynomial x^3 and the exponential function 3^x are very different, as this table demonstrates. In fact, it turns out that 3^x is larger than x^3 for almost all values of x.
Example Negative number exponents $3^{-2} = \frac{1}{3^2} = \boxed{\frac{1}{9}}$ ← Answer (Flipped)	You can evaluate an exponential function like 3^x at negative values of x. Just remember the properties of exponents.
Example Fraction number exponents $3^{\frac{3}{2}} = (\sqrt{3})^3$ $= \boxed{3\sqrt{3}}$ ← Answer	Fractional exponents like 3/2 are no problem either. Just convert the expression with a fractional exponent into an expression with a radical sign.
Example $2^{\sqrt{5}} = ?$ $\sqrt{5} = 2.2360...$ and so on $2^{2.236} = 2^{\frac{2236}{1000}} = (\sqrt[1000]{2})^{2236}$ $= \boxed{4.7105...\text{ and so on}}$ ← Approximate Answer	What if the exponent is a number that cannot be written as a fraction, like $\sqrt{5}$? In this case, approximate the value of the radical using the decimal. In this example, $2^{\sqrt{5}}$ is approximately equal to $2^{2.236}$.
More exact answer: $= 4.71111313332...$ and so on	You can approximate the value of $2^{\sqrt{5}}$ more accurately by using more digits in the decimal form. As the approximation increases in accuracy, it approaches some number. The value of $2^{\sqrt{5}}$ is this number.
What are exponential functions good for? Answer: exponential functions are used in our real world to measure growth, interest rates, and items that have half lives.	Why study exponential functions? As it turns out, they show up everywhere!

Sample problems:

1. True or False: $3^{\frac{\sqrt{7}}{2}} \approx 4.29$.

   Solution: True

   Explanation: Use a calculator to find $\sqrt{7}$: $3^{\frac{2.65}{2}}$. Simplify exponents: $3^{1.325}$.

   Use the calculator to simplify: $3^{1.325} = 4.29$. Or, enter the entire problem into the graphing calculator using the following key sequences:

   [3] [^] [(] [√(] [7] [)] [/] [2] [)] [Enter], which gives 4.278.

2. Which one of the following is not an exponential function? $a(x) = 7^{2x+3}$, $b(x) = \frac{5^{x-1}}{2}$, $c(x) = 1^{5x}$.

   Solution: $c(x)$

   Explanation: There are three requirements for exponential functions: 1) the base must be a positive real number; 2) the base cannot equal 1; 3) exponents must include a variable.

   Therefore, $c(x) = 1^{5x}$ is not an exponential function since the base is 1.

3. Given the functions $f(x) = x^4$ and $g(x) = 4^x$, which function increases faster as x increases?
   Solution: $g(x) = 4^x$
   Explanation: Substitute several increasing x values into the function, for example 2, 3, and 4: $f(2) = 16,\ f(3) = 81,\ f(4) = 256$ and $g(2) = 16,\ g(3) = 64,\ g(4) = 256$. So, it appears that they increase in a similar way. However, try a few more increasing x values: $f(5) = 625,\ f(6) = 1296,\ f(7) = 2401$ and $g(5) = 1024,\ g(6) = 4096,\ g(7) = 16{,}384$. Now, it is apparent that $g(x)$ increases faster than $f(x)$ as x increases.

Practice problems: *(Answers on page: 750)*

1. True or False: $7^{-\sqrt{2}} = 0.064$.
2. Which one of the following is not an exponential function? $a(x) = -(6)^x,\ b(x) = 3^{\pi x},\ c(x) = 4x^{\sqrt{3}}$.
3. Given the functions $f(x) = \left(\frac{1}{x}\right)^5$ and $g(x) = 5^{\frac{1}{x}}$, which function decreases faster as x increases?

Review questions: *(Answers to odd questions on page: 750)*

1. Simplify: $5^{-\sqrt{3}}$
2. Simplify: $7^{\frac{\pi}{\sqrt{5}}}$
3. True or false: $f(x) = 1^x$ is an exponential function.
4. Which of the following is not an exponential function? $f(x) = 3^{\pi x},\ g(x) = -(6)^x,\ h(x) = (-6)^x$
5. Given the functions $f(x) = x^{\frac{1}{3}}$ and $g(x) = \frac{1}{3}^{x}$, which function decreases as x increases?

Graphing Exponential Functions: Useful Patterns

- Exponential functions are functions where the variable is in the exponent.
- The graphs of exponential functions like $y = a^x$ where $a > 1$ all have the same basic shape. The graph grows rapidly for positive x and shrinks gradually to zero for negative x. The x-axis is a horizontal asymptote.
- The larger the base of an exponential function, the more rapidly it grows for positive values of x and the more rapidly it decreases for negative values of x.

Example

$f(x) = 2^x$

x	$f(x)$
0	1
1	2
2	4
3	8
−1	1/2
−2	1/4

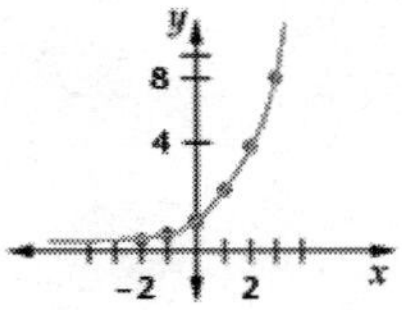

Let's graph an exponential function to get an idea of what they look like.

As you can see from the graph of $f(x) = 2^x$, exponential functions grow quickly for positive values of x and gradually approach zero for negative values of x.

The x-axis is a horizontal asymptote for all exponential functions.

Notice that exponential functions are never zero or negative; they are always positive.

Example

$g(x) = 3^x$

x	$f(x)$
0	1
1	2
2	4
3	8
−1	1/2
−2	1/4

x	$g(x)$
0	1
1	3
2	9
3	27
−2	1/9

The higher the base, the faster it grows, and the faster it shrinks.

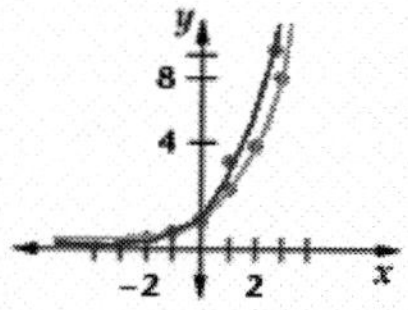

Here, the function $g(x) = 3^x$ has been graphed along with the graph of $f(x) = 2^x$. You can see how increasing the base to 3 has changed the graph.

Example

$g(x) = 5^x$

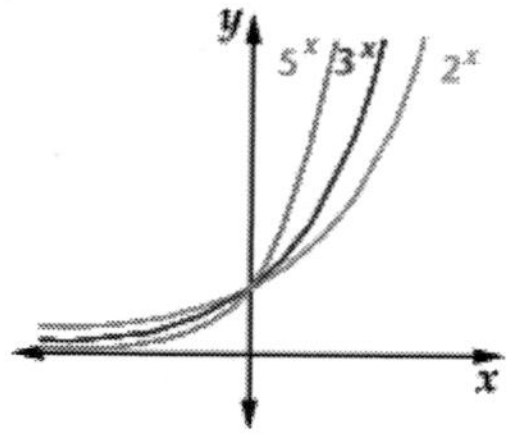

The larger the base of the exponential function, the more quickly it grows for positive x and the more quickly it approaches zero for negative values of x.

Notice, though, that no matter what the base, the graph goes through the point (0, 1).

$g(x) = \left(\frac{1}{2}\right)^x$ Same as $= (2)^{-x}$

The negative sign's effect flips the picture.

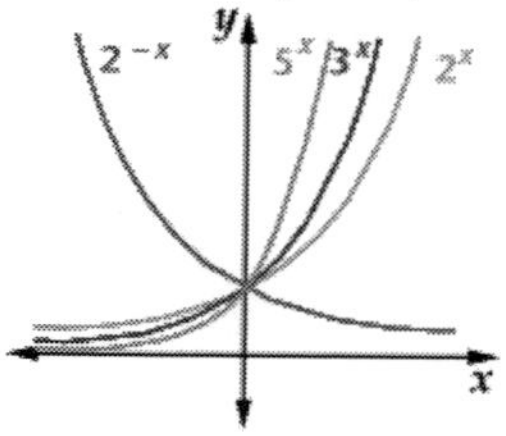

If the base is a number between 0 and 1, you can use the properties of exponents to rewrite the function using a negative exponent.

The effect of the negative sign is to reflect the graph across the y-axis.

Sample problems:

1. True or false: The function $u(x) = \left(\frac{1}{2}\right)^x$ increases as x increases.

   Solution: False

   Explanation: It appears that $u(x)$ increases as x increase since the exponent is a positive x. However, $u(x) = \left(\frac{1}{2}\right)^x$ is not in standard form since a is not greater than 1. Express the function in standard form, $y = a^x$, where $a > 0$ by rewritting the base to the -1 power: $u(x) = \left(\frac{1}{2}\right)^x = (2^{-1})^x = 2^{-x}$. For all exponential functions in standard form, $y = a^x$, where $a > 1$, if the exponent is a negative x, then the function decreases as x increases. So, $u(x)$ does not increase as x increases.

2. Given the functions $f(x) = \left(\frac{4}{5}\right)^x$ and $g(x) = \left(\frac{5}{4}\right)^x$, which function increases as x increases?

   Solution: $g(x)$

   Explanation: $g(x)$ is already in standard form, $y = a^x$, where $a > 1$. So, since the exponent is a positive x, $g(x)$ increases as x increases. It appears that $f(x)$ also increases, but express it in standard form: $f(x) = (\frac{4}{5})^x = \left((\frac{5}{4})^{-1}\right)^x = \frac{5}{4}^{-x}$.
   In standard form the exponent is a negative, so $f(x)$ decreases as x increases.

3. Given the functions $c(x) = \left(\frac{1}{3}\right)^x$ or $d(x) = \left(\frac{1}{3}\right)^{-x}$, which function decreases as x increases?

   Solution: $c(x)$

   Explanation: Express both functions in standard form, $y = a^x$, where $a > 1$: $c(x) = (\frac{1}{3})^x = (3^{-1})^x = 3^{-x}$ and $d(x) = (\frac{1}{3})^x = (3^{-1})^{-x} = 3^x$. Therefore, since the exponent is a negative x in $c(x)$, the function decreases as x increases.

Practice problems: *(Answers on page: 750)*

1. Given the functions $h(x) = 5^{-x}$ or $k(x) = \left(\frac{1}{5}\right)^x$, which function increases as x increases?
2. To the right of the y-axis, which graph rises faster, $m(x) = 5^x$ or $h(x) = 8^x$?
3. For which x-values is the graph of $y = 4^x$ above the x-axis?

Review questions: *(Answers to odd questions on page: 750)*

1. To the right of the y-axis, which graph rises faster, $m(x) = 5^x$ or $h(x) = 6^x$?
2. To the right of the y-axis, which graph rises faster, $f(x) = 5x$ or $g(x) = 2x$?
3. Which of the following functions rises to the right of the y-axis: $f(x) = 4^x$ or $g(x) = \left(\frac{1}{4}\right)^x$?
4. Which of the following functions rises to the left of the y-axis: $f(x) = \left(\frac{8}{1}\right)^x$ or $g(x) = \left(\frac{1}{8}\right)^x$?
5. Given the functions $f(x) = \left(\frac{2}{3}\right)^x$ and $g(x) = \left(\frac{3}{2}\right)^x$, which function increases as x increases?

Graphing Exponential Functions: More Examples

- Exponential functions are functions where the variable is in the exponent.
- You can graph many exponential functions by translating or reflecting the graphs of basic exponential functions like $f(x) = a^x$.
- The base of an exponential function can never be negative.

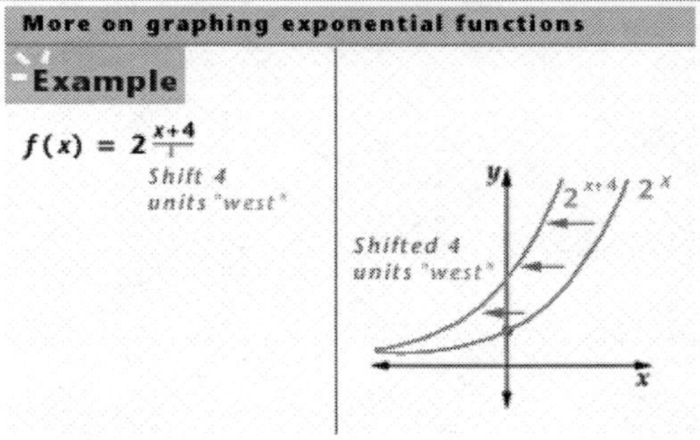

To graph this exponential function, first graph the simpler function $y = 2^x$ and then shift the graph 4 units to the left.

REMEMBER: "Add to x, go west."

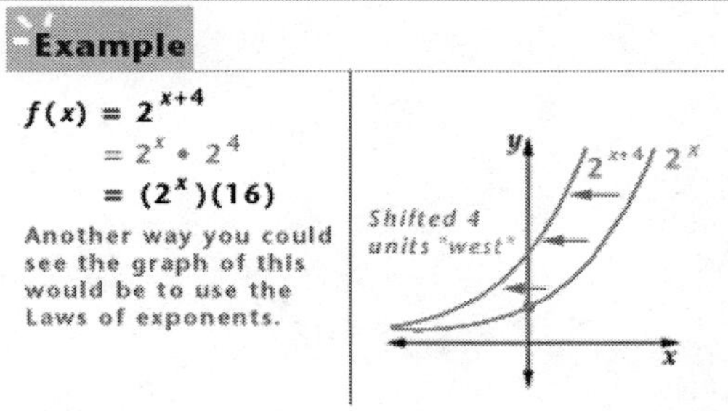

Another way you could graph $f(x)$ is to use the properties of exponents.

In this example, rewrite the function as a constant times the function 2^x.

The constant stretches the graph of $y = 2^x$ out in the vertical direction.

Example $g(x) = 2^x + 4$ $2^x + 4$ 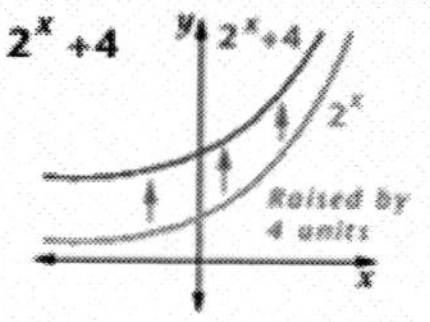	Now, take that same example and move the constant out of the exponent. You can graph this function by shifting the graph of the function $y = 2^x$ upwards by 4 units. **NOTICE:** The graphs of the functions $f(x) = 2^{x+4}$ and $g(x) = 2^x + 4$ are not the same!
Example $f(x) = (-3)^x$ ← Will Never graph!! $= (-3)^2 = 9$ $= (-3)^{\frac{1}{2}} = \sqrt{-3}$ — Not a real number	What happens if the base of an exponential function is a negative number? If the base is a negative number, then the exponential function will be undefined for many values of x. So, exponential functions are not allowed to have negative bases.
$f(x) = (-3)^x \neq 3^{-x}$ — Sorry, Two different things!!	Don't confuse these two expressions! They are not the same.

Sample problems:

1. What change is made to the graph of $f(x) = 7^x$ when the function $g(x) = 7^{x+10}$ is graphed?
   Solution: the graph shifted to the left 10 units
   Explanation: In $g(x)$ the exponent is $x + 10$. Since this function has 10 added to x, the graph of $f(x)$ should be shifted to the left 10 units to form the graph of $g(x)$.

2. True or false: the graph of $a(x) = 5^{x+2}$ is the same as the graph of $n(x) = 25 \cdot 5^x$.
   Solution: True
   Explanation: Use the rules of exponents to split up the exponent in $a(x)$:
   $a(x) = 5^{x+2} = 5^x(5^2) = 25 \cdot 5^x$. The graphs are the same since $a(x) = n(x)$.

3. What is the resulting function if the graph of $y = 2^x$ is shifted up 5 units?
   Solution: $y = 2^x + 5$
   Explanation: To shift a graph vertically add or subtract to the entire equation, so to shift the graph up 5 units, add 5 to 2^x: $y = 2^x + 5$.

Practice problems: *(Answers on page: 750)*

1. True or false: the graph of $w(x) = 3^{x+2}$ is the same as the graph of $v(x) = 9 \cdot 3^x$.
2. What change do you have to make to the graph of $v(x) = 2.5^x$ in order to graph the function $w(x) = 2.5^{x+1} + 3$?
3. What is the resulting function if the graph of $y = 4^x$ is shifted up 2 units?

Review questions: *(Answers to odd questions on page: 750)*

1. Which of the following functions will have the same graph as $w(x) = 3^{x+2}$?
   a) $a(x) = 9^x$ b) $b(x) = 9 \cdot 3^x$ c) $c(x) = 3^x + 2$ d) $d(x) = 3x + 2$
2. True or false: the graph of $g(x) = 9^{x+2}$ is the same as the graph of $h(x) = 18 \cdot 9^x$
3. What change is made to the graph of $f(x) = 6^x$ when the function $g(x) = 6^{x+8}$ is graphed?

4. What is the resulting function if the graph of $y = 10^x$ is shifted 1 unit up and 2 units left?

5. What is the resulting function if the graph of $y = 2^x$ is shifted 6 units down and 1 units right?

Using Properties of Exponents to Solve Exponential Equations

- Exponential equations are equations where the variable is in the exponent.
- You can solve many exponential equations by writing everything in terms of a common base.

Where the unknown is in exponents **Example** $2^x = 4$ $2^x = 4 = 2^2$ *Now the bases are the same* $x = \boxed{2}$ ← *Answer*	One method you can use to solve exponential equations is to express both sides of the equality in terms of the same base. Take a look at this example problem. You can write the right-hand side of the equation using base 2. When the bases are the same, the exponents must also be the same. Use this fact to solve for x.
Example $8^x = 2$ $8^x = (2^3)^x = 2^{3x}$ $2^{3x} = 2^1$ *To check answer, plug into x* $3x = 1$ $x = \boxed{\frac{1}{3}}$ *Answer* ✓	In this example, you can use the laws of exponents to write the left-hand side of the equation using base 2. After writing both sides of the equality using the common base, set the exponents equal to each other and solve for x. **REMEMBER:** You can always check your answer by plugging back into the original equation.
Example $8^x = 4$ $2^{3x} = 2^2$ $x = \boxed{\frac{2}{3}}$ *Answer*	You need to change the bases of both the left-hand and right-hand side of the equality in this example. After the bases are the same, set the exponents equal to each other and solve for x.
Example $(\frac{1}{3})^x = 27$ $3^{-x} = 3^3$ $x = \boxed{-3}$ *Answer*	Follow the same procedure to solve this problem. Remember that exponents can be negative as well as positive.
Example $x^{\frac{1}{3}} = 27$ $(x^{\frac{1}{3}})^3 = (27)^3$ $x = \boxed{19{,}683}$ ← *Answer*	What about this problem? It looks very similar to the last one. Be careful! The variable is in the base, not the exponent. To solve this equation for x, just raise both sides of the equation to the third power.

Sample problems:

1. Solve for x: $4^{2x+1} = 64$.
   Solution: $x = 1$
   Explanation: Express each side with a common base: $4^{2x+1} = 4^3$. Set the exponents equal to each other and solve for x: $2x+1=3$; $2x=2$; $x=1$.

2. Solve for x: $\left(\frac{3}{5}\right)^{x+7} = \frac{9}{25}$.

<u>Solution:</u> $x = -5$

<u>Explanation:</u> Express each side with a common base. $\left(\frac{3}{5}\right)^{x+7} = \left(\frac{3}{5}\right)^2$. Set the exponents equal to each other and solve for x: $x + 7 = 2$; $x = -5$.

3. Solve for x: $27^{x+2} = 81^{1-x}$.

<u>Solution:</u> $x = -\frac{2}{7}$

<u>Explanation:</u> Express each side with a common base: $3^{3(x+2)} = 3^{4(1-x)}$.
Set the exponents equal to each other and solve for x: $3(x+2) = 4(1-x)$;
$3x + 6 = 4 - 4x$; $7x = -2$; $x = -\frac{2}{7}$.

Practice problems: *(Answers on page: 750)*

1. Solve for x: $10^{7x+1} = 10{,}000$
2. Solve for x: $5^{x-6} = 25$
3. Solve for x: $c^{9x+2} = c^{3-x}$

Review questions: *(Answers to odd questions on page: 750)*

1. Solve for h: $h^{\frac{4}{3}} = 16$.
2. Solve for r: $\frac{4}{9} = r^{\frac{2}{5}}$.
3. Solve $\left(\frac{100}{9}\right)^x = \left(\frac{1000}{27}\right)^{x+2}$.
4. Solve $8^{2x+6} = 16^{7-x}$.
5. Solve $100^{x-4} = 0.01^{2x}$.

Finding Present Value and Future Value

- The value of an investment over time is described by an exponential equation.
- The **compound interest formula**: $A = P\left[1 + \frac{r}{m}\right]^{mt}$.
- You can use the compound interest formula to find the present and future values of investments.

Present & future values $A = P\left(1+\frac{r}{m}\right)^{mt}$ (A = future value)	You can use this formula to solve for the present and future values of investments. ***A*** is the future value of the investment. ***P*** is the present, or initial, value of the investment. ***r*** is the rate of interest. ***m*** is the number of interest payments, or compoundings, per year. ***t*** is the number of years the money is invested.

Example Suppose you put \$9,000 into a 5% bearing interest account that compounded semi-annually (2 times per year). How much money would be in the account at the end of 9 years? $A = 9{,}000\left(1+\frac{.05}{2}\right)^{18}$ $A = \boxed{14{,}036.93}$	Here is a typical problem. You are asked how much money the account will have after nine years. To find out, plug the information you are given into the formula: $\boldsymbol{P} = 9{,}000$ $\quad \boldsymbol{r} = .05$ $\boldsymbol{m} = 2$ $\quad \boldsymbol{t} = 9$ Evaluate the exponential expression and the result is your answer. **NOTICE:** The rate is 5%, so $\boldsymbol{r}$ =.05, not 5!
Suppose: The account compounded quarterly. $A = 9{,}000\left(1+\frac{.05}{4}\right)^{36}$ $A = \boxed{14{,}075.49}$ ← Answer A noticeable difference	What happens if the same account is compounded quarterly instead of semiannually? Everything in the formula stays the same except for $\boldsymbol{m}$, the number of interest payments per year; $\boldsymbol{m}$ is now equal to 4. Notice the difference in the future values of these two very similar investments!
Example Suppose that in 10 years you want to have \$25,000 in a 6% bearing interest account that compounds monthly. How much should you initially put into the account? $25{,}000 = P\left(1+\frac{.06}{12}\right)^{120}$ $P = 25{,}000\left(1+\frac{.06}{12}\right)^{-120}$ $= \boxed{13{,}740.82}$ ← Answer	This problem asks you to find the initial value of an investment given that the future value is \$25,000. Plug everything you know into the formula and solve for $\boldsymbol{P}$. The result is the initial value of the investment.

Sample problems:

1. Suppose you charged an entertainment system for \$449 and paid it off at the end of three years with 16.5% accumulated interest. How much did you pay if the interest was compounded monthly?
   Solution: \$734.10
   Explanation: Substitute $P = 449$, $r = 0.165$, $m = 12$, and $t = 3$ into the formula $A = P\left(1+\frac{r}{m}\right)^{mt}$ and simplify: $A = 449\left(1+\frac{0.165}{12}\right)^{12\cdot 3}$; $A = 449\left(1+\frac{0.165}{12}\right)^{36}$; $A = 449(1+0.01375)^{36}$; $A = 449(1.01375)^{36}$; $A = 449(1.634975)$; $A = 734.10$. The amount paid is \$734.10.

2. A teacher in London wants to end up with \$64,000 at retirement, 23 years away, by making a one-time contribution to a 7.2% trust fund today. Use the compound interest formula to determine the amount of his one-time contribution if the fund compounds interest annually.
   Solution: \$12,933.02
   Explanation: Identify the values of the known variables: $A = 64{,}000$, $r = .072$, $m = 1$, and $t = 23$. Substitute these values into the compound interest formula, $A = P\left(1+\frac{r}{m}\right)^{mt}$:
   $64{,}000 = P\left(1+\frac{.072}{1}\right)^{1\cdot 23}$. Simplify and solve for P: $64{,}000 = P(1+.072)^{23}$;
   $P = \frac{64{,}000}{(1+.072)^{23}} = \frac{64{,}000}{4.94857393} = 12933.02$. So, he must contribute \$12,933.02.

3. A couple wish to move to Palm Springs 14 years from now. They'll need $1,000,000 at that time. How much must they invest now, at 6.4% compounded monthly, to reach their goal?
   Solution: $411,451.91
   Explanation: Substitute the values from the problem into the compound interest formula: $1{,}000{,}000 = P\left(1+\frac{.064}{12}\right)^{12(14)}$. Simplify and solve for P:
   $1{,}000{,}000 = P(1.0053)^{168}$; $1{,}000{,}000 = 2.4304P$; $P = 411{,}454.91$. So, they must invest $411,454.91.

Practice problems: *(Answers on page: 750)*

1. A fisherman borrows 213,480 yen over 75 months at 17% compounded monthly. How much will he have to pay back?
2. You charge a $769.41 washer at 3.95% over $10\frac{1}{2}$ years. How much will that washer really cost if interest is compounded twice a year?
3. A 5% car loan runs for 57 months, with daily compounding of interest. Find the amount the car cost originally if the amount paid back was $20,651.66.

Review questions: *(Answers to odd questions on page: 750)*

1. Fifteen years from now Juanita Bushlueter wants to buy the farm she and her husband are now leasing. She figures they will need $485,000 to make this purchase. How much should they invest now, at 5.5% compounded daily, to reach their goal?
2. How much money should a mother now place in a 9% college trust fund (compounded twice a year), for her daughter, if she wants it to grow to $40,000 12 years from now?
3. Mr. McGoo wants to accumulate $7,500 for his LASIK eye surgery 8 years from now, by making a one-time contribution to a 6% trust fund today. What is McGoo's contribution if interest is compounded monthly?
4. A worker wants to end up with $150,000 at retirement, 20 years away, by making a one-time contribution to a 6% charitable gift annuity today. What is that one-time contribution if the charity compounds interest quarterly?
5. It is Jan 1 of a leap year (like 2008). Charles Keating invests $92,707.64 at 7.99% compounded daily. How much will he have in exactly one year?

Finding an Interest Rate to Match Given Goals

- The value of an investment over time is described by an exponential equation.
- The compound interest formula: $A = P\left[1+\frac{r}{m}\right]^{mt}$.
- You can use the compound interest formula to solve for interest rates given goals for the future value of an investment.

Formula for finding interest rate: $A = P\left(1+\frac{r}{m}\right)^{tm}$	This formula is designed to find the present and future values of investments. It can also be used to find interest rates.

Example **You want to invest \$100,000 for 6 months into an account that compounds monthly, and at the end you want to have \$102,000.** What does the account's interest rate need to be? $102{,}000 = 100{,}000\left(1+\frac{r}{12}\right)^6$	This example problem asks you to find the interest rate necessary for your \$100,000 investment to reach a value of \$102,000 after six months. To solve this problem, substitute into the formula: You start with \$100,000, so $P = 100{,}000$. You want to end with \$102,000, so $A = 102{,}000$. The length of time for the investment is six months, or half a year, so $t = 0.5$. The account compounds monthly, or twelve times a year, so $m = 12$.
$\frac{102}{100} = \left(1+\frac{r}{12}\right)^6$ $\sqrt[6]{\frac{102}{100}} = 1+\frac{r}{12}$ $\frac{r}{12} = \sqrt[6]{\frac{102}{100}} - 1$ $r = 12\left(\sqrt[6]{\frac{102}{100}} - 1\right)$ $r = .03967$	Now solve for ***r***. Evaluate this expression to find the value of ***r***.
$r = $ 3.967% ← *Answer* 	And your rate as a percentage moves the decimal two places, 3.967%.

Sample problems:

1. Suppose you want to invest \$75,000 into an account that compounds semi-annually, and at the end of 63 months you want to have \$100,000. What does the account's interest rate need to be?
   Solution: 5.6%
   Explanation: Substitute values from the problem into the compound interest formula: $100{,}000 = 75{,}000\left(1+\frac{r}{2}\right)^{2(5.25)}$, (63 months = $\frac{63}{12}$ years = 5.25 years). Simplify and solve for r: $1.333 = \left(1+\frac{r}{2}\right)^{10.5}$; $\sqrt[10.5]{1.333} = 1+\frac{r}{2}$; $1.028 = 1+\frac{r}{2}$; $\frac{r}{2} = .028$; $r = .056$. So the interest rate needs to be 5.6%

2. Suppose \$220.80 is compounded annually for 3 years. At what rate would it need to be invested to yield \$330? Express your answer to the nearest hundredth of a percent.
   Solution: 14.33%
   Explanation: Substitute the given values into $A = P\left(1+\frac{r}{m}\right)^{mt}$: $330 = 220.80(1+r)^3$; $(1+r)^3 = \frac{330}{220.80}$; $1+r = \left(\frac{330}{220.80}\right)^{\frac{1}{3}}$; $r = \left(\frac{330}{220.80}\right)^{\frac{1}{3}} - 1$; $r = 0.1433$. Thus, the answer is 14.33%.

3. Suppose you want to invest \$5,000 into an account that compounds quarterly, and at the end of $2\frac{1}{2}$ years you want to have \$6,000. What does the account's interest rate need to be?
   Solution: 7.36%
   Explanation: Substitute $A = 6{,}000$, $P = 5{,}000$, $m = 4$, and $t = 2.5$ into the compound interest formula: $A = P\left(1+\frac{r}{m}\right)^{mt}$; $6{,}000 = 5{,}000\left(1+\frac{r}{4}\right)^{4(2.5)}$. Simplify and solve for r: $6{,}000 = 5{,}000\left(1+\frac{r}{4}\right)^{10}$; $\frac{6{,}000}{5{,}000} = \left(1+\frac{r}{4}\right)^{10}$; $1.2 = \left(1+\frac{r}{4}\right)^{10}$; $\sqrt[10]{1.2} = 1+\frac{r}{4}$; $1.0184 = 1+\frac{r}{4}$; $\frac{r}{4} = .0184$; $r = .0736$. So the account's interest rate needs to be 7.36%.

Practice problems: *(Answers on page: 751)*

1. Suppose \$100 is compounded twice a year for 12 years. At what rate would it need to be invested to achieve a balance of \$236.13? Express your answer to the nearest hundredth of a percent.
2. Suppose \$4386 is compounded annually for 4 years. At what rate would it need to be invested to yield \$9652.90? Express your answer to the nearest tenth of a percent.
3. Suppose \$80,000 is compounded monthly for 42 months. At what rate would it need to be invested to achieve a balance of \$90,000. Express your answer to the nearest hundreth of a percent.

Review questions: *(Answers to odd questions on page: 751)*

1. \$2 million is compounded quarterly for 22 years at what rate to yield \$ 5 million? Express your answer to the nearest hundredth of a percent.
2. \$1750 is compounded daily for 2 years at what rate to rise to \$ 1891.96? Express your answer to the nearest tenth of a percent.
3. \$721.88 is compounded quarterly for 8 years at what rate to reach \$2455.63? Express your answer to the nearest tenth of a percent.
4. \$2507 is compounded quarterly for 5 years at what rate to yield \$3725.28?
5. \$650 is compounded monthly for 9 years at what rate to rise to \$1084.38? Express your answer to the nearest tenth of a percent.

e

- The **number *e*** is approximately equal to 2.71828.
- The number *e* is very important for measuring population growth and decay, among many other things.

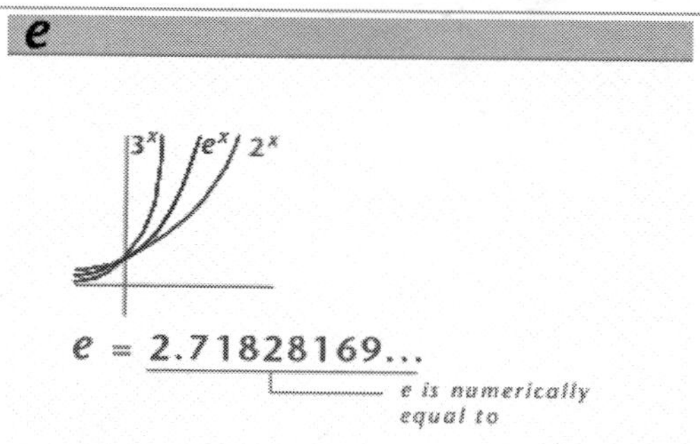

The value of *e* is connected to the slope of tangents to the exponential curve.

The slope of the line that just grazes the graph of $y = 2^x$ when $x = 0$ is less than 1.

The slope of the corresponding line for $y = 3^x$ is greater than 1.

The **number *e*** is the base that yields the tangent with slope exactly equal to 1 when $x = 0$.

Numerically, the number *e* is an infinite decimal.

Estimating *e* numerically

$$\left(1+\frac{1}{n}\right)^n \longrightarrow e$$

e can be approximated by this expression. As *n* gets larger and larger, the expression gets closer and closer to the value *e*.

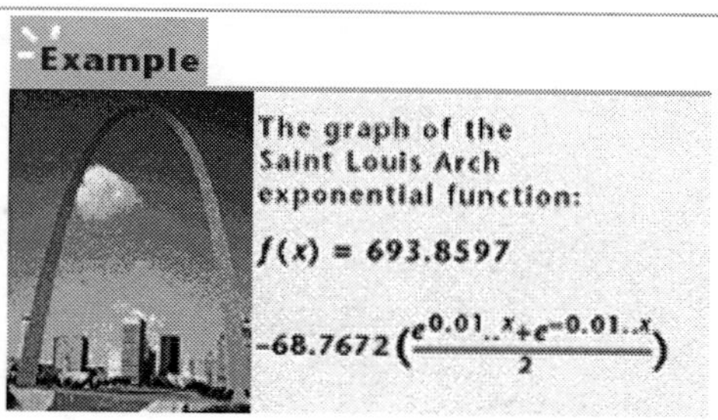

The number *e* is extremely useful. It shows up everywhere in the world around us.

For example, the shape of the Saint Louis Arch is described by an exponential function involving the base *e*.

Example **The more population you have, the greater the rate of population growth.** **This also indirectly involves the notion of e.**  	The number e is also used to predict population growth or, working backwards, to calculate probable populations during specific historical eras. The rate of population growth is proportional to population; that is, the more people there are, the faster the population will grow. As it turns out, population growth (and decay) is described by exponential functions and the number e.

Applying Exponential Functions

- The number $\boldsymbol{e}$ is approximately equal to 2.71828.
- The number $\boldsymbol{e}$ is very important for measuring population growth and decay.
- The population of the world can be modeled using an exponential function with base $\boldsymbol{e}$.

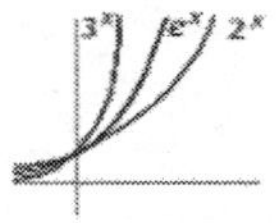 $e = 2.71828169\ldots$ ← *e is numerically equal to*	Exponential functions and the number $\boldsymbol{e}$ are very important in mathematically describing population growth.
Applying exponential functions **Example** $P(t) = 2600e^{.018t}$ t = Years after 1950	Here, $P(t)$ describes the world's population as a function of time, where t is the number of years after 1950.
Applying exponential functions with e will give highly accurate models of population growth for future planning.  **Applying exponential functions** **Example** $P(t) = 2600e^{.018t}$ $P(20) = 2600e^{(.018)(20)}$ ← in 1970 $= 3726.65$ $\approx$ 3700 million ← *Real Answer*	You can use the formula from above to calculate the number of people in the world in 1970. Since 1970 is twenty years after 1950, just plug in $t = 20$. Using the formula results in an answer very close to the actual population of the world in 1970. The exponential model does a good job!
$P(t) = 2600e^{.018t}$ $P(40) = 2600e^{(.018)(40)}$ ← in 1990 $= 5341.5$ $\approx$ 5320 million ← *Real Answer*	You can also calculate the model's prediction for the world's population for any other year after 1950. For 1990, just plug in $t = 40$ (because 1990 is forty years after 1950). The model does a good job here too.

Sample problems:

1. The number of milligrams of a certain drug that remain in a person's bloodstream after h hours is given by the exponential function $D = 5e^{-0.4h}$. Find the number of milligrams present after 5 hours.
   Solution: 0.68 milligrams
   Explanation: Substitute $h = 5$ into the function and simplify: $D = 5e^{-0.4h} = 5e^{-0.4(5)} = 5e^{-2} = 0.68$.

2. The number of milligrams of a certain drug that remain in a person's bloodstream after h hours is given by the exponential function $D = 5e^{-0.4h}$. Find the number of milligrams present after 2 hours and 30 minutes.
Solution: 1.84 milligrams
Explanation: Substitute $h = 2.5$ into the function and simplify: $D = 5e^{-0.4h} = 5e^{-0.4(2.5)} = 5e^{-1} = 1.84$.

3. In a population of size P, the number of people who have heard a rumor d days since the rumor began is given by the function $N = P\left(1 - e^{-0.15d}\right)$. In a population of 350 people, how many will have heard the rumor after 2 days?
Solution: 91 people
Explanation: Substitute $P = 350$ and $d = 2$ into the function and simplify:
$N = P\left(1 - e^{-0.15d}\right) = 350\left(1 - e^{-0.15(2)}\right) = 350\left(1 - e^{-0.3}\right) = 90.7.$
So, after 2 days 91 people will have heard the rumor.

Practice problems: *(Answers on page: 751)*

1. In a population of size P, the number of people who have heard a rumor d days since the rumor began is given by the function $N = P\left(1 - e^{-0.15d}\right)$. In a population of 700 people, how many will have heard the rumor after 3 days?
2. The probability that a customer will arrive t minutes before closing time at a certain store is given by the function $F(t) = 1 - e^{-0.006t}$. Find the probability that a customer will arrive 15 minutes before closing.
3. The probability that a customer will arrive t minutes before closing time at a certain store is given by the function $F(t) = 1 - e^{-0.006t}$. Find the probability that a customer will arrive 20 minutes before closing.

Review questions: *(Answers to odd questions on page: 751)*

1. The number of debit card transactions expected in a certain year in the U.S. can be approximated by the function $y = 0.08e^{0.42x}$, where $x = 0$ corresponds to 1990 and y is in billions. Find the number of debit card transactions in 1996.
2. The number of debit card transactions expected in a certain year in the U.S. can be approximated by the function $y = 0.08e^{0.42x}$, where $x = 0$ corresponds to 1990 and y is in billions. Predict the number of debit card transactions in 2010.
3. The percentage of U.S. households whose members are related by marriage, birth, or adoption is given by the function $p = 89.7e^{-0.0058t}$, where t is the number of years since 1950. What was the percentage of U.S. households whose members were related by marriage, birth, or adoption in 1965?
4. The percentage of U.S. households whose members are related by marriage, birth, or adoption is given by the function $p = 89.7e^{-0.0058t}$, where t is the number of years since 1950. Predict the percentage of U.S. households whose members will be related by marriage, birth, or adoption in 2009.
5. The percentage of U.S. households whose members are related by marriage, birth, or adoption is given by the function $p = 89.7e^{-0.0058t}$, where t is the number of years since 1950. Predict the percentage of U.S. households whose members will be related by marriage, birth, or adoption in 2020.

An Introduction to Logarithmic Functions

- **Logarithms** and exponential functions are inverses of each other. You can use logs to "untangle" expressions involving exponential functions.
- A log is an exponent: the statement $\boldsymbol{y = \log_b x}$ is equivalent to the statement $\boldsymbol{b^y = x}$.

log = exponent **Example** $\log_2 8 = ? \iff 2^? = 8$ *log is the exponent that 2 is raised to equal 8.* $? = 3$ $2^{③} = 8$ $\log_2 8 = ③$	Logs are nothing to be afraid of. Remember the chant: "A log is an exponent." What is the value of $\log_2 8$? "A log is an exponent." $\log_2 8$ is the exponent that 2 is raised to in order to get 8. Since 2 raised to the third power is equal to 8, $\log_2 8 = 3$. The log is the exponent, or in this case, 3.
$y = \log_b x \iff b^y = x$	In general, if $y = \log_b x$, then y is equal to the exponent that b is raised to in order to get x. In other words, $b^y = x$.
Example $\log_2 \frac{1}{4} = ?$ $2^? = \frac{1}{4}$ $? = -2$ ✓work $2^{-2} = \frac{1}{2^2} = \frac{1}{4}$	How can you evaluate the expression $\log_2 \frac{1}{4}$? "A log is an exponent." $\log_2 \frac{1}{4}$ is equal to the exponent that 2 is raised to in order to get $\frac{1}{4}$. $2^{-2} = \frac{1}{4}$ Therefore, $\log_2 \frac{1}{4} = -2$. **Check your answer:** Raise the base to your log value. If it is correct, you will derive your x-value, in this case $\frac{1}{4}$.
Example $\log_2 (-3) = ?$ $2^? $ **Never take logs of Negatives !** *What does ? equal*	Can you evaluate the expression $\log_2(-3)$? 2 raised to any power will always be positive. Thus the log expression $\log_2(-3)$ is meaningless. **REMEMBER:** Never take the log of a negative number!

Sample problems:

1. True or False: If $w = \log_b z$ then $b^z = w$.
   Solution: False
   Explanation: The statement "If $w = \log_b z$" means: assume that $w = \log_b z$ is true. So, apply the rule of logarithms which states that when $y = \log_b x$, $b^y = x$ must also be true, and vice versa.
   Thus, if $w = \log_b z$ then $b^w = z$, not $b^z = w$.

2. Evaluate: $\log_3 81$.
   Solution: 4
   Explanation: To evaluate $\log_3 81$, find the exponent that applies to 3 to get 81: $3^x = 81$. To solve this exponential function express each side with a common base: $3^x = 3^4$. So, $x = 4$.

3. Evaluate: $\log_2 \frac{1}{8}$.

Solution: -3

Explanation: Apply the rule of logarithms: $\log_2 \frac{1}{8} = x \Rightarrow 2^x = \frac{1}{8}$. Rewrite the fraction with a negative exponent: $2^x = 8^{-1}$. Express each side with a common base: $2^x = 2^{-3}$. So $x = -3$.

Practice problems: *(Answers on page: 751)*

1. Evaluate: $\log_4 \frac{1}{4}$.
2. True or False: If $\log_b c = a$, then $b^a = c$.
3. Evaluate: $\log_5 \frac{1}{125}$.

Review questions: *(Answers to odd questions on page: 751)*

1. Evaluate: $\log_6 36$
2. Evaluate: $\log_2 32$
3. Evaluate: $\log_3 \frac{1}{27}$
4. Evaluate: $\log_2 \frac{1}{16}$
5. Evaluate: $\log_8 4$

Converting between Exponential and Logarithmic Functions

- When converting from logarithmic form to exponential form, remember that "a log is an exponent." This means that the number the log is equal to becomes the exponent in the new form. The base of the log is the base of the exponent too.

A log is an exponent $y = \log_b x \iff b^y = x$	An easy way to remember how logarithms and exponents convert is to remember the statement "a log is an exponent." Whatever is on the other side of the equal sign in the logarithmic form becomes the exponent of the base in the exponential form.
Example *Rewrite as a log statement* $2^5 = 32$ $5 = \log_2 32$ 5 *(log)* is what 2 *(base)* needs to be raised to equal 32	Let's look at this idea in action. Since a log is an exponent, the exponent of this expression will become the log's answer. The bases stay the same. The exponent moves to the other side of the equal sign. The other number fills in the hole.
Example *Rewrite as a log statement* $(\frac{2}{3})^{-2} = \frac{9}{4}$ $-2 = \log_{\frac{2}{3}} \frac{9}{4}$ -2 log, base $\frac{2}{3}$ of $\frac{9}{4}$	Now let's try a harder example. Since a log is an exponent, the exponent of this expression will become the log value alone on one side of the equal sign. The base doesn't change from one form to the other. The value of the base raised to the exponent fills its hole.

Example *Rewrite as an exponential statement* $\log_6 6 = 1 \iff 6^1 = 6$	This time we will work the other way. A log is an exponent. So the exponent is 1. The base is 6. The other number fills in its hole.
Example *Rewrite as an exponential statement* $\log_{\sqrt{3}} 9 = 4 \iff (\sqrt{3})^4 = 9$ $= ((\sqrt{3})^2)^2$ $= 3^2 = 9$	Let's look at one last example. A log is an exponent. So the exponent is 4. The base is $\sqrt{3}$. The final number fills in its hole. Simplifying the expression leaves you with 3^2, which is equal to 9.

Sample problems:

1. Express $3^4 = 81$ in logarithmic form.
   Solution: $\log_3 81 = 4$
   Explanation: Apply the law of logarithms: $b^y = x \Rightarrow \log_b x = y$. So, $3^4 = 81 \Rightarrow \log_3 81 = 4$

2. Convert $\log_p q = r$ into an exponential equation.
   Solution: $p^r = q$
   Explanation: Apply the law of logarithms: $\log_b x = y \Rightarrow b^y = x$. So, $\log_p q = r \Rightarrow p^r = q$.

3. Express $\log_4 1024 = 5$ in an exponential form.
   Solution: $4^5 = 1024$
   Explanation: Apply the law of logarithms: $\log_b x = y \Rightarrow b^y = x$. So, $\log_4 1024 = 5 \Rightarrow 4^5 = 1024$.

Practice problems: *(Answers on page: 751)*

1. Express $6^2 = 36$ in logarithmic form.
2. Express $m^z = k$ in exponential form.
3. Express $\log_{16} 2 = \frac{1}{4}$ in exponential form.

Review questions: *(Answers to odd questions on page: 751)*

1. Express $\log_7 1 = 0$ in exponential form.
2. Express $7^3 = 343$ in logarithmic form.
3. Express $\log_{10} 0.01 = -2$ in exponential form.
4. Express $\log_3 2187 = 7$ in exponential form.
5. Express $4^{-\frac{3}{2}} = 0.125$ in logarithmic form.

Finding the Value of a Logarithmic Function

- When calculating logs, think of the expression in terms of the exponential form. Ask yourself "what exponent would I need to make this statement true."

More log Problems **Example** *solve the log* $\log_6 36 = 2$ $6^? = 36$	To solve logs, convert them to exponential form and see if you know what exponent you will need. 6 raised to what power is 36? $6^2 = 36$. The second power!
~~More~~ *hard* **log Problems** **Example** *solve the log* $\log_4\left(\frac{\sqrt[3]{4}}{2}\right)$ write everything as $\sqrt{4}$ — change roots to exponents $\frac{\sqrt[3]{4}}{\sqrt{4}} = \frac{4^{1/3}}{4^{1/2}} = 4^{1/3-1/2} = 4^{-1/6}$ $\log_4 \frac{\sqrt[3]{4}}{2} = \log_4 4^{-1/6} = ?$ $\Rightarrow 4^? = 4^{-1/6}$, so $? = \frac{-1}{6}$ $\boxed{\log_4 \frac{\sqrt[3]{4}}{2} = \frac{-1}{6}}$	In some problems, you will need to simplify pieces of the logarithm in order to see a good answer. You can't see what the question is asking for when the expressions aren't simplified. Make it your first priority to try to reduce them so you can work the problem. Notice that this radical expression simplifies to $4^{-1/6}$. Substituting that into the log problem makes it a lot easier: what exponent do you raise 4 to if you want $4^{-1/6}$? To $-1/6$!
really hard ~~More~~ **log Problems** *solve the log* $6^{\log_6 28}$ · express the exponential expression as a logarithmic expression $6^{\log_6 28} = ?$ $\log_6 ? = \log_6 28$ $? = 28$ $\boxed{6^{\log_6 28} = 28}$	In this problem, the log statement is the exponent. Look for a way to simplify things. The statement $\log_6 28$ equals some value: $\log_6 28 = ?$ or in exponential form: $6^? = 28$. With this information, you realize you are looking for the exponent for 6 that produces 28.

Sample problems:

1. Find the value of the logarithmic expression $\log_2 32$ without using a calculator.
   Solution: 5
   Explanation: Express the logarithmic equation $\log_2 32 = x$ as an exponential equation: $2^x = 32$. To solve for x, express each side with a common base: $2^x = 2^5$, so $x = 5$. Thus, $\log_2 32 = 5$.

2. Find the value of the logarithmic expression $\log 0.0001$ without using a calculator.
   Solution: -4
   Explanation: Express the logarithmic equation $\log 0.0001 = x$ as an exponential equation using 10 as the base: $10^x = 0.0001$. To solve for x, express each side with a common base: $10^x = 10^{-4}$, so $x = -4$. Thus, $\log 0.0001 = -4$.

3. Find the value of the logarithmic expression $\log_8\left(\frac{\sqrt[5]{16}}{2}\right)$, without using a calculator.

Solution: $-\frac{1}{15}$

Explanation: Begin by simplifying the expression inside the parentheses:

$\frac{\sqrt[5]{16}}{2} = \frac{16^{\frac{1}{5}}}{2} = \frac{\left(2^4\right)^{\frac{1}{5}}}{2} = \frac{2^{\frac{4}{5}}}{2} = 2^{\frac{4}{5}-1} = 2^{-\frac{1}{5}}$. So, $\log_8\left(\frac{\sqrt[5]{16}}{2}\right) = \log_8\left(2^{-\frac{1}{5}}\right)$.

Express the logarithmic equation $\log_8\left(2^{-\frac{1}{5}}\right) = x$ as an exponential equation: $8^x = 2^{-\frac{1}{5}}$.

To solve for x, express each side with a common base: $2^{3x} = 2^{-\frac{1}{5}}$; $3x = -\frac{1}{5}$; $x = -\frac{1}{15}$.

Practice problems: *(Answers on page: 751)*

1. Find the value of the logarithmic expression $\log_7\left(\frac{1}{49}\right)$ without using a calculator.
2. Find the value of the logarithmic expression $\log 1{,}000{,}000$ without using a calculator.
3. Find the value of the logarithmic expression $\log_9\left(\frac{\sqrt[4]{27}}{3}\right)$ without using a calculator.

Review questions: *(Answers to odd questions on page: 751)*

1. Find the value of $\log_{10} 10{,}000{,}000$ without using a calculator.
2. Find the value of $\log_8 64$ without using a calculator.
3. Find the value of $\log_9 9$ without using a calculator.
4. Find the value of $\log_3\left(\frac{1}{27}\right)$ without using a calculator.
5. Find the value of $\log_5 0.2$ without using a calculator.

Solving for x in Logarithmic Equations

- When solving logarithmic equations, convert them back to exponential form and figure out what the missing piece should be to make the statement true.

Example Find Your X $x = \log_2 32$ $2^x = 32$ $x = 5$	To solve logs, convert them to exponential form and see if you know what the x-value should be. What power do you have to raise 2 to get 32? 2 raised to the fifth power is 32.
$\log_x 25 = -2$ $x^{-2} = 25$ $\frac{1}{x^2} = 5^2$ *multiply through by x* $1 = 5^2 x^2$ *divide both sides by 5^2* $\frac{1}{5^2} = x^2$ *take square roots* $x = \frac{\pm 1}{5}$ **Remember: the base of a log MUST be positive!** $\boxed{x = \frac{1}{5}}$	Here is a slightly trickier problem. Convert the logarithm to an exponential equation first. It is a good idea to simplify expressions with strange pieces. Cross-multiply to isolate the x, then take the square root of each side. Since the base of a logarithm must be non-negative, x=1/5 only.

$\log_x\left(\frac{1}{16}\right) = -2$	Here's another example.
$x^{-2} = \frac{1}{16}$	Convert the log to exponential form.
$x^2 = 16$	Simplify the negative exponent.
$x = \pm 4$	Solve the equation.
$\boxed{x = 4}$	Taking the square root gives a positive and negative answer.
✓ Check your work!	It is always a good idea to check your work.

Sample problems:

1. Solve for x: $\log_x(-25) = 2$, if $x > 0$.
   Solution: No real solution
   Explanation: The log of a negative number does not exist, regardless of the base. So, there is no solution.

2. Solve for x: $\log_x\left(\dfrac{1}{64}\right) = 2$, if $x > 0$.
   Solution: $x = \dfrac{1}{8}$
   Explanation: Express the logarithmic equation as an exponential equation: $x^2 = \frac{1}{64}$. Solve for x: $\sqrt{x^2} = \sqrt{\frac{1}{64}}$; $x = \pm\frac{1}{8}$. Theoretically there are two solutions, but $x = -\frac{1}{8}$ must be rejected because there cannot be a negative base in the logarithmic equation. Thus, $x = \frac{1}{8}$.

3. Solve for x: $4x = \log_{\sqrt{3}} 27$.
   Solution: $x = \dfrac{3}{2}$
   Explanation: Express the logarithmic equation as an exponential equation: $\sqrt{3}^{4x} = 27$.
   Convert the radical to a fractional exponent, then simplify the exponents: $3^{\frac{1}{2}\cdot 4x} = 27$; $3^{2x} = 27$. To solve for x, express each side with a common base: $3^{2x} = 3^3$; $2x = 3$; $x = \frac{3}{2}$.

Practice problems: *(Answers on page: 751)*

1. Solve for x: $\log_x 0 = 5$, if $x > 0$.
2. Solve for x: $5x = \log_3 81$.
3. Solve for x: $3x = \log_{\sqrt{5}} 25$.

Review questions: *(Answers to odd questions on page: 751)*

1. Solve $\log_x 1000 = 3$, if $x > 0$.
2. Solve $\log_8 2x = -1$, if $x > 0$.
3. Solve $\log_5 125 = 11 - x$.
4. Solve $\log_{10} x = 4$, if $x > 0$.
5. Solve $\log_{16} 2 = x$.

Graphing Logarithmic Functions

- **Graphs of logarithmic functions** all have the same basic shape. One of the ways you can make them different is by changing the base.

Example $f(x) = \log_2 x$

$x = 2^{f(x)}$

x	$f(x)$
1	0
2	1
4	2
$\frac{1}{2}$	-1
$\frac{1}{4}$	-2

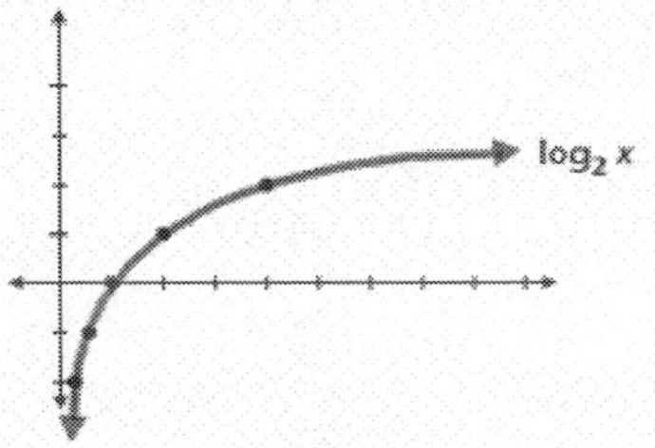

Now you can begin investigating how logarithmic functions behave graphically.

Set up a table to plot some points.

Notice that the curve does not touch the y-axis. This is because exponential functions never equal zero.

Example $g(x) = \log_3 x$

$x = 3^{g(x)}$

x	$g(x)$
1	0
3	1
9	2
$\frac{1}{3}$	-1

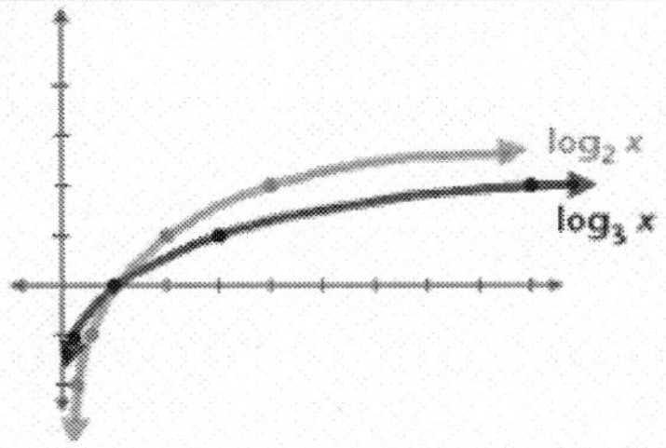

Compare the graph of $\log_2 x$ with $\log_3 x$.

Once again, the graph never crosses the y-axis.

In addition, notice how the graph with the larger base is greater then the graph with the smaller base until $x = 1$, then they switch.

Example How will the graph change when the base is increased to 10?

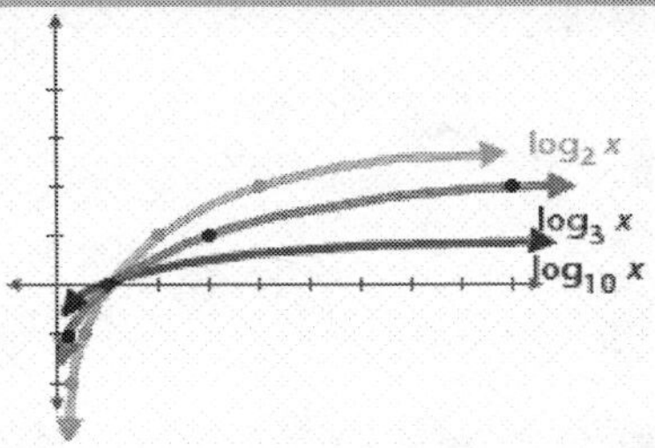

Consider when the base is equal to 10.

Reading from left to right, the graph with the larger base is greater (higher) than the smaller base until $x = 1$.

After $x = 1$, the graph with the larger base is lower than the graph with the smaller base.

Example $m(x) = \log_{\frac{1}{2}} x$

$x = \frac{1}{2}^{m(x)}$ or $x = 2^{-m(x)}$

x	$m(x)$
2	-1

$2 = 2^{-(-1)}$

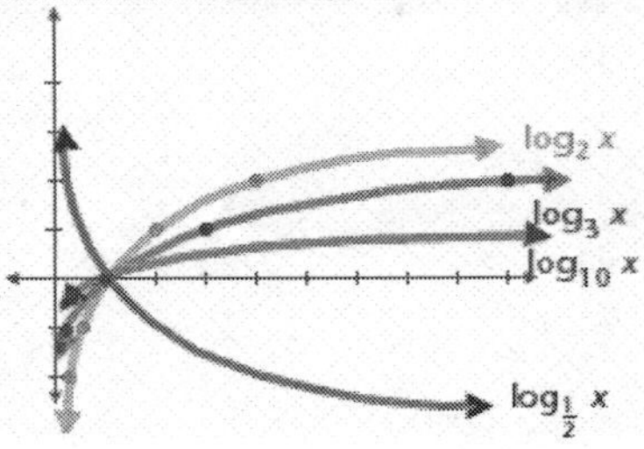

What about fractional bases?

Try plotting some points.

Notice that the graph of $\log_{\frac{1}{2}} x$ is the reflection of $\log_2 x$ across the x-axis.

Sample problems:

1. Where does the graph of $f(x) = \log_2 x$ intersect the graph of $g(x) = \log_5 x$?
   Solution: (1, 0)

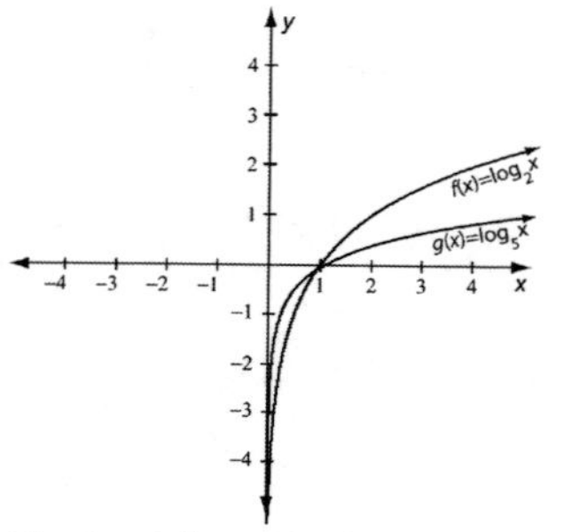

Explanation: As base values increase, the graph of $\log_b x$ changes in two ways:
1) it increases faster when the domain is greater than 0, but less than 1 and
2) it increases slower when the domain is greater than 1.
But for all base values greater than 1, $\log_b x$ passes through (1, 0).
Therefore, the graphs of $f(x)$ and $g(x)$ intersect at (1, 0).

2. True or False: If $f(x) = \log_b x$ increases faster than $g(x) = \log_4 x$ when the domain is greater than 1, then $b > 4$.
Solution: False
Explanation: As base values increase, the graph of $\log_b x$ gets closer to the x – axis when the domain is greater than 1. So, to create a logarithmic function that increases faster than $\log_4 x$ when the domain is greater than 1, the base value must be less than 4.

3. Describe the graph of $f(x) = \log_3 x$ as compared to the graph of $g(x) = \log_{\frac{1}{3}} x$.
Solution: $f(x)$ is the reflection of $g(x)$ across the x – axis
Explanation: Evaluate each function for several x values:
Find $f(1)$: $3^y = 1$; $y = 0$, so $f(1) = 0$. Find $f(2)$: $3^y = 2$, that's too hard, try another x value.
Find $f(3)$: $3^y = 3$; $y = 1$, so $f(3) = 1$. Use another easy x value, find $f(9)$: $3^y = 9$; $y = 2$, so $f(9) = 2$.

$f(x)=\log_3 x$

x	$y=\log_3 x$ or $3^y=x$	y	point
1	$3^y=1$	0	(1,0)
3	$3^y=3$	1	(3,1)
9	$3^y=9$	2	(9,2)
27	$3^y=27$	3	(27,3)

$g(x)=\log_{1/3} x$

x	$y=\log_{1/3} x$ or $1/3^y=x$	y	point
1	$1/3^y=1$	0	(1,0)
3	$1/3^y=3$	1	(3,1)
9	$1/3^y=9$	2	(9,2)
27	$1/3^y=27$	3	(27,3)

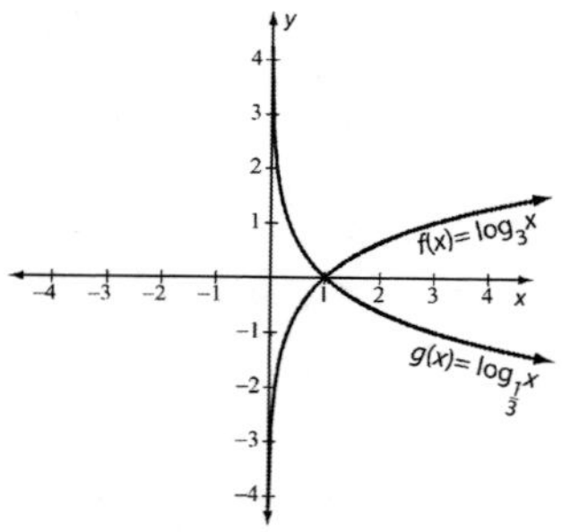

The points from $f(x)$ are all reflections across the x – axis of $g(x)$ since the x – coordinates are the same and the y – coordinates are always opposites. Therefore, the graph of $f(x)$ is the reflection of $g(x)$ across the x – axis.

Practice problems: *(Answers on page: 751)*

1. True or False: For $0 < x < 1$; $f(x) = \log_9 x$ increases faster than $g(x) = \log_7 x$.
2. Where do the graphs of $f(x) = \log_2 x$ and $f(x) = \log_{\frac{1}{4}} x$ intersect?
3. Given the function $f(x) = \log_a x$ and $g(x) = \log_{\frac{1}{2}} x$, when $a > 1$, suppose that $f(4) = 7$. Find $g(4)$.

Review questions: *(Answers to odd questions on page: 751)*

1. Graph $f(x) = \log_{\frac{1}{4}} x$.
2. Graph $f(x) = \log_4 x$.
3. Where does the graph of $f(x) = \log_5 x$ intersect the graph of $g(x) = \log_9 x$?
4. How does the graph of $g(x) = \log_2 x$ compare to the graph of $f(x) = \log_{\frac{1}{2}} x$?
5. Which graph increases faster as x increases, when $x > 0$, $f(x)\log_{10} x$ or $g(x)\log_{20} x$?

Matching Logarithmic Functions with Their Graphs

- Since all the **logarithmic functions** have the same basic shape, all you really need to know is where the graph crosses the x-axis and approximately how high it gets.

Example

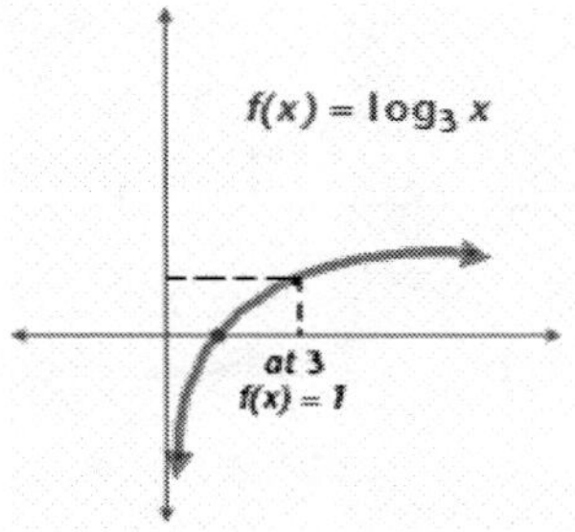

One of the key pieces of information about logarithms is the point where they cross the x-axis (sometimes called the x-intercept).

To find the x-intercept:
set the log equal to zero and solve:
$f(x) = \log_3 x = 0$.
That means: $3^0 = x$
leading to $x = 1$ when $y = 0$.

In this particular graph, the x-intercept is equal to 1.

Example

$f(x) = \log_3 x$

$g(x) = \log_3 \left(\frac{x}{3}\right)$

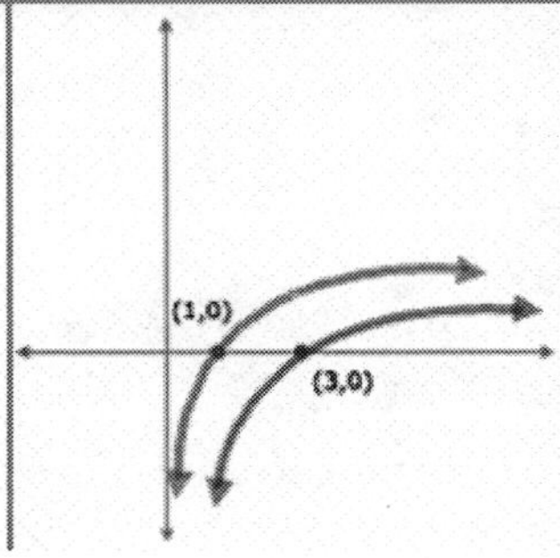

If you change x-term, you can change the x-intercept.

Building on the first example, replace x with $x/3$.
Now repeat your process from the first example:
Set $f(x) = 0$: $f(x) = \log_3 (x/3) = 0$
leading to: $3^0 = x/3$
$1 = x/3$
$x = 3$ when $y = 0$.

With this change, you move the x-intercept from $x = 1$ to $x = 3$. The new intercept is three times farther from the origin.

Dividing by 3 also flattened the curve out some. It still gets infinitely large, but not as fast as the first curve.

Example

$f(x) = \log_3 x$

$g(x) = \log_3 (\frac{x}{3})$

$h(x) = \log_3 (3x)$

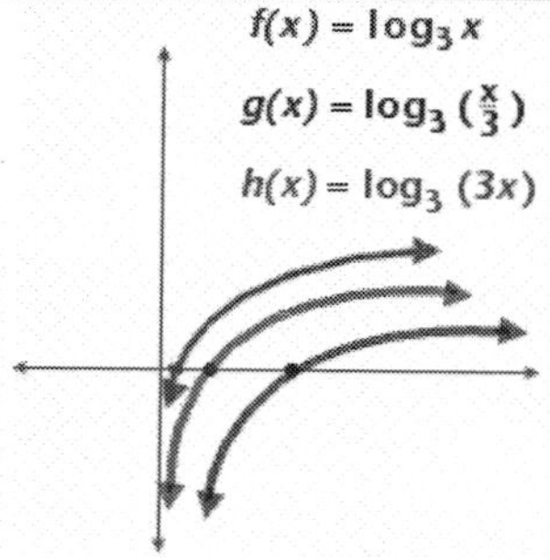

Again building on the first example, what happens when you multiply the x-term by 3?

Repeat your process again:
Set $f(x) = 0$: $f(x) = \log_3 3x = 0$
leading to: $3^0 = 3x$
$1 = 3x$
$x = 1/3$ when $y = 0$.

With this change the x-intercept is three times closer to the origin than in the first example.

The graph also gets larger more quickly.

Example

$f(x) = \log_3 x$

$s(x) = \log_3 (x\text{-}2)$

(x-2) creates a shift on the x-axis

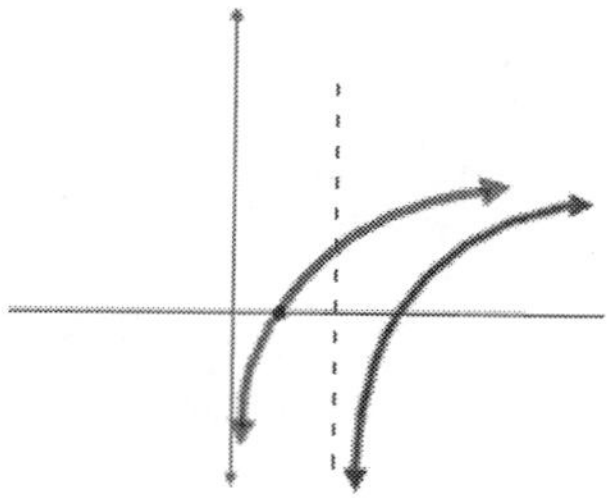

You can do more to a variable than just multiply.

What happens if you subtract 2 from the x ?

Repeat your process again:
Set $f(x) = 0$: $f(x) = \log_3 (x - 2) = 0$
leading to: $3^0 = x - 2$
$1 = x - 2$
$x = 3$ when $y = 0$.

This change has added 2 to the x-value for each y-value. The entire graph shifts 2 units to the right. This is called a translation.

The graph will have the same basic shape as the main graph. It will just be 2 units farther away.

Example

$f(x) = \log_3 x$

$s(x) = \log_3 (x\text{-}2)$

$l(x) = \log_3 (\text{-}x)$

$f(x) = \log_3 1$
$x = 0$

$f(x) = \log_3 (- \text{-}1)$
$x = 0$

creates a mirror image

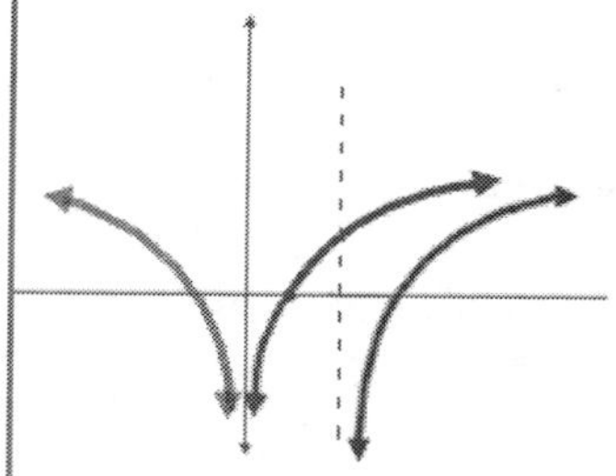

Finally, what happens if you multiply the x by a negative number?

Logarithms normally only work for values greater than 0. But if you multiply by negative one, they work only for x-values less than zero!

Use your process to see how it works:
Set $f(x) = 0$: $f(x) = \log_3 (x - 2) = 0$
leading to: $3^0 = -x$
$1 = -x$
$x = -1$ when $y = 0$.

In fact, the graph of the log of negative x is like a mirror image across the y-axis of the log of x.

Sample problems:

1. Determine the x-intercept of the graph $y = \log_7 \dfrac{x}{4}$?

   Solution: 4

   Explanation: The x-intercept is the point where the graph intersects the x – axis, thus where $y = 0$. So, substitute 0 into the equation for y: $0 = \log_7 \frac{x}{4}$. Apply the law of logarithms, $y = \log_b x \Rightarrow b^y = x$, to express the logarithmic equation as an exponential equation: $0 = \log_7 \frac{x}{4} \Rightarrow 7^0 = \frac{x}{4}$. Solve for x: $1 = \frac{x}{4}$; $x = 4$. So, the x-intercept is 4 or the point (4, 0).

2. Given the functions $f(x) = \log_2 \frac{5x}{3}$ and $g(x) = \log_2(5x-3)$, which function has the largest x-intercept?
Solution: $g(x)$
Explanation: Find the x-intercept of $f(x)$ by substituting 0 for $f(x)$, expressing the logarithmic equation as
an exponential equation, and solving for x: $0 = \log_2 \frac{5x}{3} \Rightarrow 2^0 = \frac{5x}{3}$; $1 = \frac{5x}{3}$; $3 = 5x$; $x = \frac{3}{5}$. So the x-intercept of $f(x)$ is $\frac{3}{5}$. Find the x-intercept of $g(x)$: $0 = \log_2(5x-3) \Rightarrow 2^0 = 5x-3$; $1 = 5x-3$; $4 = 5x$; $x = \frac{4}{5}$. Therefore, the x-intercept of $g(x)$ is larger.

3. From the graph below, which curve accurately represents the graph of $\log_8(x-3)$: $g(x)$ or $h(x)$?

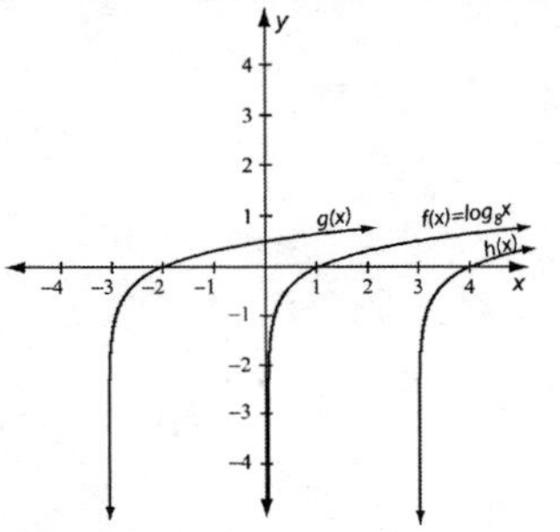

Solution: $h(x)$
Explanation: If $f(x)$ is $\log_8 x$, then $h(x)$ represents the graph of $\log_8(x-3)$ because it is shifted three units to the right. Remember: "add to x, go west". Since 3 is being subtracted from x, go east (right) 3 units.

Practice problems: *(Answers on page: 751)*

1. Which of these equations will produce a curve with the smallest x-intercept: $y = \log_9(7x)$ or $y = \log_{10}(2x)$?
2. How is the curve of $j(x) = \log_8(x-2)$ different from that of $f(x) = \log_8 x$?
3. Determine the x-intercept of the graph of $f(x) = \log_5\left(\frac{3x+1}{4}\right)$.

Review questions: *(Answers to odd questions on page: 752)*

1. True or false? All logarithmic functions pass trough the point (0, 1).
2. Which of these equations will produce a curve with the largest x-intercept?

   a) $y = \log_6(\frac{x}{2})$ b) $y = \log_8(6x)$ c) $y = \log_9(8x)$ d) $y = \log_7(\frac{x}{4})$

3. If $f(x) = \log_4 x$, graph $2 + \log_4 x$.

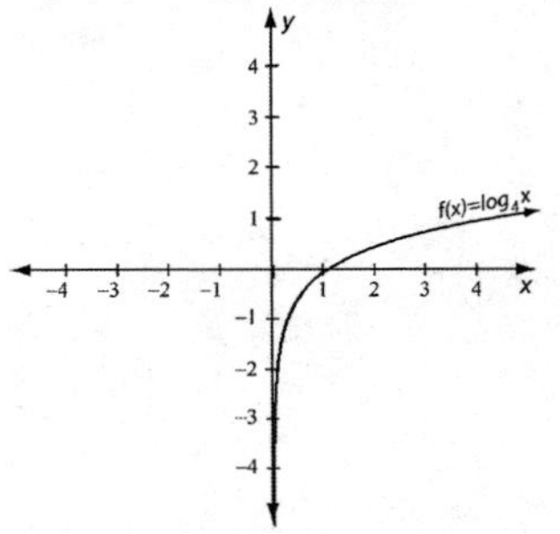

4. If $f(x)=\log_4 x$, graph $\log_4(x-2)$.

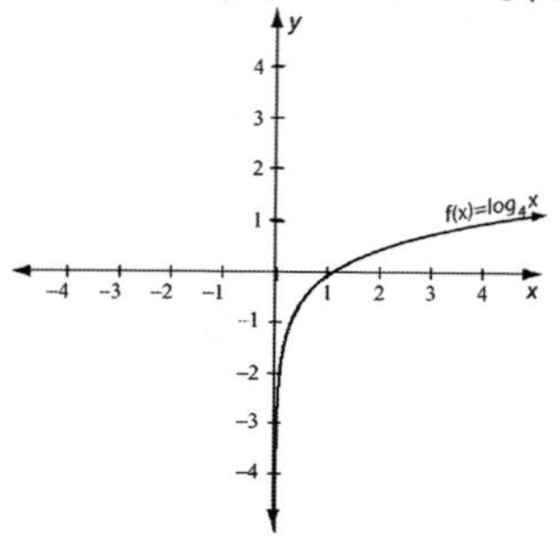

5. If $f(x)=\log_8 x$, graph $\log_8(x+1)$.

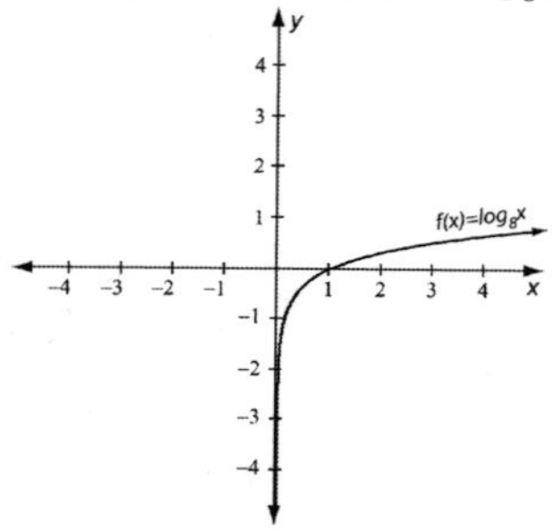

Properties of Logarithms

- The properties of **logarithms** follow directly from the properties of exponents. Keep in mind that "a log is an exponent."
- **REMEMBER:** A log is an exponent!

The log of a product $\log_b(xy) = \log_b x + \log_b y$ *sum of two logs*	When dealing with a product of exponents of the same base, you add the exponents. When dealing with the log of a product, you add the logs.
The log of a quotient $\log_b\left(\frac{x}{y}\right) = \log_b x - \log_b y$ *difference of two logs*	When you have a quotient of bases raised to different exponents, you subtract the exponents. When you have the log of a quotient, you subtract the logs.
The log of a power $\log_b(x^y) = y\log_b x$	When you raise a number with an exponent to another power, you multiply the exponents. When taking the log of a number raised to another power, you multiply that number by the log.
$\log_b b = 1$ $\quad b^1 = b$	Here is another useful property of logs. **REMEMBER:** $\log_b b = x$ means $b^x = b$. The only exponent that produces its base is 1. So, the log$b$ that produces b has to be 1.
$\log_b 1 = 0$ $\quad b^0 = 1$	**CHECK THIS OUT:** $\log_b 1 = x$ means $b^x = 1$. The only exponent that lets $b = 1$ is 0. So the log of 1 is 0!

False Formulas **$\log(x+y) \neq \log x + \log y$** *no standard form for adding* **False Formulas** **$\log_b\left(\frac{\log x}{\log y}\right) \neq \log x - \log y$** *the quotient of two logs*	*NEVER USE THESE FORMULAS*! They are examples of some common log mistakes! The log of a sum is **NOT** equal to the sum of the logs! You add two logs when you are dealing with a product of two numbers. The quotient of two logs is **NOT** equal to the difference of the logs! You subtract two logs when you are dealing with two numbers dividing, not two logs dividing.

Sample problems:

1. Expand: $\log_{10}(0.75 \cdot 293)$
   Solution: $\log_{10} 0.75 + \log_{10} 293$
   Explanation: Apply the log of a product property, $\log_b(xy) = \log_b x + \log_b y$:
   $\log_{10}(0.75 \cdot 293) = \log_{10} 0.75 + \log_{10} 293$.

2. Expand: $\log_5(7.6 + m)$
   Solution: Cannot be expanded
   Explanation: There is no rule for taking the log of a sum.

3. Expand: $\log_8\left(\frac{\sqrt[3]{x}}{y^2}\right)$

   Solution: $\frac{1}{3}\log_8 x - 2\log_8 y$

   Explanation: Express the radical as an exponent: $\log_8\left(\frac{\sqrt[3]{x}}{y^2}\right) = \log_8 \frac{x^{\frac{1}{3}}}{y^2}$.

   Apply the log of a quotient property, $\log_b\left(\frac{x}{y}\right) = \log_b x - \log_b y$: $\log_8 \frac{x^{\frac{1}{3}}}{y^2} = \log_8 x^{\frac{1}{3}} - \log_8 y^2$.

   Apply the log of a power property, $\log_b\left(x^y\right) = y\log_b x$: $\frac{1}{3}\log_8 x - 2\log_8 y$.

Practice problems: *(Answers on page: 752)*

1. Expand: $\log_1 xy^3$
2. Expand: $\log_2 \frac{2p}{q}$
3. Expand: $\log_6 \frac{x-2}{y}$

Review questions: *(Answers to odd questions on page: 752)*

1. Expand: $\log_4 j\sqrt[6]{k}$
2. Expand: $\log_e(w-4)$
3. Expand: $\log_5 \frac{x^3}{5}$

4. Expand: $\log_{10}\left(\frac{xy^2}{\sqrt{z}}\right)$

5. Expand: $\log_2\left(\frac{t}{8}\right)$

Expanding a Logarithmic Expression Using Properties

- To simplify logs, expand them out using the log properties.

log properties: • $\log_b b = 1$ • $\log_b 1 = 0$ • $\log_b (xy) = \log_b x + \log_b y$ • $\log_b (\frac{x}{y}) = \log_b x - \log_b y$ • $\log_b (x^y) = y\log_b x$	Here is a quick list of the properties of logs.
Example *simplify log* $\log_3 (\frac{3A}{B}) =$ $\log_3 3A - \log_3 B =$ $\log_3 3 + \log_3 A - \log_3 B =$ $1 + \log_3 A - \log_3 B$	Use the properties of logs to create as many small pieces as possible. The log of a quotient is equal to the difference of the logs. The log of a product is equal to the sum of the logs. The log of a value equal to the base is equal to 1. Now you've simplified the log!
Example *simplify log* $\log_6 (\frac{6\sqrt{5}}{\sqrt{6}})$ $= \log_6 (6\sqrt{5}) - \log_6 \sqrt{6}$ $= \log_6 6 + \log_6 \sqrt{5} - \log_6 \sqrt{6}$ $= 1 + \log_6 (5^{\frac{1}{2}}) - \log_6 (6^{\frac{1}{2}})$ $= 1 + \frac{1}{2}\log_6 5 - \frac{1}{2}\log_6 6 \; ((\frac{1}{2})(1))$ $\frac{1}{2} + \frac{1}{2}\log_6 5$	Again, simplify by creating small pieces. Rewrite a quotient as the difference of the logs. Rewrite a product as the sum of the logs. Rewrite square roots as exponents. Then simplify some more. Where possible, do some arithmetic. Then, you're done.
Example *simplify log* $\log_3 (A + 3B)$ * *cannot be simplified any further*	**REMEMBER:** The log of a sum cannot be simplified. Don't make the classic mistake!

Example *simplify log*	
$\log_{10}\sqrt[5]{\frac{A^2B^4}{C^3}}$	Problems that look horribly complex can actually be manipulated much more easily with the log properties.
$=\frac{1}{5}\log_{10}(\frac{A^2B^4}{C^3}) = \log_{10}((\frac{A^2B^4}{C^3})^{\frac{1}{5}})$	Because products and quotients are so easy to work, they don't cause cancellation errors.
$=\frac{1}{5}[\log_{10}(A^2B^4) - \log_{10}C^3]$	
$=\frac{1}{5}[\log_{10}A^2 + \log_{10}B^4 - \log_{10}C^3]$	Exponents are even easier. See?
$=\frac{1}{5}[2\log_{10}A + 4\log_{10}B - 3\log_{10}C]$	Now the problem is simplified!
$=\frac{2}{5}\log_{10}A + \frac{4}{5}\log_{10}B - \frac{3}{5}\log_{10}C$	

Sample problems:

1. Expand and simplify $\log_{10}(10^7c^{24})$. Assume all variables represent positive real numbers.

   Solution: $\log_{10}(10^7c^{24}) = 7 + 24\log c$

   Explanation:

Apply property	$\log_{10}10^7c^{24}$
log of a product:	$\log_{10}10^7 + \log_{10}c^{24}$
log of a power:	$7\log_{10}10 + 24\log_{10}c$
$\log_b b = 1$:	$7\cdot 1 + 24\log_{10}c$

   So, $\log_{10}(10^7c^{24}) = 7 + 24\log_{10}c$.

2. Expand and simplify $\log_5\left[\frac{(a+3)}{(a-4)}\right]$. Assume all variables represent positive real numbers.

   Solution: $\log_5(a+3) - \log_5(a-4)$

   Explanation: Apply "the log of a quotient" property: $\log_5\left[\frac{(a+3)}{(a-4)}\right] = \log_5(a+3) - \log_5(a-4)$.

   There is no "log of a sum" property, so the equation cannot be simplified any further.

3. Expand and simplify $\log_3\left(\frac{x\sqrt{y}}{3}\right)$. Assume all variables represent positive real numbers.

   Solution: $\log_3 x + \frac{1}{2}\log_3 y - 1$

   Explanation:

Apply property:	$\log_3\frac{x\sqrt{y}}{3}$
log of a quotient:	$\log_3 x\sqrt{y} - \log_3 3$
$\log_b b = 1$:	$\log_3 x\sqrt{y} - 1$
log of a product:	$\log_3 x + \log_3\sqrt{y} - 1$
$\sqrt{y} = y^{\frac{1}{2}}$:	$\log_3 x + \log_3 y^{\frac{1}{2}} - 1$
log of a power:	$\log_3 x + \frac{1}{2}\log_3 y - 1$

Practice problems: *(Answers on page: 752)*

1. Expand and simplify $\log_{10}\frac{\sqrt{2p}}{h^6}$. Assume all variables represent positive real numbers.
2. Expand and simplify $\log_2(8x^2 - y^2)$. Assume all variables represent positive real numbers.
3. Expand and simplify $\log_2\left(\frac{8t^4}{3n^2}\right)$. Assume all variables represent positive real numbers.

Review questions: *(Answers to odd questions on page: 752)*

1. Expand and simplify $\log_4\left(\frac{d^2g^7}{4m^3}\right)$. Assume all variables represent positive real numbers.
2. Expand and simplify $\log_6\left(\frac{19c}{36}\right)$. Assume all variables represent positive real numbers.
3. Expand and simplify $\log_7\left(\sqrt[6]{ab}+\sqrt{49}\right)$. Assume all variables represent positive real numbers.
4. Expand and simplify $\log_b\left(a^5k^7\right)$. Assume all variables represent positive real numbers.
5. Expand and simplify $\log_e\sqrt[3]{\frac{a}{b}}$. Assume all variables represent positive real numbers.

Combining Logarithmic Expressions

- To combine logarithms, use their properties backward to convert addition and subtraction into multiplication and division.
- A **common logarithm** is one with no base stated. The base is understood to be 10.
- A **natural logarithm** (ln) has ***e*** as its base.

log properties: • $\log_b b = 1$ • $\log_b 1 = 0$ • $\log_b (xy) = \log_b x + \log_b y$ • $\log_b (\frac{x}{y}) = \log_b x - \log_b y$ • $\log_b (x^y) = y\log_b x$	Here is a quick review of the log properties.
Note: Naked log is $\log x = \log_{10} x$	When you encounter a logarithm without a base listed, it is understood to be the common log or base 10.
Example Convert into 1 log $\log_{10}(x+5) + 2\log_{10} x$ $= \log(x+5) + \log x^2$ * bases must match up in order to combine the logs ! $= \log((x+5)(x^2))$	Sometimes you will be asked to convert multiple logs into one statement. To do so, use the multiplication and division properties to work backwards. The bases **must** be the same! In this example, since the expression is the sum of two logs, you can combine them into the log of a product.
Example Convert into 1 log $3\log_4 x - 2\log_4 z + 2\log_4 w$ $= \log_4 x^3 - \log_4 z^2 + \log_4 w^2$ difference of 2 logs $= \log_4(\frac{x^3}{z^2}) + \log_4 w^2$ sum of 2 logs $= \log_4(\frac{x^3}{z^2})(w^2)$ $= \log_4(\frac{x^3w^2}{z^2})$	Multiple terms aren't any harder. The difference of two logs is equal to the log of their quotient. The sum of two logs is equal to the log of their product. Simplify the expression next. Now you are done!
Note: Natural log is $\log_e x = \ln x$	The natural log occurs so often that mathematicians use $\ln x$ as a shortcut.

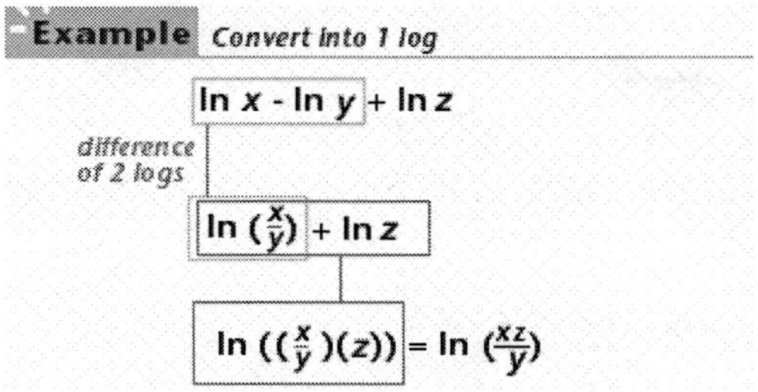

Remember: $\ln x = \log_e x$

Use your properties again:
The difference of logs becomes a quotient.
The sum of logs becomes a product.

Simplify and you're done!

Sample problems:

1. Write $3\log_2 y + \log_2(y-3) + \log_2 8$ as a single log and simplify if possible. Assume all variables represent positive real numbers.
   Solution: $\log_2[y^3(y-3)]+3$

Explanation:	Apply property	$3\log_2 y + \log_2(y-3) + \log_2 8$
	log of a power:	$\log_2 y^3 + \log_2(y-3) + \log_2 8$
	evaluate $\log_2 8$:	$\log_2 y^3 + \log_2(y-3) + 3$
	log of a product:	$\log_2[y^3(y-3)] + 3$

2. Write $\frac{1}{2}\log(x+1) + \frac{1}{2}\log(x-1)$ as a single log and simplify if possible. Assume all variables represent positive real numbers.
   Solution: $\log\sqrt{(x^2-1)}$
   Explanation: Move the $\frac{1}{2}$'s to exponents using the "log of a power" property: $\log(x+1)^{\frac{1}{2}} + \log(x-1)^{\frac{1}{2}}$. Combine the terms using the "log of a product" property: $\log(x+1)^{\frac{1}{2}}(x-1)^{\frac{1}{2}}$. Now that the expression is a single log, simplify further if possible: $\log[(x+1)(x-1)]^{\frac{1}{2}} = \log\sqrt{(x^2-1)}$. Note: the base in this logarithmic expression is 10.

3. Write $\ln\left(\frac{y^7}{z^2}\right) - \ln\left(\frac{y^3}{z}\right) - \ln\left(\frac{y^4}{z}\right)$ as a single log and simplify if possible. Assume all variables represent positive real numbers.
   Solution: 0
   Explanation: Combine the first 2 terms using the "log of a quotient" property: $\ln\left(\frac{y^7}{z^2}/\frac{y^3}{z}\right) - \ln\left(\frac{y^4}{z}\right)$. To divide the rationals, multiply by the reciprocal: $\ln\left(\frac{y^7}{z^2}\cdot\frac{z}{y^3}\right) - \ln\frac{y^4}{z} = \ln\frac{y^4}{z} - \ln\frac{y^4}{z}$. The two remaining terms are identical, thus the expression simplifies to 0.

Practice problems: *(Answers on page: 752)*

1. Write $\frac{2\log a + \log x}{4} - \log 1000$ as a single log and simplify if possible. Assume all variables represent positive real numbers.
2. Write $3\log_6 y - \log_6(y+5) + \log_6 36$ as a single log and simplify if possible. Assume all variables represent positive real numbers.
3. Write $5\ln x - \ln 8 + \ln e$ as a single log and simplify if possible. Assume all variables represent positive real numbers.

Review questions: *(Answers to odd questions on page: 752)*

1. Write the expression $\log_b\left(a^2-t^2\right)-\log_b\left(a+t\right)$ as a single log and simpify.
   Assume all variables represent positive real numbers.
2. Write the expression $\dfrac{\log(x-5)-\log y-2\log z}{3}$ as a single log and simpify.
   Use radicals instead of fractional exponents and assume all variables represent positive real numbers.
3. Write the expression $\left(\dfrac{3}{2}\right)\log_2 u+\left(\dfrac{3}{4}\right)\log_2 w$ as a single log and simpify.
   Use radicals instead of fractional exponents and assume all variables represent positive real numbers.
4. Write the expression $2\log_{10}5x+\log_{10}4$ as a single log and simpify if possible.
   Assume all variables represent positive real numbers.
5. Write the expression $2\ln x+4\ln y-3\ln z$ as a single log and simpify if possible.
   Assume all variables represent positive real numbers.

Evaluating Logarithmic Functions Using a Calculator

- When using a calculator to find the value of a logarithmic function, use the log properties to make your work easier.

log = $\log_{10}$ **ln** = $\log_e$

When finding logarithms with a calculator, you will need to find these two keys first.

Example

log 50 = 1.689...

$10^? = 50$

estimate: $10^1 = 10$, $10^2 = 100$

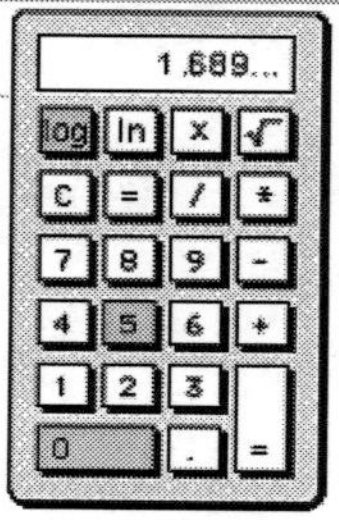

Start by finding the common log of 50.

To make sure that the calculator answer makes sense, it is probably a good idea to estimate first. What exponent would you need to raise the base, 10, to get 50? Somewhere between 1 and 2.

Punch in 50 and hit log . The answer, 1.689, fits into your range of 1 to 2.

Example

ln 50 = 3.912...

estimate: $e = 2.7\ldots$ round to 3

$3^3 = 27$

$3^4 = 81$

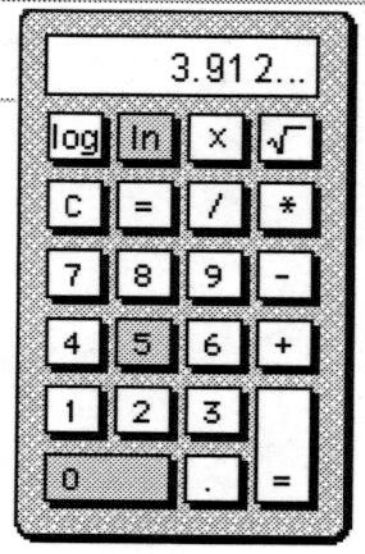

Estimating natural logs is trickier, but you can do it by figuring e about equal to 3. Notice that 50 is between 3^3 and 3^4.

Punch in 50. Hit ln . The answer, 3.912, fits into your range of 3 to 4.

WARNING: Some calculators work a little bit differently. You might have to hit ln *before* you punch in 50.

Example

log e^2 = 0.8685...
or **2log e**

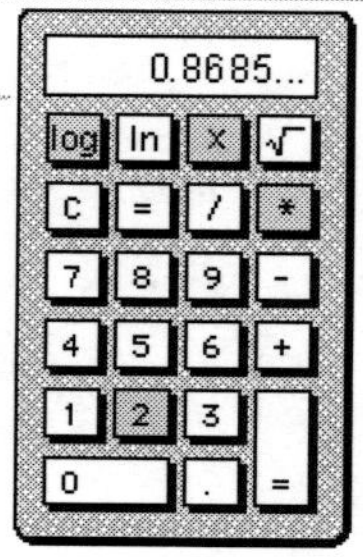

To find the log of e-squared, you can **either** find e-squared first and then hit log :

Punch in 2.7 and multiply by 2.7, then hit log .

or use the exponent rule and move the exponent outside the logarithm:

Punch in 2.7, hit log , then multiply that by 2.

Example

$\ln e^2 = 2$

$2\ln e = 2\log_e e = 2 \cdot 1 = 2$

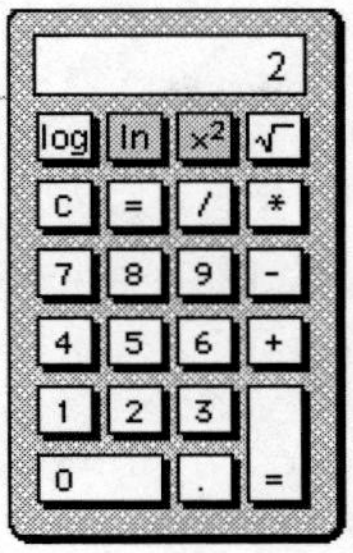

Finding the natural log of *e*-squared is actually pretty easy.

Punch in $\boxed{e}$. Square it. Hit $\boxed{\ln}$.

Notice how the answer matches what you could find using the logarithm properties. You know that $\ln e = 1$ and $1 \cdot 2 = 2$.

Sample problems:

1. Use a calculator to evaluate $\log 0.257$ to four decimal places.
   Solution: -0.5901
   Explanation: Complete the following key sequence for most scientific calculators: .257, LOG. So, $\log 0.257 = -0.5901$. Complete the following key sequence for a graphing calculator: LOG, 0.257, ENTER. Again, $\log 0.257 = -0.5901$.

2. Use a calculator to evaluate $\log 1{,}000{,}000$ (the log of a million) to four decimal places.
   Solution: 6
   Explanation: Complete the following key sequence for most scientific calculators: 1000000, LOG. So, $\log 1{,}000{,}000 = 6$. Complete the following key sequence for a graphing calculator: LOG, 1000000, ENTER. Again, $\log 1{,}000{,}000 = 6$.

3. Use a calculator to evaluate $\ln\left(\frac{5}{2}\right)$ to four decimal places.
   Solution: 0.9163
   Explanation: Complete the following key sequence for most scientific calculators: 5, ÷, 2, =, LN. So, $\ln\left(\frac{5}{2}\right) = 0.9163$ when rounded to four decimal places. Complete the following key sequence for a graphing calculator: LN, (, 5, / , 2,), ENTER. Again, $\ln\left(\frac{5}{2}\right) = 0.9163$.

Practice problems: *(Answers on page: 752)*

1. Use a calculator to evaluate $\log\left(5\frac{3}{4}\right)$ to four decimal places.
2. Use a calculator to evaluate $\log 25{,}300$ to four decimal places.
3. Use a calculator to evaluate $\ln 0.0104$ to four decimal places.

Review questions: *(Answers to odd questions on page: 752)*

1. Use a calculator to evaluate $\log 35.2$ to four decimal places.
2. Use a calculator to evaluate $\log 65.200$ to four decimal places.
3. Use a calculator to evaluate $\log\left(\frac{2}{3}\right)$ to four decimal places.
4. Use a calculator to evaluate $\log\left(\frac{6}{7}\right)$ to four decimal places.
5. Use a calculator to evaluate $\ln 25.3$ to four decimal places.

Using the Change of Base Formula

- The **change of base formula**: $\log_b x = \dfrac{\log_a x}{\log_a b}$.
- When a log has a base different from 10 or e, it can be difficult to manipulate. But you can use the **change of base formula** to make the problem easier.

$\log_7 12$ $\log_3 \frac{1}{2}$ $\log_{\frac{3}{2}} 2$ ***How would you calculate these?***	Calculating logarithms with base 10 or e is fairly straightforward. But what about logs with different bases? You can't figure these on your calculator. But there must be a way to work with strange bases.
Change of Base Formula $\log_b x = \dfrac{\log_a x}{\log_a b}$ *changing base b to base a*	And here it is! The change of base formula will enable you to turn one log of a given base into a quotient of logs with a different base (a). Notice how you can choose anything for a.
Proving the change of base formula let $y = \log_b x \longleftrightarrow b^y = x$ $\log_a (b^y) = \log_a x$ $y \log_a b = \log_a x$ $\boxed{y = \dfrac{\log_a x}{\log_a b}}$	In case you are skeptical, let's look at how the change of base formula is derived. The log equation can be rewritten as an exponential equation. Take the log base a of both sides. Use the log properties to simplify. Solve for y.
Example *solve these logs using change of base formula* A) $\log_3 \frac{1}{2} = \dfrac{\ln \frac{1}{2}}{\ln 3} = -.6309...$ B) $\log_{\frac{3}{2}} 2 = \dfrac{\log 2}{\log \frac{3}{2}} = 1.7095$ ☺ **log and ln can be used interchangably**	Examples show the change of base formula at work. In this problem the base is changed from 3 to e and the problem is easily solved. This example changes the base from 3/2 to 10 and is just as straightforward as the first example. Notice you can use 10 or e as bases easily and in any problem.

Sample problems:

1. True or False: $\log_7 12 = \dfrac{\log 7}{\log 12}$.

   Solution: False

   Explanation: Use the change of base formula, $\log_b x = \frac{\log_a x}{\log_a b}$, where $b = 7$ and $x = 12$, to change the base from 7 to 10, so $a = 10$: $\log_7 12 = \frac{\log_{10} 12}{\log_{10} 7} = \frac{\log 12}{\log 7}$, not $\frac{\log 7}{\log 12}$.

2. Express $\log_{\sqrt{3}} 4$ as a quotient of common logs.

   Solution: $\dfrac{\log 4}{\log \sqrt{3}}$

   Explanation: A common log is a log where the base is understood to be 10 and does not need to be stated. Use the change of base formula to change the base from $\sqrt{3}$ to 10: $\log_{\sqrt{3}} 4 = \dfrac{\log 4}{\log \sqrt{3}}$.

3. Express $\log_{\frac{1}{2}} \sqrt{5}$ as a quotient of natural logs.

   Solution: $\dfrac{\ln\sqrt{5}}{\ln\frac{1}{2}}$

   Explanation: A natural log is a log with base e, expressed ln. Use the change of base formula to change the base from $\frac{1}{2}$ to e: $\log_{\frac{1}{2}} \sqrt{5} = \dfrac{\ln\sqrt{5}}{\ln\frac{1}{2}}$.

Practice problems: *(Answers on page: 752)*

1. Express $\log_{20}\left(\dfrac{1541}{3.29}\right)$ as a quotient of common logs.
2. Express $\log_4 0.287$ as a quotient of natural logs.
3. True or False: $\log_{\sqrt{3}} 5 = \dfrac{\log_2 5}{\log_2 \sqrt{3}}$

Review questions: *(Answers to odd questions on page: 752)*

1. Express $\log_9 20$ as a quotient of natural logs.
2. Express $\log_5 3$ as a quotient of natural logs.
3. Express $\log_9 35$ as a quotient of common logs.
4. Express $\log_6 5$ as a quotient of common logs.
5. Express $\log_{\frac{1}{2}} 8$ as a quotient of common logs.

The Richter Scale

- The Richter scale formula: $R = \log\dfrac{I}{I_0}$.

Since logarithms give you an easy way to manipulate exponents, they turn out to have hundreds of real world applications.

One of the real world applications is in seismology, dealing with the intensity of earthquakes. You have probably heard of the **Richter scale**. The Richter scale is how scientists rate the severity of earthquakes.

The Richter scale is a logarithmic scale found by taking the log of the intensity of the earthquake divided by the intensity of normal seismic activity.

398,107,000 I_0	For one particular earthquake, scientists recorded an intensity of 398,107,000I_o, meaning 398,107,000 times normal intensity.
$R = \log\left(\frac{398,107,000\ I_0}{I_0}\right)$	They can find this earthquake's value on the Richter scale by substituting this value in for ***I***.
$R = \log(398,107,000)$ $R = \boxed{8.599...}$ ← *Answer*	Then they do the calculations.
	That was a pretty severe earthquake!

Sample problems:

1. The Richter scale magnitude R of an earthquake of intensity I is defined as $R = \log\left(\frac{I}{I_o}\right)$, where I_0 is a small threshold intensity. Find the magnitude of an earthquake if the intensity is 68 million I_0.
   Solution: 7.83
   Explanation: Use the formula $R = \log\left(\frac{I}{I_0}\right) = \log\left(\frac{68\text{ million } I_0}{I_0}\right) = \log(68\text{ million}) = 7.83$.

2. The Richter scale magnitude R of an earthquake of intensity I is defined as $R = \log\left(\frac{I}{I_o}\right)$, where I_0 is a small threshold intensity. Find the magnitude of an earthquake if the intensity is 10.5 million I_0.
   Solution: 7.02
   Explanation: Use the formula $R = \log\left(\frac{I}{I_0}\right) = \log\left(\frac{10.5\text{ million } I_0}{I_0}\right) = \log(10{,}500{,}000) = 7.02$.

3. The Richter scale magnitude R of an earthquake of intensity I is defined as $R = \log\left(\frac{I}{I_o}\right)$, where I_0 is a small threshold intensity. Find the magnitude of an earthquake if the intensity is 205 million I_0.
   Solution: 8.3
   Explanation: Use the formula $R = \log\left(\frac{I}{I_0}\right) = \log\left(\frac{205\text{ million } I_0}{I_0}\right) = \log(205{,}000{,}000) = 8.3$.

Practice problems: *(Answers on page: 752)*

1. The Richter scale magnitude R of an earthquake of intensity I is defined as $R = \log\left(\frac{I}{I_o}\right)$, where I_0 is a small threshold intensity. Find the magnitude of an earthquake if the intensity is 9 million I_0.

2. The Richter scale magnitude R of an earthquake of intensity I is defined as $R = \log\left(\frac{I}{I_o}\right)$, where I_0 is a small threshold intensity. Find the magnitude of an earthquake if the intensity is 74 million I_0.

3. The Richter scale magnitude R of an earthquake of intensity I is defined as $R = \log\left(\frac{I}{I_o}\right)$, where I_0 is a small threshold intensity. Find the magnitude of an earthquake if the intensity is 5.4 million I_0.

Review questions: *(Answers to odd questions on page: 752)*

1. The Richter scale magnitude R of an earthquake of intensity I is defined as $R = \log\left(\frac{I}{I_o}\right)$, where I_0 is a small threshold intensity. Find the magnitude of an earthquake if the intensity is 3 million I_0.

2. The Richter scale magnitude R of an earthquake of intensity I is defined as $R = \log\left(\frac{I}{I_o}\right)$, where I_0 is a small threshold intensity. Find the magnitude of an earthquake if the intensity is 15 million I_0.

3. The Richter scale magnitude R of an earthquake of intensity I is defined as $R = \log\left(\frac{I}{I_o}\right)$, where I_0 is a small threshold intensity. Find the magnitude of an earthquake if the intensity is 20.5 million I_0.

4. The Richter scale magnitude R of an earthquake of intensity I is defined as $R = \log\left(\frac{I}{I_o}\right)$, where I_0 is a small threshold intensity. Find the magnitude of an earthquake if the intensity is 0.2 million I_0.

5. The Richter scale magnitude R of an earthquake of intensity I is defined as $R = \log\left(\frac{I}{I_o}\right)$, where I_0 is a small threshold intensity. Find the magnitude of an earthquake if the intensity is 180 million I_0.

The Distance Modulus Formula

- The **distance modulus formula**: $\mathrm{M} = 5\log r - 5$.
- The variables in the distance modulus formula are:
  - **M**, for magnitude, which uses a star's brightness as measured by the observer to calculate its distance from the observer.
  - ***r***, the star's distance measured in parsecs, a value equal to approximately 3.3 light years.
- The distance modulus formula is used to calculate high distances.

	Since logarithms empower you to manipulate exponents with great ease and efficiency, they turn out to have numerous real world applications.
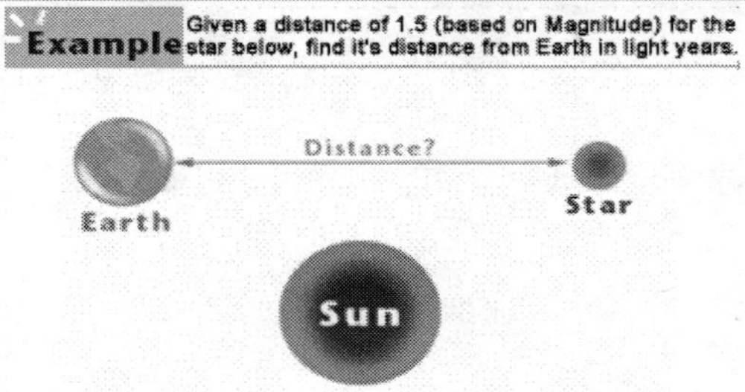	The numbers involved in astronomy are very large. In fact, they are so large that astronomers do not discuss them in terms of traditional units like seconds and miles. The large numbers involved in astronomy create a perfect opportunity for logarithms to help make calculations easier.
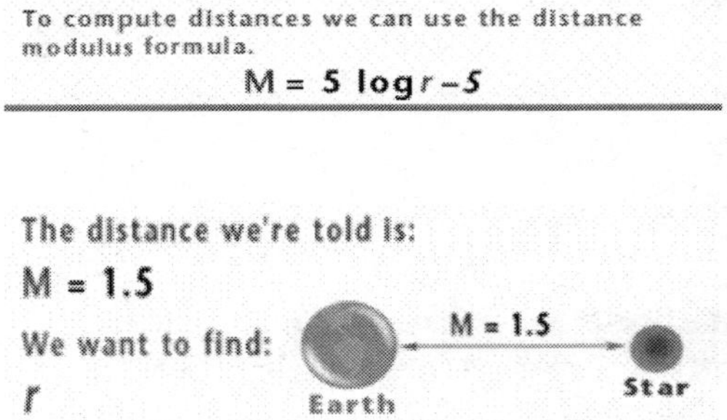	Given one of the variables of the distance modulus formula, you can use the logarithm properties to solve for the other variables. In this example, you are told the distance based on magnitude, or brightness of the star to the observer. You are asked to find the distance in light years.
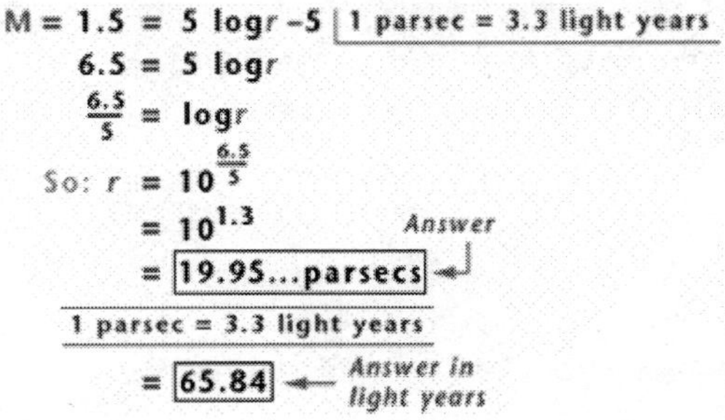	Substitute in what you know and try to isolate the log term. Once you have done this, convert back to exponential form and solve. The answer to the distance modulus formula is in parsecs. You can convert the answer to light-years by multiplying by 3.3.

Sample problems:

1. The distance modulus , M, of a star is given by the formula $M = 5\log r - 5$, where r is the distance from Earth to the star measured in parsecs. If a star is 153 parsecs away, what is its distance modulus?
   Solution: 5.925
   Explanation: $M = 5\log r - 5 = 5\log(153) - 5 = 5(2.185) - 5 = 5.925$.

2. The distance r to a star is measured in parsecs and can be obtained by solving the distance modulus formula $M = 5\log r - 5$ for r. If Vega has a distance modulus M of -0.48, how far is Vega from Earth?
   Solution: 8.02 parsecs
   Explanation: Substitute $M = -0.48$ into the distance modulus formula and solve for r:
   $-0.48 = 5\log r - 5$; $4.52 = 5\log r$; $\frac{4.52}{5} = \log r$; $0.904 = \log r$; $r = 10^{0.904} = 8.02$.

3. The distance r to a star is measured in parsecs and can be obtained by solving the distance modulus formula $M = 5\log r - 5$ for r. If Proxima Centauri has a distance modulus of -4.466, how far is Proxima Centauri from Earth in light years?
   Solution: 4.22 light years
   Explanation: Substitute $M = -4.466$ into the distance modulus formula and solve for r:
   $-4.466 = 5\log r - 5$; $0.534 = 5\log r$; $\frac{0.534}{5} = \log r$; $0.1068 = \log r$; $r = 10^{0.1068} = 1.2788$.
   Convert 1.2788 parsecs to light years: $1.2788(3.3) = 4.22$ light years.

Practice problems: *(Answers on page: 752)*

1. The distance modulus , M, of a star is given by the formula $M = 5\log r - 5$, where r is the distance from Earth to the star measured in parsecs. If a star is 79.5 parsecs away, what is its distance modulus?
2. The distance r to a star is measured in parsecs and can be obtained by solving the distance modulus formula $M = 5\log r - 5$ for r. If a star has a distance modulus M of -1.27, how far is the star from Earth?
3. The distance r to a star is measured in parsecs and can be obtained by solving the distance modulus formula $M = 5\log r - 5$ for r. If the Andromeda Galaxy has a distance modulus of 24.12, how far is the Andromeda Galaxy from Earth in light years?

Review questions: *(Answers to odd questions on page: 752)*

1. The distance modulus , M, of a star is given by the formula $M = 5\log r - 5$, where r is the distance from Earth to the star measured in parsecs. If a star is 105.2 parsecs away, what is its distance modulus?
2. The distance r to a star is measured in parsecs and can be obtained by solving the distance modulus formula $M = 5\log r - 5$ for r. If a star has a distance modulus M of -0.65, how far is the star from Earth?
3. The distance r to a star is measured in parsecs and can be obtained by solving the distance modulus formula $M = 5\log r - 5$ for r. If a star has a distance modulus M of 2.31, how far is the star from Earth?
4. The distance r to a star is measured in parsecs and can be obtained by solving the distance modulus formula $M = 5\log r - 5$ for r. If the Magellanic Clouds have a distance modulus of 18.56, how far are the Magellanic Clouds from Earth in light years?
5. The distance r to a star is measured in parsecs and can be obtained by solving the distance modulus formula $M = 5\log r - 5$ for r. If a star has a distance modulus of 32.25, how far is the star from Earth in light years?

Solving Exponential Equations

- When solving for variables in the exponents, either the bases will be the same or they will be different.
  - When the bases are the same, you can set the exponents equal to each other.
  - When the bases are different, you must use logarithms to turn the exponents into coefficients. Then isolate for your variable by using the logarithm properties.

when solving for exponents, equal bases have equal exponents **what value for x makes the equation true?** $(\frac{3}{4})^x = \frac{16}{9}$ *try to make each base the same value* $(\frac{3}{4})^x = (\frac{4}{3})^2$ *flip to make bases equal* $(\frac{3}{4})^x = (\frac{3}{4})^{-2}$ $x = -2$	When you are asked to solve equations with variables in the exponents, start by checking the bases. If they are the same, you can set the exponents equal to each other. It is often a good idea to try to manipulate the bases using exponential properties to make them the same. This process can save you time later.
Example *find the value of x that makes this true* $3^{x-2} = 4^{2x+1}$ $\log(3^{x-2}) = \log(4^{2x+1})$ *take log (base 10) of both sides* *exponents become coefficients* $(x-2)\log 3 = (2x+1)\log 4$ *don't forget to distribute* $(\log 3)x - 2\log 3 = (2\log 4)x + \log 4$ $(\log 3)x - (2\log 4)x = 2\log 3 + \log 4$ *solve for x* $(\log 3 - \log 16)x = \log 9 + \log 4$ *simplify* $(\log(3/16))x = \log 36$ $x = \frac{\log 36}{\log(3/16)} = -2.1407\ldots$	When the bases are not the same, you can still solve the equation. Since the two expressions are equal, you can equate the logs of both sides and solve for x. By using the logarithmic properties, you can transform the exponents into coefficients. Use parentheses, especially when variables are nearby. Distribute across the parentheses. Isolate x. If you want to clear the logs from your answer, plug these values into your calculator.
Example *find the value of x when:* $2^{2x-3} = 5^{-x-1}$ $\log(2^{2x-3}) = \log(5^{-x-1})$ *take logs of each side* *exponent becomes coefficient* $(2x-3)\log 2 = (-x-1)\log 5$ $(2\log 2)x - (3\log 2) = (-\log 5)x - \log 5$ *distribute* $(\log 4 + \log 5)x = \log 8 - \log 5$ *isolate x's* $(\log 20)x = \log(8/5)$ $x = \frac{\log(8/5)}{\log 20}$ *solve for x* $x = .15689\ldots$	The expressions are equal so you can set up the logs of both sides. Move the exponents down to be coefficients.Distribute, being very careful.Isolate the x-terms.Solve for x. Plug the values into your calculator.

Sample problems:

1. Solve for x: $7^{3x^2-12} = 1$
   Solution: $x = \pm 2$.
   Explanation: NOTE: $1 = 7^0$. Express each side with equal bases: $7^{3x^2-12} = 7^0$. Since equal bases have equal exponents, equate the exponents and solve for x: $3x^2 - 12 = 0$; $3x^2 = 12$; $x^2 = 4$; $x = \pm\sqrt{4} = \pm 2$.

2. Solve for x: $3^{4x} = 7^{x+2}$
   Solution: $x = 1.589$
   Explanation: This equation cannot be expressed with equal bases, so equate the logs and apply the logarithmic properties: $\log 3^{4x} = \log 7^{x+2}$; $4x\log 3 = (x+2)\log 7$; $4x\log 3 = x\log 7 + 2\log 7$. Subtract $x\log 7$ from both sides: $4x\log 3 - x\log 7 = 2\log 7$. Factor out the x: $x(4\log 3 - \log 7) = 2\log 7$. Divide each side by $(4\log 3 - \log 7)$: $x = \frac{2\log 7}{4\log 3 - \log 7} = \frac{1.69}{1.9085 - .8451} = 1.589$.

3. Solve for x: $5^{7x-4} = 3^{2x+1}$
   Solution: $x = 0.831$
   Explanation: This equation cannot be expressed with equal bases, so equate the logs and apply the logarithmic properties: $\log 5^{7x-4} = \log 3^{2x+1}$; $(7x-4)\log 5 = (2x+1)\log 3$;
   $7x\log 5 - 4\log 5 = 2x\log 3 + \log 3$. Subtract $2x\log 3$ from both sides and add $4\log 5$ to both sides:
   $7x\log 5 - 2x\log 3 = \log 3 + 4\log 5$. Factor out the x: $x(7\log 5 - 2\log 3) = \log 3 + 4\log 5$. Divide each side by $(7\log 5 - 2\log 3)$: $x = \frac{\log 3 + 4\log 5}{7\log 5 - 2\log 3} = \frac{.477+2.796}{4.893-.954} = 0.831$.

Practice problems: *(Answers on page: 752)*

1. Solve for x: $\left(\frac{7}{10}\right)^{3x^2-10} = 0.49$
2. Solve for x: $6^{1-4x} = 319$
3. Solve for x: $2^{5x+1} = 3^{2x-4}$

Review questions: *(Answers to odd questions on page: 752)*

1. Solve for x: $2^{3x+1} = 128$
2. Solve for x: $5^{2-x} = 125$
3. Solve for x: $\left(\frac{5}{2}\right)^{4x-1} = \frac{8}{125}$
4. Solve for x: $3^{x} = \frac{5}{8}$
5. Solve for x: $5^{x-2} = 3^{3x+2}$

Solving Logarithmic Equations

- When solving an equation made up of logarithms, isolate the logs and then convert to exponential form.
- Always check your answers for extraneous roots. Remember that you can only take the log of positive numbers.

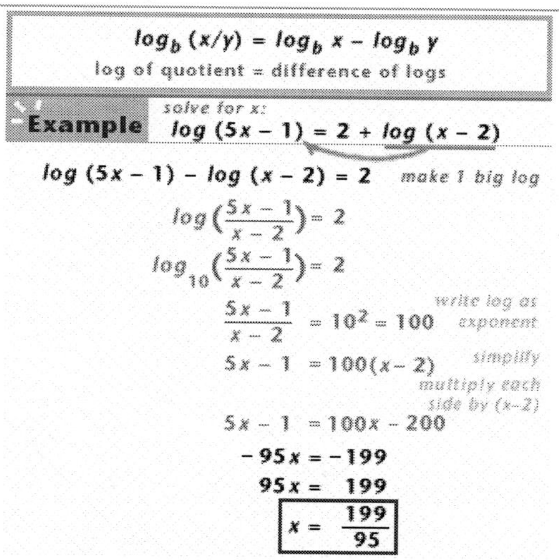

When solving log equations, start by isolating the logs on one side of the equal sign.

Next, combine the logs using the log properties.

Now write the statement in exponent form.

Simplify by cross-multiplying.

Finally, solve for x.

Example *solve for x:* $\ln x = \frac{1}{2}\ln\left(2x + \frac{5}{2}\right) + \frac{1}{2}\ln 2$

$0 = \ln\left(\frac{\sqrt{4x+5}}{x}\right)$	*distribute*
$0 = \ln_e\left(\frac{\sqrt{4x+5}}{x}\right)$	
$1 = \frac{\sqrt{4x+5}}{x}$	
$x = \sqrt{4x+5}$	*multiply through by x*
$(x = \sqrt{4x+5})^2$	*square both sides to remove the radical*
$x^2 = 4x + 5$	
$x^2 - 4x - 5 = 0$	*a quadratic*
$(x-5)(x+1) = 0$	*factor*

Remember:
always check answer for extraneous roots

$x = 5$ ~~$x = -1$~~ ← can't take log of a negative

Start by simplifying things if you see an easy way..

Then move all the logs on one side of the equal sign and combine the logs.

Convert to exponential form and solve for x.

Remember: Your log statement is telling you that e^0 equals the radical expression. You know that $e^0 = 1$.

After you have found the roots, verify that they are answers for the equation. With logarithms, you have to make sure that the roots do not require you to take the log of a negative number.

Sample problems:

1. Solve for x: $\log x + \log(x+15) = 2$
   Solution: 5
   Explanation: Use the logarithmic properties to combine the logs: $\log x(x+15) = 2$. Express the log as an exponential equation: $10^2 = x(x+15)$. Simplify and manipulate the equation until it is equal to 0: $100 = x^2 + 15x$; $0 = x^2 + 15x - 100$. Factor and solve for x: $0 = (x-5)(x+20)$; $x = 5$ or $x = -20$. But -20 is an extraneous root, so $x = 5$.

2. Solve for x: $\log_7(x^2 - x - 6) - \log_7(x+2) = 1$
   Solution: 10
   Explanation: Use the logarithmic properties to combine the logs: $\log_7 \frac{x^2-x-6}{x+2} = 1$. Express the log as an exponential equation: $7^1 = \frac{x^2-x-6}{x+2}$. Factor the trinomial in the numerator and cancel any common factors: $7 = \frac{(x-3)\cancel{(x+2)}}{\cancel{x+2}}$; $7 = x - 3$. Solve for x: $x = 10$.

3. Solve for x: $2\ln(x-3) = \ln(x+5) + \ln 4$
   Solution: 11
   Explanation: Use the logarithmic properties to combine the logs and move the coefficient: $\ln(x-3)^2 = \ln 4(x+5)$. Simplify and manipulate the equation until it is equal to 0: $\ln(x-3)^2 - \ln(4x+20) = 0$. Use the logarithmic properties again to combine the logs: $\ln\frac{(x-3)^2}{4x+20} = 0$. Express as an exponential equation: $e^0 = \frac{(x-3)^2}{4x+20}$. Simplify and manipulate the equation until it is equal to 0: $1 = \frac{(x-3)^2}{4x+20}$; $4x + 20 = (x-3)^2$; $4x + 20 = x^2 - 6x + 9$; $0 = x^2 - 10x - 11$. Factor and solve for x: $0 = (x+1)(x-11)$; $x = -1$ or $x = 11$. But $x = -1$ is an extraneous root, so $x = 11$.

Practice problems: *(Answers on page: 753)*

1. Solve for x: $\ln(x^2 - x - 12) - \ln(2x+6) = \ln\frac{1}{2}$
2. Solve for x: $\log(x-3) = 1 - \log x$
3. Solve for x: $\log_2(x+1) + \log_2(x-1) = 3$

Review questions: *(Answers to odd questions on page: 753)*

1. Solve for x: $\log_2(25 - x) = 3$
2. Solve for x: $\log_2(x+2) = 5$

3. Solve for x: $\log(x+2)+\log(x-1)=1$
4. Solve for x: $4+3\log(2x)=16$
5. Solve for x: $2-\ln(3-x)=0$

Solving Equations with Logarithmic Exponents

- When working with equations with logarithmic expressions, you can use the fact that a logarithm is an exponent to untangle the log pieces and simplify the equation.

Example solve for x: $e^{\ln(x-1)}=4$

$e^{\boxed{\ln(x-1)}}=4$

↑

the power needed to raise e to

$x-1=4$

$x=4+1=\boxed{5}$

By really understanding the properties and definition of logs, you can perform some pretty slick manipulations in very few steps.

Another way to demonstrate this problem is to rewrite this exponent sentence as a logarithmic statement:
$\log_e 4 = \ln(x-1)$.
$\log_e 4 = \ln 4$, so:
$\ln 4 = \ln(x-1)$, so
$4 = x-1$, and
$x = 5$

Example solve for x: $e^{\ln(x-1)}=4$

$\ln(e^{\ln(x-1)})=\ln 4$ — take nat. log of both sides

$\ln(x-1)\ln e=\ln 4$ — exponent becomes a coefficient

$\boxed{\log_e e}$ ← what do you raise e to in order to get e? answer: 1

$\ln(x-1)(1)=\ln 4$

$x-1=4$

$\boxed{x=5}$

If the above example didn't make sense, don't worry. Here's another approach using natural logs.

Just take the natural log of each side and use your logarithmic properties to simplify.

You are still going to need to know that the log of a number that is the same as the base is 1.

Remember: If the logs are equal, then the stuff you took the logs of is equal too.

Example solve for x: $\log(\log x)=1$

$\log_{10}(\log x)=1$ — when not written, log is base 10

$10^1=\log x$

$10^1=\log_{10}x$

$\boxed{x=10^{10}}$ — 10 = exponent needed to raise 10 to in order to get x

When dealing with logs of logs, use the definition of logarithms to untangle the logs.

Since a log is an exponent, then 10 raised to the first is equal to $\log x$.

Since a log is an exponent, then 10 raised to 10 is x.

Example solve for x: $\ln(e^{3x})=6$

$\ln(e^{3x})=6$ — exponent becomes a coefficient

$3x\ln e=6$

$3x(1)=6$

$\boxed{x=2}$

In some cases, applying one of the logarithmic properties will allow you to simplify away the logs in the equation.

Since the natural log of e is equal to 1, you can simplify and solve.

Sample problems:

1. Solve for x: $e^{\ln(x-3)}=9-2x$
   Solution: 4
   Explanation: Since $e^{\ln x}=x$, $e^{\ln(x-3)}=9-2x$; $x-3=9-2x$. Solve for x: $3x=12$; $x=4$.

2. Solve for x: $\ln(e^{5x+1}) = 7x$

   Solution: $\frac{1}{2}$

   Explanation: Apply the logarithmic property of exponents: $\ln(e^{5x+1}) = 7x$; $5x + 1(\ln e) = 7x$. Since $\ln e = 1$: $5x + 1 = 7x$. Solve for x: $1 = 2x$; $x = \frac{1}{2}$.

3. Solve for x: $1 = \log_2(\log_2 3x)$

   Solution: $\frac{4}{3}$

   Explanation: Express the log as an exponential equation: $2^1 = \log_2 3x$. Again, express the log as an exponential equation: $2^2 = 3x$. Solve for x: $4 = 3x$; $x = \frac{4}{3}$.

Practice problems: *(Answers on page: 753)*

1. Solve for x: $e^{\ln(4-x)} = 2x + 1$
2. Solve for x: $1 + x = e^{\ln(4x)}$
3. Solve for x: $\log_{\frac{1}{2}}(\log_{\frac{1}{2}} 5x - 1) = 0$

Review questions: *(Answers to odd questions on page: 753)*

1. Solve for x: $e^{\ln(x+4)} = 10 - x$
2. Solve for x: $\ln\left(e^{2x}\right) = x + 5$
3. Solve for x: $3x + 7 = \ln\left(e^{x+10}\right)$
4. Solve for x: $3 = \log_2\left(\log_2 4x\right)$
5. Solve for x: $2 = \log_3\left(\log_2\left(5x - 3\right)\right)$

Compound Interest

- The **compound interest formula**: $A = P\left(1 + \left(\frac{r}{m}\right)\right)^{tm}$.

Example Professor Burger's Car Problem Professor Burger wants to buy a car. It costs \$30,000, and he only has \$27,000. If he invests it in a bank account at 6% interest compounded quarterly, how long will he have to wait before it matures to \$30,000?  Burger's Dreamboat	To solve this problem, you will need to use the techniques for solving exponential equations. You are asked to find out how many years it will take for Dr. Burger to accumulate the necessary funds.
Logarithmic formula: $A = P(1+(\frac{r}{m}))^{tm}$ A = The future value P = Present value r = The interest rate m = Number of compounding per year t = Number of years	The **compound interest formula** is designed for such situations. Substitute in the facts you know and you will be able to determine what you want to know.
$30{,}000 = 27{,}000\left(1+\frac{.06}{4}\right)^{4t}$ Do not know the number of years we invest	After all the facts are substituted, the only variable left is t for the amount of time required.

$\frac{30{,}000}{27{,}000} = \left(1+\frac{.06}{4}\right)^{4t}$ *Now to get coefficients, take logs of both sides*	Begin to solve. Isolate the exponential term. Simplify the fraction because you can.
$\ln\left(\frac{30}{27}\right) = \ln\left(\left(1+\frac{.06}{4}\right)^{4t}\right)$ *Becomes a coefficient*	Now take the natural log of both sides.
$\ln\left(\frac{30}{27}\right) = 4t\ln\left(1+\frac{.06}{4}\right)$ ← *now solve for t* $t = \frac{\ln\left(\frac{30}{27}\right)}{4\ln\left(1+\frac{.06}{4}\right)}$	Using the log properties, transform the exponent to be a coefficient. Simplify for t and solve with your calculator.
$t =$ **1.769...years** ← *Answer* 	You are proudly able to announce to Dr. Burger that he will need 1.769 years if he follows this plan to save up the money for his dream car.

Sample problems:

1. Suppose you invest \$3,000 into an account with a 7.5% interest rate where the interest is compounded monthly. What will the balance be after 9 months?
   Solution: \$3,173.03
   Explanation: Substitute $P = 3{,}000$; $r = 7.5\% = .075$; $m = 12$; and $t = 9$ months (0.75 years) into the compound interest formula, $A = P\left(1+\frac{r}{m}\right)^{tm}$ and simplify:
   $$A = 3{,}000\left(1+\frac{0.075}{12}\right)^{0.75(12)} = 3{,}000(1.00625)^9 = 3{,}000(1.057676951) = 3173.03.$$
   So, the balance will be \$3,173.03.

2. If you take out a loan of \$19,000 at 12% interest, compounded daily, after how many years would the balance owed become \$25,000?
   Solution: 2.29 years
   Explanation: From the problem: $P = 19{,}000$; $r = 12\% = .12$; $m = 365$; $A = 25{,}000$. Substitute these values into the compound interest formula: $A = P\left(1+\frac{r}{m}\right)^{tm} \Rightarrow 25{,}000 = 19{,}000\left(1+\frac{.12}{365}\right)^{365t}$.
   Solve for t, divide each side by 19,000 and simplify within the parentheses: $\frac{25}{19} = 1.000329^{365t}$.
   Take a natural log of each side: $\ln\frac{25}{19} = \ln 1.000329^{365t}$. Apply the log of a power property: $\ln\frac{25}{19} = 365t(\ln 1.000329)$. Find each natural log with a calculator: $.27443685 = 365t(.00032895)$.
   Solve for t: $365t = 834.28135$; $t = 2.29$.

3. Suppose you invested \$5,000 into an account where the interest was compounded weekly. If after 35 years you had \$116,500, what was the interest rate?
   Solution: 9%
   Explanation: Substitute the values from the problem into the compound interest formula:
   $116{,}500 = 5{,}000\left(1+\frac{x}{52}\right)^{52(35)}$. Simplify and solve for x: $\frac{116{,}500}{5{,}000} = \left(1+\frac{x}{52}\right)^{1820}$;
   $23.3 = \left(1+\frac{x}{52}\right)^{1820}$; $\sqrt[1820]{23.3} = 1+\frac{x}{52}$; $1.001731417 = 1+\frac{x}{52}$; $\frac{x}{52} = 0.001731417$;
   $x = .09$. So the interest rate was 9%.

Practice problems: *(Answers on page: 753)*

1. Using the compound interest formula, how much would you need to invest at 6.5% interest to have \$200,000 in 6 years, compounded monthly?

2. If Nick has $2,500 to invest and he wants to invest in a program that compounds twice a year so that he will have $3,000 in 3 years, what rate of interest must he find for his investment to be successful?

3. If you invest $10,000at 9.5% interest, compounded semi-monthly, how long will it take for the balance to reach $50,000?

Review questions: *(Answers to odd questions on page: 753)*

1. Suppose you invest $5, 000 at 9% interest. How long would it take your money to double if it if the interest is compounded semiannually (twice a year).
2. Using the compound interest formula, how much would you have to invest at 7% interest, compounded quarterly, to have $15,000 in 20 years?
3. If you take out a loan of $ 19,000 at 12% interest, compounded daily, in how many years would it accumulate to a $ 25,000 loan?
4. Kris invests $800 at 3% compounded monthly. How long will it take her investment to reach $930?
5. How much should be deposited in an account paying 4% interest compounded monthly in order to have a balance of $14,500 after 6 years?

Predicting Change

- When working with equations with log expressions, you can use the definition of logarithms to untangle the log and simplify the equation.

	Here is another practice problem to show you how to manipulate equations that have logarithmic parts. **THE SET-UP:** Dr. Burger conjectures that the number of used car dealers in a town increases logarithmically in relation to the amount of time since the first used car dealership was introduced.
$P = 500\log(2t+3)$ — Solve for t P = Number of used cars dealers t = Number of months since 1st car dealership was introduced	This is the equation Dr. Burger gives. Anytime you get a scientific equation it is a very good idea to make sure you know what all the variables represent. A list is a great way to check.
$P = 500\log(2t+3)$ $\frac{P}{500} = \log_{10}(2t+3)$ $10^{P/500} = 2t+3$ $10^{P/500} - 3 = 2t$ $\boxed{t = \frac{10^{P/500}-3}{2}}$ ← Answer	The equation is set up to solve for *P*. If you wanted to find the *t*, you would rewrite the equation in terms of *P*. You are going to need your log properties to do that.

How long will it take for 600 car dealers to come about? $t = \frac{10^{P/500}-3}{2}$ ← Answer $t = \frac{10^{\frac{600}{500}}-3}{2} = \frac{10^{\frac{6}{5}}-3}{2}$ 	You are asked to determine how long it will be until there are 600 used car salesmen living in your town. Substitute in the value of P and solve for t. Simplify the equation. Let your calculator help you with the final answer.
$t =$ 6.4244...months ← Answer	After a little manipulation, your answer is 6.4244 months. That isn't very much time for 600 car dealers to move to their new homes!

Sample problems:

1. The longevity (in years) of ancient empires can be estimated by $T = (500)\ln\frac{F}{B}$, where B and F are the populations at the beginning and end of the empire, respectively. One of the Han dynasties lasted for 550 years and the beginning population was 100,000. Estimate the end population of that Han dynasty.
   Solution: 300,417
   Explanation: Substitute $T = 550$ and $B = 100{,}000$ into the equation $T = (500)\ln\frac{F}{B}$:
   $550 = (500)\ln\frac{F}{100{,}000}$. Solve for F: $\frac{550}{500} = \ln\frac{F}{100{,}000}$; $1.1 = \ln\frac{F}{100{,}000}$; $e^{1.1} = e^{\ln\frac{F}{100{,}000}}$; $3.004166 = \frac{F}{100{,}000}$;
   $F = 300{,}416.6024$. So the end population is estimated to have been 300,417.

2. The population of Boomtown has been rising according to the model $A = pe^{0.03t}$, where p is the population in 1998 and A is the population t years later. The population in 1998 was 10,000. According to this model, how many years should it take for the population to increase by 9,350?
   Solution: 22
   Explanation: From the problem, $p = 10{,}000$ and $A = 10{,}000 + 9{,}350 = 19{,}350$. Substitute the value into $A = pe^{0.03t}$ and solve for t: $19{,}350 = 10{,}000e^{0.03t}$; $e^{0.03t} = \frac{19{,}350}{10{,}000}$; $e^{0.03t} = 1.935$;
   $\ln e^{0.03t} = \ln 1.935$; $0.03t = .660107$; $t = 22$. So, after 22 years the population will increase by 9,350.

3. A certain model of car depreciates according to the function $V = Ne^{-0.23t}$, where N is the cost of the car when it was new and V is its value t years later. How old is a car of this type if it cost \$18,000 new and is now worth \$2,000?
   Solution: $9\frac{1}{2}$
   Explanation: Substitute $N = 18{,}000$ and $V = 2{,}000$ into $V = Ne^{-0.23t}$ and solve for t:
   $2{,}000 = 18{,}000e^{-0.23t}$; $e^{-0.23t} = \frac{2{,}000}{18{,}000}$; $e^{-0.23t} = \frac{1}{9}$; $\ln e^{-0.23t} = \ln\frac{1}{9}$; $-0.23t = -2.1972246$;
   $t = 9.55$. So, the car is worth \$2,000 after 9.55, or about $9\frac{1}{2}$ years.

Practice problems: *(Answers on page: 753)*

1. In chemistry, pH is given by the formula: $\text{pH} = -\log[H_3O^+]$, where H_3O^+ is the hydronium ion concentration in moles per liter. Given that the pH of hydrochloric acid is equal to 2.0, what is the concentration of the hydronium ion in moles per liter?

2. In recent years the number of cell phones c (in millions) in use in the U.S. has followed the exponential curve $c = 2150(1 - e^{-0.017t})$, where t is the number of years since 1998. Predict the year in which cell phone usage will reach 208.5 million.

3. The percent of children growing in the US without a father in the years since 1900 can be represented by this formula: $f(x) = \dfrac{25}{1+1364.3e^{-\frac{x}{9.316}}}$ such that x = number of years since 1900 and $f(x)$ = the number of children as a percent who are growing up without a father. Predict the year in which 24.1% of the children in the US will be without a father.

Review questions: *(Answers to odd questions on page: 753)*

1. The trout population in an Alaskan lake is increasing according to $f = 8000/(1+18e-0.2t)$, where t is the number of months since the ice broke. How many trout f are there in that lake 6 months after the ice broke?
2. The number of Allied troops that landed in France in World War II, beginning with June 6, 1944 ('D Day'), follows the logistics curve $A = 2{,}000{,}000(1-e-0.217t)$, where t is the number of months after D Day. Find the number of troops landed by the Battle of the Bulge (6 months after D Day).
3. In an amplifier, the power gain, P, is given by the function $P = 10\log\dfrac{P_{OUT}}{P_{IN}}$ where P_{IN} is the power input in watts and P_{OUT} is the power output in watts. If an amplifier has a power gain of 20 watts and the input power was .15 watts, find the power output in watts.
4. According to Dr . Burger's model, the population of used car salesmen in a city increases according to the following formula: $P = 500\log(2t+3)$, where P is the population of used car salesmen and t is the time in months since the first used car dealership opens. When will the population of used car salesmen equal 300?
5. The garment industry approximates the percentage P (between 1 and 100) of young adult women who are x inches tall or less by $P = \dfrac{100}{[1+e(43+0.67x)]}$. Find the percentage of women who are 5'5" tall or less.

An Introduction to Exponential Growth and Decay

- Population growth is one example of an exponential function. Radioactive decay is also an exponential function.
- When working with exponential functions, use logarithms to turn exponents into coefficients.

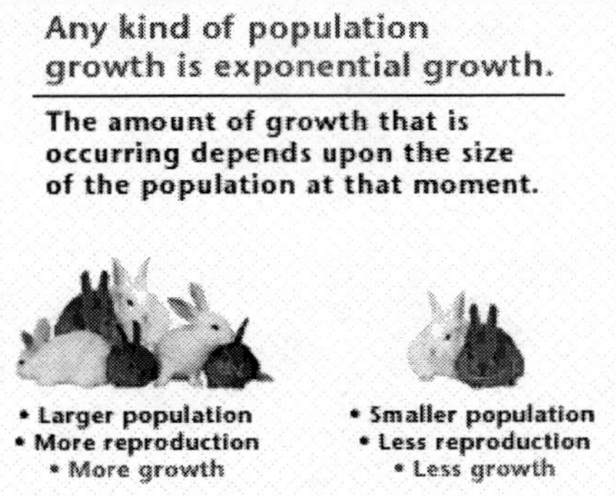

Populations tend to increase exponentially. The reason for this is that when populations are larger, there are more members producing more offspring.

Smaller populations have to grow more slowly since they don't have as many members to reproduce.

Decay is also exponential.

In radioactive decay, radioactive materials have something called a half-life. This is the amount of time it takes for the material to reduce in radioactivity by half. Each time this interval of time passes, the material becomes half as much radioactive. Notice that it never becomes non-radioactive.

Example

Population of Williamstown, MA

Model: $P(t) = 12{,}400(1.14)^t$

A) What is the population in 3 years?

$$P(3) = 12{,}400(1.14)^3$$

$$\approx 18{,}371$$

Given this formula, calculate the population after three years.

This question is pretty basic. You can just substitute and solve.

B) What is the population in 4.25 years?

$$p(4.25) = 12{,}400(1.14)^{4.25}$$

An exponent within a log can be pulled out as a coefficient of that log.

$$= 12{,}400\left(e^{\ln((1.14)^{4.25})}\right)$$

Now you can use your calculator.

$$= 12{,}400\left(e^{4.25 \ln 1.14}\right)$$

$$\approx 21{,}640$$

Here is the formula used another way.

By setting 1.14 raised to 4.25 equal to its natural log all to base e, you gain the ability to use the log properties on the exponent.

Now solving the equation is much easier!

Sample problems:

1. The number of streptococcus bacteria in a petri dish, kept in a medical laboratory, is $A = pe^{0.047t}$, where p is the initial number (when the culture was first brought in) and A is the final number of bacteria after t hours. If a culture containing 40,000 bacteria was brought in, how many will there be after 10 hours? After a week?
   Solution: 64,000 and 107,460,590
   Explanation: To determine the number of bacteria in the dish after 10 hours, substitute $t = 10$ and $p = 40{,}000$ into $A = pe^{0.047t}$ and simplify:
   $A = 40{,}000e^{0.047(10)} = 40{,}000e^{0.47} = 40{,}000(1.599994193) = 63{,}999.8 \approx 64{,}000.$
   So, after 10 hours there are about 64,000 bacteria in the dish. After a week ($24 \cdot 7 = 168$ hours):
   $A = 40{,}000e^{0.047(168)} = 40{,}000e^{7.896} = 40{,}000(2{,}686.514748) = 107{,}460{,}589.9.$
   So, after a week there are 107,460,590 bacteria in the dish.

2. The population of a certain city is given by the function $P(t) = 45{,}000e^{0.05t}$, where t is the time in years. How many years will it take for the city's population reach 90,000?
   Solution: 14
   Explanation: Substitute $P(t) = 90{,}000$ into $P(t) = 45{,}000e^{0.05t}$ and solve for t:
   $90{,}000 = 45{,}000e^{0.05t}; e^{0.05t} = 2;\ \ln e^{0.05t} = \ln 2;\ 0.05t = 0.6931471806;$
   $t = 13.86 \approx 14$. So, the population will reach 90,000 after 14 years.

3. The number of streptococcus bacteria in a Petri dish kept in a medical laboratory is $A = pe^{0.047t}$ where p is the initial number (when the culture was first brought in) and A is the final number of bacteria after t hours. If a culture has grown from 75,000 to 2.2 million, how long did that take?
Solution: 72
Explanation: Substitute $p = 75,000$ and $A = 2.2$ million $= 2,200,000$ into $A = pe^{0.047t}$ and solve for t: $2,200,000 = 75,000e^{0.047t}$; $e^{0.047t} = \frac{88}{3}$; $\ln e^{0.047t} = \ln(\frac{88}{3})$; $0.047t = 3.378724526$; $t = 71.89 \approx 72$. To grow from 75,000 to 2.2 million took almost 72 hours.

Practice problems: *(Answers on page: 753)*

1. The population of a certain city is given by the function $P(t) = 45,000e^{0.05t}$, where t is the time in years. Whatis the population of the city when $t = 6$?
2. The number of deer in a wildlife preserve is given by the function $D(t) = 184 \cdot (1.1)^{0.5t}$, where p is the population in 1990 and t is the number of years after 1990. If the population in 1990 was 184, how long will it take for the population to double?
3. Suppose that the population of New York City between the years of 1950 and 1960 can be approximated by the function $P(t) = 1050 \cdot (1.005)^t$, where t is in years, $t = 0$ corresponds to 1950, and $P(t)$ is in the thousands. Between what 2 years from 1950 and 1960 was the population of NYC 1.09 million?

Review questions: *(Answers to odd questions on page: 753)*

1. If not refrigerated, a perishable food item, t days after packing, reaches a bacteria count b according to the formula $b = 5000e^{0.1t}$. How many bacteria will there be in 18 days?
2. A semi-perishable food item should no longer be consumed if its bacteria count b reaches 2.8 million. How long will this take if $b = 500e^{0.1t}$, where t is the number of days since the food was packed?
3. The growth of a city is described by the population function $P(t) = P_0e^{kt}$, where P_0 is the initial population of the city, t is the time in years, and k is a constant. If the population of the city at $t = 0$ is 13,000 and the population of the city at $t = 2$ is 16,000, what is the population of the city at $t = 4$?
4. Suppose that the population of New York City from 1990 to the present can be modelled by the function $P(t) = 9013 \cdot e^{.08t}$, where t is in years, $t = 0$ corresponds to 1990, and $P(t)$ is in thousands. Assuming that New York City continues to grow at this rate, when will its population reach 25 million?
5. The weight of a certain growing walrus between one and five years old is described by the function $W(t) = 135 \cdot (1.22)2t$, where t is its age in years and $W(t)$ is in pounds. How much weight does the walrus gain over the four year period between $t = 1$ and $t = 5$?

Half-Life

- The **half-life** of a substance is the amount of time it takes for a radioactive material to decay to half of itself. Radioactive decay is an exponential function.

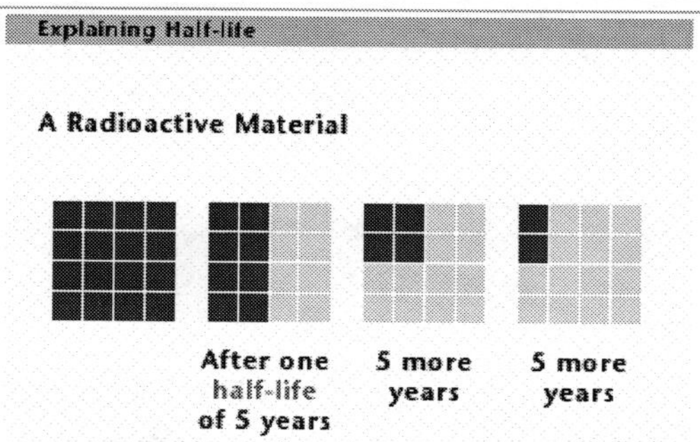

The **half-life** tells you how much time has to pass for a radioactive material to reduce to half of its current mass.

Each time the half-life interval passes, you lose one-half of the material that you had at the beginning of the interval. Think of it like a store that drops its prices 50% every two hours. The price will never equal zero although it will get darn close!

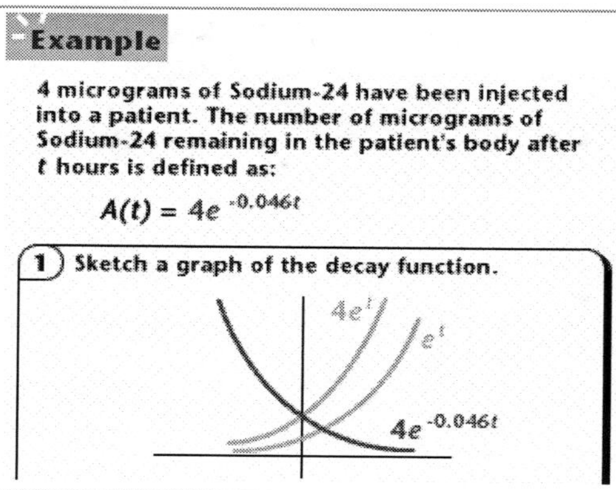

Consider the example of Sodium-24. This is a radioactive isotope that doctors use to track certain events in the health of patients.

The radioactive decay of Sodium-24 is given by $A(t)$.

The graph of the radioactive decay function looks like a regular exponential function, but stretched four times in the y-direction and then flipped across the y-axis.

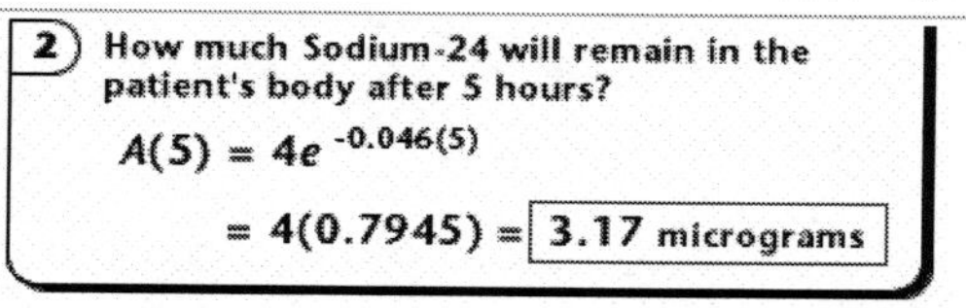

To find out how much of the material is present in the patient at a given time, just substitute the value of t and solve.

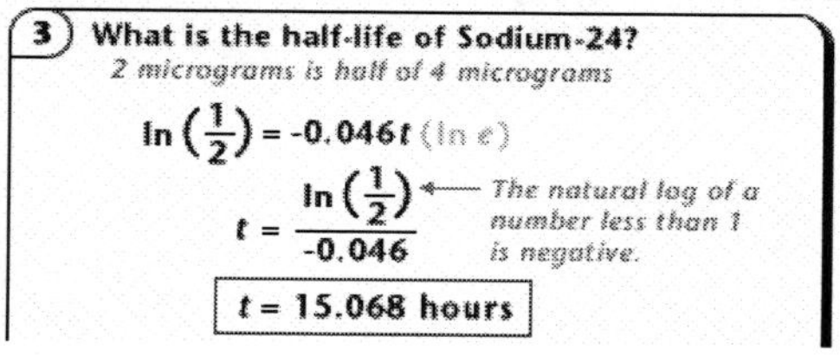

To find the half-life, set the function equal to half of the original amount of Sodium-24.

Simplify using natural logs (e is already involved) and your log properties.

Then solve for t !

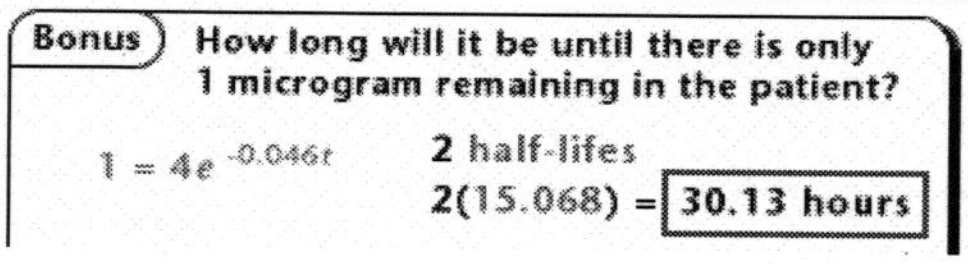

You can set the equation equal to 1 and solve. You also have a more elegant choice, thanks to your previous work.

You know the half-life. And, you know that 4 goes to 2, then goes to 1 in two half-lives. So, you have a simple multiplication problem.

Sample problems:

1. The age t (in years) of mummified organic materials can be determined by the function:
$t = (8300)\ln\frac{100}{x}$, where x is the percentage of carbon-14 still remaining. (For example, if $\frac{1}{4}$ remains, then $x = 25$). Find the age of a mummified Egyptian ruler if 61% of the carbon-14 remains in his burial wrappings.
Solution: 4103
Explanation: Substitute $x = 61$ into $t = (8300)\ln\frac{100}{x}$ and simplify:
$t = (8300)\ln\frac{100}{61} = (8300)(.4942963218) = 4102.66 \approx 4103.$
The mummy is 4,103 years old.

2. Carbon-14 is a radioactive substance used by scientists to determine the age of objects. When a plant or animal dies, the carbon-14 within its system begins decaying. The amount of carbon-14 remaining is given by $A = Ce^{-kt}$, where C is the initial amount of carbon-14 in the plant or animal t years after it dies. Given that the half - life of carbon-14 is about 5500 years, how old is a fossilized plant when it has 80% of its original carbon-14 remaining?
Solution: 1,771

3. Polonium radioactively decays from 410 grams to 0.4 grams in 35 years. What is its half - life (the number of years it takes until half of it remains)? Use the formula $A = pe^{-kt}$, where p is the initial amount, t is the time in years, and A the (smaller) final amount .
Solution: 3.5
Explanation: Begin by finding k. Substitute $A = 0.4$, $p = 410$, and $t = 35$ into $A = pe^{-kt}$ and solve for k: $0.4 = 410e^{-k(35)}$; $\frac{0.4}{410} = e^{-35k}$; $e^{-35k} = .00097561$; $\ln e^{-35k} = \ln .00097561$; $-35k = -6.93245$; $k = 0.19807$. But that is not the answer to the question. Find the half-life by substituting $k = 0.19807$, $p = 410$, and $A = \frac{410}{2} = 205$ (because that is half the original amount) into $A = pe^{-kt}$ and solve for t: $205 = 410e^{-0.19807t}$; $.5 = e^{-0.19807t}$; $\ln e^{-0.19807t} = \ln .5$; $-0.19807t = -0.6931472$; $t = 3.4995 \approx 3.5$. So the half-life is 3.5 years.

Practice problems: *(Answers on page: 753)*

1. Suppose that the decay of polonium, a radioactive element, is described by the function $P(t) = P_0 \cdot (.5)^{.047t}$, where t is the time in years and P_0 is the initial amount of polonium in grams. What percentage of a sample of polonium will remain after 4 years?
2. Sodium-24 is a radioactive substance used for medical purposes. Suppose that a patient is injected with 5mg of sodium-24 at $t = 0$ and that the amount of sodium-24 in the patient's body in milligrams is given by $S(t) = 5e^{-.35t}$, where t is the time in hours. What is the half-life of sodium-24?
3. The amount of radium in a sample after t years is given by the equation $A = pe^{-kt}$, where p is the initial amount of radium in the sample. If the half-life of radium is 1690 years and a sample contains 10g of radium, how much radium will remain after 50 years?

Review questions: *(Answers to odd questions on page: 753)*

1. The half-life of strontium-90 is 25 years. How long will it take a 50 mg sample to decay to a mass of 32 mg?
2. The decay of a radioactive substance is described by the function $A(t) = 5e^{-.1t}$, where t is the time in minutes and $A(t)$ is the mass of the substance in ounces. How many ounces of the substance are left at $t = 8$ minutes?
3. The age t (in years) of an ancient icebound corpse can be determined by the function $t = 7950 \ln\left(\frac{100}{x}\right)$ where x is 100 times the percentage of carbon-14 still remaining in its bones . (For example, if $\frac{1}{2}$ remains, then $x = 50$). Find the percentage of carbon-14 remaining in the bones of the 6,200 year-old Alpine ice man.
4. If 40 milligrams of strontium-90 radioactively decays to 12 milligrams in 30 years, find its half-life (the number of years it takes until half of it remains). Use the formula $A = p \cdot e^{-kt}$, where p is the amount and A the (smaller) final amount.

5. A certain radioactive element has a half-life of 120 years. At $t = 0$ an 80 pound chunk of the element begins decaying away. Find the function $A(t)$ that gives the amount of the element remaining after t years.

Newton's Law of Cooling

- Exponential and logarithmic equations occur frequently in real-world applications. Even refrigeration happens according to an exponential equation.
- **Newton's law of cooling**: $T(t) = A + (T_0 - A)e^{-kt}$.

Consider a Refrigerator  	Logarithmic and exponential functions have a habit of showing up in everyday situations. Did you know that refrigerating your sodas uses an exponential function?
Newton's Law of Cooling $T(t) = A + (T_0 - A)e^{-kt}$ T = temp of the soda t = time in minutes A = temp of refrigerator T_0 = initial temp of soda k = constant of the soda	Sir Isaac Newton discovered a relationship between the temperature of an object and the temperature of its environment. This relationship is demonstrated by **Newton's law of cooling**.
Calculating the Constant k $T(t) = A + (T_0 - A)e^{-kt}$ $75 - 34$ $T(t) = 34 + (41)e^{-kt}$ $65 = 34 + 41e^{-5k}$ $31 = 41e^{-5k}$ $\frac{31}{41} = e^{-5k}$ $\ln\left(\frac{31}{41}\right) = \ln\left(e^{-5k}\right)$ $\ln\left(\frac{31}{41}\right) = -5k(\ln e)$ $k = \frac{\ln\left(\frac{31}{41}\right)}{-5}$ $k = 0.0559...$	To use Newton's law of cooling, you need to know the cooling constant of the soda. Since you are given that the soda cools from 75° to 65° in 5 minutes, then you can find the cooling constant by substituting into the law and solving for k.
$T(t) = 34 + (41)e^{-0.0559t}$ **1)** What will the temperature of the soda be after 30 minutes? $T(30) = 34 + 41e^{-0.0559(30)}$ $= 41.6°$	Now that you know the constant of cooling, you can answer questions about the formula. To find the temperature of the soda at a given time, just plug in t. If your calculator can't take non-integer powers of e, then you will need to simplify using logarithms.
2) How long until the soda is 36°? $36 = 34 + 41e^{-0.0559t}$ $2 = 41e^{-0.0559t}$ $\frac{2}{41} = e^{-0.0559t}$ $\ln\left(\frac{2}{41}\right) = \ln\left(e^{-0.0559t}\right)$ $\ln\left(\frac{2}{41}\right) = -0.0559t(\ln e)$ $t = \frac{\ln\left(\frac{2}{41}\right)}{-0.0559}$ $t = 54.03$ minutes	To find a specific time, plug in all the other values and solve for t.

Sample problems:

1. The temperature of a 16 pound turkey in a 325° oven after t minutes is given by the function $T(t) = 325 - 260e^{-0.001822t}$. Find the temperature of the turkey after 2 hours.
   Solution: 141°
   Explanation: Substitute $t = 2$ hours $= 120$ minutes into $T(t) = 355 - 260e^{-0.001822t}$ and simplify: $T(120) = 355 - 260e^{-0.001822(120)} = 350 - 260e^{-0.21864} = 350 - 260(0.803612) = 350 - 208.94$ $= 141.06 \approx 141°$. So the turkey will be 141° after 2 hours.

2. According to Julia Child's The Way to Cook a turkey must be cooked to 165°F. The temperature of a 16 pound turkey in a 325° oven after t minutes is given by the function $T(t) = 325 - 260e^{-0.001822t}$. If Beth wants to serve the turkey at 6:00pm, after letting it cool for 1 hour, what time should she put the turkey in the 325° oven?
   Solution: 12:30pm
   Explanation: Find the time it takes for the turkey to reach 165° by substituting $T(t) = 165$ into $T(t) = 325 - 260e^{-0.001822t}$ and solve for t: $165 = 325 - 260e^{-0.001822t}$; $-160 = -260e^{-0.001822t}$; $\frac{8}{13} = e^{-0.001822t}$; $\ln\frac{8}{13} = \ln e^{-0.001822t}$; $-0.001822t = \ln\frac{8}{13}$; $t = \frac{\ln\frac{8}{13}}{-0.001822} = 266.5$. The turkey must cook for about 267 minutes, or 4.45 hours $\approx 4\frac{1}{2}$ hours. She needs to put the turkey in the oven $4\frac{1}{2}$ cook time and 1 cool time $= 5\frac{1}{2}$ hours before 6:00, or at 12:30pm.

3. Suppose a pie is removed from an oven when it reaches 350°F. The pie is let to cool in a room that is 70°F. After 45 minutes, the pie cools to 150°F. Use Newton's Law of cooling to write a function that gives the temperature of the pie, T, as a function of time, t.
   Solution: $T(t) = 70 + 280e^{-0.02784t}$

Practice problems: *(Answers on page: 753)*

1. A soda is placed in a regrigerator maintaining a constant temperature of 36 degrees F at time $t = 0$. The temperature of the soda after t minutes in the refrigerator is described by the function $S(t) = 36 + 34e^{-0.021t}$. Based on this model, how cold will the soda be after 45 minutes?
2. A soda is placed in a regrigerator maintaining a constant temperature of 36 degrees F at time $t = 0$. The temperature of the soda after t minutes in the refrigerator is described by the function $S(t) = 36 + 34e^{-0.021t}$. Based on this model, how long will it take for the soda to reach 40°?
3. Suppose a juice box that is 75° is placed into a 40° refrigerator. After 30 minutes the juice had cooled to 60°. Write a function for the temperature of the juice as a function of time.

Review questions: *(Answers to odd questions on page: 753)*

1. A cup of tea with a temperature of 200° Fahrenheit is placed in a room that has a temperature of 70°F. After 10 minutes the tea's temperature has cooled to 150°F. What is the tea's temperature after 15 minutes? Use the formula $T(t) = T_s + D_0e^{-kt}$.
2. A 150° cup of tea cools to 140° in a 70° room after one minute. How long will it take for the tea to cool to 91°?
3. A chocolate chip cookie is removed from the oven when it is 170°. The cookie cools to 145° after two minutes in a 72° room. What is the temperature of the cookie 15 minutes after it is removed from the oven?
4. When a can of soda is placed in a 30° freezer for 5 minutes, the temperature decreases from 70° to 67°. How long must the soda remain in the freezer before the temperature decreases to 40°?

5. The temperature of a soda t minutes after it is placed in a refrigerator is given by the function $S(t) = 36 + 34e^{-0.021t}$. Based on this model, how long will it take for the temperature of the soda to reach 46 degrees?

Continuously Compounded Interest

- Another real-world application of exponential formulas can be found in the world of finance. Banks use exponential equations to continuously compound interest.
- **Continuously compounded interest formula**: $A = Pe^{rt}$.

The Compounded Interest Formula $A = P\left(1 + \frac{r}{m}\right)^{tm}$ $A = P\left(1 + \frac{r}{m}\right)^{tm}$ $\left(1 + \frac{1}{n}\right)^{n} \rightarrow e$ *Putting in larger and larger values of n, you approach e.* $e = 2.718\ldots$	The more often a bank compounds the interest on your money, the more money you will make. Wouldn't it be nice if they compounded the interest continuously instead of quarterly or annually? Using the definition of the number ***e***, you can find a formula that computes the interest compounded continuously.
The Compounded Interest Formula $A = Pe^{rt}$ *formula for continuously compounded interest* **A = amount accumulated** **P = principal** **t = number of years** **r = interest rate** **m = compoundings per year**	So the formula for **continuously compounded interest** looks easier than the compound interest formula. Solving continuously compounded interest questions will often require that you use logarithms to "bring down" the exponents. Keep in mind that ln*e* is the same as $\log_e e$. They are both equal to 1.
Example **Suppose you invest \$300 into an account that compounds continuously at 5.25%. How long would you have to wait to double your money?** $A = Pe^{rt}$ $2\not{P} = \not{P}e^{0.0525t}$ $2 = e^{0.0525t}$ $\ln 2 = \ln(e^{0.0525t})$ $\ln 2 = 0.0525t\ (\ln e)$ $t = \frac{\ln 2}{0.0525} = \boxed{13.202 \text{ years}}$	In this example, you are asked to find how long it will take to double your money. Write the formula. Substitute in the known factors. Note how a potentially frustrating problem simplifies when you convert it to a logarithm problem. Then solve, as requested, for *t*. In 13.202 years, you will double the money you invested in your continuously compounding bank account.

Sample problems:

1. The government of Monaco borrowed \$10,000,000 from the U.S. at 6%. How much will Monaco owe the U.S. in 20 years, continuously compounded?
   Solution: \$33,201,169
   Explanation: Substitute $P = 10,000,000$, $r = 6\% = .06$, and $t = 20$ into $A = Pe^{rt}$ and simplify: $A = 10,000,000e^{(.06)(20)} = 10,000,000(3.320116923) = 33,201,169.23$.
   So, Monaco will owe the US \$33,201,169 after 20 years.

2. Manuel is considering investing some money in an account where the interest is compounded continuously at 10%. How long would it take for his investment to double?
   Solution: Almost 7 years
   Explanation: It may appear that there is not enough information to answer this question, but if the investment is doubled the $A = 2P$. Substitute $A = 2P$ and $r = 10\% = .1$ into $A = Pe^{rt}$ and solve for t: $2P = Pe^{.1t}$; $\frac{2P}{P} = e^{.1t}$; $2 = e^{.1t}$; $\ln 2 = \ln e^{.1t}$; $.1t = \ln 2$; $t = \frac{\ln 2}{.1} = 6.93 \approx 7$. So, it takes almost 7 years for an investment to double in this account.

3. Suppose $12,000 is invested at 9%. If the interest is compounded continuously, how long will it take for the investment to mature to $13,000?
   Solution: Almost a year
   Explanation: Substitute $A = 13,000$, $P = 12,000$, and $r = 9\% = .09$ into $A = Pe^{rt}$ and solve for t: $13,000 = 12,000e^{.09t}$; $\frac{13}{12} = e^{.09t}$; $\ln\frac{13}{12} = \ln e^{.09t}$; $.09t = \ln\frac{13}{12}$; $t = \dfrac{\ln\frac{13}{12}}{.09} = .89 \approx 1$.
   So, the investment will mature to $13,000 after almost 1 year.

Practice problems: *(Answers on page: 753)*

1. If $24,000 is invested at an annual interest rate of 8.5% and the interest compounds continuously, find the balance after 6 years.
2. If $5,000 is invested in an account with 7.5% interest compounded continuously, how long will it take for the investment to increase by $2,000?
3. Suppose an account offers 15.5% interest compounded continuously. How long does it take for investments in this account to triple?

Review questions: *(Answers to odd questions on page: 753)*

1. If you want to invest $6,000 and have it increase to $7,500 in 3 years, what rate of interest is necessary if your investment is compounded continuously?
2. Joe invests $25,000 at 4.25% compounded continuously. How long will it take for the money to double? Use $A = Pe^{rt}$.
3. If you want to invest $2,500 and have it grow to be $3,000 in two years, what rate of interest is necessary if your investment is compounding continuously.
4. Suppose an account offers 8.9% interest compounded continuously. How long does it take for investments in this account to quadruple?
5. In which account will a given balance double faster, an account that is compounded monthly at 8% or an account that is coumpounded continously at 7%?

6

The Trigonometric Functions

Finding the Quadrant in Which an Angle Lies

- Angles are measured from the positive side of the *x*-axis. Positive angles sweep out in a counterclockwise direction and negative angles sweep out in a clockwise direction.
- The plane is split into four regions, or quadrants, in which angles can lie.
- **Acute angles** measure between 0° and 90°.
- **Obtuse angles** measure between 90° and 180°.
- Angles that measure exactly 90° are **right angles**.
- Angles that measure exactly 180° are **straight angles**.
- **Coterminal angles** are angles whose initial sides and terminal sides are the same.

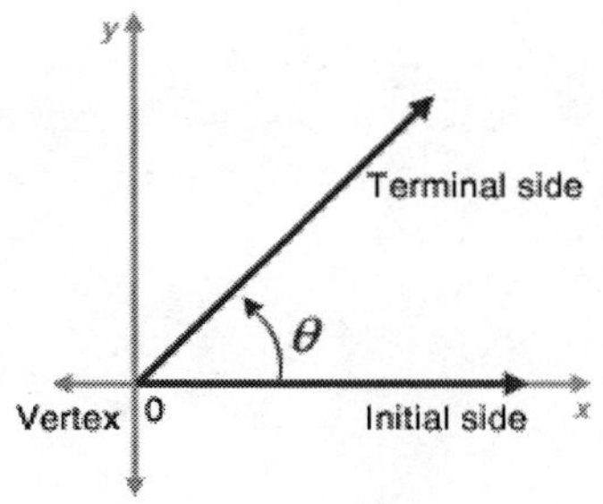

When measureing angles, always begin on the positive side of the *x*-axis.

Positive angles are measured in a counterclockwise direction from the positive *x*-axis and negative angles are measured in a clockwise direction.

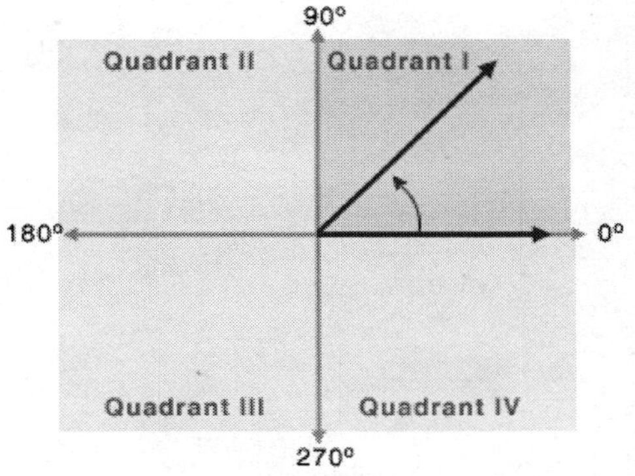

The plane can be broken up into four regions, or quadrants. **Acute angles**, those angles whose measure is less than 90°, lie in quadrant I.

Obtuse angles, those angles whose measure is between 90° and 180°, lie in quadrant II.

Other angles with special names include **right angles**, which measure exactly 90°, and **straight angles**, which measure exactly 180°.

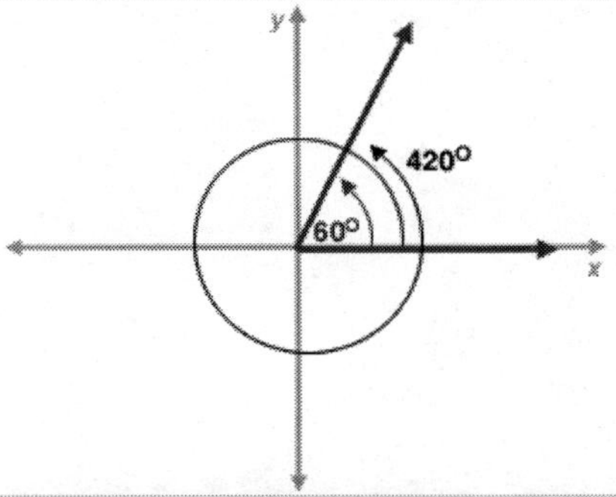

Angles with the same initial side and terminal side are coterminal angles.

The two angles in the diagram on the left measure 60° and 420°. These angles have the same **initial side** and the same **terminal side**, but have different amounts of rotation.

Angles with the same initial and terminal sides are called **coterminal angles**. Thus, 60° and 420° are coterminal angles.

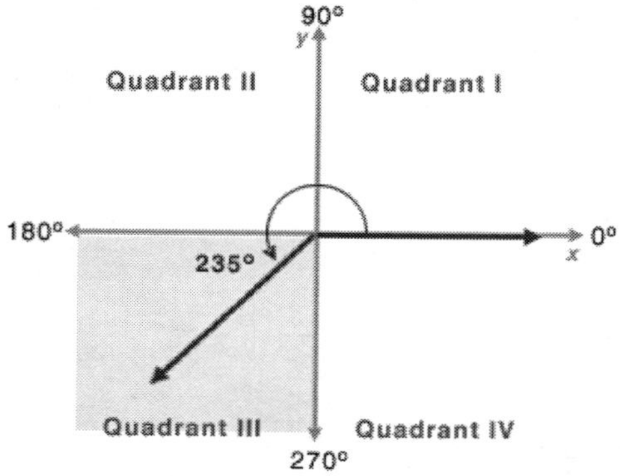	To determine in which region an angle lies, graph the angle. Since 235° is positive, begin at the positive x-axis and move in a counterclockwise direction. Use the axes to estimate the location. The angle with measure 235° is greater than 180° but less than 270°; therefore, 235° is in quadrant III.
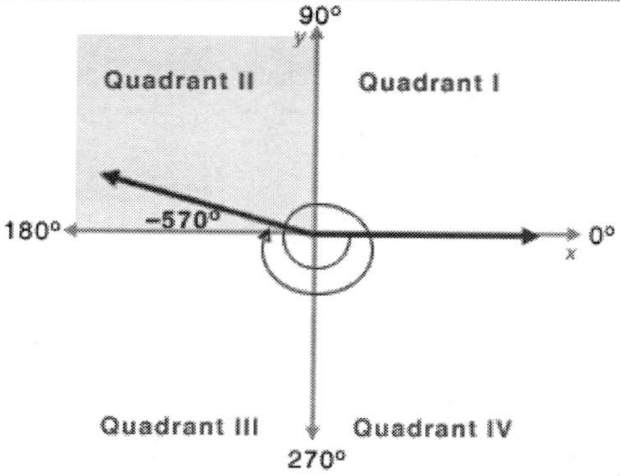	To determine in which region an angle measuring -570° lies, begin at the positive x-axis and move in a clockwise direction. Sweep one full cycle, -360°, to return to the positive x-axis. Next, move an additional -210° in the clockwise direction to land in quadrant II.

Sample problems:

1. In which quadrant does the terminal side of an angle measuring 133° lie?
   Solution: Quadrant II
   Explanation: Since 133° is an obtuse angle between 90° and 180°, the terminal side lies in the second quadrant.

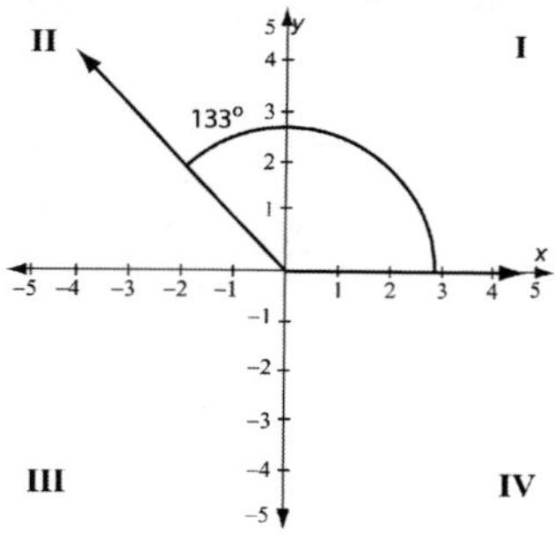

2. In which quadrant would the angle $\theta = -1100°$ be located?
   Solution: Quadrant IV
   Explanation: Since θ is negative, add 360° to $-1100°$ repeatedly until a number between 0 and 360 is reached: $-1100° + 360° = -740° + 360° = -380 + 360° = -20°$ to produce $-20° + 360° = 340°$. 340° is greater than 270° but less than 360°. Thus, θ lies in the fourth quadrant.

3. True or False: Angle θ could be $-75°$.

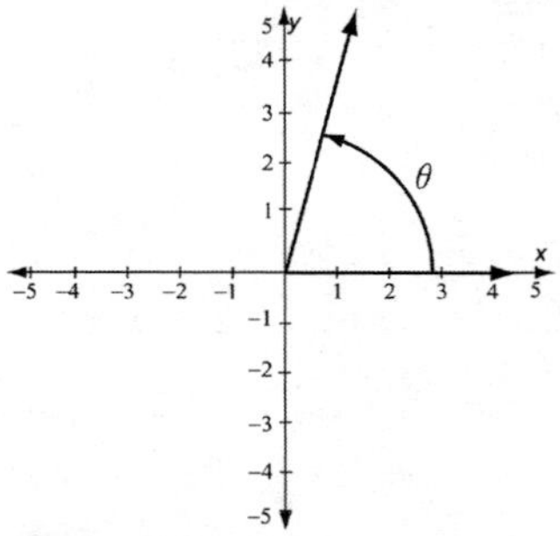

Solution: False

Explanation: The angle θ in the graph is in quadrant I. However, an angle with measure $-75°$ is located in quadrant IV.

Practice problems: *(Answers on page: 753)*

1. In which quadrant would an angle measuring 788° be located?
2. In what quadrant does the terminal side of an angle measuring $-165°$ lie?
3. True or False: Angle θ could be 585°.

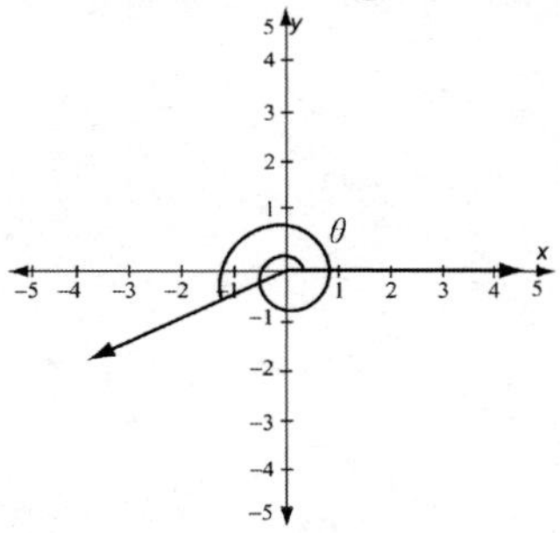

Review questions: *(Answers to odd questions on page: 753)*

1. In what quadrant does the terminal side of an angle measuring 95° lie?
2. In what quadrant does the terminal side of an angle measuring 200° lie?
3. In what quadrant does the terminal side of an angle measuring $-310°$ lie?
4. True or false: Angles measuring 10° and 397° lie in the same quadrant.
5. True or false: Angles measuring 950°, 223° and $-190°$ lie in the same quadrant.

Finding Coterminal Angles

- **Review**: **Coterminal angles** are angles whose **terminal sides** lie in the same place.
- The measures of coterminal angles differ by a multiple of 360°.

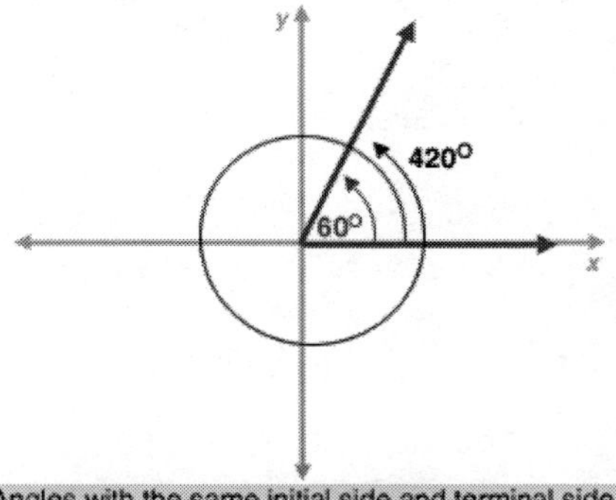

Angles with the same initial side and terminal side are coterminal angles.

Recall that **coterminal angles** are angles that have **terminal sides** in the same location.

The difference of the measures of coterminal angles is a multiple of 360° (some number of full circles).

Example Is 360° coterminal with 0°?

$360° - 0° = \boxed{360°}$ *A multiple of 360, so these are coterminal angles.*

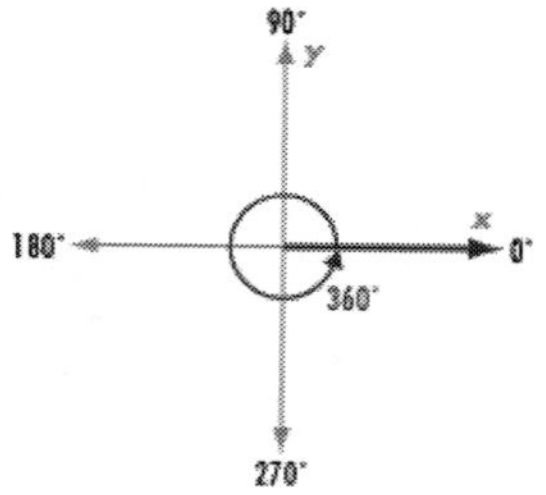

To determine if 360° is coterminal with 0°, find the difference of the measures of the two angles:

$$360° - 0° = 360°$$

The difference, 360°, is a multiple of 360°. Thus, 360° is coterminal with 0°.

Example Are −570° and 150° coterminal angles?

$-570° - 150° = \boxed{-720°}$ *A multiple of 360, so these are coterminal angles.*

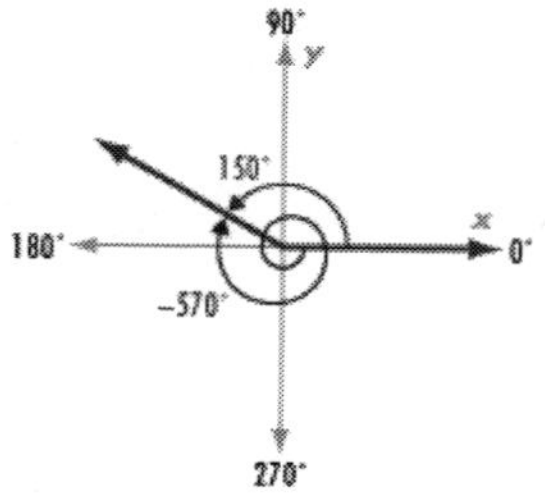

What about – 570° and 150°? Are these two angles coterminal?

The difference of the measures of the two angles is – 720°. Since – 720° is a multiple of 360°, they are coterminal angles.

Example Are −800° and −80° coterminal angles?

$-800° - (-80°) =$
$-800° + 80° = \boxed{-720°}$ *A multiple of 360, so these are coterminal angles.*

Notice that even though these are both negative angles, they are coterminal because their difference is a multiple of 360°.

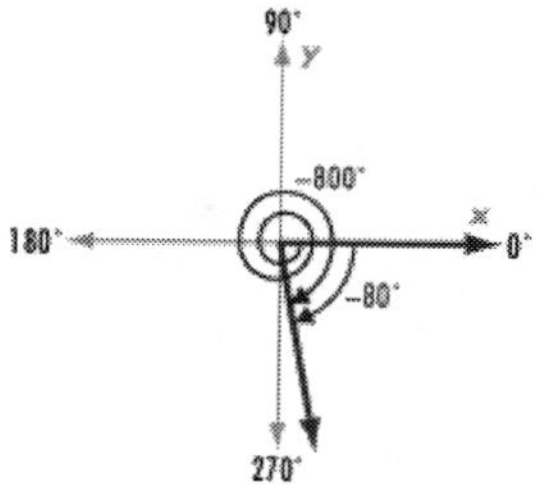

Are .– 800° and – 80° votermial? Yes, since their measures differ by a multiple of 360°

REMEMBER: Coterminal angles are not the same angle; they just have terminating sides in the same location.

Sample problems:

1. True or False: If $\theta = 494°$ and $\alpha = -1306°$, then θ and α are coterminal.
   Solution: True
   Explanation: Two angles are coterminal if the difference in their measurements is a multiple of 360. Subtract the angles: $494° - (-1306°) = 1800°$. Divide the difference by 360°: $1800°/360° = 5$. Since there is no remainder, 1800° is a multiple of 360. Thus, θ and α are coterminal.

2. What is the smallest positive angle that is coterminal with 560°?
   Solution: 200°
   Explanation: The smallest postive angle that is coterminal with 560° is 360° less than 560°, or 200°.

3. Find the negative angle closest to zero and coterminal with 655°.
   Solution: $-65°$
   Explanation: Subtract 360° from 655° repeatedly until the 1st negative angle measurement is obtained: $655° - 360° = 295° - 360° = -65°$.

Practice problems: *(Answers on page: 753)*

1. True or false: The difference of measures of coterminal angles is always 360°.
2. True or false: If $\theta = -35°$, $\alpha = 1405°$ and $\sigma = 865°$, then θ, α and σ are coterminal.
3. What is the smallest positive angle that is coterminal with $-795°$?

Review questions: *(Answers to odd questions on page: 753)*

1. True or false: For two angles to be coterminal, the difference in their measures must be a multiple of 360.
2. True or false: If $\theta = 125°$ and $\alpha = 465°$, then θ and α are coterminal.
3. True or false: If $\theta = 15°$ and $\alpha = 1095°$, then θ and α are coterminal.
4. True or false: If $\theta = -317°$ and $\alpha = 403°$, then θ and α are coterminal.
5. What is the smallest negative angle that is coterminal with 547°?

Finding the Complement and Supplement of an Angle

- Two positive angles are **complementary** if their measures add up to 90°.
- Two positive angles are **supplementary** if their measures add up to 180°.

Two positive angles are **complementary** if their measures add up to 90°. 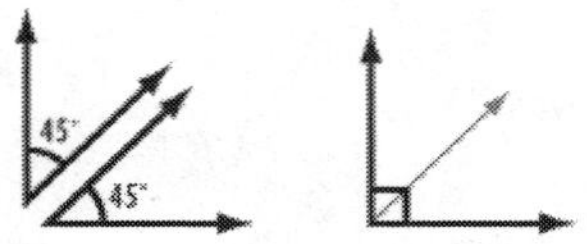 45° + 45° = 90° 45° and 45° are complementary angles.	**Complementary angles** are two positive angles whose measures add up to 90°. Since $45° + 45° = 90°$, 45° and 45° are complementary angles.
Example What is the complementary angle of 62°? 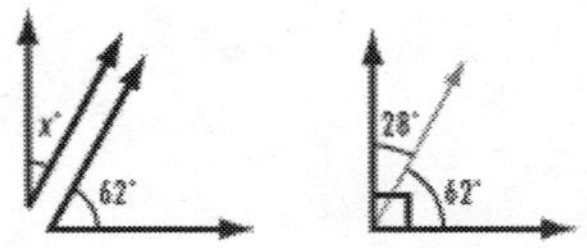 $62° + x = 90°$ $x = 28°$	To find the complementary angle, or **complement**, of 62°, solve for x in the equation. $62° + x = 90°$. The complement of 62° is 28°. **REMEMBER**: Complementary angles are always positive.
Two positive angles are **supplementary** if they add up to 180°. 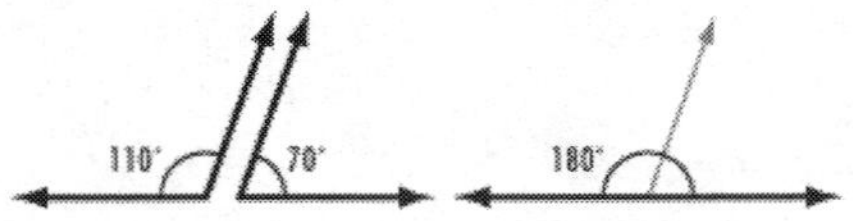 110° + 70° = 180° 110° and 70° are supplementary angles.	**Supplementary angles** are two positive angles whose measures add up to 180°. Since 110° + 70° = 180°, 110° and 70° are supplementary angles.

Example What is the supplementary angle of 90°?	To find the **supplement** of 90°, solve for x in the equation $90° + x = 180°$.

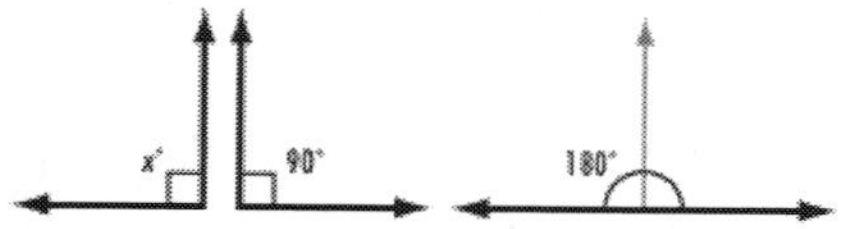

$90° + x = 180°$
$x = 90°$

Since $90° + 90° = 180°$, 90° and 90° are supplementary angles.

Sample problems:

1. What is the complementary angle of 2°?
   Solution: 88°
   Explanation: Let x be the complementary angle of 2°. Then $x + 2 = 90°$.
   Solve for x: $x + 2 = 90°$; $x = 88°$.

2. Suppose that angles measuring $2x$ and $4x + 6$ are supplementary. What are the measures of the angles?
   Solution: 58° and 122°
   Explanation: The sum of supplementary angles is 180°, or $(2x) + (4x + 6) = 180$.
   Solve for x: $2x + 4x + 6 = 180$; $6x + 6 = 180$; $6x = 174$; $x = 29$. Substitute 29 into $2x$ and $4x + 6$ to find the measures of the angles: $2(29) = 58$ and $4(29) + 6 = 122$. The two angle measures are 58° and 122°.

3. Suppose that two angles measuring $2a + 7$ and $3a + 4$ degrees are complementary. What are measures of the two angles?
   Solution: 38.6° and 51.4°
   Explanation: Since the two angles are complementary, their sum is 90°, or $(2a + 7) + (3a + 4) = 90$. Solve for a: $(2a + 7) + (3a + 4) = 90$; $5a + 11 = 90$; $5a = 79$; $a = \frac{79}{5} = 15.8$. Substitute 15.8 into $2a + 7$ and $3a + 4$ to find the measures of the angles: $2(15.8) + 7 = 38.6$ and $3(15.8) + 4 = 51.4$. The two angle measures are 38.6° and 51.4°.

Practice problems: *(Answers on page: 753)*

1. True or false: Supplementary angles are two angles whose measures add up to 90°.
2. Suppose that an angle measures x (degrees). Write an expression for its supplement in terms of x.
3. The supplement of an angle y measures $10x + 4$ and the complement of the angle measures $4x$. What is the measure of angle y?

Review questions: *(Answers to odd questions on page: 753)*

1. True or false: Complementary angles are two positive angles whose measures add up to 180°.
2. What angle is its own complement?
3. What is the measure of the supplementary angle for an angle of 58°?
4. Suppose two angles are complementary and the measure of one angle is twice the measure of the other. What are the measures of the angles?
5. Suppose that the complement of angle θ measures $5x + 4$ and the supplement of angle θ measures $15x - 6$. Find the measure of θ.

Converting between Degrees and Radians

- Mathematicians prefer to measure angles in **radians**. In **radian measure**, there are 2π radians in one complete circle.
- Use the conversion 2π radians = 360° to convert between degrees and radians.

Once around a circle will now be 2π radians

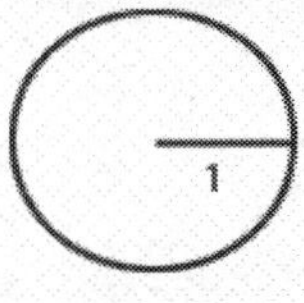

radius = 1
circumference (distance around the circle) = $2\pi r$

Up to this point, we have measured angles in degrees. But why? The choice of 360° for a complete circle is an arbitrary one.

Consider a circle of radius 1. Its circumference is 2π. Why not let once around the circle be equal to 2π instead of 360°?

Mathematicians call this method of measuring angles **radian measure**. In radian measure, one complete circle is equal to 2π radians.

Converting from degrees to radians

$$\frac{360°}{360} = \frac{2\pi \text{ radians}}{360} \quad \textit{(divide both sides by 360)}$$

$$\boxed{1° = \frac{\pi}{180} \text{ radians}}$$

Converting from radians to degrees

$$\frac{360°}{2\pi} = \frac{2\pi \text{ radians}}{2\pi} \quad \textit{(divide both sides by } 2\pi\textit{)}$$

$$\boxed{\frac{180°}{\pi} = 1 \text{ radian}}$$

To convert between degrees and **radians**, just remember that 2π radians = 360°.

Dividing both sides by 360 gives you the radian equivalent of 1°.

Dividing both sides by 2π gives you the degree equivalent of 1 radian.

Example 180° = ? radians

$$1° = \frac{\pi}{180} \text{ radians}$$

$$(180)(1°) = \left(\frac{\pi}{180} \text{ radians}\right)(180)$$

$$\boxed{180° = \pi \text{ radians}}$$

To convert 180° to radian measure, use the equation $1° = \pi/180$ radians.

Multiply both sides by 180 and you're done!

Another method for converting degrees to radians is to multiply the degrees by $\pi/180$ radians, which is acceptable since $\pi/180$ radians = 1°. So,

$$180° = 180°(1°) = \cancel{180°}\left(\frac{\pi}{\cancel{180}} \text{ radians}\right) = \pi \text{ radians.}$$

Example ?° = 3π radians

$$\frac{180°}{\pi} = 1 \text{ radian}$$

$$(3\cancel{\pi})\left(\frac{180°}{\cancel{\pi}}\right) = (1 \text{ radian})(3\pi)$$

$$\boxed{540° = 3\pi \text{ radians}}$$

To convert 3π radians to degrees,
start with the equation $180°/\pi = 1$ radian.
Multiply both sides by 3π.

Again, a second method is to multiply the given radian measurement by $180°/\pi$; since $180°/\pi = 1$ radian, the multiplication does not change the value.

So, 3π radians $= 3\cancel{\pi}\left(\frac{180°}{\cancel{\pi}}\right) = 540°.$

REMEMBER: If you forget how to convert between degrees and radians, start with the formula 2π radians = 360°.

Sample problems:

1. Convert 20° to radian measure, leave your answer in terms of π.

Solution: $\frac{\pi}{9}$ radians

Explanation: To convert from degrees to radians, multiply the degree measurement by $\frac{\pi}{180°}$: $20° \cdot \frac{\pi}{180°} = \frac{\pi}{9}$.

2. Convert $\frac{\pi}{5}$ radians to degree measure.

   Solution: 36°

   Explanation: To convert from radians to degrees, multiply the radian measurement by $\frac{180°}{\pi}$: $\frac{\pi}{5}\cdot\frac{180°}{\pi}=\frac{180°}{5}=36°$.

3. Convert $-\frac{80\pi}{7}$ radians to degree measure.

   Solution: $-2057.14°$

   Explanation: Multiply by $\frac{180°}{\pi}$: $\left(-\frac{80\pi}{7}\right)\cdot\left(\frac{180°}{\pi}\right)=-\frac{80(180°)}{7}=-2057.14°$.

Practice problems: *(Answers on page: 753)*

1. How many degrees are there in 3 radians? Leave your answer in terms of π.
2. Convert $-\frac{20\pi}{3}$ radians to degree measure.
3. A wall clock reads exactly 4 o'clock. What is the radian measure of the smaller angle formed by the hour and minute hands of the clock?

Review questions: *(Answers to odd questions on page: 754)*

1. Convert 45° to radian measure. Leave your answer in terms of π.
2. Convert $\frac{7\pi}{8}$ radians to degree measure.
3. Convert 132° to radian measure. Leave your answer in terms of π.
4. Convert $\frac{5\pi}{12}$ to degree measure.
5. Which angle is greater, 1° or 1 radian?

Using the Arc Length Formula

- The **arc length** of an **arc** of a circle is given by the formula $s = r\theta$, where s is the length of the arc, r is the radius of the circle, and θ is the central angle subtended, measured in **radians**.

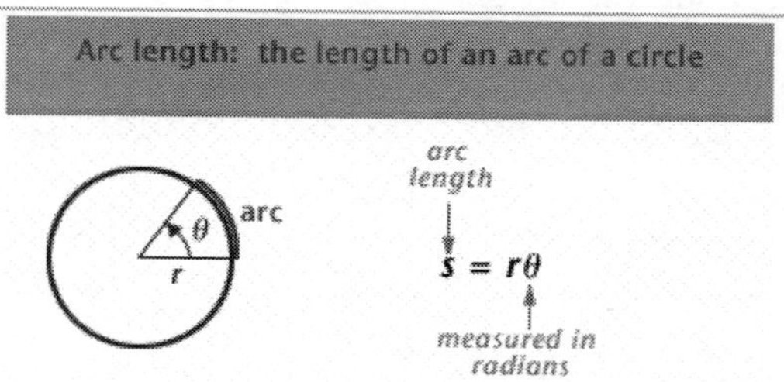	Measuring **arc length** is one example of why it is often more convenient to measure angles in **radians** instead of degrees. This formula, $s = r\theta$, says that the length of the **arc** of a circle is equal to the radius of the circle times the angle subtended by the arc, measured in radians.
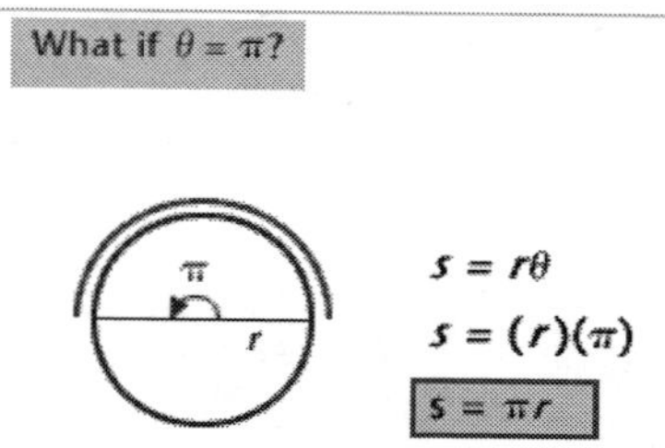	Try the formula out on an arc that subtends an angle measuring π radians (one-half of the circle). Plug in the known values and solve. The length of this arc is equal to πr, where r is the radius of the circle.

Example What is the arc length of the clock between 2:00 and 3:00? 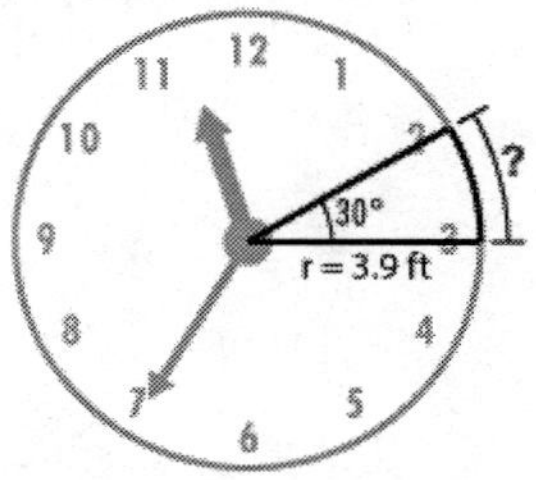 	You can use the formula for arc length to find the measure of the arc from 2:00 to 3:00 on the clock illustrated to the left. Use the arc length formula, $s = r\theta$, and plug in the known values.
Remember $1° = \frac{\pi}{180}$ Convert to radians using either method: $(30)1° = \frac{\pi}{180}(30)$ $30° = \frac{\pi}{6}$ OR: $30°\left(\frac{\pi}{180}\right) = \frac{30\pi}{180} = \frac{\pi}{6}$	First, convert 30° to radians so you can use the formula for arc length. There are 2 ways to convert from degrees to radians, use whatever method you find easier. **REMEMBER**: The formula for arc length only works when the angle is measured in radians.
$s = r\theta$ Plug in the known values: $s = (3.9')\frac{\pi}{6}$ $s = 2.04'$ 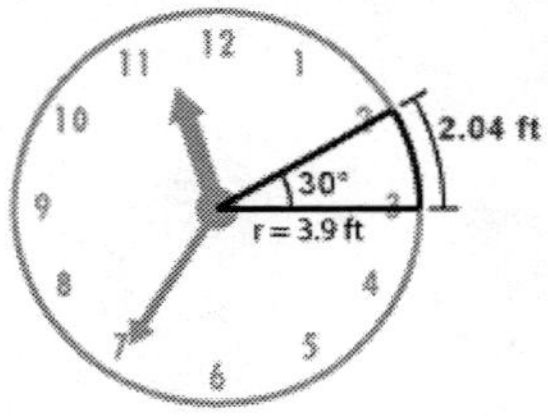 	Plugging into the formula $s = r\theta$ results in measure for the arc length for the clock between 2:00 and 3:00. The arc length of the clock between 2:00 and 3:00 is 2.04 feet.

Sample problems:

1. A string on a pendulum with a length of 2 ft subtends an angle of 35°. Find the length of the arc the pendulum swings through.
   Solution: 1.22 feet
   Explanation: Think of the pendulum as making a circle with a 2 ft. radius. To find the arc length, convert 35° to radians: $35° = 35 \cdot \left(\frac{\pi}{180}\right) = \frac{7\pi}{36}$ radians. Use the arc length formula: $s = r\theta = (2\text{ ft})\left(\frac{7\pi}{36}\right) = 1.22$ ft. The arc length of the pendulum is 1.22 ft.

2. The cities of Vandora and Lachistan are located on the same longitude, but different latitudes. Vandora is on the latitude 58° N, while Lachistan is at 10° S. What is the distance (along the surface of the Earth) between the two cities? Assume that the radius of the Earth is 3700 miles.
   Solution: 4391 miles
   Explanation: The distance between two cities along the surface of the Earth is an arc of a circle. The angle subtended by the arc is 68°.
   Convert this to radians: $68° = 68 \cdot \left(\frac{\pi}{180}\right)$ radians $= \frac{17\pi}{45}$ radians.
   Now use the arc length formula: $s = r\theta = (3700\text{ miles})\left(\frac{17\pi}{45}\right) = 4391.2$ miles.

3. The wheels on Jan's bicycle have a radius of 50 centimeters. Jan rides her bicycle so that its wheels rotate at 1 revolution per second. Determine Jan's speed in meters per second.
   Solution: 3.14 meters/sec
   Explanation: In 1 second, the wheels make 1 revolution. A full revolution of a circle is equal to 2π radians, so in 1 second, the wheel rotates $1(2\pi) = 2\pi$ radians. Convert 50 cm to meters: 50 cm = .5m. Use the arc length formula to calculate the linear distance Jan travels in 1 second: $s = r\theta = (0.5 \text{ meters})(2\pi) = 3.14$ meters. In one second, Jan travels 3.14 meters, so she is riding at 3.14 meters/sec.

Practice problems: *(Answers on page: 754)*

1. What is the length of the arc intercepted by an angle of 10° on a circle with a radius of 10 meters?
2. The clock in the tower of City Hall has a circular face that measures 15 feet in diameter. What is the arc length between the number 3 and the number 8 (passing through 4, 5, 6, and 7)?
3. At a birthday party, a circular cake with a diameter of 14 inches is cut into 16 equal pieces. What is the length of the curved end of each piece of cake?

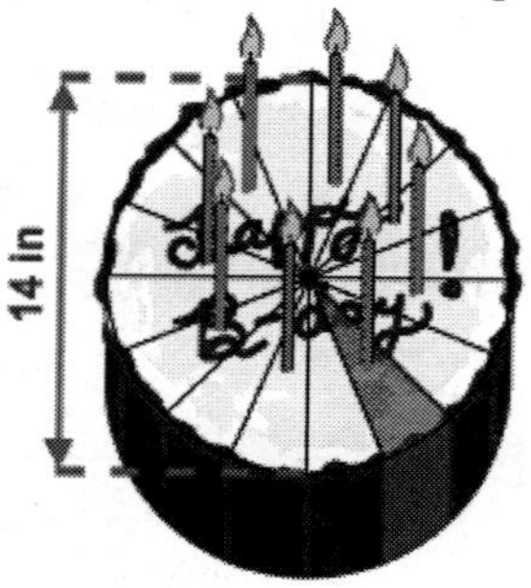

Review questions: *(Answers to odd questions on page: 754)*

1. In the arc length formula, what quantity does s represent?
2. Compute the length of the arc that subtends angle B if its measure is 110°.

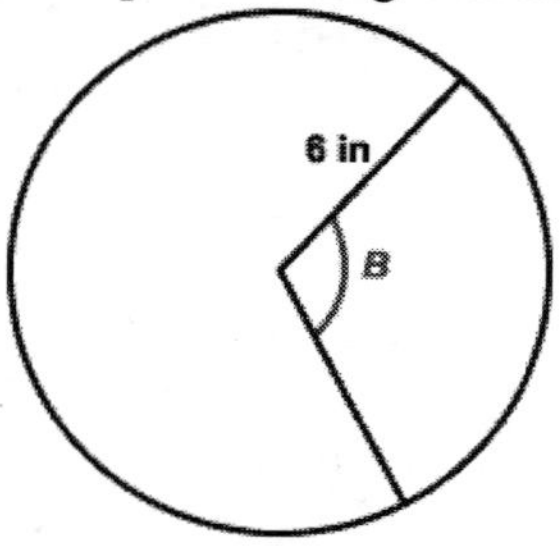

3. Compute the length of the arc that subtends angle C if its measure is 12°.

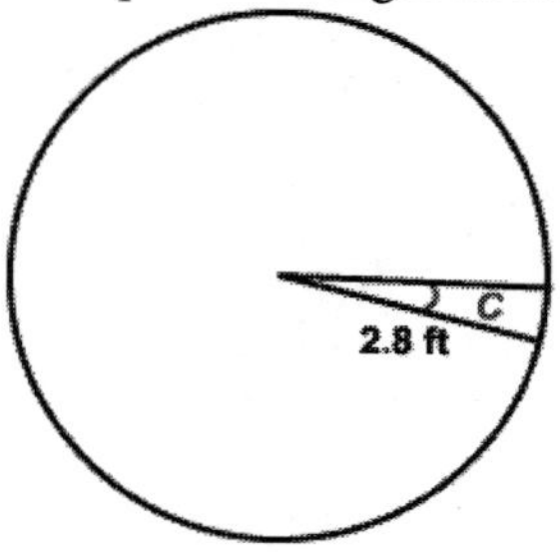

4. On a certain clock, the minute hand is 4.5 inches long. How far does the tip of the minute hand travel in 40 minutes?

5. Find the radius of the circle to the nearest hundredth of an inch.

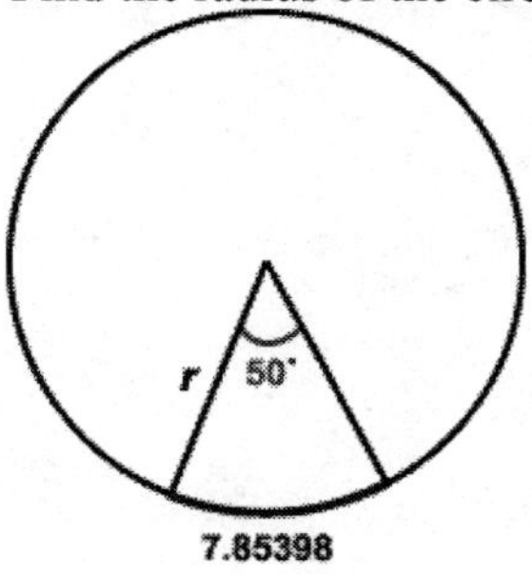

An Introduction to the Trigonometric Functions

- The **trigonometric functions** of an angle θ are defined to be the ratios of the side lengths of a right triangle having θ as an angle.
- The three basic trig functions are **sine**, **cosine**, and **tangent**. They are defined as follows:
  - $\sin\theta = \dfrac{opposite}{hypotenuse}$
  - $\cos\theta = \dfrac{adjacent}{hypotenuse}$
  - $\tan\theta = \dfrac{opposite}{adjacent}$

  Their reciprocals are the **cosecant**, **secant**, and **cotangent** functions, respectively.
- Every angle can be expressed in **radians** regardless of starting position.

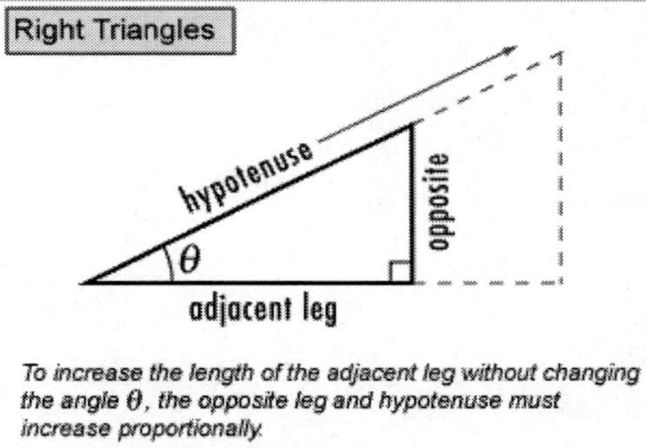

If you wish to lengthen the adjacent side without changing the angle θ, you must increase the other two sides of the triangle proportionally.

All right triangles with the same angle θ are **similar**; the lengths of their sides are in the same proportions.

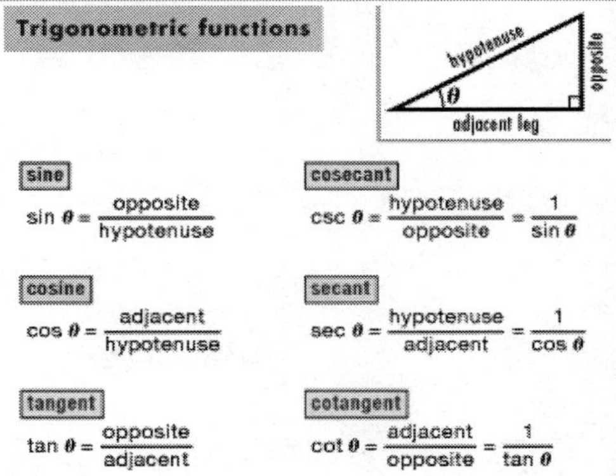

The **trigonometric functions** of an angle θ are defined to be the ratios of the sides of a right triangle having θ for an angle. The three basic trig functions are **sine**, **cosine**, and **tangent**; **cosecant**, **secant**, and **cotangent** are their reciprocals, respectively.

NOTICE: The reciprocal of sine is cosecant, and the reciprocal of cosine is secant. It's easy to mix these up.

Example

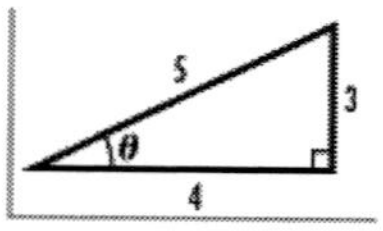

$\sin\theta = \frac{\text{opp}}{\text{hyp}} = \frac{3}{5}$ $\csc\theta = \frac{\text{hyp}}{\text{opp}} = \frac{5}{3}$

$\cos\theta = \frac{\text{adj}}{\text{hyp}} = \frac{4}{5}$ $\sec\theta = \frac{\text{hyp}}{\text{adj}} = \frac{5}{4}$

$\tan\theta = \frac{\text{opp}}{\text{adj}} = \frac{3}{4}$ $\cot\theta = \frac{\text{adj}}{\text{opp}} = \frac{4}{3}$

Compute the trig functions for the angle θ in this 3-4-5 right triangle.

For this triangle, the opposite side has length 3, the adjacent side has length 4, and the hypotenuse has length 5. Substitute these values into the formulas to find the values of the different trig functions.

Example

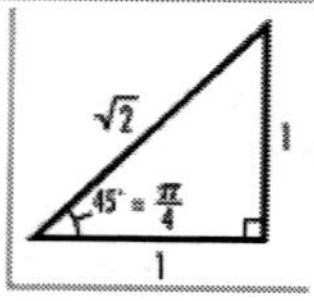

$\sin\frac{\pi}{4} = \frac{\text{opp}}{\text{hyp}} = \frac{1}{\sqrt{2}} = \frac{\sqrt{2}}{2}$ $\csc\frac{\pi}{4} = \frac{\text{hyp}}{\text{opp}} = \frac{\sqrt{2}}{1} = \sqrt{2}$

$\cos\frac{\pi}{4} = \frac{\text{adj}}{\text{hyp}} = \frac{1}{\sqrt{2}} = \frac{\sqrt{2}}{2}$ $\sec\frac{\pi}{4} = \frac{\text{hyp}}{\text{adj}} = \frac{\sqrt{2}}{1} = \sqrt{2}$

$\tan\frac{\pi}{4} = \frac{\text{opp}}{\text{adj}} = \frac{1}{1} = 1$ $\cot\frac{\pi}{4} = \frac{\text{adj}}{\text{opp}} = \frac{1}{1} = 1$

Find the trig functions for $\pi/4$ (**radian measure**), the acute angle in an isosceles right triangle.

If each of the legs of the triangle have length 1, use the **Pythagorean theorem** to find the length of the hypotenuse, $\sqrt{2}$.

Substitute to find the values of the trig functions for $\pi/4$.

Example

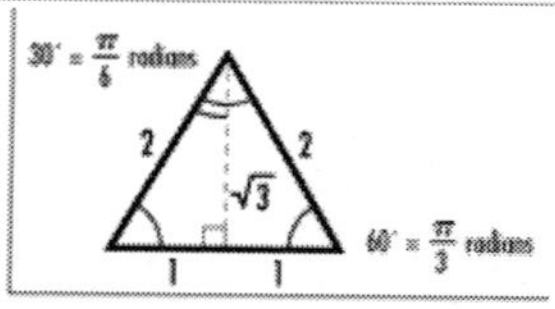

$\sin\frac{\pi}{3} = \frac{\text{opp}}{\text{hyp}} = \frac{\sqrt{3}}{2}$ $\sin\frac{\pi}{6} = \frac{\text{opp}}{\text{hyp}} = \frac{1}{2}$

$\cos\frac{\pi}{3} = \frac{\text{adj}}{\text{hyp}} = \frac{1}{2}$ $\cos\frac{\pi}{6} = \frac{\text{adj}}{\text{hyp}} = \frac{\sqrt{3}}{2}$

$\tan\frac{\pi}{3} = \frac{\text{opp}}{\text{adj}} = \frac{\sqrt{3}}{1} = \sqrt{3}$ $\tan\frac{\pi}{6} = \frac{\text{opp}}{\text{adj}} = \frac{1}{\sqrt{3}} = \frac{\sqrt{3}}{3}$

Find the trig functions for $\pi/6$ **radians** and $\pi/3$ radians.

Use an equilateral triangle with sides of length 2. Drop an altitude, forming two 30°-60°-90° right triangles. Each of these triangles has an angle measuring $30° = \pi/6$ radians and $60° = \pi/3$ radians.

It is important to be familiar with the trig functions of the angles $\pi/6$, $\pi/4$, and $\pi/3$ radians.

Sample problems:

1. Given the right triangle below, compute the cosine of angle C.

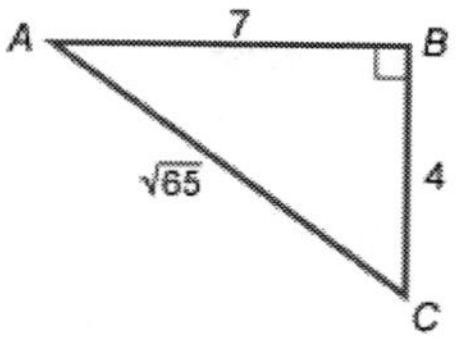

Solution: $\frac{4\sqrt{65}}{65}$

Explanation: By definition, $\cos\theta = \frac{\text{adjacent}}{\text{hypotenuse}}$. The side adjacent to $\angle C$ is $\overline{BC} = 4$.

The hypotenuse is $\overline{AC} = \sqrt{65}$ Therefore, $\cos C = \frac{\text{adj}}{\text{hyp}} = \frac{\overline{BC}}{\overline{AC}} = \frac{4}{\sqrt{65}}$. Now rationalize:

$$\frac{4}{\sqrt{65}}\left(\frac{\sqrt{65}}{\sqrt{65}}\right) = \frac{4\sqrt{65}}{65}.$$

2. Given the right triangle below, compute the tangent of angle D.

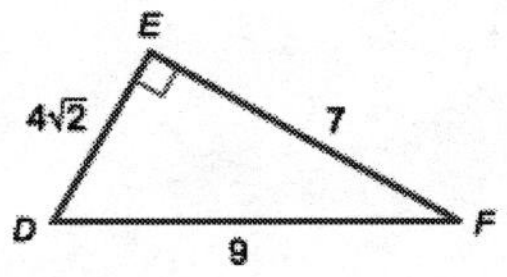

Solution: $\frac{7\sqrt{2}}{8}$

Explanation: By definition, $\tan\theta = \frac{\text{opposite}}{\text{adjacent}}$. The side opposite $\angle D$ is $\overline{EF} = 7$.

The side adjacent to $\angle D$ is $\overline{DE} = 4\sqrt{2}$. Therefore, $\tan D = \frac{7}{4\sqrt{2}}$. Rationalize:

$$\frac{7}{4\sqrt{2}}\left(\frac{\sqrt{2}}{\sqrt{2}}\right) = \frac{7\sqrt{2}}{8}.$$

3. Given the right triangle below, compute the sine of angle E.

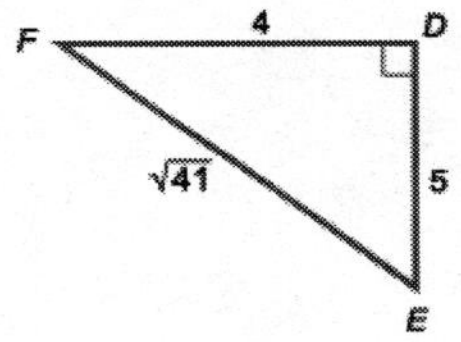

Solution: $\frac{4\sqrt{41}}{41}$

Explanation: By definition, $\sin\theta = \frac{\text{opposite}}{\text{hypotenuse}}$. The side opposite $\angle E$ is $\overline{DF} = 4$.

The hypotenuse of the triangle is $\overline{EF} = \sqrt{41}$. Therefore, $\sin E = \frac{4}{\sqrt{41}}$.

Rationalize: $\frac{4}{\sqrt{41}}\left(\frac{\sqrt{41}}{\sqrt{41}}\right) = \frac{4\sqrt{41}}{41}$.

Practice problems: *(Answers on page: 754)*

1. True or false: The ratio $\frac{\overline{AB}}{\overline{BC}}$ represents the tangent of $\angle A$ in the triangle below.

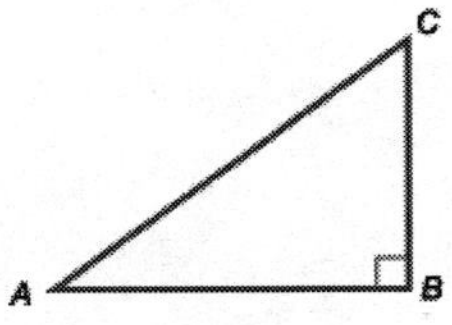

2. Given the triangle below, compute the secant of angle F.

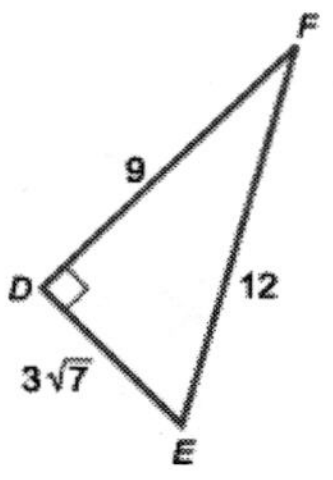

3. What is the value of $\sin\theta$?

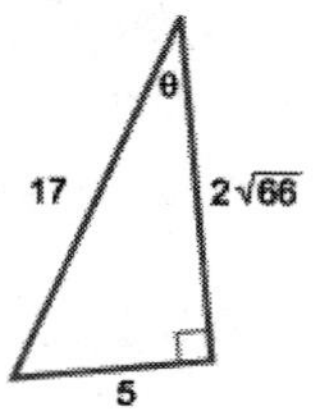

Review questions: *(Answers to odd questions on page: 754)*

1. True or false: The ratio adj/hyp defines the cosine function.
2. What is the value of $\sec\theta$?

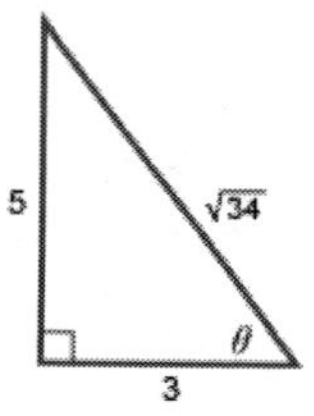

3. What is the value of $\tan\theta$?

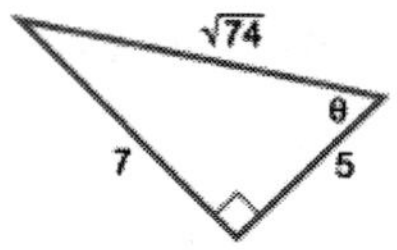

4. Suppose $\csc\theta = \frac{\sqrt{265}}{12}$ and $\sec\theta = \frac{\sqrt{265}}{11}$, what is the value of $\sin\theta$?

5. What is the value of $\cot\theta$?

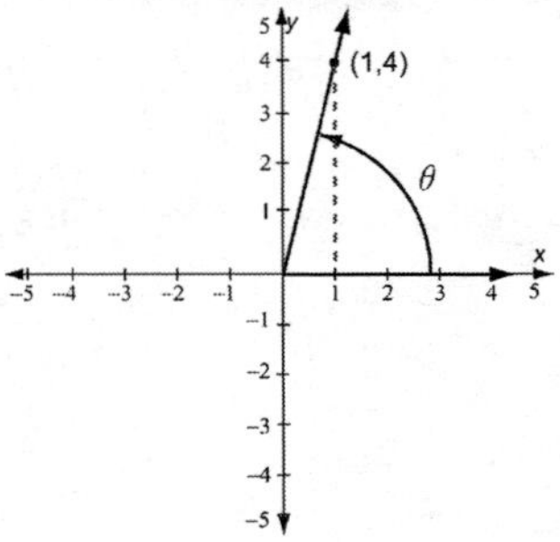

Evaluating Trigonometric Functions for an Angle in a Right Triangle

- Use the **Pythagorean theorem** to find the missing side of a right triangle before computing the **trigonometric functions** for an angle in a given triangle.
- When given the value of a trig function for an **acute angle** θ, find the other trig functions for θ by drawing a right triangle having θ as an angle.

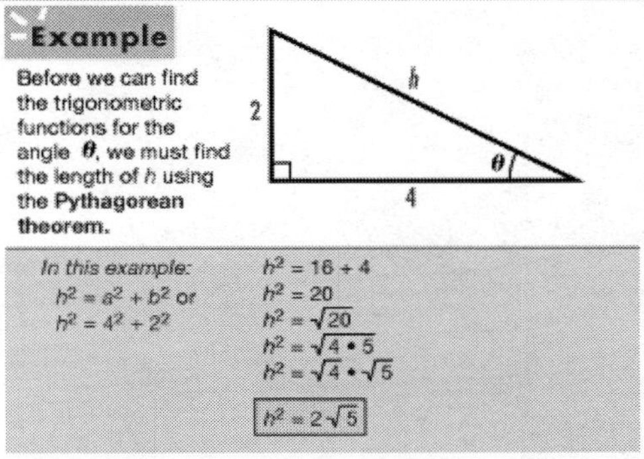

Given the right triangle illustrated here, find the values of the **trigonometric functions** for the angle θ. Before taking the ratios of the sides, find the length of the hypotenuse.

Find the length of the hypotenuse using the **Pythagorean theorem**.

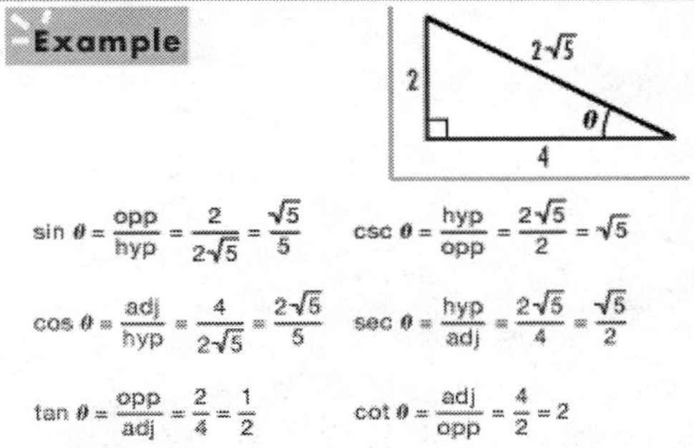

Once all three sides of the right triangle are known, plug the lengths of the sides into the trig functions to find their values.

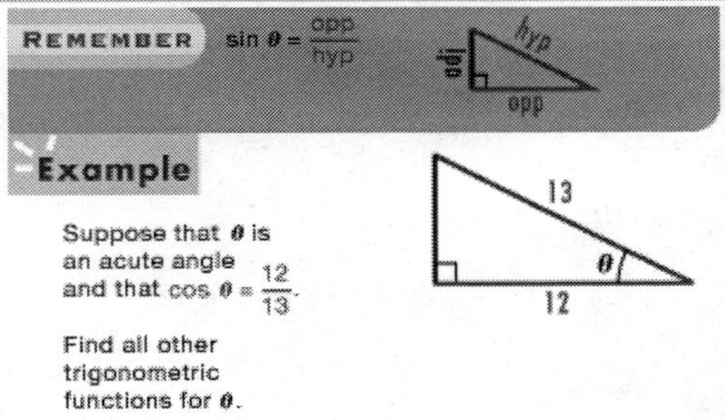

Consider the following: given that an angle θ is an **acute angle**, and given that the value for $\cos\theta$ is 12/13, find the other trig functions for θ.

Begin by sketching a right triangle having θ for an angle. Label the side adjacent θ and the hypotenuse using the fact that $\cos\theta$ = *adjacent/hypotenuse* = 12/13.

Example

By knowing one trigonometric function of an acute angle we can figure out the others.

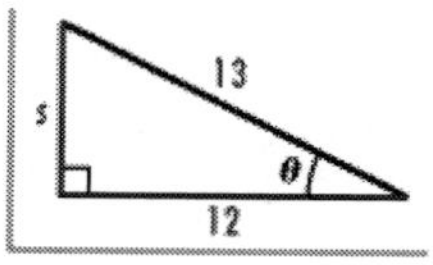

$\sin\theta = \frac{opp}{hyp} = \frac{5}{13}$ $\csc\theta = \frac{hyp}{opp} = \frac{13}{5}$

$\cos\theta = \frac{adj}{hyp} = \frac{12}{13}$ $\sec\theta = \frac{hyp}{adj} = \frac{13}{12}$

$\tan\theta = \frac{opp}{adj} = \frac{5}{12}$ $\cot\theta = \frac{adj}{opp} = \frac{12}{5}$

Then use the Pythagorean theorem to find the unknown side of the triangle. In this case, the missing leg has length 5.

Knowing all three sides of the right triangle, plug the lengths of the sides into the trigonometric functions to find their values.

Sample problems:

1. Given the triangle below, compute the cotangent of angle G.

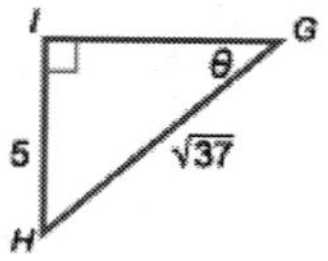

Solution: $\frac{2\sqrt{3}}{5}$

Explanation: Find the missing length using the Pythagorean theorem: $a^2 + b^2 = c^2$; $5^2 + b^2 = \left(\sqrt{37}\right)^2$; $25 + b^2 = 37$; $b^2 = 12$; $b = 2\sqrt{3}$. By definition, $\cot\theta = \frac{\text{adjacent}}{\text{opposite}}$. The side adjacent to angle G is $\overline{GI}$. The side opposite angle G is $\overline{HI}$. Therefore, $\cot G = \frac{\overline{GI}}{\overline{HI}} = \frac{2\sqrt{3}}{5}$.

2. Suppose that θ is an acute angle and that $\tan\theta = \frac{5}{7}$. Use a right triangle to find the value of $\sin\theta$.

Solution: $\frac{5\sqrt{74}}{74}$

Explanation: Since θ is acute, it can be an angle in a right triangle. The value of $\tan\theta$ is $\frac{5}{7}$. Although that is a ratio, you can let the side opposite θ be 5 and the side adjacent θ be 7. Use the Pythagorean theorem to find the length of the hypotenuse, h: $7^2 + 5^2 = h^2$; $49 + 25 = h^2$; $74 = h^2$; $h = \sqrt{74}$.

Find $\sin\theta$: $\sin\theta = \frac{\text{opposite}}{\text{hypotenuse}} = \frac{5}{\sqrt{74}}$. Rationalize: $\frac{5\sqrt{74}}{74}$

3. Suppose θ is the angle between AF and the base $BCDF$ in the right triangular prism below. Find cos θ.

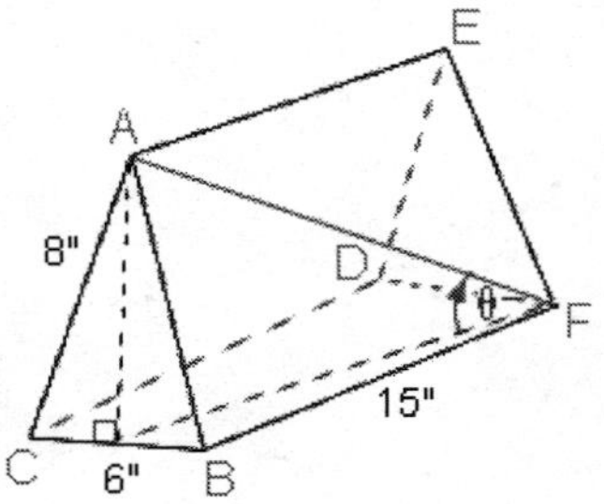

Solution: $\frac{3\sqrt{26}}{17}$

Explanation: Let G be the point where the altitude from A intersects the side BC. The angle between AF and the base $BCDF$ is the angle θ in the right triangle AGF. Since cosine relates the adjacent side, GF, and the hypotenuse, AF, use the Pythagorean theorem to calculate the lengths of GF and AF: $(GF)^2 = (BG)^2 + (BF)^2 = 3^2 + 15^2 = 9 + 225 = 234$; $GF = \sqrt{234} = 3\sqrt{26}$. Find the length of AF: $(AB)^2 + (BF)^2 = (AF)^2$; $8^2 + 15^2 = (AF)^2$; $289 = (AF)^2$; $AF = 17$. Therefore, $\cos\theta = \frac{3\sqrt{26}}{17}$.

Practice problems: *(Answers on page: 754)*

1. Given the triangle below, compute the cosecant of angle H.

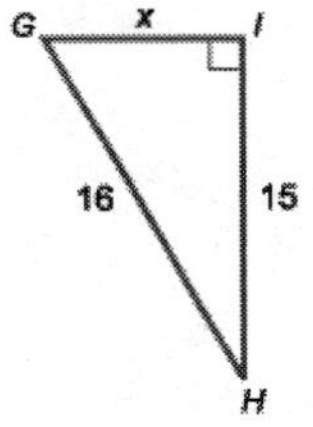

2. Suppose that θ is an acute angle and that $\sec\theta = \frac{8}{3}$. Use a right triangle to find the value of $\tan\theta$.

3. Suppose you are given that $\sin\theta = \frac{1}{2}$. If the area of the square is 36, what is the area of the triangle?

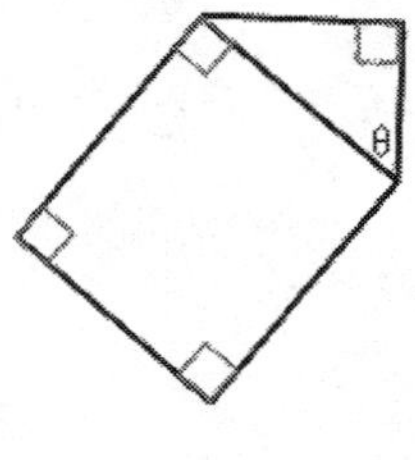

Review questions: *(Answers to odd questions on page: 754)*

1. Given the triangle below, compute the secant of angle I.

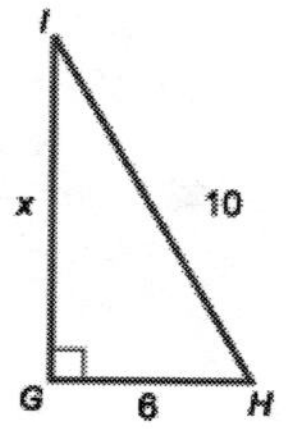

2. What is the value of $\cos\theta$?

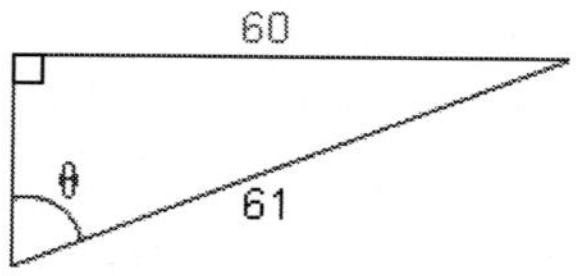

3. Compute the value of $\csc\theta$.

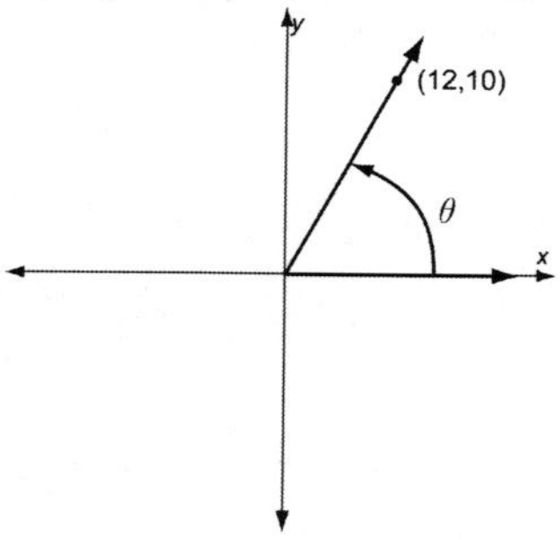

4. What are the ratios of the sides of a right triangle with θ, an acute angle, as one of its angles if $\cos\theta = 25$?

5. True or false: If θ is an acute angle and $\cos\theta = \frac{5}{9}$, then $\sin\theta$ is greater than $\tan\theta$.

Finding an Angle Given the Value of a Trigonometric Function

- You can sometimes find the measure of an angle θ given the value of one of its **trigonometric functions** by analyzing a right triangle with θ as one of its angles.

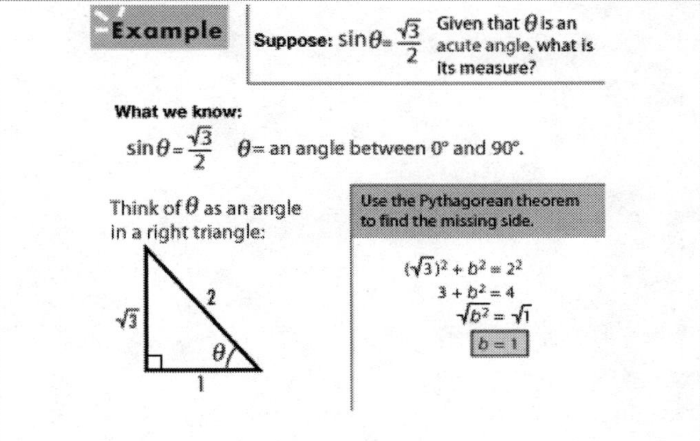

You have learned how to compute **trigonometric functions** given an angle. What about finding an angle given the value of a trig function?

For example, can you find the acute angle θ, given the value of **sin**θ ?

First, sketch a right triangle having θ as an angle. Use the fact that $\sin\theta = \dfrac{\text{opposite}}{\text{hypotenuse}} = \dfrac{\sqrt{3}}{2}$ to label the legs and hypotenuse of the triangle. Then, use the **Pythagorean theorem** to find the length of the missing leg.

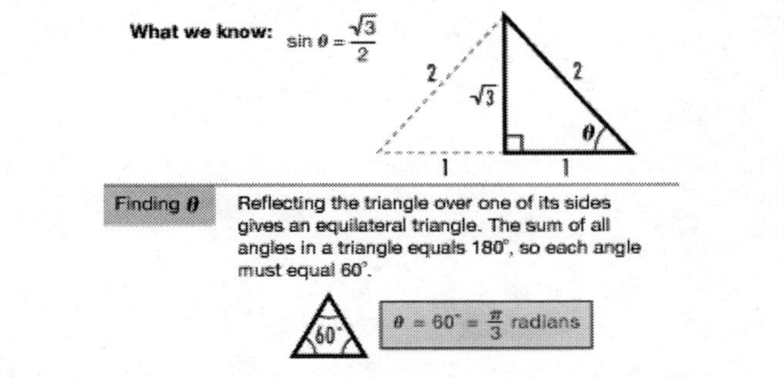

Reflecting the triangle over the side of length $\sqrt{3}$ results in an equilateral triangle.

The angles of an equilateral triangle all measure 60°, or $\pi/3$ **radians**. Therefore, $\theta = 60°$ or $\pi/3$ radians.

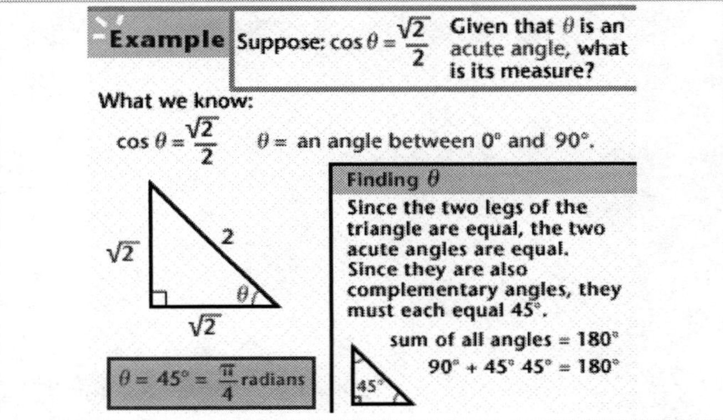

Consider this example: find θ if it is an acute angle whose **cosine** is $\sqrt{2}/2$.

Sketch a right triangle with θ as one of its angles. Label the adjacent leg with $\sqrt{2}$ and the hypotenuse with 2. Use the Pythagorean theorem to find that the missing leg.

Since both legs measure $\sqrt{2}$, this right triangle is isosceles. Therefore, $\theta = 45°$ or $\pi/4$ radians.

Sample problems:

1. Suppose $\cot\theta = 1$. Given that θ is an acute angle in a right triangle, what is its measure in radians?

   Solution: $\dfrac{\pi}{4}$

   Explanation: By definition, $\text{cotangent}\,\theta = \dfrac{\text{adjacent}}{\text{opposite}}$. Since $\cot\theta = 1$, $\dfrac{\text{adjacent}}{\text{opposite}} = 1$.

   Cross-multiply: $\dfrac{\text{adjacent}}{\text{opposite}} = 1$; adjacent = opposite. The sides must be the same length.

   Since the sides are equal, this is an isosceles right triangle. Therefore, $\theta = 45° = \dfrac{\pi}{4}$.

2. Suppose $\sin\theta = \frac{\sqrt{2}}{2}$. Given that θ is an acute angle in a right triangle, what is its measure in radians?

Solution: $\frac{\pi}{4}$ rad

Explantion: By definition, $\sin\theta = \frac{\text{opposite}}{\text{hypotenuse}} = \frac{\sqrt{2}}{2}$. Therefore, let the length of the side opposite the angle θ be $\sqrt{2}$, and let the length of the hypotenuse be 2. Use the Pythagorean theorem to find the missing length: $a^2 + b^2 = c^2$; $\left(\sqrt{2}\right)^2 + x^2 = 2^2$; $2 + x^2 = 4$; $x^2 = 2$; $x = \sqrt{2}$. Since both legs of the triangle are equal, the triangle is isosceles. Therefore, $\theta = 45° = \frac{\pi}{4}$ rad.

3. Suppose $\cos\theta = \frac{\sqrt{3}}{2}$. Given that θ is an acute angle in a right triangle, what is its measure in radians?

Solution: $\frac{\pi}{6}$ rad

Explanation: By definition, $\cos\theta = \frac{\text{adjacent}}{\text{hypotenuse}} = \frac{\sqrt{3}}{2}$. Therefore, let the length of the adjacent side be $\sqrt{3}$, and the length of the hypotenuse be 2. Use the Pythagorean theorem to find the missing length. $a^2 + b^2 = c^2$; $\left(\sqrt{3}\right)^2 + x^2 = 2^2$; $3 + x^2 = 4$; $x^2 = 1$; $x = 1$. The sides are not equal, so reflect the triangle across the leg with the greater length to form an equilateral triangle. An equilateral triangle has equal angles of 60°. Since θ is adjacent to the longer leg, it is added to itself to form one of the 60° angles. Divide by 2 to find the original measure: $\frac{60°}{2} = 30° = \frac{\pi}{6}$ rad.

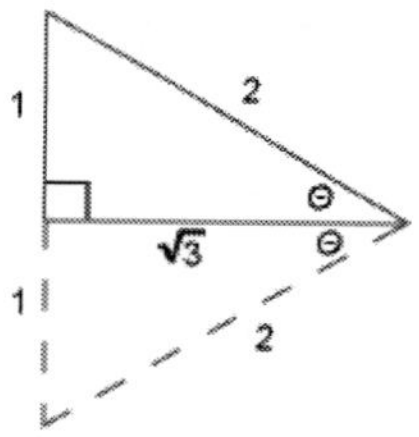

Practice problems: *(Answers on page: 754)*

1. What is the measure of θ if it represents an acute angle in a right triangle with $\sin\theta = \frac{1}{2}$?

2. Suppose $\sec\theta = \frac{2\sqrt{3}}{3}$. Given that θ is an acute angle in a right triangle, what is its measure in radians?

3. Suppose $\cos\theta = \frac{1}{2}$. Given that θ is an acute angle in a right triangle, what is its measure in radians?

Review questions: *(Answers to odd questions on page: 754)*

1. Suppose $\tan\theta = \sqrt{3}$. Given that θ is an acute angle in a right triangle, what is its measure in radians?

2. Suppose $\tan\theta = \frac{1}{2}$. Given that θ is an acute angle in a right triangle, what is its measure in radians?

3. Suppose $\csc\theta = \frac{2\sqrt{3}}{3}$. Given that θ is an acute angle in a right triangle, what is its measure in radians?

4. What is the measure of θ if it represents an acute angle with $\tan\theta = \frac{\sqrt{3}}{3}$?

5. Suppose $\sin\theta = \frac{1}{2}$. Given that θ is an acute angle in a right triangle, what is its measure?

Using Trigonometric Functions to Find Unknown Sides of Right Triangles

- You can use trigonometry to solve for an unknown side of a right triangle, given the length of one side and the measure of an angle (other than the right angle, 90°).

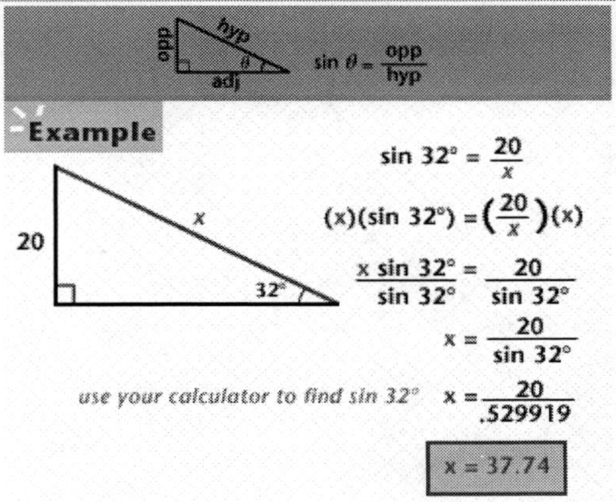

Consider the triangle illustrated here. To find x, the length of the hypotenuse, use one the of the trigonometric functions.

The **sine** function relates the side opposite the 32° angle to the hypotenuse. Use it to write an equation involving x, then solve for x.

Use a calculator to evaluate sin 32°. (Be sure the calculator is in degree mode)

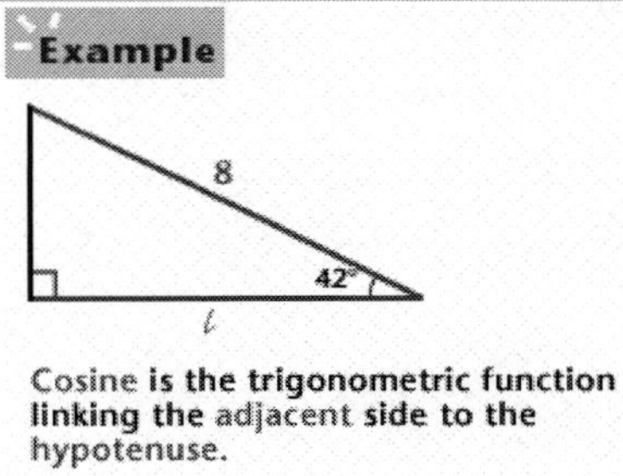

Determine the length of side l for the triangle illustrated here. This time, use the **cosine function**.

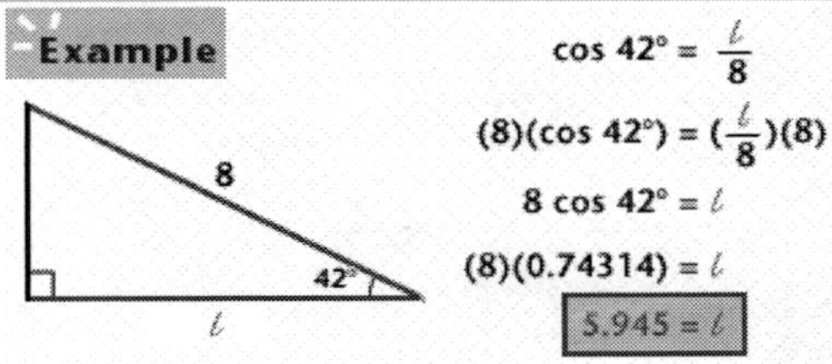

The side adjacent to the 42° angle is l and the hypotenuse is 8, so $\cos 42° = l/8$. Solve this equation for l.

Use a calculator to evaluate the expression.

Sample problems:

1. Given a right triangle with one angle measuring 38° and the opposite side of length 7, find the length x of the side adjacent to the angle.

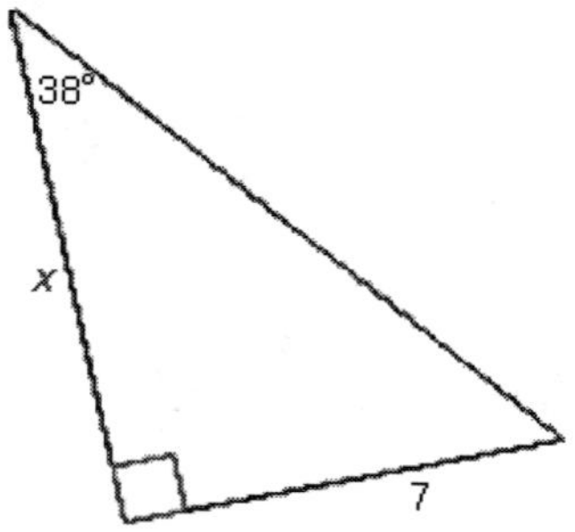

Solution: 8.96

Explanation: The tangent function relates the given angle with the known side and the unknown side. Write an equation using the tangent function and solve for x:

$\tan 38° = \frac{7}{x}$; $x \tan 38° = 7$; $x = \frac{7}{\tan 38°} = 8.96$.

2. A plane is flying over an uncharted island. What is the length of the island (represented by x)?

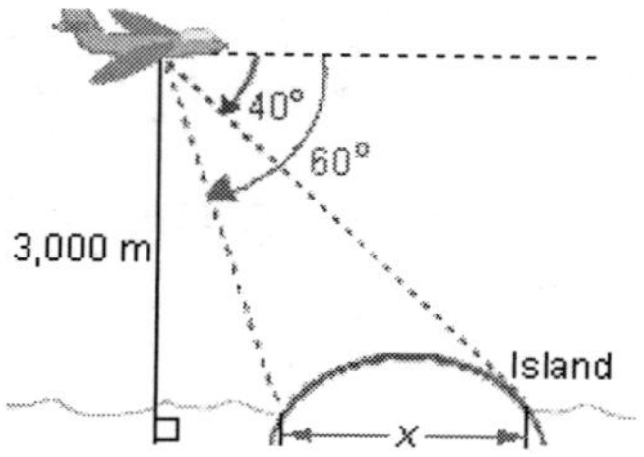

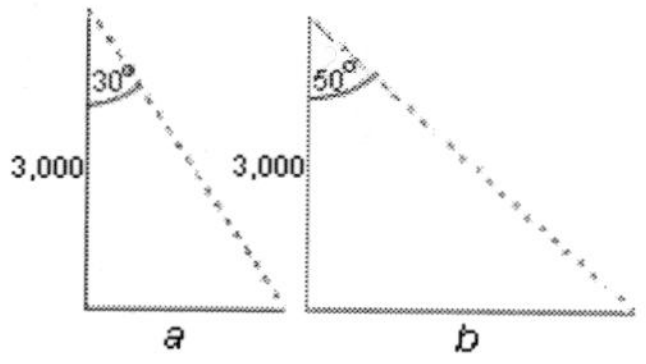

Solution: 1843 m

Explanation: There are two right triangles in the diagram. Using the first, smaller one, find the horizontal distance from the plane to the near side of the island:

$\tan 30° = \frac{a}{3,000}$; $a = 3000 \tan 30° = 1732$. Using the second, larger, right triangle, find the horizontal distance from the plane to the far side of the island:

$\tan 50° = \frac{b}{3,000}$; $b = 3,000 \tan 50° = 3575$. The difference of these two distances is the size of the island. The island is 1843 meters across.

3. An isosceles triangle has a base of length 5. The angle opposite the base measures $\frac{\pi}{5}$ radians. What are the lengths of the two equal sides?

Solution: 8.1

Explanation: An altitude from the vertex of the triangle to the base forms two congruent right triangles. The base of one of these triangles has length 2.5 and the angle opposite this base is $\frac{\pi}{5} \div 2$, or $\frac{\pi}{10}$ radians. The sine function relates the known side to the unknown: $\sin \frac{\pi}{10} = \frac{2.5}{x}$. Solve for x (calculator needs to be in radian mode): $x = \frac{2.5}{\sin \frac{\pi}{10}} = 8.1$.

Practice problems: *(Answers on page: 754)*

1. Consider the triangle ABC shown below. If $c = 12$, what is the value of a?

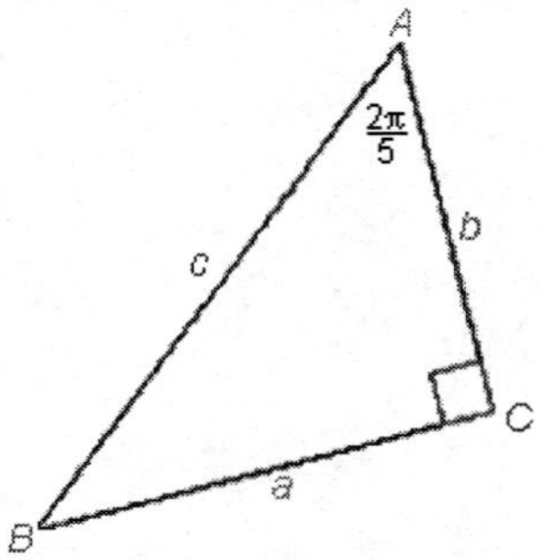

2. Find the missing length x.

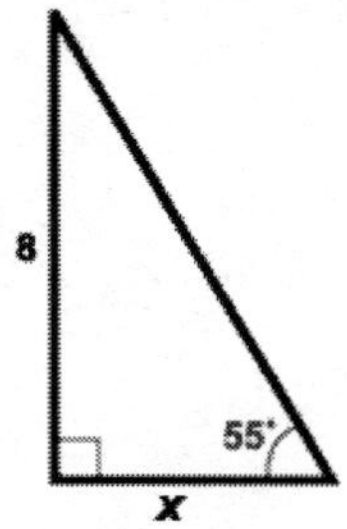

3. A 50 ft ladder is leaning against a wall so that the top of the ladder makes a 20° angle with the wall. How high up the wall does the ladder reach?

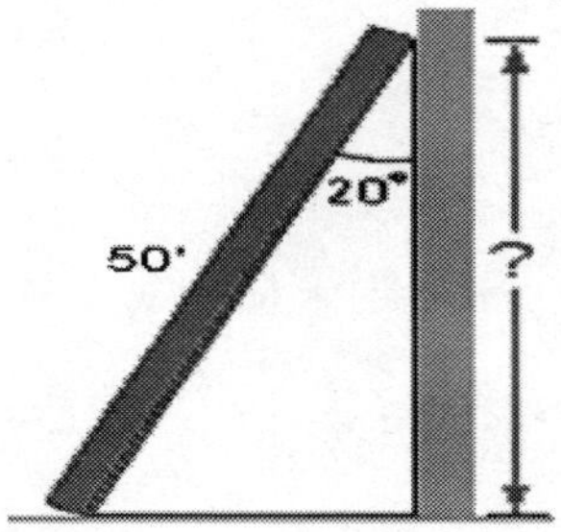

Review questions: *(Answers to odd questions on page: 754)*

1. Which trigonometric function could best be used to find the length x?

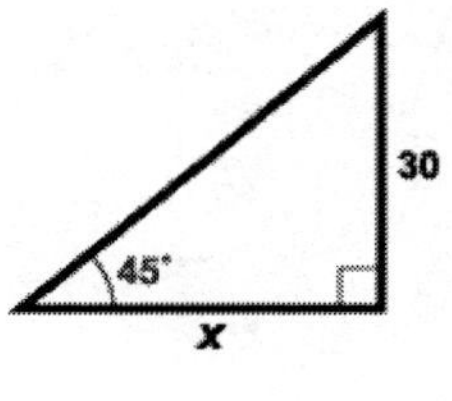

2. True or false: $\sin 30° = \dfrac{x}{15}$ could be used to solve for the unknown length of the triangle below.

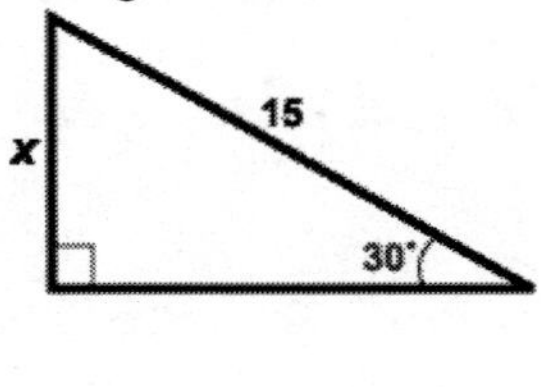

3. Find the missing length x.

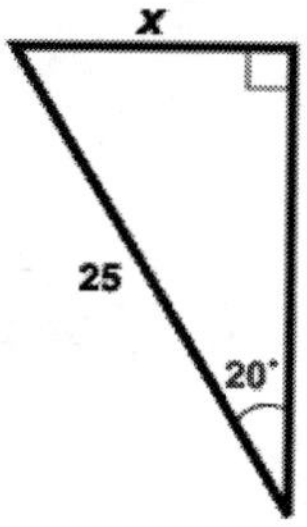

4. What is the length of x?

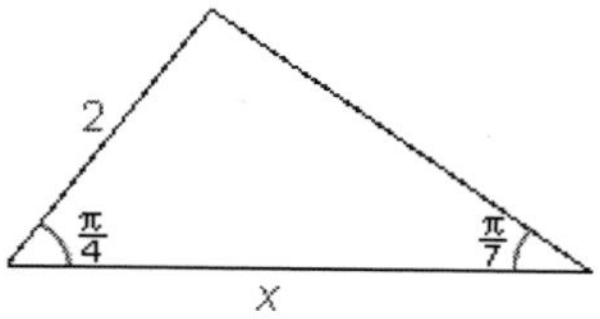

5. A distance of 60 ft is marked off from the foot of a building. The angle of elevation measured to the top of the building from that point is 82°. What is the height of the building to the nearest foot?

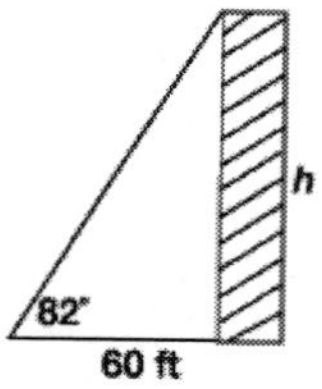

Finding the Height of a Building

- **Review:** You can use trigonometry to solve for an unknown side of a right triangle, given the length of one side and the measure of an angle (other than the right angle, 90°).
- Trigonometry has many real-world applications such as finding the height of a building and other tall structures.

Trigonometry can be used to find the height of a building. 	Trigonometry applies directly to the real world; for example, finding the height of a tall building. Simply measuring the building from the bottom to the top isn't always feasible, so we use trigonometric tools instead.

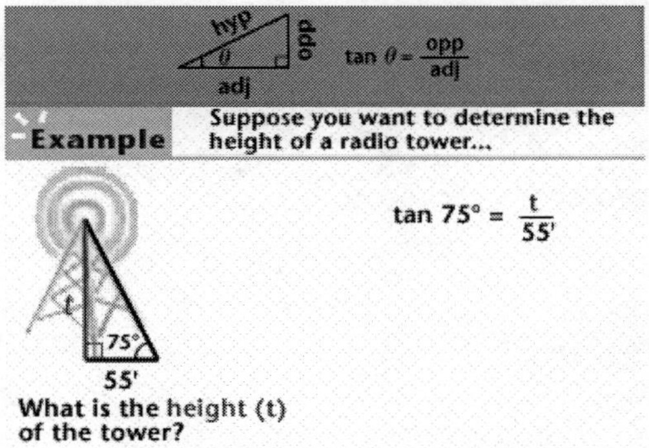

In this example you're asked to find t, the height of the radio tower. From a point on the ground 55 feet away from its base, you measure the angle to the top of the tower to be 75°.

The **tangent** function gives an equation involving t.

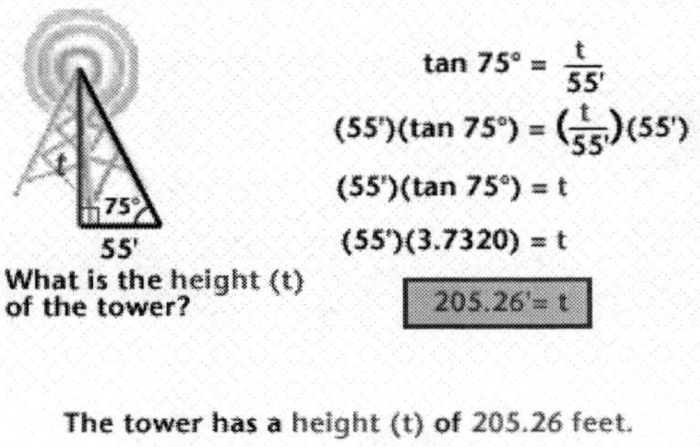

Solve the equation for t.

Use a calculator to evaluate tan75°. (Be sure the calculator is in degree mode!)

The height of the tower is 205.26 ft.

Sample problems:

1. Find the height of the building.

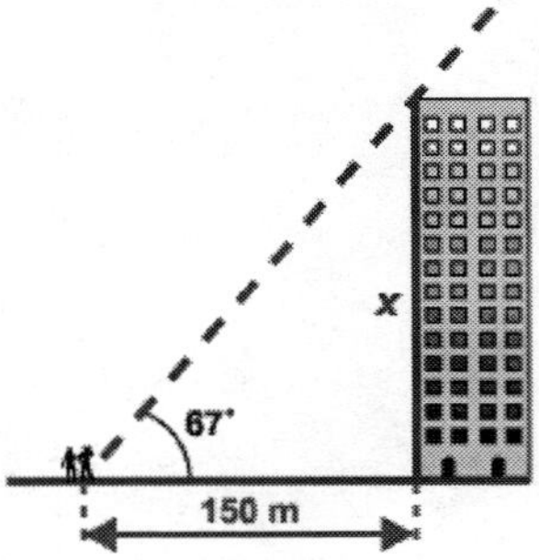

Solution: 353 m
Explanation: The tangent function relates the given angle to the known and unknown side. Use the tangent function to write an equation and solve for x:

$\tan 67° = \frac{x}{150}$; $x = 150(\tan 67°) = 353$ m.

2. A blimp is flying at an elevation of 6000 feet. The camera under the blimp has to swivel up 58° from the vertical to focus on the football stadium. What is the distance from the blimp to the stadium?

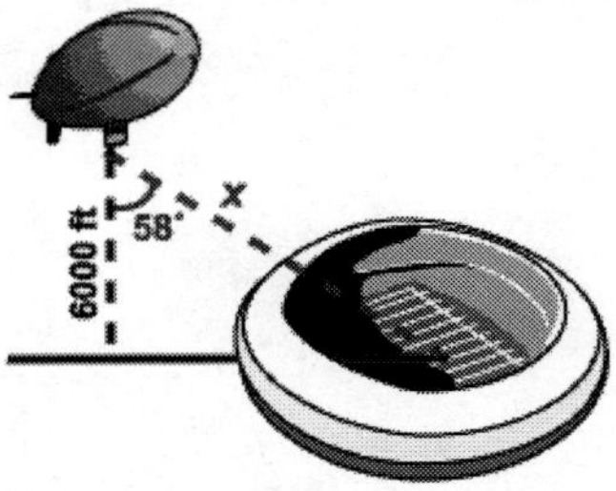

Solution: 11,322.5 ft
Explanation: Use the cosine function to write an equation and solve for x:
$\cos 58° = \frac{6000}{x}$; $x = \frac{6000}{\cos 58°}$; $x = 11{,}322.5$

3. Two buildings are 200 feet apart. If the angle of elevation from the top of the shorter building to the top of the taller building is 8°, what is the difference in the heights of the two buildings?
Solution: 28 feet
Explanation: Let y be the difference in heights between the buildings. From the diagram you can see that $\tan 8° = \frac{\text{opposite}}{\text{adjacent}} = \frac{y}{200}$. Thus $y = 200 \tan 8° \approx 28$. The difference in the heights of the buildings is 28 feet.

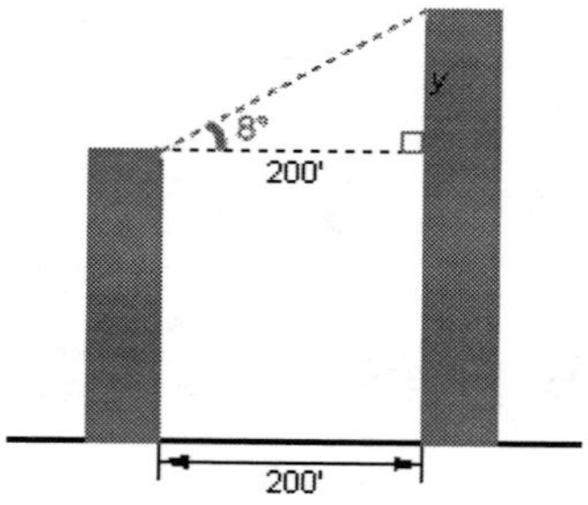

Practice problems: *(Answers on page: 754)*

1. Find the altitude of the airplane.

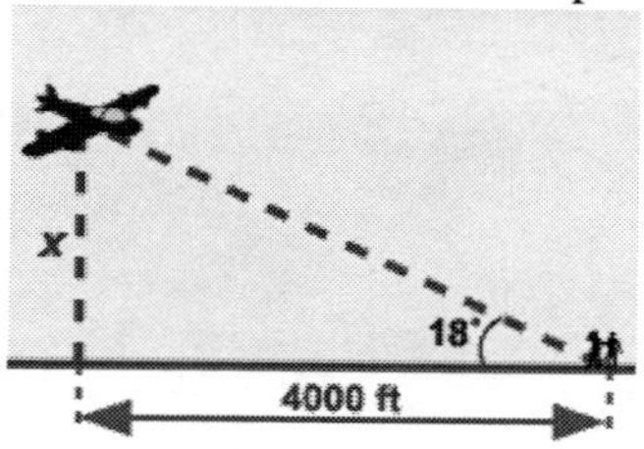

2. In a football game, the field goal kicker has to kick the ball from a point 53 yards from the goalpost at an angle of 40° in order to score points. How far will the ball travel from the kicking tee to the goalpost?

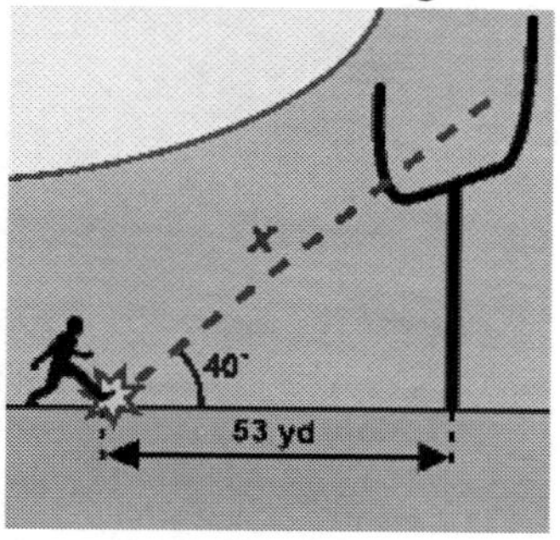

3. The roof of a particular house is 25 feet above the ground. For safety reasons, the angle that a ladder makes with the ground should be no greater than 70 degrees. What is the length of the shortest ladder that will reach the roof of the house safely?

Review questions: *(Answers to odd questions on page: 754)*

1. True or false: $\tan 40° = \dfrac{x}{200}$ can be used to find the height of the flagpole.

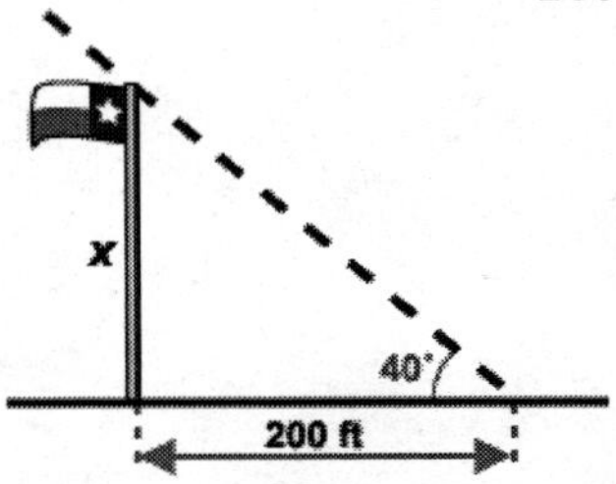

2. Find the height x of the indicated mountain.

3. Find the altitude of the hot air balloon.

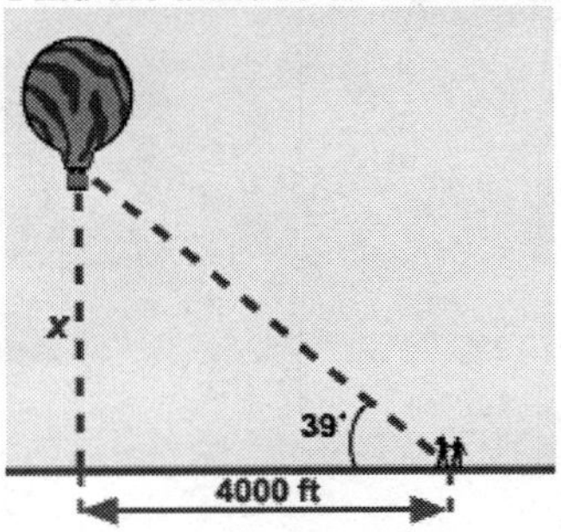

4. Find the distance from the lighthouse to the boat.

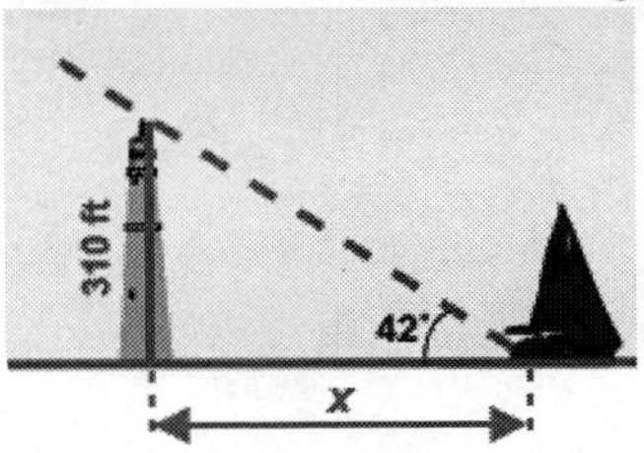

5. A man 1.5 miles away from a rocket launchpad observes a rocket launch. The man determines that the angle of elevation to the rocket is 23°, and then a few moments later he determines the angle of elevation to be 31°. How far did the rocket travel between the two observations? Assume that the rocket travels directly upwards.

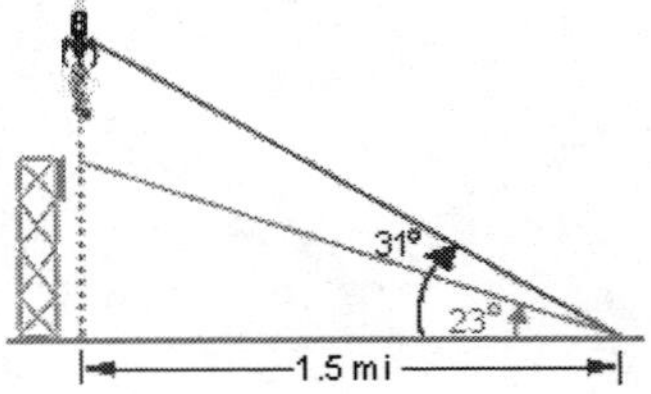

Evaluating Trigonometric Functions for an Angle in the Coordinate Plane

- If (x, y) is a point on the **terminal side** of an angle θ, then

  $\mathbf{sin}\theta = y/r$, $\mathbf{cos}\theta = x/r$, $\mathbf{tan}\theta = y/x$, $\mathbf{csc}\theta = r/y$, $\mathbf{sec}\theta = r/x$, and $\mathbf{cot}\theta = x/y$, where $r = \sqrt{x^2 + y^2}$.
- For angles in quadrant I, **A**ll trigonometric functions are positive.
  For angles in quadrant II, only **S**ine and its recipricocal function, cosecant, are positive.
  For angles in quadrant III, only **T**angent and its recipricocal function, cotangent, are positive.
  For angles in quadrant IV, only **C**osine and its recipricocal function, secant, are positive.

  You can remember this with the saying "**A**ll **S**tudents **T**ake **C**alculus."

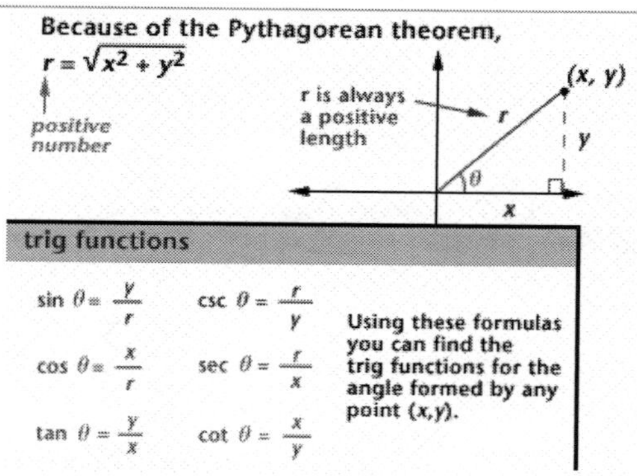

Thus far we have defined the **trigonometric functions** as ratios of sides of right triangles.

The trigonometric functions for an angle can also be defined using a point *(x, y)* on the **terminal side** of the angle.

Using these definitions, the trigonometric functions of any angle can be found.

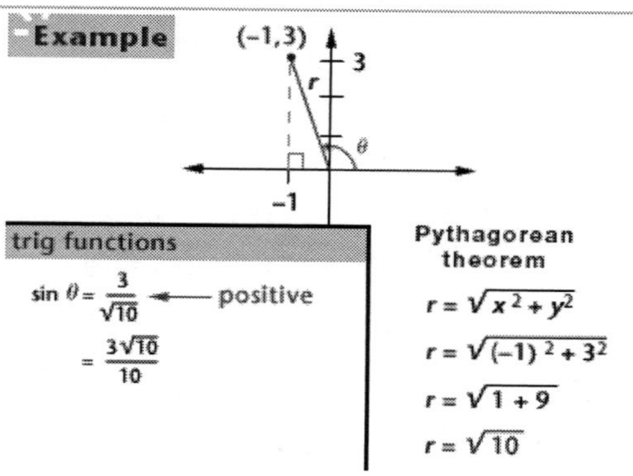

In this example, the terminal side of the angle θ goes through the point $(-1, 3)$. Notice that θ is not an acute angle.

First, find r using the **Pythagorean theorem**. Remember that r is always a positive length.

Then plug in $x = -1$, $y = 3$, and $r = \sqrt{10}$ into the formulas above to get the trig functions for θ.

"All Students Take Calculus"

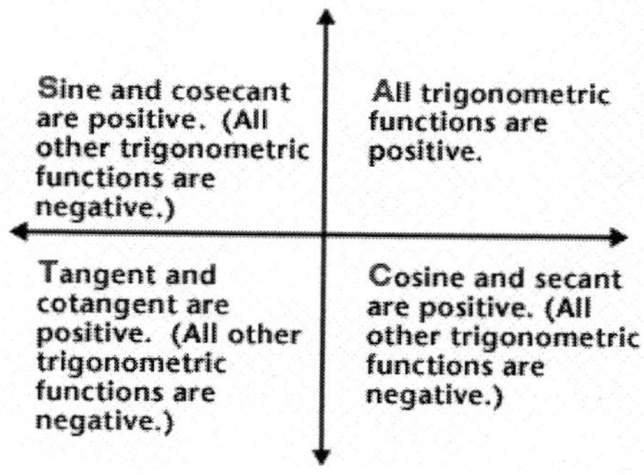

Figure out the signs of the trig functions for angles in each **quadrant**.

For example, for angles that lie in quadrant III, only the **tangent** and **cotangent** functions are positive.

REMEMBER: The saying "**A**ll **S**tudents **T**ake **C**alculus" tells which trig functions are positive in each quadrant.

Sample problems:

1. Which trig functions would be positive in the quadrant containing the point $(2, -4)$?
   Solution: Cosine and Secant
   Explanation: In Quadrant IV, x is positive. The ratios for cosine and secant use the values of x and r. Since r is always positive, cosine and secant are positive whenever x is.

2. Find $\cot\theta$ if θ is in the standard position on the coordinate plane and the point $(-4,-2)$ is on the terminal side of θ.
   Solution: 2

   Explanation: By definition, $\cot\theta$ is $\cot\theta = \frac{x}{y}$ and $x=-4$ and $y=-2$, so $\cot\theta = \frac{-4}{-2} = 2$.

3. Find $\csc\theta$ and $\cot\theta$ if θ is in the standard position on the coordinate plane and the point $(-2,-3)$ is on the terminal side of θ.

   Solution: $\csc\theta = -\frac{\sqrt{13}}{3}$; $\cot\theta = \frac{2}{3}$

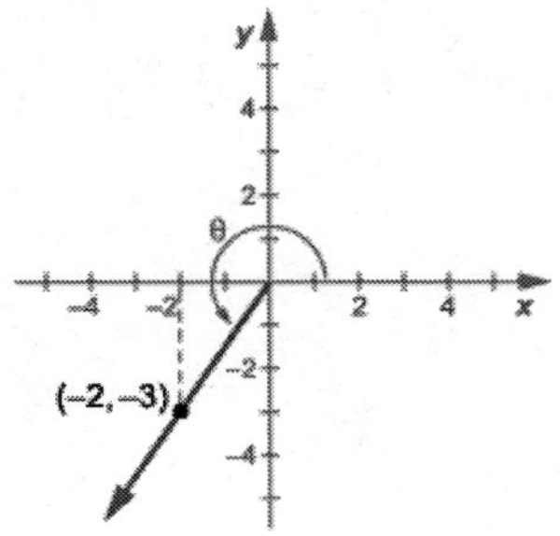

   Explanation: Use the basic definition $\csc\theta = \frac{r}{y}$. Use the Pythagorean theorem to find the value of the radius: $r = \sqrt{(-2)^2 + (-3)^2} = \sqrt{4+9} = \sqrt{13}$. Thus, $r = \sqrt{13}$ and $y=-3$, so $\csc\theta = \frac{\sqrt{13}}{-3}$. For cotangent, substitute the values of x and y into the basic definition: $\cot\theta = \frac{x}{y} = \frac{-2}{-3} = \frac{2}{3}$.

Practice problems: *(Answers on page: 754)*

1. True or false: The point $(3,-2)$ lies in a quadrant where $\csc\theta$ and $\tan\theta$ are both negative.
2. Find $\sin\theta$ if θ is in the standard position on the coordinate plane and the point (3,4) is on the terminal side of θ.
3. Find the values of $\sin\theta$ and $\cos\theta$ for the angle θ in the standard position on the coordinate plane with the point $(6,-3)$ on its terminal side.

Review questions: *(Answers to odd questions on page: 754)*

1. Find $\tan\theta$ if θ is in the standard position on the coordinate plane and the point (3, 4) is on the terminal side of θ.
2. In which quadrant(s) are the values of tangent and cotangent positive?
3. In what quadrant does an angle lie if the sine of the angle is negative and the cosine is positive?
4. What is the value of the tangent of the angle in the standard position on the coordinate axes whose terminal side passes through the point $(6,-3)$?
5. What is the value of $\sin\theta$ if θ is the angle formed by the positive x-axis and a line segment passing through the origin and the point $(-3, 4)$?

Evaluating Trigonometric Functions Using the Reference Angle

- The **reference angle** for an angle θ is the positive, **acute** angle made by the **terminal side** of θ and the x-axis.
- To find the value of a trig function for an angle θ using its reference angle:
  1. Find the value of the trig function for the reference angle.
  2. Change the sign appropriately depending on which **quadrant** θ is in.

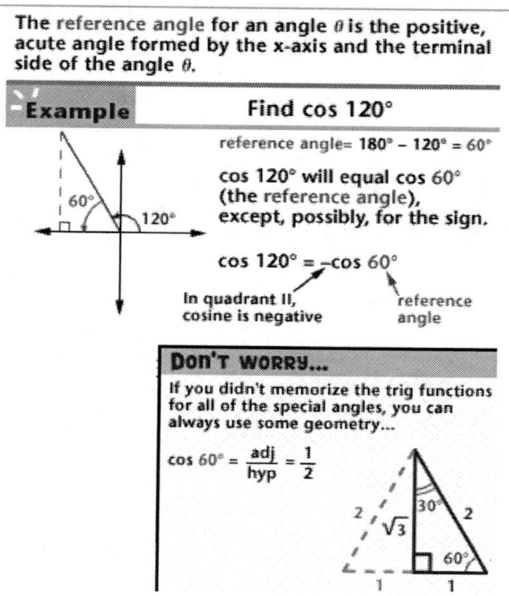

The notion of a **reference angle** is very useful for computing trigonometric functions.

What is the cosine of 120°? First, find the reference angle by subtracting 120° from 180°.

The cosine of 120° will equal the cosine of the reference angle (in this case, 60°) up to a difference in sign. Determine the sign using the fact that 120° lies in **quadrant II.**

REMEMBER: "**A**ll **S**tudents **T**ake **C**alculus."

If you don't have the value of cos 60° memorized, you can figure it out using a 30°-60°-90° right triangle. As you can see, cos 60° = 1/2.

Therefore, cos 120° = –cos 60° =–1/2.

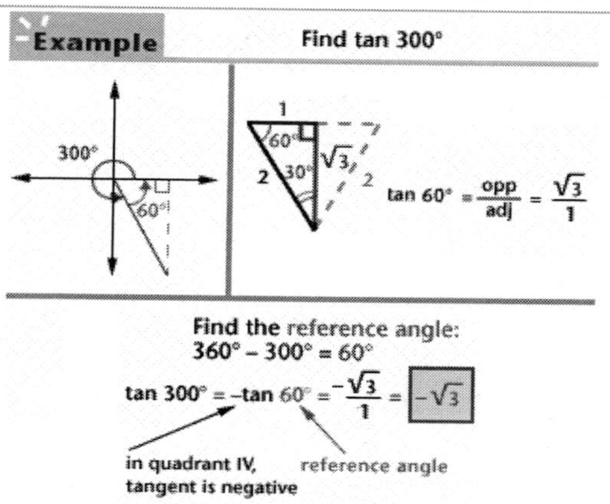

What is the tangent of 300°?

First find the reference angle for 300°. It is the **acute angle** made by the **terminal side** of 300° and the x-axis. The reference angle measures 60°.

Now find the value of tan 60°. If you don't have it memorized, use some right triangle geometry.

The value of tan 300° is equal to either tan 60° or –tan 60°. Since tangent is negative in quadrant IV, tan 300° = –tan 60° = $-\sqrt{3}$.

Sample problems:

1. What is the reference angle for the angle $\theta = \dfrac{9\pi}{7}$?

   Solution: $\dfrac{2\pi}{7}$

   Explanation: The reference angle for $\dfrac{9\pi}{7}$ is the acute angle made by the terminal side of θ and the x-axis. This angle is $\dfrac{9\pi}{7} - \pi = \dfrac{2\pi}{7}$.

2. Calculate: $\sin 210°$

   Solution: $-\dfrac{1}{2}$

   Explanation: The angle measuring 210° lies in quadrant III, where sine is negative. Subtract 180° to find the angle formed by the terminal ray of the original angle and the x-axis: $\sin 210° = -\sin 30° = -\left(\dfrac{1}{2}\right) = -\dfrac{1}{2}$

3. Calculate: $\sin\left(-\frac{\pi}{3}\right)$

<u>Solution</u>: $-\frac{\sqrt{3}}{2}$

<u>Explanation</u>: The reference angle for $-\frac{\pi}{3}$ is $\frac{\pi}{3}$. The sine function is negative in the fourth quadrant. Thus, $\sin\left(-\frac{\pi}{3}\right) = -\sin\frac{\pi}{3} = -\frac{\sqrt{3}}{2}$.

Practice problems: *(Answers on page: 754)*

1. Find the reference angle for $\alpha = 890°$.
2. Calculate: $\cos(-60°)$
3. True or false: $\tan\frac{7\pi}{8} = -\tan\frac{\pi}{8}$

Review questions: *(Answers to odd questions on page: 754)*

1. Determine the reference angle for $\theta = 210°$.
2. Find the reference angle for 460°.
3. Find the reference angle for $-50°$.
4. Find $\tan 225°$.
5. Evaluate $\cos\left(-\frac{7\pi}{3}\right)$ without the use of a calculator.

Finding the Value of Trigonometric Functions Given Information about the Values of Other Trigonometric Functions

- It is possible to find the value of trigonometric functions for an angle θ given only information about other trigonometric functions for θ. Here is one method of solving these problems:
  1. Determine which quadrant θ lies in.
  2. Sketch a picture of θ and its right triangle in the *x-y* plane.
  3. Use the **Pythagorean theorem** to find the length of the unknown side of the triangle.
  4. Use the triangle to compute the values of the trigonometric functions.

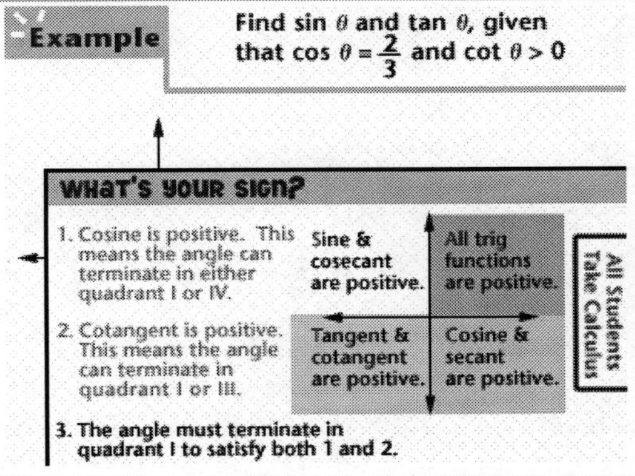

Find the value of $\sin\theta$ and $\tan\theta$ if $\cos\theta = 2/3$ and $\cot\theta > 0$.

The first step is to determine which quadrant θ lies in. Use the fact that both $\cos\theta$ and $\cot\theta$ are positive.

In order for $\cos\theta$ and $\cot\theta$ to both be positive, θ must lie in quadrant I.

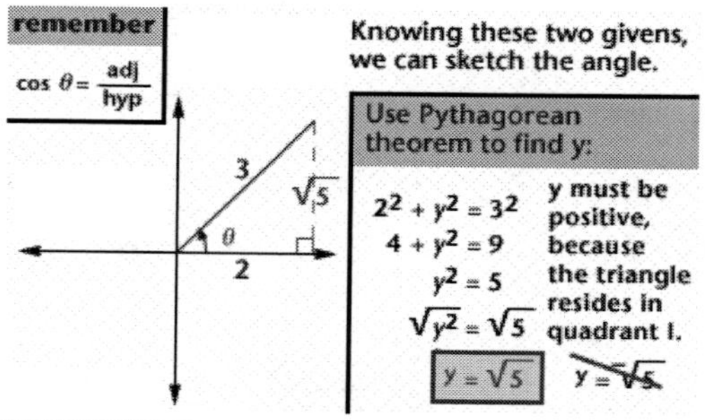	Sketch a picture of the angle θ in the first quadrant. Since $\cos\theta = 2/3$, you can label the adjacent leg with a 2 and the hypotenuse with a 3. Use the **Pythagorean theorem** to find the length of the unknown side y. Notice that y must be positive since θ is in the first quadrant.
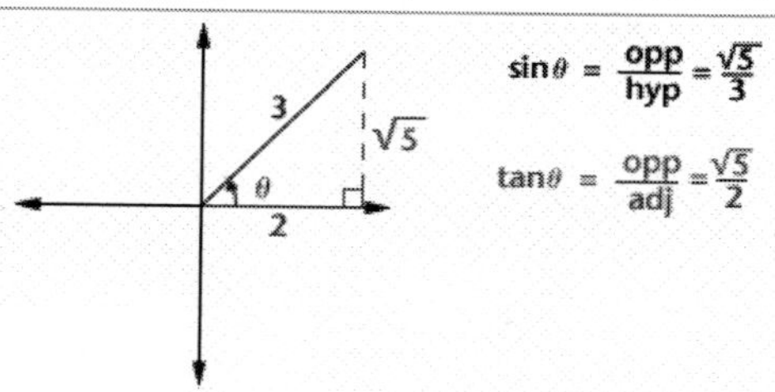	Once all three sides of the triangle are labeled, compute the values of $\sin\theta$ and $\tan\theta$.

Sample problems:

1. Find $\cos\theta$ and $\tan\theta$ given that $\sin\theta = \frac{2}{5}$ and $\tan\theta$ is greater than zero.

   Solution: $\cos\theta = \frac{\sqrt{21}}{5}$; $\tan\theta = \frac{2\sqrt{21}}{21}$

   Explanation: θ must be in quadrant I since $\sin\theta > 0$ and $\tan\theta > 0$.
   Sketch a right triangle and label the opposite side 2 and the hypotenuse 5.
   Use the Pythagorean theorem to find the unknown side, x:

   $x = \sqrt{5^2 - 2^2} = \sqrt{21}$, so $\cos\theta = \frac{\sqrt{21}}{5}$; $\tan\theta = \frac{2}{\sqrt{21}}$ or $\frac{2\sqrt{21}}{21}$.

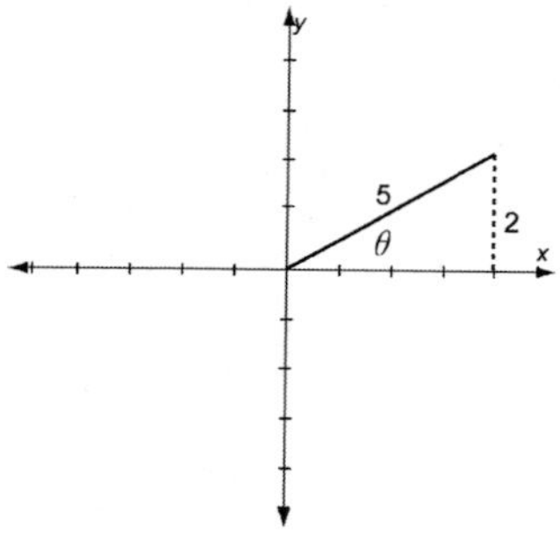

2. If you know $\sin\theta = \frac{4}{5}$, can you find $\cos\theta$?

   Solution: No

   Explanation: Using the Pythagorean theorem, we find that $x = 3$ or -3, so both $\cos\theta = \frac{3}{5}$ or $\cos\theta = -\frac{3}{5}$ are possible, but you do not have enough information to determine which is correct.

3. Suppose that $\sin\theta < 0$ and $\cos\theta = a$, where $0 < a < 1$. Find the value of $\csc\theta$ in terms of a.

   Solution: $-\frac{1}{\sqrt{1-a^2}}$

Explanation: First, determine what quadrant θ is in using the facts that $\sin\theta < 0$ and $\cos\theta = a > 0$. Since the sine function is negative in Quadrants III and IV, and the cosine function is positive in Quadrants I and IV, θ must lie in Quadrant IV. Sketch a picture of θ and its reference triangle. Use the fact that $\cos\theta = \frac{\text{adjacent}}{\text{hypotenuse}} = a = \frac{a}{1}$ to label the sides of the triangle. Then use the Pythagorean theorem to find the length of the unknown side y in terms of a: $a^2 + y^2 = 1$; $y^2 = 1 - a^2$; $y = -\sqrt{1-a^2}$. Notice that y is negative because θ lies below the x-axis.

Compute $\csc\theta$: $\csc\theta = \frac{\text{hypotenuse}}{\text{opposite}} = \frac{1}{-\sqrt{1-a^2}} = -\frac{1}{\sqrt{1-a^2}}$.

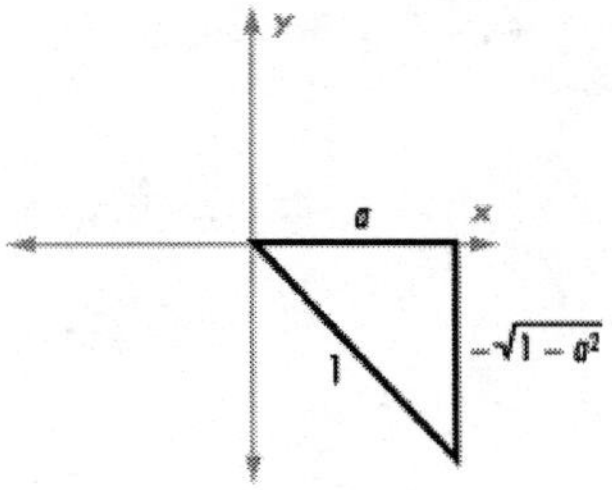

Practice problems: *(Answers on page: 754)*

1. Find $\sin\theta$ and $\cos\theta$ given that $\tan\theta = -\frac{12}{5}$ and $\sin\theta < 0$.
2. Find $\sin\theta$ and $\tan\theta$, given that $\cos\theta = -\frac{3}{5}$ and $\sin\theta > 0$.
3. Find $\csc\theta$, given that $\cos\theta = -\frac{\sqrt{2}}{2}$ and $\cot\theta = 1$.

Review questions: *(Answers to odd questions on page: 755)*

1. In which quadrant(s) are the values of tangent and cotangent positive?
2. In what quadrant does an angle lie if the sine of the angle is negative and the cosine is positive?
3. Find $\tan\theta$ given that $\sin\theta = \frac{2}{3}$ and $\cos\theta = \frac{\sqrt{5}}{3}$.
4. Find $\cos\theta$, given that $\tan\theta = \frac{1}{2}$ and $\cos\theta > 0$.
5. Find $\tan\theta$, given that $\cos\theta = -\frac{2}{\sqrt{5}}$ and $\sin\theta < 0$.

Trigonometric Functions of Important Angles

- Memorize the trigonometric functions for important angles: 0, π/6, π/4, π/3, and π/2 (or 0°, 30°, 45°, 60°, and 90°).

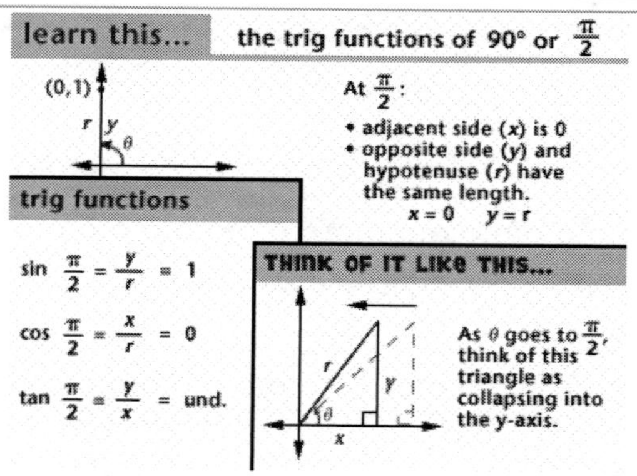

There are some trigonometric values for important angles that should be memorized. One such angle is 90°, or $\pi/2$.

The angle $\pi/2$ lies directly on the y-axis.

Calculate the values of the trig functions using the point (0, 1) on its **terminal side**.

NOTICE: The tangent function for $\pi/2$ is undefined!

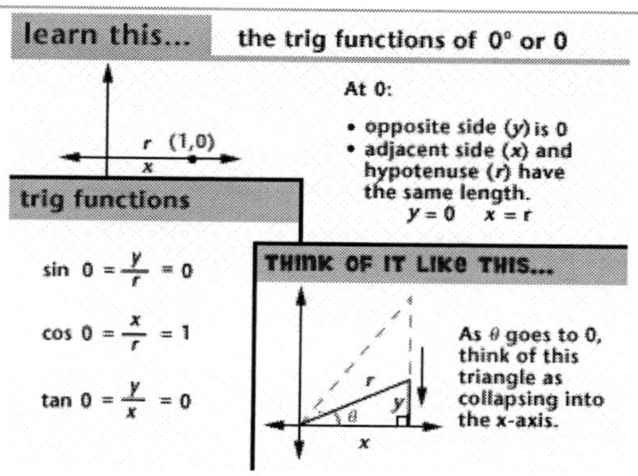

Calculate the trigonometric functions for 0 in the same way.

The angle 0 also has a degenerate right triangle, but like before, calculate its trigonometric functions using the point (1, 0) on its terminal side.

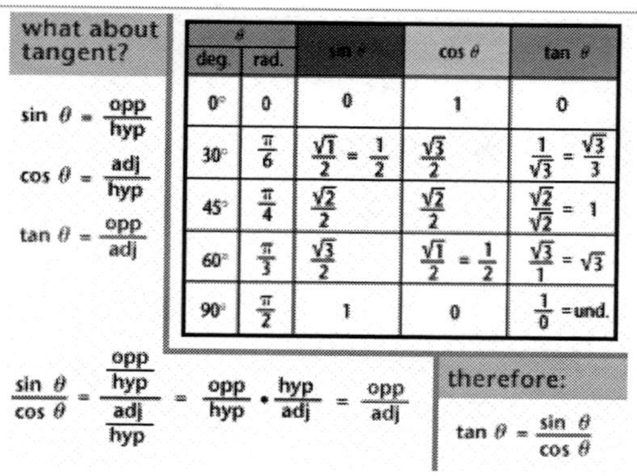

This is a table with the important angles between 0 and $\pi/2$ (or 90°) and their trigonometric functions. These angles and values are worth memorizing-- you'll see them a lot in the future!

By dividing fractions, you can check that the tangent function is equal to the sine function divided by the cosine function.

Sample problems:

1. Find the value of $\sin\frac{5\pi}{6}$. (Do not use a calculator.)

   Solution: 1/2

   Explanation: The reference angle for $\frac{5\pi}{6}$ is $\frac{\pi}{6}$. Since $\sin\frac{\pi}{6} = \frac{1}{2}$ and since $\frac{5\pi}{6}$ is in the second quadrant where the sine function is positive, $\sin\frac{5\pi}{6} = \sin\frac{\pi}{6} = \frac{1}{2}$.

2. Evaluate: $\sin\left(\frac{\pi}{6}\right) + \cos\left(\frac{\pi}{3}\right) + \tan\left(\frac{\pi}{4}\right)$. (Do not use a calculator.)

   Solution: 2

   Explanation: Recall the values of the trigonometric functions for the angles $\frac{\pi}{6}$, $\frac{\pi}{4}$, and $\frac{\pi}{3}$: $\sin\frac{\pi}{6} = \frac{1}{2}$; $\cos\frac{\pi}{3} = \frac{1}{2}$; $\tan\frac{\pi}{4} = 1$. Therefore,
   $\sin\frac{\pi}{6} + \cos\frac{\pi}{3} + \tan\frac{\pi}{4} = \left(\frac{1}{2}\right) + \left(\frac{1}{2}\right) + (1) = \frac{1}{2} + \frac{1}{2} + 1 = 2.$

3. Find the value of $\cos 45°$. (Do not use a calculator.)

Solution: $\frac{\sqrt{2}}{2}$

Explanation: The point (1,1) lies on the terminal side of the angle measuring 45°.
Let $x = 1$ and $y = 1$. Use the Pythagorean theorem to find r: $1^2 + 1^2 = r^2$; $r^2 = 2$;
$r = \sqrt{2}$. Therefore, $\cos 45° = \frac{x}{r} = \frac{1}{\sqrt{2}} = \frac{\sqrt{2}}{2}$.

Practice problems: *(Answers on page: 755)*

1. What is the value of $\tan 45°$? (Do not use a calculator.)
2. What is the exact value of $\tan\left(-\frac{4\pi}{3}\right)$? (Do not use a calculator.)
3. What is the value of $\sin\frac{\pi}{2}$? (Do not use a calculator.)

Review questions: *(Answers to odd questions on page: 755)*

1. What is the value of $\cos\frac{\pi}{2}$? (Do not use a calculator.)
2. What is the value of $\sin\frac{\pi}{4}$? (Do not use a calculator.)
3. What is the value of $\sin\frac{\pi}{3}$? (Do not use a calculator.)
4. Evaluate $\tan\left(-\frac{13\pi}{4}\right)$. (Do not use a calculator.)
5. What is the value of $\tan 30°$? (Do not use a calculator.)

An Introduction to the Graphs of Sine and Cosine Functions

- The graph of the sine function oscillates and repeats without end. The graph of the cosine function is the same as that of the sine function shifted to the left by $\pi/2$ units.
- The **amplitude** of an oscillating function is half the difference between the maximum and minimum values of the function.
- The **period** of an oscillating function is the length of the interval over which the function goes through one full cycle before it repeats.

Graphing $y = \sin x$

independent variable

$y = \sin x$		
x (radians)	x (degrees)	$\sin x$
0	0°	0
$\pi/6$	30°	1/2
$\pi/4$	45°	$\sqrt{2}/2$
$\pi/3$	60°	$\sqrt{3}/2$
$\pi/2$	90°	1
π	180°	0
$3\pi/2$	270°	-1
2π	360°	0

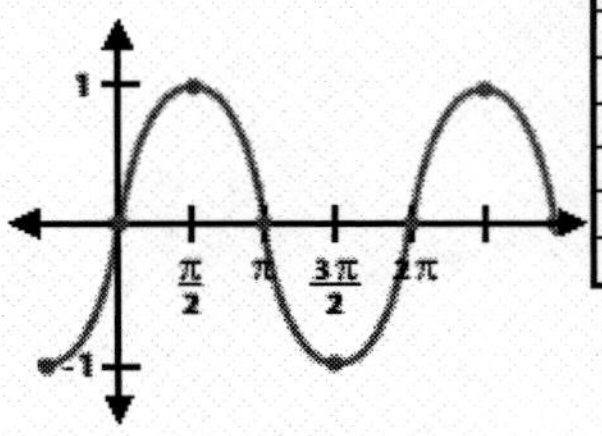

Graph the function $y = \sin x$ by making a table of values and plotting the points.

The graph of the sine function is pictured to the left. It repeats itself without stopping.

NOTE: On the graph, x is given in **radians**, not degrees.

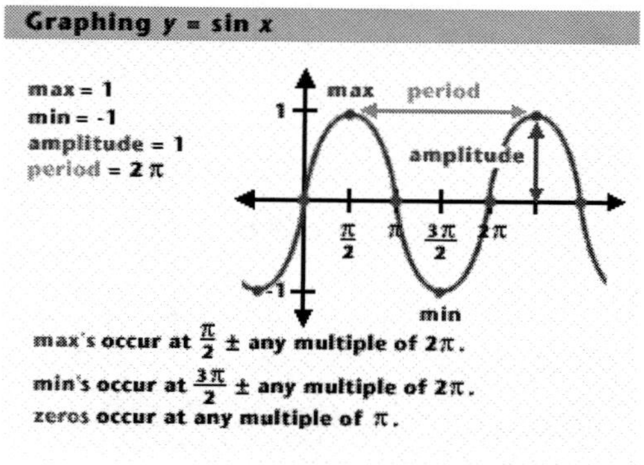

There are terms that describe the graphs of oscillating functions like
$y = \sin x$:

1. The **amplitude** is equal to half the difference between the maximum height and the minimum height. For $y = \sin x$, the amplitude is $(1/2)[1 - (-1)] = 1$. You can think of the amplitude as the half of vertical distance that the function covers.
2. The **period** is the length of the largest interval the function covers without repeating. The sine function repeats every 2π radians, so the period of sine is 2π.

Since the sine function repeats every 2π radians, its **maxima**, **minima**, and **zeros** also repeat themselves regularly.

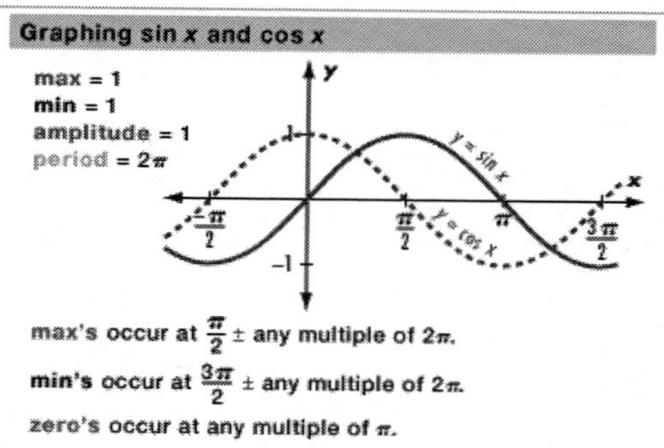

Look at the graph of the cosine function $y = \cos x$.

The amplitude, period, and maximum and minimum values of the cosine function are all the same as the corresponding values for the sine function.

Notice, though, that the locations of the maxima, minima, and zeros are different.

Sample problems:

1. What is the equation for this graph?

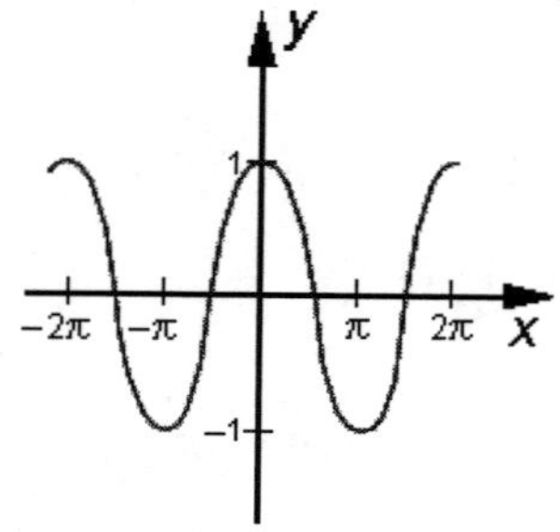

Solution: $y = \cos x$
Explanation: The graph has a maximum value of 1 at $x = 0$, minimum values of -1 at $x = -\pi$ and $x = \pi$, zeros at odd multiples of $\pi / 2$, and period of 2π. Thus, the equation is $y = \cos x$.

2. What is the amplitude of this curve?

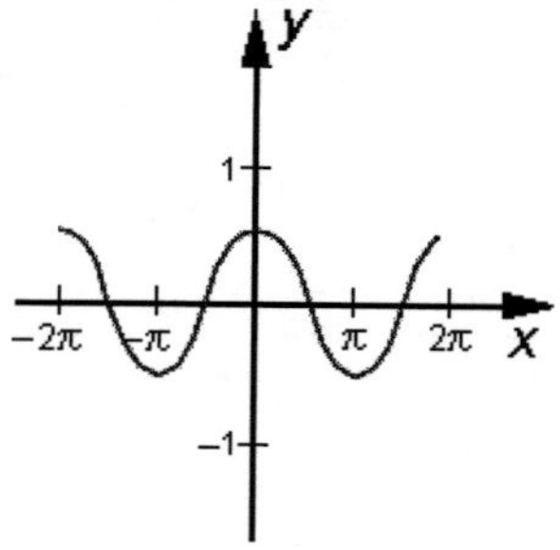

Solution: $\frac{1}{2}$

Explanation: Subtract the minimum value from the maximum value and divide by 2: $\frac{[\frac{1}{2}-(-\frac{1}{2})]}{2}=\frac{1}{2}$.

3. What is the period of this curve?

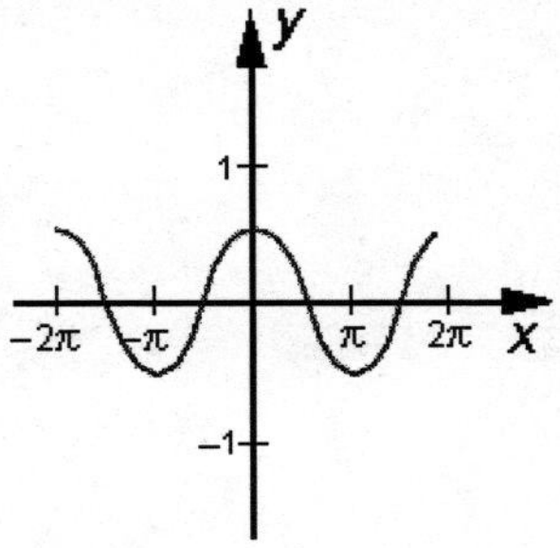

Solution: 2π

Explanation: The period is the length of the largest interval the function covers without repeating. In this graph, the non-repeating interval is from -2π to 0 or from 0 to 2π. Therefore, the period is 2π.

Practice problems: *(Answers on page: 755)*

1. What is the equation for this graph?

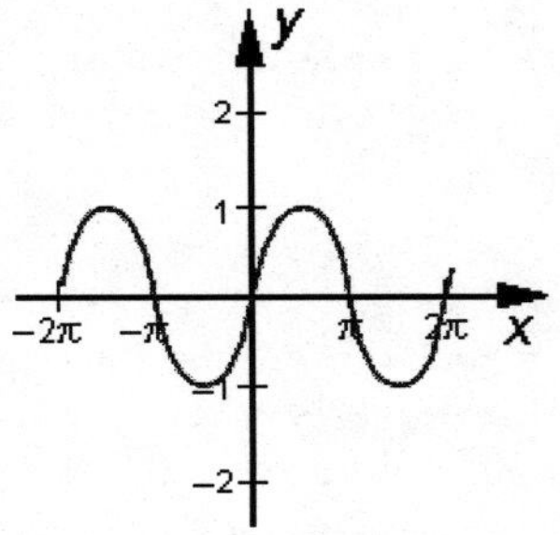

2. What is the amplitude of this sine curve?

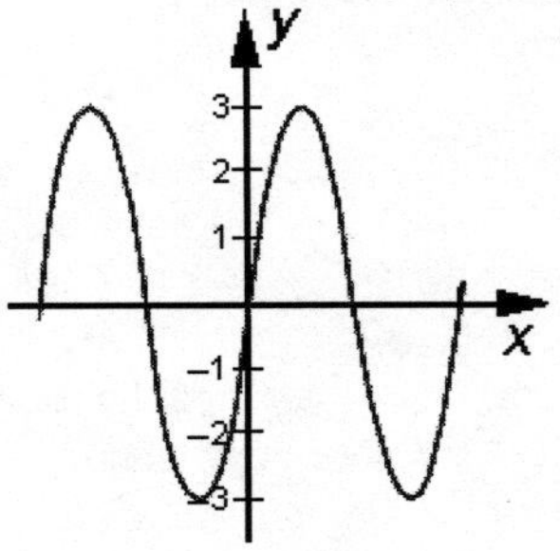

3. What is the period of this curve?

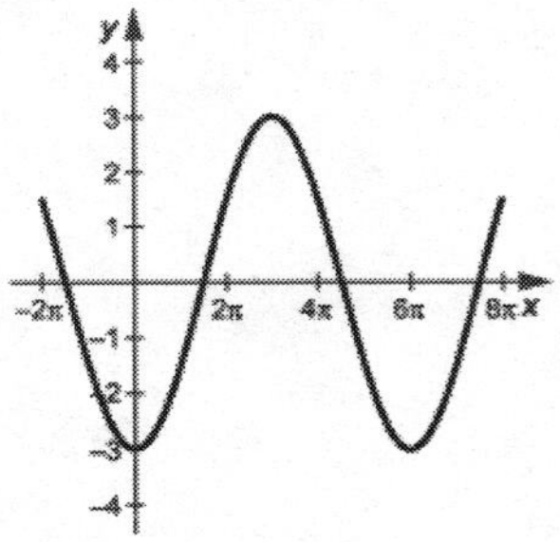

Review questions: *(Answers to odd questions on page: 755)*

1. True or false: The amplitude is the height of the function from the lowest point to its highest point.
2. True or false: The period is the distance in the x-direction that covers exactly one repetition of the function.
3. True or false: The amplitudes of $y = \sin x$ and of $y = \cos x$ are the same.
4. True or false: $y = \cos x$ has a zero at 2π.
5. True or false: The maximum value of $y = \cos x$ occurs at 2π.

Graphing Sine or Cosine Functions with Different Coefficients

- The coefficients in the functions $y = a\sin(bx)$ or $y = a\cos(bx)$ determine the **amplitude** and **period** of the functions.
- The amplitude of the function $y = a\sin x$ or $y = a\cos x$ is equal to $|a|$.
- The period of the function $y = \sin(bx)$ or $y = \cos(bx)$ is equal to $2\pi/|b|$.

Graphing $y = 2\sin x$

This coefficient changes the amplitude.

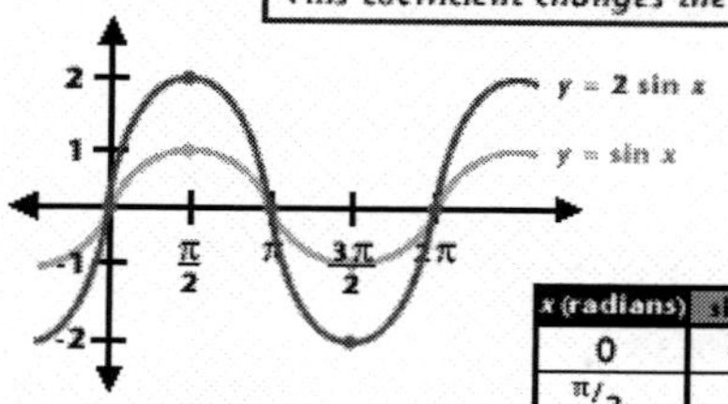

x (radians)	sin x	2 sin x
0	0	0
π/2	1	2
π	0	0
3π/2	-1	-2
2π	0	0

To graph the function $y = 2\sin x$, stretch the graph of $y = \sin x$ vertically by a factor of 2. The **amplitude** of the new graph is 2. A coefficient larger than 1 stretches the graph out vertically (as in this case), and a coefficient smaller than 1 compresses the graph vertically.

In general, the graph of the function $y = a\sin x$ (or $y = a\cos x$) has an amplitude of the **absolute value** of a. Note also that a coefficient that is negative will flip the graph over the x-axis.

Example Graphing $y = \cos\left(\frac{1}{4}\right)x$

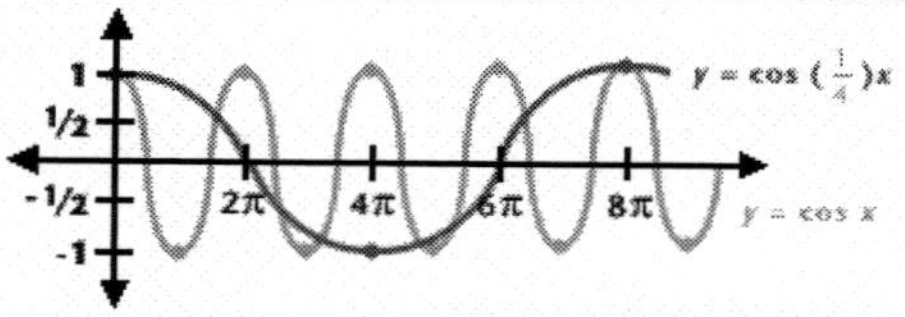

① Find the period: $\frac{2\pi}{|1/4|} = \frac{2\pi}{1/4} \cdot \frac{4}{4} = 8\pi$

② Amplitude = 1

absolute value of the coefficient of the trig function

x (radians)	cos x	cos (¼)x
0	1	1
2π	1	0
4π	1	-1
6π	1	0
8π	1	1

What if the coefficient being changed is inside the **argument** of the function, as in the function $y = \cos(x/4)$?

The coefficient inside the argument changes the **period** of the function. Since the coefficient is smaller than one, it lengthens the period of the graph. If it had been greater than one, it would have shortened the period.

In general, the period of the function $y = \sin(bx)$ or $y = \cos(bx)$ is $2\pi/|b|$.

Example Graphing $y = -2\cos\frac{1}{2}x$

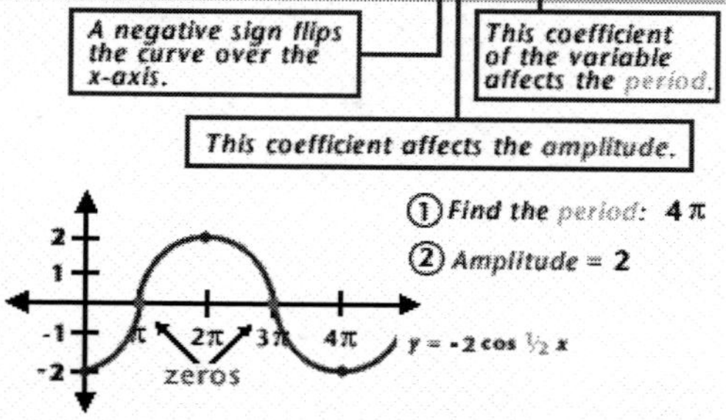

Consider the equation $y = -2\cos 1/2x$. First, graph the regular cosine function $y = \cos x$, then consider the coefficients. The negative sign flips the graph over the x-axis. The coefficient of 2 in front stretches the graph vertically so that the amplitude is 2. Finally, the coefficient of 1/2 inside the argument gives the graph a period of 4π instead of 2π. The result is the graph to the left.

Sample problems:

1. What is the amplitude of the function $y = \frac{3}{2}\cos 3x$?

   Solution: $\frac{3}{2}$

   Explanation: Since the amplitude is equal to the absolute value of the coefficient in front of the trigonometric function, amplitude $= \left|\frac{3}{2}\right| = \frac{3}{2}$.

2. Identify the period and amplitude of $y = 3\cos 2x$.

   Solution: The period is π, and the amplitude is 3

   Explanation: The period of a function of the form $y = a\cos(bx)$ is 2π divided by the absolute value of the coefficient b. The period of the given function is therefore $\frac{2\pi}{|2|} = \pi$. The amplitude of a function of the form $y = a\cos(bx)$ is the absolute value of the coefficient a. The amplitude of the given function is therefore $|3| = 3$.

3. True or false: The equation $y = 3\sin 4x$ is graphed below.

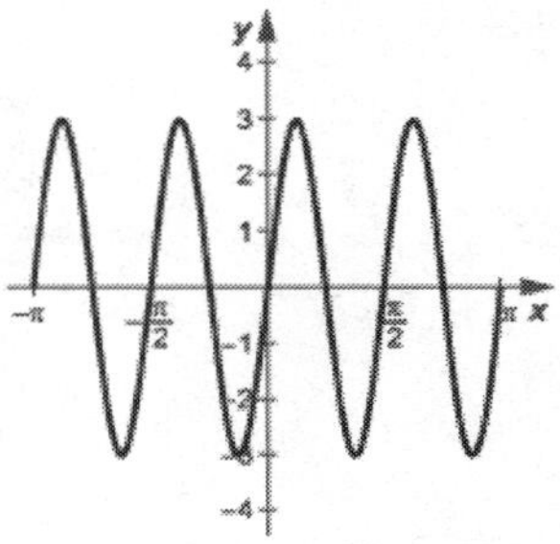

   Solution: True

   Explanation: Compared to the graph of $y = \sin x$, the amplitude of this graph has been increased by a factor of 3. The graph has not been flipped, so the coefficient must be 3 and not -3. Compared to the graph of $y = \sin x$, the period of this graph has been decreased. The period is now $\frac{\pi}{2}$ instead of 2π. Thus $\frac{2\pi}{b} = \frac{\pi}{2}$, so $b = 4$. Therefore, the coefficient of the argument is 4.

Practice problems: *(Answers on page: 755)*

1. What is the amplitude of the function $y = -4\sin\frac{1}{2}x$?
2. Identify the period and amplitude of $y = -2\sin 5x$.
3. True or false: The equation $y = 3\cos 2x$ is graphed below.

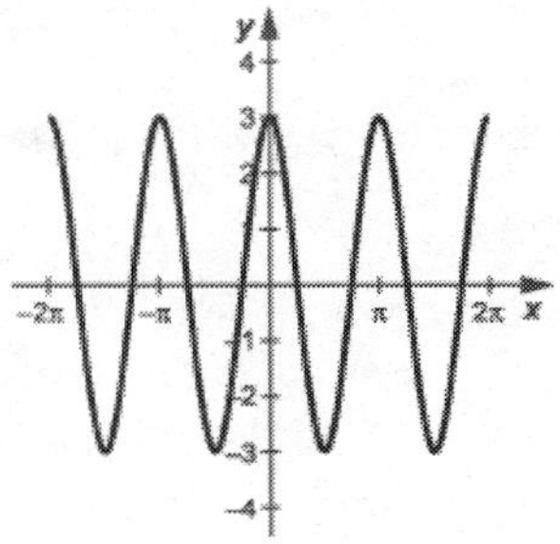

Review questions: *(Answers to odd questions on page: 755)*

1. What is the period of the function $y = -4\sin\frac{1}{2}x$?
2. What is the period of the function $y = \frac{3}{2}\cos 3x$?
3. What is the amplitude of the function $y = 2\cos x$?
4. Identify the period and amplitude of $y = -\frac{1}{2}\cos\frac{x}{3}$.
5. True or false: $y = -\sin 2x$ is the equation for the following graph.

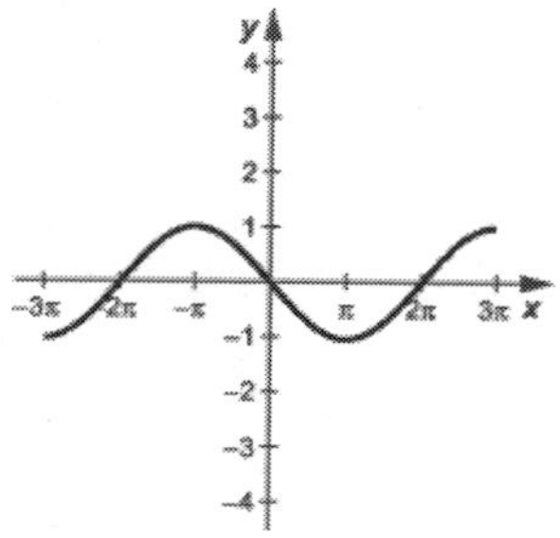

Finding Maximum and Minimum Values and Zeros of Sine and Cosine

- When graphing trigonometric functions, there are points on the graph where important things happen:
  - **Maxima** occur at the highest points of the graph and repeat each **period**.
  - **Minima** occur at the lowest points of the graph and repeat each period.
  - **Zeros** occur where the function crosses the x-axis.
- Adding or subtracting a constant to a trigonometric function produces a vertical shift, moving the graph up or down.

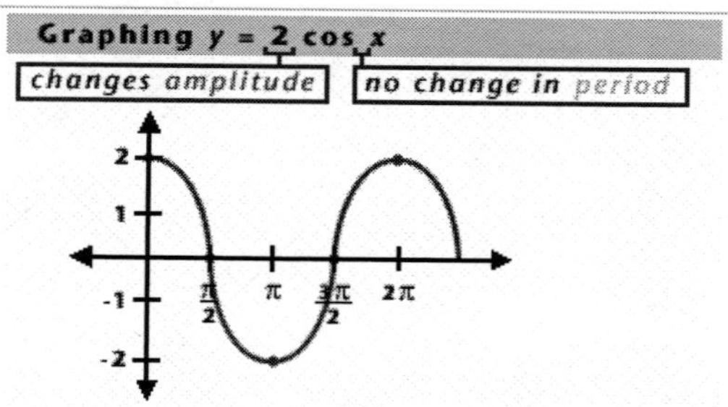

One way to find the important points of a trigonometric function is to graph it.

Consider the function $y = 2\cos x$. The coefficients of the trigonometric function change the appearance of the graph, but the function still looks fundamentally the same.

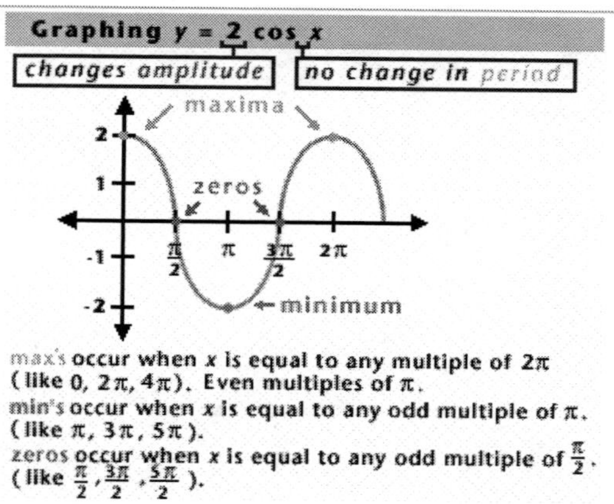

Three important points you might be asked to find for a trig function are the **maxima**, **minima**, and **zeros**.

- maxima (singular: **maximum**) occur wherever the graph reaches the highest point.
- minima (singular: **minimum**) occur wherever the graph drops to the lowest point.
- Zeros occur where the graph crosses the x-axis (or the y-value equals zero)

Maxima and minima occur once per period for sine and cosine. Per period, zeros can occur twice, once, or not at all, depending on the function and its vertical shift and amplitude.

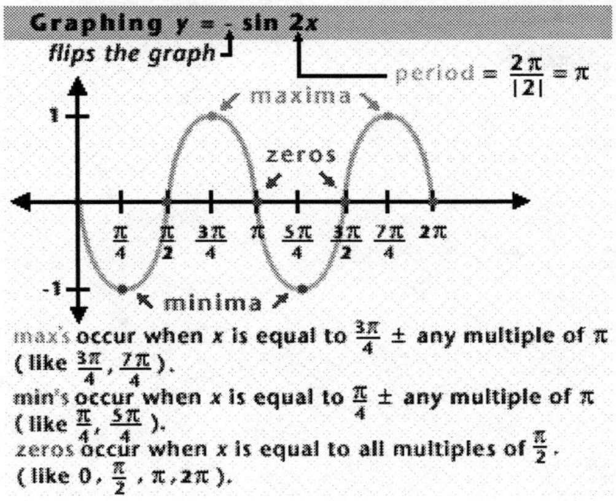

Notice that for this example there are two maxima and two minima in the 2π interval. By reducing the period, the number of times the curve oscillates increases. As such, the curve "tops out" and "bottoms out" more often.

By adding multiples of the period to a maximum or minimum point or to all of the zeros in a single period of the trig function, you can describe all of the maxima, minima, and zeros for a trig function.

Sample problems:

1. Find the maximum for $y = -\frac{3}{2}\cos\left(\frac{2\pi}{3}x\right)$.

   Solution: $\frac{3}{2}$

   Explanation: The amplitude $= \frac{3}{2}$, which corresponds to the highest point on the graph and is the maximum.

2. Find the the maximum for $y = 3\sin 2x + 3$.
   Solution: 6
   Explanation: The vertical shift of this function is 3 so the graph moves up 3 units. Since the maximum value is equal to the shift of the sine function plus the amplitude, the result is $3 + 3 = 6$. Notice that the argument does not play any role in finding the maximum value.

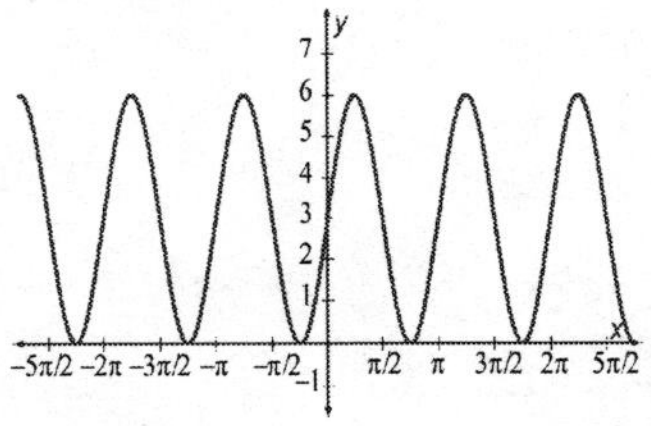

3. A group of scientists conducting a statistical survey found that traffic in a local mall over the course of a day could be estimated by the equation: $P(t) = -3500\cos\left(\frac{\pi}{5}t\right) + 3500$ where P is the population and t is the time after the mall opens, in hours. After the mall opens, how much time passes before the number of people in the mall reaches its maximum?
   Solution: 5 hours
   Explanation: Start by finding the maximum number of people, $P(t)$. The maxima is found by adding the vertical shift, 3500, to the amplitude; $\max = 3500 + |-3500| = 3500 + 3500 = 7000$.

   Substitute into the formula and solve for t: $7000 = -3500\cos\left(\frac{\pi}{5}t\right) + 3500$;

   $3500 = -3500\cos\left(\frac{\pi}{5}t\right); -1 = \cos\left(\frac{\pi}{5}t\right)$. Determine when $\cos\left(\frac{\pi}{5}t\right)$ equals -1. The value of $\cos x$ is -1 when x is an odd multiple of π. Since you want the time after the mall opens, use the smallest positive value, π, and replace x with $\frac{\pi}{5}t$. $x = \pi$; $\frac{\pi}{5}t = \pi$; $t = 5$. The number of people in the mall is maximized when $t = 5$.

Practice problems: *(Answers on page: 755)*

1. Estimate the maximum value of this sine wave.

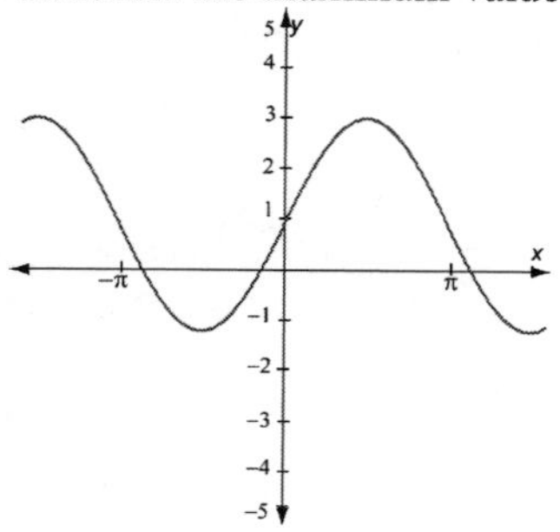

2. Find the minimum value of $y = -\frac{1}{2}\sin 3x - \frac{3}{2}$.

3. In a particular wildlife refuge, the number of white spotted owls varies according to the following formula where P is the population and t is the time in months since January 1, 1991: $P(t) = 15\sin\left(\frac{\pi}{6}t\right) + 20$. What is the maximum population of white spotted owls in the wildlife refuge?

Review questions: *(Answers to odd questions on page: 755)*

1. What is the maximum value of the function $y = 4\cos 3\pi x$?
2. Find the minimum for $y = 3\cos 2x - 5$.
3. Find the maximum for $y = 3\cos 2x$.
4. What is the minimum value of the function $y = 3\cos 2\pi x + 8$?
5. What is the maximum value of the function $y = 5\sin\frac{2x}{5}$?

Solving Word Problems Involving Sine or Cosine Functions

- One application of the sine or cosine functions can be seen in wave motion, such as the movement of water and sound. Wave motion can be modeled by these functions. As such, they appear often in word problems.

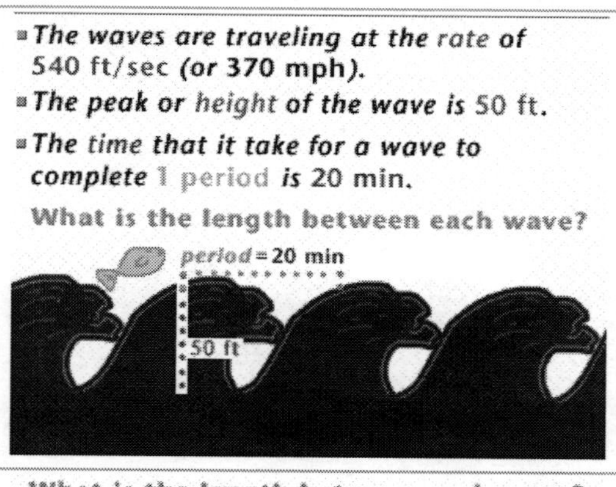	Given that a tsunami wave is moving at a rate of 540 feet per second and that the peak of the wave is 50 feet, and given that the time it takes the wave to move one **period** is 20 minutes, find the distance between each wave.
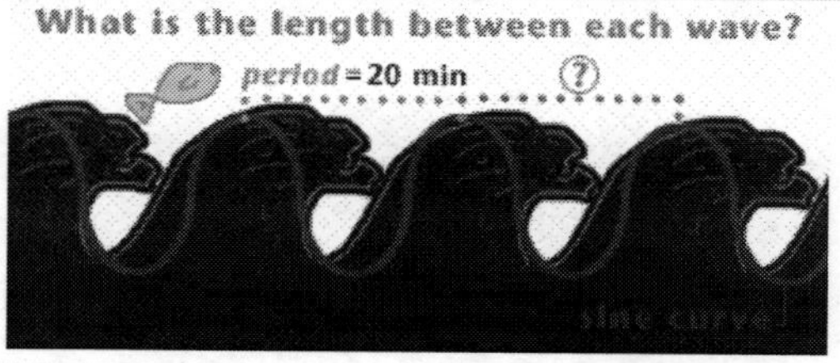	Tsunami waves, like many waves in nature, are **sinusoidal**. This means that they behave like a sine wave. If you know the speed of the wave and the time it takes the wave to travel one period, you can find the distance between the waves.

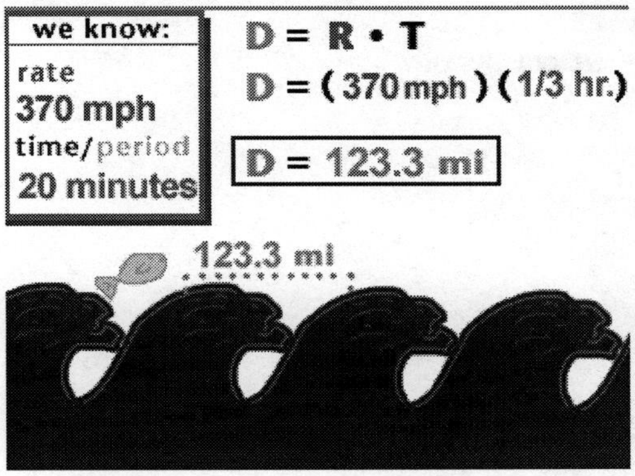

Since rate is equal to the distance divided by time, then distance must be equal to the rate times time. Use 370 mph then convert 20 minutes to 1/3 hour. Plug in the values and simplify.

The waves are 123.3 miles apart!

Notice how we did not need to know the **amplitude** of the sine wave.

Be very careful with your units when solving word problems. Many mistakes made in this type of problem are caused by not canceling units correctly.

Sample problems:

1. The waves of a tsunami have peaks 50 m high and are 200 km apart. They are traveling at a rate of 400 km/hr. How much time does it take to complete one period?
   Solution: 30 min
   Explanation: Substitute the known values into $d = rt$ and solve for t:

$$200 \text{ km} = \frac{400 \text{ km}}{1 \text{ hr}} t; \; t = \left(\frac{(200 \cancel{\text{km}}) 1 \text{ hr}}{400 \cancel{\text{km}}} \right) = 0.5 \text{ hr} = 30 \text{ minutes.}$$

2. A wave in a pond with an amplitude of 3 feet and a period of 6 seconds has an equation at a fixed position of the form $y = A \sin Bt$. How high is the wave from trough to crest?
   Solution: 6 feet
   Explanation: The height from the trough to crest is equal to twice the amplitude. The height is 3(2) = 6 feet.

3. The temperature of a particular patient in a hospital is modeled by the following function where t is the time in hours: $T(t) = 3\sin\frac{\pi t}{14} + 98$. What is the maximum temperature that the patient can attain?
   Solution: 101°F
   Explanation: The sine function ranges from -1 to 1. Multiply that range by the amplitude, which is 3, to obtain the range $[-3,3]$. Finally, add 98 to obtain [95,101]. Thus the maximum temperature of the patient will be 101°F.

Practice problems: *(Answers on page: 755)*

1. A surfer is riding a wave with an amplitude of 20 feet and a period of 40 feet. If the wave completes a period in 10 seconds, what is the speed of the surfer?
2. The waves of a tsunami are traveling at 400 ft/sec. The waves are 40 ft high, and their period is 15 min. What is the length of each wave in miles?
3. The temperature of a particular patient in a hospital is modeled by the following function where t is the time in hours: $T(t) = 4\sin\frac{\pi t}{7} + 98$. How long will it take for the patient's temperature to reach its first maximum?

Review questions: *(Answers to odd questions on page: 755)*

1. The waves of a tsunami are 50 ft high and 528 miles apart. It takes a wave 20 minutes to complete one period. How fast are the waves traveling?

2. The waves of a tsunami are 50 ft high, 100 miles apart and traveling at a rate of 1000 miles per hour. How long does it take for the waves to complete one period?

3. The waves of a tsunami have peaks 60 m high and 200 km apart. At what speed are the waves traveling?

4. The waves of a tsunami are traveling at 0.1 mi/sec. It takes a wave 20 min to complete one period. What is the length between wave peaks?

5. The temperature of a particular patient in a hospital ranges between 94°F and 100°F as modeled by the following function where t is the time in hours: $T(t) = 3\sin\frac{\pi t}{14} + C$. What is the value of C for this function?

Graphing Sine and Cosine Functions with Phase Shifts

- A **phase shift** is a horizontal **translation** of a trig function.
  - Phase shifts occur when adding or subtracting from the x-term in the trig function.
  - A phase shift will move the graph of the function to the left or the right, depending on whether the constant is added or subtracted.
  - Adding or subtracting an entire **period** does not change the appearance of the graph.

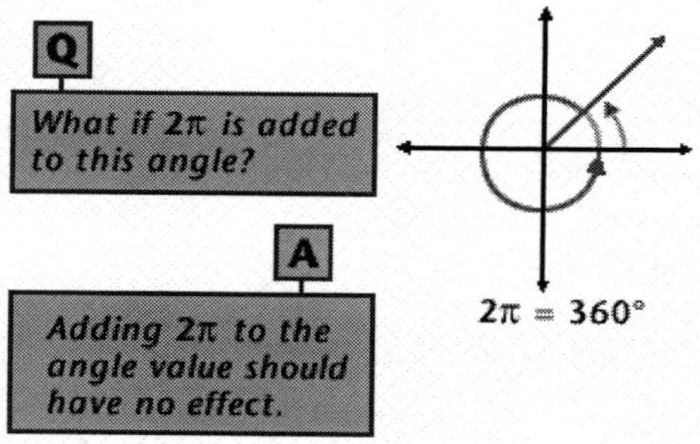

Recall that adding 2π to an angle results in a **coterminal angle**. So, adding 2π to an angle has no effect on the value of trig functions for that angle.

Adding 360° has the same effect as adding 2π.

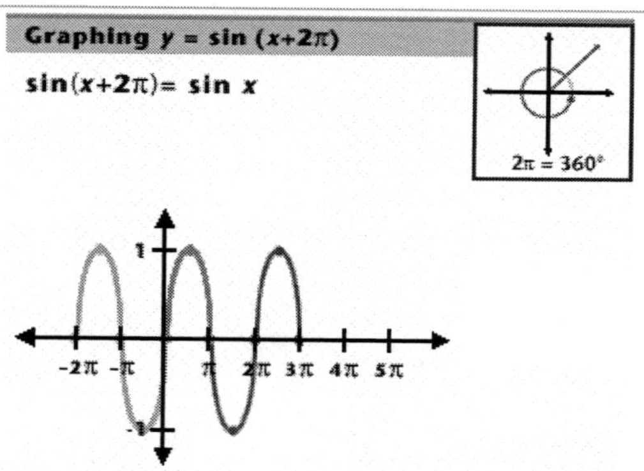

A **phase shift** is a horizontal movement of a trig function. Phase shifts occur any time you add or subtract from the x-term in a trigonometric function.

Since adding or subtracting 2π from an angle doesn't affect the sine of the angle, and since adding any multiple of 2π is the same as adding 2π several times, adding any multiple of 2π to the angle in the **argument** of the sine function doesn't change the appearance of the graph. The graph shifts on top of itself.

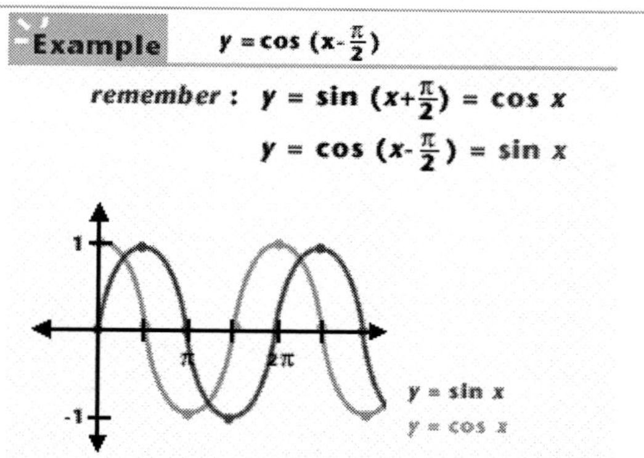

Consider the equation $y = \cos(x - \pi/2)$. Subtracting from the x-term causes a translation in the graph, moving the function to the right.

The new graph should look familiar. Moving the cosine curve to the right $\pi/2$ units, it becomes the sine curve.

By the same logic, moving the sine curve to the left $\pi/2$ units, it becomes the cosine curve.

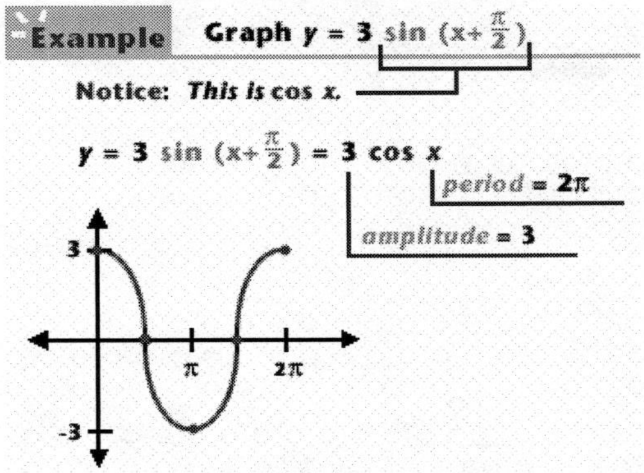

Knowing the patterns of phase shifts can allow for substitution to take place—making the graphing process of the trig functions much easier.

Consider the example illustrated here:
Graph $y = 3\sin(x + \pi/2)$. Notice that adding $\pi/2$ to the sine curve produces the cosine curve. $\sin(x + \pi/2) = \cos x$

Therefore, substitute $\cos x$ for $\sin(x + \pi/2)$ and graph.

Be careful not to make the common **shifting function mistake**. Many people think that if you add to the x-term then the graph moves in the positive direction, which is false.

Remember, if you add to x, go west (or left).

If you add to y, go high.

Sample problems:

1. What is the phase shift for the function $y = \frac{2}{3}\cos\left(x + \frac{\pi}{4}\right)$?

Solution: $\frac{\pi}{4}$ to the left

Explanation: Adding to x moves the graph left. In this case, $\frac{\pi}{4}$ is the quantity added to x.

2. True or false: The function $y = \frac{5}{2}\sin 2\left(x + \frac{\pi}{2}\right) + 1$ is graphed below.

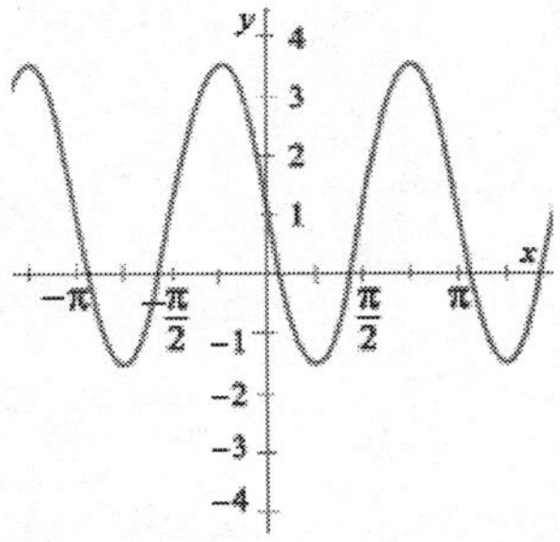

Solution: True

Explanation: The amplitude is $\frac{5}{2}$, the period is π, and the function is shifted upward by 1 unit. There is also a phase shift $\frac{\pi}{2}$ units to the left.

3. True or false: The graph of $y = \cos\left(x + \frac{\pi}{2}\right)$ is the graph of $y = \cos x$ shifted $\frac{\pi}{2}$ units to the right.
Solution: False
Explanation: Adding a constant to the argument of the cosine function shifts the curve west, or to the left, by that many units.

Practice problems: *(Answers on page: 755)*

1. What is the phase shift of the function $y = \frac{\pi}{2}\sin(x-3)$?
2. True or false: The graph of $y = \sin(x + 4\pi)$ is the same as the graph of $y = \sin x$.
3. True or false: The graph of $y = \cos(x - \frac{\pi}{3})$ is the graph of $y = \cos x$ shifted $\frac{\pi}{3}$ units to the right.

Review questions: *(Answers to odd questions on page: 755)*

1. True or false: The function $y = 2\sin\left(x + \frac{\pi}{2}\right)$ is graphed below.

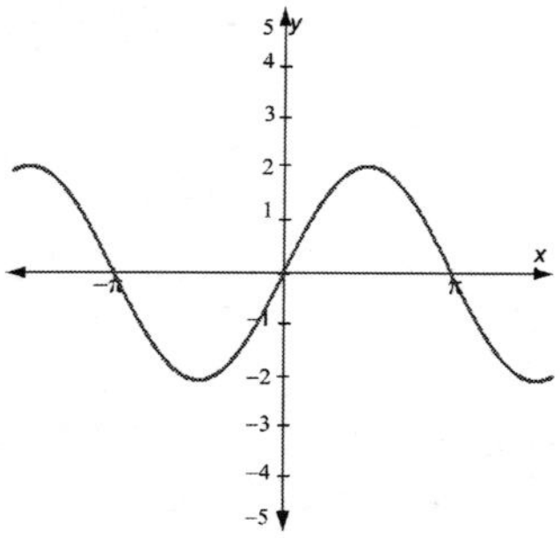

2. True or false: The graphs of $y = -2\cos(x - 4\pi)$ and $y = -2\cos x$ are identical.
3. What is the phase shift of the function $y = -\frac{1}{2}\cos\left(x + \frac{\pi}{2}\right)$?
4. What is the phase shift for the function $y = \frac{3}{4}\sin\left(x - \frac{\pi}{6}\right)$?
5. What is the phase shift for the function $y = \frac{\pi}{3}\cos 3(x+4)$?

Fancy Graphing: Changes in Period, Amplitude, Vertical Shift, and Phase Shift

- **Review**: Use information about the **period**, **amplitude**, **vertical shift**, and **phase shift** to accurately graph very involved sine and cosine functions.
  - Graph the function with just the change in period and amplitude (and any flips) first.
  - Translate the graph appropriately according to the phase shift.
  - Translate the graph appropriately according to the vertical shift.

fancy graphing	Determine the **amplitude**, **period**, **vertical shift**, and the **phase shift** to graph trigonometric functions.

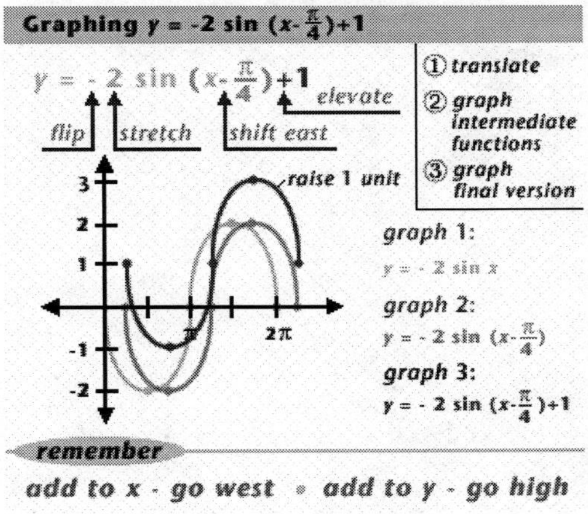

When asked to graph a function with more than one coefficient change , its helpful to draw several intermediate graphs to help keep the information straight.

Remember which constants affect which aspects of the graph:

- Multiplying the trig function by a constant stretches the graph vertically, changing the amplitude.
- Negative signs in front flip the graph upside down. This does not change the amplitude.
- Adding or subtracting from the *x*-term creates a phase shift, moving the graph left or right.
- Adding or subtracting from the entire expression creates a vertical shift.

Graph the function, taking into account any changes in period and amplitude. Then draw another graph taking into account the phase shift. Finally, take the vertical shift into account.

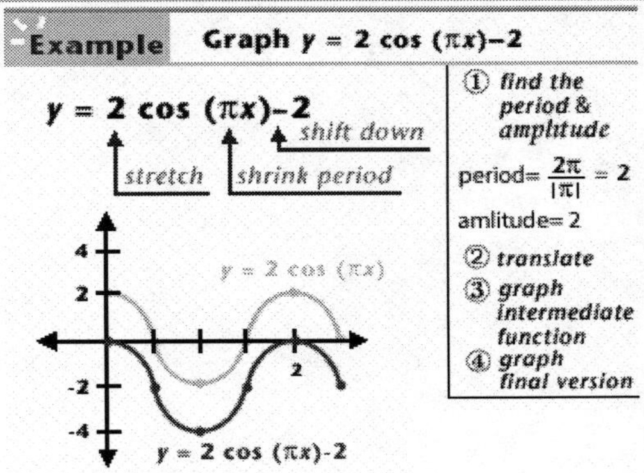

How would you go about graphing this equation: $y = 2\cos(\pi x) - 2$?

Start by finding the period and amplitude. Notice that the period is equal to 2 radians, *not* 2π radians.

After graphing the function with just the period and amplitude change, translate the graph by the vertical shift (which is –2).

Sample problems:

1. Determine the period of the function $y = \frac{3}{\pi}\sin\left(\frac{2\pi}{3}x - 1\right) + \frac{3}{4}$.

   Solution: 3

   Explanation: To find the period, divide 2π by the absolute value of the coefficient of the argument: $2\pi \div \left|\frac{2\pi}{3}\right| = 2\pi\left(\frac{3}{2\pi}\right) = 3$.

2. Find the amplitude, period, phase shift and vertical shift of $y = -4\sin(3x - \pi) + 1$.

   Solution: amplitude = 4, period = $\frac{2\pi}{3}$, phase shift is $\frac{\pi}{3}$ to the right, vertical shift is up one.

   Explanation: The absolute value of the constant multiplying the trigonometric function is the amplitude, so amplitude = $|-4| = 4$. To find the period, find b by factoring the coefficient of x out of the argument; $(3x - \pi) = 3\left(x - \frac{\pi}{3}\right)$, so $b = 3$ and the period is $\frac{2\pi}{|b|} = \frac{2\pi}{3}$. Subtracting a constant from the argument means the functions shifts east or to the right. The constant being added to the entire expression is the vertical shift, so the graph moves up 1 unit.

3. Give the equation of the graph of $y = 2\cos 3x + 1$ after it has been stretched vertically by a factor of 2, flipped upside down, and stretched horizontally by a factor of 3.
   Solution: $y = -4\cos x + 1$
   Explanation: To stretch the graph vertically by a factor of 2, multiply the cosine expression by 2. To flip the graph upside down, multiply the cosine expression by -1. To stretch the graph horizontally by a factor of 3, divide the argument of the cosine function by 3.

Practice problems: *(Answers on page: 755)*

1. Determine the phase shift of the function $y = \frac{2}{3}\cos\left(x + \frac{\pi}{6}\right) - \frac{3}{2}$.
2. Give the equation of the graph obtained by shifting $y = 4\cos x$ up 2 units and to the right 3 units.
3. Give the equation of the graph obtained by shifting $y = \sin x$ down 1 unit, to the right π units, and by increasing its amplitude to 3.

Review questions: *(Answers to odd questions on page: 755)*

1. What is the vertical translation of $y = -3\cos 5x - 4$?
2. What is the phase shift of the equation $y = 3\sin(2x - 5) - 3$?
3. True or false: $y = \cos(2x - \pi) - 2$ has a phase shift of $\frac{\pi}{2}$ units to the right and a vertical shift of 2 units down.
4. What is the phase shift of $y = 5\sin(\pi + 2x)$?
5. True or false: $y = 2\sin\pi(x - 1) + 2$ is graphed below.

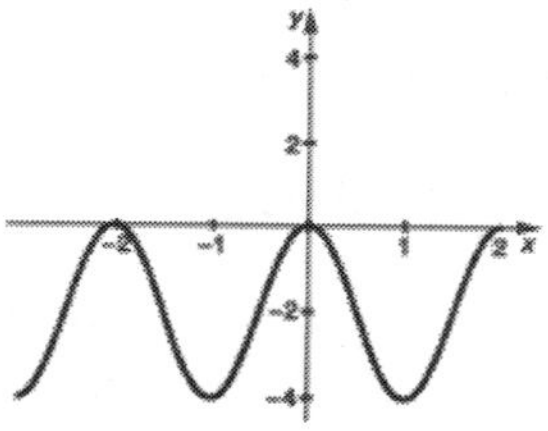

Graphing the Tangent, Secant, Cosecant, and Cotangent Functions

- The **tangent**, **secant**, **cosecant**, and **cotangent** functions are all defined in terms of the **sine** and **cosine** functions. Knowing how to graph sine and cosine empowers you to graph the other four.

Graphing tangent

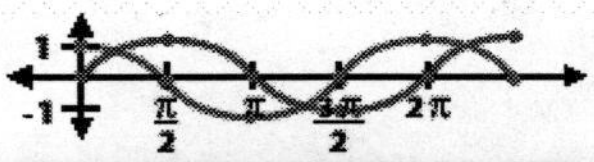

x (radians)	sin x	cos x	tan x
0	0	1	0
$\pi/4$	$\sqrt{2}/2$	$\sqrt{2}/2$	1
$\pi/2$	1	0	**undefined**
$3\pi/4$	$\sqrt{2}/2$	$-\sqrt{2}/2$	-1
π	0	-1	0
$3\pi/2$	-1	0	**undefined**
2π	0	1	0

$\tan x = \frac{\sin x}{\cos x}$

Tangent has a vertical asymptote here.

Another vertical asymptote.

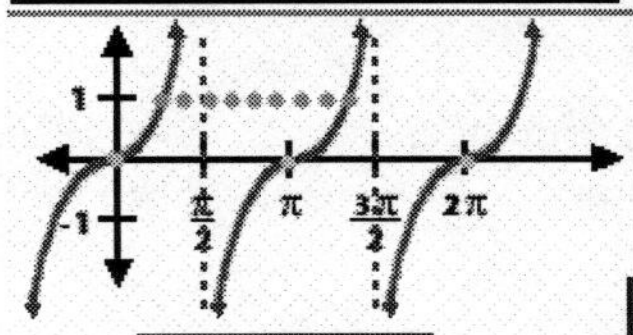

y = tan x

$\tan x = \frac{\sin x}{\cos x}$

***Asymptotes** are at the odd multiples of $\frac{\pi}{2}$.*

Period = π.

Zeros occur at multiples of π.

Note:

To find the period of tangent or cotangent use $\frac{\pi}{|b|}$.

***Don't** use the same formula that you use to find the period for sine and cosine.*

The tangent function is equal to the **sine** function divided by the **cosine** function. Start by making a table of values. For any given x-value (in the first column), the value of sine and cosine (in the second and third columns) are known. Divide sine by cosine. This is the value of the tangent function.

For example, if $x = 0$, then $\sin x = 0$, $\cos x = 1$, and $\tan x = 0/1$ or 0.

If the value of the tangent is undefined, that means there is a **vertical asymptote** at that point.

There are asymptotes at every odd multiple of $\pi/2$. Therefore, the tangent function is undefined at these points.

Notice that tangent completes a **period** in π radians instead of 2π radians like sine and cosine. Finding the period of tangent requires the formula $\pi/|b|$.

The **zeros** of the tangent function occur at the multiples of π.

Graphing secant

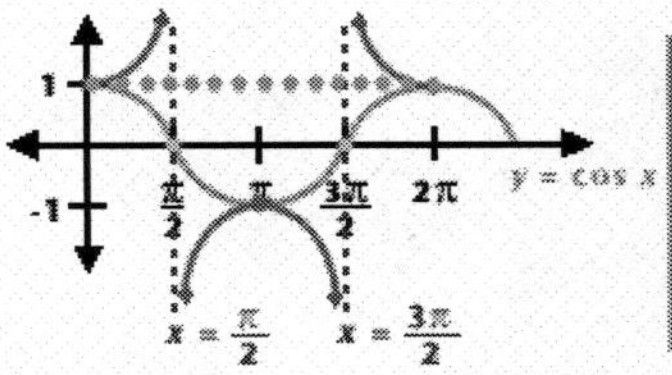

***to graph** y = sec x*

remember

$\sec x = \frac{1}{\cos x}$

- *Secant has asymptotes where cosine equals zero.*
- *Period = 2π.*

$\frac{1}{\text{very small number}} = \text{very large number}$

example: $\frac{1}{\frac{1}{1{,}000}} = 1{,}000$

The **secant** function is defined to be the reciprocal of the cosine function. So, take the values of cosine and put them under 1.

Because secant is defined as the reciprocal of cosine, secant will be undefined wherever cosine is equal to zero. Wherever the cosine is really small, the secant will be really big. Wherever the cosine is one, the secant will be one.

Secant has no zeros unless it is affected by a **vertical shift**. The period is equal to the period of cosine. Secant has asymptotes wherever cosine has zeros.

Graphing cosecant

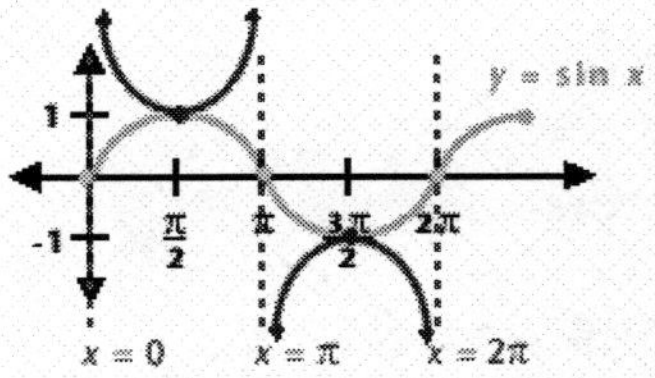

***to graph** y = csc x*

remember

$\csc x = \frac{1}{\sin x}$

Cosecant has asymptotes at zeros of sine.

Notice:

Cosecant graph is identical to secant, but shifted over.
(Just like the sine and cosine relationship)

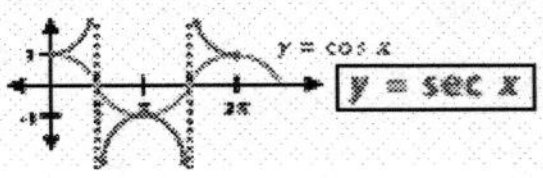

The **cosecant** function is the reciprocal of the sine function. To plot some points take the values of sine and put them under 1.

Just like secant, cosecant is defined to be the reciprocal of a trig function (in this case, the sine function). Wherever sine is really small, the cosecant will be really big. Wherever sine is 1, the cosecant will be 1.

Just like secant, cosecant has no zeros unless it is affected by a vertical shift. The period of cosecant is equal to the period of sine. Cosecant has asymptotes where sine has zeros.

Also, just like the sine and cosine relationship, the secant and cosecant are identical, except that one is shifted over slightly.

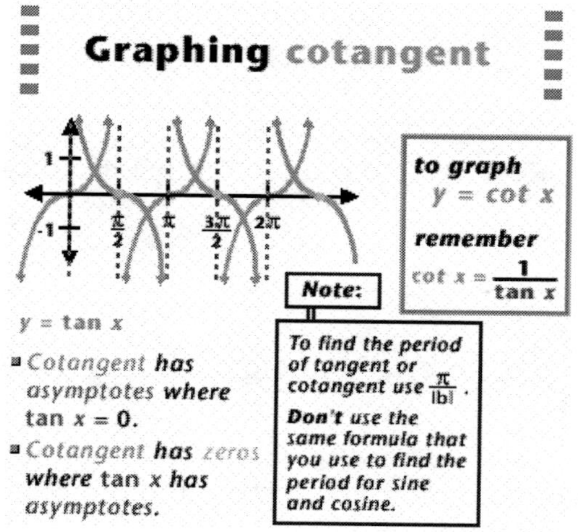

The **cotangent** function is the reciprocal of the tangent function.
Wherever the tangent function equals 1, the reciprocal equals 1 as well.

Wherever the tangent function equals zero, the cotangent is undefined and has an asymptote.

Wherever the tangent function is undefined, the cotangent function equals zero.

Just like the tangent curve, cotangent has a period of π.

Be very careful when finding the period of tangent and cotangent —do not use the wrong formula. They get their own formula since their periods are different.

Sample problems:

1. What is the period of $y = \cot x$?
   Solution: π
   Explanation: To determine the period of a tangent or cotangent function, use the formula $\frac{\pi}{|b|}$: $\frac{\pi}{|1|} = \pi$. Thus, the period is π.

2. Where are the vertical asymptotes of the graph of $y = \cot x$?
   Solution: $x = k\pi$ (multiples of π)
   Explanation: Because $\cot x$ is the reciprocal of $\tan x$, its asymptotes occur at values of x for which $\tan x = 0$. These are the same values that make $\sin x = 0$. They are given by $x = k\pi$.

3. True or false: The function $y = -\cot x$ is graphed below.

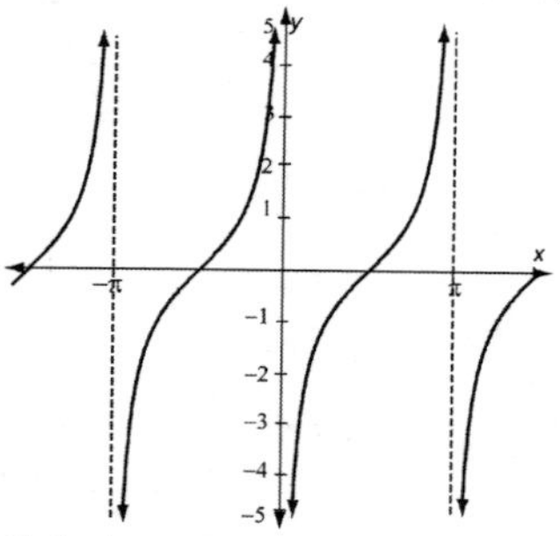

   Solution: True
   Explanation: First graph the function $y = -\tan x$. Wherever $y = -\tan x$ has a zero, $y = -\cot x$ will have a vertical asymptote and wherever $y = -\tan x$ has a vertical asymptote, $y = -\cot x$ will have a zero.

Practice problems: *(Answers on page: 755)*

1. What is the period of $y = \tan 2x$?
2. Where are the zeros of $y = \tan(x - \pi)$?

3. True or false: The function $y = -\sec x$ is graphed below?

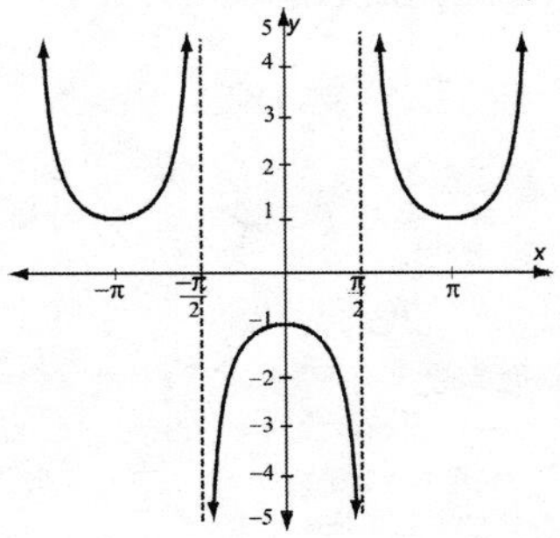

Review questions: *(Answers to odd questions on page: 755)*

1. What is the period of $y = \tan x$?
2. Where are the zeros of $y = \sec x$?
3. Where are the vertical asymptotes of $y = \csc x$?
4. True or false: The function $y = \sec 2x$ has zeros at $x = \frac{\pi}{4}$ and $x = \frac{3\pi}{4}$.
5. True or false: The function $y = -\tan x$ is graphed below.

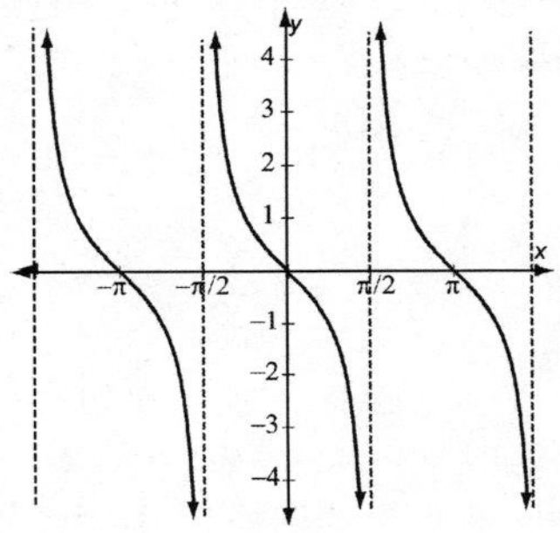

Fancy Graphing: Tangent, Secant, Cosecant, and Cotangent

- Graph **tangent**, **secant**, **cosecant**, and **cotangent** step by step, changing the graph to match the coefficients.
  - First graph the normal version of the function (with the proper period).
  - Alter this graph according to the other coefficients. This step might stretch or compress the graph and/or move it vertically or horizontally.

Easy 2-step process for graphing trig functions: 1) Graph the regular version. 2) Alter this graph according to the other coefficients.	When asked to graph more involved trig functions, graph them bit by bit, figuring out how the coefficients affect the graph.

$y = \frac{1}{2}\tan x$ 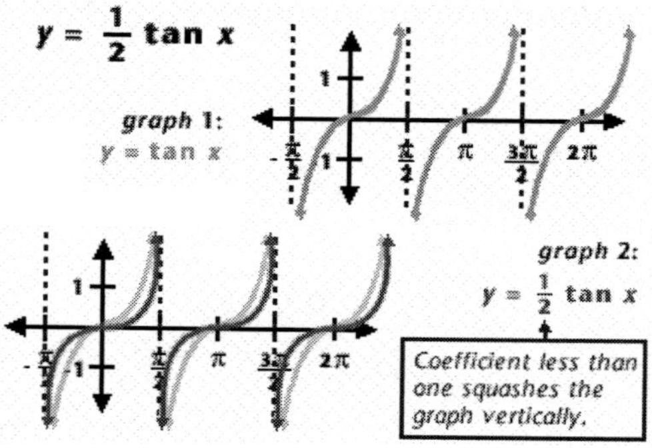 $y = 4\tan x$ 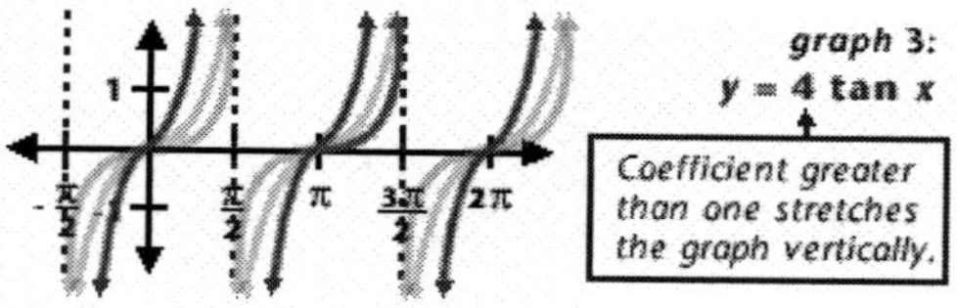	To graph $y = 1/2\ \tan x$, start by graphing **tan**x. The coefficient in front of the tangent will multiply each y-value by one-half; therefore, each point on the graph gets closer to the x-axis. The coefficient compresses the graph. To graph y = 4 tanx, remember that the coefficient will multiply each y-value by 4; therefore each point on the graph will be stretched upwards. A coefficient that is greater than one will always elongate the graph.
$y = \csc(2x) = \frac{1}{\sin(2x)}$ period of $\sin(2x) = \frac{2\pi}{\lvert 2\rvert} = \pi$ 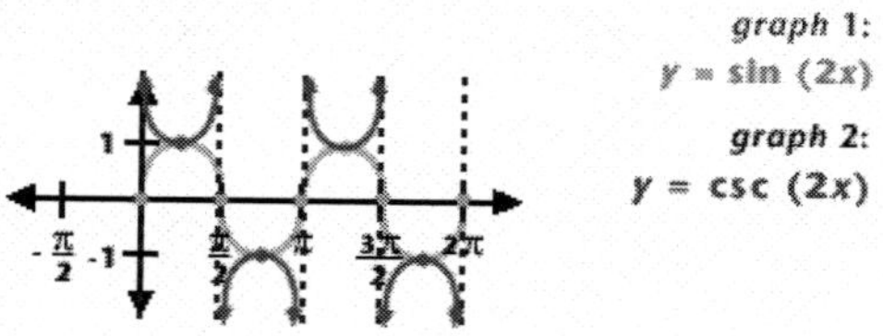 *Cosecant has asymptotes where sine has zeros.*	To graph the cosecant function, remember that **cosecant** is the reciprocal of the **sine** function. Start by graphing the sine curve with the proper period. Now take the reciprocal. Remember that cosecant will have **asymptotes** wherever sine has **zeros**. Changing the period will compress the graph horizontally.
$y = 2\csc x = 2\left(\frac{1}{\sin x}\right)$ 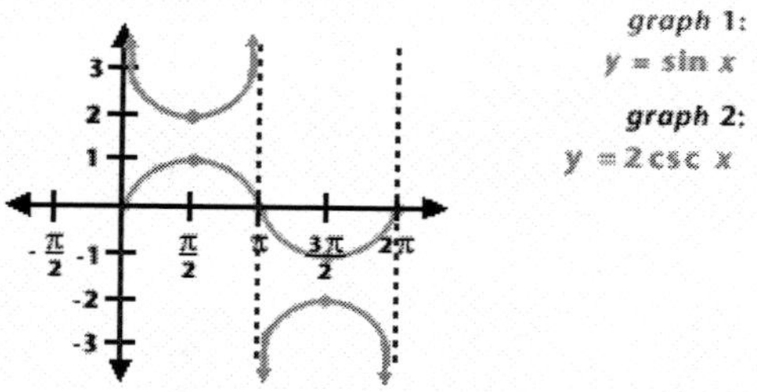	At first glance, the function of $y = 2\csc x$ looks a lot like the function of $y = \csc(2x)$, but notice that the coefficient has been moved. Therefore, the graph is going to look very different. The period of $y = 2\csc x$ is 2π. Because of the coefficient in front of the trig function, each of the y-terms of the cosecant curve has to be multiplied by 2. So, the cosecant curve moves away from the sine curve.
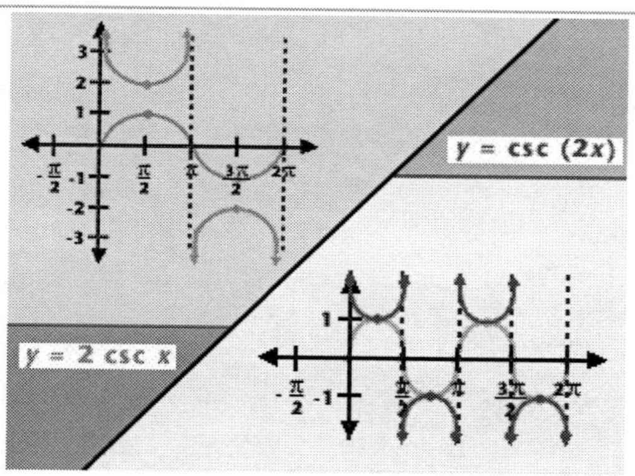	Notice here, the graphs of $y = 2\csc x$ and $y = \csc(2x)$ are very different. The placement of the coefficient greatly effects the graph.

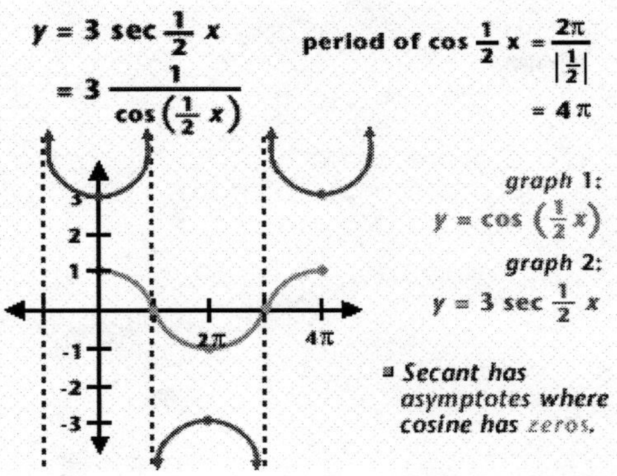

Graph $y = 3\ \sec(1/2x)$.

Follow the same steps to graph **secant** that were used to graph cosecant. Start by graphing the cosine function. Remember that secant is the reciprocal of **cosine**.

Then graph the secant function, multiplying it by 3 (stretching it away from the x-axis).

Remember that secant has asymptotes where the cosine curve has zeros.

Sample problems:

1. True or false: The following is a graph of one period of $y = \cot 2x$.

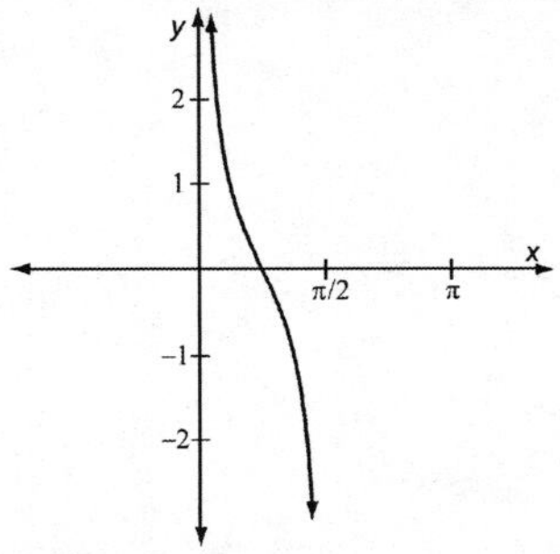

Solution: True

Explanation: The period is $\dfrac{\pi}{2}$ and there are no phase shifts or vertical translations.

2. Describe the steps for graphing $y = \sec 2x$.
Solution: Find the period, graph $y = \cos 2x$ and then graph the reciprocal
Explanation: Use the coefficient of x, 2, to calculate the period: $\dfrac{2\pi}{2} = \pi$. Graph $y = \cos 2x$ and then graph its reciprocal.

3. In the graph of $y = 2\tan \pi x$, where do the zeros occur?
Solution: At every integer
Explanation: The period of this function is $\pi/\pi = 1$. Since $\tan 0 = 0$, the zeros occur at every integer.

Practice problems: *(Answers on page: 755)*

1. True or false: One period of $y = \dfrac{1}{2}\csc x + 1$ is graphed below.

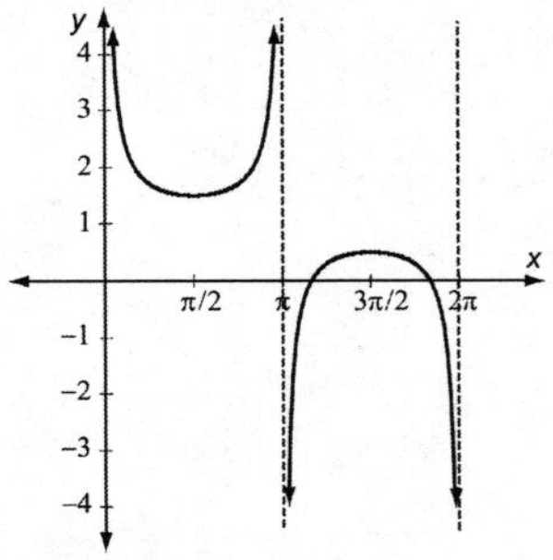

2. What is the period of $y = 2\tan 3(x - 2) + 7$?
3. How does the graph of $y = 2\sec x$ differ from the graph of $y = \sec 2x$?

Review questions: *(Answers to odd questions on page: 756)*

1. What is the period of $y = \tan 6x$?

2. True or false: $x = \dfrac{\pi}{2}$ is an equation of a vertical asymptote of $y = \sec x$.

3. True or false: The function $y = 5\tan 4x$ is graphed below.

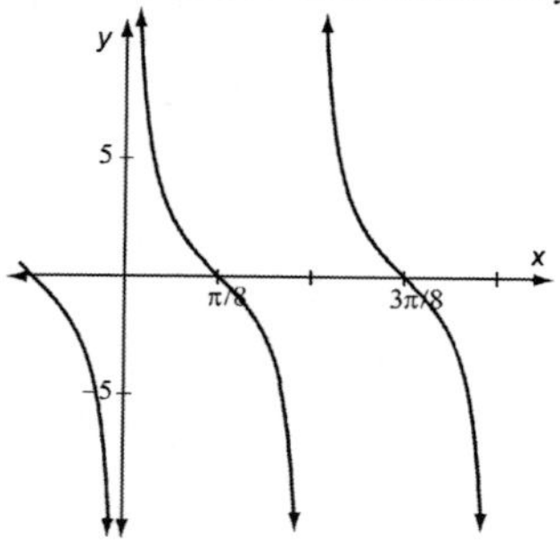

4. Describe the steps for graphing the function $y = \dfrac{1}{2}\csc x$.

5. How does the graph of $y = -3\sec 2x$ differ from the graph of $y = \sec 2x$?

Identifying a Trigonometric Function from its Graph

- To identify which **trig function** a graph might represent, graph the reciprocal of the function.

<table>
<tr>
<td>

Identify the function:

Is it:

y = −2tan x

y = sec 2x

y = cot x

y = −csc x

?

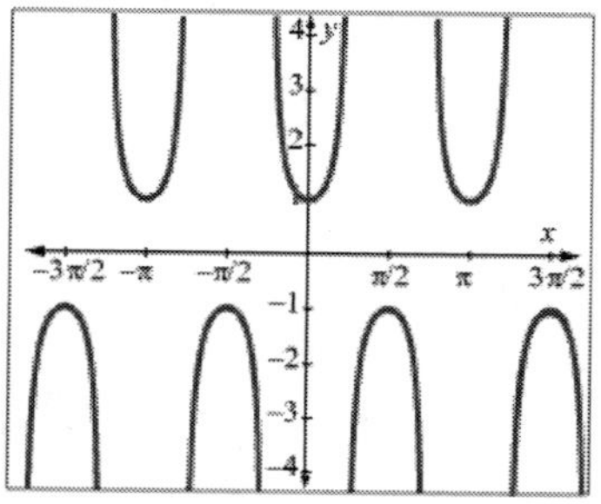

</td>
<td>

Identifying **trig functions** can be made easier by sketching a graph of the reciprocal of the given function.

</td>
</tr>
<tr>
<td>

Where there are asymptotes in the original function, its reciprocal will have zeros.

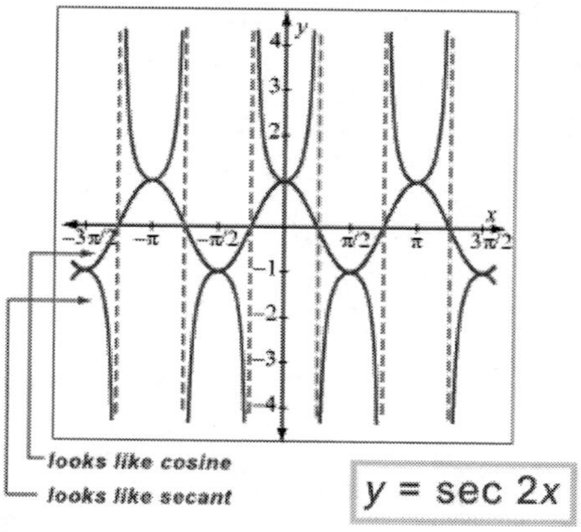

</td>
<td>

To sketch the reciprocal of the graph you are interested in, remember that **asymptotes** become **zeros** and zeros become asymptotes.

The reciprocal function of the graph given here makes a graph similar to the cosine curve, so the original graph must be a secant curve.

</td>
</tr>
</table>

Identify the function:

Is it:

$y = -2\tan x$

$y = \sec 2x$

$y = \cot x$

$y = -\csc x$

?

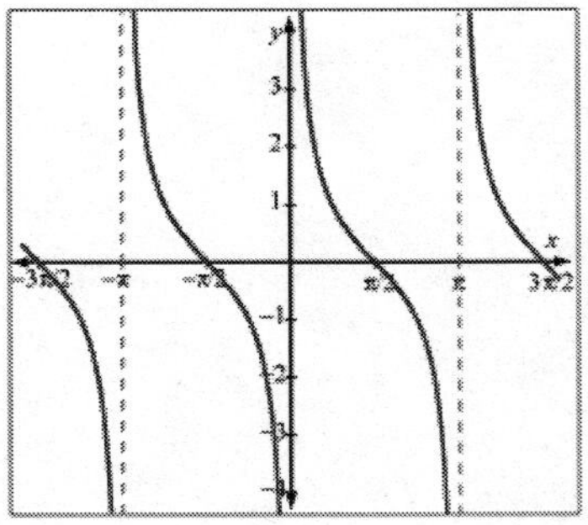

Identify the trig function that produces this graph.

Where there are asymptotes in the original function, its reciprocal will have zeros.

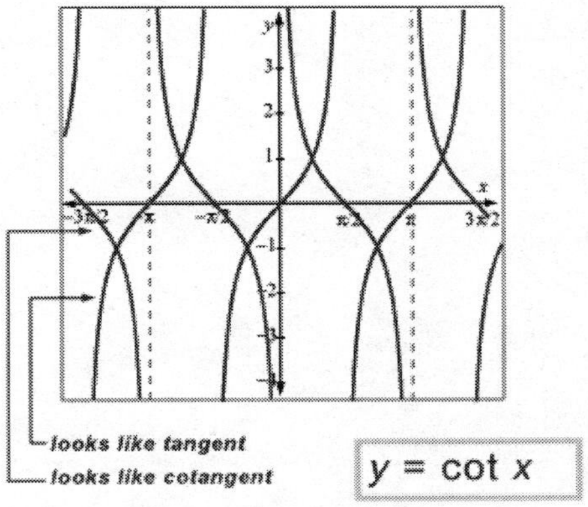

First, find the reciprocal graph by turning zeros into asymptotes and asymptotes into zeros.

The reciprocal graph looks like the tangent function. So, the original graph must be the cotangent function.

Sample problems:

1. True or false: The function $y = 3\csc\left(x + \frac{\pi}{2}\right)$ is graphed below.

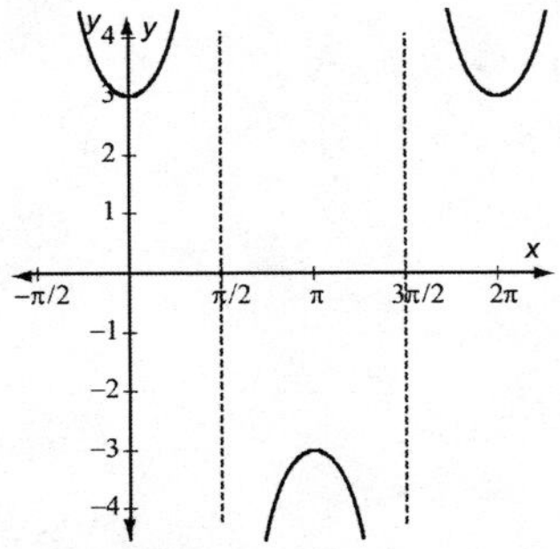

Solution: True
Explanation: The corresponding reciprocal function has an amplitude of 3 and a period of 2π. The function is either a secant function or a cosecant function shifted to the left by $\pi/2$.

2. Determine the equation of the following graph.

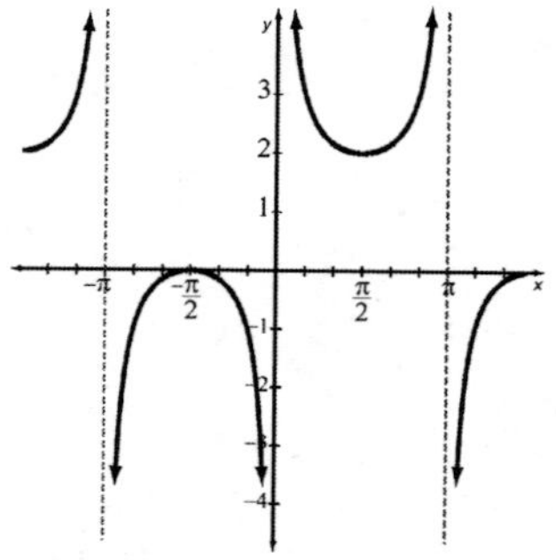

Solution: $y = \csc x + 1$

Explanation: Sketch the graph of the reciprocal function. Use the asymptotes of the function as zeros of the reciprocal function and zeros of the function as asymptotes of the reciprocal function. Because the reciprocal resembles the graph of $y = \sin x$ moved up one unit, the graph must be that of $y = \csc x + 1$.

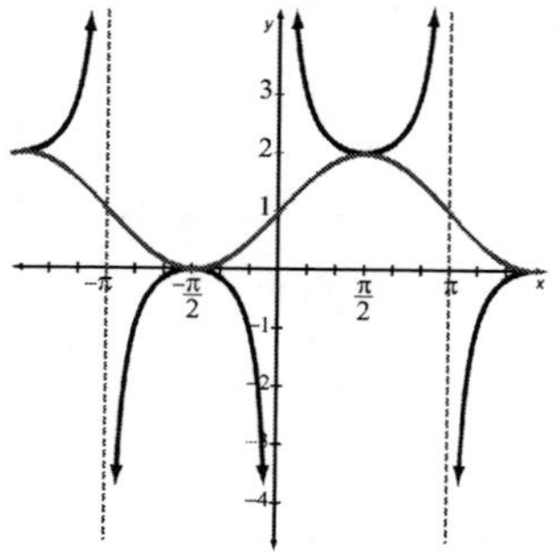

3. True or false: The function $y = \cot 2x$ is graphed below.

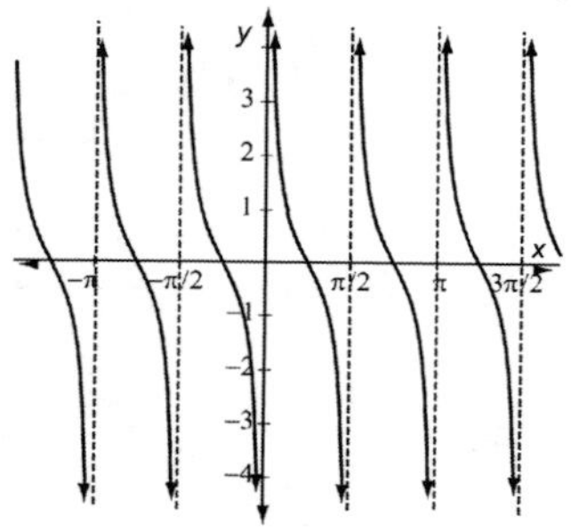

Solution: True

Explanation: Sketch the graph of the reciprocal function. Use the asymptotes of the function as zeros of the reciprocal and the zeros of the function as asymptotes of the reciprocal function. Because the reciprocal resembles the graph of $y = \tan 2x$, the graph must be that of $y = \cot 2x$.

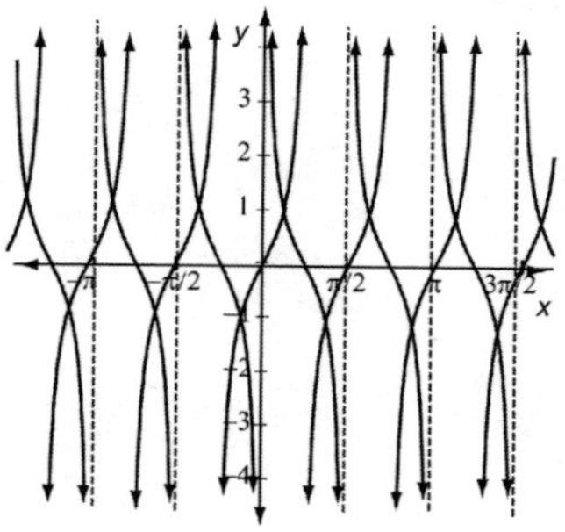

Practice problems: *(Answers on page: 756)*

1. Determine an equation for the graph below.

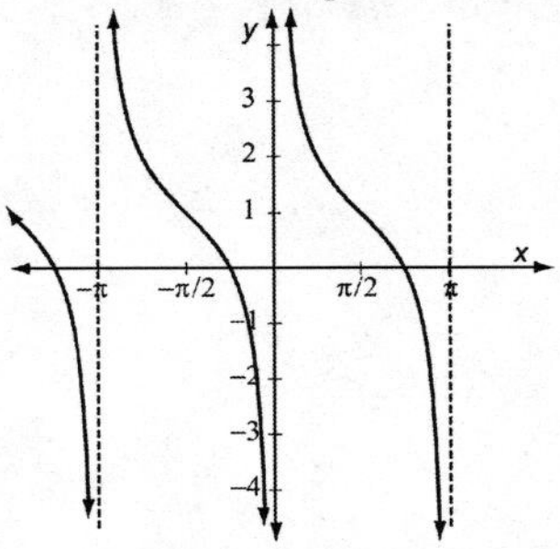

2. True or false: The function $y = -3\cot x$ is graphed below.

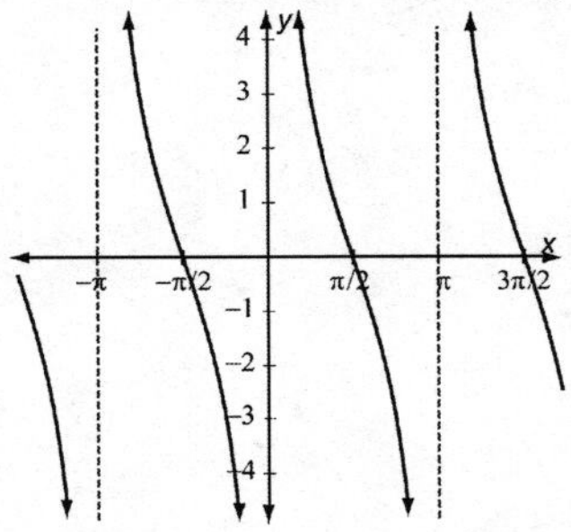

3. True or false: The function $y = 2\sec x$ is graphed below.

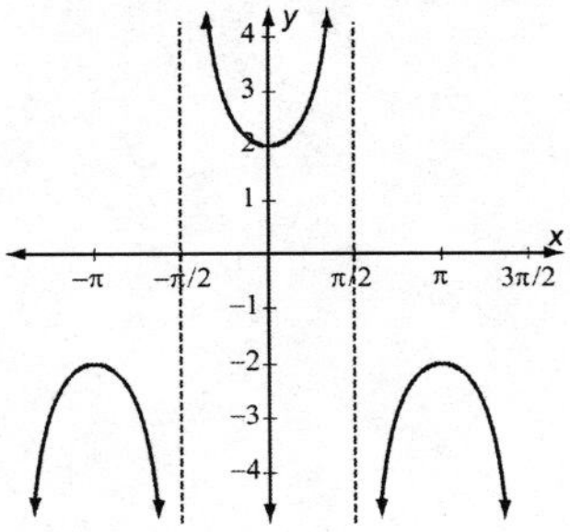

Review questions: *(Answers to odd questions on page: 756)*

1. Determine an equation for the graph below. The graph shows one complete period.

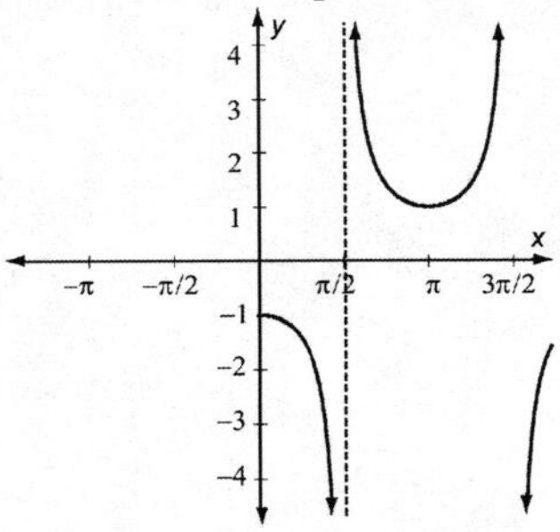

2. Determine an equation for the graph below.

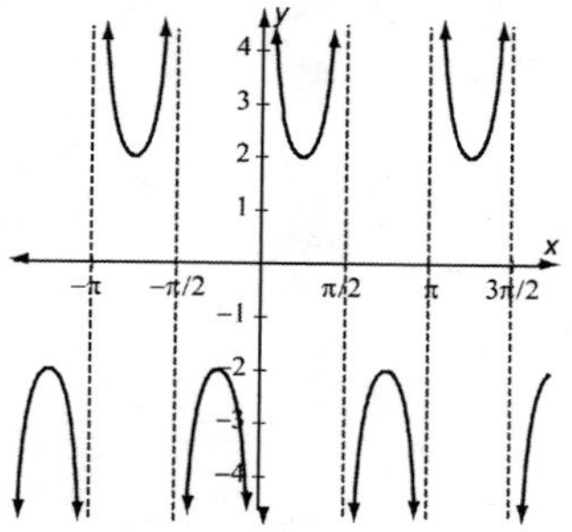

3. Determine an equation for the graph below.

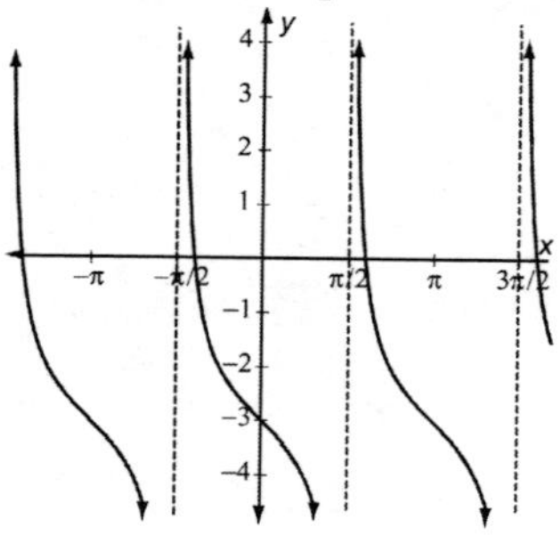

4. True or false: The function $y = \csc x$ is graphed below.

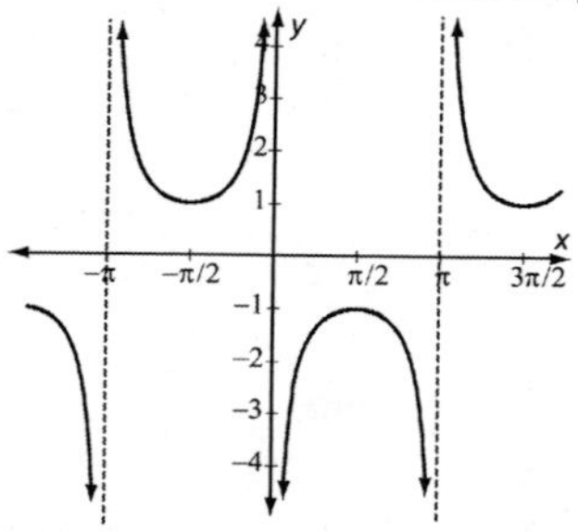

5. True or false: The function $y = -\cot x$ is graphed below.

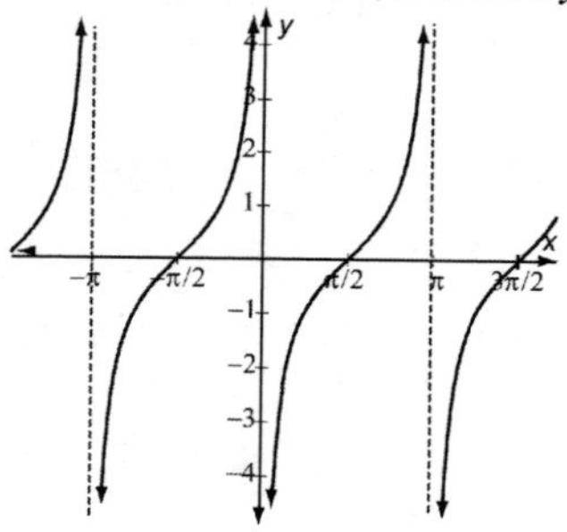

An Introduction to Inverse Trigonometric Functions

- **Review**: In order for a function, $f(x)$, to have an **inverse** , $f^{-1}(x)$, it must be a one-to-one function (ie: it must pass the **horizontal line test**).
- The basic trigonometric functions have inverses if their **domains** are restricted. These inverse functions are known as the **inverse trigonometric functions**:
  - The **inverse sine function** is written $y = \sin^{-1}x$. (Think of $\sin^{-1}x$ as "the angle whose sine is x.")

  The domain for $y = \sin^{-1}x$ is $-1 \le x \le 1$ and the **range** is $-\pi/2 \le y \le \pi/2$.

  - The **inverse cosine function** is written $y = \cos^{-1}x$. (Think of $\cos^{-1}x$ as "the angle whose cosine is x.")

  The domain for $y = \cos^{-1}x$ is $-1 \le x \le 1$ and the range is $0 \le y \le \pi$.

  - The **inverse tangent function** is written $y = \tan^{-1}x$. (Think of $\tan^{-1}x$ as "the angle whose tangent is x.")

  The domain for $y = \tan^{-1}x$ is any real number and the range is $-\pi/2 \le y \le \pi/2$

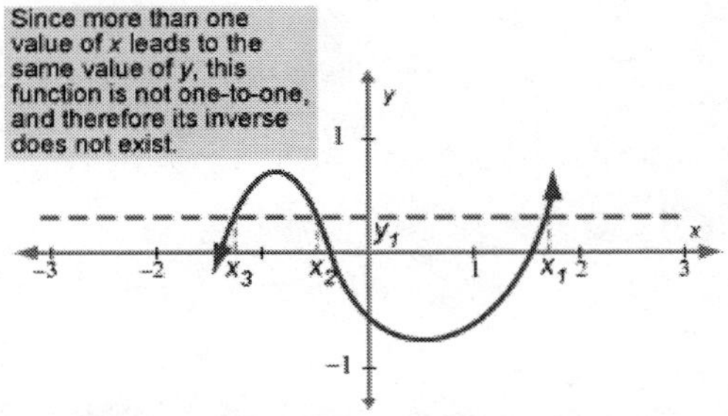

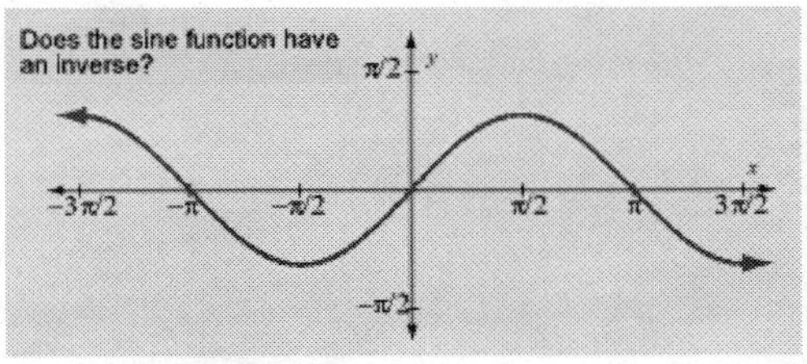

Remember, in order for a function, $f(x)$, to have an inverse, $f^{-1}(x)$, it must pass the horizontal line test. If it fails the horizontal line test, the function is not one-to-one and, therefore, the inverse of that function does not exist.

Consider the sine function, $y = \sin x$. Does $y = \sin^{-1} x$ exist?

From the graph of the sine function, it is clear that $y = \sin x$ is not a one-to-one function, therefore its inverse does not exist.

By restricting the **domain** of the sine function, however, a one-to-one function can be defined.

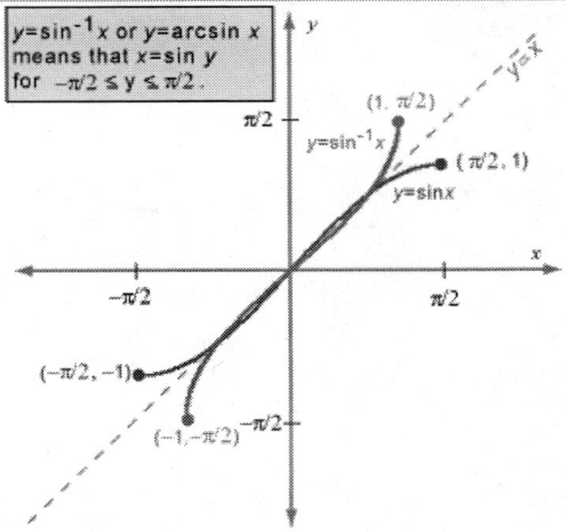

Consider the piece of the sine function between $x = -\pi/2$ and $x = \pi/2$. This piece by itself passes the horizontal line test, so it has an inverse.

Find the inverse by reflecting the restricted piece across the line $y = x$.

The result is the **inverse sine function**, written $y = \sin^{-1}x$.

The meaning of the inverse sine function, $y = \sin^{-1}x$, is "y is the angle whose sine is x," or $x = \sin y$.

Don't forget, $y = \sin^{-1}x$ is NOT the same as $y = \sin x^{-1}$.

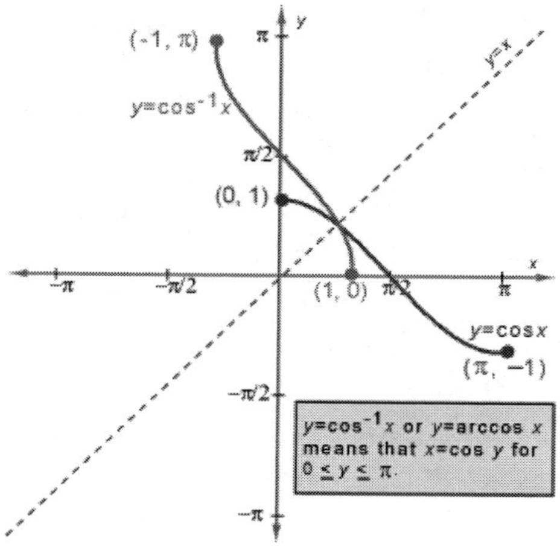

The inverse of the cosine function, $y = \cos^{-1} x$ is defined by restricting the domain of the cosine function, $y = \cos x$, and then by reversing the roles of x and y.

Restrict the domain of the cosine function $y = \cos x$ to x-values between 0 and π.

Reflect this piece of the graph over the line $y = x$. The result is the **inverse cosine function**, written $y = \cos^{-1}x$.

If $y = \cos^{-1}x$, then "y is the angle whose cosine is x," or $\cos y = x$.

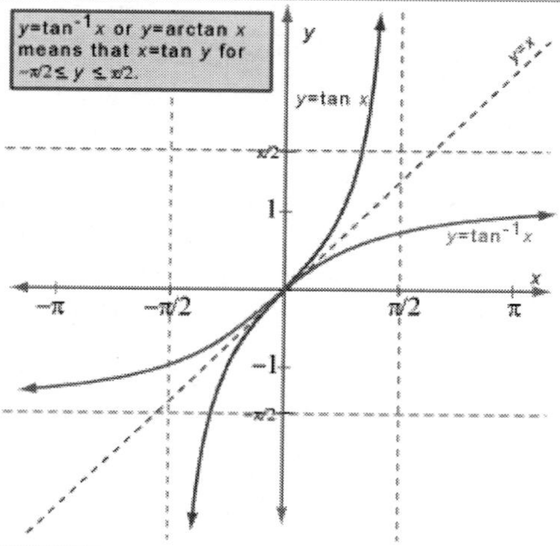

The inverse of the tangent function, $y = \tan^{-1} x$ is defined by restricting the domain of the tangent function, $y = \tan x$, and then by reversing the roles of x and y.

For $y = \tan x$, restrict the domain to the interval between $-\pi/2$ and $\pi/2$ and reflect this piece of the graph over the line $y = x$.

The **inverse tangent function** is notated $y = \tan^{-1}x$, and means "y is the angle whose tangent is x."

Sample problems:

1. What is the range of the inverse cosine function?
   Solution: $0 \le y \le \pi$
   Explanation: In order to produce an inverse function, the domain of cosine must be reduced to $[0, \pi]$. On this interval, cosine passes the horizontal line test. Since this interval is the restricted domain of cosine, it is the range of the inverse cosine function.

2. What is the domain of the inverse tangent function?
   Solution: All real numbers
   Explanation: To pass the horizontal line test, the domain of the tangent function must be restricted to the interval $\left[-\frac{\pi}{2}, \frac{\pi}{2}\right]$. However, over this restricted domain, the range of tangent is still all real numbers. Thus the domain of the inverse tangent function is also all real numbers.

3. True or false: The inverse tangent function is graphed below.

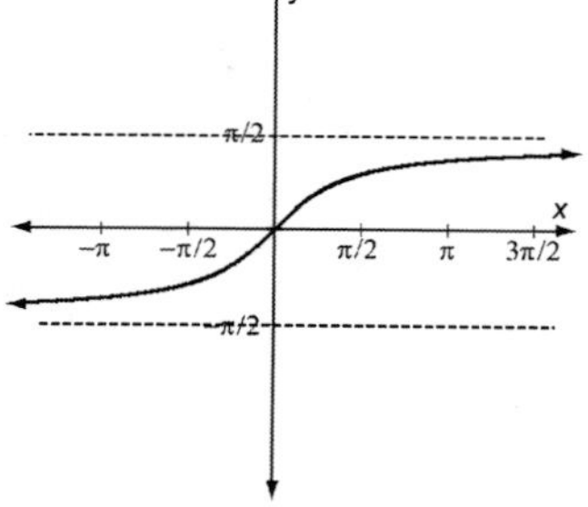

Solution: True

Explanation: The domain of this function is any real number, and the range is $-\frac{\pi}{2} < y < \frac{\pi}{2}$. This is the graph of the inverse tangent function.

Practice problems: *(Answers on page: 756)*

1. True or false: $\sin x^{-1} = \sin \frac{1}{x}$
2. What is the domain of the function $y = 3\sin^{-1} t$?
3. True or false: The function $y = \sin^{-1} x$ is graphed below.

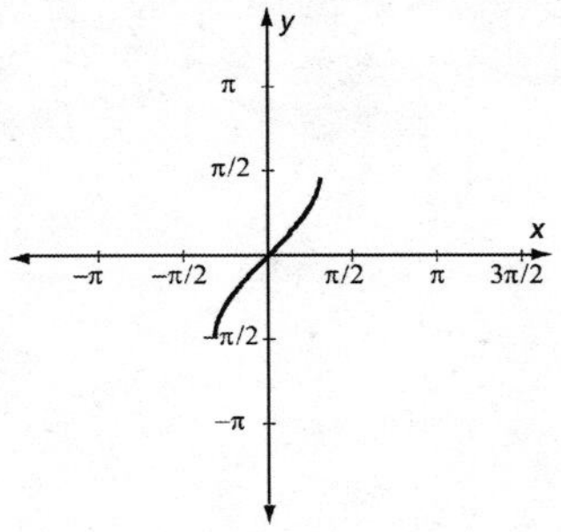

Review questions: *(Answers to odd questions on page: 756)*

1. True or false: The function $y = \frac{1}{2}\tan^{-1} x$ is graphed below.

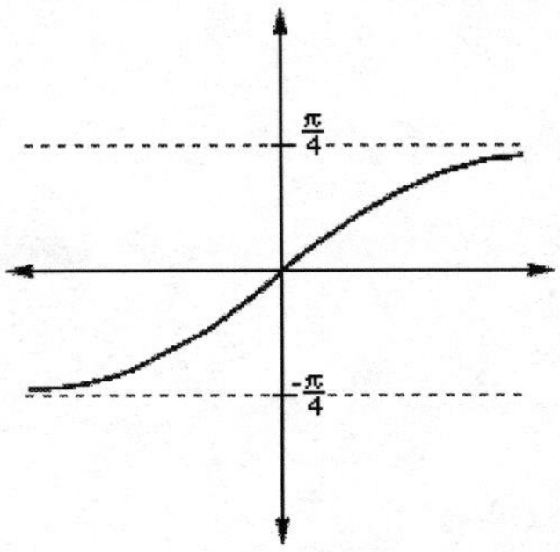

2. True or false: If $\tan^{-1} A = B$, then $\tan B = A$.
3. True or false: The function $y = \cos^{-1} x$ graphed below.

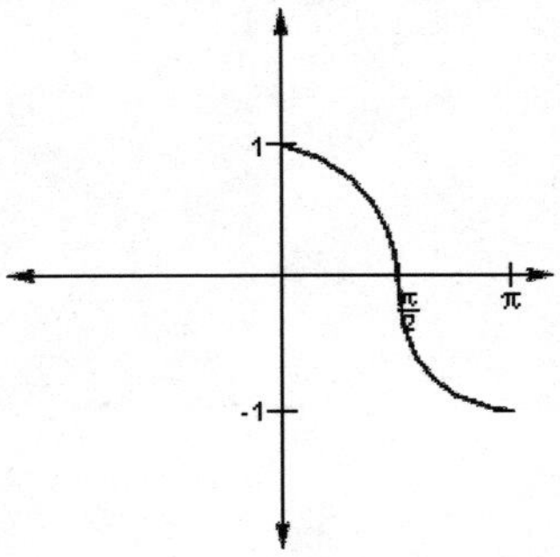

4. What is the range of $y = \cos^{-1} x$?
5. What is the range of $y = \frac{1}{3}\tan^{-1} x$?

Evaluating Inverse Trigonometric Functions

- When evaluating an **inverse trigonometric function**:
  - Think of the answer as "the angle whose ________ is...."
    For example, $\mathbf{sin^{-1}}$ 0.5 is equal to "the angle whose sine is 0.5."
  - Verify that the answer is in the correct **range** for the inverse trig function.
  - The graph of the appropriate trig function is often helpful.

Evaluate: $\sin^{-1}(\frac{\sqrt{3}}{2})$

Q: What is the angle whose sine is $\frac{\sqrt{3}}{2}$? A: π/3 or 60°

y=sin x		
x radians	x degrees	sin x
0	0	0
π/6	30°	1/2
π/4	45°	√2/2
π/3	60°	√3/2
π/2	90°	1
π	180°	0
3π/2	270°	−1
2π	360°	0

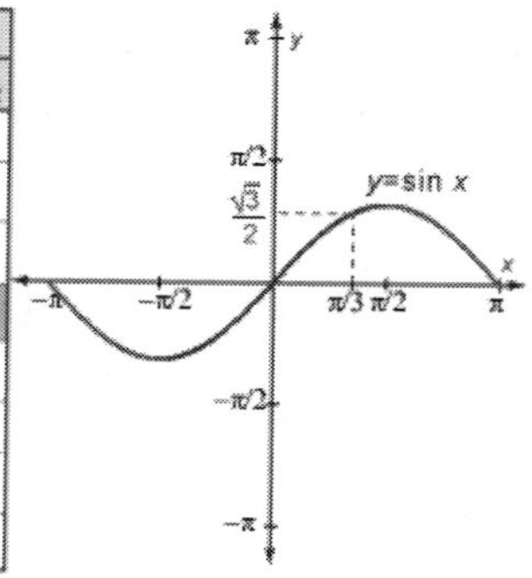

Evaluate: $\mathbf{sin}^{-1}\frac{\sqrt{3}}{2}$.

$\mathbf{sin}^{-1}(\frac{\sqrt{3}}{2})$ is equal to "the angle whose sine is $\frac{\sqrt{3}}{2}$." Notice that the solution must be in the interval (−π/2, π/2), the **range** of the inverse sine function.

Since $\sin\frac{\pi}{3} = \frac{\sqrt{3}}{2}$, the solution is π/3, or 60°.

So, $\sin^{-1} = \frac{\sqrt{3}}{2} = \frac{\pi}{3}$

Evaluate: $\cos^{-1}(\frac{-1}{2})$

Q: What is the angle whose cosine is $\frac{-1}{2}$? A: 2π/3 or 120°

y=cos x		
x radians	x degrees	cos x
0	0	1
π/6	30°	√3/2
π/4	45°	√2/2
π/3	60°	1/2
π/2	90°	0
2π/3	120°	−1/2
3π/4	135°	−√2/2
5π/6	150°	−√3/2
π	180°	−1

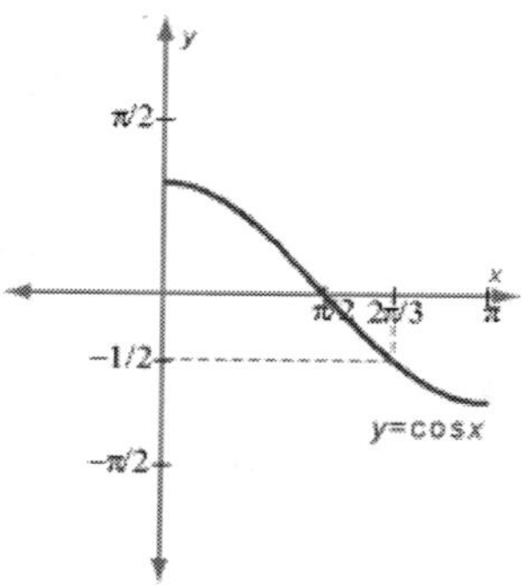

Evaluate: $\mathbf{cos}^{-1}(-\frac{1}{2})$.

$\cos^{-1}(-\frac{1}{2})$ is "the angle whose cosine is −1/2." Notice that the answer must be between 0 and π.

Use the graph of the cosine function and the fact that $\cos\frac{\pi}{3} = \frac{1}{2}$, to determine that the solution is the angle 2π/3.

Use a calculator in radian mode to find the following:

$\sin^{-1}(0.362) = 0.3704$
$\tan^{-1}(-12.6) = -1.491...$

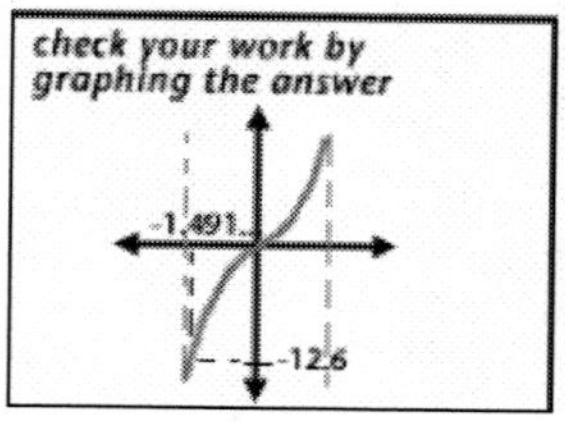

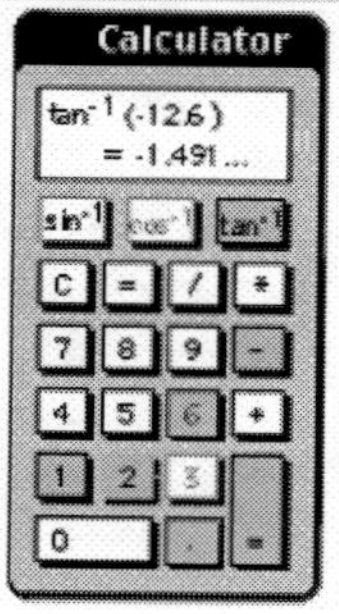

It's also possible to compute inverse trig functions using a calculator. Be sure your calculator is in the appropriate mode: degrees or radians.

Use the graph of the appropriate trig function to check the answer.

Sample problems:

1. Use a calculator to evaluate $\cos^{-1} 0.319$ to the nearest degree.
   Solution: 71°
   Explanation: Set the calculator to degree mode.
   For a scientific calculator: 0.319, 2nd, $\cos^{-1}$.
   For a graphing calculator: 2nd, $\cos^{-1}$, 0.319, enter.

2. Use a calculator to evaluate $\sin^{-1}\left(\frac{\sqrt{2}}{2}\right)$ in radians to the nearest thousandth.

Solution: 0.785
Explanation: Set the calculator to radian mode.
For a scientific calculator: 2, 2nd, $\sqrt{\ }$, ÷, 2, =, 2nd, $\sin^{-1}$.
For a graphing calculator: 2nd, $\sin^{-1}$, 2nd, $\sqrt{\ }$, 2,), ÷, 2, enter.

3. Find the exact value of $\tan^{-1}\left(-\sqrt{3}\right)$ in radians.

Solution: $-\frac{\pi}{3}$

Explanation: The range of the inverse tangent function is $\left[-\frac{\pi}{2}, \frac{\pi}{2}\right]$. Thus, $\tan^{-1}\left(-\sqrt{3}\right)$ is equal to the angle between $-\frac{\pi}{2}$ and $\frac{\pi}{2}$ whose tangent is $-\sqrt{3}$. Since $\tan\left(-\frac{\pi}{3}\right) = -\sqrt{3}$, and $-\frac{\pi}{3}$ is in the correct range of angles, $\tan^{-1}\left(-\sqrt{3}\right) = -\frac{\pi}{3}$.

Practice problems: *(Answers on page: 756)*

1. Use a calculator to evaluate $\tan^{-1} 4.65$ to the nearest degree.
2. Use a calculator to evaluate $\cos^{-1}\left(\frac{\sqrt{3}}{2}\right)$ to the nearest degree.
3. Find the exact value of $\cos^{-1}\left(-\frac{\sqrt{2}}{2}\right)$ in radians.

Review questions: *(Answers to odd questions on page: 756)*

1. Use a calculator to evaluate $\sin^{-1} 0.753$ in radians to the nearest thousandth.
2. Use a calculator to evaluate $\tan^{-1}\left(-\frac{\sqrt{3}}{3}\right)$ in radians to five decimal places.
3. Use a calculator to evaluate $\cos^{-1}\left(\frac{7\pi}{4}\right)$ in radians to five decimal places.
4. Find the exact value of $\sin^{-1}\left(\frac{1}{2}\right)$.
5. Find the exact value of $\tan^{-1} 1$.

Solving an Equation Involving an Inverse Trigonometric Function

- To solve an equation containing an **inverse trigonometric function**:
  - Determine what the equation says by 'untangling' it. Think of the inverse trig function as "the angle whose _______ is...." For example, think of $\mathbf{sin^{-1}}\ \frac{1}{2}$ as "the angle whose sine is $\frac{1}{2}$."
  - After untangling, solve the equation normally.
  - Graph the function to check that all solutions were found.

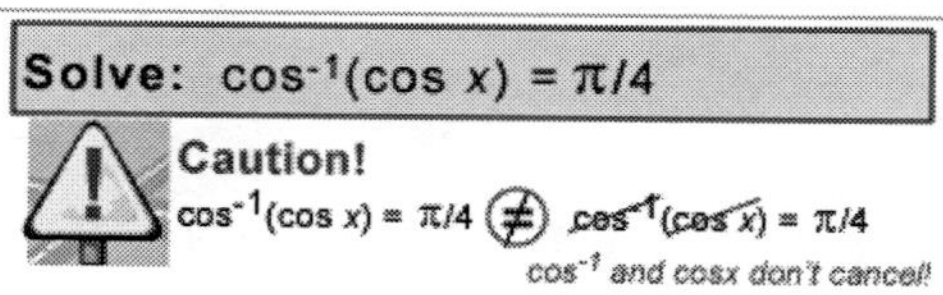

Remember, when solving an equation that contains an inverse trig function, determine what the equation is saying by 'untangling' it.

Take a look at the equation to the left. You might be tempted to cancel the cos and **cos^{-1}** to produce a solution. Unfortunately, the cosine and inverse cosine functions do not cancel in this way!

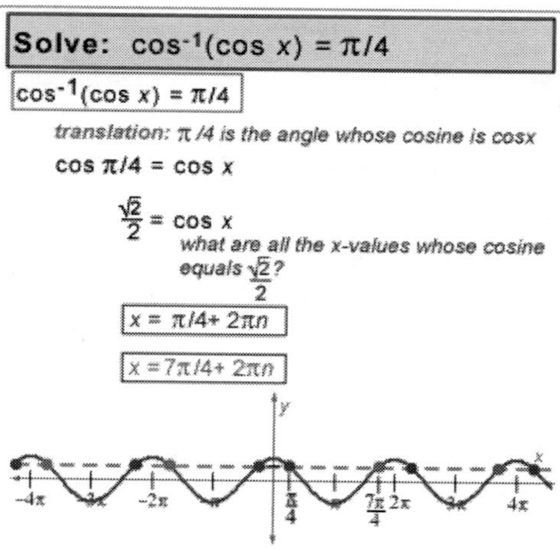

Given the equation to the left:

1. Untangle. $\cos^{-1}(\cos x)$ means "the angle whose cosine is $\cos x$."

2. Determine the value of $\cos\frac{\pi}{4}$: $\cos\frac{\pi}{4} = \frac{\sqrt{2}}{2}$

3. Solve the equation for all possible values of x. There will be two answers per **period**.

4. Check the graph of cosine to make sure your answer is right.

Remember, you can't be too careful when dealing with these functions. Take your time! Many of these solution sets will be infinite--watch out for them.

Sample problems:

1. Find all solutions: $2(\cos x + 1) = 2$

   Solution: $\frac{\pi}{2} + k\pi$, where k is any integer

   Explanation: Simplify: $2(\cos x + 1) = 2$; $2\cos x + 2 = 2$; $2\cos x = 0$; $\cos x = 0$.

   Observe from the graph of $y = \cos x$ that $\cos x = 0$ at $\frac{\pi}{2}$ and at $-\frac{\pi}{2}$.

   Additionally, $\cos x = 0$ at $\frac{\pi}{2}$ plus any multiple of 2π.

   Thus, all solutions can be described as $\frac{\pi}{2} + k\pi$, where k is any integer.

2. Find all solutions: $\tan^{-1}(\tan x) = \frac{\pi}{6}$

   Solution: $x = \frac{\pi}{6} + \pi n$

   Explanation: Simplify: $\tan^{-1}(\tan x) = \frac{\pi}{6}$; $\tan\frac{\pi}{6} = \tan x$; $\frac{\sqrt{3}}{3} = \tan x$. The x-value whose tangent is $\frac{\sqrt{3}}{3}$ is $\frac{\pi}{6}$ given that the period of tangent is π. Therefore, $x = \frac{\pi}{6} + \pi n$.

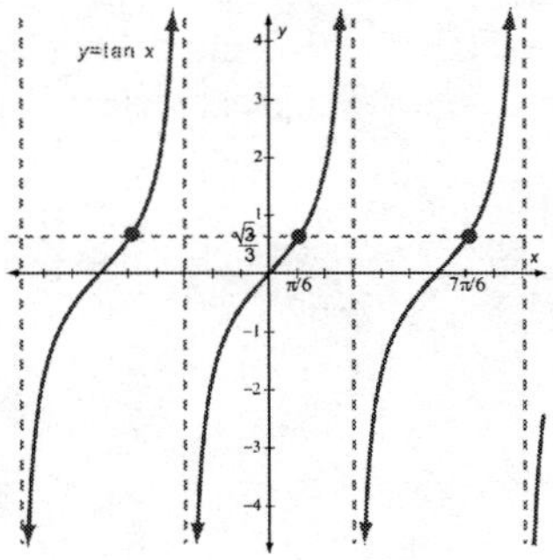

3. Find all solutions: $\tan^{-1}(\sin x) = \frac{\pi}{3}$

Solution: No solution

Explanation: Simplify: $\tan^{-1}(\sin x) = \frac{\pi}{3}$; $\sin x = \tan\frac{\pi}{3}$; $\sin x = \sqrt{3}$.

However, $\sqrt{3} \approx 1.73205$, is not in the range of the sine function. Thus, there is no solution.

Practice problems: *(Answers on page: 756)*

1. Find all solutions: $\sin^{-1}(\sin x) = \frac{\pi}{2}$
2. Find all solutions: $\tan^{-1}(\tan x) = -\frac{\pi}{4}$
3. Find all solutions: $\cos^{-1}(\cos x) = \frac{5\pi}{6}$

Review questions: *(Answers to odd questions on page: 756)*

1. Find all solutions: $\frac{4}{3}\tan^{-1}\frac{\theta}{2} = \pi$
2. Find all solutions: $\cos^{-1}\left(\cos x\right) = \frac{\pi}{3}$
3. Find all solutions: $\sin^{-1}\left(\sin x\right) = 0$
4. Find all solutions: $\cos^{-1}\left(\cos x\right) = \frac{2\pi}{3}$
5. Find all solutions: $\sin^{-1}\left(\cos x\right) = \frac{\pi}{6}$

Evaluating the Composition of a Trigonometric Function and Its Inverse

- To evaluate a **composite** trigonometric function:
  - First find the value of the inner expression.
  - Then evaluate the outer expression (usually an inverse) at that value.
- Always consider the **range** of the inverses. Certain answers are not allowed when solving an **inverse trig function**.
  - The range of $\mathbf{sin}^{-1}x$ is the interval $[-\pi/2, \pi/2]$.
  - The range of $\mathbf{cos}^{-1}x$ is the interval $[0, \pi]$.
  - The range of $\mathbf{tan}^{-1}x$ is the interval $(-\pi/2, \pi/2)$.

Ranges for inverse trigonometric functions:

$y=\sin^{-1}x$: $-\pi/2 \le y \le \pi/2$

$y=\cos^{-1}x$: $0 \le y \le \pi$

$y=\tan^{-1}x$: $-\pi/2 < y < \pi/2$

To evaluate a composite trig function:

1) Find the value of the inner expression
2) Find the inverse*

*-*The solution must be within the range of allowable values for the inverse trig function*

To evaluate the **composition** of a trig function and its **inverse**, find the value of the inner expression and then take its inverse.

Remember, the solution for the composite trig function must be within the range of allowable values for the inverse trig function.

Evaluate: $\sin^{-1}(\sin(7\pi/6))$

$\sin^{-1}(\sin(7\pi/6)) \longrightarrow \sin(7\pi/6) = -1/2$

$\sin^{-1}(-1/2) = \boxed{-\pi/6}$

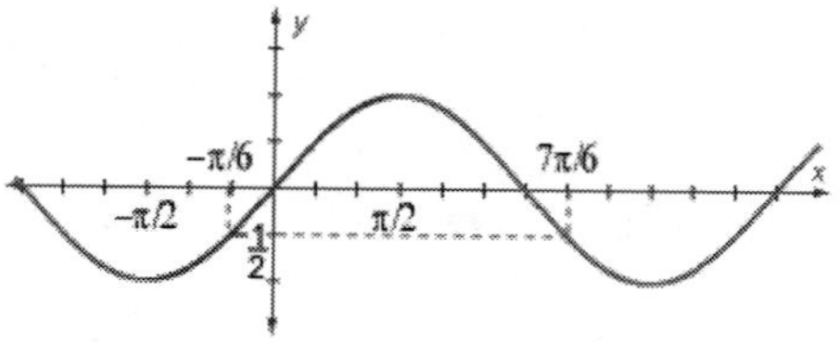

y=sin x		
x radians	x degrees	sin x
0	0	0
π/6	30°	1/2

Consider the composite function, $\sin^{-1}(\sin(7\pi/6))$.

Begin by finding the value of the inner expression, $\sin(7\pi/6)$. The **reference angle** turns out to be $\pi/6$, and sine is negative in the third quadrant, so this value is $-1/2$.

Now find the **inverse sine** of $-1/2$. Remember, the answer has to be between $-\pi/2$ and $\pi/2$, the range of inverse sine.

What is the angle whose sine is $-1/2$? The angle is $-\pi/6$.

Evaluate: $\tan^{-1}(\tan(3\pi/4))$

$\tan^{-1}(\tan(3\pi/4)) \longrightarrow \tan(3\pi/4) = -1$

$\tan^{-1}(-1) = \boxed{-\pi/4}$

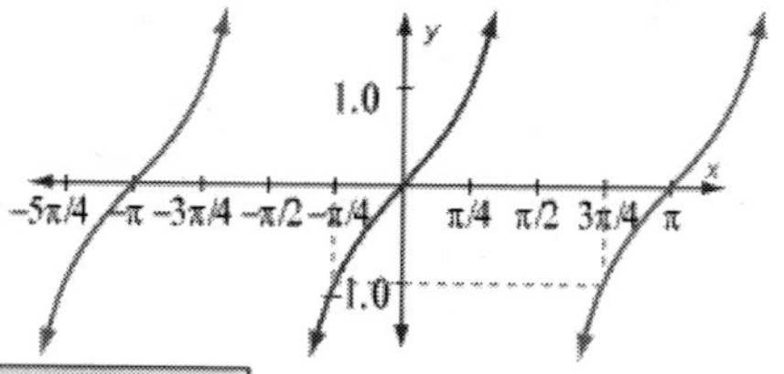

y=tan x		
x radians	x degrees	tan x
0	0	0
π/4	45°	1

Consider the composite function, $\tan^{-1}(\tan(3\pi/4))$.

Begin by finding the value of the inner expression. The reference angle is $\pi/4$, and tangent is negative in the second quadrant, so the inner expression equals -1.

Now take the inverse **tangent** of -1.

What is the angle whose tangent is -1?
The angle is $-\pi/4$. Since the range of inverse tangent is between $-\pi/2$ and $\pi/2$, the answer must be $-\pi/4$.

Evaluate: $\sin(\sin^{-1}\frac{1}{2})$

Recall: if f and f^{-1} are inverse functions, then $f(f^{-1}(x))=x$ and $f^{-1}(f(x))=x$

Therefore, $\sin(\sin^{-1}\frac{1}{2}) = \frac{1}{2}$

check:

$\sin($*the angle whose sin is* $\frac{1}{2}) \longrightarrow \sin(30°) = \frac{1}{2}$

y=sin x		
x radians	x degrees	sin x
0	0	0
π/6	30°	1/2

Consider the example given here: evaluate $\sin(\sin^{-1} 1/2)$.

Remember the rule that if f and f^{-1} are inverse functions then $f(f^{-1}(x)) = x$ and $f^{-1}(f(x)) = x$; therefore $\sin(\sin^{-1} 1/2) = 1/2$.

You can check this by remembering that $\sin^{-1} 1/2$ means "find the angle whose sine is 1/2." Since you know that $\sin(30°) = 1/2$, then $\sin(\sin^{-1} 1/2) = \sin(30°) = 1/2$.

Evaluate: $\sin\left(\tan^{-1}\frac{7}{24}\right)$

Translate:
sin(*the angle whose tangent is* $\frac{7}{24}$)

$\tan\theta = \frac{7}{24}$

Sketch a right triangle:
recall: $\tan\theta = \frac{\text{opp}}{\text{adj}}$

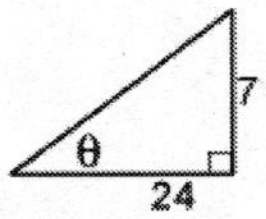

$\sin\theta = \frac{\text{opp}}{\text{hyp}}$

$\sin\theta = \frac{7}{25}$

find the hypotenuse:
$7^2 + 24^2 = c^2$
$625 = c^2$
$25 = c$

Therefore, $\sin\left(\tan^{-1}\frac{7}{24}\right) = \frac{7}{25}$

Use the right-triangle method to evaluate inverse trig functions when appropriate.

Consider the example illustrated here, $\sin\left(\tan^{-1}\frac{7}{24}\right)$.

The problem is asking you to find the sine of the angle whose tangent is 7/24.

Finding the value of the inner expression is too difficult to do without a calculator. Instead, use the right triangle method to evaluate the expression.

Draw a triangle in the first quadrant (since tangent is positive) and use the Pythagorean theorem to find the hypotenuse.

Knowing all the sides of the triangle, use the trig identities to solve.

Sample problems:

1. Determine the exact value of $\tan(\tan^{-1} 10)$.
   Solution: 10
   Explanation: Remember the rule that if f and f^{-1} are inverse functions then $f(f^{-1}(x)) = x$ and $f^{-1}(f(x)) = x$. So, $\tan(\tan^{-1}10) = 10$. The value 10 is in the domain of the inverse tangent function. Therefore, the tangent of the angle whose tangent is 10 equals 10.

2. Determine the exact value of $\tan\left(\sin^{-1}\frac{3}{5}\right)$.
   Solution: $\frac{3}{4}$
   Explanation: Draw a right triangle with an angle whose measure is equal to $\sin^{-1}\frac{3}{5}$. Since $\frac{3}{5}$ is a ratio, let the opposite side be 3 and the hypotenuse be 5. Use the Pythagorean theorem to find the length of the unknown side. $3^2 + x^2 = 5^2$; $9 + x^2 = 25$; $x^2 = 16$; $x = 4$. Thus, $\tan\left(\sin^{-1}\frac{3}{5}\right) = \frac{\text{opposite}}{\text{adjacent}} = \frac{3}{4}$.

3. Determine the exact value of $\sin^{-1}\left(\sin\left(-\frac{3\pi}{7}\right)\right)$.
   Solution: $-\frac{3\pi}{7}$
   Explanation: The inverse sine function of x produces the angle between $-\frac{\pi}{2}$ and $\frac{\pi}{2}$ whose sine is x. The angle in this expression is in the range of the inverse sine function. $-\frac{\pi}{2} \le -\frac{3\pi}{7} \le \frac{\pi}{2}$.
   Thus, $\sin^{-1}\left(\sin\left(-\frac{3\pi}{7}\right)\right) = -\frac{3\pi}{7}$.

Practice problems: *(Answers on page: 756)*

1. Determine the exact value of $\sin^{-1}\left(\sin\left(\frac{5\pi}{3}\right)\right)$.

2. Determine the exact value of $\cos^{-1}\left(\cos\left(\frac{5\pi}{3}\right)\right)$.

3. Determine the exact value of $\tan^{-1}\left(\tan\left(\frac{7\pi}{6}\right)\right)$.

Review questions: *(Answers to odd questions on page: 756)*

1. Determine the exact value of $\cos^{-1}(\cos 1.7)$.

2. Determine the exact value of $\cos^{-1}\left(\cos\left(\frac{7\pi}{4}\right)\right)$.

3. Determine the exact value of $\tan^{-1}\left(\tan\left(\frac{4\pi}{3}\right)\right)$.

4. Determine the exact value of $\sin^{-1}\left(\sin\left(\frac{7\pi}{4}\right)\right)$.

5. Determine the exact value of $\sin^{-1}\left(\sin\left(\frac{11\pi}{6}\right)\right)$.

Applying Trigonometric Functions: Is He Speeding?

- **Review**:

  $\sin\theta = \frac{opposite}{hypotenuse}$ $\cos\theta = \frac{adjacent}{hypotenuse}$ $\tan\theta = \frac{opposite}{adjacent}$
- An **angle of depression** is the angle formed by looking straight out to the horizon and then looking down at an object.
- An **angle of elevation** is the angle formed by looking straight out to the horizon and then looking up at an object.
- The angle of depression looking down from a height to a location is the same as the angle of elevation looking up from that location to that height.
- **Review**: *rate = distance /time*

Is the truck illustrated here exceeding the 65 miles per hour speed limit?

To determine that, first find out how far the truck traveled in 3 seconds. From this you can calculate the speed of the truck in miles per hour.

Given the two angles and the height of the building, use the fundamental trig functions to solve.

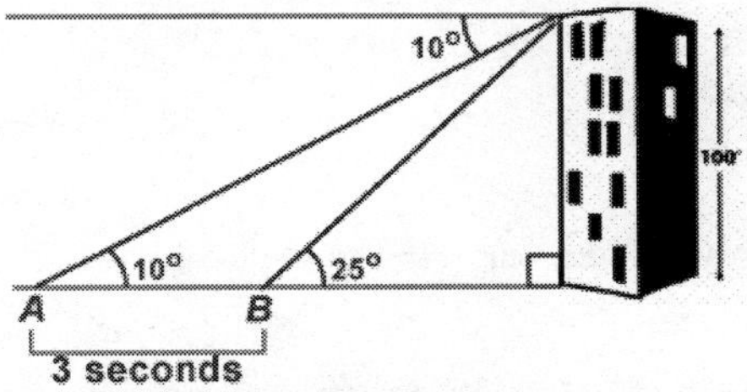

Find the distance from point A to the building

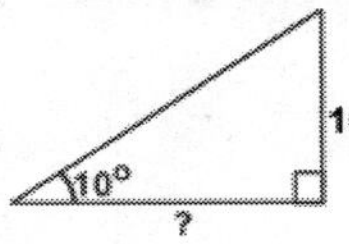

$\tan 10° = \frac{100}{?}$

$? = \frac{100}{\tan 10°}$

use a calculator $? = 567.13'$

First find the distance from point *A* to the building.

The angle from point *A* to the ground is 10° because the angle of elevation is equal to the angle of depression that is given in the example. Also given is the height of the building.

Set up a right triangle diagram to solve.

Given the angle, 10°, and the opposite side length, 100 feet, find the length of the adjacent side. Use the tangent function to solve.

You find that the distance from point *A* to the building is 567.13 feet.

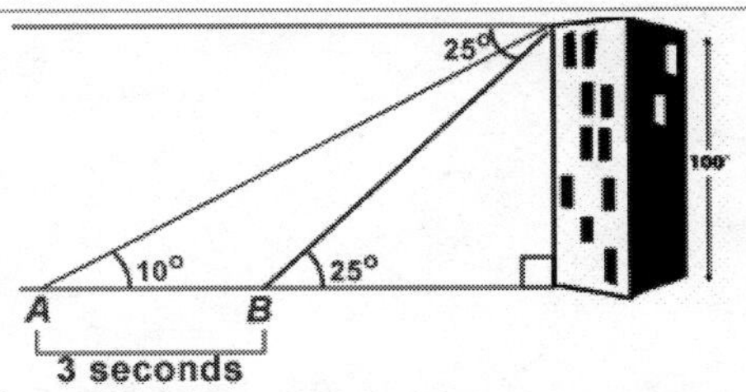

Find the distance from point B to the building

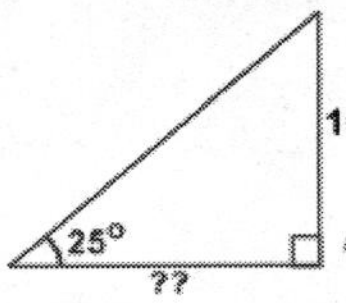

$\tan 25° = \frac{100}{?}$

$?? = \frac{100}{\tan 25°}$

use a calculator $?? = 214.45'$

Next, find the distance from the point *B* to the building. This involves the same process as finding the distance from point *A*— an angle measure and and opposite side length are given, set up a right triangle diagram to solve.

To find the length of the adjacent side, use the tangent function again. Use a calculator to find that the length from point *B* to the building is 214.45 feet.

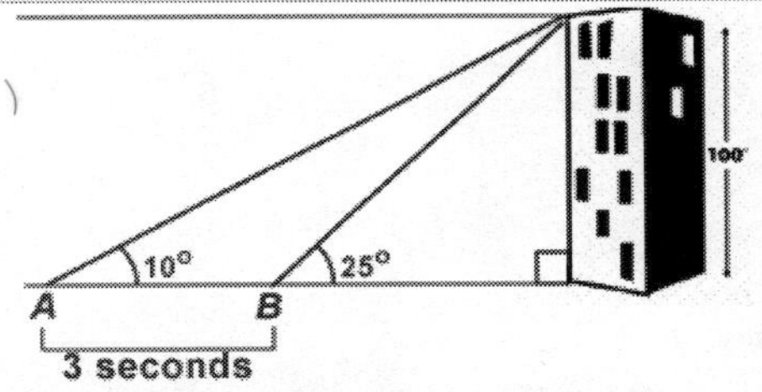

Subtract to find the distance from *A* to *B*

$567.13' - 214.45' = 352.68'$

convert to miles

352.68 feet = 0.0668 miles

Distance = 0.0668 miles

The distance the truck moved is the difference between these two answers, converted to miles from feet. (Divide the number of feet by 5,280 feet/mile.)

Subtract to find the distance from *A* to *B*

$567.13' - 214.45' = 352.68'$

convert to miles

352.68 feet = 0.0668 miles

Distance = 0.0668 miles

Find the rate

Use the distance formula:

Distance = Rate × Time

(0.0668 miles) = Rate × (3 seconds)

$\frac{0.0668}{3 \text{ seconds}} = \text{Rate}$

$\frac{0.02226}{\text{second}} = \text{Rate}$

convert to miles per hour

Rate = 80.15 miles per hour

Finding the truck's speed is a matter of dividing distance traveled by time used.

Use the distance formula to solve.

Convert the answer, 0.02226 miles per second, to miles per hour.

The final answer is 80.15 miles per hour.

	80.148 mph is definitely faster than the stated limit of 65 mph. Give this guy a ticket and tell him to slow down.

Sample problems:

1. A hiker is hiking up a 14° slope. If he hikes at a constant rate of 2 mph, how much altitude does he gain in 4 hours of hiking?

Solution: 1.9 mi
Explanation: Find the distance that he has hiked after 4 hours: $d = rt = 4\text{hr} \cdot 2 \text{ mile/hr} = 8$ miles. Let y be the altitude gained by the hiker. Use the sine function to find the altitude:
$\sin 14° = \frac{y}{8}$; $8\sin 14° = y$; $y = 1.9$. The hiker gains 1.9 miles of altitude in his 4 hours of hiking.

2. A motorcyclist traveling along a road can see the top of a 75 foot tall observation tower by looking up at an angle of 7°. Eight seconds later, the same motorcyclist has to crane his neck to an angle of 45° to see the top of the tower. Was the motorcyclist speeding on a road that has a speed limit of 35 mph? What is the difference between the speed of the motorcycle and the speed limit?

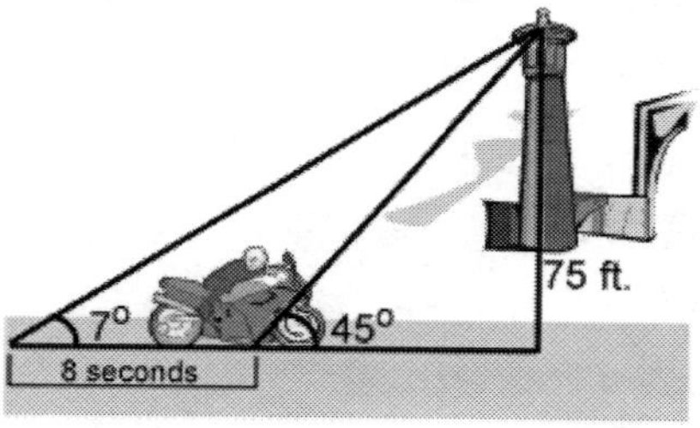

Solution: He is speeding by traveling 10.67 mph over the speed limit.
Explanation: Let x be the distance from the starting point to the tower.

Use the tangent function to find x: $\tan 7° = \frac{75}{x}$; $x = \frac{75}{\tan 7°}$; $x = 610.83$.
Let y be the distance from the motorcyclist after 8 seconds to the tower.
Use the tangent function to find y: $\tan 45° = \frac{75}{y}$; $y = \frac{75}{\tan 45°}$; $y = 75$.
Subtract to find the distance traveled by the motorcycle: $610.83 - 75 = 535.83$ ft.
Find the distance in miles: $535.83 \div 5280 = 0.101483$ miles.
Find the speed, r: $r = d/t = 0.101483/8 = 0.012685$ mi/s.
Find the speed in miles per hour: $0.012685 \frac{\text{mi}}{\text{s}} \times 60 \frac{\text{s}}{\text{min}} \times 60 \frac{\text{min}}{\text{hr}} = 45.666$ mph.
Find the miles per hour over the speed limit: $45.666 - 35 = 10.666 \approx 10.67$.

3. A helicopter is hovering 300 feet over the finish line of a boat race. The crew of Boat A can see the helicopter by looking up at an angle of 3°. At that exact same moment, the crew of Boat B has to look at an angle of 3.5° to see the chopper. After 2 minutes, the crew of Boat A has to look at an angle of 32° to see the chopper, while the crew of Boat B has to look at an angle of 32.2° to see it. Assuming that both boats will continue to travel at the same speed they have demonstrated over the last 2 minutes, which boat will win the race, and by how many seconds?

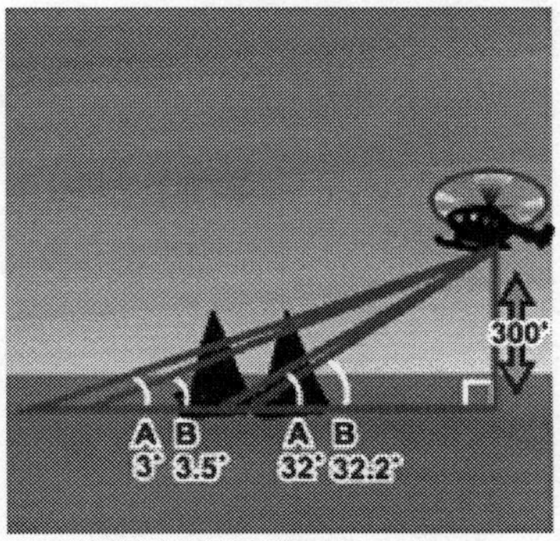

Solution: Boat A by 1.9 seconds
Explanation: Use the tangent function to find the missing distances:
Boat A → $\tan 3° = \frac{300}{x}$; $x = \frac{300}{\tan 3°} = 5724.34$, and $\tan 32° = \frac{300}{x}$; $x = \frac{300}{\tan 32°} = 480.1$,
so the distance traveled by Boat A is $5724.34 - 480.1 = 5244.24$ ft.
Boat B → $\tan 3.5° = \frac{300}{x}$; $x = \frac{300}{\tan 3.5°} = 4904.96$, and $\tan 32.3° = \frac{300}{x}$; $x = \frac{300}{\tan 32.2°} = 476.39$,
so the distance traveled is $4904.96 - 476.39 = 4428.57$ ft.
Divide each distance by 120 (120 secs = 2 min) to find the speed for each boat in ft/sec:
Boat A → $5244.24/120 = 43.7$ ft/sec, and Boat B → $4428.57/120 = 36.9$ ft/sec.
Divide the remaining distance for each boat by the speed of each boat to find the time required to finish the race: Boat A → $480.1 \div 43.7 = 10.99$ s, and
Boat B → $476.39 \div 36.9 = 12.91$ s. Thus, Boat A will win the race by 1.9 seconds.

Practice problems: *(Answers on page: 756)*

1. Ada spots the cities of Gary and Smithville from her hot air balloon at an altitude of 3 miles. The angles of depression to the cities are 23° and 60°. How far apart are the cities?

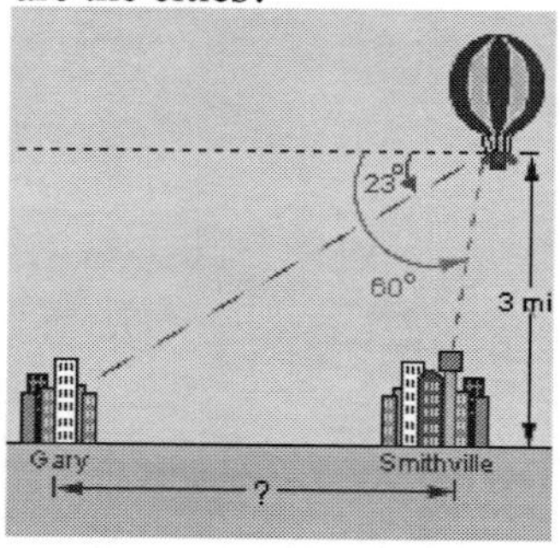

2. A helicopter is hovering 1000 feet above the surface of a lake. The helicopter is observed by the crew of a boat as they look upwards at an angle of 25°. Twenty seconds later, the crew has to look at an angle of 70° to see the helicopter. How fast was the boat traveling?

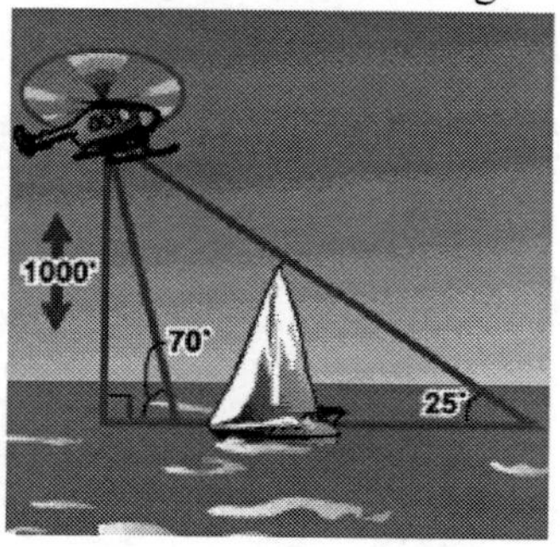

3. An announcer at a race track, sitting on the observation platform 100 feet above the track, spots a horse running on the track. The announcer has to look at an angle of depression of 4°. Some time later during the race (28.6 seconds later to be exact) he spots the same horse. This time he has to look at an angle of depression of 48°. How does the speed of the horse (in miles per hour) compare to that of the horse who set the record for the 1.25 mile Kentucky Derby at 1 minute, 59 seconds?

Review questions: *(Answers to odd questions on page: 756)*

1. A submarine has an enemy battleship in its sights. If the battleship is 800 feet long and subtends an angle of 30°, how far away is the battleship? Assume that the submarine is approaching the exact center of the battleship.

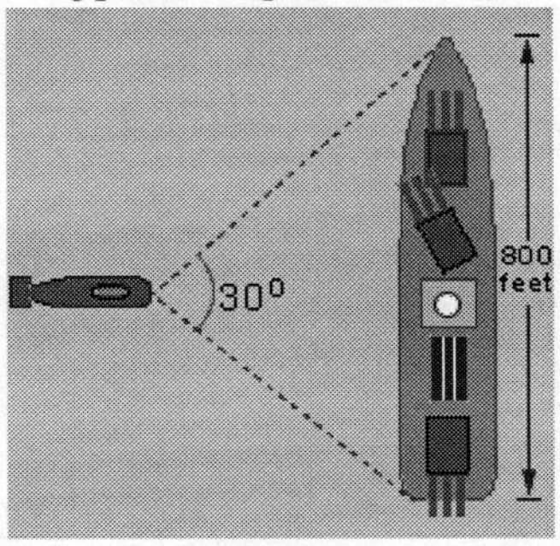

2. What is the height of this building?

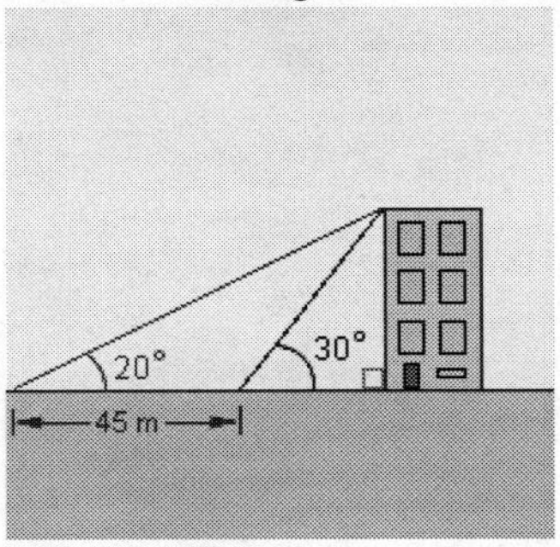

3. Find the distance across the river. Give your answer in miles, rounded to 4 decimal places.

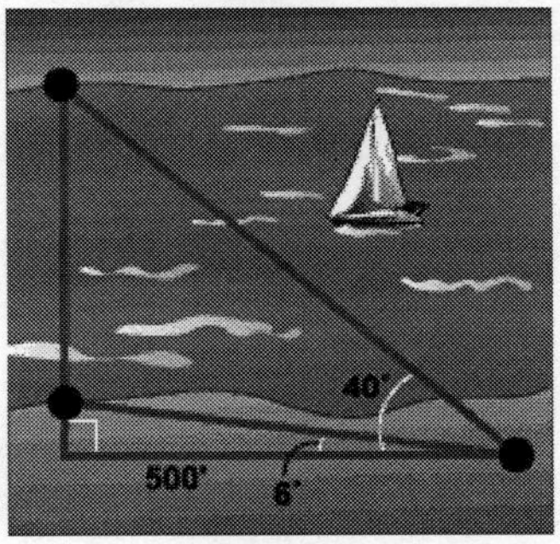

4. A fountain sits in the courtyard 50 feet from a building. A person at the fountain looking up at a 30° angle can see a flower pot in a window. Looking at a 75° angle from the same position, the person sees a dog in a window. How many yards higher is the dog than the flower pot? Round your answer to 2 decimal places.

5. A passenger in a car at an intersection sees laundry drying on the roof of a building in the distance. The passenger can see the laundry by looking up at a 10° angle. At the next intersection, the passenger can see the laundry, but only by sticking his head out of the car and looking up at a 35° angle. The car he is riding in had traveled from the first intersection to the second intersection in 5 seconds. What is the difference between the speed of the car and the street speed limit of 25 mph?

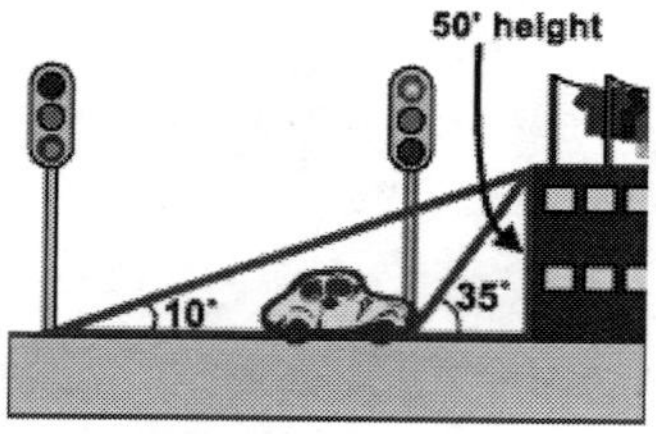

7

Trigonometric Identities

Fundamental Trigonometric Identities

- An **identity** is an equation that is true for all meaningful values of the variable(s) involved.
- Four basic **trigonometric identities**:
  - $\tan\theta = \dfrac{\sin\theta}{\cos\theta}$
  - $\cos^2\theta + \sin^2\theta = 1$ (the **Pythagorean identity**)
  - $1 + \tan^2\theta = \sec^2\theta$
  - $1 + \cot^2\theta = csc^2\theta$

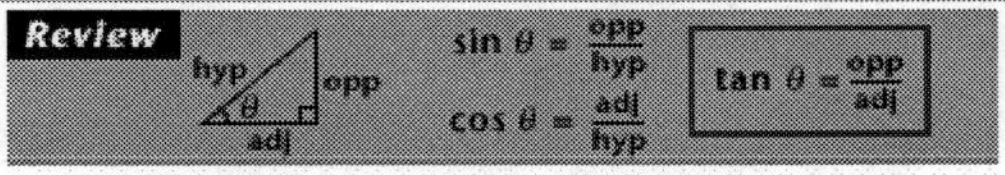 $\dfrac{\sin\theta}{\cos\theta} = \dfrac{\frac{opp}{hyp}}{\frac{adj}{hyp}} = \dfrac{opp}{hyp} \cdot \dfrac{hyp}{adj} = \boxed{\dfrac{opp}{adj}} = \tan\theta$ $\boxed{\tan\theta = \dfrac{\sin\theta}{\cos\theta}}$	Let's get back to the basics. Think back to the three basic trigonometric functions: sine, cosine, and tangent. If you divide sine by cosine and do some canceling, the result is tangent. This is our first **trigonometric identity**! An **identity** is an equation that is always true.
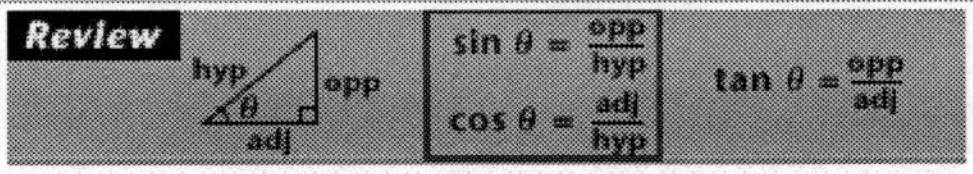 $opp^2 + adj^2 = hyp^2$ *divide by hyp²* $\dfrac{opp^2}{hyp^2} + \dfrac{adj^2}{hyp^2} = \dfrac{hyp^2}{hyp^2}$ $\left(\boxed{\dfrac{opp}{hyp}}\right)^2 + \left(\boxed{\dfrac{adj}{hyp}}\right)^2 = 1$ $\boxed{\sin^2\theta + \cos^2\theta = 1}$	To identify other trig identities, begin with the familiar right triangle and apply the **Pythagorean theorem:** $a^2 + b^2 = c^2$ Plug in opposite, adjacent, and hypotenuse for *a*, *b*, and *c*, respectively. The result is one of the most important trigonometric identities, the **Pythagorean identity**: $\sin^2\theta + \cos^2\theta = 1$
$\sin^2\theta + \cos^2\theta = 1$ $\left(\dfrac{\sin\theta}{\cos\theta}\right)^2 + \left(\dfrac{\cos\theta}{\cos\theta}\right)^2 = \dfrac{1}{\cos^2\theta}$ $\left(\dfrac{\sin\theta}{\cos\theta}\right)^2 + 1 = \dfrac{1}{\cos^2\theta}$ $\boxed{\tan^2\theta + 1 = \sec^2\theta}$	Manipulating the Pythagorean identity produces other important trig identities. Given $\sin^2\theta + \cos^2\theta = 1$, if you divide both sides by $\cos^2\theta$ the result is another useful identity, $\tan^2\theta + 1 = \sec^2\theta$.
$\sin^2\theta + \cos^2\theta = 1$ *divide by sin² θ* $\left(\dfrac{\sin\theta}{\sin\theta}\right)^2 + \left(\dfrac{\cos\theta}{\sin\theta}\right)^2 = \dfrac{1}{\sin^2\theta}$ *reciprocal of tan θ* $1 + \cot^2\theta = \csc^2\theta$	Now let's go back to the Pythagorean identity and divide everything by $\sin^2\theta$. The resulting identity, $1 + \cot^2\theta = \csc^2\theta$, is very similar to the one we just found. It involves cotangent and cosecant instead of tangent and secant.

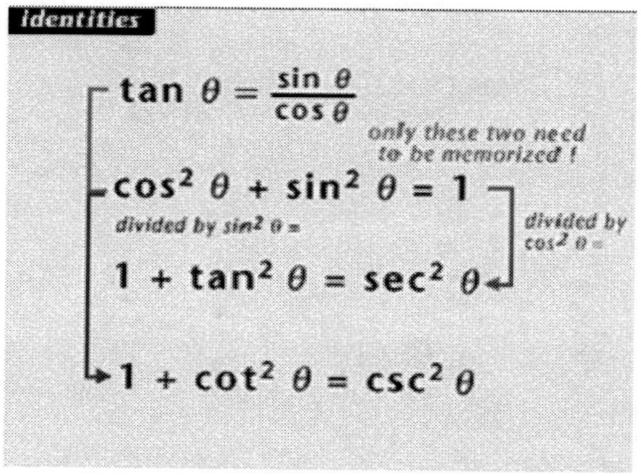

Notice that you really only need to memorize two of these four identities because the other two are derived from the Pythagorean identity.

Sample problems:

1. True or false: The result of dividing $\text{opp}^2+\text{adj}^2=\text{hyp}^2$ by opp^2 is $1+\cot^2\theta=\csc^2\theta$.
   Solution: True

   Explanation: Divide each term by opp^2: $\dfrac{\text{opp}^2}{\text{opp}^2}+\dfrac{\text{adj}^2}{\text{opp}^2}=\dfrac{\text{hyp}^2}{\text{opp}^2}$; $1+\dfrac{\text{adj}^2}{\text{opp}^2}=\dfrac{\text{hyp}^2}{\text{opp}^2}$. Recall that $\dfrac{\text{adj}^2}{\text{opp}^2}=\cot^2\theta$ and $\dfrac{\text{hyp}^2}{\text{opp}^2}=\csc^2\theta$, substitute: $1+\dfrac{\text{adj}^2}{\text{opp}^2}=\dfrac{\text{hyp}^2}{\text{opp}^2}\Rightarrow 1+\cot^2\theta=\csc^2\theta$.

2. True or false: $\tan^2\theta+1=\csc^2\theta$
   Solution: False

   Explanation: To prove that $\tan^2\theta+1=\csc^2\theta$ is false, divide the identity $\sin^2\theta+\cos^2\theta=1$ by $\cos^2\theta$: $\sin^2\theta+\cos^2\theta=1$; $\dfrac{\sin^2\theta}{\cos^2\theta}+\dfrac{\cos^2\theta}{\cos^2\theta}=\dfrac{1}{\cos^2\theta}$. Simplify: $\dfrac{\sin^2\theta}{\cos^2\theta}+1=\dfrac{1}{\cos^2\theta}$.
   Recall that $\dfrac{\sin^2\theta}{\cos^2\theta}=\tan^2\theta$ and $\dfrac{1}{\cos^2\theta}=\sec^2\theta$, substitute: $\dfrac{\sin^2\theta}{\cos^2\theta}+1=\dfrac{1}{\cos^2\theta}\Rightarrow$ $\tan^2\theta+1=\sec^2\theta$. Thus, $\tan^2\theta+1$ is equal to $\sec^2\theta$, not $\csc^2\theta$.

3. Simplify: $\left(\sin^2\dfrac{\pi}{8}+3+\cos^2\dfrac{\pi}{8}\right)^3$
   Solution: 64

   Explanation: Use the identity $\sin^2 x+\cos^2 x=1$ to substitute and simplify:
   $$\left(\sin^2\frac{\pi}{8}+3+\cos^2\frac{\pi}{8}\right)^3=\left[\left(\sin^2\frac{\pi}{8}+\cos^2\frac{\pi}{8}\right)+3\right]^3=\left[(1)+3\right]^3=4^3=64.$$

Practice problems: *(Answers on page: 756)*

1. True or false: The result of dividing $\text{adj}^2+\text{opp}^2=\text{hyp}^2$ by adj^2 is $1+\tan^2\theta=\sec^2\theta$.
2. True or false: $\cot^2\theta+1=\sec^2\theta$
3. Simplify: $\left(2x+\sin^2\dfrac{2\pi}{3}+2+\cos^2\dfrac{2\pi}{3}\right)^2$

Review questions: *(Answers to odd questions on page: 756)*

1. True or False: The result of dividing $\text{opp}^2+\text{adj}^2=\text{hyp}^2$ by hyp^2 is $\sin^2\theta+\cos^2\theta=1$.
2. True or False: $\cot\theta+1=\sec^2\theta$
3. True or False: $\tan^2\theta=\sec^2\theta-1$

4. Simplify: $\left(\cos^2\frac{\pi}{2}+5+\sin^2\frac{\pi}{2}\right)^2$

5. Simplify: $\left(\sin^2\pi+5x-\left(4-\cos^2\pi\right)\right)^2$

Finding All Function Values

- **Review**: The four basic **trigonometric identities**:
  1. $\tan\theta=\dfrac{\sin\theta}{\cos\theta}$
  2. $\sin^2\theta+\cos^2\theta=1$ (The **Pythagorean identity**)
  3. $1+\tan^2\theta=\sec^2\theta$
  4. $1+\cot^2\theta=\csc^2\theta$
- Given the value of a trigonometric function for an angle and the **quadrant** that the angle lies in, you can use trigonometric identities to find the values of the other trigonometric functions.

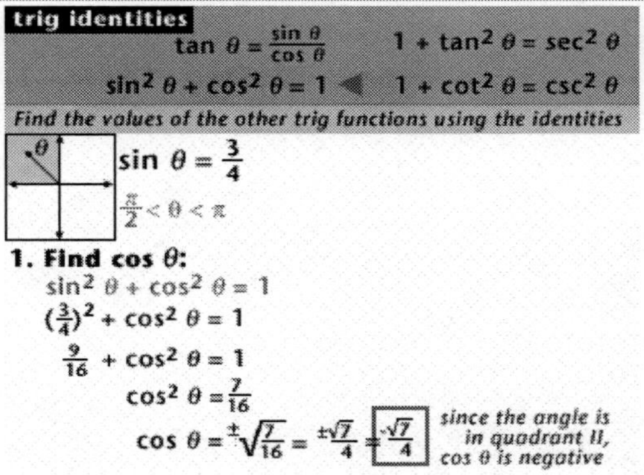 	Use the basic trig identities to find the value of trigonometric functions. Consider the following example, given $\sin\theta=\frac{3}{4}$ and $\frac{\pi}{2}<\theta<\pi$, find cos *θ*. Since you are given the value of sin *θ* and the **quadrant** that *θ* lies in, you can use a basic trig identity to find cos *θ*. Plug sin *θ* = 3/4 into the **Pythagorean identity** to find cos *θ*. Solving for cos *θ* produces two answers: $+\frac{\sqrt{7}}{4}$ and $-\frac{\sqrt{7}}{4}$; however, since *θ* lies in quadrant II, cos *θ* must be negative. Therefore, the answer is the negative square root.
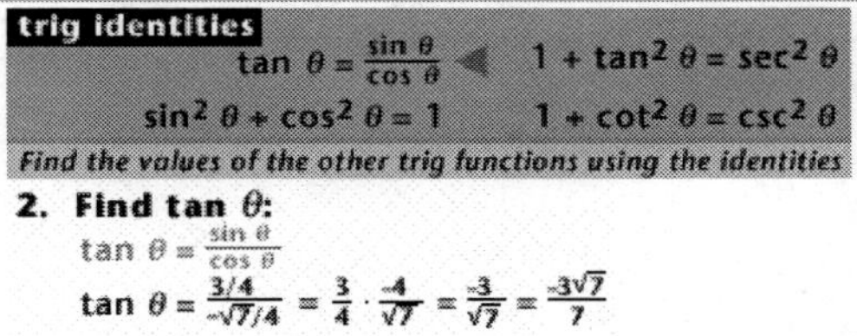 	This example asks you to find tan *θ* given $\sin\theta=\frac{3}{4}$ and $\frac{\pi}{2}<\theta<\pi$. Plugging sin *θ* and cos *θ* into the identity $\tan\theta=\frac{\sin\theta}{\cos\theta}$ produces a value of $-\frac{3\sqrt{7}}{7}$ for tan *θ*.

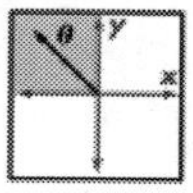

$\sin\theta = \frac{3}{4}$

$\frac{\pi}{2} < \theta < \pi$

1. $\cos\theta = \boxed{\frac{-\sqrt{7}}{4}}$

2. $\tan\theta = \frac{\sin\theta}{\cos\theta}$

$= \frac{-3}{\sqrt{7}} = \boxed{\frac{-3\sqrt{7}}{7}}$

3. Find $\csc\theta$:

$\csc\theta = \frac{1}{\sin\theta}$

$= \frac{1}{3/4} = \boxed{\frac{4}{3}}$

4. Find $\sec\theta$:

$\sec\theta = \frac{1}{\cos\theta}$

$= \frac{1}{\sqrt{7}/4}$

$= \frac{-4}{\sqrt{7}} = \boxed{\frac{-4\sqrt{7}}{7}}$

5. Find $\cot\theta$:

$\cot\theta = \frac{1}{\tan\theta}$

$= \frac{1}{3/\sqrt{7}}$

$= \boxed{\frac{-\sqrt{7}}{3}}$

Finding the values of cosecant, secant, and cotangent simply involves taking the reciprocal of sine, cosine, and tangent repsectively.

Sample problems:

1. If the secant of θ is 2, what is the cosine of θ?

   Solution: $\frac{1}{2}$

   Explanation: The cosine of θ is equal to the reciprocal of the secant of θ, or $\cos\theta = \frac{1}{\sec\theta}$.

   Thus, $\cos\theta = \frac{1}{\sec\theta} = \frac{1}{2}$.

2. Find $\cos\theta$, if $\sin\theta = \frac{\sqrt{3}}{2}$. (The angle is in the first quadrant).

   Solution: $\frac{1}{2}$

   Explanation: Substitute $\sin\theta = \frac{\sqrt{3}}{2}$ into the Pythagorean identity and simplify:

   $\sin^2\theta + \cos^2\theta = 1 \Rightarrow \left(\frac{\sqrt{3}}{2}\right)^2 + \cos^2\theta = 1;\ \frac{3}{4} + \cos^2\theta = 1.$

   Solve for $\cos\theta$: $\frac{3}{4} + \cos^2\theta = 1;\ \cos^2\theta = \frac{1}{4};\ \sqrt{\cos^2\theta} = \sqrt{\frac{1}{4}};\ \cos\theta = \pm\frac{1}{2}.$

   Because the angle is in the first quadrant, cosine has to be the positive square root.

   Therefore, $\cos\theta = \frac{1}{2}$.

3. If $\sec\theta = 12$, find the value of $\csc\theta$ assuming that $\sin\theta < 0$.

   Solution: $-\frac{12\sqrt{143}}{143}$

   Explanation: Since $\sec\theta = 12$ and $\cos\theta = \frac{1}{\sec\theta}$, $\cos\theta = \frac{1}{12}$.

   Use the Pythagorean identity to find $\sin\theta$:

   $\sin^2\theta + \cos^2\theta = 1;\ \sin^2\theta + \left(\frac{1}{12}\right)^2 = 1;\ \sin^2\theta + \frac{1}{144} = 1;\ \sin^2\theta = \frac{143}{144};\ \sin\theta = \pm\frac{\sqrt{143}}{12}.$

   Since $\sin\theta < 0$, $\sin\theta = -\frac{\sqrt{143}}{12}$. Thus, $\csc\theta = \frac{1}{\sin\theta} = -\frac{12}{\sqrt{143}} = -\frac{12\sqrt{143}}{143}$.

Practice problems: *(Answers on page: 756)*

1. Find $\cos\theta$, if $\sin\theta = \frac{1}{2}$. (The angle is in the first quadrant).
2. If the cotangent of θ is 2 in the first quadrant, what is the secant of θ?

3. Suppose $\csc\theta = 6$ and $\cos\theta < 0$. What is $\cot\theta$?

Review questions: *(Answers to odd questions on page: 756)*

1. If the cosine of θ is $\frac{1}{2}$ and the sine of θ is $\frac{\sqrt{3}}{2}$, what is the tangent of θ?
2. If $\cos q = 1$, what is the value of $\sin q$?
3. Given that $\sin\theta = .65$ and θ is in the first quadrant, what is the value of $\tan\theta$?
4. What is the cosecant of θ if the cosine of θ is equal to $\frac{\sqrt{3}}{2}$ and θ lies in Quadrant I?
5. If $\sec^2 q = 5$, and q lies in Quadrant I, what is the value of $\tan q$?

Simplifying a Trigonometric Expression Using Trigonometric Identities

- **Review**: The four basic **trigonometric identities**:
  1. $\tan\theta = \dfrac{\sin\theta}{\cos\theta}$
  2. $\sin^2\theta + \cos^2\theta = 1$ (the **Pythagorean identity**)
  3. $1 + \tan^2\theta = \sec^2\theta$
  4. $1 + \cot^2\theta = \csc^2\theta$
- You can use trigonometric identities to help you simplify complicated trigonometric expressions.
- Writing a trigonometric function in terms of just sines and cosines often makes it easier to simplify.

trig identities $\tan\theta = \frac{\sin\theta}{\cos\theta}$ $\quad 1 + \tan^2\theta = \sec^2\theta$ $\sin^2\theta + \cos^2\theta = 1$ $\quad 1 + \cot^2\theta = \csc^2\theta$ *simplify the expression* $\tan x \cos x$ $\tan x \cos x = \frac{\sin x}{\cancel{\cos x}} \cdot \cancel{\cos x} = \boxed{\sin x}$ *can only cancel if $\cos x \neq 0$*	You have seen how using **trigonometric identities** can help you find the values of trigonometric functions. They can also help you simplify complicated trigonometric expressions. In this example, you can simplify the expression $\tan x \cos x$ by rewriting $\tan x$ as the fraction $\sin x / \cos x$. After canceling and restricting the value of x, $\tan x \cos x$ simplifies to $\sin x$.
trig identities $\tan\theta = \frac{\sin\theta}{\cos\theta}$ $\quad 1 + \tan^2\theta = \sec^2\theta$ $\sin^2\theta + \cos^2\theta = 1$ $\quad 1 + \cot^2\theta = \csc^2\theta$ *simplify the expression* $\frac{1 + \tan^2\theta}{\csc^2\theta} = \frac{\sec^2\theta}{\csc^2\theta}$ $= \frac{1/\cos^2\theta}{1/\sin^2\theta}$ *convert to sin and cos* $= \frac{1}{\cos^2\theta} \cdot \frac{\sin^2\theta}{1}$ $= \frac{\sin^2\theta}{\cos^2\theta} = \frac{\sin\theta}{\cos\theta} \cdot \frac{\sin\theta}{\cos\theta}$ $= \boxed{\tan^2\theta}$	Consider the example, $\frac{1+\tan^2\theta}{\csc^2\theta}$. To simplify, first rewrite the numerator, $1 + \tan^2\theta$, as $\sec^2\theta$. Next, convert everything to sines and cosines. **REMEMBER**: It is often easier to simplify a trigonometric expression when it is written in terms of just sines and cosines. The answer is pretty simple!

simplify the expression $\frac{1-\cos^2 t}{\sin t} = \frac{\sin^2 t}{\sin t}$ $= \frac{\sin t\ \sin t}{\sin t}$ (the common factor sin t struck out) $= \boxed{\sin t}$	To simplify the expression given here, first use the **Pythagorean identity** to simplify the numerator. Next, express the numerator in factored form. Cancel the common factor, sin *t*, from the numerator and denominator. **NOTICE**: You can only cancel terms from the numerator and denominator if you promise that the denominator will never equal 0.

Sample problems:

1. Simplify: $\dfrac{\sin^3 x}{\cos x} + \sin x \cos x$

   Solution: $\tan x$

   Explanation: Find a common denominator and add the terms: $\dfrac{\sin^3 x}{\cos x} + \sin x \cos x = \dfrac{\sin^3 x}{\cos x} + \dfrac{\sin x \cos^2 x}{\cos x} = \dfrac{\sin^3 x + \sin x \cos^2 x}{\cos x}$.

   Factor the numerator: $\dfrac{\sin^3 x + \sin x \cos^2 x}{\cos x} = \dfrac{\sin x(\sin^2 x + \cos^2 x)}{\cos x}$.

   Use the Pythagorean identity to simplify: $\dfrac{\sin x(\sin^2 x + \cos^2 x)}{\cos x} = \dfrac{\sin x(1)}{\cos x} = \dfrac{\sin x}{\cos x} = \tan x$.

2. Simplify: $\dfrac{\sec^2 - \tan^2 \theta}{\cot^2 \theta - \csc^2 \theta}$

   Solution: -1

   Explanation: Use the identities $(1 + \tan^2 \theta = \sec^2 \theta$ and $1 + \cot^2 \theta = \csc^2 \theta)$ to simplify:

   $$\frac{\sec^2 - \tan^2 \theta}{\cot^2 \theta - \csc^2 \theta} = \frac{\left(1 + \tan^2 \theta\right) - \tan^2 \theta}{\cot^2 \theta - \left(1 + \cot^2 \theta\right)} = \frac{1}{-1} = -1.$$

3. Simplify: $\left(\csc^2 t - 1\right)\left(\csc^2 t \cdot \dfrac{1}{\sec^2 t}\right)$

   Solution: $\cot^4 t$

   Explanation: Rewrite the identity $1 + \cot^2 \theta = \csc^2 \theta$ as $\cot^2 \theta = \csc^2 \theta - 1$ and simplify:

   $$\left(\csc^2 t - 1\right)\left(\csc^2 t \cdot \frac{1}{\sec^2 t}\right) = \cot^2 t\left(\csc^2 t \cdot \frac{1}{\sec^2 t}\right), \text{ since } \cot^2 t = \csc^2 t - 1.$$

   Use the identities $\csc^2 t = \dfrac{1}{\sin^2 t}$ and $\dfrac{1}{\sec^2 t} = \cos^2 t$ to further simplify:

   $$\cot^2 t\left(\csc^2 t \cdot \frac{1}{\sec^2 t}\right) = \cot^2 t\left(\frac{1}{\sin^2 t} \cdot \cos^2 t\right) = \cot^2 t\left(\frac{\cos^2 t}{\sin^2 t}\right) = \cot^2 t\left(\cot^2 t\right) = \cot^4 t.$$

Practice problems: *(Answers on page: 756)*

1. Simplify: $\dfrac{\sec^2 x - 1}{\sec^2 x}$
2. Simplify: $\sin^2 t \csc^2 t - \cos^2 t$
3. Simplify: $(\sec^2 \theta - 1)(\csc^2 \theta \cos^2 \theta)$

Review questions: *(Answers to odd questions on page: 756)*

1. Simplify: $\csc \theta \tan \theta$

2. Simplify: $\tan^2 x \csc^2 x$
3. Simplify: $\tan x \sin x \sec x$
4. Simplify: $\tan^2 x(1+\cot^2 x)$
5. Simplify: $\sin^2 x(1+\cot^2 x)$

Simplifying Trigonometric Expressions Involving Fractions

- **Review**: The four basic **trigonometric identities**:
  1. $\tan\theta = \dfrac{\sin\theta}{\cos\theta}$
  2. $\sin^2\theta + \cos^2\theta = 1$(the **Pythagorean identity**)
  3. $1+\tan^2\theta = \sec^2\theta$
  4. $1+\cot^2\theta = \csc^2\theta$
- **Review**: You can use trigonometric identities to help you simplify complicated trigonometric expressions.
- **Review**: Writing a trig function in terms of just sines and cosines often makes it easier to simplify.

simplify the expression $\dfrac{1+\tan x}{1+\cot x} = \dfrac{1+\frac{\sin x}{\cos x}}{1+\frac{\cos x}{\sin x}}$ *convert to sin and cos* $= \dfrac{\frac{\sin x+\cos x}{\cos x}}{\frac{\sin x+\cos x}{\sin x}}$ *get a common denominator* $= \dfrac{\cos x+\sin x}{\cos x}\cdot\dfrac{\sin x}{\cos x+\sin x}$ *invert and multiply* $= \dfrac{(\sin x+\cos x)\sin x}{(\sin x+\cos x)\cos x}$ $= \dfrac{\cancel{(\sin x+\cos x)}\sin x}{\cancel{(\sin x+\cos x)}\cos x}$ $= \dfrac{\sin x}{\cos x} = \boxed{\tan x}$	Consider the given expression. To simplify, first convert the numerator to an expression involving just sines and cosines. Next, convert the denominator. Add the terms in the numerator and the terms in the denominator by using a common denominator for each. (Notice that in the numerator the number 1 had to be rewritten as $\cos x/\cos x$ and in the denominator the number 1 had to be rewritten as $\sin x/\sin x$.) Invert and multiply to get rid of the complex fraction. Cancel common factors and simplify. Notice that the given expression, $(1+\tan x)/(1+\cot x)$, simplifies to just $\tan x$.
simplify the expression $\dfrac{\sec^2\theta-\tan^2\theta}{\cos^2\theta+\sin^2\theta} = \dfrac{1+\tan^2\theta-\tan^2\theta}{\cos^2\theta+\sin^2\theta}$ $= \dfrac{1+\cancel{\tan^2\theta}-\cancel{\tan^2\theta}}{1}$ $= \dfrac{1}{1} = \boxed{1}$	To simplify the expression illustrated here, replace the $\sec^2\theta$ term in the numerator with $1+\tan^2\theta$. The $\tan^2\theta$ terms in the numerator cancel, and the **Pythagorean identity** tells you that the denominator is equal to 1.
simplify the expression $\dfrac{\sec\theta}{\sin\theta}-\dfrac{\sin\theta}{\cos\theta} = \dfrac{\cos\theta}{\cos\theta}\dfrac{\sec\theta}{\sin\theta}-\dfrac{\sin\theta}{\sin\theta}\dfrac{\sin\theta}{\cos\theta}$ *get a common denominator* $= \dfrac{\cos\theta\sec\theta}{\sin\theta\cos\theta}-\dfrac{\sin^2\theta}{\sin\theta\cos\theta}$ $= \dfrac{\cancel{\cos\theta}\,\cancel{\frac{1}{\cos\theta}}}{\sin\theta\cos\theta}-\dfrac{\sin^2\theta}{\sin\theta\cos\theta}$ $= \dfrac{1-\sin^2\theta}{\sin\theta\cos\theta}$ $= \dfrac{\cos^{\cancel{2}}\theta}{\sin\theta\cancel{\cos\theta}} = \dfrac{\cos\theta}{\sin\theta} = \boxed{\cot\theta}$	To simplify the expression $\dfrac{\sec\theta}{\sin\theta}-\dfrac{\sin\theta}{\cos\theta}$, begin by finding a common denominator. Next, rewrite the numerator of the first fraction, $\cos\theta\cdot\sec\theta$, as $\cos\theta\cdot 1/\cos\theta$. $1/\cos\theta$ and $\cos\theta$ cancel to produce 1. Subtract the fractions and simplify. The Pythagorean identity tells you that $1-\sin^2\theta=\cos^2\theta$, so the numerator can be rewritten as $\cos^2\theta$. Cancel a common factor of $\cos\theta$ and simplify.

Sample problems:

1. Simplify: $\dfrac{\sin x-1}{\cos x}-\dfrac{\cos x}{\sin x-1}$

   Solution: $2\tan x$

   Explanation: Find a common denominator and subtract:

   $$\frac{\sin x-1}{\cos x}\left(\frac{\sin x-1}{\sin x-1}\right)-\frac{\cos x}{\sin x-1}\left(\frac{\cos x}{\cos x}\right)=\frac{(\sin x-1)^2-\cos^2 x}{\cos x(\sin x-1)}=\frac{\sin^2 x-2\sin x+1-\cos^2 x}{\cos x(\sin x-1)}.$$

   Use the Pythagorean identity to substitute $\sin^2 x$ for $1-\cos^2 x$ and simplify:

   $$\frac{\sin^2 x-2\sin x+(1-\cos^2 x)}{\cos x(\sin x-1)}=\frac{\sin^2 x-2\sin x+\sin^2 x}{\cos x(\sin x-1)}=\frac{2\sin^2 x-2\sin x}{\cos x(\sin x-1)}.$$

   Factor the numerator and simplify: $\dfrac{2\sin x(\sin x-1)}{\cos x(\sin x-1)}=\dfrac{2\sin x}{\cos x}=2\tan x.$

   (Note that $\sin x\neq 1$ when the factors of $\sin x-1$ are canceled.)

2. Simplify: $\dfrac{1-\tan^2\theta}{1+\tan^2\theta}$

   Solution: $\cos^2\theta-\sin^2\theta$

   Explanation: Express in terms of $\sin\theta$ and $\cos\theta$: $\dfrac{1-\tan^2\theta}{1+\tan^2\theta}=\dfrac{1-\dfrac{\sin^2\theta}{\cos^2\theta}}{1+\dfrac{\sin^2\theta}{\cos^2\theta}}.$

   Multiply by $\dfrac{\cos^2\theta}{\cos^2\theta}$ and simplify: $\dfrac{1-\dfrac{\sin^2\theta}{\cos^2\theta}}{1+\dfrac{\sin^2\theta}{\cos^2\theta}}\cdot\dfrac{\cos^2\theta}{\cos^2\theta}=\dfrac{\left(1-\dfrac{\sin^2\theta}{\cos^2\theta}\right)\cdot\cos^2\theta}{\left(1+\dfrac{\sin^2\theta}{\cos^2\theta}\right)\cdot\cos^2\theta}=$

   $$\frac{\cos^2\theta-\sin^2\theta}{\cos^2\theta+\sin^2\theta}=\frac{\cos^2\theta-\sin^2\theta}{1}=\cos^2\theta-\sin^2\theta.$$

3. Simplify: $\dfrac{\sec^2\theta}{1+\tan^2\theta}+\dfrac{\tan^2\theta}{\sec^2\theta-1}$

   Solution: 2

   Explanation: Use the Pythagorean identity $(1+\tan^2\theta=\sec^2\theta)$ to substitute:

   $$\frac{\sec^2\theta}{1+\tan^2\theta}+\frac{\tan^2\theta}{\sec^2\theta-1}=\frac{\sec^2\theta}{\sec^2\theta}+\frac{\tan^2\theta}{\tan^2\theta}=1+1=2.$$

Practice problems: *(Answers on page: 757)*

1. Simplify: $\csc\theta\left(\sin\theta+\dfrac{1}{\sec\theta}\right)$

2. Simplify: $\dfrac{(1+\sin^2\theta)-(1-\cos^2\theta)}{\sec^2\theta-1}$

3. Simplify: $\dfrac{\cot^2 x}{(1-\sin^2 x)}+\dfrac{\tan^2 x}{(1-\cos^2 x)}$

Review questions: *(Answers to odd questions on page: 757)*

1. Simplify: $\dfrac{\cos x\csc x}{\cot x}$

2. Simplify: $\dfrac{\tan x}{\cos x} \cdot \dfrac{\sec x}{\cot x}$

3. Simplify: $\dfrac{\sec\theta \tan\theta}{\cot\theta \csc\theta}$

4. Simplify: $\dfrac{\tan x + \cot x}{\cot x - \tan x}$

5. Simplify: $\dfrac{\tan^2 t}{\sec^2 t} + \dfrac{\cot^2 t}{\csc^2 t}$

Simplifying Products of Binomials Involving Trigonometric Functions

- **Review:** Four basic **trigonometric identities**:
  - $\tan\theta = \dfrac{\sin\theta}{\cos\theta}$
  - $\cos^2\theta + \sin^2\theta = 1$ (the **Pythagorean identity**)
  - $1 + \tan^2\theta = \sec^2\theta$
  - $1 + \cot^2\theta = cs\,c^2\theta$
- To simplify a product of trigonometric expressions, first multiply everything out. Then use trig identities to simplify the result.
- **Review:** Rewriting expressions in terms of sines and cosines often makes simplifying easier.

simplify the expression $(\cos\theta + 1)(\cos\theta - 1) = \cos^2\theta + \cos\theta - \cos\theta - 1$ (the middle terms $\cos\theta - \cos\theta$ struck through) $= \cos^2\theta - 1$ *$\cos^2\theta + \sin^2\theta = 1$* *$\cos^2\theta + \sin^2\theta - 1 = 0$* *$\cos^2\theta - 1 = -\sin^2\theta$* $= \boxed{-\sin^2\theta}$	To simplify this product of two binomials, first multiply the terms using the **FOIL** method. Next, use the **Pythagorean identity** to simplify: $\cos^2\theta - 1$ becomes $-\sin\theta$. Therefore, $(\cos\theta + 1)(\cos\theta - 1)$ simplifies to $-\sin^2\theta$.
simplify the expression $(\csc x - \sin x)^2 = (\csc x - \sin x)(\csc x - \sin x)$ $= \csc^2 x - \sin x \csc x - \sin x \csc x + \sin^2 x$ $= \csc^2 x - 2\sin x \csc x + \sin^2 x$ $= \csc^2 x - 2\sin x \cdot \frac{1}{\sin x} + \sin^2 x$ $= \csc^2 x - 2(1) + \sin^2 x$ *rewrite in terms of sin x and cos x* $= \frac{1}{\sin^2 x} - 2 + \sin^2 x$ *get a common denominator* $= \frac{1}{\sin^2 x} + \frac{\sin^4 x}{\sin^2 x} - \frac{2\sin^2 x}{\sin^2 x}$ $= \frac{1 + \sin^4 x - 2\sin^2 x}{\sin^2 x}$ *$s^2 - 2s + 1 = (s-1)(s-1) = (s-1)^2$* $= \frac{(\sin^2 x)^2 - 2(\sin^2 x) + 1}{\sin^2 x}$ *$\cos^2 x + \sin^2 x = 1$* *$\cos^2 x + \sin^2 x - 1 = 0$* *$\sin^2 x - 1 = -\cos^2 x$* $= \frac{(\sin^2 x - 1)(\sin^2 x - 1)}{\sin^2 x}$ $= \frac{(-\cos^2 x)(-\cos^2 x)}{\sin^2 x}$ $= \frac{\cos^4 x}{\sin^2 x}$ *Remember: $\cot x = \frac{\cos x}{\sin x}$* $= \boxed{\cos^2 x \cot^2 x}$	Consider the example illustrated here. Begin rewriting the squared expression as a product of two binomials. Use the FOIL method to multiply. Next, combine like terms. Rewrite $2\sin x \cdot \csc x$ as $2\sin x \cdot 1/\sin x$. Cancel a common factor of $\sin x$ and simplify. Rewrite $\csc^2 x$ as $1/\sin^2 x$. Find a common denominator and combine fractions. Notice, $\sin^4 x$ can be expressed as $(\sin^2 x)^2$. Treat the $\sin^2 x$ terms as you would treat a regular variable, like *s,* and factor the numerator. Simplify using the Pythagorean identity. Eliminate the fraction by writing the expression using the cotangent function.

simplify the expression	
$(\csc x - \sin x)^2 = (\frac{1}{\sin x} - \sin x)^2$ *convert to sin and cos*	Take a look at that problem again. This time, convert everything to sines and cosines first before doing any simplifying.
$= (\frac{1}{\sin x} - \frac{\sin^2 x}{\sin x})^2$ *get a common denominator*	Combine terms using a common denominator.
$= (\frac{1 - \sin^2 x}{\sin x})^2$	
$= (\frac{\cos^2 x}{\sin x})^2$	Use the Pythagorean identity to simplify the numerator.
$= \frac{\cos^4 x}{\sin^2 x}$	You get the same answer with a lot less work!
$= \boxed{\cos^2 x \cot^2 x}$	**REMEMBER:** Converting everything to sines and cosines often makes simplifying a trig function easier.

Sample problems:

1. Simplify: $\dfrac{2}{\sin\theta+1} - \dfrac{2}{\sin\theta-1}$

   Solution: $4\sec^2\theta$

   Explanation: Find a common denominator and subtract:

   $$\frac{2}{\sin\theta+1} - \frac{2}{\sin\theta-1} = \frac{2(\sin\theta-1)-2(\sin\theta+1)}{(\sin\theta+1)(\sin\theta-1)} = \frac{2\sin\theta-2-2\sin\theta-2}{(\sin\theta+1)(\sin\theta-1)} = \frac{-4}{(\sin\theta+1)(\sin\theta-1)}.$$

   Multiply the binomials in the denominator and simplify using the Pythagorean identity:

   $$\frac{-4}{(\sin\theta+1)(\sin\theta-1)} = \frac{-4}{\sin^2\theta-1} = \frac{-4}{-\cos^2\theta} = \frac{4}{\cos^2\theta} = 4\sec^2\theta.$$

2. Simplify: $(\csc x + \cot x)(\csc x - \cot x)$

   Solution: 1

   Explanation: Multiply the binomials: $(\csc x + \cot x)(\csc x - \cot x) =$ $\csc^2 x - \csc x\cot x + \cot x\csc x - \cot^2 x = \csc^2 x - \cot^2 x$. Use the identity $\csc^2 x = \cot^2 x + 1$ to simplify: $\csc^2 x - \cot^2 x = \cot^2 x + 1 - \cot^2 x = 1$.

3. Simplify: $[\csc x - (\sec^2 x - \tan^2 x)][\csc x + (\sec^2 x - \tan^2 x)]$

   Solution: $\cot^2 x$

   Explanation: Use the Pythagorean identity to rewrite $(\sec^2 x - \tan^2 x)$ as 1 then multiply the binomials: $[\csc x - (\sec^2 x - \tan^2 x)][\csc x + (\sec^2 x - \tan^2 x)] = (\csc x - 1)(\csc x + 1) = \csc^2 x - 1$. Use the Pythagorean identity to rewrite $\csc^2 x - 1$ as $\cot^2 x$: $\csc^2 x - 1 = \cot^2 x$.

Practice problems: *(Answers on page: 757)*

1. Simplify: $(1+\sin^2\theta)(1+\cot^2\theta)$
2. Simplify: $(\cos t - \sec t)^2$
3. Simplify: $[\cot\theta + (\cos^2\theta + \sin^2\theta)][\cot\theta - (\cos^2\theta + \sin^2\theta)]$

Review questions: *(Answers to odd questions on page: 757)*

1. Simplify: $(\sin x - 1)(\sin x + 1)$
2. Simplify: $(\sec t - 1)(\sec t + 1)$
3. Simplify: $(\tan x - \sin x)(\tan x + \sin x)$
4. Simplify: $(\sin\alpha + \cos\alpha)^2$
5. Simplify: $(\cot x - \cos x)(\cot x + \cos x)$

Factoring Trigonometric Expressions

- **Review:** Four basic **trigonometric identities**:
  - $\tan\theta = \dfrac{\sin\theta}{\cos\theta}$
  - $\cos^2\theta + \sin^2\theta = 1$ (the **Pythagorean identity**)
  - $1 + \tan^2\theta = \sec^2\theta$
  - $1 + \cot^2\theta = csc^2\theta$
- Trigonometric expressions can be **factored** just like **polynomials**. When factoring a trigonometric expression, use trigonometric identities to rewrite or simplify the expression.
- **Review:** Rewriting expressions in terms of sine or cosine often makes simplifying easier.

factor the trig expression $\sin^2\theta + \sin^2\theta\tan^2\theta = \sin^2\theta(1+\tan^2\theta)$ *factor out $\sin^2\theta$* $= \sin^2\theta\sec^2\theta$ $= \sin^2\theta \cdot \frac{1}{\cos^2\theta}$ $= (\frac{\sin\theta}{\cos\theta})^2$ $= \boxed{\tan^2\theta}$	Just as you can multiply out trigonometric expressions, you can also **factor** them. Consider this example. For the given expression, $\sin^2\theta + \sin^2\theta\cdot\tan^2\theta$, you can factor out $\sin^2\theta$ to produce $\sin^2\theta(1+\tan^2\theta)$. Next, rewrite $1 + \tan^2\theta$ term as $\sec^2$. Simplify further and the final answer is $\tan^2\theta$.
factor the trig expression $\sin x - \cos^2 x - 1 = \sin x - (1 - \sin^2 x) - 1$ *rewrite in terms of sin x* $= \sin x - 1 + \sin^2 x - 1$ $= \sin^2 x + \sin x - 2$ $s^2 + s - 2 = (s+2)(s-1)$ $\quad = (\sin x + 2)(\sin x - 1)$	The expression given here has sines and cosines in it. How can you possibly factor it? Use the **Pythagorean identity** to write everything in terms of $\sin x$. Then factor as you would factor a regular **polynomial**, treating the $\sin x$ term as you would treat a regular variable.
factor the trig expression $\sin^2 x + \frac{2}{\csc x} + 1 = \sin^2 x + \frac{2}{1/\sin x} + 1$ $= \sin^2 x + (2\cdot\frac{\sin x}{1}) + 1$ $= \sin^2 x + 2\sin x + 1$ $= (\sin x + 1)(\sin x + 1)$ $= \boxed{(\sin x + 1)^2}$	To factor this example, first replace $\csc x$ with $\sin x$ so that everything is in terms of sine. This expression factors like a perfect square.

Sample problems:

1. Simplify: $\sec^2 x + 6\tan x + 8$

   Solution: $(\tan x + 3)^2$

   Explanation: Use the identity $\sec^2 x = \tan^2 x + 1$ to write the expression in terms $\tan x$: $\sec^2 x + 6\tan x + 8 = (\tan^2 x + 1) + 6\tan x + 8 = \tan^2 x + 6\tan x + 9$ (which is a perfect square trinomial). Factor: $\tan^2 x + 6\tan x + 9 = (\tan x + 3)(\tan x + 3) = (\tan x + 3)^2$.

2. Simplify: $\dfrac{\sin^3 x + \cos^3 x}{\cos x + \sin x}$

Solution: $1 - \sin x \cos x$

Explanation: The numerator is the sum of two cubes and can be factored:

$$\frac{\sin^3 x + \cos^3 x}{\cos x + \sin x} = \frac{(\sin x + \cos x)(\sin^2 x - \sin x \cos x + \cos^2 x)}{\cos x + \sin x} = \sin^2 x - \sin x \cos x + \cos^2 x.$$

Use the Pythagorean identity:

$\sin^2 x - \sin x \cos x + \cos^2 x = (\sin^2 x + \cos^2 x) - \sin x \cos x = 1 - \sin x \cos x.$

(Note: $\cos x + \sin x \neq 0$.)

3. Simplify: $\cos^2 t + 4 + \dfrac{4}{\sec t}$

Solution: $(\cos t + 2)^2$

Explanation: Express in terms of cosine:

$$\cos^2 t + 4 + \frac{4}{\sec t} = \cos^2 t + 4 + \frac{4}{\frac{1}{\cos t}} = \cos^2 t + 4 + 4\cos t.$$

Factor this perfect square trinomial:

$\cos^2 t + 4\cos t + 4 = (\cos t + 2)(\cos t + 2) = (\cos t + 2)^2.$

Practice problems: *(Answers on page: 757)*

1. Simplify: $2\cos^2\theta + 10\cos\theta + 12$
2. Simplify: $\cos\theta\tan\theta + \cos\theta\cot\theta$
3. Simplify: $\dfrac{\sin^2 a - \cos^2 a}{\sin^2 a - \sin a \cos a}$

Review questions: *(Answers to odd questions on page: 757)*

1. Simplify: $\sin^2 q + \cot^2 q \sin^2 q$
2. Simplify: $\sin x - \cos^2 x \sin x$
3. Simplify: $\cos^2 x + \tan^2 x \cos^2 x$
4. Simplify: $\sin^2 x + \sin^2 x \cot^2 x$
5. Simplify: $\csc^2\theta - \cot^2\theta$

Determining Whether a Trigonometric Function Is Odd, Even, or Neither

- **Review:** A function $f(x)$ is **odd** if $f(-x) = -f(x)$ and **even** if $f(-x) = f(x)$. The graphs of odd functions are symmetric about the origin and the graphs of even functions are symmetric about the y-axis. A function can also be neither even nor odd.
- The sine and tangent functions are odd and the cosine function is even.

sine

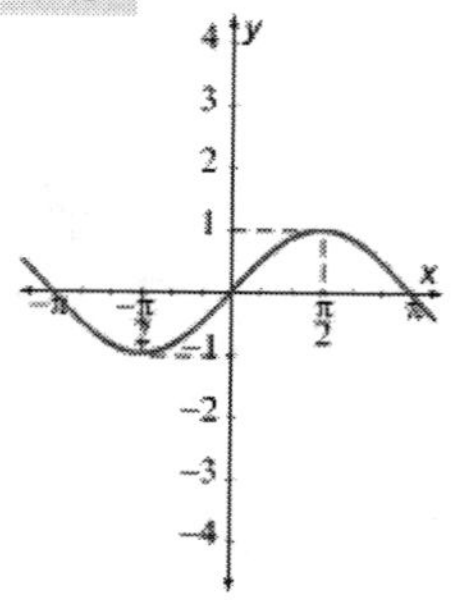

odd
sin (−x) = −sin x

cosine

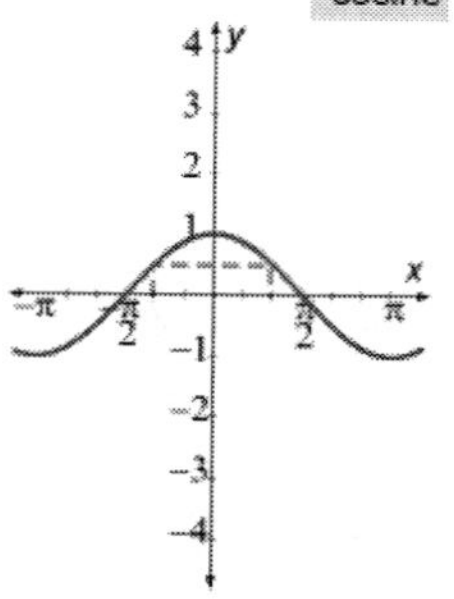

even
cos (−x) = cos x

Recall that a function $f(x)$ is **odd** if $f(-x) = -f(x)$ and **even** if $f(-x) = f(x)$. The graphs of odd functions are symmetric about the origin while the graphs of even functions are symmetric about the y-axis.

The sine function is symmetric about the origin; therefore, sine is an odd function.

The cosine function is symmetric across the y-axis; therefore, cosine is an even function.

$f(x) = \tan x$ a) look at the graph. 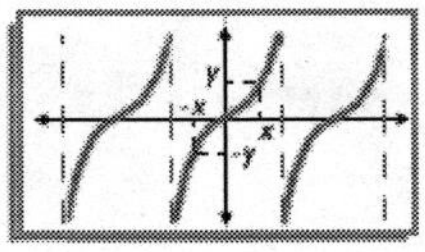 **odd** b) find f(−x). $f(x) = \tan x$ $= \frac{\sin x}{\cos x}$ *replace x with −x* $f(-x) = \frac{\sin(-x)}{\cos(-x)}$ $= \frac{-\sin x}{\cos x}$ $= -\tan x = -f(x)$ *So f(−x) = −f(x), therefore the function is* **odd.**	The graph of $y = \tan x$ is symmetric about the origin. Therefore, the tangent function is an odd function. Check this algebraically by computing the value of $\tan(-x)$. The sine function is odd; $\sin(-x) = -\sin x$. The cosine function is even; $\cos(-x) = \cos x$. Since $\tan x = \frac{\sin x}{\cos x}$, then $\tan(-x) = \frac{-\sin x}{\cos x} = -\tan x$; therefore, the tangent function is odd.
Example $f(x) = \frac{\sin x}{x}$ $f(-x) = \frac{\sin(-x)}{(-x)}$ $= \frac{-\sin x}{-x}$ $\frac{(odd)}{(odd)}$ $= \frac{\sin x}{x}$ $= f(x)$ So f(−x) = f(x), therefore the function is **even.** $\frac{\text{odd}}{\text{odd}} = \text{even}$	Consider the example here: $f(x) = \sin x/x$. To determine whether the function is odd, even, or neither, compute the value of $f(-x)$. Substituting $-x$ for x and simplifying yields $f(-x) = f(x)$; therefore, the function is even. Another way to see this is to note that both $\sin x$ and x are odd functions. Think of them as you would the signs on numbers: negative/negative = positive. In the same way, when dealing with functions, odd/odd = even.

Sample problems:

1. Is the function $f(x) = \sin x + \cos x$ odd, even, or neither?
   Solution: Neither
   Explanation: A function $f(x)$ is even if $f(-x) = f(x)$ and odd if $f(-x) = -f(x)$. Evaluate $f(-x)$: $f(-x) = \sin(-x) + \cos(-x) = -\sin x + \cos x$. Since $f(-x) \neq \sin x + \cos x$ and $f(-x) \neq -(\sin x - \cos x)$, the function is neither even nor odd.

2. Is the function $f(x) = x^2 \sin x \cos x$ odd, even, or neither?
   Solution: Odd
   Explanation: A function $f(x)$ is even if $f(-x) = f(x)$ and odd if $f(-x) = -f(x)$. Evaluate $f(-x)$, remembering that $\sin(-x) = -\sin x$ and $\cos(-x) = \cos x$: $f(-x) = (-x)^2 \sin(-x)\cos(-x) = x^2(-\sin x)(\cos x) = -x^2 \sin x \cos x = -f(x)$. Since $f(-x) = -f(x)$, the function is odd.

3. Is the function $f(x) = \sec x + \sin^2 x$ odd, even, or neither?
   Solution: Even
   Explanation:
   Evaluate $f(-x)$: $f(-x) = \sec(-x) + \sin^2(-x)$
   $$= \frac{1}{\cos(-x)} + (\sin(-x))(\sin(-x))$$
   $$= \frac{1}{\cos x} + (-\sin x)(-\sin x)$$
   $$= \sec x + \sin^2 x.$$
   Therefore, $f(-x) = f(x)$, so $f(x) = \sec x + \sin^2 x$ is an even function.

Practice problems: *(Answers on page: 757)*

1. Is this the graph of even or odd function?

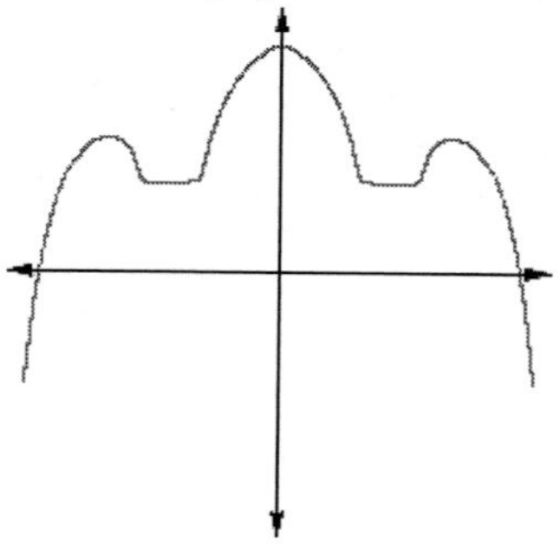

2. Is the function $f(x) = \csc x$ even, odd, or neither?
3. Is the function $f(x) = \tan x \sec x$ even, odd, or neither?

Review questions: *(Answers to odd questions on page: 757)*

1. Is the function $g(x) = 2\sin x \cos x \tan^2 x$ odd, even or neither?
2. Is the function $f(x) = \csc x \cot x$ odd, even or neither?
3. Is the function $h(x) = \cos x\left(\sin x + 2\right)$ odd, even or neither?
4. Is the function $f(x) = 3\sin x \tan x$ odd, even or neither?
5. Is the function $g\left(x\right) = \dfrac{(x-1)^3 \tan^2 x}{\sin^3 x}$ odd, even or neither?

Proving an Identity

- **Review:** An **identity** is a mathematical statement that is true for all meaningful values of the variable(s) involved.
- When proving an identity, treat each side of the equal sign as its own expression. Do not treat the identity as an equality until it is proven that both sides are equal.

Proving an Identity -manipulate each side of the equal sign independently -try to make both sides the same	Often in trigonometry you are given an equation and asked to show whether or not the statement is true. When proving an **identity**, remember to only manipulate one side of the proposed equality at a time.
Fundamental Identities $\tan\theta = \dfrac{\sin\theta}{\cos\theta}$ $\sec\theta = \dfrac{1}{\cos\theta}$ $\csc\theta = \dfrac{1}{\sin\theta}$ $\sin^2\theta + \cos^2\theta = 1$	The four basic trigonometric identities will be used often.

Example $\tan x + \cot x = \sec x \csc x$

steps:

1. Convert to sine and cosine
2. Multiply to get a common denominator
3. Add
4. Trig identity $\sin^2 x + \cos^2 x = 1$

$$= \frac{\sin x}{\cos x} + \frac{\cos x}{\sin x} \quad \Big| \quad \frac{1}{\cos x} \cdot \frac{1}{\sin x} =$$

$$= \frac{\sin^2 x}{\sin x \cos x} + \frac{\cos^2 x}{\sin x \cos x}$$

$$= \frac{\sin^2 x + \cos^2 x}{\sin x \cos x}$$

$$\boxed{= \frac{1}{\sin x \cos x}} = \boxed{\frac{1}{\sin x \cos x}}$$

When proving an identity, it is often useful to draw a line down the middle. Only work on one side of the line at a time.

Consider the given example. First express both sides of the identity in terms of sine and cosine.

Next, try to manipulate the left side of the identity until it is identical to the right side of the identity.

Working on the left side of the equal sign, find a common denominator in order to add $\sin x/\cos x + \cos x/\sin x$. Combine like terms.

You can use trig identities to simplify the expression. In this case the numerator, $\sin^2 x + \cos^2 x$, was replaced with the number 1 by the basic identity $\sin^2 x + \cos^2 x = 1$.

Now that both sides of the identity are identical, the proof is finished and the stated identity is true.

---

remember: $\sin^2 x + \cos^2 x = 1$
so, $1 - \sin^2 x = \cos^2 x$

Example $\tan x + \sec x = \dfrac{\cos x}{1 - \sin x}$

steps:

1. Convert to sine and cosine
2. Add
3. Multiply to get a common denominator
4. Foil

$$= \frac{\sin x}{\cos x} + \frac{1}{\cos x}$$

$$= \frac{\sin x + 1}{\cos x} \cdot 1$$

$$= \left(\frac{1 - \sin x}{1 - \sin x}\right)\left(\frac{\sin x + 1}{\cos x}\right)$$

$$= \frac{\sin x + 1 - \sin^2 x - \sin x}{(1 - \sin x)(\cos x)}$$

$$= \frac{\cos^2 x}{(1 - \sin x)(\cos x)}$$

$$\boxed{= \frac{\cos x}{1 - \sin x}} = \boxed{\frac{\cos x}{1 - \sin x}}$$

Draw a line down the middle to separate the equality into two expressions.

Change $\tan x + \sec x$ to an expression in terms of sine and cosine. Add like terms.

Next, multiply by a well-chosen fraction equal to 1 and simplify.

Both sides are the same; therefore the identity must be true.

Sample problems:

1. True or false: $\dfrac{\csc\theta - \cot\theta}{\sec\theta - \tan\theta} = \cot\theta$ is an identity.

   Solution: False

   Explanation:

   Express each side in terms of sine and cosine: $\dfrac{\csc\theta - \cot\theta}{\sec\theta - \tan\theta} = \cot\theta \Rightarrow \dfrac{\frac{1}{\sin\theta} - \frac{\cos\theta}{\sin\theta}}{\frac{1}{\cos\theta} - \frac{\sin\theta}{\cos\theta}} = \dfrac{\cos\theta}{\sin\theta}$.

   Subtract the terms in the numerator and denominator: $\dfrac{\frac{1-\cos\theta}{\sin\theta}}{\frac{1-\sin\theta}{\cos\theta}} = \dfrac{\cos\theta}{\sin\theta}$.

   Complete the division on the left side: $\dfrac{1-\cos\theta}{\sin\theta} \cdot \dfrac{\cos\theta}{1-\sin\theta} = \dfrac{\cos\theta}{\sin\theta} \Rightarrow \dfrac{1-\cos\theta}{1-\sin\theta} \cdot \dfrac{\cos\theta}{\sin\theta} = \dfrac{\cos\theta}{\sin\theta}$.

   On either side of the equal sign, there is a factor of $\dfrac{\cos\theta}{\sin\theta}$. So, in order for the equation to be an identity, $\dfrac{1-\cos\theta}{1-\sin\theta}$ must equal 1: $\dfrac{1-\cos\theta}{1-\sin\theta} = 1$; $1-\cos\theta = 1-\sin\theta$; $\cos\theta = \sin\theta$.

   Since $\cos\theta$ does not equal $\sin\theta$, $\dfrac{1-\cos\theta}{1-\sin\theta}$ does not equal 1. Therefore, the equation is not an identity.

2. True or false: $\cot x + \csc x = \dfrac{\sin x}{1-\cos x}$ is an identity.

   Solution: True

   Explanation:

   Express the left in terms of sine and cosine: $\cot x + \csc x = \dfrac{\sin x}{1-\cos x}$;

   $\dfrac{\cos x}{\sin x} + \dfrac{1}{\sin x} = \dfrac{\sin x}{1-\cos x}$; $\dfrac{\cos x + 1}{\sin x} = \dfrac{\sin x}{1-\cos x}$.

   Multiply the left hand side of the equation by a well chosen 1: $\dfrac{(1-\cos x)}{(1-\cos x)} \cdot \dfrac{\cos x + 1}{\sin x} = \dfrac{\sin x}{1-\cos x}$.

   Foil the numerator to set $\dfrac{1-\cos^2 x}{\sin x(1-\cos x)} = \dfrac{\sin x}{1-\cos x}$;

   Use the Pythagorean identity: $\dfrac{\sin^2 x}{\sin x(1-\cos x)} = \dfrac{\sin x}{1-\cos x}$.

   Cancel a $\sin x$: $\dfrac{\sin x}{1-\cos x} = \dfrac{\sin x}{1-\cos x}$

   The equation is an identity.

3. True or false: $(\sec\theta - \tan\theta)^2 = \dfrac{(1-\sin\theta)^2}{(1+\sin\theta)^2}$ is an identity.

Solution: False
Explanation:

Express the left in terms of sine and cosine: $\left(\dfrac{1}{\cos\theta} - \dfrac{\sin\theta}{\cos\theta}\right)^2 = \dfrac{(1-\sin\theta)^2}{(1+\sin\theta)^2}$;
$\dfrac{(1-\sin\theta)^2}{\cos^2\theta} = \dfrac{(1-\sin\theta)^2}{(1+\sin\theta)^2}$.

Use the Pythagorian identity: $\dfrac{(1-\sin\theta)^2}{1-\sin^2\theta} = \dfrac{(1-\sin\theta)^2}{(1+\sin\theta)^2}$.

The numerators are the same, so for this statement to be true, $1-\sin^2\theta$ must equal $(1+\sin\theta)^2$; however $1-\sin^2\theta \neq (1+\sin\theta)^2$.

The equation is not an identity.

Practice problems: *(Answers on page: 757)*

1. True or false: $\dfrac{1-\cos t}{\sin t} + \dfrac{\sin t}{1-\cos t} = 2\csc t$ is an identity.
2. True or false: $\dfrac{\csc x}{1+\csc x} = \dfrac{1-\sin x}{\cos^2 x}$ is an identity.
3. True or false: $\dfrac{\csc^2 t + 1 + \cot^2 t}{1-\sin^2 t} = \dfrac{2}{\sin^2 t\cos^2 t}$ is an identity.

Review questions: *(Answers to odd questions on page: 757)*

1. True or false: $(\sec x\cot x)^2 - 1 = \cot^2 x$ is an identity.
2. True or false: $4\cos^2 t + 3\sin^2 t = 3\cos^2 t + 1$ is an identity.
3. True or false: $\dfrac{2\cot^2\theta}{1+\cot^2\theta} = 2\cos^2\theta$ is an identity.
4. True or false: $(\sin x - \cos x)^2 + (\sin x + \cos x)^2 = 2$ is an identity.
5. True or false: $\dfrac{1-\tan^2\theta}{1-\tan^4\theta} = \dfrac{1}{\sec^2\theta}$ is an identity.

Proving an Identity: Other Examples

- **Review:** An **identity** is a mathematical statement that is true for all meaningful values of the variable(s) involved.
- **Review:** When proving an identity, treat each side of the equal sign as its own expression. Do not treat the identity as an equality until its proven that both sides are equal.

Proving an Identity -manipulate each side of the equal sign independently -try to make both sides the same	To prove an **identity** manipulate the expressions on either side of the equal sign independently. The expression is not an equality until it is proven to be one.
Fundamental Identities $\tan\theta = \dfrac{\sin\theta}{\cos\theta}$ $\sec\theta = \dfrac{1}{\cos\theta}$ $\csc\theta = \dfrac{1}{\sin\theta}$ $\sin^2\theta + \cos^2\theta = 1$	Remember the four basic identities.

Example $\frac{\cos^2 x - 1}{\cos x} \overset{?}{=} -\tan x \sin x$

$\sin^2\Theta + \cos^2\Theta = 1$
$\sin^2\Theta + \cos^2\Theta - 1 = 0$
$\cos^2\Theta - 1 = -\sin^2\Theta$

$= \frac{-\sin^2 x}{\cos x}$

$= \frac{-\sin x \sin x}{\cos x}$

$= \boxed{-\tan x \sin x} = \boxed{-\tan x \sin x}$

Consider the example illustrated here. Choose one side of the expression to manipulate until it is identical to the expression on the other side of the equal sign.

Use the Pythagorean identity to restate $\cos^2 x - 1$ as $-\sin^2 x$.

Break the sine-squared term into its factors. Put one of the sine terms over the cosine to get an identity (tangent).

Since both sides of the expression are identical, the statement is true; therefore, it is an identity.

Example $\frac{1}{\tan\theta} + \tan\theta \overset{?}{=} \sec\theta \csc\theta$

steps:

❶ *convert to sine and cosine* $= \frac{\cos\theta}{\sin\theta} + \frac{\sin\theta}{\cos\theta}$ $\qquad \frac{1}{\cos\theta}\cdot\frac{1}{\sin\theta} =$

❷ *multiply to get a common denominator* $= \left(\frac{\cos\theta}{\cos\theta}\right)\left(\frac{\cos\theta}{\sin\theta}\right) + \left(\frac{\sin\theta}{\sin\theta}\right)\left(\frac{\sin\theta}{\cos\theta}\right)$

$= \frac{\cos^2\theta}{\sin\theta\cos\theta} + \frac{\sin^2\theta}{\sin\theta\cos\theta}$

❸ *add* $= \frac{\cos^2\theta + \sin^2\theta}{\sin\theta\cos\theta}$

❹ *trig identity* $\sin^2 x + \cos^2 x = 1$ $\qquad = \boxed{\frac{1}{\sin\theta\cos\theta}} = \boxed{\frac{1}{\sin\theta\cos\theta}}$

For this example, first put everything in terms of sine and cosine. Then, select one side of the expression to manipulate until it is identical to the other side of the expression.

To add the two fractions on the left-hand side, find a common denominator. Then, combine the like terms.

Use the Pythagorean identity to complete the proof.

Since both sides are identical, the equation is an identity.

Sample problems:

1. Form an identity from the following expression: $\sec^2\theta - \sec^2\theta\cos^2\theta$

   Solution: $\sec^2\theta - \sec^2\theta\cos^2\theta = \tan^2\theta$

   Explanation: Factor: $\sec^2\theta - \sec^2\theta\cos^2\theta = \sec^2\theta(1-\cos^2\theta)$.

   Use a Pythagorean identity to write $(1-\cos^2\theta)$ as $\sin^2\theta$: $\sec^2\theta(1-\cos^2\theta) = \sec^2\theta(\sin^2\theta)$.

   Express in terms of sine and cosine and multiply: $\sec^2\theta(\sin^2\theta) = \frac{1}{\cos^2\theta}\cdot\frac{\sin^2\theta}{1} = \frac{\sin^2\theta}{\cos^2\theta} = \tan^2\theta$.

   Therefore, $\sec^2\theta - \sec^2\theta\cos^2\theta = \tan^2\theta$ is an identity.

2. Form an identity from the following expression: $\frac{\sin^2 x - 1}{\sin x}$

   Solution: $\frac{\sin^2 x - 1}{\sin x} = -\cot x \cos x$

   Explanation: Use the Pythagorean identity: $\frac{\sin^2 x - 1}{\sin x} = \frac{-\cos^2 x}{\sin x}$.

   Factor $-\cos^2 x$ into $-\cos x$ and $\cos x$: $\frac{-\cos^2 x}{\sin x} = \frac{-\cos x \cdot \cos x}{\sin x}$.

   Combine one of the $\cos x$ factors with the $\sin x$ factor in the denominator to arrive at a $\cot x$ factor:

   $\frac{-\cos x\cdot\cos x}{\sin x} = \frac{-\cos x}{\sin x}\cos x = -\cot x \cos x$.

   Therefore $\frac{\sin^2 x - 1}{\sin x} = -\cot x\cos x$ is an identity.

3. Form an identity from the following expression: $\tan t \cot t - \sin^2 t$

<u>Solution</u>: $\tan t \cot t - \sin^2 t = \cos^2 t$

<u>Explanation</u>: Express in terms of sine and cosine: $\tan t \cot t - \sin^2 t = \frac{\sin t}{\cos t} \cdot \frac{\cos t}{\sin t} - \sin^2 t.$

Multiply and cancel like terms: $\frac{\sin t}{\cos t} \cdot \frac{\cos t}{\sin t} - \sin^2 t = \frac{\sin t \cos t}{\sin t \cos t} - \sin^2 t = 1 - \sin^2 t.$

Use a Pythagorean identity: $1 - \sin^2 t = \cos^2 t$. Thus, $\tan t \cot t - \sin^2 t = \cos^2 t$.

Therefore, $\tan t \cot t - \sin^2 t = \cos^2 t$ is an identity.

Practice problems: *(Answers on page: 757)*

1. Form an identity from the following expression: $\csc^2 \theta - \csc^2 \theta \sin \theta$
2. Form an identity from the following expression: $\frac{1}{\cot x} + \cot x.$
3. Form an identity from the following expression: $\frac{1 + 2\tan^2 x + \tan^4 x}{1 - \tan^2 x}$

Review questions: *(Answers to odd questions on page: 757)*

1. Form an identity from the following expression: $\sec^2 x \cot x - \cot x$
2. Form an identity from the following expression: $\cot^2 \theta \left(\sec^2 \theta - 1\right)$
3. Form an identity from the following expression: $(\sec\theta + \cos\theta)(\sec\theta - \cos\theta)$
4. Form an identity from the following expression: $\frac{\csc^4 x - 2\csc^2 x + 1}{\cot^2 x}$
5. Form an identity from the following expression: $\sqrt{\frac{(1 - \cos\theta)^2}{1 - \cos^2 \theta}}$

Solving Trigonometric Equations

- Since trig functions are **periodic**, trig equations will often have many solutions. To find all the possible solutions to a trig equation, first find the solutions for a single period and then add multiples of the period to those solutions.

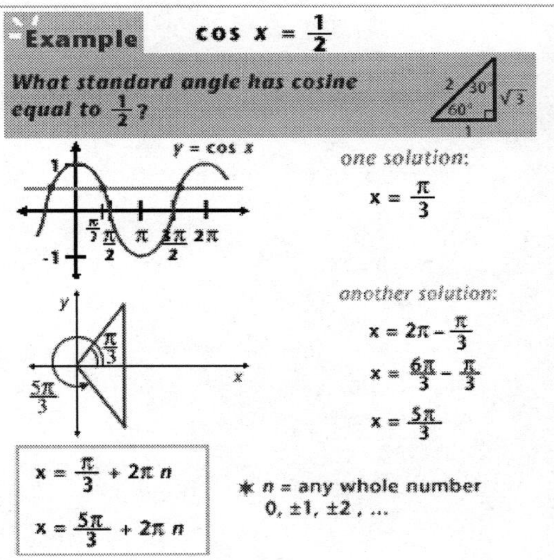

Consider the following question: what standard angle has cosine equal to 1/2?

Cos$x$ is equal to 1/2 every time the graph of $y = \cos x$ intersects the graph of $y = 1/2$.

To find the smallest angle value, think about the angle x in a right triangle; 1 is the adjacent leg and 2 is the hypotenuse. This triangle is the 30:60:90 triangle, and the angle is $\pi/3$ or 60°.

But notice that the graph of cosine is equal to 1/2 more often than just once in a **period**. 1/2 occurs again in the 4th **quadrant**. The distance the angle covers from zero to the first solution is the same as the distance from 2π to the second solution. Subtract that distance from 2π to get the second solution.

These solutions are only for the first period. To get all the solutions, add multiples of the period 2π.

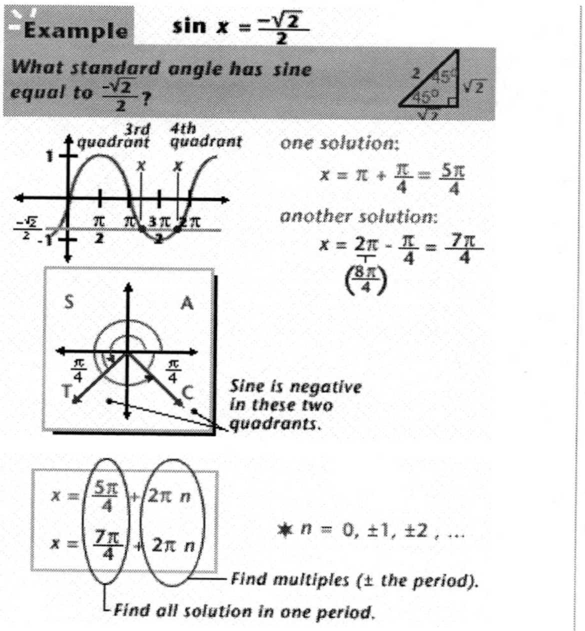

Consider the example given here. First, find the **reference angle** by ignoring the negative sign.

The reference angle is $\pi/4$ or 45°. Now, how do you find the actual value of x?

Remember that sine is negative in the third and fourth quadrants and that reference angles are measured from the x-axis.

To find the solution in the third quadrant, add π to the reference angle. To find the solution in the fourth quadrant, subtract the reference angle from 2π.

REMEMBER: This process only gives the answers in the first period of the function. Add multiples of the period to describe all the rest of the solutions.

Sample problems:

1. Find all values of x for which $\sin x = \frac{1}{2}$.

   Solution: $x = \frac{\pi}{6} + 2\pi n$ or $x = \frac{5\pi}{6} + 2\pi n$

   Explanation: $\text{Sin}\,x > 0$ in quadrant I or quadrant II; therefore, the specific solutions to the equation $\sin x = \frac{1}{2}$ must be in the interval $0 \le x \le \pi$. $\text{Sin}\,30° = \sin\frac{\pi}{6} = \frac{1}{2}$ and $\sin 150° = \sin\frac{5\pi}{6} = \frac{1}{2}$. The period of the sine function is 2π. Adding any multiple of $2\pi (2\pi n)$ produces another angle value where $\sin x = \frac{1}{2}$.

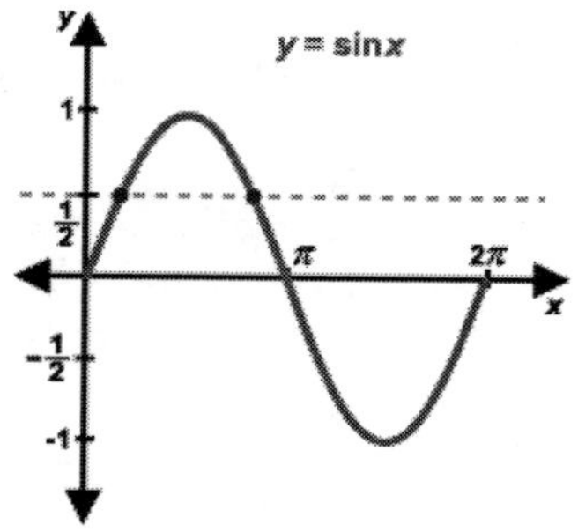

2. Solve for x: $\sin x = 0.8192$

   Solution: $x = 0.96 + 2\pi n$ and $x = 2.18 + 2\pi n$

   Explanation: Notice that the line $y = 0.8192$ passes through the graph of the sine in several places. Looking at the first period you can see that there are two solutions, one in quadrant one and the other in quadrant two. Use the arcsine function to find the value of the reference angle. Subtract that angle from π to determine the solution in the second quadrant. Finally, notice that these solutions repeat in each period, so all of the solutions are given by $x = 0.96 + 2\pi n$ and $x = 2.18 + 2\pi n$ where n is any integer.

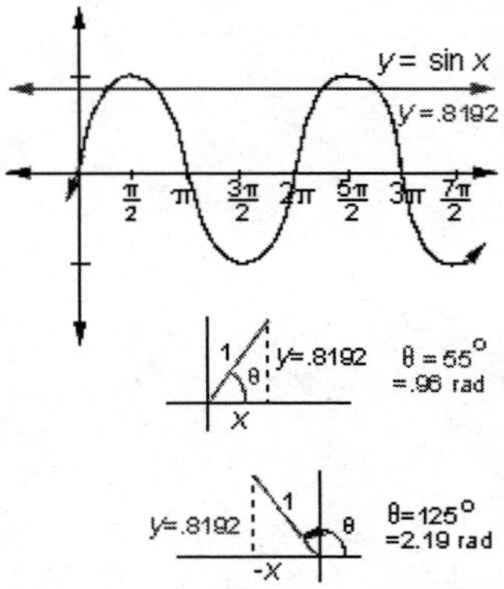

3. Solve for x: $\sin 2x = \dfrac{1}{2}$

<u>Solution:</u> $x = \dfrac{\pi}{12} + \pi n$ and $x = \dfrac{5\pi}{12} + \pi n$

<u>Explanation:</u> Notice that the period of sine has changed. Also notice that the line $y = \dfrac{1}{2}$ passes through the graph of $\sin 2x$ at several places. Looking at the first period, there are two solutions. In a triangle, sine is equal to the opposite over the hypotenuse, so the length of the opposite leg is 1 and the hypotenuse 2. This triangle is the 30:60:90 triangle and the angle is 30° or $\dfrac{\pi}{6}$. Sine is positive in the first and second quadrant because of the coefficient in the argument, $2 = \dfrac{\pi}{2}$ (in the first quadrant) and $2 = \dfrac{5\pi}{6}$ (in the second quadrant). But notice that the solution repeats each period, so all of the solutions are $x = \dfrac{\pi}{12}\pi n$ and $x = \dfrac{5\pi}{12} + \pi n$ where n is any integer.

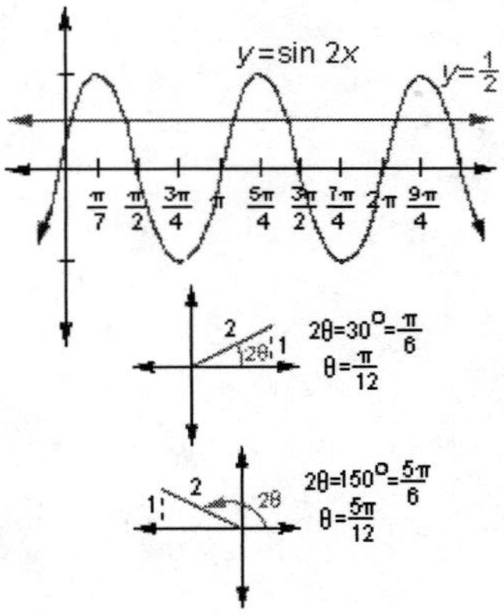

Practice problems: *(Answers on page: 757)*

1. Solve for x: $\cos x = \dfrac{\sqrt{2}}{2}$
2. Solve for x: $\sec x = -1$.
3. Solve for x: $\cos^2 x = 1$

Review questions: *(Answers to odd questions on page: 757)*

1. Find all solutions to the equation $\cos x = -1$.

2. Find all solutions to the equation $\cos x = \frac{\sqrt{3}}{2}$.

3. True or false: The equation $\sec x = \frac{1}{2}$ has no solutions.

4. Find all solutions to the equation $\sin^2 x = 1$.

5. Find all solutions to the equation $\tan x = 1$.

Solving Trigonometric Equations by Factoring

- When solving trig equations by factoring, try to isolate all the terms on one side of the equation and set it equal to zero. Then, **factor** that side of the equation so that the equation equals zero where the factors equal zero.
- **Review:** Since trig functions are **periodic**, trig equations can have many solutions. To find all the possible solutions to a trig equation, find the solutions for a single period and then add multiples of the **period** to those solutions.

Example $\tan x \sin^2 x = \tan x$ *steps:* 1) *factor* 2) *solve separately* $\tan x \sin^2 x - \tan x = 0$ $\tan x (\sin^2 x - 1) = 0$ $\tan x = 0$ *or* $\sin^2 x - 1 = 0$ $\sin^2 x = 1$ $\sin x = \pm 1$	When solving trig equations by factoring, isolate all of the expressions on the same side (setting it equal to zero) and **factor**. If two factors multiply together to equal zero, then either the first factor, the second factor, or both factors equals zero. In this example, first subtract $\tan x$ from both sides of the equation. Next, factor the left side of the equation. Set each factor equal to zero and solve. You find that either $\tan x = 0$ or $\sin x = 1$ or -1.
$x = \pi n$ $n = 0, \pm1, \pm2, \ldots$ 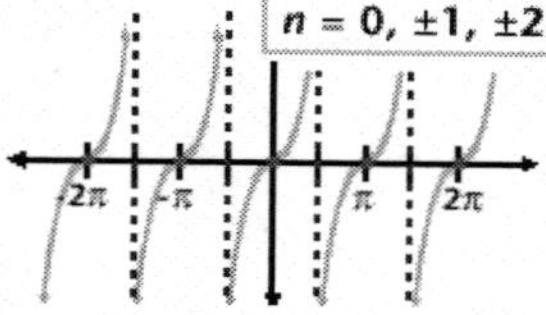 *Zeros occur at all multiples of* π.	Once the equation is broken into factors, there are several distinct equations to solve. Find all the solutions for each factor. Find the solutions of $\tan x = 0$ by looking at the graph. You find that $\tan x = 0$ at all multiplicities of pi.
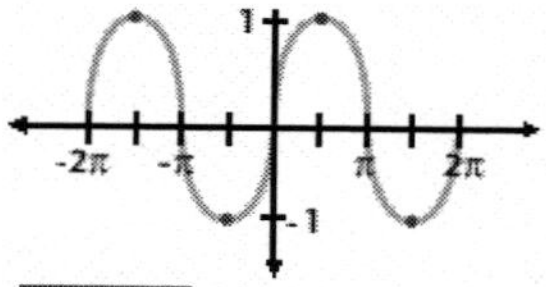 *Where does sine equal +1 or −1?* **note:** *These are the odd multiples which can be combined into the equation.* $x = \frac{\pi}{2} \pm 2\pi n$ *and* $x = \frac{3\pi}{2} \pm 2\pi n$ $x = \frac{(2n+1)\pi}{2}$ $n = 0, \pm1, \pm2, \ldots$ Solution: $x = \pi n$ OR $\frac{(2n+1)}{2}\pi$ for $n = 0, \pm1, \pm2, \ldots$	Now find when $\sin x = \pm1$ by looking at the graph. $\sin\frac{\pi}{2} = 1$, $\sin\frac{3\pi}{2} = -1$. Remember to add multiples of the **period** to the answers. The answers can be combined to get a solution that is easier to express. The solution set is made up of the solutions for the tangent and the solutions for the sine.

Sample problems:

1. Find all solutions in the interval $[0,2\pi)$ of the equation $2\cos\theta\sin\theta+\cos\theta=0$.

   Solution: $\theta=\frac{\pi}{2},\frac{7\pi}{6},\frac{3\pi}{2}$, or $\frac{11\pi}{6}$

   Explanation: Factor: $(\cos\theta)(2\sin\theta+1)=0$. Set each factor equal to zero: $\cos\theta=0$ or $2\sin\theta+1=0$. For the first factor: $\cos\theta=0$, cosine is equal to zero when θ is equal to $\frac{\pi}{2}$ and $\frac{3\pi}{2}$. Solve the second factor for θ: $2\sin\theta+1=0$; $2\sin\theta=-1$; $\sin\theta=\frac{-1}{2}$, sine is equal to $\frac{-1}{2}$ when θ is equal to $\frac{7\pi}{6}$ and $\frac{11\pi}{6}$. So, the solutions within $[0,2\pi)$ are $\theta=\frac{\pi}{2},\frac{7\pi}{6},\frac{3\pi}{2}$, or $\frac{11\pi}{6}$.

2. Solve the equation $\sin^2 x+\sin x=0$ on $[0,2\pi]$.

   Solution: $x=0,\ \pi,\ \frac{3\pi}{2}$, or 2π

   Explanation: Factor: $\sin x(\sin x+1)=0$. Set each factor equal to zero: $\sin x=0$ or $(\sin x+1)=0$. For the first factor: $\sin x=0$, therefore $x=0$, $x=\pi$ or $x=2\pi$. Solve the second factor for x: $\sin x+1=0$; $\sin x=-1$, therefore $x=\frac{3\pi}{2}$. So the solutions are $x=0$, $x=\pi$, $x=\frac{3\pi}{2}$, and $x=2\pi$.

3. Find all solutions to the equation $2\cos^2 x-5\cos x=-2$.

   Solution: $x=\frac{\pi}{3}+2\pi n$ or $\frac{5\pi}{3}+2\pi n$

   Explanation: Manipulate the terms: $2\cos^2 x-5\cos x+2=0$. Factor: $(2\cos x-1)(\cos x-2)=0$. Solve the first factor for x: $2\cos x-1=0$; $\cos x=\frac{1}{2}$, then $x=\frac{\pi}{3}$ or $x=\frac{5\pi}{3}$. Solve the second factor for x: $\cos x-2=0$; $\cos x=2$, however this is impossible because the range of $\cos x$ is restricted to values between -1 and 1. The general solution is $x=\frac{\pi}{3}+2\pi n$ or $x=\frac{5\pi}{3}+2\pi n$.

Practice problems: *(Answers on page: 757)*

1. Find all solutions in the interval $[0,2\pi)$ of the equation $\sin^2\theta=\frac{1}{2}\sin\theta$.
2. Solve the equation $\sin x\tan x=\sin x$ on the interval $[0,2\pi)$.
3. Solve the equation $\tan^2 x\csc x=\tan^2 x$ on $[0,2\pi)$.

Review questions: *(Answers to odd questions on page: 757)*

1. Find all solutions in the interval $[0,\ 2\pi)$ of the equation $\sin x=\tan x$.
2. Find all solutions in the interval $[0,\ 2\pi)$ of the equation $\cos^2 x-1=-\sin x$.
3. Find all solutions in the interval $[0,\ 2\pi]$ of the equation $\sin x\cos x=0$.
4. Find all solutions to the equation $2\sin x\cos x=\sin x$ in $[0,\ 2\pi)$.
5. Find all solutions to the equation $2\cos^2 x+\cos x=1$ in $[0,\ 2\pi)$.

Solving Trigonometric Equations with Coefficients in the Argument

- Coefficients in the **argument** of a trig function change the **period** of the function. To solve an equation involving trig functions with coefficients in the arguments, first solve the equation ignoring the coefficients. Then divide the solutions through by the coefficients appropriately.
- **Review:** Since trig functions are **periodic**, they often have many solutions. To find all the possible solutions to a trig equation, find the solutions for a single period and then add multiples of the period to those solutions.

Example Find all the solutions for one period of the given function.

$2\sin(3\theta) = 1$

Let $ø = 3\theta$

$2\sin ø = 1$

$\sin ø = \frac{1}{2}$

$\sin ? = \frac{1}{2}$

$\sin\frac{\pi}{6} = \frac{1}{2}$

So, $3\theta = \frac{\pi}{6}$ and $3\theta = \pi - \frac{\pi}{6}$

$3\theta = \frac{5\pi}{6}$

Therefore,

$\theta = \frac{\pi}{18}$ and $\theta = \frac{5\pi}{18}$

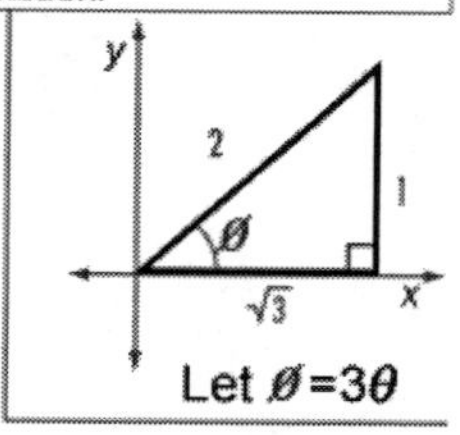

To solve trig equations with coefficients in the **argument**, start by factoring (if needed) or isolating the trig function.

NOTICE: In this example we're treating 3θ as if it were a different angle called $ø$ and then finding the values of $ø$ that make $\sin ø = 1/2$.

Divide through by the coefficient of θ to get the answers.

Example Find all the solutions for **two** periods of the given function.

$\tan^2(2x) = 1$

Take the square root

$\tan(2x) = \pm 1$

Let $ø = 2x$

$\tan ø = \pm 1$

$\tan ? = 1 \qquad \tan ? = -1$

$\tan\frac{\pi}{4} = 1 \qquad \tan -\frac{\pi}{4} = -1$

So, $ø = \frac{\pi}{4} = 2x$

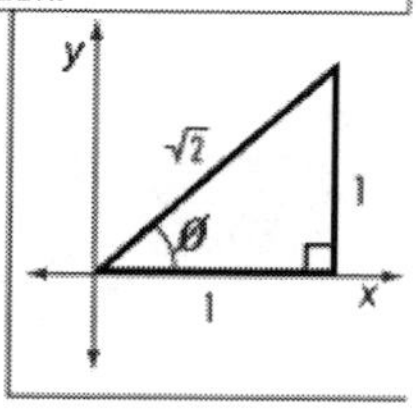

$2x = \frac{\pi}{4}$ or $2x = \frac{\pi}{4} + \pi$ or $2x = \pi - \frac{\pi}{4}$ or $2x = 2\pi - \frac{\pi}{4}$

$2x = \frac{5\pi}{4} \qquad 2x = \frac{3\pi}{4} \qquad 2x = \frac{7\pi}{4}$

$x = \frac{\pi}{8} \qquad x = \frac{5\pi}{8} \qquad x = \frac{3\pi}{8} \qquad x = \frac{7\pi}{8}$

Consider this example: find all the solutions for two periods of $\tan^2(2x) = 1$.

Begin by taking the square root of both sides.

Solve for the two possible equations: $\tan 2x = 1$ and $\tan 2x = -1$.

The normal tangent curve equals 1 at $\pi/4$ and $5\pi/4$, and it equals -1 at $3\pi/4$ and $7\pi/4$ in the frist two periods.

Divide these answers by the coefficient of the argument to find the solutions.

Example Find all the solutions in the interval $[0, 2\pi]$ of the given function

$(\sin 2x)(\tan 2x) + \sin 2x = 0$

$(\sin 2x)(\tan 2x + 1) = 0$

$\sin 2x = 0$ *or* $\tan 2x + 1 = 0$

Substitute $\theta = 2x$

$\sin\theta = 0$ *or* $\tan\theta = -1$

Interval is $0 < \theta < 4\pi$

So, $\theta = 0, \pi, 2\pi, 3\pi, 4\pi$ *or* $\theta = \frac{3\pi}{4}, \frac{7\pi}{4}, \frac{11\pi}{4}, \frac{15\pi}{4}$

Substitute $\theta = 2x$

$2x = 0, \pi, 2\pi, 3\pi, 4\pi$ *or* $2x = \frac{3\pi}{4}, \frac{7\pi}{4}, \frac{11\pi}{4}, \frac{15\pi}{4}$

Divide by 2

$x = 0, \frac{\pi}{2}, \pi, \frac{3\pi}{2}, 2\pi \qquad x = \frac{3\pi}{8}, \frac{7\pi}{8}, \frac{11\pi}{8}, \frac{15\pi}{8}$

Conisder the example illustrated here: find all solutions in the interval $[0, 2\pi]$ for $(\sin 2x)(\tan 2x) + \sin 2x$.

Since $0 \le x \le 2\pi$, multiply by 2 to find the interval for $2x$: $0 \le 2x \le 4\pi$.

To solve, first factor the equation and then set each factor equal to zero. Let $\theta = 2x$ and solve for θ.

Remember the interval is now $[0, 4\pi]$.

Substitute back $2x$ for θ and divide the answers by 2 to finish the problem.

Sample problems:

1. Solve the equation $\sin 2\theta = 1$ in $[0, 2\pi]$.

   Solution: $\frac{\pi}{4}$ or $\frac{5\pi}{4}$

   Explanation: Since $0 \le \theta \le 2\pi$, multiply by 2 to find the interval for 2θ: $0 \le 2\theta \le 4\pi$.

   Let $x = 2\theta$, and find all values of x on $[0, 4\pi]$ where $\sin x = 1$: $x = \frac{\pi}{2}$ or $x = \frac{5\pi}{2}$.

   Substitute 2θ into each equation and solve for x: $2\theta = \frac{\pi}{2}$ or $2\theta = \frac{5\pi}{2}$; $\theta = \frac{\pi}{4}$ or $\theta = \frac{5\pi}{4}$.

2. Find all solutions to the equation $\tan\frac{x}{2} = \sqrt{3}$ on $[0, 2\pi]$.

   Solution: $x = \frac{2\pi}{3}$

   Explanation: Since $0 \le x \le 2\pi$, divide by 2 to find the interval for $\frac{x}{2}$: $0 \le \frac{x}{2} \le \pi$.

   Let $\theta = \frac{x}{2}$, and find all values of θ on $[0, \pi]$ where $\tan\theta = \sqrt{3}$: $\theta = \frac{\pi}{3}$. Substitute $\frac{x}{2}$ into the equation for θ and solve for x: $\frac{x}{2} = \frac{\pi}{3}$, then $x = \frac{2\pi}{3}$.

3. Find all solutions to the equation $2\cos\left(\frac{x}{2}\right) - \sqrt{3} = 0$ on $[0, 2\pi]$.

   Solution: $x = \frac{\pi}{3}$

   Explanation: Isolate the trig function: $2\cos\left(\frac{x}{2}\right) - \sqrt{3} = 0$; $\cos\left(\frac{x}{2}\right) = \frac{\sqrt{3}}{2}$. Since $0 \le x \le 2\pi$, divide by 2 to find the interval for $\frac{x}{2}$: $0 \le \left(\frac{x}{2}\right) \le \pi$. Let $\frac{x}{2} = \theta$ and find all values of θ on $[0, \pi]$ where $\cos\theta = \frac{\sqrt{3}}{2}$: $\theta = \frac{\pi}{6}$. Substitute $\frac{x}{2}$ into the equation and solve for x: $\frac{x}{2} = \frac{\pi}{6}$; $x = \frac{\pi}{3}$.

Practice problems: *(Answers on page: 757)*

1. Solve the equation $\sin 2\theta = \frac{1}{2}$ on $[0, 2\pi]$.
2. Find all solutions to the equation $\tan\frac{x}{3} = 1$ on $[0, 2\pi]$.
3. Solve the equation $\sec\frac{3\theta}{2} = -2$ on $[0, 2\pi]$.

Review questions: *(Answers to odd questions on page: 757)*

1. Find all solutions in the interval $[0, 2\pi)$ of the equation $\sin^2 2\theta = \frac{1}{4}$.
2. Find all solutions in the interval $[0, 2\pi)$ of the equation $\sin 2\theta = \frac{-\sqrt{3}}{2}$.
3. Find all solutions in the interval $[0, 2\pi)$ of the equation $2\cos 2\alpha = 1$.

4. Find all solutions in the interval $[0, 2\pi)$ of the equation $\sin 3x \cos 2x = 0$.

5. Find all solutions in the interval $[0, 2\pi]$ of the equation $1 - \sin\left(\frac{x}{2}\right) = 0$.

Solving Trigonometric Equations Using the Quadratic Formula

- Some quadratic trigonometric equations cannot be easily solved by factoring, so use the **quadratic formula**.
- **Review:** Coefficients in the **argument** of a trig function change the **period** of the function. To solve an equation involving trig functions with coefficients in the arguments, first solve the equation ignoring the coefficients. Then divide the solutions through by the coefficients.
- **Review:** Since trig functions are **periodic**, trig equations often have many solutions. To find all the possible solutions to a trig equation, find the solutions for a single period and then add multiples of the period to those solutions.

If a quadratic trig equation cannot be factored, try using the **quadratic formula** $x = \frac{-b \pm \sqrt{b^2-4ac}}{2a}$	If a quadratic trig equation cannot be factored, try using the **quadratic formula**.
Example Solve in the interval $[0,\pi]$ $3\sin^2(2x) + \sin(2x) - 1 = 0$ if $[S = \sin(2x)]$ $3S^2 + S - 1 = 0$ $a = 3$ $b = 1$ $c = -1$ $S = \frac{-1 \pm \sqrt{1 - -12}}{2(3)}$ *Plug into quadratic formula.* $S = \frac{-1 + \sqrt{13}}{6}$ *and* $S = \frac{-1 - \sqrt{13}}{6}$ $S = .43425...$ *and* $S = -.7675918...$ **But, this is only *S*, we want to find *x*.** $\sin(2x) = .43425...$ *and* $\sin(2x) = -.7675918...$ 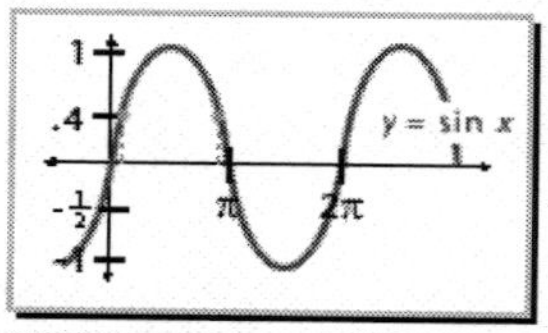 *Find the reference angle by finding arc sine on your calculator.* Since $0 \le x \le \pi$, multiply by 2 to find the interval for 2x: $0 \le 2x \le \pi$. $\sin(2x) = .43425...$ *and* $\sin(2x) = -.7675918...$ $\sin^{-1}(.43425) = .4492$ | $\sin^{-1}(-.7675918) = -.8751$ $\pi - .4492 = 2.693$ | $-.8751 + 2\pi$ or $-.8751 + \pi$ $2x = .4492$ or 2.693 | $2x = 5.408$ or 4.0167 *therefore,* *x=.2246 radians* *x=2.704 radians* *x=1.3462 radians* *x=2.008 radians*	Consider this example: Solve $3\sin^2(2x) + \sin(2x) - 1 = 0$ for the interval $[0,\pi]$. Treat the $\sin(2x)$ term like its own variable—so, let $S = \sin x$. $3\sin^2(2x) + \sin(2x) - 1 = 0$ becomes $S^2 + 2S - 1 = 0$. This expression is quadratic and cannot be easily factored, so use the quadratic formula. Plug the coefficients into the formula. The result is the solution for *S*. Substitute $\sin(2x)$ back in for *S* to solve for *x*. Since $0 \le x \le \pi$ multiply by 2 to find the interval for $2x$: $0 \le 2x \le 2\pi$. Find the **reference angle** in radians by taking the inverse sine on the calculator. Given the reference angle use the graph of sine to determine the solution. Find all solutions in the given interval. For the second sine function, notice that the calculator gives a negative answer for the second expression. Add 2π to that answer to move it into the correct interval.

Sample problems:

1. Find all solutions to $\tan^2 x + 2\tan x - 1 = 0$ on $[0,2\pi]$. (Round solutions to 3 decimal places)
   Solution: $x = 0.393,\ 1.963,\ 3.534,$ and 5.105
   Explanation: Let $\tan x = z$: $z^2 + 2z - 1 = 0$. Solve using the quadratic formula:
   $$z = \frac{-2 \pm \sqrt{(2)^2 - 4(1)(-1)}}{2(1)} = \frac{-2 \pm \sqrt{4+4}}{2} = \frac{-2 \pm \sqrt{8}}{2} = \frac{-2 \pm 2\sqrt{2}}{2} = -1 \pm \sqrt{2}.$$
   So, $\tan x = -1 \pm \sqrt{2}$. Solve the first equation for x: $x = \tan^{-1}(-1+\sqrt{2}) = 0.3927$, which is an angle in Quadrant I. Find all solutions in the given interval: since $\tan x$ is also positive in Quadrant III, use 0.3927 as the reference angle to find the quadrant III solution, $\pi + 0.3927 = 3.5343$ (round to three decimal places to get 0.393 and 3.534). Solve the second equation for x: $x = \tan^{-1}(-1-\sqrt{2}) = -1.1781$, which leads to quadrant II and quadrant IV solutions: $\pi - 1.1787 = 1.963$ and $2\pi - 1.1781 = 5.105$.

2. Find all solutions in the interval $[0,2\pi)$ of the equation $10\sec^2\theta - 10 = 7\tan\theta + 2$.
   Solution: $\theta = 0.743,\ 2.972,\ 3.884,$ and 6.069 radians
   Explanation: Use the Pythagorean identity to express $\sec^2\theta$ in terms of tangent, simplify, and set the equation equal to zero: $10\sec^2\theta - 10 = 7\tan\theta + 2$; $10(\tan^2\theta + 1) - 10 = 7\tan\theta + 2$; $10\tan^2\theta + 10 - 10 = 7\tan\theta + 2$; $10\tan^2\theta = 7\tan\theta + 2$; $10\tan^2\theta - 7\tan\theta - 2 = 0$. Use the quadratic formula to solve for $\tan\theta$:
   $$\tan\theta = \frac{-(-7) \pm \sqrt{(-7)^2 - 4(10)(-2)}}{2(10)} = \frac{7 \pm \sqrt{49+80}}{20} = \frac{7 \pm \sqrt{129}}{20} = \frac{7 \pm 11.358}{20},$$
   $\tan\theta = 0.9179$ or $\tan\theta = -0.2179$. Solve each equation for θ (use the inverse tangent function and find all solutions in the given interval): $\theta = 0.743,\ 2.927,\ 0.884,$ and 6.069 radians.

3. Find all solutions in the interval $[0,2\pi)$ of the equation $5\sin\theta - \cos^2\theta = 1$.
   Solution: $\theta = .382$ and 2.760 radians
   Explanation: Use the Pythagorean identity to substitute sine for cosine, simplify, and set the equation equal to zero: $5\sin\theta - \cos^2\theta = 1$; $5\sin\theta - (1 - \sin^2\theta) = 1$; $5\sin\theta - 1 + \sin^2\theta = 1$; $\sin^2\theta + 5\sin\theta - 2 = 0$. Use the quadratic formula to solve for $\sin\theta$: $\sin\theta = \dfrac{-(5) \pm \sqrt{(5)^2 - 4(1)(-2)}}{2(1)} = \dfrac{-5 \pm \sqrt{25+8}}{2} = \dfrac{-5 \pm 5.7446}{2}$, so $\sin\theta = 0.3723$ and -5.3723. The range of sine does not include values less than -1, so discard -5.3723. Therefore, $\sin\theta = 0.3723$. Solve for θ (use the inverse sine function and find all solutions in the given interval): $\theta = .382$ and 2.760 radians.

Practice problems: *(Answers on page: 757)*

1. Find all solutions in the interval $[0,2\pi)$ of the equation $2\cos^2 3x + 6\cos 3x = 3$.
2. Find all solutions to the equation $5\sin x + 2 = 0$ on $[0, 2\pi]$, rounding your answers to three decimal places.
3. Solve the equation $\sin^2(2x) - 3\sin(2x) + 1 = 0$ on $[0, 2\pi]$, rounding your answers to three decimal places.

Review questions: *(Answers to odd questions on page: 757)*

1. Find all solutions in the interval $[0, 2\pi)$ of the equation $\sin^2 2\theta - 4\sin 2\theta - 3 = 0$.
2. Solve the equation $4\cos x + 3 = 0$ on $[0, 2\pi]$, rounding your answers to three decimal places.

3. True or false: The equation $\sin^2 x - \sin x + 1 = 0$ has no solution on $[0, 2\pi]$.

4. Solve the equation $\sin x^2 + \sin x - 1 = 0$ on $[0, 2\pi]$, rounding your answers to three decimal places.

5. Solve the equation $\cos^2 x - 3\cos x + 1 = 0$ on $[0, 2\pi]$, rounding your answer to three decimal places.

Solving Word Problems Involving Trigonometric Equations

- One application of the trig functions can be seen in **harmonic motion**, such as the movement of a spring. The length or location of the spring can be modeled using trig functions. As such, many word problems involving harmonic motion will require you to solve trigonometric equations.
- **Review**: Since trig functions are **periodic**, they will often have many solutions. To find all the possible solutions to a trig equation, find the solutions for a single period and then add multiples of the period to those solutions.

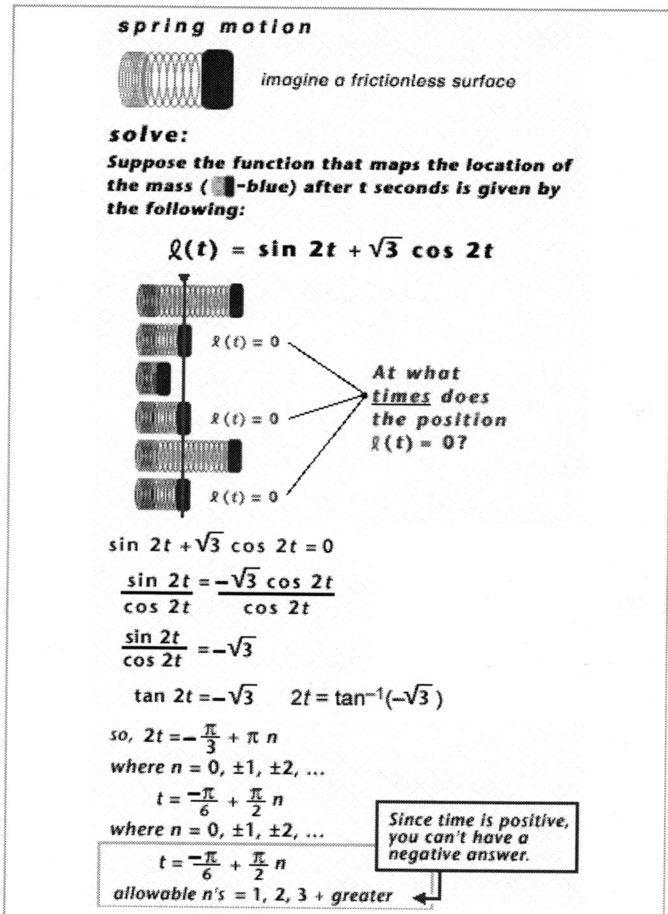

There are many applications of trigonometry in the real world. One such application is spring motion.

In this example, you're given the function that maps the location of a spring mass after t seconds. It has an oscillating motion due to the spring. Given this equation, find the times when the **position** equals zero.

Notice that the answer occurs several times because the spring motion is periodic.

To solve, start by setting the position function equal to zero.

Isolate the variables. Notice that sine over cosine is tangent. It is easier to solve an equation with only one trig function than to solve an equation with several.

Find the angle whose tangent is $\sqrt{3}$. (Use a calculator, if necessary.)

Remember, tangent has a period of π, so to list every possible solution add multiples of π to the answer. Now divide by the coefficient of the argument.

Discard any negative answers because a negative time is physically meaningless.

Sample problems:

1. In an electric circuit, the electromotive force is $E(t)$ volts where $E(t) = 2\cos 50\pi t$. Find the smallest positive value of t for which the electromotive force is 2 volts.

   Solution: $\frac{1}{25}$

   Explanation: Substitute $E(t) = 2$ and solve for t: $2 = 2\cos 50\pi t$; $1 = \cos 50\pi t$; $\cos^{-1}(1) = 50\pi t$. Cosine equals 1 at intervals of 2π, so: $\cos^{-1}(1) = 50\pi t$; $2\pi n = 50\pi t$.

   Solve for t: $t = \frac{1}{25}n$, where n is any integer. The smallest possible value of t will occur when $n = 1$, so $t = \frac{1}{25}$.

2. An electric generator produces a 30-cycle alternating current described by the equation $I(t) = 40\sin\left(60\pi\left(t - \frac{7}{72}\right)\right)$, where $I(t)$ amps is the current at t seconds. Find the smallest positive value of t for which the current is 20 amps.

   Solution: $\frac{1}{90}$

   Explanation: Substitute $I(t) = 20$ and solve for t: $20 = 40\sin\left(60\pi\left(t - \frac{7}{72}\right)\right)$;

   $\frac{1}{2} = \sin\left(60\pi\left(t - \frac{7}{72}\right)\right)$; $60\pi\left(t - \frac{7}{72}\right) = \sin^{-1}\left(\frac{1}{2}\right)$. The arcsine of $\frac{1}{2}$ is $\frac{\pi}{2}$ and $\frac{5\pi}{6}$ and occur every period, so add multiples of 2π: $60\pi\left(t - \frac{7}{72}\right) = \frac{\pi}{6} + 2\pi n$

   or $60\pi\left(t - \frac{7}{72}\right) = \frac{5\pi}{6} + 2\pi n$; $t - \frac{7}{72} = \frac{1}{360} + \frac{1}{30}n$ or $t - \frac{7}{72} = \frac{1}{72} + \frac{1}{30}n$;

   $t = \frac{1}{10} + \frac{1}{30}n$ or $t = \frac{1}{9} + \frac{1}{30}n$; $t = \frac{3}{30} + \frac{1}{30}n$ or $t = \frac{10}{90} + \frac{3}{90}n$, where n can be any integer. By observation, the smallest positive value of t will occur in the second equation when $n = -3$, $t = \frac{1}{90}$.

3. A weight suspended from a spring is vibrating vertically according to the equation $y = 2\sin\left(4\pi\left(t + \frac{1}{8}\right)\right)$, where y is the distance in cm from the central position t seconds after the motion is started. Determine the three smallest possible values of t for which the weight is 1 cm above its central position.

   Solution: $\frac{1}{12}, \frac{5}{12}, \frac{7}{12}$

   Explanation: To determine the values of t for which the weight is 1 cm above its central position, let $y = 1$ and solve for t: $1 = 2\sin\left(4\pi\left(t + \frac{1}{8}\right)\right)$; $\frac{1}{2} = \sin\left(4\pi\left(t + \frac{1}{8}\right)\right)$;

   $4\pi\left(t + \frac{1}{8}\right) = \sin^{-1}\left(\frac{1}{2}\right)$; $4\pi\left(t + \frac{1}{8}\right) = \frac{\pi}{6} + 2\pi n$ or $4\pi\left(t + \frac{1}{8}\right) = \frac{5\pi}{6} + 2\pi n$;

   $t + \frac{1}{8} = \frac{1}{24} + \frac{n}{2}$ or $t + \frac{1}{8} = \frac{5}{24} + \frac{n}{2}$; $t = -\frac{1}{12} + \frac{n}{2}$ or $t = \frac{1}{12} + \frac{n}{2}$; so

   $t = -\frac{1}{12}, \frac{5}{12}, \frac{11}{12}, \frac{17}{12}, \frac{23}{12}\ldots$ or $t = \frac{1}{12}, \frac{7}{12}, \frac{13}{12}, \frac{19}{12}\ldots$ The three smallest, positive values are $t = \frac{1}{12}, \frac{5}{12}, \frac{7}{12}$.

Practice problems: *(Answers on page: 758)*

1. A weight suspended from a spring is vibrating vertically according to the equation $f(t)=10\sin\left(\frac{3}{4}\pi(t-3)\right)$ where $f(t)$ is the directed distance (in cm) of the weight from its central position at t seconds. Find the smallest positive value of t for which the weight will be at its central position.
2. The equation of motion for a weight suspended from a particular spring is given by: $p(t)=3\sin\frac{t}{2}+4\cos\frac{t}{2}$ where p is the displacement from the equilibrium position in centimeters and t is the time elapsed in seconds. At what time does the weight first reach the equilibrium position?
3. The equation of motion for a weight suspended from a particular spring is given by: $p(t)=-5\cos 2t+8\sin 2t$ where p is the displacement from the equilibrium position in centimeters and t is the time elapsed in seconds. At what times does the weight pass through the equilibrium position within the first minute?

Review questions: *(Answers to odd questions on page: 758)*

1. A baseball was thrown from first base at an angle q with the horizontal and with an initial velocity of $V_0=80$ ft/sec. The ball was caught by the second base player who was 100 ft. away. Find q if the horizontal distance covered by the ball, r, is given by the equation $r=\frac{1}{32}V_0^2\sin 2\theta$. Express the answer in degrees.
2. A weight is oscillating on the end of a spring. The position of the weight relative to the point of the equilibrium is given by the equation $y=\frac{1}{12}\left(\sqrt{3}\cos 8t-3\sin 8t\right)$ where y is the displacement (in meters) and t is the time (in seconds). Find the smallest positive value of t when the weight is at the point of equilibrium.
3. The equation of motion for a weight suspended from a particular spring is $p(t)=4\sin 2t-2\cos 2t$ where p is the displacement from the equilibrium position in centimeters and t is the time elapsed in seconds. Find the smallest positive value of t when the weight is at the point of equilibrium. (Use degrees to measure t.)
4. The equation of motion for a weight suspended from a particular spring is given by: $p(t)=-5\sin 2t-6\cos 2t$ where p is the displacement from the equilibrium position in centimeters and t is the time elapsed in seconds. When does the weight pass through the equilibrium position within the first three periods?
5. The equation of motion for a weight suspended from a particular spring is given by $p(t)=2\sin\frac{t}{3}+5\cos\frac{t}{3}$, where $p(t)$ is the displacement from the equilibrium position in centimeters and t is the time elapsed in seconds. At what time does the weight first reach the equilibrium position?

Identities for Sums and Differences of Angles

- The **sum and difference identities**:
  - The sine of a sum of angles: $\sin(\theta_1+\theta_2)=\sin\theta_1\cos\theta_2+\cos\theta_1\sin\theta_2$
  - The sine of a difference of angles: $\sin(\theta_1-\theta_2)=\sin\theta_1\cos\theta_2-\cos\theta_1\sin\theta_2$
  - The cosine of a sum of angles: $\cos(\theta_1+\theta_2)=\cos\theta_1\cos\theta_2-\sin\theta_1\sin\theta_2$
  - The cosine of a difference of angles: $\cos(\theta_1-\theta_2)=\cos\theta_1\cos\theta_2+\sin\theta_1\sin\theta_2$
  - The tangent of a sum of angles: $\tan(\theta_1+\theta_2)=\dfrac{\tan\theta_1+\tan\theta_2}{1-\tan\theta_1\tan\theta_2}$
  - The tangent of a difference of angles: $\tan(\theta_1-\theta_2)=\dfrac{\tan\theta_1-\tan\theta_2}{1+\tan\theta_1\tan\theta_2}$

$\sin\left(\frac{\pi}{2}+\frac{\pi}{2}\right)\overset{?}{=}\sin\left(\frac{\pi}{2}\right)+\sin\left(\frac{\pi}{2}\right)$ $\sin(\pi)\overset{?}{=}\sin\left(\frac{\pi}{2}\right)+\sin\left(\frac{\pi}{2}\right)$ $0\overset{?}{=}1+1$ $0\neq 2$	This example shows that the sine of a sum of two angles is not equal to the sine of the first angle added to the sine of the second. sin (π/2 + π/2) = 0, while sin (π/2) + sin (π/2) = 2. Therefore, the sine of a sum of two angles does not equal the sine of the first angle plus the sine of the second.
sum of angles formulas: $\sin(\theta_1+\theta_2)=\sin\theta_1\cos\theta_2+\cos\theta_1\sin\theta_2$ $\sin\left(\frac{\pi}{2}+\frac{\pi}{2}\right)=\sin\left(\frac{\pi}{2}\right)\cos\left(\frac{\pi}{2}\right)+\cos\left(\frac{\pi}{2}\right)\sin\left(\frac{\pi}{2}\right)$ $\sin(\pi)=(1)(0)+(0)(1)$ $0\overset{\checkmark}{=}0$	The example shown is the proper way to find the sine of a sum of angles. To simplify, first substitute in the values for each trig function. Then do the arithmetic.
sin is *good* • shares the limelight • signs are the same **cos is** *evil* • it wants it all; needs to be 1st • so obnoxious it switches signs Just memorize tangent.	Here is Dr. Burger's "crutch" for remembering these formulas. They do help. Memorizing these formulas will save time and will make many problems simple and quick to solve.

Sample problems:

1. Use the subtraction formula for sine to evaluate $\sin 105°$.
   Solution: $\frac{\sqrt{2}+\sqrt{6}}{4}$
   Explanation: Express 105° as the difference of two common angles: $\sin 105° = \sin(150°-45°) =$
   $\sin 150°\cos 45° - \cos 150°\sin 45° = \left(\frac{1}{2}\right)\left(\frac{\sqrt{2}}{2}\right)-\left(\frac{-\sqrt{3}}{2}\right)\left(\frac{\sqrt{2}}{2}\right)=\frac{\sqrt{2}}{4}+\frac{\sqrt{6}}{4}=\frac{\sqrt{2}+\sqrt{6}}{4}$.

2. Find $\sin(x+y)$ if $\sin x = -\frac{5}{13}$ and $\cos y = -\frac{3}{5}$ with x and y being in quadrant III.

Solution: $\frac{63}{65}$

Explanation: Use the "sine of a sum of angles" formula to expand $\sin(x+y)$: $\sin(x+y) = \sin x\cos y + \cos x\sin y = \left(-\frac{5}{13}\right)\left(-\frac{3}{5}\right) + \cos x\sin y$. Find $\cos x$ and $\sin y$ to complete the formula. Use $\sin x = -\frac{5}{13}$ to find $\cos x$: if $\sin x = -\frac{5}{13}$ then $a^2 + (-5)^2 = 13^2$; $a^2 + 25 = 169$; $a^2 = 144$; $a = 12$, so $\cos x = -\frac{12}{13}$ (since cosine is negative in quadrant III). Use $\cos y = -\frac{3}{5}$ to find $\sin y$: if $\cos y = -\frac{3}{5}$ then $(-3)^2 + b^2 = (5)^2$; $9 + b^2 = 25$; $b^2 = 16$; $b = 4$, so $\sin y = -\frac{4}{5}$ (since sine is negative in quadrant III). Substitute these values into the formula: $\sin x\cos y + \cos x\sin y = \left(-\frac{5}{13}\right)\left(-\frac{3}{5}\right) + \left(-\frac{12}{13}\right)\left(-\frac{4}{5}\right) = \frac{15}{65} + \frac{48}{65} = \frac{63}{65}$.

3. Find $\sin(x-y)$ if $\tan x = -\frac{5}{12}$ and $\cos y = \frac{3}{5}$ with x and y being in quadrant IV.

Solution: $\frac{33}{65}$

Explanation: Use the "sine of a difference of angles" formula to expand $\sin(x-y)$: $\sin(x-y) = \sin x\cos y - \cos x\sin y = \sin x\left(\frac{3}{5}\right) - \cos x\sin y$. Find $\sin x$, $\cos x$, and $\sin y$ to complete the formula. Use $\tan x = -\frac{5}{12}$ to find $\sin x$ and $\cos x$: if $\tan x = -\frac{5}{12}$ then $c^2 = (5)^2 + (12)^2$; $c^2 = 25 + 144$; $c^2 = 169$; $c = 13$, so $\sin x = -\frac{5}{13}$ (since sine is negative in quadrant IV) and $\cos x = \frac{12}{13}$ (since cosine is positive in quadrant IV). Use $\cos y = \frac{3}{5}$ to find $\sin y$: if $\cos y = \frac{3}{5}$ then $a^2 + (3)^2 = (5)^2$; $a^2 + 9 = 25$; $a^2 = 16$; $a = 4$, so $\sin y = -\frac{4}{5}$. Substitute these values into the formula: $\sin x\cos y - \cos x\sin y = \left(-\frac{5}{13}\right)\left(\frac{3}{5}\right) - \left(\frac{12}{13}\right)\left(-\frac{4}{5}\right) = -\frac{15}{65} + \frac{48}{65} = \frac{33}{65}$.

Practice problems: *(Answers on page: 758)*

1. Use the addition formula for cosine to evaluate $\cos 105°$.
2. Use the addition of sines identity to evaluate $\sin 255°$.
3. Find $\tan(a+b)$ given that $\cos a = \frac{5}{13}$ and $\sin b = \frac{\sqrt{3}}{2}$ and both a and b are in quadrant I. (Use a calculator to simplify answer.)

Review questions: *(Answers to odd questions on page: 758)*

1. True or false: You would use the identity $\sin 45°\cos 60° + \cos 45°\sin 60°$ to find $\sin(45° + 60°)$.
2. Use the addition formula for cosine to evaluate $\cos 195°$.
3. Use the addition formula for sine to evaluate $\sin 105°$.
4. Find $\cos(x+y)$ for $\cos x = -\frac{4}{5}$ and $\sin y = \frac{5}{13}$ with x and y being in quadrant II.
5. Determine $\tan(a-b)$, given that $\cos a = \frac{3}{5}$, $\sin b = \frac{1}{2}$, and both a and b are in quadrant I. (Use a calculator to simplify answer.)

Using Sum and Difference Identities

- When finding trigonometric function values for an angle, it helps to write the angle as the sum or difference of two angles whose function values are already known. Then, find the desired values using a **sum or difference identity**.
- The sine of a difference of angles: $\sin(\theta_1 - \theta_2) = \sin\theta_1 \cos\theta_2 - \cos\theta_1 \sin\theta_2$.

<table>
<tr>
<td>

Difference of Two Sines:

$\sin(\theta_1 - \theta_2) = \sin\theta_1 \cos\theta_2 - \cos\theta_1 \sin\theta_2$

Example $\sin(15°) =$ not a standard formula angle

$\sin(45° - 30°) =$ *We know the sine of 45° and 30°*

</td>
<td>

In this example you're asked to find the value of sin (15°).

Notice that 15° = 45°–30°. Substituting (45°–30°) for 15° makes it possible to use the difference of angles formula.

</td>
</tr>
<tr>
<td>

$\sin(45° - 30°) =$

$\sin(45°)\cos(30°) - \cos(45°)\sin(30°) =$

$\left(\frac{\sqrt{2}}{2}\right)\left(\frac{\sqrt{3}}{2}\right) - \left(\frac{\sqrt{2}}{2}\right)\left(\frac{1}{2}\right)$

<table>
<tr><th>angles</th><th>0°</th><th>30°</th><th>45°</th><th>60°</th><th>90°</th></tr>
<tr><td>sine</td><td>0</td><td>$\frac{1}{2}$</td><td>$\frac{\sqrt{2}}{2}$</td><td>$\frac{\sqrt{3}}{2}$</td><td>1</td></tr>
<tr><td>cosine</td><td>1</td><td>$\frac{\sqrt{3}}{2}$</td><td>$\frac{\sqrt{2}}{2}$</td><td>$\frac{1}{2}$</td><td>0</td></tr>
</table>

</td>
<td>

Plug 45° and 30° into the appropriate places and evaluate.

</td>
</tr>
<tr>
<td>

$= \frac{\sqrt{6}}{4} - \frac{\sqrt{2}}{4}$

$\sin(15°) = \frac{\sqrt{6} - \sqrt{2}}{4}$

</td>
<td>

Simplify to find that $\sin(15°) = \frac{\sqrt{6} - \sqrt{2}}{4}$

</td>
</tr>
<tr>
<td>

</td>
<td>

This is how to calculate the trigonometric functions for an unusual angle like 15° using the **sum and difference identities**.

Finding the trig functions of different angles will be possible using the sum and difference identities.

</td>
</tr>
</table>

Sample problems:

1. Find the exact value of $\cos 15°$.

   Solution: $\frac{\sqrt{6}+\sqrt{2}}{4}$

   Explanation: Use the "cosine of a difference of angles" formula to express the $\cos 15°$ as the difference of two common angles: $\cos(15°) = \cos(45° - 30°) = \cos 45° \cos 30° + \sin 45° \sin 30° =$ $\left(\frac{\sqrt{2}}{2}\right)\left(\frac{\sqrt{3}}{2}\right) + \left(\frac{\sqrt{2}}{2}\right)\left(\frac{1}{2}\right) = \frac{\sqrt{6}}{4} + \frac{\sqrt{2}}{4} = \frac{\sqrt{6}+\sqrt{2}}{4}$.

2. Find the exact value of $\tan\frac{7\pi}{12}$.

Solution: $-2-\sqrt{3}$

Explanation: Use the "tangent of a sum of angles" formula to express $\tan\frac{7\pi}{12}$ as the sum of two common angles: $\tan\frac{7\pi}{12}=\tan\left(\frac{4\pi}{12}+\frac{3\pi}{12}\right)=\tan\left(\frac{\pi}{3}+\frac{\pi}{4}\right)$

$$=\frac{\tan\frac{\pi}{3}+\tan\frac{\pi}{4}}{1-\tan\frac{\pi}{3}\tan\frac{\pi}{4}}$$

$$=\frac{\sqrt{3}+1}{1-(\sqrt{3})(1)}=\frac{\sqrt{3}+1}{1-\sqrt{3}}.$$

Rationalize the denominator: $\frac{\sqrt{3}+1}{1-\sqrt{3}}\left(\frac{1+\sqrt{3}}{1+\sqrt{3}}\right)=\frac{1+2\sqrt{3}+3}{1+\sqrt{3}-\sqrt{3}-3}=\frac{4+2\sqrt{3}}{-2}=-2-\sqrt{3}.$

3. If $\cos x=-\frac{4}{5}$ with x in quadrant III and $\cos y=\frac{5}{13}$ with y in quadrant IV, find $\cos(x-y)$.

Solution: $\frac{16}{65}$

Explanation: Expand using the cosine of a difference of angles formula:

$\cos(x-y)=\cos x\cos y+\sin x\sin y\Rightarrow\left(-\frac{4}{5}\right)\left(\frac{5}{13}\right)+\sin x\sin y$. Find $\sin x$ and $\sin y$.

Use $\cos x=-\frac{4}{5}$ to find $\sin x$: $a^2+4^2=5^2$; $a^2+16=25$; $a^2=9$; $a=3$, so $\sin x=-\frac{3}{5}$ (sine is negative since x is in quadrant III). Use $\cos y=\frac{5}{13}$ to find $\sin y$: $a^2+5^2=13^2$; $a^2+25=169$; $a^2=144$; $a=12$, so $\sin y=-\frac{12}{13}$ (sine is negative since y is in quadrant IV). Complete the formula:

$\cos(x-y)=\cos x\cos y+\sin x\sin y$; $\left(-\frac{4}{5}\right)\left(\frac{5}{13}\right)+\left(-\frac{3}{5}\right)\left(-\frac{12}{13}\right)=\left(-\frac{20}{65}\right)+\left(\frac{36}{65}\right)=\frac{16}{65}.$

Practice problems: *(Answers on page: 758)*

1. Find the exact value of $\sin 75°$.
2. Find the exact value of $\tan\frac{11\pi}{12}$.
3. If $\cos p=-\frac{4}{5}$ with p in quadrant III, and $\cos q=\frac{5}{13}$ with q in quadrant IV, find $\tan(p-q)$.

Review questions: *(Answers to odd questions on page: 758)*

1. Find the exact value of $\cos 75°$.
2. Find the exact value of $\cos 195°$.
3. Find the exact value of $\tan 255°$.
4. Find the exact value of $\cos\frac{5\pi}{12}$.
5. If $\sin x=-\frac{4}{5}$ with x in quadrant III and $\cos y=\frac{5}{13}$ with y in quadrant IV, find $\sin(x+y)$.

Using Sum and Difference Identities to Simplify an Expression

- Sum and difference identities can be useful in simplifying trigonometric expressions.
- **Review**:
  - The sine of a sum of angles: $\sin(\theta_1+\theta_2)=\sin\theta_1\cos\theta_2+\cos\theta_1\sin\theta_2$
  - The sine of a difference of angles: $\sin(\theta_1-\theta_2)=\sin\theta_1\cos\theta_2-\cos\theta_1\sin\theta_2$
  - The cosine of a sum of angles: $\cos(\theta_1+\theta_2)=\cos\theta_1\cos\theta_2-\sin\theta_1\sin\theta_2$
  - The cosine of a difference of angles: $\cos(\theta_1-\theta_2)=\cos\theta_1\cos\theta_2+\sin\theta_1\sin\theta_2$
  - The tangent of a sum of angles: $\tan(\theta_1+\theta_2)=\dfrac{\tan\theta_1+\tan\theta_2}{1-\tan\theta_1\tan\theta_2}$
  - The tangent of a difference of angles: $\tan(\theta_1-\theta_2)=\dfrac{\tan\theta_1-\tan\theta_2}{1+\tan\theta_1\tan\theta_2}$

Example $\sin\frac{\pi}{9}\cos\frac{7\pi}{18}+\sin\frac{7\pi}{18}\cos\frac{\pi}{9}$ $=\sin\left(\frac{\pi}{9}+\frac{7\pi}{18}\right)$	Consider the expression to the left. While it may initially look complicated, further inspection reveals that the expression is equal to the sine of a sum of angles.
$=\sin\left(\frac{2\pi}{18}+\frac{7\pi}{18}\right)$ $=\sin\left(\frac{9\pi}{18}\right)$	To evaluate, first find a common denominator and add the fractions.
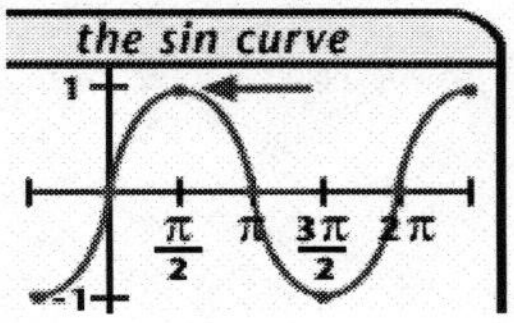 $=\sin\left(\frac{9\pi}{18}\right)$ $=\sin\frac{\pi}{2}$ $=1$	The expression $\sin\frac{9\pi}{18}$ is equivalent to $\sin\frac{\pi}{2}$, which is equal to 1. Therefore, $\sin\frac{\pi}{9}\cos\frac{7\pi}{18}+\sin\frac{7\pi}{18}\cos\frac{\pi}{9}=1.$
Example $\dfrac{\tan 47^\circ-\tan 2^\circ}{1+\tan 47^\circ\tan 2^\circ}$ $=\tan(47^\circ-2^\circ)$ $=\tan(45^\circ)$ $=1$	Consider the example illustrated here. The given expression is equal to the tangent of the difference of two angles. The difference is 45° and the tangent of 45° is one.

Sample problems:

1. Simplify: $\sin 20^\circ\cos 80^\circ-\cos 20^\circ\sin 80^\circ$

   Solution: $-\frac{\sqrt{3}}{2}$

   Explanation: Use the sine of a difference of angles formula, $\sin\theta_1\cos\theta_2-\cos\theta_1\sin\theta_2=\sin(\theta_1-\theta_2)$, to simplify: $\sin 20^\circ\cos 80^\circ-\cos 20^\circ\sin 80^\circ=\sin(20^\circ-80^\circ)=\sin(-60^\circ)=-\sin 60^\circ=-\frac{\sqrt{3}}{2}$.

2. Simplify: $\dfrac{\tan 20^\circ+\tan 25^\circ}{1-\tan 20^\circ\tan 25^\circ}$

   Solution: 1

   Explanation: Simplify using the identity for the tangent of a sum, $\tan(\theta_1+\theta_2)=\dfrac{\tan\theta_1+\tan\theta_2}{1-\tan\theta_1\tan\theta_2}$: $\dfrac{\tan 20^\circ+\tan 25^\circ}{1-\tan 20^\circ\tan 25^\circ}=\tan(20^\circ+25^\circ)=\tan 45^\circ=1.$

3. Find the exact value of $\cos\frac{5\pi}{12}\cos\frac{7\pi}{12} - \sin\frac{5\pi}{12}\sin\frac{7\pi}{12}$.
   Solution: -1
   Explanation: Use the identity for the cosine of a sum, $\cos(\theta_1 + \theta_2) = \cos\theta_1\cos\theta_2 - \sin\theta_1\sin\theta_2$, to simplify: $\cos\frac{5\pi}{12}\cos\frac{7\pi}{12} - \sin\frac{5\pi}{12}\sin\frac{7\pi}{12} = \cos\left(\frac{5\pi}{12} + \frac{7\pi}{12}\right) = \cos\pi = -1$.

Practice problems: *(Answers on page: 758)*

1. Simplify: $\cos 70°\cos 20° - \sin 70°\sin 20°$
2. Find the exact value of $\dfrac{\tan 40° - \tan 10°}{1 + \tan 40°\tan 10°}$.
3. Find the exact value of $\cos\dfrac{\pi}{12}\cos\dfrac{5\pi}{12} + \sin\dfrac{\pi}{12}\sin\dfrac{5\pi}{12}$.

Review questions: *(Answers to odd questions on page: 758)*

1. Simplify: $\sin 20°\cos 10° + \cos 20°\sin 10°$
2. Find the exact value of $\cos 40°\cos 10° + \sin 40°\sin 10°$.
3. Find the exact value of $\sin\dfrac{\pi}{18}\cos\dfrac{5\pi}{18} + \cos\dfrac{\pi}{18}\sin\dfrac{5\pi}{18}$.
4. Write $\sin\dfrac{7}{6}\cos\dfrac{1}{6} + \cos\dfrac{7}{6}\sin\dfrac{1}{6}$ as a single sine or cosine term.
5. Express $\cos(x+y)\cos y + \sin(x+y)\sin y$ as a single term.

Confirming a Double-Angle Identity

- The **double-angle identities** arise from the sum identities (from the **sum and difference identities**) when the two angles being added are equal. It is important to remember that one side of the identity refers to double angles while the other side refers to single angles. This shift can be very useful in solving problems.
- The double-angle identities:
  - $\sin 2\theta = 2\sin\theta\cos\theta$
  - $\cos 2\theta = \cos^2\theta - \sin^2\theta$
  - $\cos 2\theta = 1 - 2\sin^2\theta$
  - $\cos 2\theta = 2\cos^2\theta - 1$
  - $\tan 2\theta = \dfrac{2\tan\theta}{1 - \tan^2\theta}$

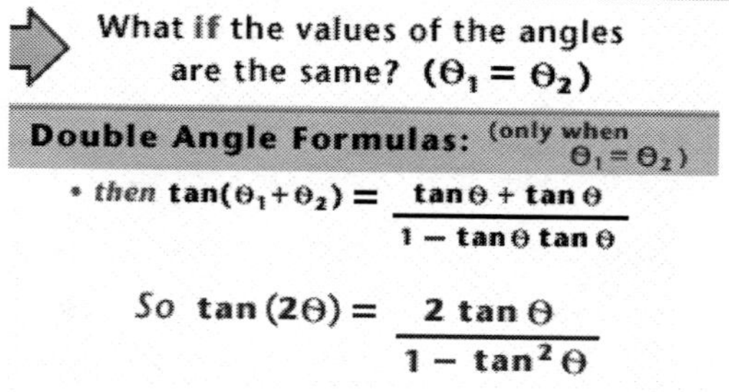	If the two angles, θ_1 and θ_2, are the same, then the tangent of $\theta_1 + \theta_2$ is just $2\tan\theta/1-\tan^2\theta$—the **double-angle identity** for tangents.
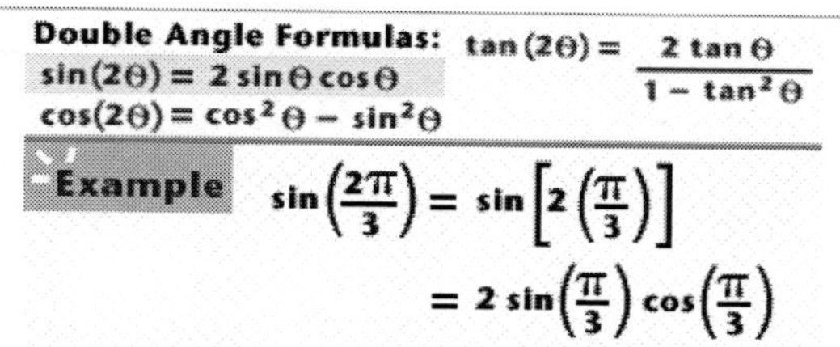	Use a double-angle identity to evaluate this trig function. Here the sine of $2\pi/3$ (the **double-angle**) can be written in terms of the sine and cosine of $\pi/3$.

$= 2\left(\frac{\sqrt{3}}{2}\right)\left(\frac{1}{2}\right)$ $= \frac{\sqrt{3}}{2}$	Plug in the values of sin (π/3) and cos (π/3). Simplify to get the answer. So, $\sin\frac{2\pi}{3} = \frac{\sqrt{3}}{2}$.
Double Angle Formulas: $\tan(2\theta) = \frac{2\tan\theta}{1-\tan^2\theta}$ $\sin(2\theta) = 2\sin\theta\cos\theta$ $\cos(2\theta) = \cos^2\theta - \sin^2\theta$ **Example** $\cos\left(\frac{2\pi}{3}\right) = \cos^2\left(\frac{\pi}{3}\right) - \sin^2\left(\frac{\pi}{3}\right)$ $= \left(\frac{1}{2}\right)\left(\frac{1}{2}\right) - \left(\frac{\sqrt{3}}{2}\right)\left(\frac{\sqrt{3}}{2}\right)$ $= \frac{1}{4} - \frac{3}{4}$ $= -\frac{2}{4}$ $= -\frac{1}{2}$	Consider the example illustrated here. Begin with the double-angle identity for cosine. Substitute in the known values and do the arithmetic.

Sample problems:

1. If $\sin x = \frac{3}{5}$ and x is in the first quadrant, find $\sin 2x$.

   Solution: $\frac{24}{25}$

   Explanation: For sine the double angle identity is $\sin 2x = 2\sin x\cos x$; $\sin 2x = 2\left(\frac{3}{5}\right)\cos x$.
   Use $\sin x = \frac{3}{5}$ to find $\cos x$: $5^2 = 3^2 + b^2$; $b^2 = 25 - 9$; $b = 4$, so $\cos x = \frac{4}{5}$. Complete the formula: $\sin 2x = 2\sin x\cos x = 2\left(\frac{3}{5}\right)\left(\frac{4}{5}\right) = 2\left(\frac{12}{25}\right) = \frac{24}{25}$.

2. If $\tan x = -\frac{5}{12}$ and x is in the second quadrant, find $\sin 2x$.

   Solution: $-\frac{120}{169}$

   Explanation: The double angle identity for sine is $\sin 2x = 2\sin x\cos x$. Use $\tan x = -\frac{5}{12}$ to find the values of $\sin x$ and $\cos x$: $c^2 = a^2 + b^2$; $c^2 = 5^2 + 12^2$; $c^2 = 25 + 144$; $c = 13$.
   In quadrant II, $\sin x$ is positive and $\cos x$ is negative, so $\sin x = \frac{5}{13}$ and $\cos x = -\frac{12}{13}$.
   Complete the formula: $\sin 2x = 2\sin x\cos x = 2\left(\frac{5}{13}\right)\left(-\frac{12}{13}\right) = 2\left(-\frac{60}{169}\right) = -\frac{120}{169}$.

3. Find the exact value of $\cos 2x$ given $\sin\theta = -\frac{24}{25}$ and $\cos\theta < 0$.

   Solution: $-\frac{527}{625}$

   Explanation: To solve for $\cos 2x$, use the double angle form that is most appropriate:
   $\cos 2x = 1 - 2\sin^2\theta \Rightarrow \cos 2x = 1 - 2\left(-\frac{24}{25}\right)^2 = 1 - 2\left(\frac{576}{625}\right) = -\frac{527}{625}$

Practice problems: *(Answers on page: 758)*

1. If $\sin x = \frac{1}{2}$ and x is in the first quadrant, find $\tan 2x$.
2. If $\tan x = \frac{3}{2}$ and x is in the first quadrant, find $\sin 2x$.

3. Simplify: $1-4\sin^2 x\cos^2 x$

Review questions: *(Answers to odd questions on page: 758)*

1. If $\sin x=\frac{\sqrt{2}}{2}$ and x is in the first quadrant, find $\cos 2x$.
2. If $\tan x=\frac{24}{7}$ and x is in the first quadrant, find $\cos 2x$.
3. If $\sin x=\frac{5}{13}$ and x is in the first quadrant, find $\tan 2x$.
4. If $\cos x=35$ and x is in the first quadrant, find $\tan 2x$.
5. Find the exact value of $\sin 2x$, given $\sin x=\frac{3}{5}$ and $0<x<\frac{\pi}{2}$.

Using Double-Angle Identities

- **Double-angle identities** can help you solve trigonometric equations.
- **Review**: The double-angle identities:
  - $\sin 2\theta = 2\sin\theta\cos\theta$
  - $\cos 2\theta = \cos^2\theta - \sin^2\theta$
  - $\cos 2\theta = 1 - 2\sin^2\theta$
  - $\cos 2\theta = 2\cos^2\theta - 1$
  - $\tan 2\theta = \frac{2\tan\theta}{1-\tan^2\theta}$

Example $\cos 2x = \sin x \quad x \in [0, 2\pi)$ *(find solution for x from 0 to 2π)* $\cos^2 x - \sin^2 x = \sin x$	In this example you are given that cos 2x = sin 2x and you are asked to find the solution for x from 0 to 2π. Since this trigonometric equation involves the angle 2x and the angle x, use a **double-angle identity** for cosine to simplify the expression. Rewrite cos 2x as $\cos^2 x - \sin^2 x$.
$1 - \sin^2 x - \sin^2 x = \sin x$ *Pythagorean identity* $\sin^2 x + \cos^2 x = 1$ *So* $\cos^2 x = 1 - \sin^2 x$	Next, use the **Pythagorean identity** to replace the $\cos^2 x$ term, leaving the equation in terms of sin$x$.
$1 - 2\sin^2 x = \sin x$ $2\sin^2 x + \sin x - 1 = 0$ $(2\sin x - 1)(\sin x + 1) = 0$ *So either* $(2\sin x - 1) = 0$ *OR* $(\sin x + 1) = 0$ $\sin x = \frac{1}{2}$ $\quad$ $\sin x = -1$	Now follow the usual procedure for solving equations: Combine like terms. Move everything to one side. Factor. Solve for the value of sin$x$.
$x = \frac{\pi}{6}$ $\quad$ $x = \frac{5\pi}{6}$ $\quad$ $x = \frac{3\pi}{2}$ 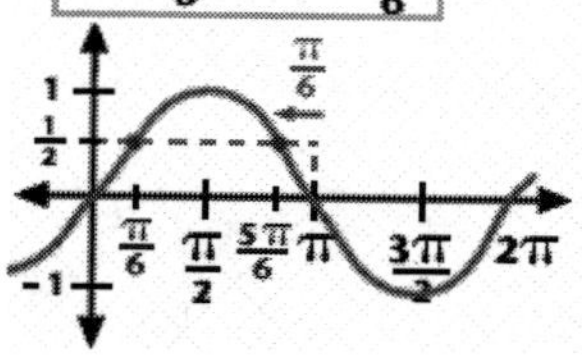 $\pi - \frac{\pi}{6} =$ $\frac{6\pi}{6} - \frac{\pi}{6} = \frac{5\pi}{6}$	Check on a graph or a table of trig values to see what angles have these values for their sine. For example, there are two angles, π/6 and 5π/6, that satisfy sin x = 1/2.

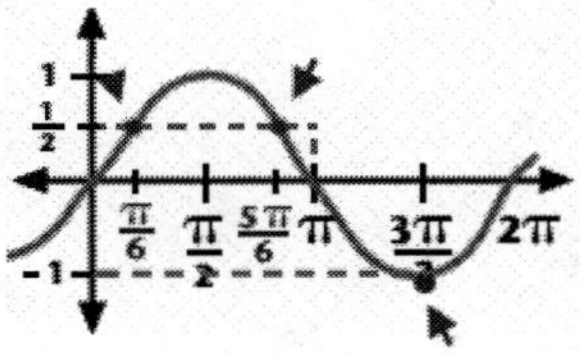

$x = \frac{\pi}{6}, \frac{5\pi}{6}$ or $\frac{3\pi}{2}$

Remember to check for all values!

What is the angle whose sine is –1? 3π/2.

So there are three solutions in all: $x = \pi/6$, $5\pi/6$, and $3\pi/2$.

Remember to always check for two values when finding the inverse of a function.

Sample problems:

1. Solve $\sin 2t = \cos t$ for t, $t \in [0, 2\pi)$.
   Solution: $\frac{\pi}{2}, \frac{3\pi}{2}, \frac{\pi}{6}, \frac{5\pi}{6}$
   Explanation: Use the double-angle formula for $\sin 2t$: $\sin 2t = \cos t \Rightarrow 2\sin t \cos t = \cos t$.
   Set the equation equal to zero, factor and solve each factor for t: $2\sin t \cos t - \cos t = 0$;
   $\cos t(2\sin t - 1) = 0$; $\cos t = 0$ or $2\sin t = 1$; $\cos t = 0$ or $\sin t = \frac{1}{2}$. Thus, $t = \frac{\pi}{2}, \frac{3\pi}{2}, \frac{\pi}{6}, \frac{5\pi}{6}$.

2. Solve $\cos 2t = \cos t$ for t, if t is in the interval $[0, 2\pi)$.
   Solution: $\frac{2\pi}{3}, \frac{4\pi}{3}, 0$
   Explanation: Use the double-angle formula for $\cos 2t$: $\cos 2t = \cos t \Rightarrow 2\cos^2 t - 1 = \cos t$. Move all terms to the left side: $2\cos^2 t - \cos t - 1 = 0$. Factor and solve each factor for t:
   $(2\cos t + 1)(\cos t - 1) = 0$; $\cos t = -\frac{1}{2}$ or $\cos t = 1$. Thus, $t = \frac{2\pi}{3}, \frac{4\pi}{3}$ or $t = 0$.

3. Solve $\cos 2t = \cos t$ for t, if t is in the interval $[0, 2\pi)$.
   Solution: $\frac{2\pi}{3}, \frac{4\pi}{3}, 0$
   Explanation:
   Use the most appropriate double-angle formula for $\cos 2t$: $\cos 2t = \cos t \Rightarrow 2\cos^2 t - 1 = \cos t$.
   Move all of the terms to the left side: $2\cos^2 t - \cos t - 1 = 0$.
   Factor and solve each factor for t: $(2\cos t + 1)(\cos t - 1) = 0$; $\cos t = -\frac{1}{2}$ or $\cos t = 1$.
   Thus, $t = \frac{2\pi}{3}, \frac{4\pi}{3}$ or $t = 0$.

Practice problems: *(Answers on page: 758)*

1. Solve $\sin 2t = 2\sin t$ for t, $t \in [0, 2\pi)$.
2. Solve $\cos 2t = 1 - \sin t$ for t, $t \in [0, 2\pi)$.
3. Solve $\sin 2t \sin t + \cos 2t \cos t = 1$ for t, $t \in [0, 2\pi)$.

Review questions: *(Answers to odd questions on page: 758)*

1. Solve $\cos 2t = 0$ for t, $t \in [0, 2\pi)$.
2. Solve $(\tan t)(\tan 2t) = 1$ for t, $t \in [0, 2\pi)$.
3. Solve $3\cos 2t - 5\cos t - 1 = 0$ for t, $t \in [0, 2\pi)$.
4. Solve $\cos 2t + 3\cos t = 1$ for t, $t \in [0, 2\pi)$.
5. Find all solutions in the interval $[0, 2\pi)$ for $\cos 4x - 7\cos 2x = 8$.

Solving Word Problems Involving Multiple-Angle Identities

- **Multiple-angle identities** involve trigonometric functions of multiples of an angle θ (such as 2θ or 3θ). The most commonly used multiple angle identities are the **double-angle identities**.
- Trigonometry has many practical applications.
- **Review**: Area of a rectangle: *base* · *height*
- **Review**:

  Area of a triangle: $\frac{1}{2} \cdot base \cdot height$
- **Review**: In the point (x,y), x represents the base, or horizontal distance from a central point, and y represents the height, or vertical distance from that same central point.

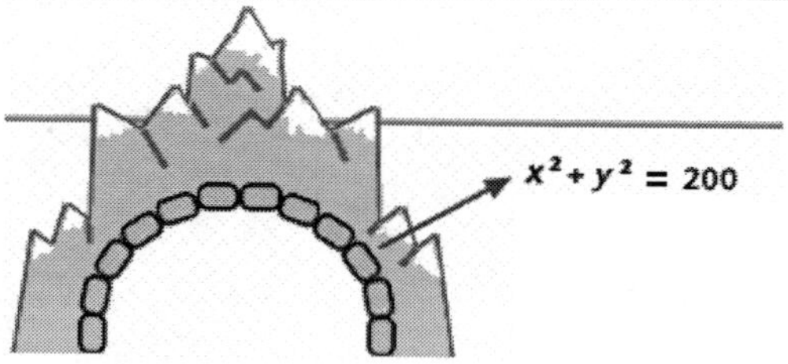 	Consider the following application: An engineer wants to build a tunnel through a mountain with the maximum cross-sectional area possible. The equation $x^2 + y^2 = 200$ is given to represent the circle, half of which is the arch for the tunnel.
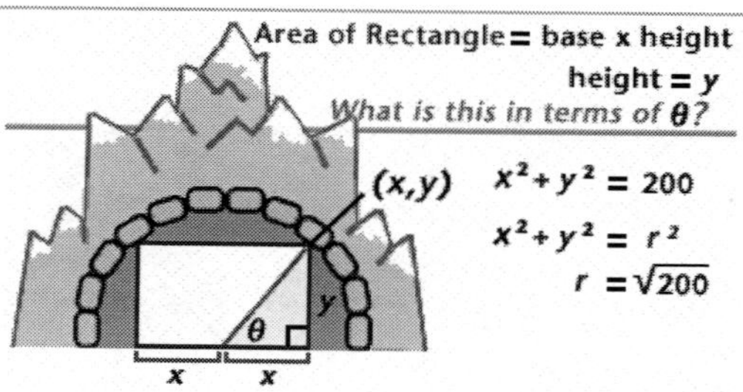 	From this equation it can be deduced that the radius of the circle is $\sqrt{200}$. (A radius extends from the center of the circle to any point on the circle.) The center of the circle is the midpoint of the base of the rectangle drawn to fill half the circle. A radius from the center to the upper corner of the rectangle will form the hypotenuse of a right triangle. (See the diagram to the left.) If (x, y) is the point that is the upper corner of the rectangle, then x is the base of the triangle and y is the height of the triangle.
$\sin\theta = \frac{opp}{hyp} = \frac{y}{\sqrt{200}}$ So $y = \sqrt{200}\sin\theta$ $\cos\theta = \frac{adj}{hyp} = \frac{x}{\sqrt{200}}$ So $x = \sqrt{200}\cos\theta$	Define θ to be the angle formed by the radius/hypotenuse and the base of the rectangle/triangle. Express y and x in terms of $\sin\theta$ and $\cos\theta$.
$A = 2xy$ $= 2x(\sqrt{200}\sin\theta)$ $= 2(\sqrt{200}\cos\theta)\sqrt{200}\sin\theta$ $= (200)(2\cos\theta\sin\theta)$ Double Angle Formula for sine $A = 200\sin 2\theta$	Now substitute into the equation for the area of the rectangle. Notice that the **double-angle identity** for sine appears on the right side.

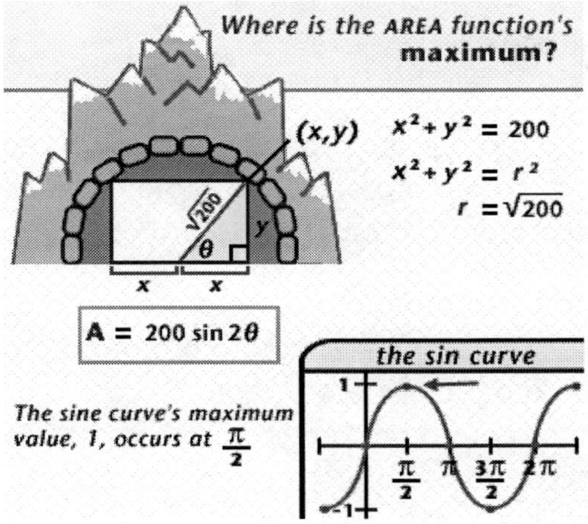	To determine the maximum area, determine where the sine value is at its maximum. The maximum value that the sine function reaches is 1. On a graph of the sine curve, this maximum is achieved when the angle is equal to $\pi/2$. Thus, $2\theta = \pi/2$.
So $2\theta = \frac{\pi}{2}$ $\theta = \frac{\pi}{4}$ $\theta = 45°$	If $2\theta = \pi/2$, or 90°, then $\theta = \pi/4$, or 45°.
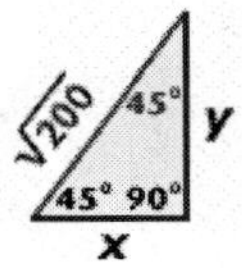	Now all the angles of the triangle are known: 180° – 90°– 45° = 45°. And, because you know that the two acute angles are equal, then you can say that $x = y$.
$x^2 + y^2 = 200$ since $x = y$ $x^2 + x^2 = 200$ $2x^2 = 200$ $x^2 = 100$ $x = 10'$ $y = 10'$	Now, return to the original equation for the circle and solve for x and y.
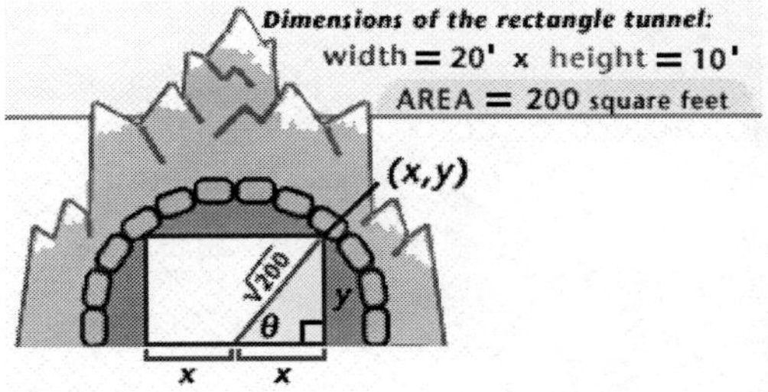	Substitute x and y into the equation for the area of the rectangle and find the maximum area for the tunnel. Notice that the width of the rectangle is $2x$ when substituting to find the area.

Sample problems:

1. A function is given by the equation $A = \cos^2\theta - \sin^2\theta$. In the interval $0 \le \theta \le 2\pi$, what is the smallest value of A?
   Solution: -1
   Explanation: The expression $\cos^2\theta - \sin^2\theta$ is equal to $\cos(2\theta)$, so $A = \cos(2\theta)$. For any equation of the form $y = \cos x$, the minimum value of y is -1.

2. A point (x, y) moves along a circle represented by $x^2 + y^2 = 400$, but never leaves the first quadrant. At any location, the point determines an angle θ. A horizontal line through the point, a vertical line through the point, and a diameter of the circle determine a triangle. Write an expression for the horizontal leg of the triangle.

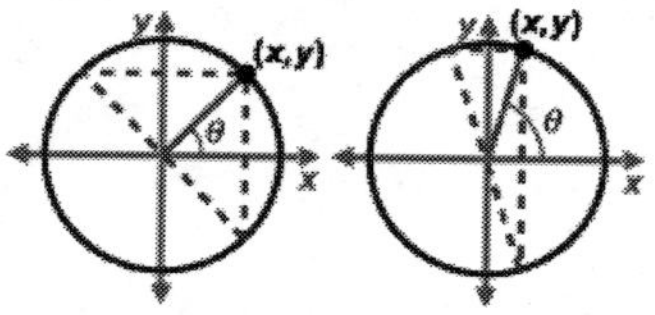

Solution: $2x$

Explanation: The horizontal leg connects the two points (x, y) and $(-x, y)$. The distance between those two points is $2x$.

3. A point moves around a circle represented by $x^2 + y^2 = 100$. At any location on the circle, the point determines an angle θ. The points (x, y), $(-x, y)$, $(-x, 0)$, and $(x, 0)$ determine a rectangle. Find an expression that uses only the variable θ to represent the shaded area of the diagram.

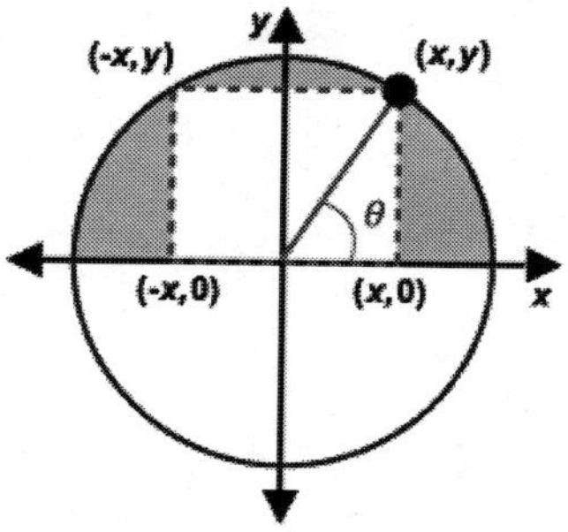

Solution: $50\pi - 200\sin\theta\cos\theta$

Explanation: The area of the half circle is $A_1 = \frac{\pi r^2}{2} = \frac{\pi(10^2)}{2} = 50\pi$. The area of the rectangle is $A_2 = lw = (2x)(y)$. Since $x = 10\cos\theta$ and $y = 10\sin\theta$, the area of the rectangle is $A_2 = 2(10\cos\theta)(10\sin\theta) = 200\cos\theta\sin\theta$. So the shaded area is $A = A_1 - A_2 = 50\pi - 200\sin\theta\cos\theta$.

Practice problems: *(Answers on page: 758)*

1. A point (x, y) moves along a circle represented by $x^2 + y^2 = 400$, but never leaves the first quadrant. At any location, the point determines an angle θ. A horizontal line through the point, a vertical line through the point, and a diameter of the circle determine a triangle. Write an expression for the vertical leg of the triangle.

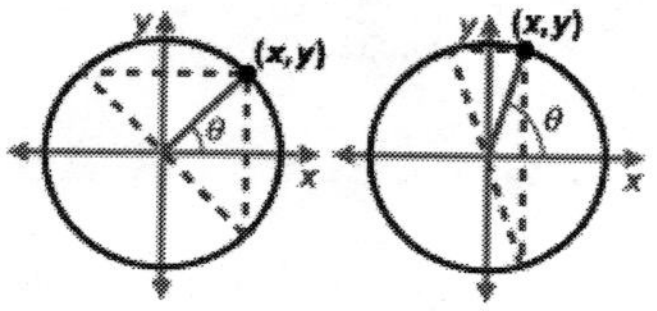

2. The area of a figure is given by the equation $A = \dfrac{(1+\cos(2\theta))}{2}$. In the interval $0 \le \theta \le \pi$, at what value of θ is the area of the figure equal to zero?

3. A point moves around a circle represented by $x^2 + y^2 = 9$. At any location on the circle, the points (x, y), $(-x, y)$, $(x, -y)$, and $(-x, -y)$ determine a rectangle. Also, for each value of θ, $x = 3\cos\theta$ and $y = 3\sin\theta$. The area of the rectangle can be expressed in terms of θ as $18\sin(2\theta)$. In the interval $0 \le \theta \le \pi$, what is the value of θ that maximizes the area of the rectangle?

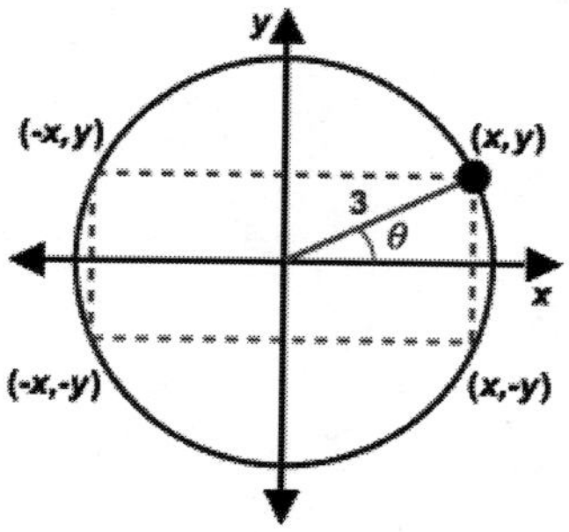

Review questions: *(Answers to odd questions on page: 758)*

1. A point (x, y) moves along a circle represented by $x^2 + y^2 = 25$, but never leaves the first quadrant. At any location, the point determines an angle θ. A horizontal line through the point, a vertical line through the point, and a diameter of the circle determine a triangle. Write x and y in terms of $\sin\theta$ and $\cos\theta$.

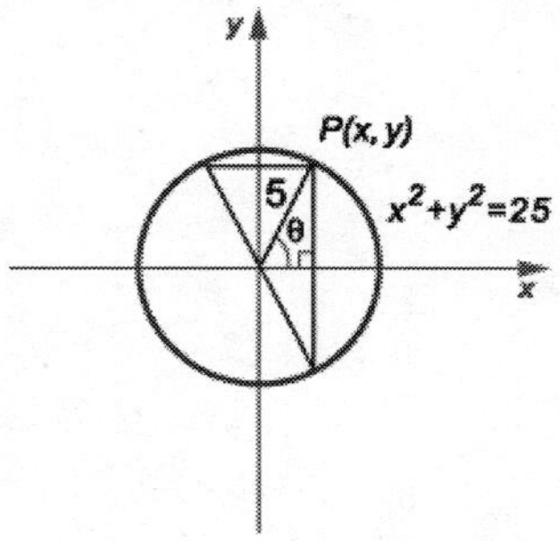

2. A point (x, y) moves along a circle represented by $x^2 + y^2 = 400$, but never leaves the first quadrant. At any location, the point determines an angle θ. A horizontal line through the point, a vertical line through the point, and a diameter of the circle determine a triangle.

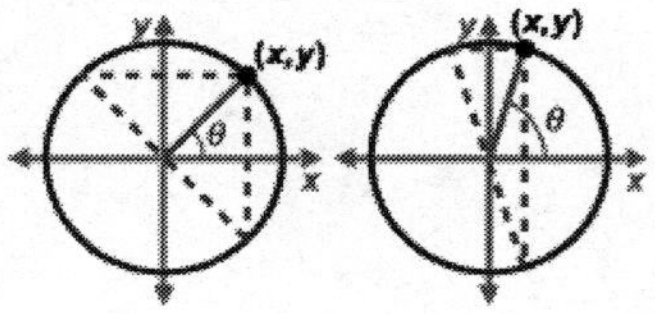

Using the formula for the area of a triangle $A = \left(\frac{1}{2}\right)bh$, what is an expression for the area of the triangle formed by the horizontal and vertical lines through (x, y) and the diameter of the circle?

3. A point (x, y) moves along a circle represented by $x^2 + y^2 = 400$, but never leaves the first quadrant. At any location, the point determines an angle θ. A horizontal line through the point, a vertical line through the point, and a diameter of the circle determine a triangle.

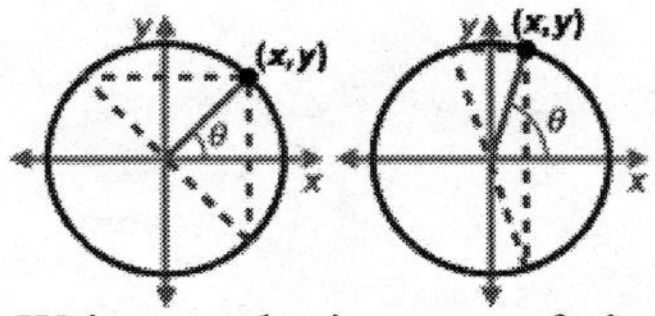

Write x and y in terms of $\sin\theta$ and $\cos\theta$.

4. A point (x, y) moves along a circle represented by $x^2 + y^2 = 400$. At any location on the circle, the point determines an angle θ. A horizontal line through the point, a vertical line through the point, and a diameter of the circle determine a triangle.

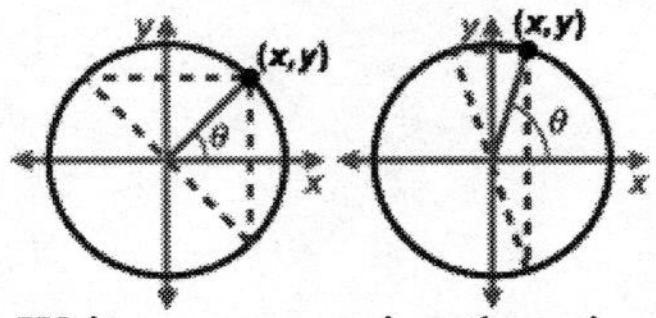

Write an expression that gives the area of the triangle in terms of $\sin\theta$ and $\cos\theta$.

5. A point (a,b) moves along a circle represented by $x^2 + y^2 = 36$, but never leaves the first quadrant. At any location, the point determines an angle q. A horizontal line through the point, a vertical line through the point, and a diameter of the circle determine a triangle. Using the formula for the area of a triangle, $A = (\frac{1}{2})(B)(H)$, what is an expression for the area of the triangle in terms of $\sin\theta$ and $\cos\theta$?.

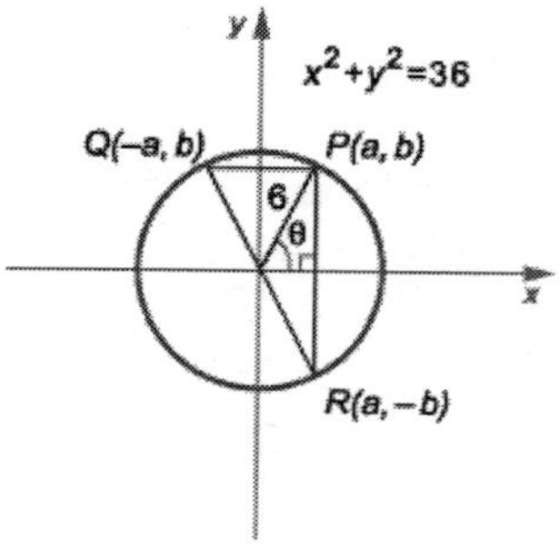

Using a Cofunction Identity

- The **cofunction identities** relate sine to cosine and tangent to cotangent:
  - cos $(x - \pi/2) = \sin x$
  - sin $(x - \pi/2) = -\cos x$
  - tan $(x - \pi/2) = -\cot x$

Example $\cos\left(x - \frac{\pi}{2}\right) \stackrel{?}{=}$

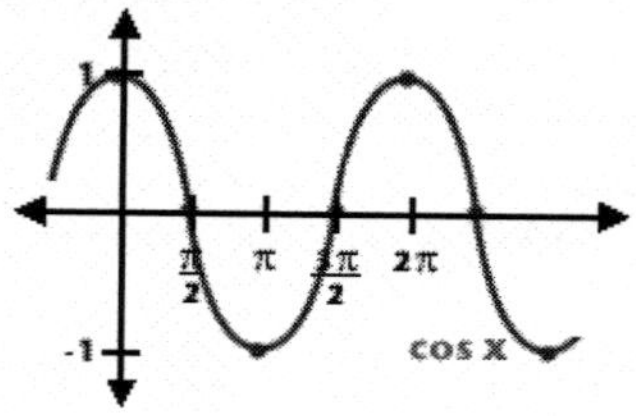

The graph of cos x is given to the left.

Find the effect of subtracting $\pi/2$ from x .

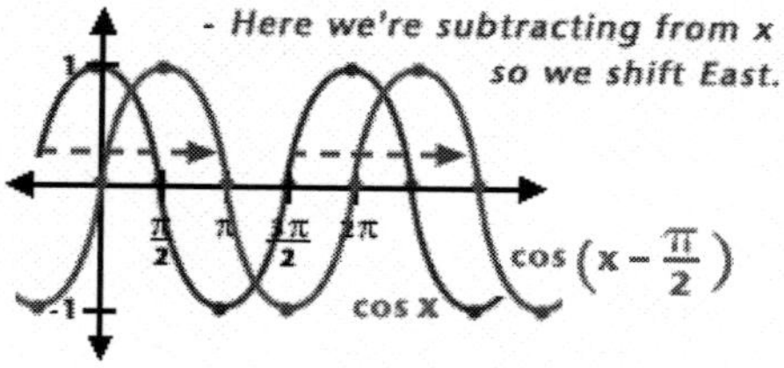

Since $\pi/2$ is subtracted from x, the graph is shifted "east," or to the right, of where it used to be.

The new graph looks a lot like the graph of sin x.

How could you determine, algebraically, if the function $\cos(x - \pi/2)$ is the same as sin x?

difference of angles:

$\cos(\theta_1 - \theta_2) = \cos\theta_1\cos\theta_2 + \sin\theta_1\sin\theta_2$

Example $\cos\left(x - \frac{\pi}{2}\right) \stackrel{?}{=} \sin x$

$$\cos\left(x - \frac{\pi}{2}\right) = \cos x \cos\frac{\pi}{2} + \sin x \sin\frac{\pi}{2}$$
$$= \cos x\ (0)\ + \sin x\ (1)$$
$$= \sin x$$

Rewrite $\cos(x - \pi/2)$ using the identity for the cosine of a difference of two angles.

Plug in x and $\pi/2$ appropriately into the formula.

Evaluate the trig functions of $\pi/2$: the cosine of $\pi/2$ is 0, and the sine of $\pi/2$ is 1.

$\cos(x - \pi/2)$ simplifies to sin x.

$\cos\left(x - \frac{\pi}{2}\right) \stackrel{\checkmark}{=} \sin x$

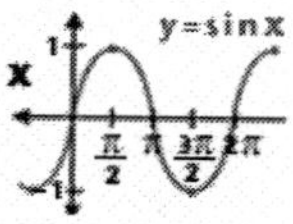

Therefore, the function cos x shifted to the right $\pi/2$ units is the same as the sine function.

Example $\sin\left(x-\frac{\pi}{2}\right) \stackrel{?}{=}$

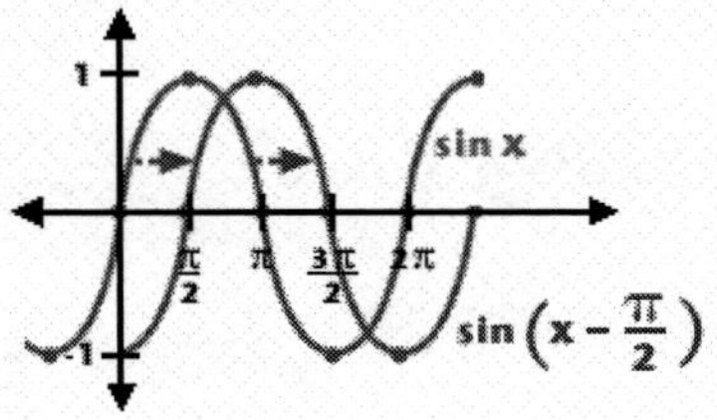

Now graph sin (x –π/2) and compare it with the graph of cos x.

Again, the curve shifts to the right, or "east." But it doesn't yield the cos x curve because, for example, the angle 0 is –1 on this new curve while it is 1 on the cos$x$ curve. However, following the curve, notice that the new curve matches the negative of the cosine curve.

Example $\sin\left(x-\frac{\pi}{2}\right) \stackrel{?}{=} -\cos x$

$$\sin\left(x-\frac{\pi}{2}\right) = \sin x \cos\frac{\pi}{2} - \cos x \sin\frac{\pi}{2}$$

$$= \sin x\ (0) \quad - \cos x\ (1)$$

$$\sin\left(x-\frac{\pi}{2}\right) \stackrel{\surd}{=} -\cos x$$

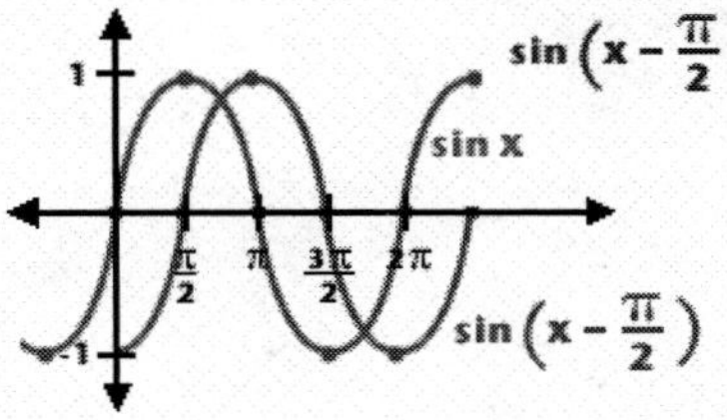

Can you determine, algebraically, that sin (x –π/2) = –cos$x$?

Use the identity for the sine of a difference of two angles.

Substitute in known values.

Simplify to find that sin (x – π/2) = –cos$x$.

---

difference of angles: $\tan(\theta_1-\theta_2) = \dfrac{\tan\theta_1 - \tan\theta_2}{1 + \tan\theta_1 \tan\theta_2}$

Example $\tan\left(x-\frac{\pi}{2}\right) \stackrel{?}{=} -\cot x$

$$\tan\left(x-\frac{\pi}{2}\right) = \left(\frac{\tan x - \tan\frac{\pi}{2}}{1 + \tan x \tan\frac{\pi}{2}}\right)\left(\frac{\frac{1}{\tan\frac{\pi}{2}}}{\frac{1}{\tan\frac{\pi}{2}}}\right)$$

same as multiplying by 1/1

Can you prove algebraically that tan (x –π/2) = –cot$x$?

First, write out the expression.

Multiply by a fraction equal to 1 to get rid of the undefined value tan (π/2).

$$= \frac{\frac{\tan x}{\tan\frac{\pi}{2}} - 1}{\frac{1}{\tan\frac{\pi}{2}} + \tan x} = \frac{\tan x \cot\frac{\pi}{2} - 1}{\cot\frac{\pi}{2} + \tan x}$$

This is the resulting fraction on the left. Substitute cotangent for tangent in the denominator.

$$= \frac{\tan x\ (0) - 1}{(0) + \tan x} = \frac{-1}{\tan x} \stackrel{\surd}{=} \boxed{-\cot x}$$

Then substitute known values in wherever possible.

Therefore: tan (x–π/2) = –cot x.

Sample problems:

1. Evaluate $\tan(\theta-90^\circ)$ if $\tan\theta = \frac{5}{3}$.

   Solution: $-\frac{3}{5}$

   Explanation: By the cofunction identities, $\tan\left(\theta-\frac{\pi}{2}\right) = -\cot\theta$ and $\frac{\pi}{2} = 90^\circ$,

   so $\tan(\theta-90^\circ) = -\cot\theta = -\frac{1}{\tan\theta} = -\frac{1}{\frac{5}{3}} = -\frac{3}{5}$.

2. Simplify: $\tan\left(x+\frac{\pi}{4}\right)$

<u>Solution</u>: $\frac{1+\tan x}{1-\tan x}$

<u>Explanation</u>: Simplify $\tan\left(x+\frac{\pi}{4}\right)$ using the identity for the tangent of a difference of two angles:

$$\tan\left(x+\frac{\pi}{4}\right)=\frac{\tan x+\tan\frac{\pi}{4}}{1-\tan x\tan\frac{\pi}{4}}=\frac{\tan x+1}{1-(\tan x)(1)}=\frac{1+\tan x}{1-\tan x}.$$

3. Simplify: $\cos\left(x+\frac{3\pi}{2}\right)$

<u>Solution</u>: $\sin x$

<u>Explanation</u>: Simplify $\cos\left(x+\frac{3\pi}{2}\right)$ using the identity for the cosine of a sum of two angles:

$\cos\left(x+\frac{3\pi}{2}\right)=\cos x\cos\frac{3\pi}{2}-\sin x\sin\frac{3\pi}{2}=(\cos x)(0)-(\sin x)(-1)=0+\sin x=\sin x.$

Practice problems: *(Answers on page: 758)*

1. Simplify: $\tan(2\pi-x)$
2. Simplify: $\cot\left(\frac{\pi}{2}-x\right)$
3. Simplify: $\sin(x-3\pi)$

Review questions: *(Answers to odd questions on page: 758)*

1. Simplify: $\cos\left(x-\frac{\pi}{2}\right)$
2. Simplify: $\sin\left(x-\frac{\pi}{2}\right)$
3. Simplify: $\sin(\pi-x)$
4. Simplify: $\cos\left(x+\frac{\pi}{2}\right)$
5. Simplify: $\cot\left(\frac{\pi}{2}+x\right)$

Using a Power-Reducing Identity

- **Power-reducing identities** allow you to write trig expressions with powers as equivalent expressions without powers.
- The power-reducing identities:
  - $\cos^2\theta=\frac{1+\cos(2\theta)}{2}$
  - $\sin^2\theta=\frac{1-\cos(2\theta)}{2}$

Example Rewrite: $\sin^4\Theta$ $\sin^4\Theta = (\sin^2\Theta)^2$ $(\sin^2\Theta)^2 = \left(\frac{1-\cos(2\Theta)}{2}\right)^2$ $= \frac{1}{4}\left[1 - 2\cos(2\Theta) + \cos^2(2\Theta)\right]$	How would you rewrite the expression $\sin^4\theta$ without using any powers? Start by writing the original expression as an expression squared. Substitute a **power- reducing** identity for the $\sin^2\theta$ term. Square the resulting expression.
$= \frac{1}{4}\left(\frac{2 - 4\cos(2\Theta) + 1 + \cos(4\Theta)}{2}\right)$ $\sin^4\Theta = \boxed{\frac{1}{8}\left[3 - 4\cos(2\Theta) + \cos(4\Theta)\right]}$	Again, substitute the power-reducing identity for the $\cos^2(2\theta)$ term. **REMEMBER**: Double the angle when using a power-reducing identity. Find a common denominator for the expression in the brackets, then simplify.
The Power of Reducing Power Formulas:  • *Reduce trig functions with powers to simpler expressions without powers.*	Power-reducing formulas can be really useful—look for opportunities to use them.

Sample problems:

1. Solve for x in the interval $0 < x < \pi$: $\sec^4 2x = 4$

   Solution: $\frac{\pi}{8}, \frac{3\pi}{8}, \frac{5\pi}{8}, \frac{7\pi}{8}$

   Explanation: $\sec^4 2x = 4$; $\sqrt{\sec^4 2x} = \sqrt{4}$; $\sec^2 2x = \pm 2$; $\frac{1}{\cos^2 2x} = \pm 2$;
   $\cos^2 2x = \pm\frac{1}{2}$; $\sqrt{\cos^2 2x} = \pm\sqrt{\frac{1}{2}}$; $\cos 2x = \pm\frac{\sqrt{2}}{2}$; $2x = \frac{\pi}{4}, \frac{3\pi}{4}, \frac{5\pi}{4}$, or $\frac{7\pi}{4}$,
   so $x = \frac{\pi}{8}, \frac{3\pi}{8}, \frac{5\pi}{8}$, or $\frac{7\pi}{8}$.

2. Express $2(\sin^4 t)$ without using any exponents other than 1.

   Solution: $\left(\frac{1}{4}\right)(3 - 4\cos 2t + \cos 4t)$

   Explanation: Write the expression in parentheses as a square: $2\left(\sin^4 t\right) = 2\left(\sin^2 t\right)^2$.

   Use the power-reducing identity: $2\left(\sin^2 t\right)^2 = 2\left(\frac{1-\cos 2t}{2}\right)^2 = 2\cdot\left(\frac{1}{4}\right)(1 - 2\cos 2t + \cos^2 2t)$.

   Use the power-reducing identity for cosine: $\left(\frac{1}{2}\right)(1 - 2\cos 2t + \cos^2 2t) = \left(\frac{1}{2}\right)\left(1 - 2\cos 2t + \frac{1+\cos 4t}{2}\right)$

   Find a common denominator and combine like terms: $\left(\frac{1}{2}\right)\left(\frac{2 - 4\cos 2t + 1 + \cos 4t}{2}\right) = \left(\frac{1}{2}\right)\left(\frac{3 - 4\cos 2t + \cos 4t}{2}\right)$

   Simplify: $\left(\frac{1}{4}\right)(3 - 4\cos 2t + \cos 4t)$.

3. Express $\cos^4 t$ without using any exponents other than 1.

Solution: $\left(\frac{1}{8}\right)(3+4\cos 2t+\cos 4t)$

Explanation: Write the original expression as an expression squared: $\cos^4 t=\left(\cos^2 t\right)^2$.

Use the power-reducing identity: $\cos^4 t=\left(\cos^2 t\right)^2=\left(\frac{1+\cos 2t}{2}\right)^2=\left(\frac{1}{4}\right)(1+2\cos 2t+\cos^2 2t)$.

Again, use the power-reducing identity: $\left(\frac{1}{4}\right)(1+2\cos 2t+\cos^2 2t)=\left(\frac{1}{4}\right)\left(1+2\cos t+\frac{1+\cos 4t}{2}\right)=$ $\left(\frac{1}{4}\right)\left(\frac{2+4\cos 2t+1+\cos 4t}{2}\right)=\left(\frac{1}{8}\right)(3+4\cos 2t+\cos 4t)$.

Practice problems: *(Answers on page: 758)*

1. Express $\cos^4 t-\sin^4 t$ without using any exponents other than 1.
2. Solve for x in the interval $0<x<\pi$: $\tan^2 2x-1=0$
3. Express $\tan^4 t$ without using any exponents other than 1.

Review questions: *(Answers to odd questions on page: 758)*

1. Express $\sin^3 t$ without using any exponents other than 1.
2. Express $\frac{\cos^4 t}{16}$ without using any exponents other than 1.
3. Express $\cos^4 t-\cos^2 t$ without using any exponents other than 1.
4. Express $\cos^3 t$ without using any exponents other than 1.
5. Express $\frac{\tan^4 t}{4}$ without using any exponents other than 1.

Using Half-Angle Identities to Solve a Trigonometric Equation

- **Half-angle identities** allow you to write trig functions of an angle $x/2$ (half of the angle x) in terms of trig functions of the angle x:
  - $\cos\frac{x}{2}=\pm\sqrt{\frac{1+\cos x}{2}}$
  - $\sin\frac{x}{2}=\pm\sqrt{\frac{1-\cos x}{2}}$
  - $\tan\frac{x}{2}=\pm\frac{1-\cos x}{\sin x}$

Reducing Power Formulas: $\cos^2\Theta=\frac{\cos(2\Theta)+1}{2}$ | $\sin^2\Theta=\frac{1-\cos(2\Theta)}{2}$	To derive the **half-angle identities**, start with the **power-reducing identities**. Note that the squared side is in terms of θ while the unsquared side is in terms of 2θ.

Half-Angle Formulas: $\cos\left(\frac{x}{2}\right)=\pm\sqrt{\frac{1+\cos x}{2}}$ $\sin\left(\frac{x}{2}\right)=\pm\sqrt{\frac{1-\cos x}{2}}$	Take the square roots of both sides of the identities. 2θ is represented as x, and therefore θ is $x/2$. **NOTE**: In the half-angle formulas, the angles are represented by $x/2$ and x instead of θ and 2θ. The angle on the right is still twice the angle on the left.
$\tan\left(\frac{x}{2}\right)=\frac{1-\cos x}{\sin x}$	Using the two identities above, the half-angle identity for tangent is derived.
Choose the sign (+ −) of your trig function based on the quadrant your angle lies in. Students ← All Take → Calculus S: sine positive; A: All trig functions are +; T: tangent positive; C: cosine positive	Pay special attention to the signs for your answer. **REMEMBER:** The **quadrant** that an angle is in determines the signs of its trig functions.
Example $\sin 15° = \sin\left(\frac{30°}{2}\right)$ $\sin\left(\frac{30°}{2}\right)=\sqrt{\frac{1-\cos(30°)}{2}}$	Consider the given example: find the value of sin 15°. Since 15° = 30°/2, use a half-angle identity.
$=\sqrt{\frac{1-\sqrt{3}/2}{2}}$ $=\sqrt{\frac{\frac{2}{2}-\sqrt{3}/2}{2}}$ $=\sqrt{\frac{2-\sqrt{3}}{4}}$ $\boxed{\sin 15° = \frac{\sqrt{2-\sqrt{3}}}{2}}$	Now substitute in the known values. Find a common denominator. Do the arithmetic to find the answer.

Sample problems:

1. Find the exact value of $\tan 67.5°$.

   Solution: $1+\sqrt{2}$

   Explanation: Express 67.5° as a fraction with a denominator of 2: $\tan 67.5° = \tan\frac{135°}{2}$.

   Use a half-angle identity to simplify: $\tan\frac{135°}{2}=\frac{1-\cos 135°}{\sin 135°}=\frac{1-\frac{\left(-\sqrt{2}\right)}{2}}{\frac{\sqrt{2}}{2}}$

   $$=\frac{\frac{2}{2}+\frac{\sqrt{2}}{2}}{\frac{\sqrt{2}}{2}}=\frac{2+\sqrt{2}}{\sqrt{2}}\cdot\frac{\sqrt{2}}{\sqrt{2}}$$

   $$=\frac{\left(2\sqrt{2}\right)+2}{2}=\sqrt{2}+1.$$

2. Find the exaxt value of $\tan\frac{\pi}{12}$.

Solution: $2-\sqrt{3}$

Explanation: Express $\frac{\pi}{12}$ as a fraction with a denominator of 2: $\tan\frac{\pi}{12}=\tan\frac{\frac{\pi}{6}}{2}$.

Use a half-angle identity to simplify: $\tan\frac{\frac{\pi}{6}}{2}=\frac{1-\cos\frac{\pi}{6}}{\sin\frac{\pi}{6}}=\frac{1-\frac{\sqrt{3}}{2}}{\frac{1}{2}}=2-\sqrt{3}$.

3. Find the value of $\cos x$ for $x=67.5$ to four decimal places.

Solution: 0.3827

Explanation: Substitute using the half-angle formula:

$$\cos(67.5)=\cos\left(\frac{135}{2}\right)=\sqrt{\frac{1+\cos 135}{2}}.$$

(Note: use the positive square root since 67.5 is in the first quadrant).

$$\sqrt{\frac{1+\cos 135}{2}}=\sqrt{\frac{1+\left(-\frac{\sqrt{2}}{2}\right)}{2}}=\sqrt{\frac{2-\sqrt{2}}{4}}=\frac{\sqrt{2-\sqrt{2}}}{2}\approx 0.3827$$

Practice problems: *(Answers on page: 759)*

1. Find the exact value for $\tan\frac{x}{2}$ given $\cos x=\frac{24}{25}$ and $\sin x>0$.
2. Find $\sin\frac{a}{2}$ if $\cos a=\frac{12}{13}$ for $0°\le a\le 90°$.
3. Find the exact value of $\sin 7.5°$.

Review questions: *(Answers to odd questions on page: 759)*

1. Find the exact value of $\cos 15°$.
2. Find the exact value of $\sin 22.5°$.
3. Find the exact value of $\tan 22.5°$.
4. Find the exact value of $\sin 67.5°$.
5. Find the exact value of $\cos 22.5°$.

8

Applications of Trigonometry

The Law of Sines

- The **law of sines** allows you to solve for sides or angles of triangles that are not right triangles.
- The law of sines:

  In a triangle with sides a, b, and c opposite angles α, β, and γ, $\frac{\sin\alpha}{a} = \frac{\sin\beta}{b} = \frac{\sin\gamma}{c}$.

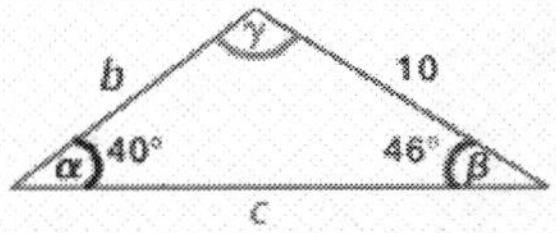 **find:** $a = 10$, $b = ?$, $c = ?$, $\alpha = 40°$, $\beta = 46°$, $\gamma = ?$ **reminder:** *the sum of all angles in a triangle is always equal to 180°*	To use the **law of sines** on a triangle you must either know two sides and one angle or two angles and one side of the triangle. In this problem, you are given two angles and one side and asked to find the missing sides and angle.
$40° + 46° = 86°$ $180° - 86° = 94°$	Finding the third angle is just a matter of subtracting the sum of the two given angles from 180°.
find b $\frac{\sin 40°}{10} = \frac{\sin 46°}{b}$	Use the law of sines to solve for side b by substituting into two of the fractions. Choose the two fractions so that you'll have one unknown to solve for.
$b = \frac{(10)(\sin 46°)}{\sin 40°}$ $\boxed{b = 11.1909}$ *make sure your calculator is set in "degrees" mode*	Solve for b and evaluate the resulting expression using a calculator. **REMEMBER**: Whenever evaluating trig functions on a calculator, be sure the calculator is in the appropriate mode.
find c $\frac{\sin 40°}{10} = \frac{\sin 94°}{c}$ $c = \frac{10(\sin 94°)}{\sin 40°}$ $c = \boxed{15.52...}$	Next, find side c, the remaining unknown side. Again, use two fractions from the law of sines. Solve for c and evaluate on a calculator.
$\frac{\sin\alpha}{a} = \frac{\sin\beta}{b} = \frac{\sin\gamma}{c}$ **applying the law of sines** 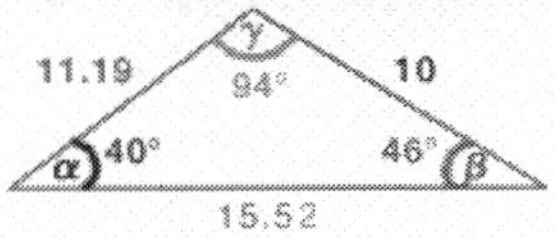 $a = 10$, $b = 11.19$, $c = 15.52$, $\alpha = 40°$, $\beta = 46°$, $\gamma = 94°$	The solution is complete, all three sides and angles are known. **TIP:** The largest angle will always be opposite the longest side - and the smallest angle will always be opposite the shortest side.

Sample problems:

1. An isosceles triangle has a base of length 49.28 meters and the angle opposite the base is 58.746°. Find the length of the legs of the triangle.
   Solution: 50.23m
   Explanation: Begin by finding the two missing angles (they are equal because the triangle is defined as being isosceles): $180° - 58.746° = 121.254°/2 = 60.627°$.
   Use the law of sines to find the length of the legs: $\frac{a}{\sin A} = \frac{c}{\sin C}$; $\frac{49.28}{\sin 58.746°} = \frac{c}{\sin 60.627°}$; $c = \frac{49.28(0.8714)}{(0.8549)} = 50.23$.

2. In the triangle $\angle 1 = \angle 2$, $\overline{CD}$ bisects $\angle ACB$, and $\overline{AD} = 224$. Find $\overline{BD}$.

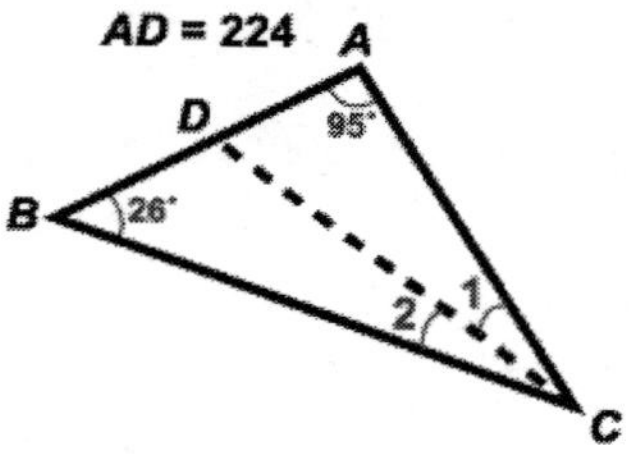

Solution: 509

Explanation: Find $\angle 1$ and $\angle 2$: $\angle 1 + \angle 2 = 180° - (95° + 26°)$; $\angle 1 + \angle 2 = 59°$,

so $\angle 1 = \angle 2 = 29.5°$. Use the law of sines to find $\overline{CD}$: $\dfrac{\sin 95°}{\overline{CD}} = \dfrac{\sin 29.5°}{224}$;

$\overline{CD} = \dfrac{224 \sin 95°}{\sin 29.5} = 453.2$. Find $\overline{BD}$: $\dfrac{\sin 29.5°}{BD} = \dfrac{\sin 26°}{453.2}$;

$\overline{BD} = \dfrac{453.2 \sin 29.5°}{\sin 26°} = 509.$

3. The three angles in a triangle correspond to the ratio $5:6:9$. The shortest side of the triangle is 3.25 inches. Find the length of the longest side of the triangle to the nearest hundredth.
   Solution: 4.54
   Explanation: Find the three angles. The angles can be represented as $5x$, $6x$, and $9x$. The sum of the angles is 180°, so $20x = 180°$ or $x = 9°$, thus the three angles are 45°, 54°, and 81°. The shortest side of the triangle is 3.25, which must be opposite the smallest angle. The longest side is opposite the 81° angle. Use the law of sines: $\dfrac{\sin 81°}{a} = \dfrac{\sin 45°}{3.25}$; $a = \dfrac{3.25(\sin 81°)}{\sin 45°} = 4.54.$

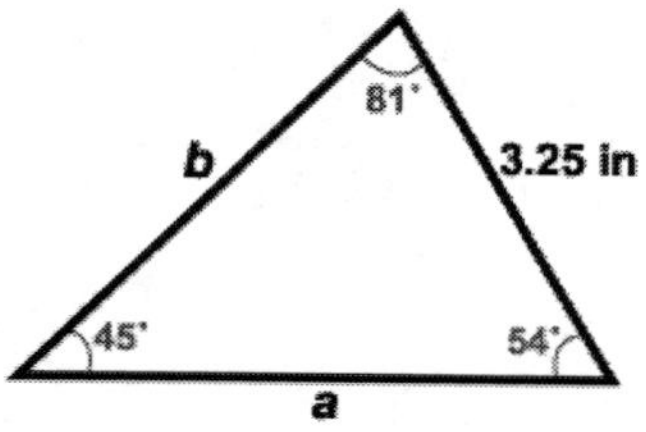

Practice problems: *(Answers on page: 759)*

1. Find the lengths a and b to the nearest millimeter.

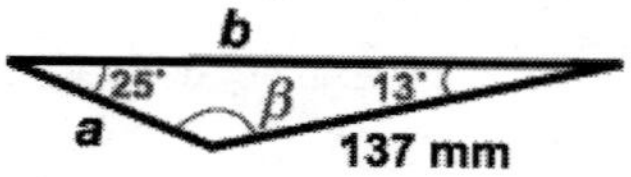

2. The angles of a triangle correspond to the ratio 3:4:5. If the longest side of the triangle is 324 mm, find the length of the shortest side.
3. The vertex angle of an isosceles triangle is 25°, and the legs of the triangle are each 10.0 in. Find the length of the third side of the triangle to the nearest tenth.

Review questions: *(Answers to odd questions on page: 759)*

1. Given that one angle of a triangle is 110°, another angle is 30°, and the side opposite the 30° angle measures 10.5 meters, find the side opposite the unknown angle.
2. AB is a line 652 feet long on one bank of a stream. C is a point on the opposite bank. Angle $A = 50°$ while angle $B = 48°$. Find the width of the stream from C to AB.
3. What is the length of side b?

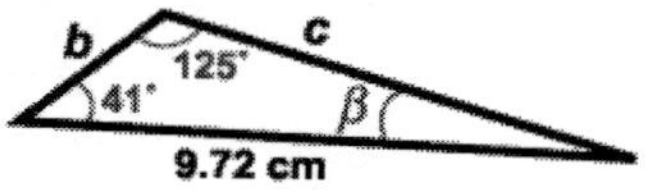

4. Determine the measure of angle α.

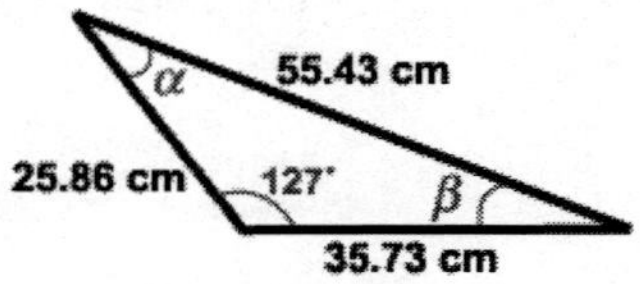

5. The base angles of an isosceles triangle are 73° and the base is 12.86 in. Find the length of the two legs of the triangle to the nearest tenth of an inch.

Solving a Triangle Given Two Sides and One Angle

- **Review**: The **law of sines** solves for sides or angles of triangles that are not right triangles.
- **Review**:

The law of sines: $\dfrac{\sin\alpha}{a} = \dfrac{\sin\beta}{b} = \dfrac{\sin\gamma}{c}$.

 applying the law of sines given: α, a, b find: β, γ, c $\alpha = 50°$ $a = 10$ $\beta = ?$ $b = 8$ $\gamma = ?$ $c = ?$	Given two sides and one angle, use the **law of sines** to solve the triangle.
finding β $\dfrac{\sin 50°}{10} = \dfrac{\sin\beta}{8}$	Start by finding the angle β. Choose the two fractions from the law of sines that leave just one unknown and plug in what is known.
$\sin\beta = \dfrac{8\sin 50°}{10}$ $\sin\beta = .6128\ldots$ *take inverse sin of β (or arcsin)* $\boxed{\beta = 37.8°}$	Solve the equation for $\sin\beta$. Evaluate the expression using a calculator. Use the **inverse sine function** to find β.
finding γ $\alpha + \beta + \gamma = 180°$ $50° + 37.8° + \gamma = 180°$ $\gamma = \boxed{92.2°}$	To find the third angle, subtract the known angles from 180°.
finding c $\dfrac{\sin 50°}{10} = \dfrac{\sin 92.2°}{c}$ $c = \dfrac{10\sin 92.2°}{\sin 50°}$ $c = \boxed{13.044\ldots}$	Now solve for the missing side c: Set up two fractions from the law of sines. Cross-multiply, then solve for c. Evaluate the expression.
$\alpha = 50°$ $a = 10$ $\beta = 37.8°$ $b = 8$ $\gamma = 92.2°$ $c = 13$	In summary, here are the findings.
tip *the largest angle will always be opposite the longest side - and the smallest angle will always be opposite the shortest side*	**REMEMBER:** the largest angle will always be opposite the longest side. The smallest angle will always be opposite the shortest side.

Sample problems:

1. Given a triangle with side $a = 91\text{m}$, side $b = 73.5\text{m}$, and angle $A = 39°$, find angle B.
   Solution: 30.55°

   Explanation: Substitute into the law of sines: $\frac{\sin A}{a} = \frac{\sin B}{b}$; $\frac{\sin 39°}{91} = \frac{\sin B}{73.5}$; $\frac{91}{\sin 39} = \frac{73.5}{\sin B}$; $\sin B = \frac{(\sin 39)(73.5)}{(91)} = 0.5083$. Use the arcsin function on a calculator: $B = 30.55°$.

2. Use the law of sines to find angle α to the nearest tenth.

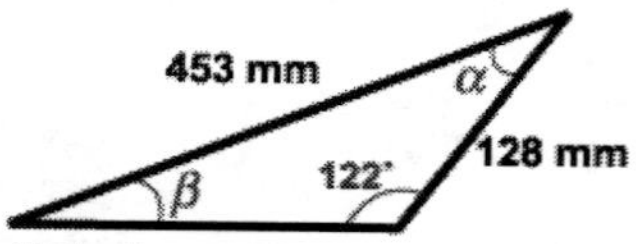

   Solution: 44.1°

   Explanation: Use the law of sines to find β: $\frac{\sin\beta}{128} = \frac{\sin 122°}{453}$; $\sin\beta = \frac{(128(\sin 122°)}{453} = 0.2396$, $\beta = 13.9°$. Find α: $\alpha = 180° - (122° + \beta) = 180° - (122° + 13.9°) = 44.1°$.

3. Find the missing side of the triangle.

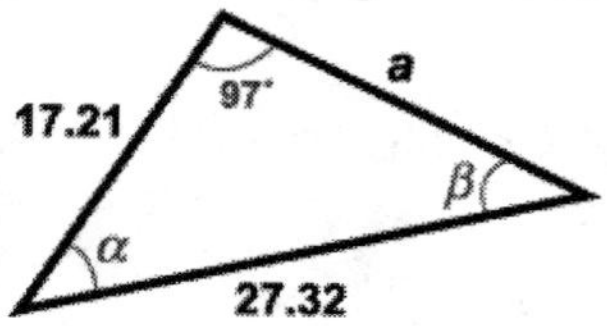

   Solution: 19.22

   Explanation: Find angle β: $\frac{\sin 97°}{27.32} = \frac{\sin\beta}{17.21}$; $\sin\beta = \frac{(17.21)(\sin 97°)}{27.32} = 0.6252$, $\beta = 38.7$. Find α: $\alpha = 180° - (97° + 38.7°) = 44.3°$. Find a: $\frac{\sin 44.3°}{a} = \frac{\sin 97°}{27.32}$;
   $a = \frac{(27.32)(\sin 44.3°)}{(\sin 97°)} = 19.22$.

Practice problems: *(Answers on page: 759)*

1. Given a triangle with side $b = 76.45\text{m}$, angle $B = 105°$ and side $a = 60\text{m}$, find angle C.
2. Use the law of sines to find the measure of angle β to the nearest degree.

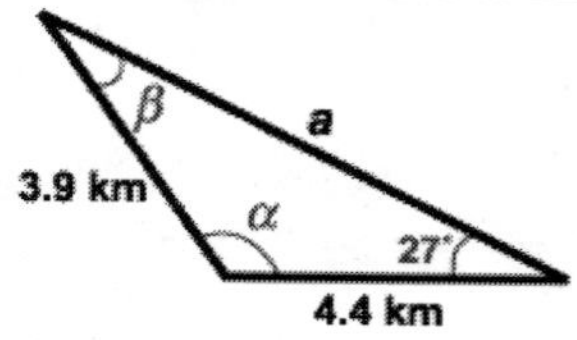

3. Find the lengths of sides a and b, each to the nearest tenth.

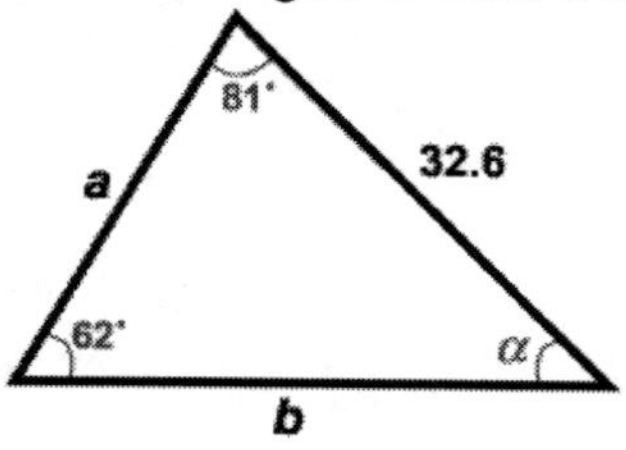

Review questions: *(Answers to odd questions on page: 759)*

1. Given the acute triangle ΔABC with side $a = 67$ cm, side $c = 49.8$ cm, and angle $C = 42°$, find angle A.
2. Given ΔABC with side $a = 68$ m, angle $A = 62.3°$, and side $c = 57.2$ m, find angle B.
3. In ΔABC, all angles are acute. Find side a and angle A, given that angle C is 61°, side c is 21 in, and side b is 15 inches.
4. Given a triangle with angle $B = 110°$, side $b = 22\ .55$ feet, and side $c = 12$ feet, find angle C and side a.
5. Find side b and angle B given angle A is 42°, side $a = 14$ inches, side $c = 18$ inches, and all angles are acute.

Solving a Triangle (SAS): Another Example

- **Review**:

  The law of sines: $\frac{\sin\alpha}{a} = \frac{\sin\beta}{b} = \frac{\sin\gamma}{c}$.
- If the side opposite the given angle is shorter than the adjacent side, there may be two triangles. If so, solve for both sets of possibilities. The possibilities are:
  - The opposite side is shorter than the altitude. If so, no triangle exists.
  - The opposite side is longer than the altitude and shorter than the adjacent side. If so, two triangles may be possible.
  - The opposite side is longer than the adjacent side. If so, one triangle is possible.

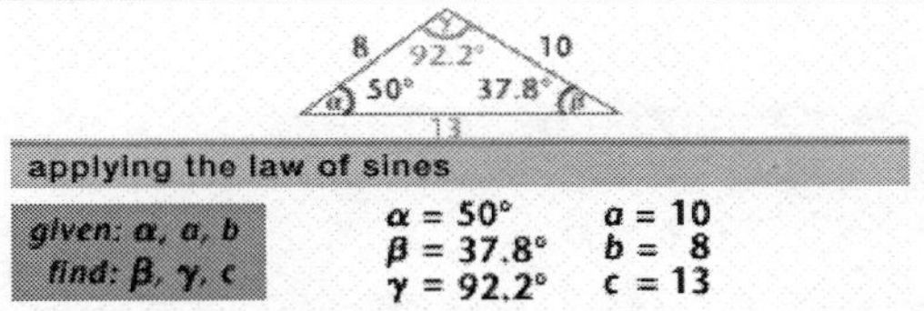	The law of sines can be used when given two angles and the side opposite one of these angles. Also, if two angles and the included side are known, then the third angle can be found by using the fact that the sum of the angles of a triangle is 180°, and then the law of sines can be applied.
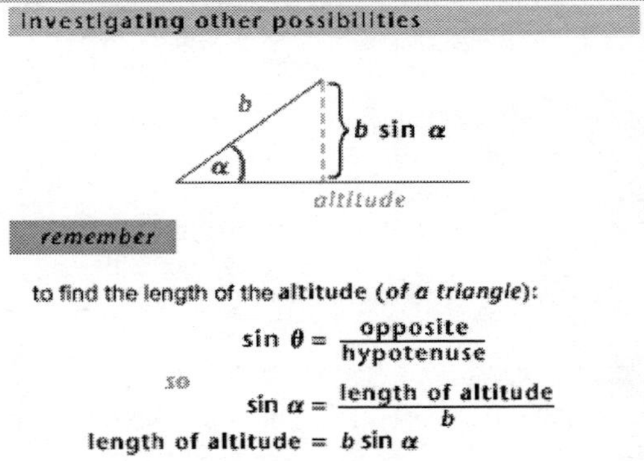	However, if you are given the lengths of two sides and the angle opposite one of them, it is possible that more than one triangle exists. The length of the altitude formed opposite a given angle determines how many triangles will exist. The length of this altitude is $b \cdot \sin a$.
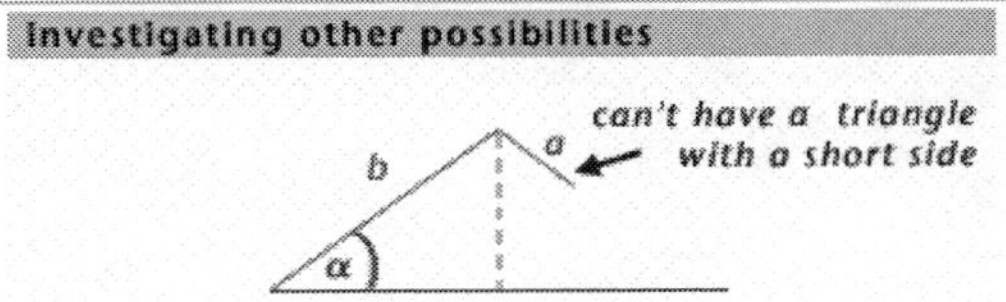	If the side opposite the angle is shorter than the altitude, no triangle is possible. Look at the illustration, notice that side a is shorter than the altitude (dotted) and does not reach the opposite side. The result does not make a triangle.
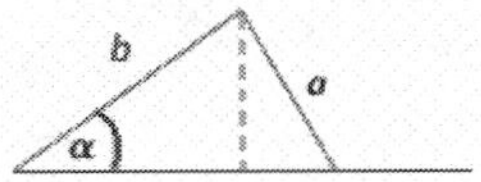	If the side opposite the angle is shorter than the adjacent side but longer than the altitude, there will be two possible triangles. One possible triangle will have three acute angles with the side in question swinging away from the angle.

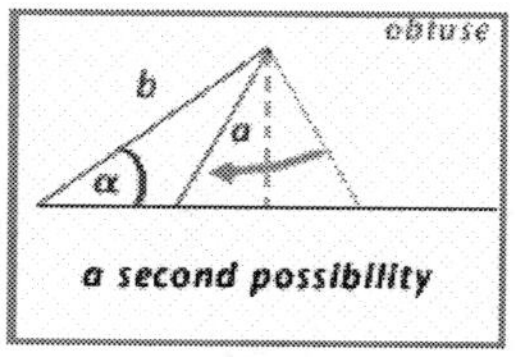	The second possibility occurs when the side opposite the angle swings in towards the angle. In this case, the triangle will have an obtuse angle.
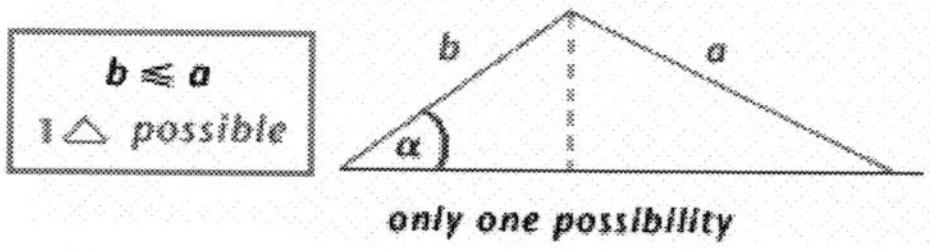	When the side opposite the angle is longer than the adjacent side, only one triangle is possible.
Example *suppose:* $\alpha = 50°$ $a = 8$ $b = 10$ *find: how will side a fall?* **there are 2 possibilities:** 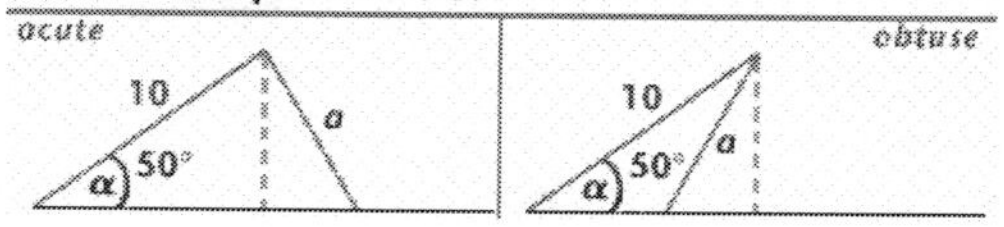	Consider the given example: suppose $\alpha = 50°$, $a = 8$, and $b = 10$. Find all the possible triangles. The altitude is $b \cdot \sin a = (10)(\sin 50) = 7.6$. Since $a = 8$ and $b = 10$, a is longer than the altitude but shorter than b. So, two triangles are possible.
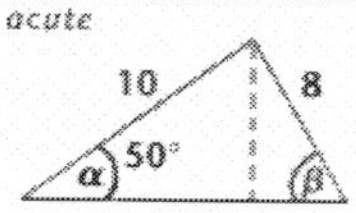$\frac{\sin 50°}{8} = \frac{\sin \beta}{10}$ $\sin \beta = \frac{10 \sin 50°}{8}$ $\sin \beta = .95755$ $\beta = 73.25°$ *so:* $\gamma = 180° - (73.25° + 50°)$ $= 56.75°$ **remember** *the sum of the angles of a triangle always equals 180°*	Consider one of the possibilities for β. Use the **law of sines** to solve for angle β. Now find γ by subtracting α and β from 180°.
find c $\frac{\sin 50°}{8} = \frac{\sin 56.75°}{c}$ $c = 8.733$	Finally, return again to the law of sines to solve for side c. The triangle is solved. All three sides and all three angles are known.
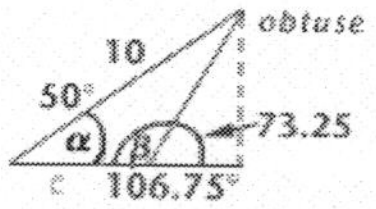$\beta = 180° - 73.25°$ $\beta = 106.75°$ $\gamma = 180° - (106.75° + 50°)$ $\gamma = 23.25°$ **remember** *the sum of the angles of a triangle always equals 180°*	Now, solve for the second possibile triangle. Start by finding β again. This time β must be obtuse, so the angle will be $180° - 73.25° = 106.75°$. Having found β, find the third angle by subtracting the two angles known for the triangle from 180°.
find c $\frac{\sin 23.25°}{c} = \frac{\sin 50°}{8}$ $c = 4.12$	Finally, solve for the third side and then the triangle is solved.
note *if the side opposite the angle given is shorter than the adjacent side, you may have 2 triangles*	Always consider the possibility that two triangles might exist.

Sample problems:

1. In the diagram, $QS = QR$. Find $\angle 4$.

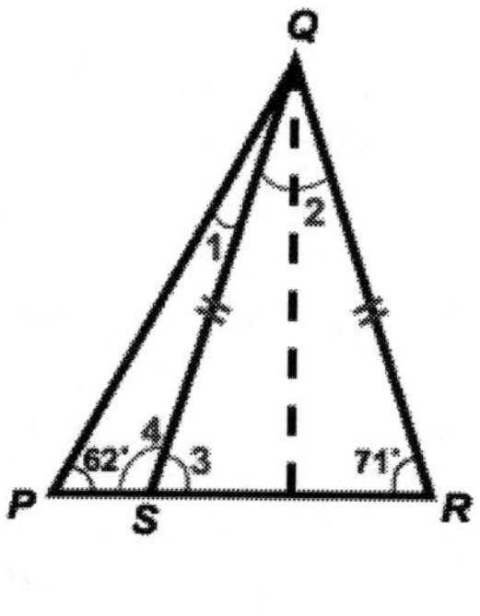

Solution: 109°
Explanation: In triangle QRS, $QS = QR$ so $\angle 3 = 71°$. $\angle 4$ and $\angle 3$ are supplementary, so $\angle 4 + \angle 3 = 180°$ and $\angle 4 = 180° - 71° = 109°$.

2. Given the triangle FGH find angle H given that side $f = 11$ km, side $g = 15$ km and angle $G = 33°$.
Solution: 123.46°
Explanation:
Find angle F using the law of sines: $\frac{\sin F}{11} = \frac{\sin 33°}{15}$; $\frac{\sin F}{11} = \frac{0.5446}{15}$;
$\sin F = \frac{(11)(0.5446)}{(15)} = 0.3994$, $F = 23.54°$.
Find angle H: $H = 180° - (33° + 23.54°) = 123.46°$.

3. In these triangles, $\alpha = 41°$, $b = 15.56$ mm, and $a = 13.05$ mm. Find the measures of $\angle 1$ and $\angle 2$ to the nearest degree.

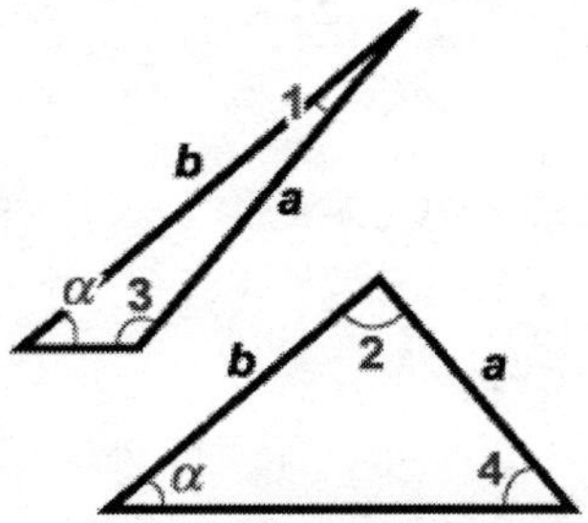

Solution: $\angle 1 = 10°$, $\angle 2 = 88°$
Explanation: Find $\angle 4$, the acute angle opposite b: $\frac{\sin 41°}{13.05} = \frac{\sin \angle 4}{15.56}$; $\sin \angle 4 = \frac{(15.56)(\sin 41°)}{13.05} = 0.7822$, $\angle 4 = 51°$. Find the remaining angles: $\angle 2 = 180° - (41° + 51°) = 88°$; $\angle 3$ and $\angle 4$ are supplementary, so $\angle 3 = 180° - 51° = 129°$; $\angle 1 = 180° - (\alpha + \angle 3) = 180° - (41° + 129°) = 10°$.

Practice problems: *(Answers on page: 759)*

1. In these two triangles, $\alpha = 52°$, $b = 22.71$ cm, and $a = 18.95$ cm.

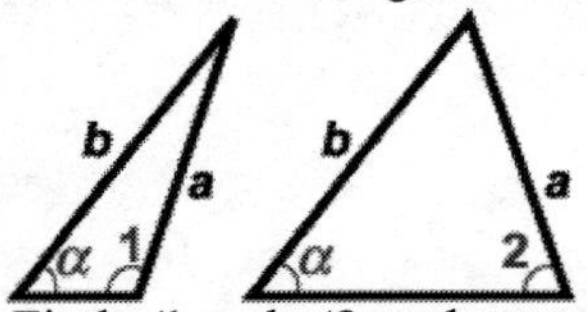

Find $\angle 1$ and $\angle 2$ to the nearest degree.

2. In triangle ABC, angle $B = 27°$, side $a = 8.2'$, and side $b = 5'$. Find two possibilities for angle C.

3. One angle of a triangle is given to be 54.93° and a side adjacent to that angle is 15.75 in. If there are two possible triangles, write an inequality to express the possible lengths for the side opposite the given angle.

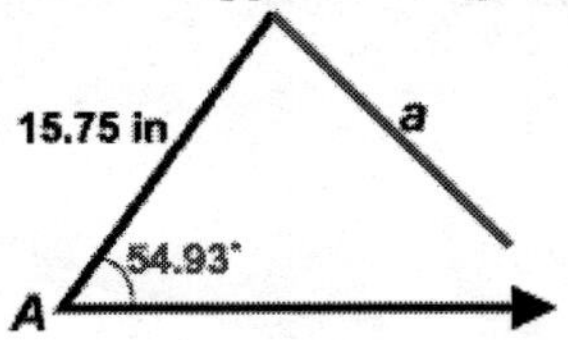

Review questions: *(Answers to odd questions on page: 759)*

1. In ΔABC, angle $A = 103°$, side $a = 37.48$ ft, and side $c = 29.73$ ft. Find angle C and side b.
2. In ΔRST, angle $R = 41°$, side $r = 18$ cm, and side $s = 57$ cm. Find all possible measures for angle S.
3. In ΔABC, find angle B, given that angle $C = 31°$, side $a = 9.4$ ft, and side $c = 7$ ft. If two possibilities exist, state both of them.
4. Given triangle FGH, find side h when angle $F = 43°$, side $f = 12$cm and side $g = 9$cm.
5. In triangle PQR, angle $P = 37°$, side $p = 45$cm and side $q = 85$cm. Find all possible measures for angle Q.

The Law of Sines: An Application

- **Review**: The **law of sines**: $\dfrac{\sin\alpha}{a} = \dfrac{\sin\beta}{b} = \dfrac{\sin\gamma}{c}$.

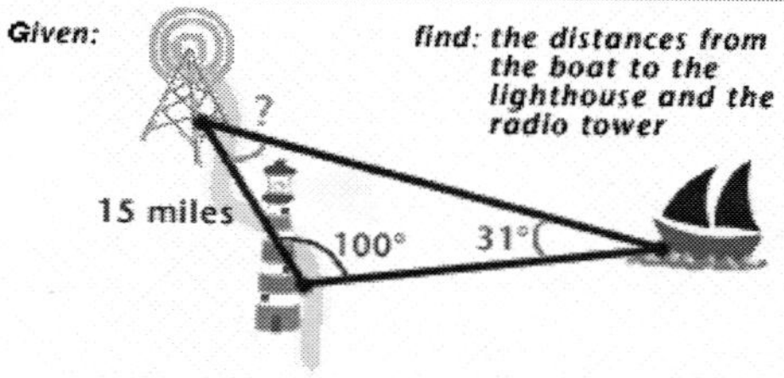

Suppose a boat at sea can observe both a radio tower and a lighthouse on the shore. If the radio tower is located 15 miles from the lighthouse, and the boat subtends a 31° angle from the shore, find the distance from the boat to the lighthouse and from the boat to the radio tower.

Begin by making a sketch of the problem. It helps to see what is known and what needs to be found.

Given two angles and one side of a triangle, find the other two sides.

find 3rd angle

$?\angle = 180° - (100° + 31°)$
$?\angle = 49°$

Find the third angle, by subtracting 100° and 31° from 180°.

applying the law of sines

$$\frac{\sin 31°}{15} = \frac{\sin 49°}{b}$$

Next, solve for one of the unknown sides. Find b, the distance from the boat to the lighthouse.

$$b = \frac{15 \sin 49°}{\sin 31°}$$

$b = 21.98$ miles

Shift the terms to solve for b.

Evaluate using a calculator.

applying the law of sines

$$\frac{\sin 31°}{15} = \frac{\sin 100°}{c}$$

Now solve for the other side, the distance to the radio tower (c), in the same way. Using the law of sines, set up the two fractions.

$$c = \frac{15 \sin 100°}{\sin 31°}$$

$c = 28.68$ miles

Shift the terms to solve for c.

Evaluate the expression using a calculator.

tip *the largest angle will always be opposite the longest side*
the smallest angle will always be opposite the shortest side

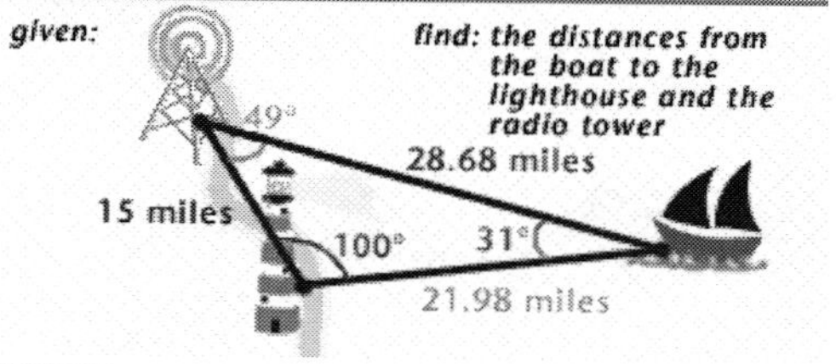

Here is the finished problem. The triangle is solved for the distance from the boat to both the radio tower and the lighthouse.

Sample problems:

1. Two wires are part of the supports of a tall pole. One wire forms an angle of 53° with the ground and the other wire forms an angle of 78° with the ground. The distance between the feet of the wires is 25 m. Find the height of the pole *CD*.

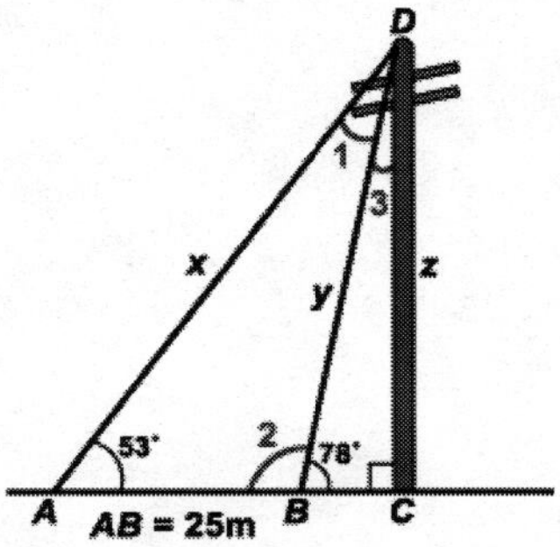

Solution: 46 m

Explanation: Start by finding the other angles in the diagram: $\angle 3 = 180° - (90° + 78°) = 12°$; $\angle 2 = 180° - 78° = 102°$; $\angle 1 = 180° - (53° + 102°) = 25°$. Use the law of sines to find x: $\frac{\sin 25°}{25} = \frac{\sin 102°}{x}$; $x = \frac{25(\sin 102°)}{\sin 25°} = 57.86$. Use the law of sines again to find z: $\frac{\sin 90°}{57.86} = \frac{\sin 53°}{z}$; $z = 46.2$. Thus, the height of the pole is 46.2 feet.

2. Two wireless telephone transmission centers are 35 km apart. A cell phone user is 19 km from one of the centers. At the cell phone user, the angle formed by the two centers is 101°. Find the distance between the cell phone user and the other transmission center.

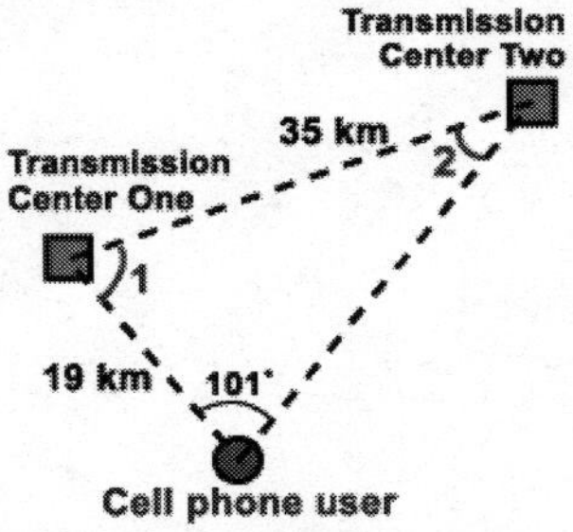

Solution: 26 km

Explanation: Let d be the distance between the cell phone user and the second transmission center. Find the two unknown angles in the triangle: $\frac{\sin \angle 2}{19} = \frac{\sin 101°}{35}$; $\sin \angle 2 = \frac{(19)(\sin 101°)}{35} = 0.5328$, so $\angle 2 = 32°$. Then $\angle 1 = 180° - (101° + 32°) = 47°$. Find the distance: $\frac{\sin 47°}{d} = \frac{\sin 101°}{35}$; $d = \frac{(35)(\sin 47°)}{\sin 101°} = 26$. The distance between the cell phone user and the other tower is 26 km.

3. Two ships are 272 km apart. A submarine lies directly below the line passing through the two ships. From the submarine, the angle formed by the ships is 41° while from ship A the angle formed by ship B and the submarine is 97°. How much farther is ship B from the submarine than ship A?

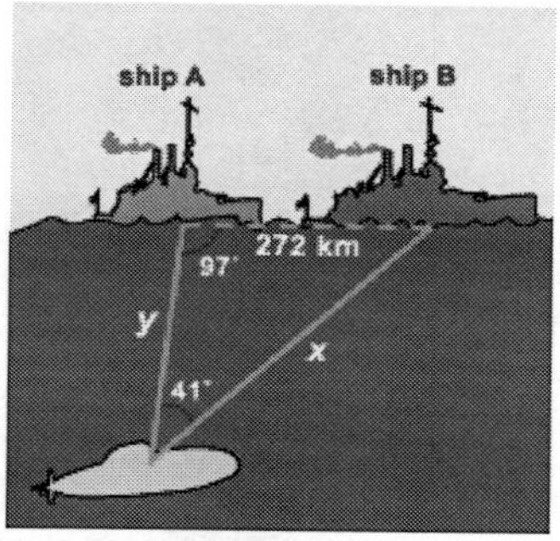

Solution: 134 km

Explanation: Find the distance from the submarine to each ship. For ship B:
$\frac{\sin 97°}{x} = \frac{\sin 41°}{272}$; $x = \frac{(272)(\sin 97°)}{\sin 41°} = 411.5$. For ship A: $180° - (41° + 97°) = 42°$;
$\frac{\sin 42°}{y} = \frac{\sin 41°}{272}$; $y = \frac{(272)(\sin 42°)}{\sin 41°} = 277.4$. The difference is $411.5 - 277.4 = 134.1$ km.

Practice problems: *(Answers on page: 759)*

1. A Scout traveled 100 m from Troop Headquarters. For the Scout, the angle formed by the Target and Headquarters was 63°. From Headquarters, the angle formed by the Target and the Scout was 58°.

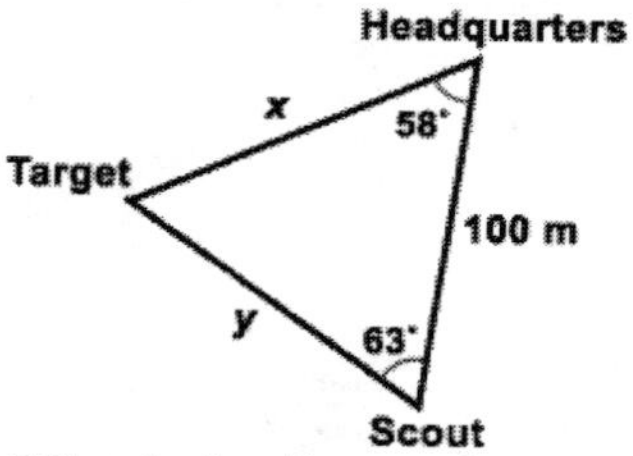

What is the distance between Headquarters and the Target?

2. Flying above the straight line segment connecting one city to another, an airplane is 174 miles from the first city and 71 miles from the second. From the first city, the angle formed by the airplane and the ground is 22°. Find the distance between the two cities.

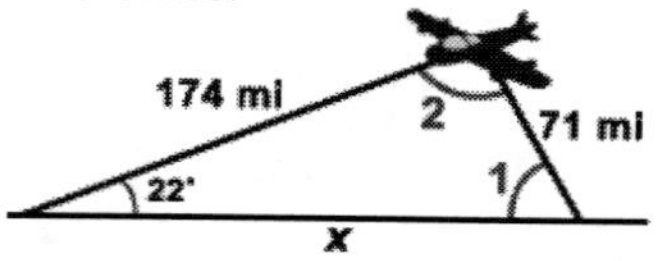

3. A radio tower sits on top of a hill. The distance along the hill from its base to the tower is 212 feet. The angle of elevation from the base of the hill to the top of the tower is 27.2°. The hill itself makes an angle of 14.3° with the horizontal. Find the height of the tower.

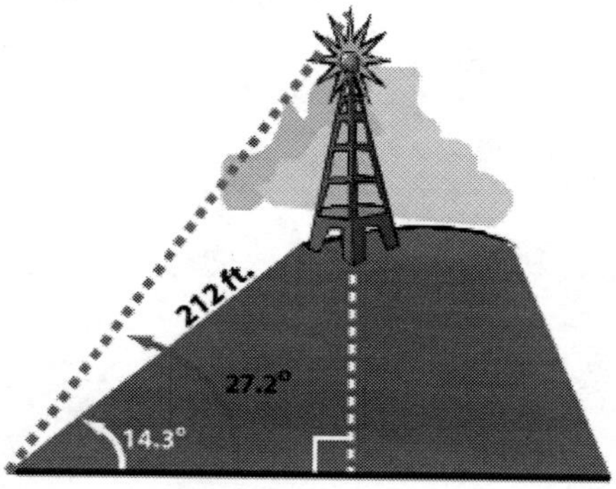

Review questions: *(Answers to odd questions on page: 759)*

1. A pilot in a helicopter sights an ambulance heading toward an accident scene. He measures the angles of depression to the ambulance and the accident to be 21° and 15°, respectively. If the helicopter is 4000 ft from the ambulance, how far does the ambulance have to travel to get to the accident?

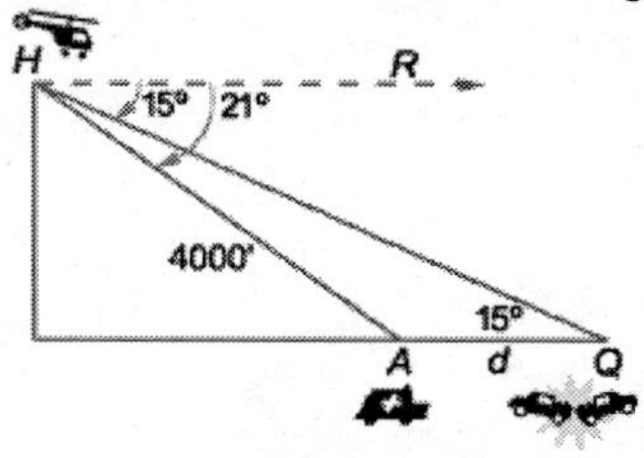

2. A person has a kite out on 1650 feet of string at an angle of 72° with the ground. An observer notes that the angle formed by the kite and the flier is 103°. Find the distance between the observer and the kite flier.

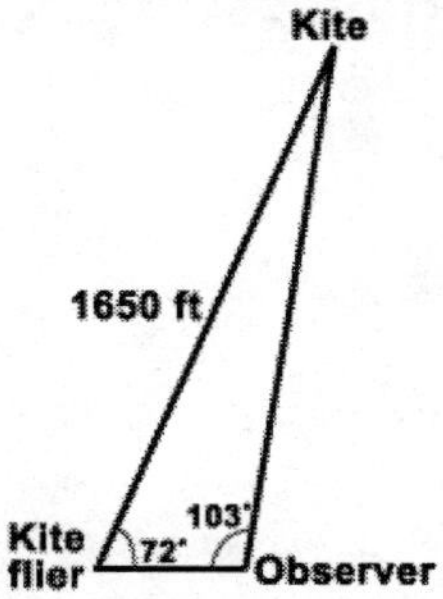

3. Smokey Bear standing on a hill can see two firewatch towers in the distance. He knows that the two towers are 8 miles from each other. He thinks he is approximately 4.8 miles from one tower. He roughly calculates the angle between his two lines of sight to the towers to be 34.6°. How far is he from the second tower?

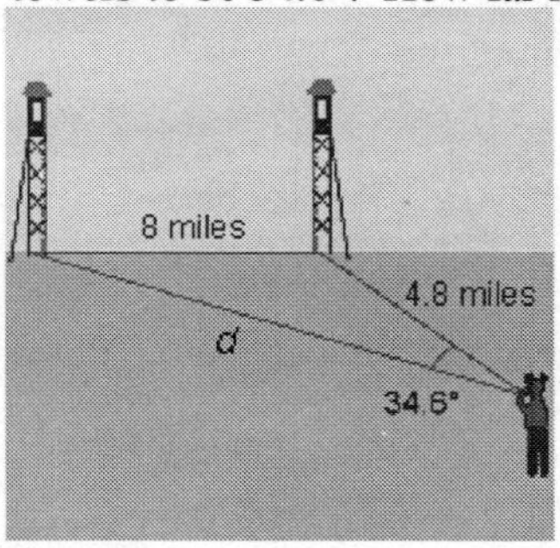

4. Ted was flying his Lear jet over Waikiki when he noticed a party on a yacht. His angle of depression was 17.5°. Then he noticed the surfer on a huge pipeline wave. His angle of depression to the surfer was 24.2°. His navigating copilot told him he was 5120 feet from the yacht. How far was he from the surfer? (Assume that all three characters are in a vertical plane.)

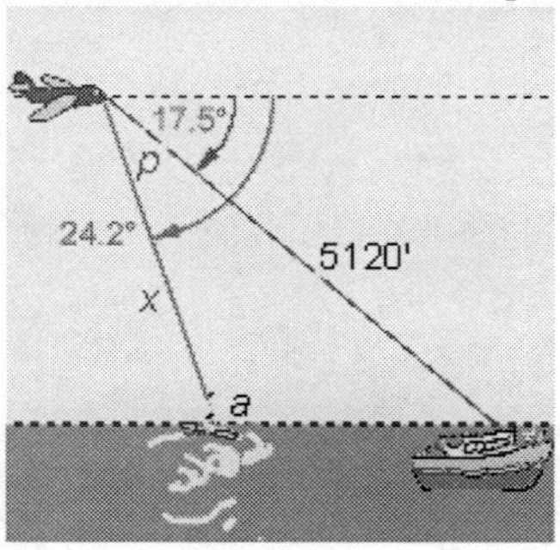

5. Troop A left base camp and hiked 6 hours at 4.4 mph. Troop B left the same camp and hiked 7 hours at 4.2 mph. That evening, Troop A noticed that the angle formed by beacons at the base camp and at Troop B's camp was 87°.
Find the distance between Troop A and Troop B.

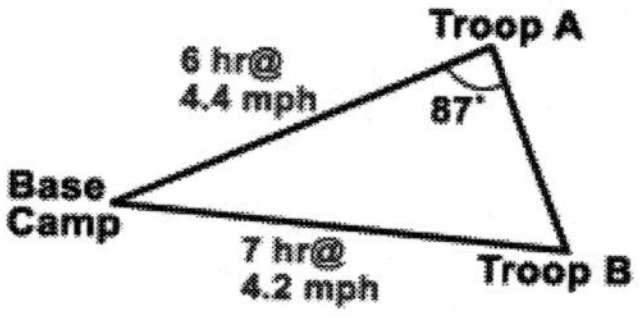

The Law of Cosines

- Like the **law of sines**, the **law of cosines** is a formula that solves for angles and sides for any given triangle, even those that are not right triangles. It is derived from the **Pythagorean theorem**.
- The law of cosines is used to solve a triangle when given three sides of a triangle or two sides plus the included angle.
- The law of cosines has three forms. In every case, the last term is 2 times the product of the two sides with the cosine of the included angle. The single term on the left is always the square of the side opposite the angle. Use the form of the identity that fits what is known about the triangle.

  In a triangle with sides a, b, c, and opposite angles α, β, γ:

  $a^2 = b^2 + c^2 - 2bc\cos\alpha \quad b^2 = a^2 + c^2 - 2ac\cos\beta \quad c^2 = a^2 + b^2 - 2ab\cos\gamma$

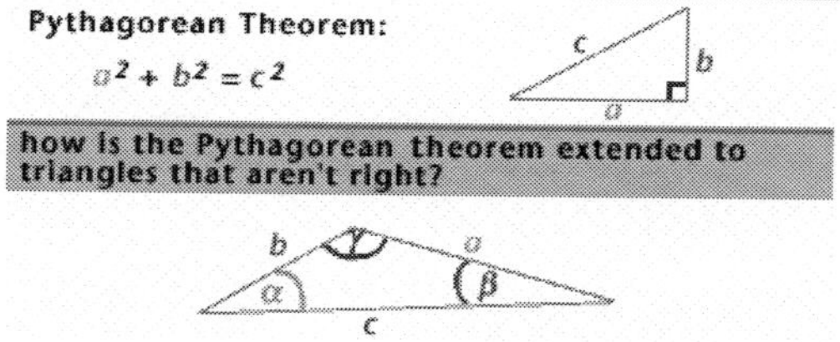	The **Pythagorean theorem** applies only to right triangles, although its influences are seen in many of the definitions and identities developed for trigonometry. It has been extended to apply to general triangles with no right angle.
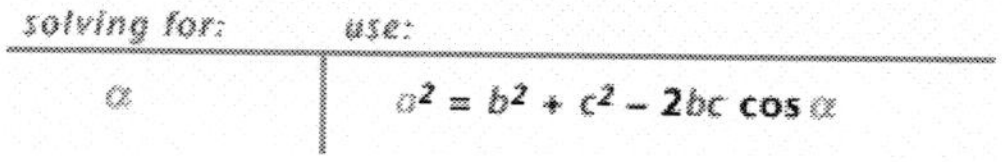	For any non-right triangle, to solve for side a or its angle, α, use this version of the **law of cosines:** $a^2 = b^2 + c^2 - 2bc\cos\alpha$.
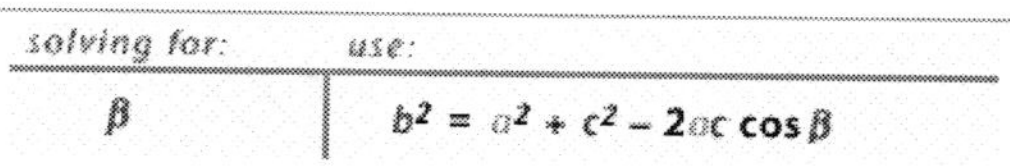	To solve for side b or its angle, β, use this version of the law of cosines: $b^2 = a^2 + c^2 - 2ac\cos\beta$.
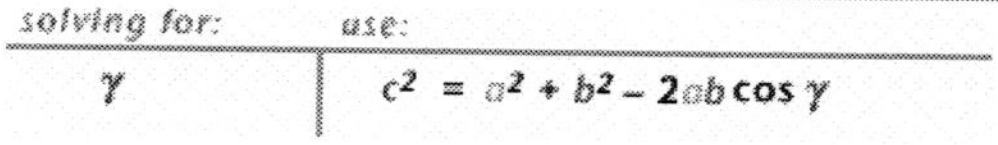	To solve for side c or its angle, γ, use this version of the law of cosines: $c^2 = a^2 + b^2 - 2ab\cos\gamma$.
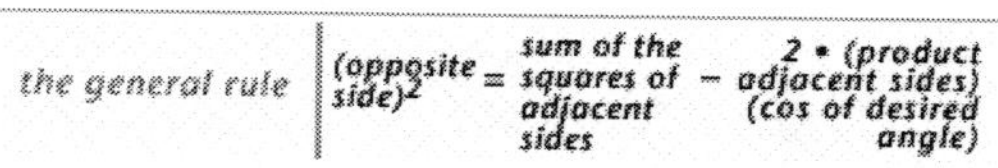	This is a general way to state the law of cosines: (opposite side)^2 = the sum of the squares of adjacent sides – 2 times the product of the adjacent sides times the cosine of the desired angle. **REMEMBER:** the angle must be the angle included between two known sides.
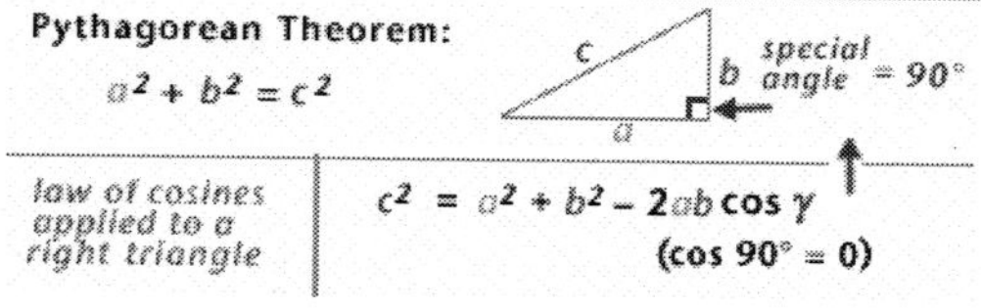	In a right triangle, the law of cosines solves for c, the hypotenuse. In a right triangle, $\cos\gamma = \cos 90° = 0$. If you plug 0 in for $\cos\gamma$, the result is that the entire $-2ab\cos\gamma$ term drops out and what's left is the Pythagorean theorem.

Sample problems:

1. True or false: The equation $a^2 = 64 + 144 - 192\cos 62°$ may be used to find the missing side of the triangle below.

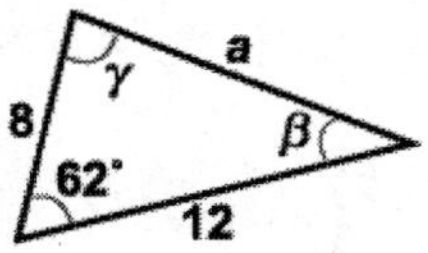

Solution: True

Explanation: In the law of cosines, $a^2 = b^2 + c^2 - 2bc\cos\alpha$, side a is the side opposite angle α, and the other two sides are b and c. Let $\alpha = 62°$, then $b = 8$ and $c = 12$. Substitute these values into the law of cosines and simplify: $a^2 = b^2 + c^2 - 2bc\cos\alpha \Rightarrow$ $a^2 = 8^2 + 12^2 - 2(8)(12)\cos 62°$; $a^2 = 64 + 144 - 192\cos 62°$, which is the equation given in the question.

2. Find the missing side for triangle FGH, if $\angle FGH = 55°$, $FG = 8.6$ cm and $GH = 5.7$cm.

Solution: 7.09 cm

Explanation: Use the law of cosines, $a^2 = b^2 + c^2 - 2bc\cos A$, to find the missing side, FH. Let $a = FH$, $b = 8.6$, $c = 5.7$, and $\angle A = 55°$. Substitute these values into the law of cosines (solved for a) and simplify: $a = \sqrt{b^2 + c^2 - 2bc\cos A} \Rightarrow FH =$ $\sqrt{8.6^2 + 5.7^2 - 2(8.6)(5.7)(\cos 55°)} = \sqrt{50.22} = 7.09$. Thus, $FH = 7.09$cm.

3. Find the missing side of triangle RST given that $\angle T = 87°$, $ST = 16$mm, and $RT = 23$mm.

Solution: 27.3mm

Explanation: Use the law of cosines $a = \sqrt{b^2 + c^2 - 2bc\cos A}$, where $a = RS$, $b = 16$, $c = 23$, and $A = 87°$: $a = \sqrt{16^2 + 23^2 - 2(16)(23)\cos 87°} = \sqrt{256 + 529 - 736(0.0523)} = \sqrt{746.51} = 27.3$.

Practice problems: *(Answers on page: 759)*

1. What must be known about a triangle in order to use the law of cosines to find a missing side?
2. Find the missing side for triangle DEF given that $\angle D = 30°$, $DE = 8$ and $DF = 10$.
3. Find the missing side for triangle ABC given that $\angle B = 110°$, side $a = 4$ and side $c = 4$.

Review questions: *(Answers to odd questions on page: 759)*

1. Find the missing side of the triangle below.

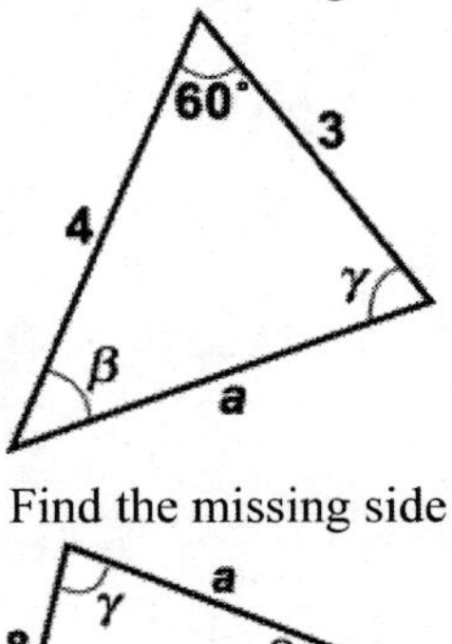

2. Find the missing side of the triangle below.

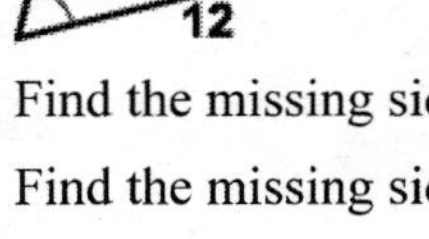

3. Find the missing side of ΔABC, given that angle C=113°, side $a = 7$, and side $b = 7$.
4. Find the missing side for ΔRST if you are given $\angle RST = 63°$, $SR = 9.3$ cm, and $ST = 6.9$ cm.

5. Find the missing side for ΔEFG if you are given $\angle F = 60°$, $EF = 11$ m, and $FG = 13$ m.

The Law of Cosines (SSS)

- **Review**: The **law of cosines** has three forms. Use the form that fits the triangle:
  $a^2 = b^2 + c^2 - 2bc\cos\alpha \quad b^2 = a^2 + c^2 - 2ac\cos\beta \quad c^2 = a^2 + b^2 - 2ab\cos\gamma$
- **Review**: The law of cosines is used to solve a triangle when given three sides of a triangle or two sides plus the included angle.
- **Review**:

The law of sines: $\dfrac{\sin\alpha}{a} = \dfrac{\sin\beta}{b} = \dfrac{\sin\gamma}{c}$.

given: $a = 8$, $b = 3$, $c = 10$ find: $\alpha = ?$, $\beta = ?$, $\gamma = ?$ 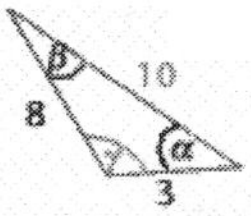	Given three sides of a triangle, $a = 8$, $b = 3$, $c = 10$, find all three angles, α, β, and γ.
$c^2 = a^2 + b^2 - 2ab\cos\gamma$ $10^2 = 8^2 + 3^2 - 2(8)(3) \cdot \cos\gamma$	First find γ. Use the version of the **law of cosines** which includes this angle: $c^2 = a^2 + b^2 - 2ab\cos\gamma$.
$100 = 73 - 48\cos\gamma$ subtract 73 from both sides $\frac{27}{-48} = \cos\gamma$ divide through by -48 $-.5625 = \cos\gamma$	Now, substitute in all the known values and solve for the angle.
$\gamma = 124.23°$	Use the **inverse cosine function** to solve for γ.
remember sine is positive cosine is negative 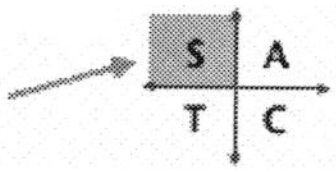	Since the cosine of γ is negative, γ should lie between 90° and 180°.
$\frac{\sin 124.2°}{10} = \frac{\sin\beta}{3}$	To find the second angle, use the **law of sines**. (It is possible to use the law of cosines again, but the arithmetic is easier when using the law of sines.)
$\sin\beta = \frac{3\sin 124.2°}{10}$ $\sin\beta = .24806$ $\beta = 14.37°$	Solve for $\sin\beta$. Then find the **inverse sine** to solve for β.
$180° = \alpha + \beta + \gamma$ $\alpha = 180° - \beta - \gamma$ $\alpha = 180° - 124.23° - 14.37°$ $\alpha = 41.40°$	Subtract the two known angles from 180° to find the third angle.
find: $\alpha = 41.40°$, $\beta = 14.37°$, $\gamma = 124.2°$ given: $a = 8$, $b = 3$, $c = 10$ 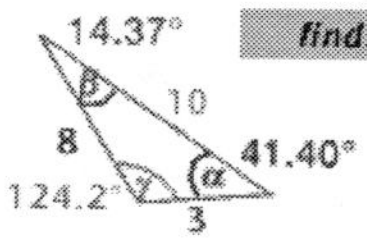	Here is the triangle fully solved.

Sample problems:

1. Use the law of cosines to prove that triangle XYZ does not exist, given that $x = 2.5$ cm, $y = 15.0$ cm, and $z = 4.5$ cm.
   Solution: -8.8222 is not in the domain of cosine
   Explanation: Substitute the known values into the law of cosines: $y^2 = x^2 + z^2 - 2xz\cos Y \Rightarrow$
   $(15)^2 = (2.5)^2 + (4.5)^2 - 2(2.5)(4.5)\cos Y$; $225 = 6.25 + 20.25 - 22.5\cos Y$;
   $198.5 = -22.5\cos Y$; $\cos Y = \dfrac{198.5}{-22.5} = -8.8222$. This is impossible, since -8.8222 is not in cosine's domain.

2. In the triangle below, $a = 4$, $b = 6$, and $c = 8$. Find angle β.

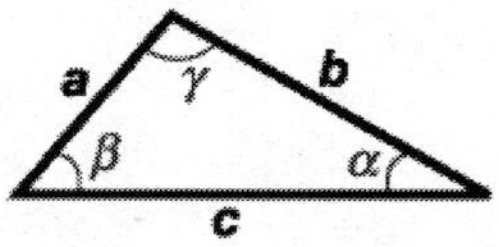

   Solution: 46.57°
   Explanation: Use the law of cosines to find an unknown angle when given the three sides.
   Substitute the values of the sides into $b^2 = a^2 + c^2 - 2ac\cos\beta$ and solve for β:
   $(6)^2 = (4)^2 + (8)^2 - 2(4)(8)\cos\beta$; $36 = 80 - 64\cos\beta$; $\dfrac{-44}{-64} = \cos\beta$; $0.6875 = \cos\beta$;
   $\beta = 46.57°$.

3. To straighten a tree, an 8.4 ft guide wire is stretched from the top of the tree trunk (6.8 ft) to a stake in the ground that is 4.9 ft from the base of the tree. What is the angle of elevation between the ground and the guide wire?

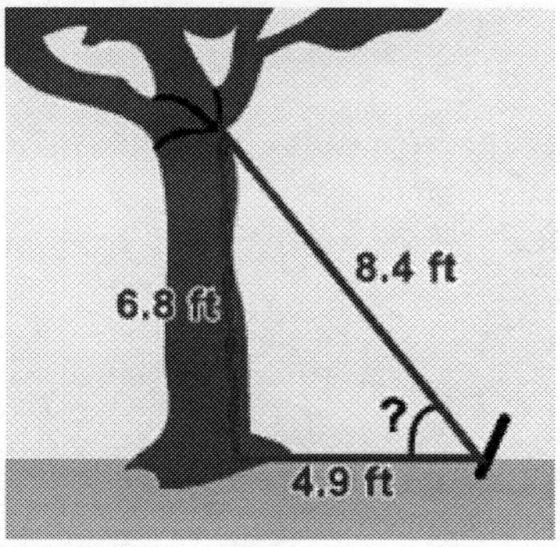

   Solution: 54.05°
   Explanation: Use the law of cosines to find the measure of the missing angle, x:
   $(6.8)^2 = (4.9)^2 + (8.4)^2 - 2(4.9)(8.4)\cos x$; $46.24 = 94.57 - 82.32\cos\beta$;
   $\dfrac{-48.33}{-82.32} = \cos\beta$; $0.587 = \cos\beta$; $\beta = 54.05°$.

Practice problems: *(Answers on page: 759)*

1. In the triangle below, $a = 5$, $b = 7$, and $c = 10.5$. Find angle β.

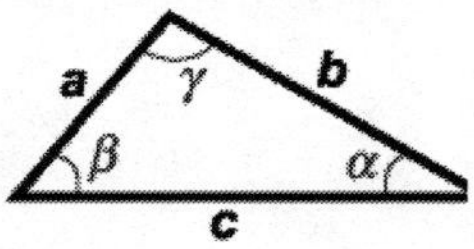

2. In triangle DEF, solve for $\angle D$ given that side $d = 80mm$, $e = 60mm$, and $f = 100mm$.

3. The triangle below has sides with lengths of 5, 9, and 12. Find the measures of all three angles.

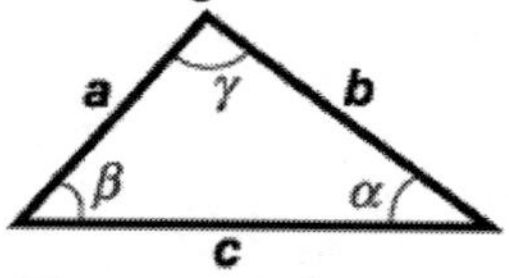

Given $a = 5$, $b = 9$, and $c = 12$, find α, β, and γ.

Review questions: *(Answers to odd questions on page: 759)*

1. For triangle PQR, find angle R given side $p = 5'$, $q = 4'$, and $r = 2'$.
2. In ΔABC solve for B given that side $a = 20'$, $b = 25'$, and $c = 30'$.
3. The sides of a parallelogram are 40 feet and 70 feet. The length of the longer diagonal is 105 feet. What is the measure of the smaller angle in the parallelogram?
4. The triangle below has sides with lengths of $a = 50$, $b = 70$, and $c = 85$. Find the measure of the largest angle.

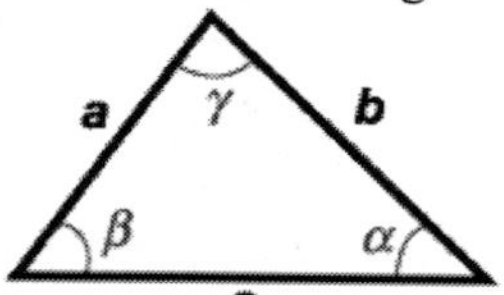

5. Find the smallest angle, given that $a : b : c = 4 : 5 : 7$.

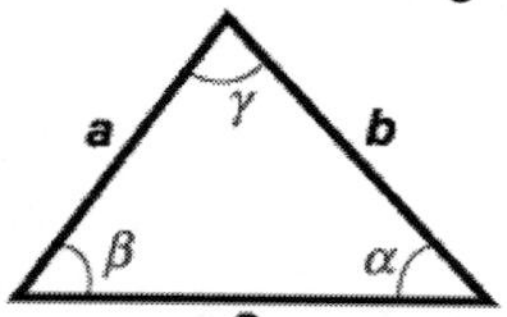

The Law of Cosines (SAS): An Application

- **Review**: The **law of cosines** has three forms depending on which angle is known:
  $a^2 = b^2 + c^2 - 2bc\cos\alpha \quad b^2 = a^2 + c^2 - 2ac\cos\beta \quad c^2 = a^2 + b^2 - 2ab\cos\gamma$
- **Review**: The law of cosines is used to solve a triangle when given three sides of a triangle, or two sides plus the included angle.
- **Review**:

  The **law of sines**: $\dfrac{\sin\alpha}{a} = \dfrac{\sin\beta}{b} = \dfrac{\sin\gamma}{c}$.

	Consider the example given here: find the length of the tunnel given two sides and the included angle of a triangle.
$t^2 = a^2 + b^2 - 2ab\cos\gamma$ $t^2 = 7^2 + 5^2 - 2(7)(5) \bullet \cos 28°$ $t^2 = 7^2 + 5^2 - 2(35) \bullet \cos 28°$	Find the third side of the triangle by letting t be the length of the tunnel and plugging it into the law of cosines.

$t^2 = 7^2 + 5^2 - 2(35) \cdot \cos 28°$
$t^2 = 49 + 25 - 70 \cdot \cos 28°$
$t^2 = 12.193$
$t = \sqrt{12.193}$
$\boxed{t = 3.491 \text{ miles}}$

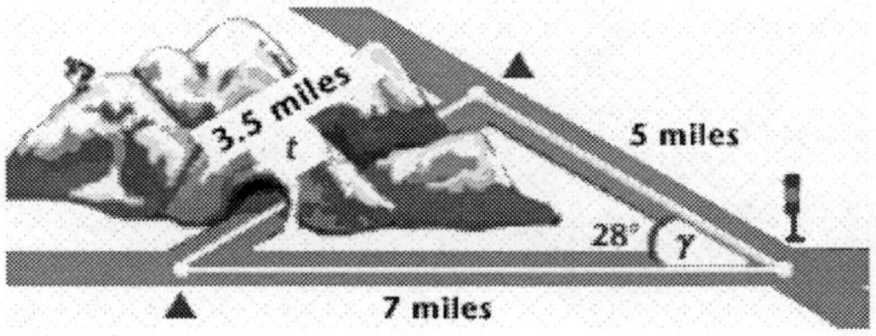

Do the arithmetic to find t^2.

Take the square root to find the length of the tunnel, t.

The length of the tunnel is 3.491 miles.

Sample problems:

1. A piece of wire is bent into the shape of a triangle. Two sides have lengths of 18 inches and 22 inches. The angle between these two sides is 45°. What is the total length of the wire?
Solution: 55.7 inches
Explanation: Use the law of cosines where a is the unknown side, $b = 18$, $c = 22$, and $\alpha = \cos 45°$:
$a = \sqrt{b^2 + c^2 - 2bc \cos\alpha} = \sqrt{247.97} = 15.7$. Add the three lengths: $15.7 + 18 + 22 = 55.7$.

2. Two runners began running at the same time, but at a 100° angle from each other. One runner averages 10 mph, the other averages 6.5 mph. How far apart are the runners after one hour?
Solution: 12.8 miles
Explanation: After one hour, the first runner will have run 10 mi, and the second one will have run 6.5 mi, these two distances form the sides of the triangle. Use the law of cosines to find the distance between the two runners after one hour:
$a = \sqrt{(6.5)^2 + (10)^2 - 2(6.5)(10)\cos 100°} = \sqrt{164.8} = 12.8$.

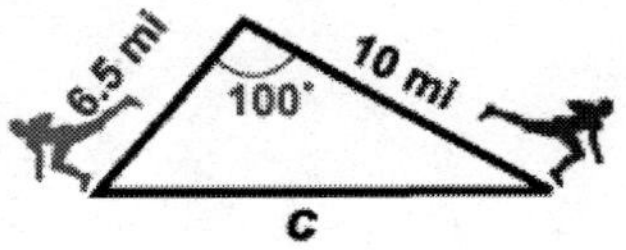

3. The lengths of the diagonals of a parallelogram are 10 feet and 16 feet. Find the lengths of the short sides of the parallelogram if the diagonals intersect at an angle of 28°.
Solution: 4.3 feet
Explanation: A triangle is formed by the short side of the parallelogram and half of each diagonal. Find the length of the sides of the triangle, a and b, formed by half of the diagonals: $a = \frac{16}{2} = 8$ and $b = \frac{10}{2} = 5$. Find c, the short side of the parallelogram, using the law of cosines, where a and b are the sides adjacent to the 28° angle:
$c = \sqrt{8^2 + 5^2 - 2(8)(5)\cos 28°} = \sqrt{18.4} = \sqrt{18.4} = 4.3$.

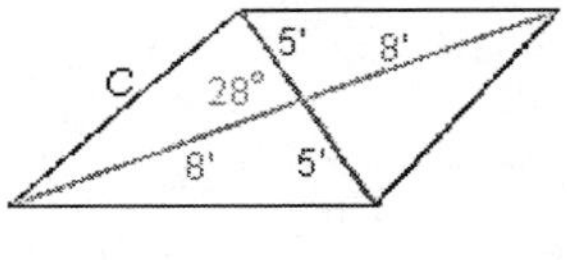

Practice problems: *(Answers on page: 759)*

1. Two sides of a triangle each measure 4 mm. The angle between these two sides has a measure of 50°. What is the length of the third side of the triangle?
2. The sides of a parallelogram are 10 cm and 5 cm, and the smallest angle has a measure of 30°. Find the length of the longer diagonal.

3. Two boats leave a dock together. Each travels in a straight line. The angle between their courses measures 54.2°. One boat travels 36.2 km/hr and the other travels 45.6 km/hr. How far apart will they be after three hours?

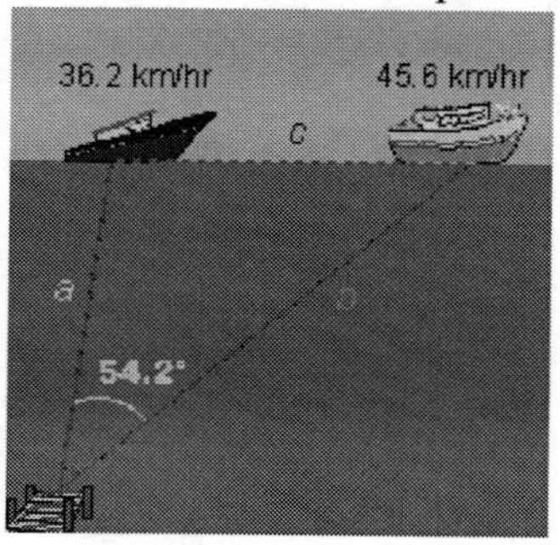

Review questions: *(Answers to odd questions on page: 759)*

1. Determine the length of Lake Manyhaha knowing the following information. A surveyor is standing at a point south of the lake. After measuring he finds he is 2125 meters from the western end of the lake and 3250 meters from the eastern end of the lake. The angle between the lines-of-sight to the two ends of the lake is 77°.

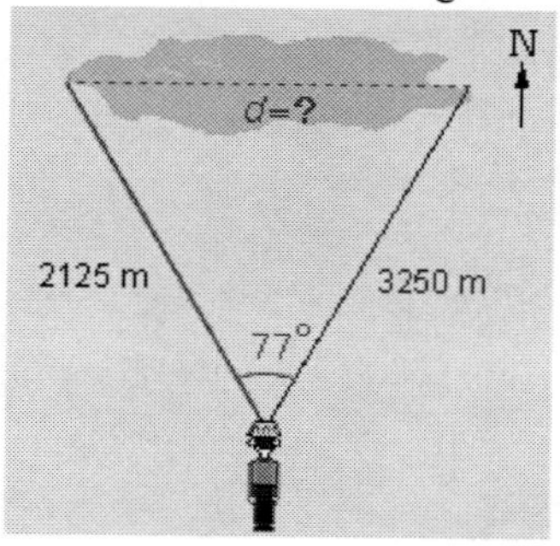

2. One angle of a triangular field measures 82°. The sides that meet at this angle are 100 meters and 120 meters long. How long is the third side?
3. Find the length of a in the figure below.

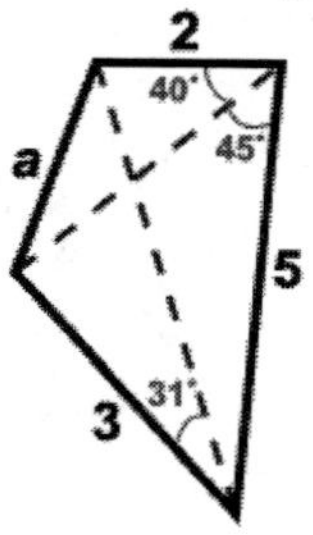

4. The two diagonals of a parallelogram meet at a 60° angle. The diagonals are 10 cm and 6 cm long. Find the lengths of the sides of the parallelogram.

5. A Chinese satellite (C) in circular orbit around the earth is sighted by a Russian tracking station (R). Radar indicates that the satellite is 734 km from the station. The angle of elevation from ground level to the satellite is 32.7°. How high is the satellite above the earth at this point? [The radius of the earth is 6393.5 km .]

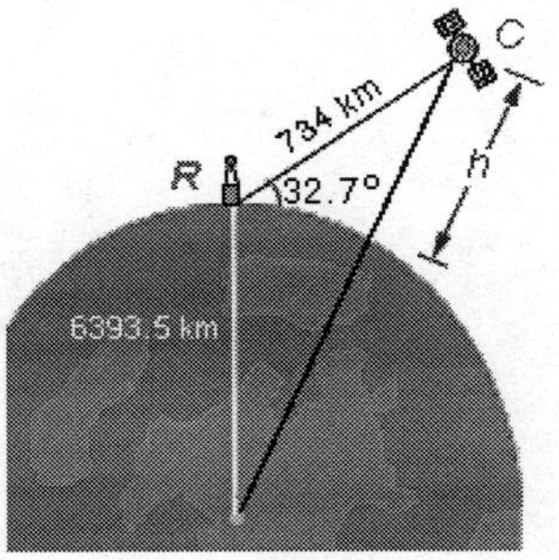

Heron's Formula

- To find the area of any triangle given its three sides, use **Heron's formula**.
- Heron's formula has two parts. For a triangle with sides a, b, and c:
  - Calculate s, 1/2 of the perimeter of the triangle, called the semi-perimeter: $s = \dfrac{a+b+c}{2}$.
  - Calculate the area of the triangle using s and the three sides: $A = \sqrt{s(s-a)(s-b)(s-c)}$

<table>
<tr><td>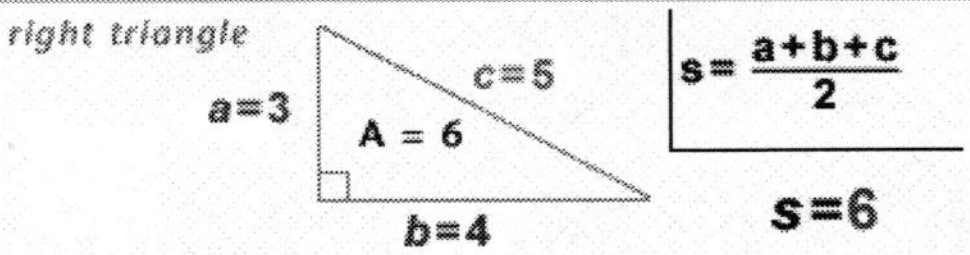
</td><td>Find the area of this right triangle using Heron's formula.

First calculate s:

$s = \dfrac{3+4+5}{2} = 12/2 = 6.$</td></tr>
<tr><td>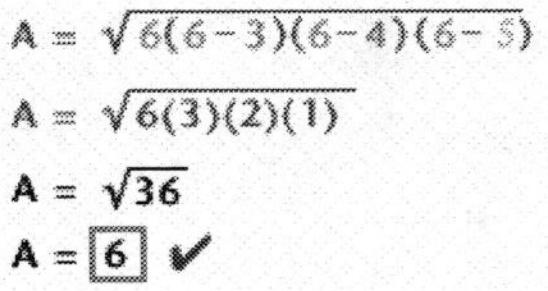
</td><td>Now that the value of s is known, plug it into the area equation and calculate the area:

$area = \sqrt{(6)(6-3)(6-4)(6-5)}$
$= \sqrt{(6)(3)(2)(1)}$
$= \sqrt{36}$
$= 6$
So, the area of the given triangle equals 6.</td></tr>
<tr><td>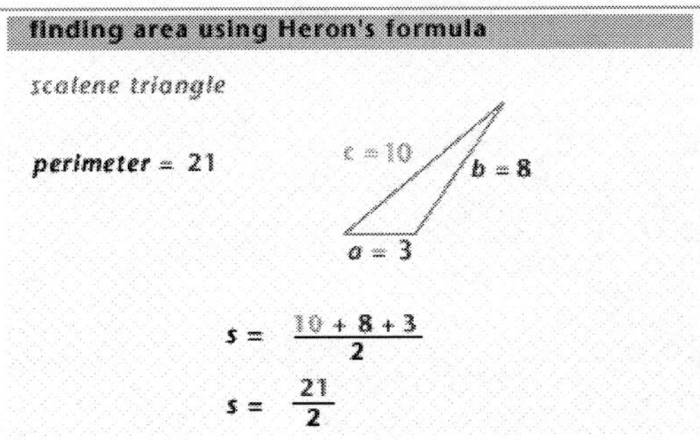
</td><td>Use Heron's formula to find the area of the triangle. First, find s, the semiperimeter, by adding all three sides and dividing by two.</td></tr>
</table>

$A = \sqrt{\frac{21}{2}\left(\frac{21}{2}-3\right)\left(\frac{21}{2}-8\right)\left(\frac{21}{2}-10\right)}$ $A = \frac{\sqrt{1575}}{4}$ $A = \frac{39.6}{4}$ $A = \boxed{9.9}$	Then, use s and the three sides to find the area. In this case, the area equals 9.9.

Sample problems:

1. Find the area of triangle *JHI* given that $j = 17$, $h = 18$, and $i = 19$ meters.
   Solution: 139.4 sq. m.

   Explanation: Find the semi-perimeter, s: $s = \frac{P}{2} = \left(\frac{17+18+19}{2}\right) = 27$. Substitute the known values into Heron's formula and simplify: $A = \sqrt{s(s-j)(s-h)(s-i)} = \sqrt{27(27-17)(27-18)(27-19)} = \sqrt{27(10)(9)(8)} = \sqrt{19440} = 139.4 \text{ m}^2$.

2. Find the area of the figure below.

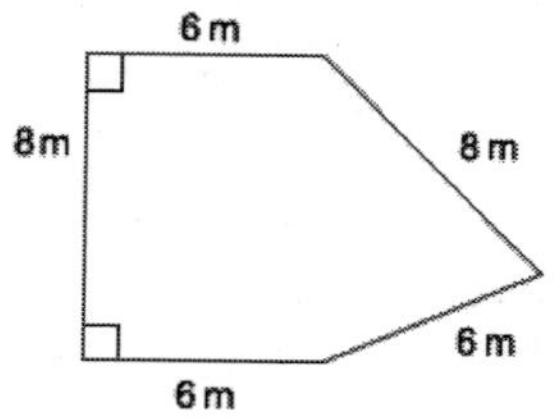

Solution: 70.2 m^2
Explanation: Divide the figure into two figures. The third side of the triangle is the same as the length of the rectangle. Find the semi-perimeter, s: $P = 22$, so $s = \frac{22}{2} = 11$.
Use Heron's area formula to find the area of the triangle:
$A = \sqrt{11(11-8)(11-8)(11-6)} = \sqrt{11(3)(3)(5)} = \sqrt{495} = 22.2 \text{ m}^2$.
Find the area of the rectangle: $8 \cdot 6 = 48 \text{ m}^2$. The total area of the figure is the sum of the two areas: $48 \text{ m}^2 + 22.2 \text{ m}^2 = 70.2 \text{ m}^2$.

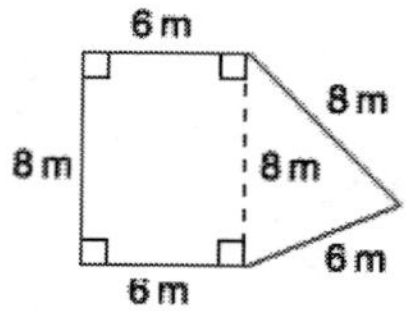

3. What is the area of a triangle with sides measuring 26, 26, and 17 inches?
   Solution: 208.9 in^2

   Explanation: Find the semi-perimeter, s, of the triangle: $P = 69$, so $s = \frac{69}{2} = 34.5$.
   To find the area, substitute the values for s, a, b, and c into Heron's area formula, $A = \sqrt{s(s-a)(s-b)(s-c)}$, and simplify: $A = \sqrt{34.5(34.5-26)(34.5-26)(34.5-17)}$
   $= \sqrt{34.5(8.5)(8.5)(17.5)} = \sqrt{43620.9375}$
   $= 208.9 \text{ in}^2$.

Practice problems: *(Answers on page: 759)*

1. For the triangle below, what is the value of s in Heron's area formula?

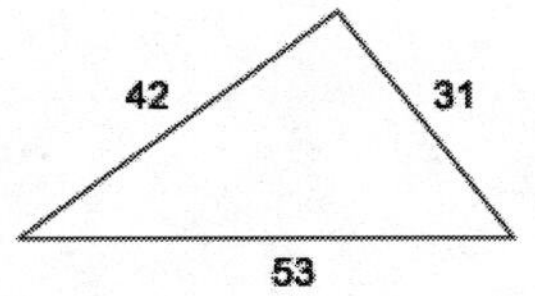

2. Find the area of triangle PQR given that side $p = 21$ in, side $r = 29$ in and $\angle Q = 53°$.
3. Find the area of the parallelogram.

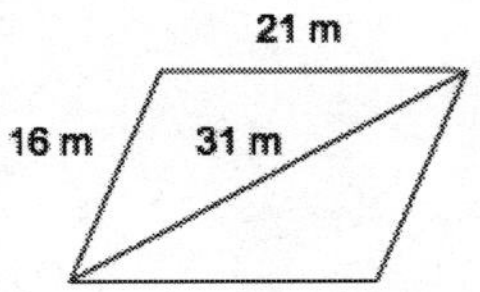

Review questions: *(Answers to odd questions on page: 759)*

1. What is the area of a triangle with sides measuring 15 inches, 12 inches, and 9 inches?
2. A triangular garden has sides that measure 35 ft, 45 ft, and 50 ft. What is the area of the garden?
3. The perimeter of a triangle is 42 cm. Two sides of the triangle have lengths of 15 cm and 20 cm. What is the area of the triangle?
4. Find the height, h, of the triangle below.

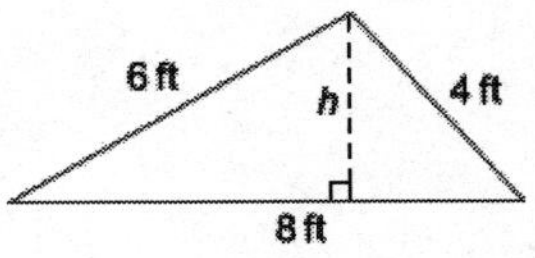

5. A lot has the shape of a quadrilateral as shown in the figure. What is its area?

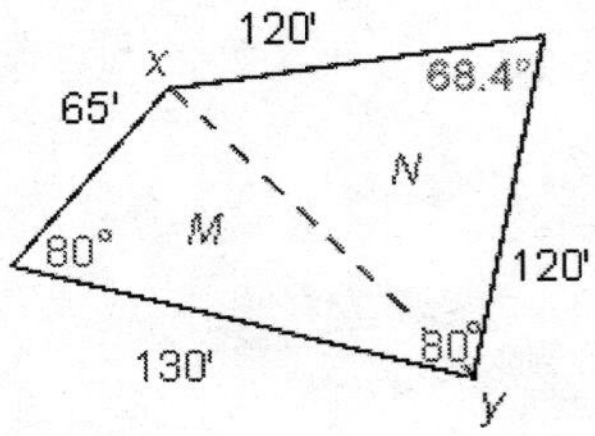

An Introduction to Vectors

- A **vector** is a mathematical object consisting of two parts: a **magnitude** and a direction.

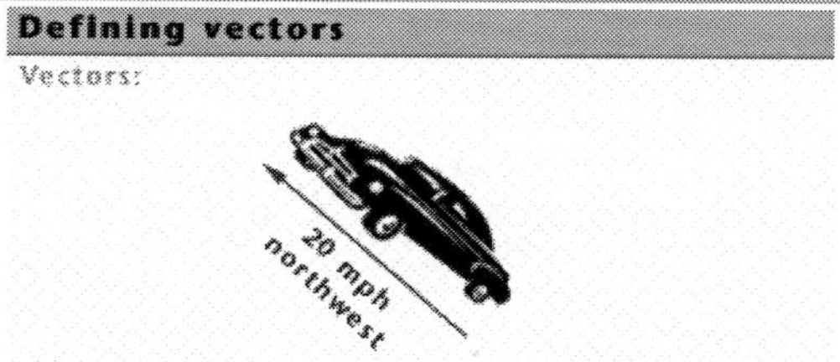

A **vector** is a mathematical object with a **magnitude** and direction.

Velocity can be expressed as a vector.

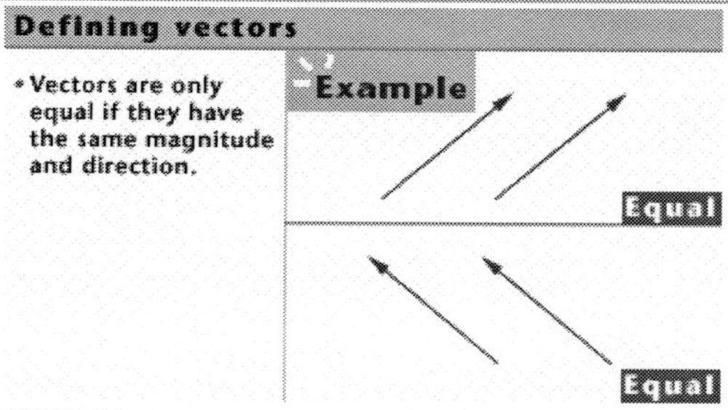

For two vectors to be equal, they must have the same length and point in the same direction. Putting one on top of the other, they would look exactly the same.

So, vectors are only equal if they have the same magnitude and direction.

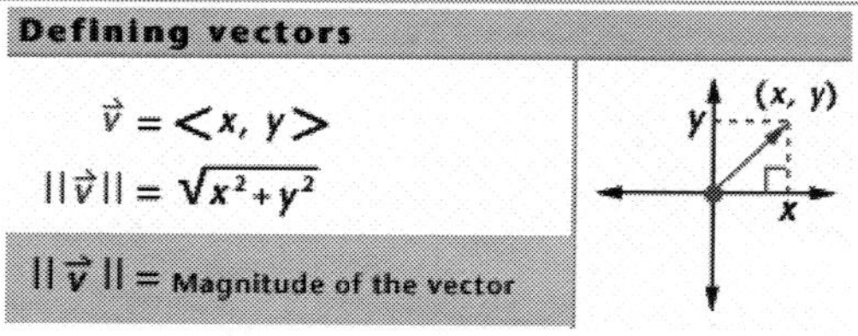

To describe a vector, list the distance it moves in the x-direction and then the distance it moves in the y-direction. These pairs of numbers look a lot like points, so mathematicians use $<x, y>$ instead of (x, y) to write them.

The magnitude of a vector is another name for its length.

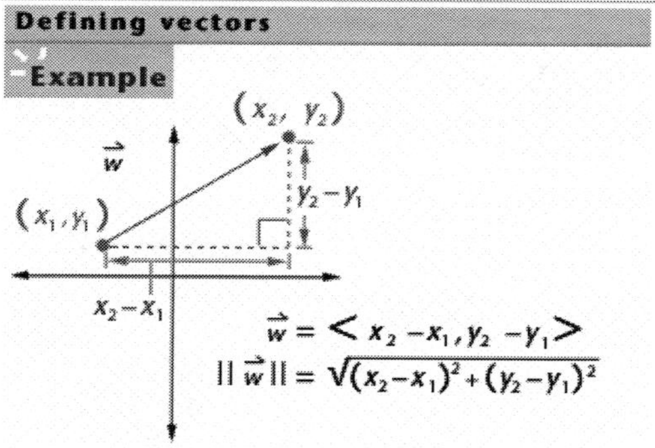

It is common to graph vectors by putting their base at the origin. Even if the vector is not lined up there, it is still possible to determine its **components**. To determine the components of a vector not on the origin, find the distance moved in the x-direction and then the distance moved in the y-direction. The magnitude of a sector is similar to the distance formula used in graphing lines.

Sample problems:

1. Find the component form of the illustrated vector.

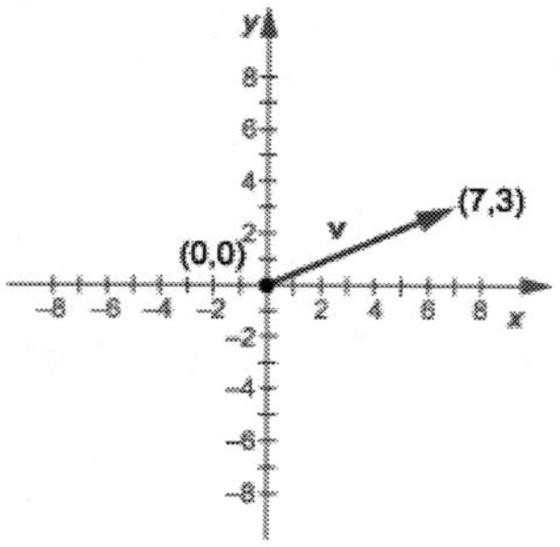

Solution: $\langle 7,3 \rangle$

Explanation: The components of the vector are found by taking the components of the terminal point and subtracting the corresponding components of the initial point. Since the terminal point is $(7,3)$ and the initial point is $(0,0)$, the vector's components are $\langle 7-0, 3-0 \rangle = \langle 7,3 \rangle$

2. What are the components of the vector below?

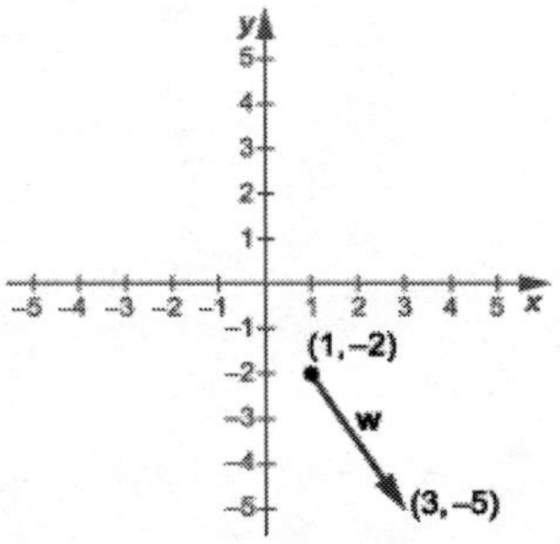

Solution: <2, − 3 >
Explanation: Use the ordered pairs at the beginning and end of vector w, (1, − 2) and (3, − 5).
Let (1, − 2) be (x_1, y_1) and (3,−5) be (x_2, y_2): $w = \langle x_2 - x_1, y_2 - y_1 \rangle = \langle 3-1, -5-(-2) \rangle = \langle 2, -3 \rangle$.

3. Find $\|w\|$ to the nearest whole number.

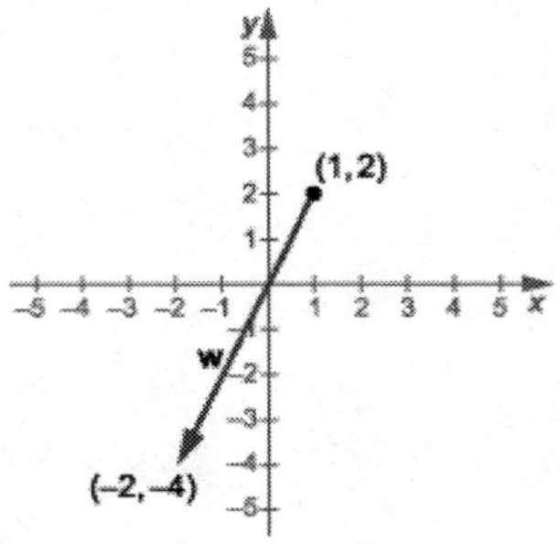

Solution: 7
Explanation: To find the magnitude, or length, of vector w, let the starting point (1,2) be (x_1, y_1) and ending point (− 2, −4) be (x_2, y_2).
Use the distance formula: $\|w\| = \sqrt{(x_2 - x_1)^2 + (y_2 - y_1)^2}$

$$= \sqrt{(-2-1)^2 + (-4-2)^2}$$
$$= \sqrt{(-3)^2 + (-6)^2}$$
$$= \sqrt{9+36} = \sqrt{45} = 3\sqrt{5}, \text{ so } \|w\| = 6.7, \text{ which rounds to 7.}$$

Practice problems: *(Answers on page: 759)*

1. What are the components of the vector shown below?

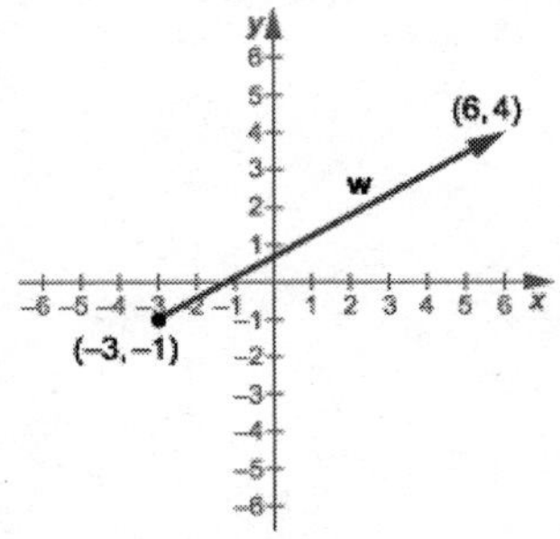

2. Consider the vectors shown below. Which two vectors are equal?

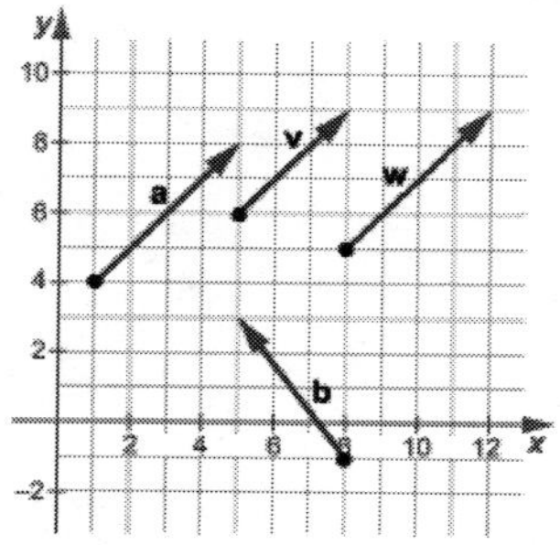

3. Find the component form of the illustrated vector.

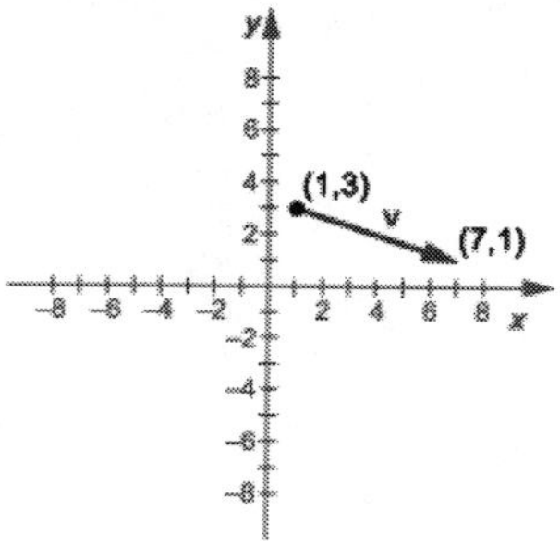

Review questions: *(Answers to odd questions on page: 759)*

1. Find the component form of the illustrated vector.

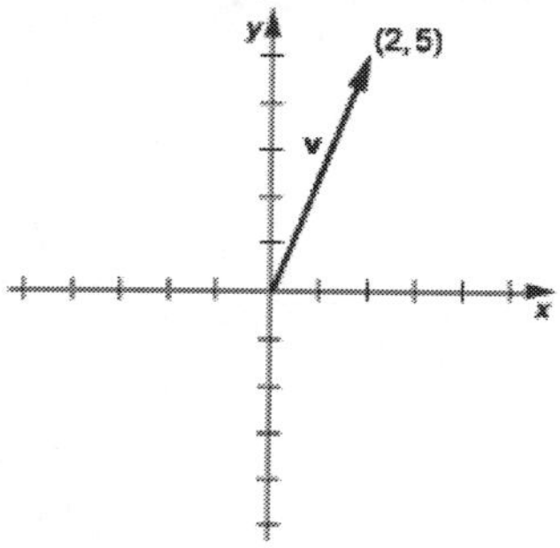

2. Find the component form of the illustrated vector.

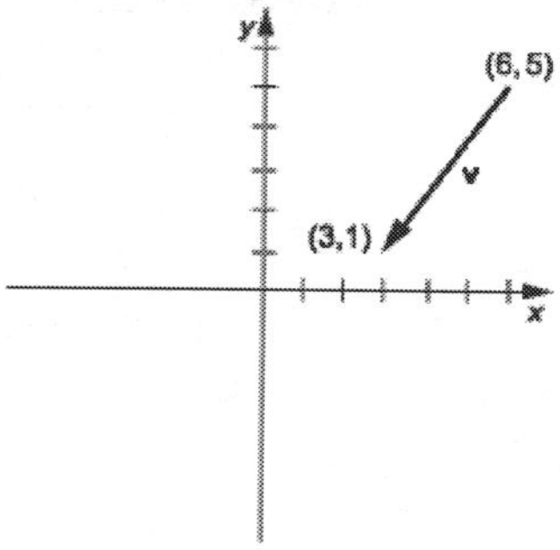

3. Find the component form of the illustrated vector.

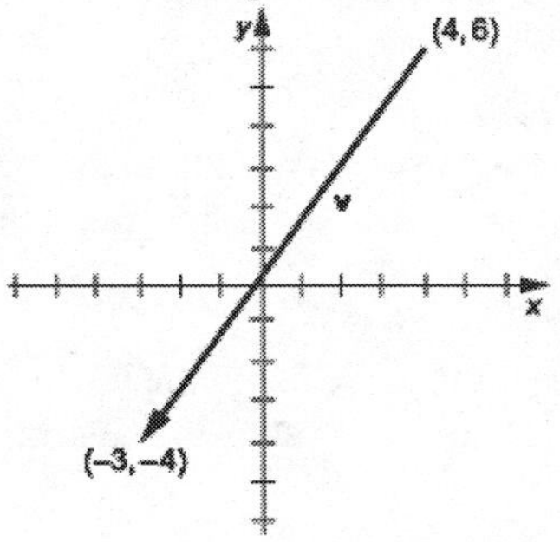

4. Find the component form of the illustrated vector.

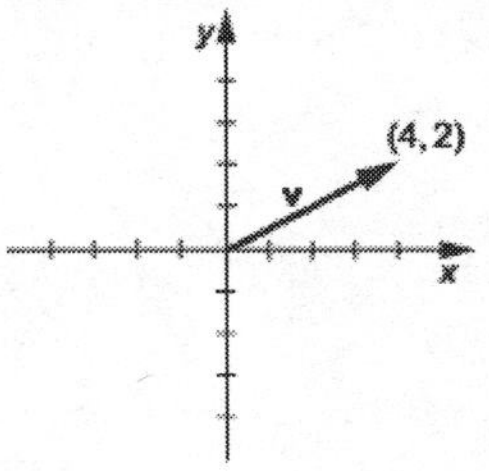

5. Find the component form of the illustrated vector.

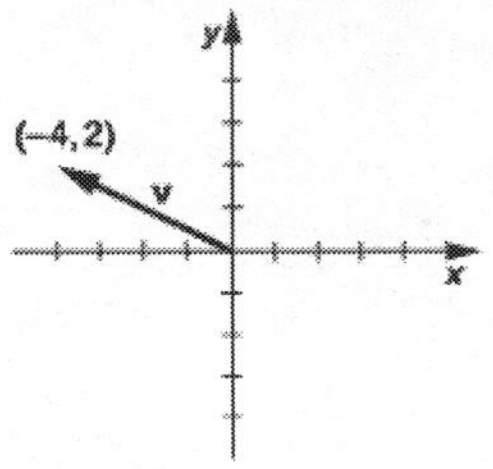

Finding the Magnitude and Direction of a Vector

- The **magnitude** of a **vector** is its length.

  The magnitude of a vector $\vec{v} = \langle v_1, v_2 \rangle$, denoted $\|\vec{v}\|$,

  is given by the formula $\|\vec{v}\| = \sqrt{v_1^2 + v_2^2}$.
- The **direction angle** of a vector is the angle measured from the positive side of the x-axis counterclockwise to the vector.

Example

$< \sqrt{3}, 1 > = \vec{v}$

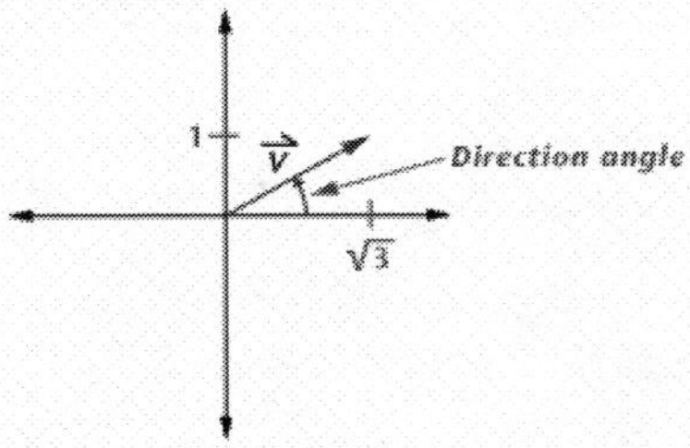

Two pieces of information that describe a **vector** are its **magnitude** and its **direction angle**.

Magnitude is just another way of saying length. For example, the magnitude of the vector $\vec{v}$ graphed to the left is the length of the arrow representing $\vec{v}$.

The direction angle of $\vec{v}$ is the angle from the positive side of the x-axis up to $\vec{v}$. Measuring direction angles is just like measuring angles in trigonometry.

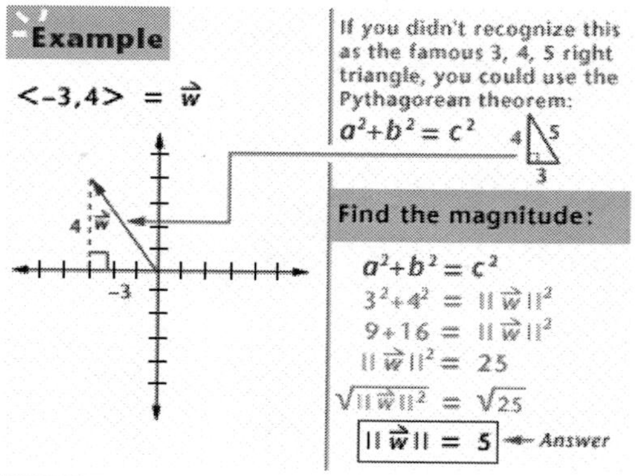

Consider the example illustrated here. How would you find the magnitude of vector $\overline{w}$?

Think of the vector as the hypotenuse of a right triangle. The x-component of the vector is one leg of the triangle and the y-component is the other leg.

Find the hypotenuse of the right triangle using the Pythagorean theorem. This length is the vector's magnitude.

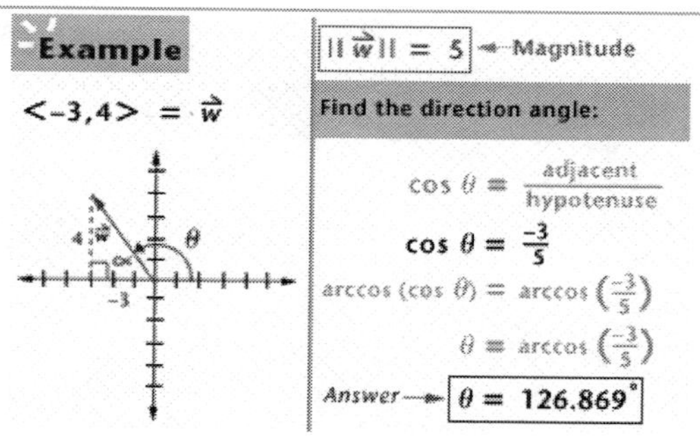

To find the **direction angle** of the vector, use the basic right-angle trigonometry rules.

The right triangle graphed here provides the values of the trig functions for the direction angle. Use any one of the trig functions to set up an equation. In this example, we used the cosine function to determine that the cosine of the direction angle is –3/5.

To solve for θ, take the **inverse cosine** of both sides of the equation. Evaluate using a calculator.

The direction angle of vector $\overline{w}$ is 126.869°

Sample problems:

1. What is the magnitude of the vector $\langle 5,-3 \rangle$?

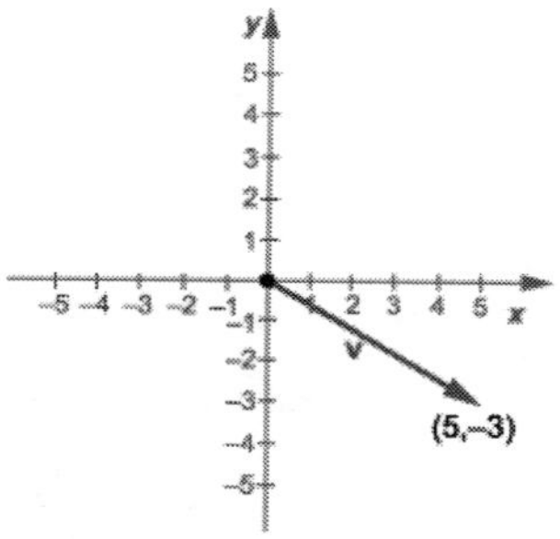

Solution: $\sqrt{34}$ or 5.8
Explanation: The vector forms a right triangle where the components are the legs and the magnitude is the hypotenuse . Use the Pythagorean theorem to determine the magnitude:
$c=\sqrt{a^2+b^2}=\sqrt{5^2+(-3)^2}=\sqrt{25+9}=\sqrt{34}=5.8.$

2. What is the magnitude and direction angle of the vector $\langle 3,6 \rangle$?

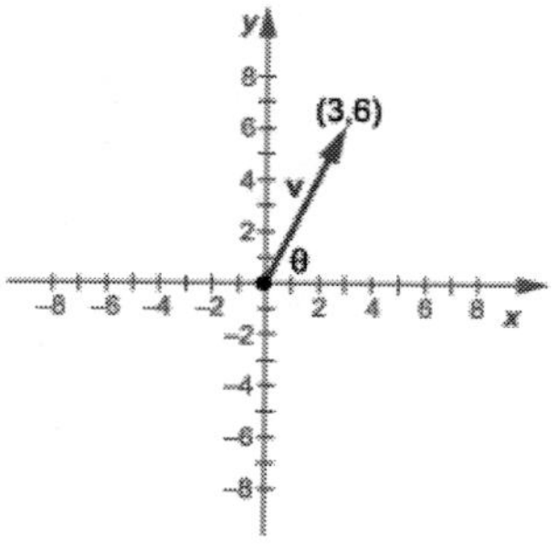

Solution: 6.7, 63.4°

Explanation: Use the Pythagorean theorem to find the magnitude: $c = \sqrt{3^2 + 6^2} = \sqrt{45}$ or 6.7.

Use a trigonometric function to set up an equation to find θ: $\tan\theta = \frac{\text{opposite}}{\text{adjacent}} = \frac{6}{3} = 2$, $\theta = 63.4°$.

The magnitude is 6.7 and the angle of direction is 63.4°.

3. What is the direction angle of the vector $v = \langle -10, -60 \rangle$?
   Solution: 260.5°
   Explanation: Use a trigonometric function to find the direction angle α:
   $\tan\alpha = \frac{\text{opposite}}{\text{adjacent}} = \frac{-60}{-10} = 6$; $\alpha = 80.5\%$. Since θ is in the third quadrant, you need to add the value of the reference angle to 180°: $180° + \alpha = \theta$; $180° + 80.5° = \theta$; $260.5° = \theta$.

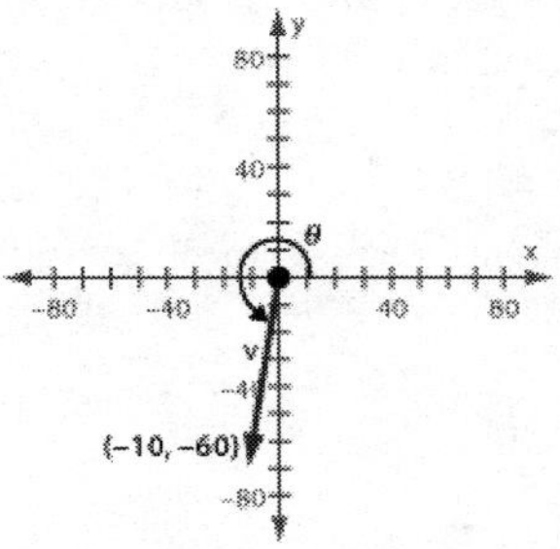

Practice problems: *(Answers on page: 759)*

1. What is the direction angle of the vector $\langle 5, -3 \rangle$?

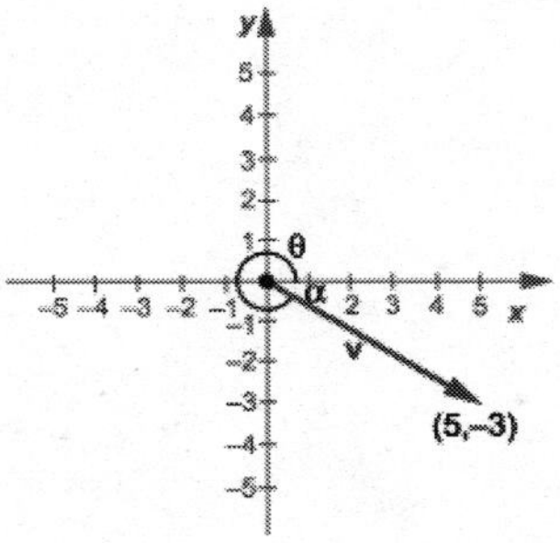

2. What is the direction angle of the vector $v = \langle 2, -30 \rangle$?
3. The direction angle of a vector is 135°. The x-component of the vector is -3. What is the y-component of this vector?

Review questions: *(Answers to odd questions on page: 759)*

1. Find the magnitude of the vector represented by $\langle 4, 5 \rangle$.
2. Find the magnitude of the vector $v = \langle -6, 8 \rangle$.
3. Find the magnitude of the vector $w = \langle -3, 3 \rangle$.
4. Find the direction angle of the vector $m = \langle 12, 5 \rangle$.
5. Determine the direction angle of the vector $u = \langle -5, -7 \rangle$.

Vector Addition and Scalar Multiplication

- A number that is multiplied into a **vector** is called a **scalar**. **Scalar multiplication** is the process of multiplying a vector by a scalar.
- Scalar multiplication can change the **magnitude** of a vector. To perform scalar multiplication, multiply each of the vector's **components** by the scalar.
- The process of adding two vectors together is called **vector addition**. To perform vector addition for two vectors, just add the *x*-components together and add the *y*-components together.

Scalar: a number to multiply a vector by. (examples: 5, −2, $\frac{1}{2}$...) *Multiply the scalar by each number in the vector.* $\vec{v} = \langle 1,2\rangle$ $2\vec{v} = \langle 2\cdot 1, 2\cdot 2\rangle$ $2\vec{v} = \langle 2,4\rangle$ $\frac{1}{2}\vec{v} = \langle \frac{1}{2}\cdot 1, \frac{1}{2}\cdot 2\rangle$ $\frac{1}{2}\vec{v} = \langle \frac{1}{2}, 1\rangle$ 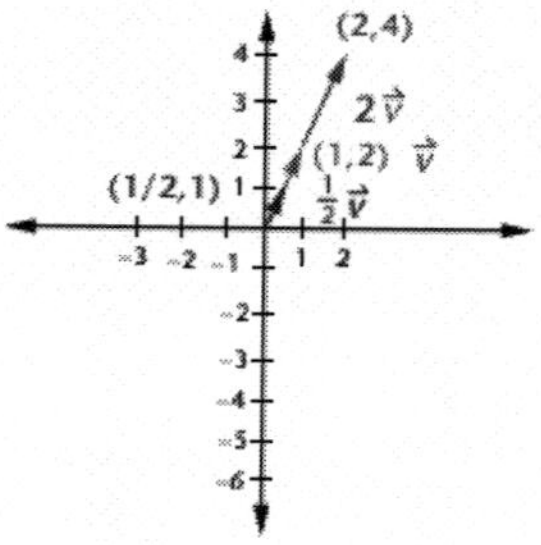 	A **scalar** is a number used to multiply a **vector**. To perform **scalar multiplication**, multiply each **component** of the vector by the scalar. Scalars greater than 1 elongate the vector, increasing the **magnitude**. Look at the illustration, notice how the vector is stretched but the **direction angle** does not change. Scalars less than 1 but greater than 0 shrink the vector, decreasing the magnitude. Once again, the vector's length changes but the direction angle remains the same.
$\vec{v} = \langle 1,2\rangle$ $-3\vec{v} = \langle -3\cdot 1, -3\cdot 2\rangle$ $-3\vec{v} = \langle -3,-6\rangle$ 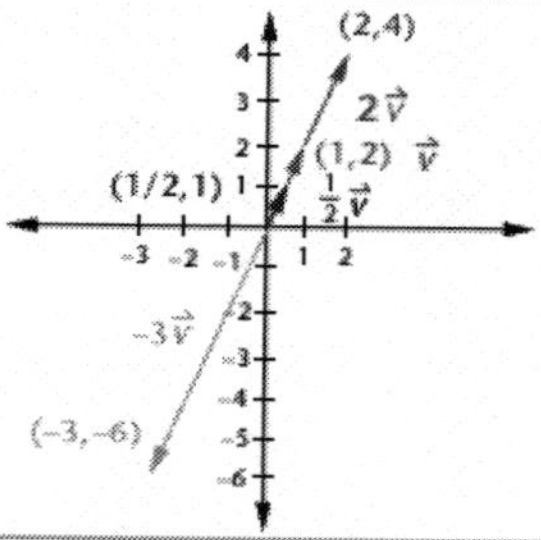 Scalar multiplication only changes the magnitude of the vector or flips it across the origin.	Negative scalars flip the vector across the origin. The absolute value of the scalar still stretches or shrinks the vector in the same manner as above.
Example Adding vectors $\langle 1,3\rangle + \langle 2,2\rangle = \langle 3,5\rangle$ (add, add)	To add two vectors together using **vector addition**, add the *x*-components together to get the new *x*-component. Then, add the *y*-components together to get the new *y*-component.
$\langle 1,3\rangle + \langle 2,2\rangle = \langle 3,5\rangle$ (add, add) 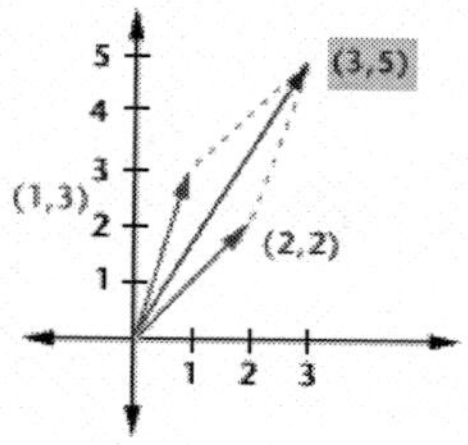 	Vector addition can also be described graphically. Start by drawing both vectors stemming from the origin. Draw a parallelogram treating the vectors like adjacent sides of the parallelogram. The diagonal that starts at the origin matches the graph of the new vector.
Example Subtracting vectors $\vec{w} - \vec{v}$ $\vec{w} + -\vec{v}$ $\langle 3,2\rangle - \langle 1,4\rangle = \langle 3,2\rangle + (-\langle 1,4\rangle)$ $= \langle 3,2\rangle + \langle -1,-4\rangle$ $= \langle 2,-2\rangle$	When asked to subtract vectors, simply subtract their respective components. Remember to take the component from the first vector minus the component from the second vector both times.

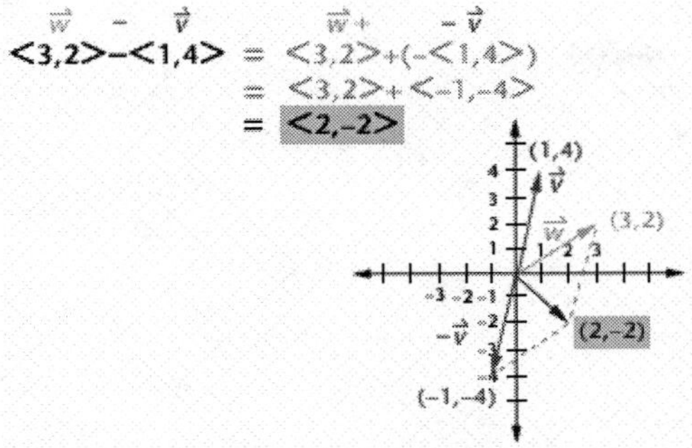

Vector subtraction can be described graphically.

Start the same way as in vector addition by putting both vectors on the origin.

Flip the vector that's being subtracted across the origin, just as if it had been multiplied by the scalar −1.

Complete the parallelogram created by the first vector and this new vector.

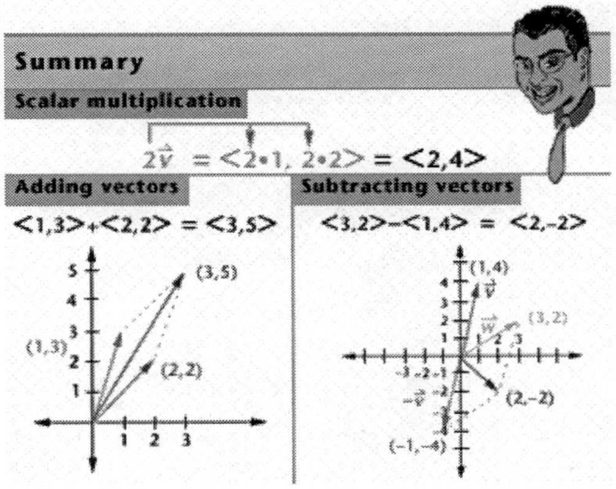

REMEMBER:

When multiplying a vector by a scalar, multiply both of the vector's components by the scalar.

When adding or subtracting vectors, combine the respective components. Do not switch them around or add x-components to y-components, keep them in order.

Graph the new vector by plotting the point or completing the parallelogram.

A SIDEBAR: You can't add a scalar to a vector since scalars do not have direction.

Sample problems:

1. If $v = \langle -6, 8 \rangle$, find the value of $\frac{1}{2}v$.

   Solution: $\langle -3, 4 \rangle$

   Explanation: A scalar is simply a number used to multiply a vector. Multiply each component of the vector by the scalar $\frac{1}{2}$: $\frac{1}{2}v = \frac{1}{2}\langle -6, 8 \rangle = \left\langle \frac{1}{2}\cdot(-6), \frac{1}{2}\cdot 8 \right\rangle = \langle -3, 4 \rangle$.

2. Add the vectors $\langle 8, -12 \rangle$ and $\langle 4, 7 \rangle$.

   Solution: $\langle 12, -5 \rangle$

   Explanation: Add the x-components together to get the new x-component and add the y-components together to get the new y-component: $\langle 8, -12 \rangle + \langle 4, 7 \rangle = \langle 8+4, -12+7 \rangle = \langle 12, -5 \rangle$.

3. Given the vectors $u = \langle 3, -2 \rangle$ and $v = \langle 2, 1 \rangle$, determine the components of $3u + v$.

   Solution: $\langle 11, -5 \rangle$

   Explanation: Perform the scalar multiplication: $3u = 3\langle 3, -2 \rangle = \langle 9, -6 \rangle$. Add the vectors: $3u + v = \langle 9, -6 \rangle + \langle 2, 1 \rangle = \langle 9+2, -6+1 \rangle = \langle 11, -5 \rangle$.

Practice problems: *(Answers on page: 760)*

1. If $\vec{v} = \langle 4.5, -5.5 \rangle$, find the value of $-4\vec{v}$.
2. Subtract: $\langle -3, 10 \rangle - \langle 1, -6 \rangle$
3. Given the vectors $r = \langle -1, -1 \rangle$ and $s = \langle -2, 4 \rangle$, determine the components of $2r - s$.

Review questions: *(Answers to odd questions on page: 760)*

1. Given the vector $u = \langle 3,-7\rangle$, determine the components of $3u$.
2. Given vectors $u = \langle 4,1\rangle$, $v = \langle 2,-1\rangle$, and $w = \langle -2,3\rangle$, determine the components of $u + v + w$.
3. Given vectors $u = \langle 4,-3\rangle$ and $v = \langle 2,\ 3\rangle$, determine the components of $2u - v$.
4. Given vectors $r = \langle -2,2\rangle$ and $s = \langle 3,-1\rangle$, determine the components of $3r - s$.
5. Given vectors $u = \langle 4,-3\rangle$ and $v = \langle 3,2\rangle$, determine the components of $5u + v$.

Finding the Components of a Vector

- When given a vector's **magnitude** and **direction** angle, it is possible to determine its **components** by using the **trigonometric functions**.

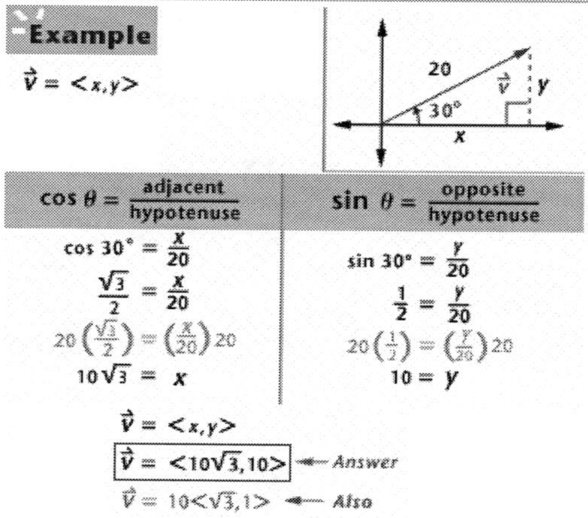

Suppose you are told that a given vector has a **magnitude** of 20 and a **direction angle** that measures 30°. How would you find its x- and y-**components**?

Using the basic trig functions can help you determine the components of a vector.

To determine the components of the vector given here, use the fact that the **cosine** of the vector's direction angle is defined as the adjacent side over the hypotenuse. For a **vector**, the adjacent side is equal to the x-component. Since the direction angle is known, find the value of the trig function and set it equal to the x-component over the magnitude.

The same thing works for **sine** and the y-component.

Write the answer in vector component form and factor out a **scalar**. (Factoring is not a requirement.)

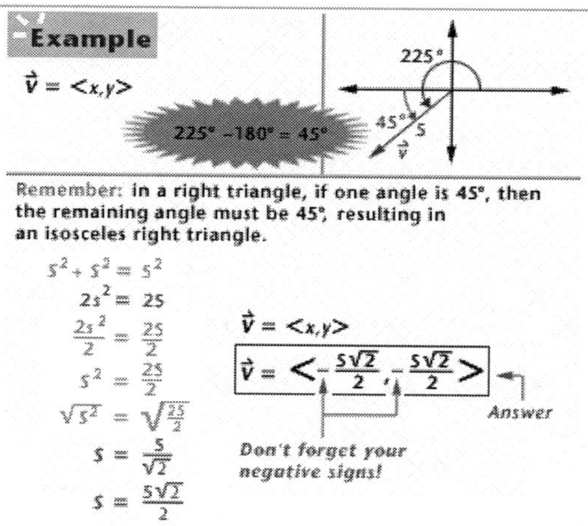

Given a vector with magnitude equal to 5 and a direction angle of 225°, find the components.

Notice that the **reference angle** is equal to 45°.

Consider the right triangle for this vector. Since one angle is 90° and the next is 45°, the last angle must be 45° as well. That fact makes the triangle an isosceles right triangle, which means the sides are equal.

Notice, it was not necessary to use the trig functions for this example. Knowing that the sides are equal and applying the Pythagorean theorem will produce the length for all the sides. Adjust the answer so that negative signs are on the correct terms given the location of the vector.

Sample problems:

1. Find the x- and y-components of a vector of magnitude $\sqrt{2}$ and at an angle 45° from the origin.
   Solution: $\langle 1,1\rangle$
   Explanation: The magnitude of the vector is the hypotenuse of a triangle where the legs are the x- and y-components. Furthermore, the 45° angle means that the triangle is isosceles. Use the Pythagorean theorem, where a and b are equal and $c=\sqrt{2}$, to find the length of the legs:
   $c^2=a^2+b^2 \Rightarrow \left(\sqrt{2}\right)^2=2\left(a^2\right);\ 2=2\left(a^2\right);\ 1=a^2;\ a=\sqrt{1}=1.$ Thus the legs are each 1, so the x- and y-components are $\langle 1,1\rangle$.

2. What are the x- and y-components of a vector with a magnitude of 40 and a direction angle of 390°?
   Solution: $\left\langle 20\sqrt{3},20\right\rangle$
   Explanation: Because the vector angle is greater than 360°, it rotates around the coordinate plane once. The vector ends up 30° above the x-axis in the first quadrant. Use a trig function to find the y-component: $\sin 30^\circ=\frac{y}{40};\ y=40(\sin 30^\circ);\ y=40\left(\frac{1}{2}\right);\ y=20.$
   Use the Pythagorean theorem to find the length of the third side, x:
   $40^2=20^2+x^2;\ x=\sqrt{1600-400}=\sqrt{1200}=20\sqrt{3}.$
   Thus, the x- and y-components are $\left\langle 20\sqrt{3},20\right\rangle$.

3. Express the vector in component form.

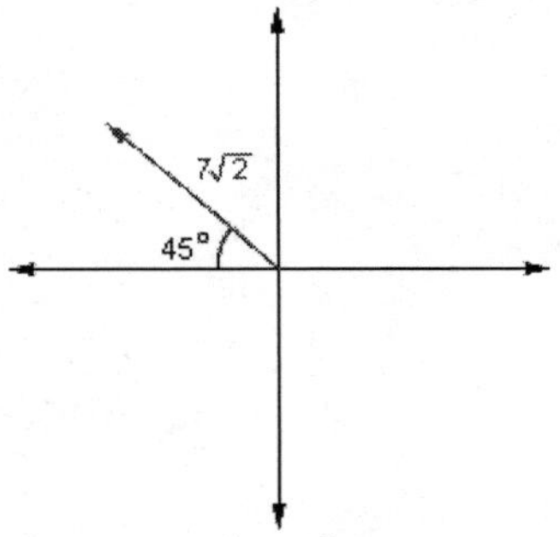

   Solution: $\langle -7,7\rangle$
   Explanation: Use a trig function to find the y-component: $\sin 45^\circ=\frac{y}{7\sqrt{2}};$
   $y=7\sqrt{2}(\sin 45^\circ)=7.$ Since the angle is 45° the triangle must be isosceles. Thus, the x- and y-components are both 7. However, the angle is in quadrant II, so x is negative: $\langle -7,7\rangle$.

Practice problems: *(Answers on page: 760)*

1. What are the x- and y-components for a vector with a magnitude of 2 and at an angle 210° from the origin?
2. What are the x- and y-components of a vector with a magnitude of $15\sqrt{2}$ and at an angle of 135° from the origin?

3. Express the vector in component form.

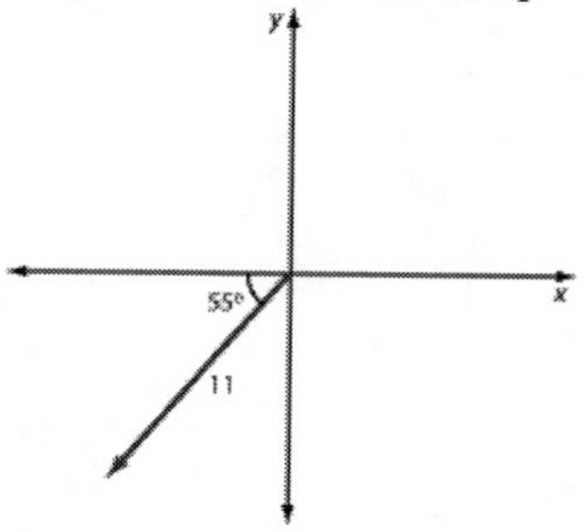

Review questions: *(Answers to odd questions on page: 760)*

1. Express the vector in component form.

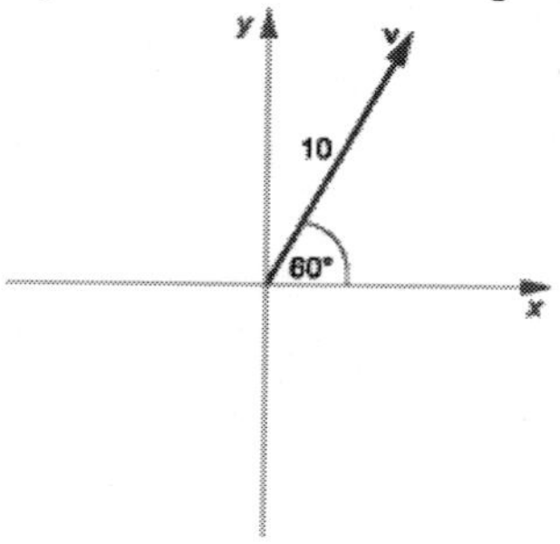

2. Express the vector in component form.

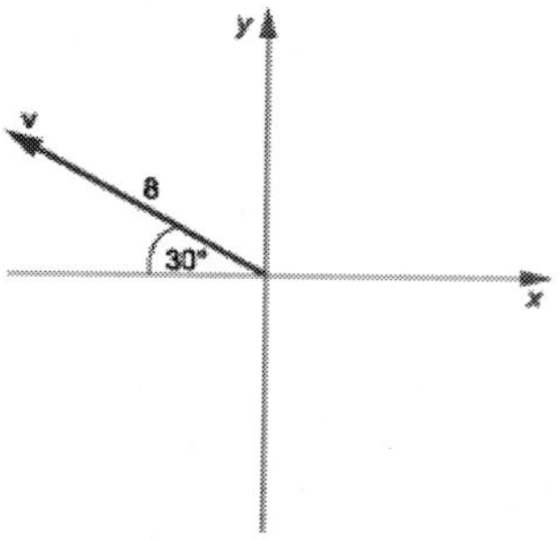

3. Express the vector in component form.

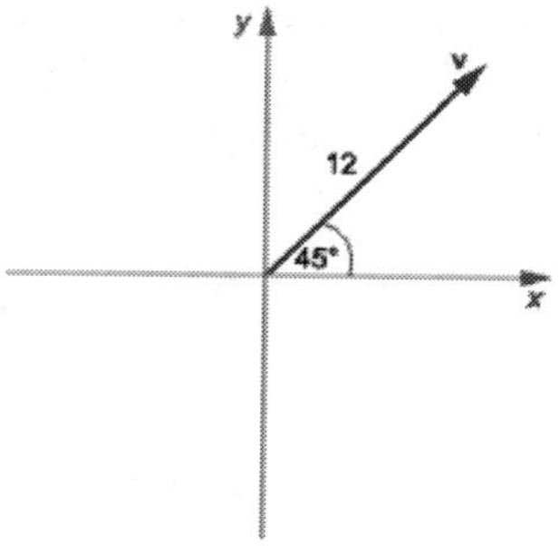

4. Express the vector in component form.

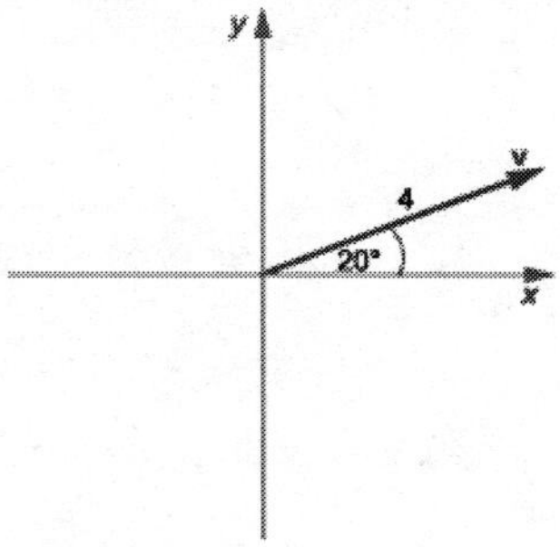

5. Express the vector in component form.

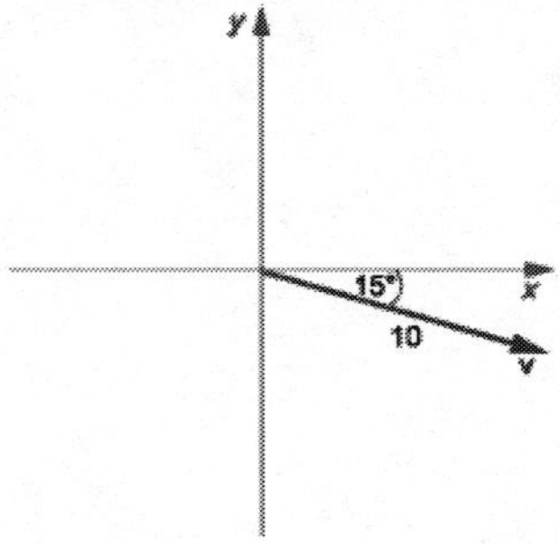

Finding a Unit Vector

- A **unit vector** is a **vector** with a **magnitude** of 1. Unit vectors are used when distance is not important and only the direction is in question.
- The unit vector in the direction of a vector $\vec{v}$ is given by the equation $\vec{u} = \frac{1}{\|\vec{v}\|}\vec{v}$.

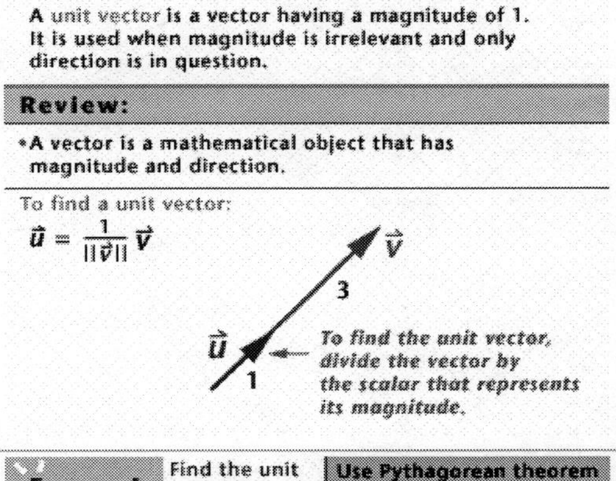	A **vector** whose **magnitude** is equal to 1 is called a **unit vector**. All vectors have corresponding unit vectors, even if the unit vector is bigger than the original vector. To find the unit vector that corresponds to a particular vector, use **scalar multiplication** to multiply the vector by the reciprocal of its magnitude (in other words, divide by the magnitude). The result is a vector in the same direction with a magnitude of 1.
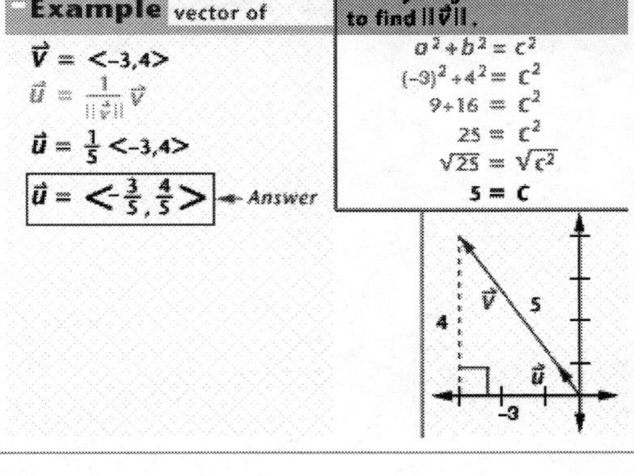	Consider the following: given the **components** <–3, 4> of a vector, find its corresponding unit vector. **REMEMBER**: The unit vector is equal to the vector divided by the magnitude, so find the magnitude first. Find the magnitude by using the Pythagorean theorem. Plug in –3 for *a* and 4 for *b*. The hypotenuse, *c*, is equal to 5. Next, divide the components of the original vector by 5. The result is the unit vector in the direction of the original vector.

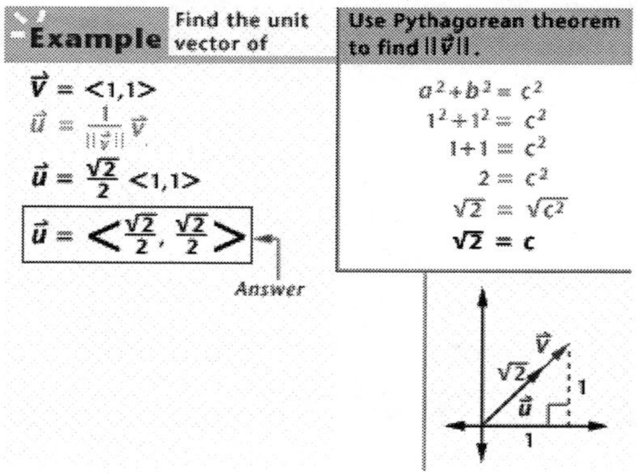

In this example it might appear that the given vector is already a unit vector, but remember, a vector's magnitude is equal to the square root of the sum of the squares of the components.

First, find the magnitude by plugging the vector's components into the Pythagorean theorem. The magnitude for the given vector is $\sqrt{2}$.

Next, divide the components by the magnitude. What you find is that the unit vector for this example is $\left\langle \frac{\sqrt{2}}{2}, \frac{\sqrt{2}}{2} \right\rangle$.

Sample problems:

1. Find a unit vector with the same directions as $w = \langle 5,12 \rangle$.

   Solution: $\left\langle \frac{5}{13}, \frac{12}{13} \right\rangle$

   Explanation: Start by finding the magnitude of the vector: $\|w\| = \sqrt{5^2 + 12^2} = \sqrt{169} = 13$. Now divide the magnitude into each of the vector's components to get the unit vector, u: $u = \left\langle \frac{5}{13}, \frac{12}{13} \right\rangle$.

2. Find a unit vector with the same direction as $r = \left\langle \frac{1}{2}, \frac{-2}{5} \right\rangle$.

   Solution: $\left\langle \frac{5\sqrt{41}}{41}, \frac{-4\sqrt{41}}{41} \right\rangle$

   Explanation: Start by finding the magnitude of the vector:
$$\begin{aligned}\|r\| &= \sqrt{\left(\frac{1}{2}\right)^2 + \left(-\frac{2}{5}\right)} \\ &= \sqrt{\frac{1}{4} + \frac{4}{25}} \\ &= \sqrt{\frac{25}{100} + \frac{16}{100}} \\ &= \sqrt{\frac{41}{100}} = \frac{\sqrt{41}}{10}.\end{aligned}$$

   Now divide the magnitude into each of the vector's components to get the unit vector, u:
$$\begin{aligned}u &= \left\langle \frac{1/2}{\sqrt{41}/10}, \frac{-2/5}{\sqrt{41}/10} \right\rangle \\ &= \left\langle \frac{1}{2} \cdot \frac{10}{\sqrt{41}}, -\frac{2}{5} \cdot \frac{10}{\sqrt{41}} \right\rangle \\ &= \left\langle \frac{1}{2} \cdot \frac{10}{\sqrt{41}}, -\frac{2}{5} \cdot \frac{10}{\sqrt{41}} \right\rangle \\ &= \left\langle \frac{5}{\sqrt{41}}, \frac{-4}{\sqrt{41}} \right\rangle \\ &= \left\langle \frac{5\sqrt{41}}{41}, \frac{-4\sqrt{41}}{41} \right\rangle\end{aligned}$$

3. What is the magnitude of a unit vector that is oriented in the same direction as a vector with a magnitude of 10?
Solution: 1
Explanation: A unit vector is produced by dividing a given vector by its magnitude. Thus, unit vectors have a magnitude of 1.

Practice problems: *(Answers on page: 760)*

1. Find a unit vector with the same direction as $t = \langle -3, -7 \rangle$.
2. Find a unit vector with the same direction as $t = \left\langle \frac{\pi}{2}, 0 \right\rangle$.
3. What is the magnitude of a unit vector in the direction of a vector with a magnitude of 472?

Review questions: *(Answers to odd questions on page: 760)*

1. True or false: A unit vector is a vector with magnitude equal to 1.
2. Find a unit vector with the same direction as $v = \langle -5, 12 \rangle$.
3. Find a unit vector with the same direction as $w = \langle -1, 1 \rangle$.
4. Find a unit vector with the same direction as $w = \left\langle \frac{3}{\sqrt{13}}, \frac{-2}{\sqrt{13}} \right\rangle$.
5. Find a unit vector with the same direction as $w = \langle 7, -24 \rangle$.

Solving Word Problems Involving Velocity or Forces

- **Velocity** can be expressed as a direction and a speed; therefore, velocity is a **vector**.
- Degree measure starts at the positive x-axis and moves counterclockwise. **Compass direction** (or **bearing**) starts at north and moves clockwise.

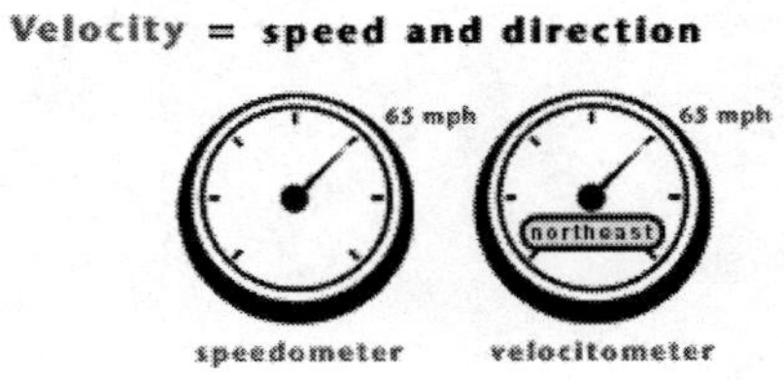

The speedometer in a car measures the rate at which the car moves, but it does not indicate the direction of movement. So, speed itself is not a **vector**.

However, if the speedometer did provide information about direction, then it would be a vector.

Velocity is a vector made up of a speed and a direction.

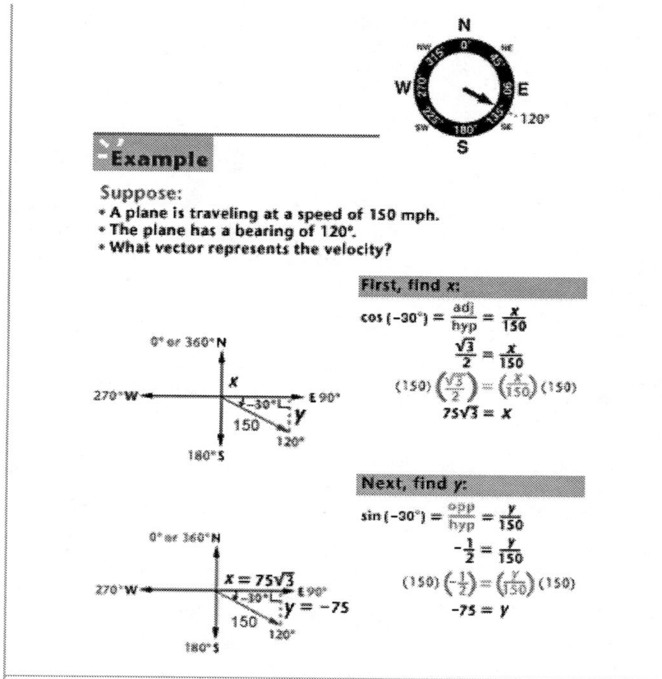

In surveying, angles are measured clockwise from north. This angle measurement is referred to as the **bearing** or **compass direction**. Beearings are measured differently than other angles in math.

Suppose you are told the following:
*A plane is traveling at a speed of 150 mi/hr
*The plane has a bearing of 120°.

How would you find the vector that represents velocity?

To find the vector that represents velocity, you need to break the velocity into x- and y-components. Use the trigonometric functions to find the value for the components.

Cosine relates to x.

Sine relates to y.

Because the vector is in the fourth quadrant, the x-component is positive and the y-component is negative.

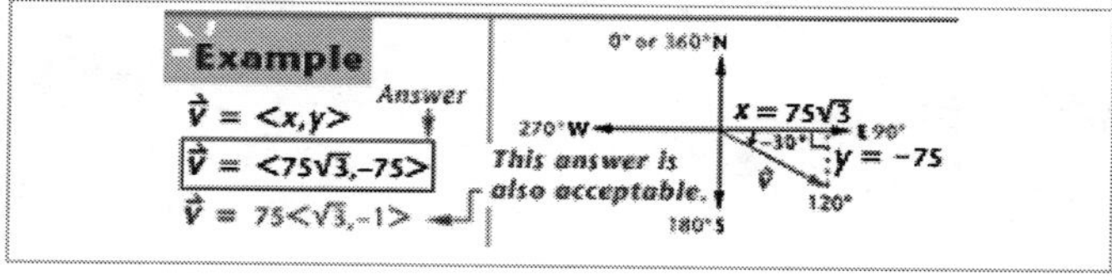

Put x and y in vector form.

You can factor out the **scalar** if you choose; however, it is not necessary.

Sample problems:

1. A boat is traveling at a speed of 48 mph. The boat has a bearing of 135°. What vector represents the velocity?

   Solution: $24\left\langle\sqrt{2},-\sqrt{2}\right\rangle$

   Explanation: First, find x: $\cos(-45°)=\frac{x}{48}$; $\frac{\sqrt{2}}{2}=\frac{x}{48}$; $24\sqrt{2}=x$. Next, find y: $\cos(-45°)=\frac{x}{48}$; $-\frac{\sqrt{2}}{2}-\frac{y}{48}$; $-24\sqrt{2}=y$. Because the vector is in the fourth quadrant, the x-component is positive and the y-component is negative. Therefore, the vector is $\left\langle 24\sqrt{2},-24\sqrt{2}\right\rangle$ or $24\left\langle\sqrt{2},-\sqrt{2}\right\rangle$.

2. A bus is traveling at a speed of 60 mph. The vector that represents the velocity is $30\left\langle -1,\sqrt{3}\right\rangle$. What is the bearing of the bus?

   Solution: 330°

   Explanation: Since the x-component is negative and the y-component is positive, the vector must be in the second quadrant. Distribute the 30 into the vector to get $\left\langle -30,30\sqrt{3}\right\rangle$. Use the x component for the cosine trig function: $\cos x=-\frac{30}{60};\cos x=-\frac{1}{2};x=120°$. This angle has a reference angle of 60° and lies in the second quadrant. The bearing is $270°+60°$, or 330°.

3. A ship sails 50 mph on a bearing of 20° for one hour and then turns and sails 30 mph on a bearing of 80° for another hour. What vector represents the velocity and what is its magnitude?

Solution: $\langle 46.6, 52.2\rangle$ $\bar{v} = 70$

Explanation: Find the x-component for the ship's first hour of travel:

$\cos 70 = \frac{x}{50}$; $50\cos 70 = x$; $x = 17.1$. Now find y: $\sin 70 = \frac{4}{50}$; $y = 47$. Find the components for the second hour (start where the first vector stopped): $\cos 10 = \frac{x}{30}$; $x = 29.5$:

$\sin 10 = \frac{y}{30}$; $y = 5.2$. Add the two vectors: $\langle 17.1, 47\rangle + \langle 29.5, 5.2\rangle$. The velocity vector is $\langle 46.6, 52.2\rangle$ Magnitude $\bar{v} = \sqrt{46.6^2 + 52.2^2} = 70$.

Practice problems: *(Answers on page: 760)*

1. A plane is traveling at a speed of 180 mph with a bearing of 300°. What vector represents the velocity?
2. A boat is traveling at a speed of 40 mph. The vector that represents the velocity is $20\langle -\sqrt{2}, -\sqrt{2}\rangle$. What is the bearing of the boat?
3. A scuba diver swims 100 ft/min on a bearing of 170°. The water is moving with a current of 30 ft/min on a bearing of 115° . Find the diver's resultant velocity.

Review questions: *(Answers to odd questions on page: 760)*

1. A plane is traveling at a speed of 250 mph. The plane has a bearing of 30° east of north. Find the vector that represents the velocity of the plane.

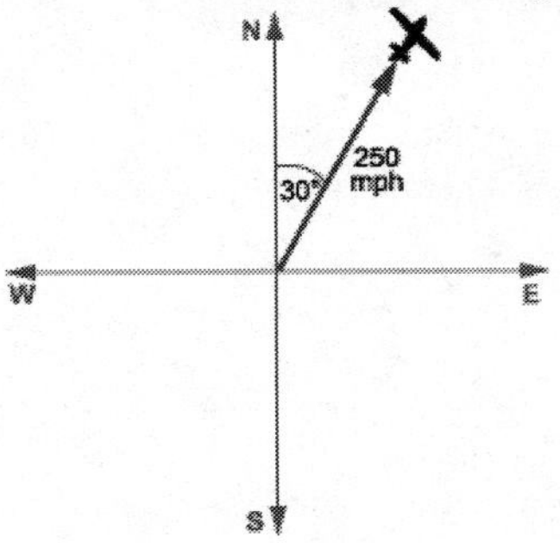

2. A plane is traveling at a speed of 400 mph on a bearing of 150°. Express the velocity of the plane as a vector.

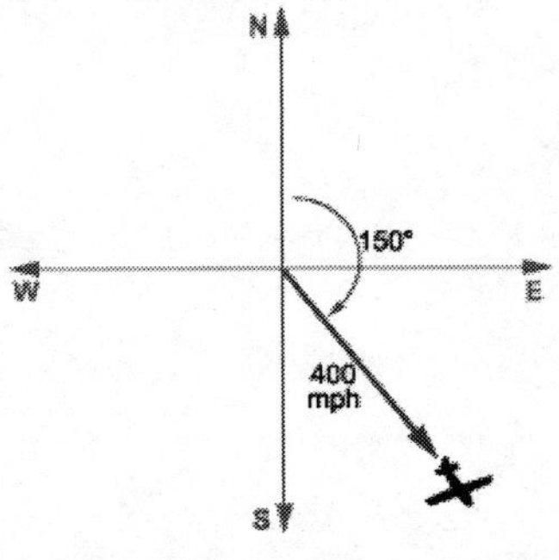

3. A baseball player throws a ball with a velocity of 30 ft/sec at an angle of 65° with the horizontal. Express the velocity of the ball as a vector. Round components to the nearest tenth.

4. A plane leaves an airport on a bearing of 130°, traveling at 450 mph. What is the velocity of the plane as a vector? Express the components to the nearest tenth.

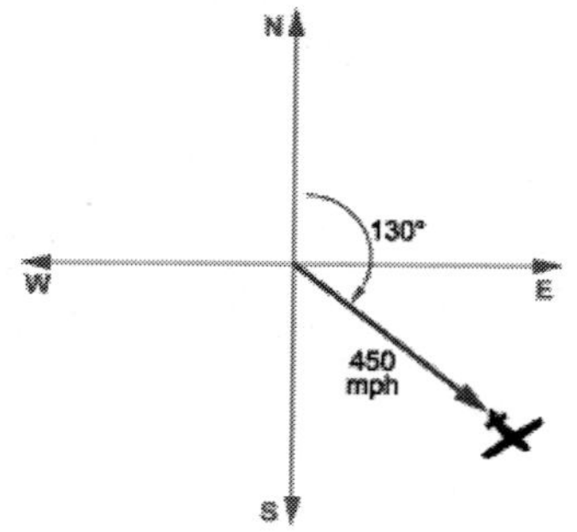

5. A plane leaves the airport on a bearing of 30° traveling at 500 mph. The wind is blowing at a bearing of 135° at a speed of 30 mph. What is the actual velocity of the plane?

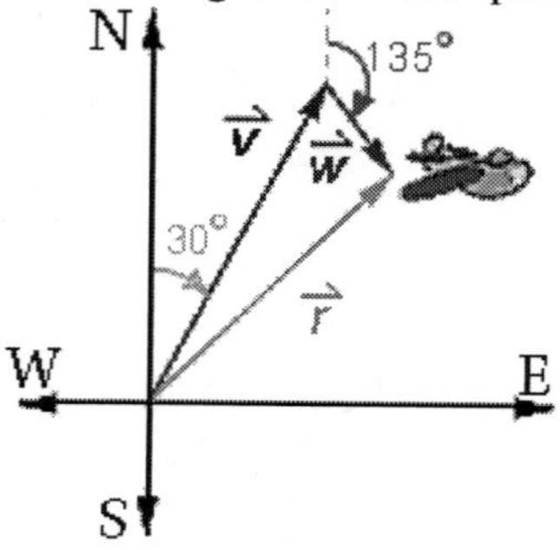

Graphing a Complex Number and Finding Its Absolute Value

- **Review**: A **complex number** $x + yi$ has a **real part**, x, and an **imaginary part**, y. The **imaginary number i** represents the quantity $\sqrt{-1}$.
- Complex numbers can be graphed in the **complex plane** just like points are graphed in the coordinate plane. The horizontal axis of the complex plane measures the real part of the complex number and the vertical axis measures the imaginary part.
- The **absolute value** or **modulus** of a complex number $z = x + yi$ is denoted $|z|$. It represents the distance of z from the origin in the complex plane. Calculate it using the **Pythagorean theorem**: $|z| = |x + yi| = \sqrt{x^2 + y^2}$.

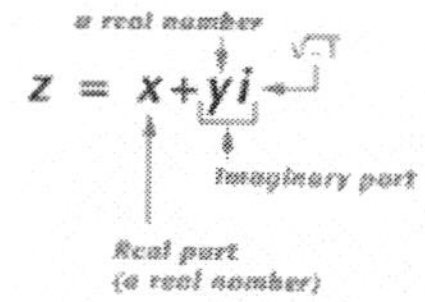

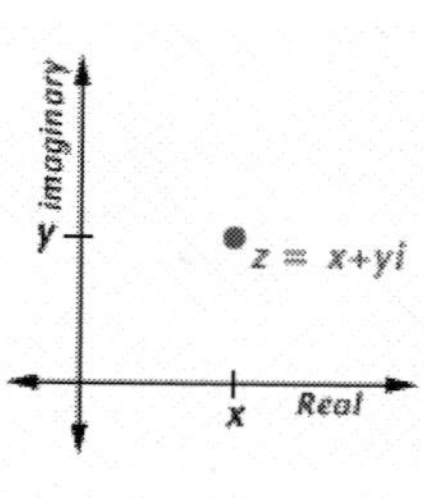

Visualize complex numbers by graphing them in the **complex plane** just as you would graph **ordered pairs**. The horizontal axis is the real axis and the vertical axis is the imaginary axis.

Example

Plot 2+3*i*

Plot −3+*i*

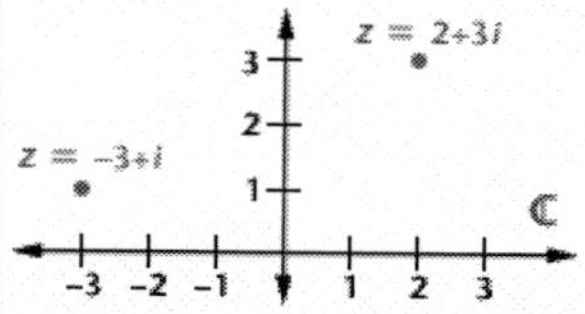

The complex numbers $-3 + i$ and $2 + 3i$ have been graphed in the complex plane on the left.

$|z| = |x+yi| = \sqrt{x^2+y^2}$

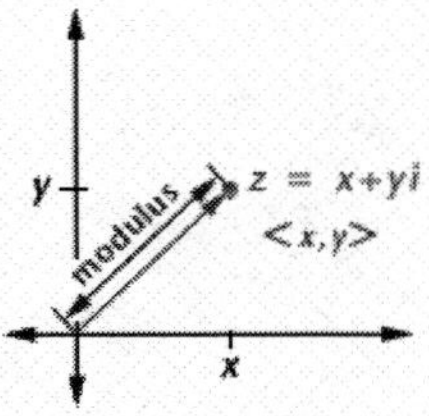

Notice that a point in the complex plane has two coordinates just like a vector does.

The absolute value or modulus of a complex number is analogous to the magnitude of a vector; calculate it using the Pythagorean theorem.

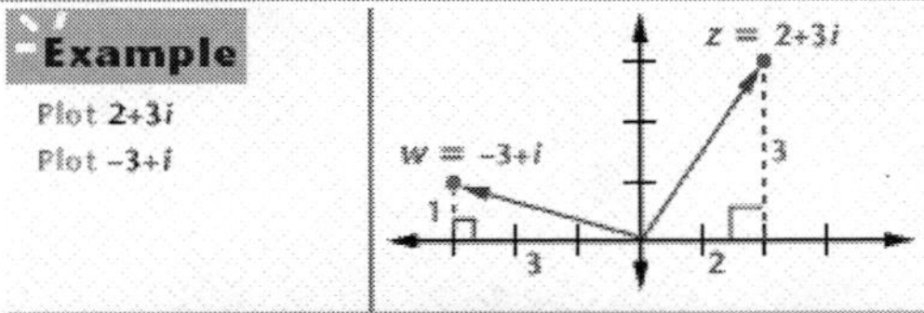

Find the modulus of:	
$w = -3+i$	$z = 2+3i$
$\lvert w\rvert = \sqrt{x^2+y^2}$	$\lvert z\rvert = \sqrt{x^2+y^2}$
$\lvert w\rvert = \sqrt{(-3)^2+1^2}$	$\lvert z\rvert = \sqrt{2^2+3^2}$
$\lvert w\rvert = \sqrt{9+1}$	$\lvert z\rvert = \sqrt{4+9}$
$\lvert w\rvert = \sqrt{10}$ Modulus	$\lvert z\rvert = \sqrt{13}$ Modulus

Calculate the moduli of the two complex numbers given here.

Use the Pythagorean theorem and plug in the known values. For the complex number $-3 + i$ plug in -3 for x and i for y. Remember $i^2 = 1$. You find that the modulus for the complex number $-3 + i = \sqrt{10}$.

The modulus is just the distance from a point to the origin.

Sample problems:

1. Determine the modulus of the complex number $-5i$.
   Solution: 5
   Explanation: Compute the modulus of $-5i$: $\sqrt{(0)^2+(-5)^2} = \sqrt{0+25} = \sqrt{25} = 5$.

2. Determine the modulus of the complex number $-4+3i$.
   Solution: 5
   Explanation: Compute the modulus of $-4+3i$ using the formula $|z| = \sqrt{a^2+b^2}$:
   $|z| = \sqrt{(-4)^2+(3)^2} = \sqrt{16+9} = \sqrt{25} = 5$.

3. True or false: The complex number $-3-2i$ is graphed below.

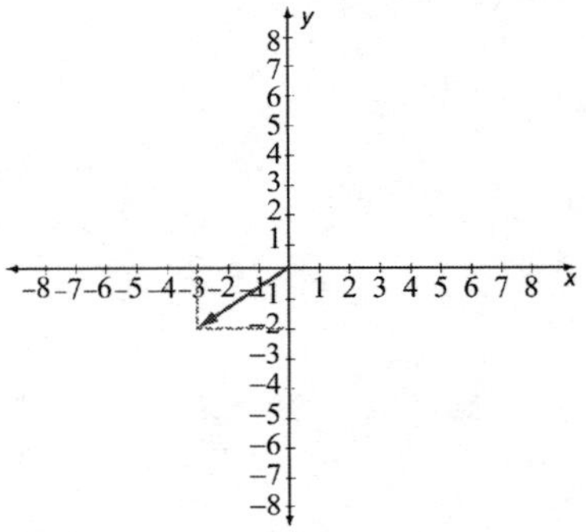

   Solution: True
   Explanation: Move 3 units to the left, according to the real number -3, and move 2 units down, according to the imaginary number $-2i$.

Practice problems: *(Answers on page: 760)*

1. What is the modulus of the complex number, $3+4i$?

2. True or false: The complex number $-4+3i$ is graphed below.

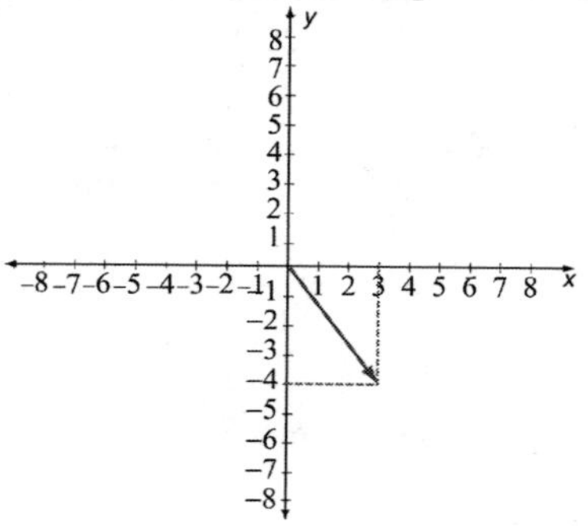

3. What is the modulus of the complex number $(3+4i)(1-2i)$?

Review questions: *(Answers to odd questions on page: 760)*

1. True or false: The absolute value of the complex number $-8i$ is 8.
2. True or false: The complex number $3+4i$ is graphed below.

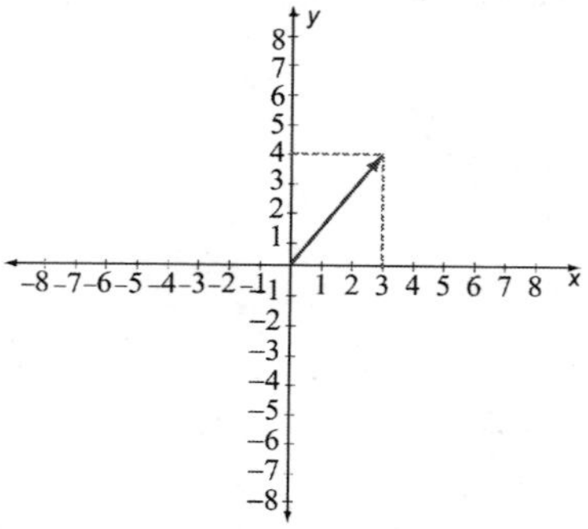

3. Determine the modulus of the complex number $6-8i$.
4. Determine the modulus of the complex number $7+3i$.
5. Determine the modulus of the complex number $(5+2i)(3-i)$.

Expressing a Complex Number in Trigonometric or Polar Form

- To express a **complex number** z in **trigonometric form** or **polar form**:
  - Start by sketching the complex number.
  - Find r, the **absolute value**, and θ, the angle from the x-axis.
  - Plug these values into the polar form: $z = r(\cos\theta + i\sin\theta)$.
- **Review**: The **standard form** of a complex number z follows the formula: $z = x + yi$

How do you express complex numbers in trig form? 1. Sketch a graph. 2. Use trig properties to find unknown values. 3. Plug the values into the trig form.	Given a **complex number** in **standard form,** $z = x + yi$, you can express that number in trigonometric or polar form by following these basic steps: 1. Sketch a graph of the complex number 2. Use trig properties to find unknown values 3. Plug the values into the trig form.

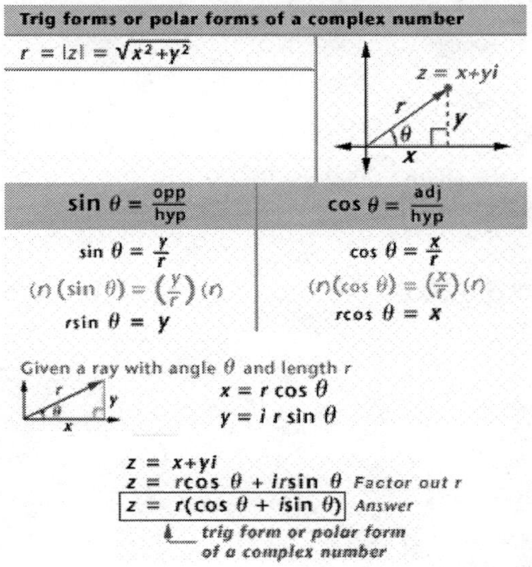

Given the complex number $z = x + yi$, first sketch a graph of the number in the complex plane.

To find r, the modulus of the complex number, use the Pythagorean theorem. The value of r will equal the square root of $x^2 + y^2$.

Now consider the angle θ. Knowing that $\cos\theta = x/r$, you can find x by multiplying both sides by r. So, $x = r\cos\theta$.

Also notice that $\sin\theta = y/r$, so $y = r\sin\theta$.

Substituting these values for x and y into the original complex number will give you that complex number expressed in terms of r and θ. This is the **trigonometric form** or **polar form** of the complex number: $z = r(\cos\theta + i\sin\theta)$.

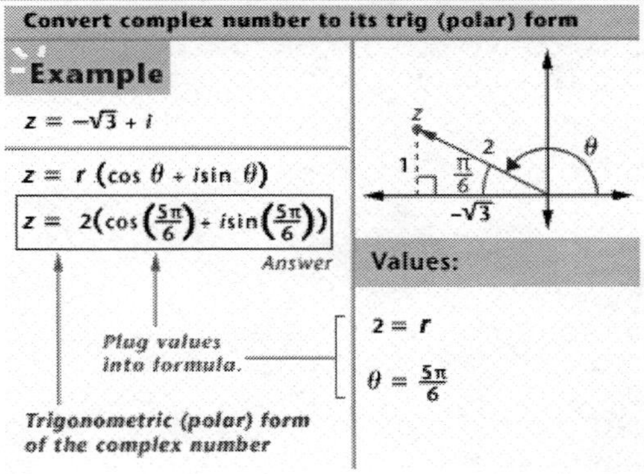

Consider the complex number $z = -\sqrt{3} + i$.

How would you express this number in polar (or trig) form?

First, sketch a graph of the complex number. Next, find the value of r, the modulus of the complex number. Remember that r is equal to the absolute value, or length, of the complex number.

Plugging the x and y values of the complex number into the Phythagorean theorem, you find that $r = 2$.

Next, find the value of θ as measured from the positive real axis. Given that the angles for a $1-2-\sqrt{3}$ triangle measure 30°, 60°, and 90°, you can label the angle formed with the negative real axis $\pi/6$. Therefore, θ equals $5\pi/6$.

Plug r and θ into the trig (or polar) form of the complex number.

So, the complex number in standard form, $z = -\sqrt{3} + i$, is equal to the complex number $z = 2\left(\cos\left(5\pi/6\right) + i\sin\left(5\pi/6\right)\right)$ in polar form.

Sample problems:

1. Convert the polar number $4(\cos 90° + i\sin 90°)$ to complex form.
   Solution: $4i$
   Explanation: Evaluate each trig function and simplify:
   $4(\cos 90° + i\sin 90°) = 4\cos 90° + 4i\sin 90° = 4(0) + 4i(1) = 4i.$

2. Convert the complex number $-3i$ to polar form.
   Solution: $3(\cos 270° + i\sin 270°)$
   Explanation: The polar form is $r(\cos\theta + i\sin\theta)$.
   Find r: $r = \sqrt{x^2 + y^2} = \sqrt{(0)^2 + (-3)^2} = \sqrt{9} = 3$.
   Find x and y: $-3i = 0 - 3i$; so, $x = 0$ and $y = -3$, which means $\cos\theta = 0$ and $\sin\theta = -1$.
   Therefore, $\theta = 270°$. Thus, $-3i = r(\cos\theta + i\sin\theta) = 3(\cos 270° + i\sin 270°)$.

3. What is the polar form of the complex number represented as point A in the graph of the complex plane below?

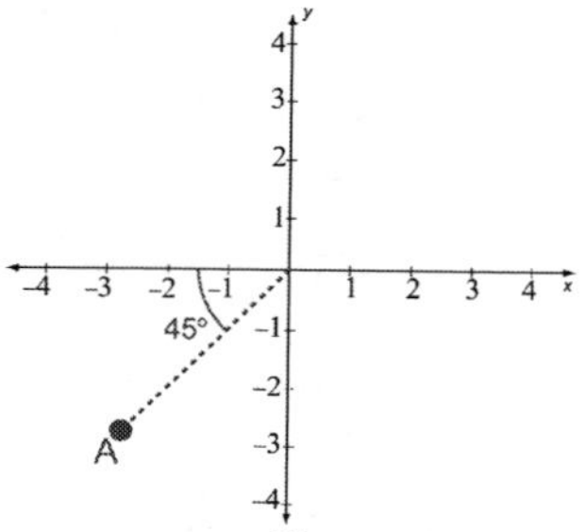

   Solution: $3\sqrt{2}(\cos 225° + i\sin 225°)$
   Explanation: The reference angle is 45° and is in the third quadrant. Therefore, $\theta = 225°$.
   Since both legs of the reference triangle are of length 3, the modulus is $3\sqrt{2}$.

Practice problems: *(Answers on page: 760)*

1. What is the polar form of the complex number $-7i$?
2. Convert the complex number $-5 + 5i$ to polar form.
3. Convert the polar number $4(\cos 225° + i\sin 225°)$ to complex form.

Review questions: *(Answers to odd questions on page: 760)*

1. Convert the complex number $z = 4 + 4i$ to polar form.
2. Convert the complex number $z = \sqrt{3} + i$ to trigonometric form.
3. Convert the complex number $z = 9i$ to polar form.
4. Convert the trigonometric form of the complex number $z = 6(\cos 60° + i\sin 60°)$ to standard form.
5. Convert the polar form of the complex number $z = 3(\cos 180° + i\sin 180°)$ to standard form.

Multiplying and Dividing Complex Numbers in Trigonometric or Polar Form

- To multiply two complex numbers:
  - Start by putting the complex numbers in **polar form**.
  - Multiply the r-terms and add the θ-terms: $z_1 z_2 = r_1 r_2\left[\cos(\theta_1 + \theta_2) + i\sin(\theta_1 + \theta_2)\right]$
- To divide two complex numbers:
  - Start by putting the complex numbers in polar form.
  - Divide the r-terms and subtract the θ-terms:

$$\frac{z_1}{z_2} = \frac{r_1}{r_2}\left[\cos(\theta_1 - \theta_2) + i\sin(\theta_1 - \theta_2)\right]$$

Multiply these two complex numbers in polar form:

$$z_1z_2 = (r_1\cos\theta_1 + ir_1\sin\theta_1)(r_2\cos\theta_2 + i\,r_2\sin\theta_2)$$

$$z_1z_2 = \underbrace{r_1r_2\cos\theta_1\cos\theta_2}_{\text{First}} - \underbrace{r_1r_2\sin\theta_1\sin\theta_2}_{\text{Last}}$$

$$+ \underbrace{i\,r_1r_2\sin\theta_1\cos\theta_2}_{\text{Inner}} + \underbrace{i\,r_1r_2\cos\theta_1\sin\theta_2}_{\text{Outer}}$$

$$z_1z_2 = r_1r_2[\cos\theta_1\cos\theta_2 - \sin\theta_1\sin\theta_2 + i(\sin\theta_1\cos\theta_2 + \cos\theta_1\sin\theta_2)]$$

$$\boxed{z_1z_2 = r_1r_2[\cos(\theta_1+\theta_2) + i\sin(\theta_1+\theta_2)]} \leftarrow \text{Answer}$$

$$\sin\theta_1\cos\theta_2 + \cos\theta_1\sin\theta_2 = \sin(\theta_1+\theta_2)$$

$$z_1 = r_1(\cos\theta_1 + i\sin\theta_1)$$

$$z_2 = r_2(\cos\theta_2 + i\sin\theta_2)$$

$$z_1z_2 = r_1r_2[\cos(\theta_1+\theta_2) + i\sin(\theta_1+\theta_2)] \leftarrow \text{Answer}$$

Multiply the moduli — Add the angles

To multiply two complex numbers in polar form
1. Multiply the moduli
2. Add the angles

$$z_1z_2 = r_1r_2[\cos(\theta_1+\theta_2) + i\sin(\theta_1+\theta_2)]$$

Multiplying two complex numbers using FOIL is complicated. Instead, look for a pattern.

Notice that when taking the product of the two complex numbers, the polar form of the result has an absolute value of r_1r_2 and an angle of $\theta_1\theta_2$.

When multiplying two complex numbers, use this shortcut: convert the complex numbers to **polar form**, then multiply the r-terms and add the θ-terms.

Trig (polar) form of a complex number:

$$z = r(\cos\theta + i\sin\theta)$$

Divide the two complex numbers in polar form:

$$z_1 = r_1(\cos\theta_1 + i\sin\theta_1)$$

$$z_2 = r_2(\cos\theta_2 + i\sin\theta_2)$$

$$\frac{z_1}{z_2} = \frac{r_1}{r_2}[\cos(\theta_1-\theta_2) + i\sin(\theta_1-\theta_2)]$$

To divide two complex numbers in polar form
1. Divide the moduli
2. Subtract the angles

$$\frac{z_1}{z_2} = \frac{r_1}{r_2}[\cos(\theta_1-\theta_2) + i\sin(\theta_1-\theta_2)]$$

There is also a shortcut for complex number division.

To divide two complex numbers, divide the r-terms and subtract the θ-terms.

Trig (polar) form of a complex number:

$$z = r(\cos\theta + i\sin\theta)$$

Example Multiply:

$$z_1 = 6(\cos 105° + i\sin 105°)$$

$$z_2 = 3(\cos 15° + i\sin 15°)$$

$$z_1z_2 = r_1r_2[\cos(\theta_1+\theta_2) + i\sin(\theta_1+\theta_2)]$$

$$z_1z_2 = 6\bullet 3[\cos(105°+15°) + i\sin(105°+15°)]$$

$$\boxed{z_1z_2 = 18(\cos 120° + i\sin 120°)} \leftarrow \text{Answer}$$

Consider this example: find the product of z_1 and z_2.

The complex number is already in polar form, so first multiply the r terms, and then add the θ terms.

REMEMBER: To multiply two complex numbers in polar form, multiply the r-terms together and add the θ-terms together.

Trig (polar) form of a complex number:

$$z = r(\cos\theta + i\sin\theta)$$

Example Divide:

$$z_1 = 6(\cos 105° + i\sin 105°)$$

$$z_2 = 3(\cos 15° + i\sin 15°)$$

$$\boxed{\frac{z_1}{z_2} = 2(\cos 90° + i\sin 90°)} \leftarrow \text{Answer in trig (polar) form}$$

Simplifying further:

$$\frac{z_1}{z_2} = 2(0+i1)$$

$$\boxed{\frac{z_1}{z_2} = 0+2i} = 2i$$

Answer

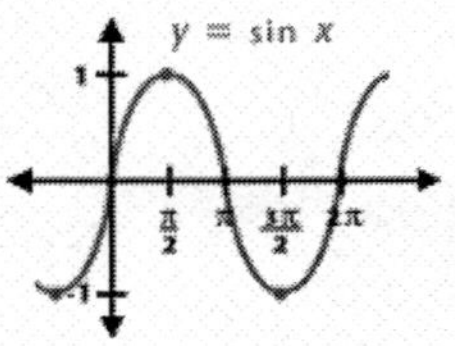

Consider the example illustrated here.

To solve, divide the first complex number by the second.

Next, divide the r-terms.

Finally, subtract the θ-terms.

The answer in polar form, $2(\cos 90° + i\sin 90°)$, can be simplified. Since the sine of 90° is 1, and the cosine of 90° is 0, the final answer is $2i$.

To multiply two complex numbers in polar form

1. Multiply the moduli
2. Add the angles

$z_1 z_2 = r_1 r_2 [\cos(\theta_1+\theta_2) + i\sin(\theta_1+\theta_2)]$

To divide two complex numbers in polar form

1. Divide the moduli
2. Subtract the angles

$\frac{z_1}{z_2} = \frac{r_1}{r_2}[\cos(\theta_1-\theta_2) + i\sin(\theta_1-\theta_2)]$

Multiplying and dividing complex numbers in polar form is pretty straightforward—just remember the shortcuts!

Sample problems:

1. If $z_1 = [5(\cos 90° + i\sin 90°)]$ and $z_2 = [6(\cos 180° + i\sin 180°)]$, find the product of $z_1 z_2$. Express your answer in polar form.
   Solution: $30(\cos 270° + i\sin 270°)$
   Explanation: To multiply the two complex numbers in trigonometric form, multiply the coefficients and add the angles:
   $z_1 z_2 = (5\cdot 6)[\cos(90°+180°) + i\sin(90°+180°)] = 30(\cos 270° + i\sin 270°)$.

2. Find $\frac{z_1}{z_2}$ when $z_1 = 12(\cos 60° + i\sin 60°)$ and $z_2 = 3(\cos 20° + i\sin 20°)$.
   Express your answer in polar form.
   Solution: $4(\cos 40° + i\sin 40°)$
   Explanation: Divide the coefficients and subtract the angles:
   $\frac{z_1}{z_2} = \frac{12(\cos 60° + i\sin 60°)}{3(\cos 20° + i\sin 20°)} = \left(\frac{12}{3}\right)[\cos(60° - 20°) + i\sin(60° - 20°)] = 4(\cos 40° + i\sin 40°)$.

3. What is the product of the three complex numbers $2(\cos 15° + i\sin 15°)$, $3(\cos 30° + i\sin 30°)$, and $4(\cos 45° + i\sin 45°)$? Express your answer in standard form.
   Solution: $24i$
   Explanation: The product of the first two numbers is $(2)(3)(\cos 45° + i\sin 45°) =$ $6(\cos 45° + i\sin 45°)$. Multiply this with the third number to get
   $(6)(4)(\cos(45°+45°) + i\sin(45°+45°)) = 24(\cos(90°) + i\sin(90°)) = 24(0+i) = 24i$.

Practice problems: *(Answers on page: 760)*

1. If $z_1 = 2(\cos 60° + i\sin 60°)$ and $z_2 = 4(\cos 150° + i\sin 150°)$ find the product of $z_1 z_2$. Express your answer in polar form.
2. If $z_1 = 6(\cos 60° + i\sin 60°)$ and $z_2 = 2(\cos 300° + i\sin 300°)$, find the quotient $\frac{z_1}{z_2}$. Express your answer in polar form.
3. What is the value of the expression $\frac{16(\cos 300° + i\sin 300°)}{8(\cos 60° + i\sin 60°)}$? Express your answer in standard form.

Review questions: *(Answers to odd questions on page: 760)*

1. If $z_1 = 4(\cos 60° + i\sin 60°)$ and $z_2 = 3(\cos 90° + i\sin 90°)$, find the product $z_1 z_2$.

2. Find $\frac{z_1}{z_2}$ where $z_1 = 20(\cos 120° + i\sin 120°)$ and $z_2 = 4(\cos 30° + i\sin 30°)$.

3. If $z_1 = 3(\cos 20° + i\sin 20°)$ and $z_2 = 5(\cos 70° + i\sin 70°)$, find the product $z_1 z_2$ in polar form.

4. Find the quotient $\frac{z_1}{z_2}$ in trigonometric form when $z_1 = 12(\cos 80° + i\sin 80°)$ and $z_2 = 6(\cos 30° + i\sin 30°)$.

5. If $z_1 = 3\sqrt{2}(\cos 135° + i\sin 135°)$ and $z_2 = 4\sqrt{2}(\cos 45° + i\sin 45°)$, find the product $z_1 z_2$ and express the answer in standard form.

Using DeMoivre's Theorem to Raise a Complex Number to a Power

- **Review**: A complex number in polar form is expressed as $r(\cos\theta + i\sin\theta)$, where r is the absolute value of the number and θ is its angle from the x-axis
- You can raise a complex number z in **polar form** to any power n using

DeMoivre's theorem: $z^n = r^n\left[\cos(n\theta) + i\sin(n\theta)\right]$.

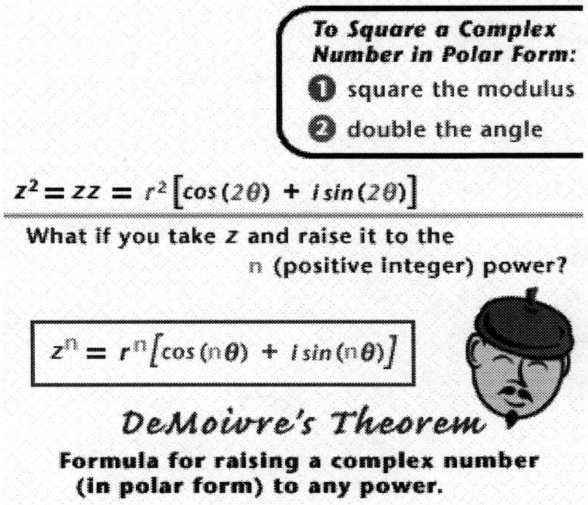

To square a complex number in **polar form**, multiply the number by itself.

To raise a complex number to a power other than two, use **DeMoivre's theorem**.

DeMoivre's theorem is a formula for raising a complex number z in polar form to the nth power.

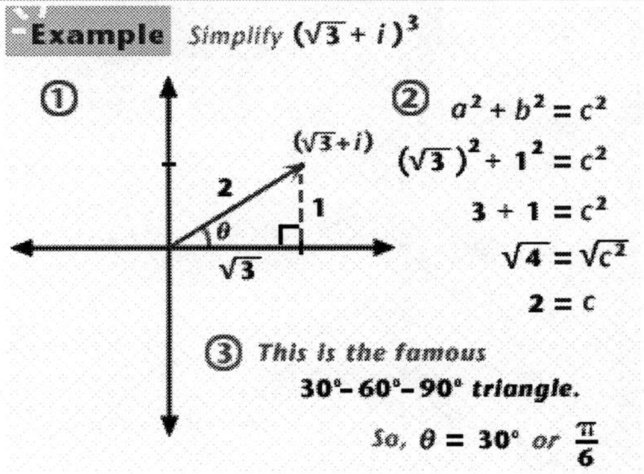

Use DeMoivre's theorem to raise this complex number to the third power.

First, convert the number into polar form:

Step 1: Graph the complex number.

Step 2: Find the **modulus**.

Step 3: Find the angle θ.

Example *Simplify* $(\sqrt{3}+i)^3$

④ $(\sqrt{3}+i)^3 = \left[2\left(\cos\frac{\pi}{6} + i\sin\frac{\pi}{6}\right)\right]^3$

⑤ $= 2^3\left[\cos\left(3\cdot\frac{\pi}{6}\right) + i\sin\left(3\cdot\frac{\pi}{6}\right)\right]$

$= 8\left(\cos\frac{\pi}{2} + i\sin\frac{\pi}{2}\right)$

$= 8(0+i)$

$(\sqrt{3}+i)^3 = \boxed{8i}$

Step 4: Plug these values into the polar form $r(\cos\theta + i\sin\theta)$.

Step 5: Apply DeMoivre's theorem and simplify.

Sample problems:

1. Use DeMoivre's theorem to express the following power in trigonometric form:

   $\left[3(\cos 100° + i\sin 100°)\right]^4$

   Solution: $81(\cos 400° + i\sin 400°)$

   Explanation: $\left[3(\cos 100° + i\sin 100°)\right]^4 = 3^4\left[\cos(4\cdot 100°) + i\sin(4\cdot 100°)\right] = 81(\cos 400° + i\sin 400°)$

2. Find $(-1-i)^4$ using DeMoivre's theorem.

   Solution: $4(\cos 900° + i\sin 900°)$

   Explanation: Convert $-1-i$ to trig form: $x=-1$ and $y=-1$, so

   $r = \sqrt{(-1)^2 + (-1)^2} = \sqrt{1+1} = \sqrt{2}$, so $\cos\theta = \frac{-\sqrt{2}}{2}$ and $\sin\theta = \frac{-\sqrt{2}}{2}$, therefore,

   $\theta = 225°$. Thus, $-1-i = \left(\sqrt{2}\right)\left[\cos(225°) + i\sin(225°)\right]$. Apply DeMoivre's theorem:

   $(-1-i)^4 = \left(\sqrt{2}\right)^4\left[\cos 4(225°) + i\sin 4(225°)\right] = 4(\cos 900° + i\sin 900°)$.

3. Find $\left(2\sqrt{2}(\cos 10° + i\sin 10°)\right)^4$

   Solution: 64(cos40°+isin40°)

   Explanation: $\left(2\sqrt{2}\right)^4\left(\cos(4\cdot 10) + i\sin(4\cdot 10)\right) = \left(\sqrt{8}\right)^4(\cos 40 + i\sin 40)$

   $= 8^2(\cos 40 + i\sin 40)$

   $= 64(\cos 40 + i\sin 40)$

Practice problems: *(Answers on page: 760)*

1. Use DeMoivre's theorem to express the following power in trigonometric form:

   $\left[2(\cos 20° + i\sin 20°)\right]^6$

2. Find $\left(\sqrt{3}+i\right)^5$ using DeMoivre's theorem.

3. Compute $(1+i)^6$.

Review questions: *(Answers to odd questions on page: 760)*

1. Use DeMoivre's theorem to express the following power in trigonometric form:

   [2(cos125°+isin125°)]^4

2. Use DeMoivre's theorem to express the following power in trigonometric form:

   $[3(\cos 40° + i\sin 40°)]^5$

3. Find $\left(1-\sqrt{3}i\right)^4$ using DeMoivre's theorem, expressing the answer in trigonometric form.

4. Use DeMoivre's theorem to express the following power in trigonometric form: $(-2+2i)^6$.

5. Compute $(4(\cos 80° + i\sin 80°))^3$.

Roots of Complex Numbers

- **Review**: A complex number in **polar form** is expressed as $r(\cos\theta + i\ \sin\theta)$, where r is the **absolute value** of the number and θ is its angle from the x-axis.
- **Review**: Use **DeMoivre's theorem** to raise a complex number in polar form to a power:

  $z_n = r^n\left[\cos(n\theta) = i\sin(n\theta)\right]$
- Also use DeMoivre's theorem to find the ***n*th roots** of a complex number in polar form. The nth roots of the complex number $z = r\ (\cos\theta + i\ \sin\theta)$ are given by the formula $\sqrt[n]{r}\left[\cos\left(\frac{\theta+2\pi k}{n}\right)+i\sin\left(\frac{\theta+2\pi k}{n}\right)\right]$, for $k = 0,1\ldots,(n-1)$.

Find all the solutions to $z^4 = 16$ • There will be 4 roots (even if some of them are complex numbers).	Consider the example here: find all the solutions for $z^4 = 16$. Notice, since z is raised to the fourth power, there will be four solutions to this equation.
$z = \sqrt[4]{16} \longrightarrow z^4 = 16$ $z^4 - 16 = 0$ *factor* $(z^2-4)(z^2+4) = 0$	One way to approach the problem would be to move all the terms to one side and factor.
$(z-2)(z+2)(z^2+4) = 0$ $(z-2) = 0 \quad (z+2) = 0$ $z = 2 \quad z = -2$	Find two real-number roots.
$(z+2)(z^2+4) = 0 \quad (z^2+4) = 0$ $z^2 = -4$ $z = \pm\sqrt{-4}$ $z = \pm 2i$	Then, using the third factor, find two **imaginary roots**.
4 Roots: **2, −2, 2*i*, −2*i***	All four roots for the equation $z^4 = 16$ have been found. They are 2, −2, 2i, −2i.
Take the nth root of $z = r(\cos\theta + i\sin\theta)$ There will be n roots. $\sqrt[n]{z} = \sqrt[n]{r}\left[\cos\left(\frac{\theta+2\pi k}{n}\right) + i\sin\left(\frac{\theta+2\pi k}{n}\right)\right]$	Consider another way to solve this problem. Convert the number to **polar form** and find the roots using **DeMoivre's theorem**.
Example *Simplify* $z^4 = 16$ $z^4 = 16(\cos 0 + i\sin 0)$ So: $z = \sqrt[4]{16}\left[\cos\left(\frac{0+2\pi k}{4}\right) + i\sin\left(\frac{0+2\pi k}{4}\right)\right]$	To convert to polar form, notice that $r = 16$ and the angle θ is 0°. Now plug into the formula for the nth roots of a complex number with $n = 4$. Let k equal 0, 1, 2, and 3 to find the four roots. Each value of k will give you one root.

when $k = 0$ $z = 2\left[\cos\left(\frac{0+2\pi\cdot 0}{4}\right) + i\sin\left(\frac{0+2\pi\cdot 0}{4}\right)\right]$ $z = 2(\cos 0 + i\sin 0)$ $z = 2(1+0)$ $\boxed{z = 2}$	Start with $k = 0$. Calculate the angle, evaluate the trigonometric functions, and simplify. The result is the first root, $z = 2$.
when $k = 1$ $z = 2\left[\cos\left(\frac{0+2\pi\cdot 1}{4}\right) + i\sin\left(\frac{0+2\pi\cdot 1}{4}\right)\right]$ $z = 2(\cos\frac{\pi}{2} + i\sin\frac{\pi}{2})$ $z = 2(0+i)$ $\boxed{z = 2i}$	Next, let $k = 1$. Again, • calculate the angle, • evaluate the trigonometric functions, • and simplify. When $k = 1$, $z = 2i$.
when $k = 2$ $z = 2\left[\cos\left(\frac{0+2\pi\cdot 2}{4}\right) + i\sin\left(\frac{0+2\pi\cdot 2}{4}\right)\right]$ $z = 2(\cos\pi + i\sin\pi)$ $z = 2(-1+0)$ $\boxed{z = -2}$	Continuing on, plug in $k = 2$ into the formula. Follow the routine. When $k = 2$, $z = -2$.
when $k = 3$ $z = 2\left[\cos\left(\frac{0+2\pi\cdot 3}{4}\right) + i\sin\left(\frac{0+2\pi\cdot 3}{4}\right)\right]$ $z = 2(\cos\frac{3\pi}{2} + i\sin\frac{3\pi}{2})$ $z = 2(0-i)$ $\boxed{z = -2i}$	Finally, plug in $k = 3$. This gives the fourth and final root, $z = -2i$.
Four Roots: 2, −2, $2i$, $-2i$ **4 Roots: 2, −2, $2i$, $-2i$**	Notice that the four roots found using DeMoivre's formula are the same as the four roots found by factoring. **REMEMBER:** When solving math problems, use the technique that is simplest for you unless you are directed to use a particular method.

Sample problems:

1. Find the fourth roots of -81. List the roots in complex form.

<u>Solution</u>: $\dfrac{3\sqrt{2}+3i\sqrt{2}}{2}, \dfrac{-3\sqrt{2}+3i\sqrt{2}}{2}, \dfrac{-3\sqrt{2}-3i\sqrt{2}}{2}, \dfrac{3\sqrt{2}-3i\sqrt{2}}{2}$

<u>Explanation</u>: Express -81 in polar form: $-81 = 81(\cos\pi + i\sin\pi)$. Use the formula,

$\sqrt[n]{r}\left[\cos\left(\dfrac{\theta+2\pi k}{n}\right)+i\sin\left(\dfrac{\theta+2\pi k}{n}\right)\right]$ where $n=4$, $r=81$, $\theta=\pi$, and $k=0,1,2,$ and 3, to find the fourth roots of -81. Substitute the values for n, r, and θ into the formula and simplify:

$$\sqrt[4]{81}\left[\cos\left(\frac{\pi+2\pi k}{4}\right)+i\sin\left(\frac{\pi+2\pi k}{4}\right)\right]=3\left[\cos\left(\frac{\pi+2\pi k}{4}\right)+i\sin\left(\frac{\pi+2\pi k}{4}\right)\right].$$

Evaluate the expression for $k=0,1,2,$ and 3:

$$k=0:\ 3\left[\cos\left(\frac{\pi+2\pi(0)}{4}\right)+i\sin\left(\frac{\pi+2\pi(0)}{4}\right)\right]=3\left[\cos\left(\frac{\pi}{4}\right)+i\sin\left(\frac{\pi}{4}\right)\right]$$
$$=3\left[\left(\frac{\sqrt{2}}{2}\right)+i\left(\frac{\sqrt{2}}{2}\right)\right]=\frac{3\sqrt{2}+3i\sqrt{2}}{2}$$

$$k=1:\ 3\left[\cos\left(\frac{\pi+2\pi(1)}{4}\right)+i\sin\left(\frac{\pi+2\pi(1)}{4}\right)\right]=3\left[\cos\left(\frac{3\pi}{4}\right)+i\sin\left(\frac{3\pi}{4}\right)\right]$$
$$=3\left[\left(\frac{-\sqrt{2}}{2}\right)+i\left(\frac{\sqrt{2}}{2}\right)\right]=\frac{-3\sqrt{2}+3i\sqrt{2}}{2}$$

$$k=2:\ 3\left[\cos\left(\frac{\pi+2\pi(2)}{4}\right)+i\sin\left(\frac{\pi+2\pi(2)}{4}\right)\right]=3\left[\cos\left(\frac{5\pi}{4}\right)+i\sin\left(\frac{5\pi}{4}\right)\right]$$
$$=3\left[\left(\frac{-\sqrt{2}}{2}\right)+i\left(\frac{-\sqrt{2}}{2}\right)\right]=\frac{-3\sqrt{2}-3i\sqrt{2}}{2}$$

$$k=3:\ 3\left[\cos\left(\frac{\pi+2\pi(3)}{4}\right)+i\sin\left(\frac{\pi+2\pi(3)}{4}\right)\right]=3\left[\cos\left(\frac{7\pi}{4}\right)+i\sin\left(\frac{7\pi}{4}\right)\right]$$
$$=3\left[\left(\frac{\sqrt{2}}{2}\right)+i\left(\frac{-\sqrt{2}}{2}\right)\right]=\frac{3\sqrt{2}-3i\sqrt{2}}{2}$$

2. Find the cube roots of $2-2i$.

Solution: $\sqrt{2}\left[\cos\left(\frac{7\pi}{12}\right)+i\sin\left(\frac{7\pi}{12}\right)\right]$, $\sqrt{2}\left[\cos\left(\frac{5\pi}{4}\right)+i\sin\left(\frac{5\pi}{4}\right)\right]$, $\sqrt{2}\left[\cos\left(\frac{23\pi}{12}\right)+i\sin\left(\frac{23\pi}{12}\right)\right]$

Explanation: Express $2-2i$ in polar form: $2-2i=2\sqrt{2}\left(\cos\frac{7\pi}{4}+i\sin\frac{7\pi}{4}\right)$. Use the formula,

$\sqrt[n]{r}\left[\cos\left(\frac{\theta+2\pi k}{n}\right)+i\sin\left(\frac{\theta+2\pi k}{n}\right)\right]$ where $n=3$, $r=2\sqrt{2}$, $\theta=\frac{7\pi}{4}$, and $k=0,1$ and 2, to find the cube roots of $2-2i$. Substitute the values for n, r, and θ into the formula and simplify:

$$\sqrt[3]{\left(2\sqrt{2}\right)}\left[\cos\left(\frac{\frac{7\pi}{4}+2\pi k}{3}\right)+i\sin\left(\frac{\frac{7\pi}{4}+2\pi k}{3}\right)\right]=\sqrt{2}\left[\cos\left(\frac{\frac{7\pi}{4}+2\pi k}{3}\right)+i\sin\left(\frac{\frac{7\pi}{4}+2\pi k}{3}\right)\right].$$

Evaluate the expression for $k=0,1$ and 2:

$$k=0:\ \sqrt{2}\left[\cos\left(\frac{\frac{7\pi}{4}+2\pi(0)}{3}\right)+i\sin\left(\frac{\frac{7\pi}{4}+2\pi(0)}{3}\right)\right]=\sqrt{2}\left[\cos\left(\frac{7\pi}{12}\right)+i\sin\left(\frac{7\pi}{12}\right)\right]$$

$$k=1:\ \sqrt{2}\left[\cos\left(\frac{\frac{7\pi}{4}+2\pi(1)}{3}\right)+i\sin\left(\frac{\frac{7\pi}{4}+2\pi(1)}{3}\right)\right]=\sqrt{2}\left[\cos\left(\frac{5\pi}{4}\right)+i\sin\left(\frac{5\pi}{4}\right)\right]$$

$$k=2:\ \sqrt{2}\left[\cos\left(\frac{\frac{7\pi}{4}+2\pi(2)}{3}\right)+i\sin\left(\frac{\frac{7\pi}{4}+2\pi(2)}{3}\right)\right]=\sqrt{2}\left[\cos\left(\frac{23\pi}{12}\right)+i\sin\left(\frac{23\pi}{12}\right)\right]$$

3. Find the square roots of $8\sqrt{2}+8i\sqrt{2}$.

Solution: $4\left[\cos\left(\frac{\pi}{8}\right)+i\sin\left(\frac{\pi}{8}\right)\right]$, $4\left[\cos\left(\frac{9\pi}{8}\right)+i\sin\left(\frac{9\pi}{8}\right)\right]$

Explanation:

Express $8\sqrt{2}+8i\sqrt{2}$ in polar form: $8\sqrt{2}+8i\sqrt{2}=16\left(\cos\frac{\pi}{4}+i\sin\frac{\pi}{4}\right)$. Use the formula,

$\sqrt[n]{r}\left[\cos\left(\frac{\theta+2\pi k}{n}\right)+i\sin\left(\frac{\theta+2\pi k}{n}\right)\right]$ where $n=2$, $r=16$, $\theta=\frac{\pi}{4}$, and $k=0$ and 1, to find the square roots of $8\sqrt{2}+8i\sqrt{2}$. Substitute the values for n, r, and θ into the formula and simplify:

$$\sqrt[2]{16}\left[\cos\left(\frac{\frac{\pi}{4}+2\pi k}{2}\right)+i\sin\left(\frac{\frac{\pi}{4}+2\pi k}{2}\right)\right]=4\left[\cos\left(\frac{\frac{\pi}{4}+2\pi k}{2}\right)+i\sin\left(\frac{\frac{\pi}{4}+2\pi k}{2}\right)\right].$$

Evaluate the expression for $k=0$ and 1:

$$k=0:\ 4\left[\cos\left(\frac{\frac{\pi}{4}+2\pi(0)}{2}\right)+i\sin\left(\frac{\frac{\pi}{4}+2\pi(0)}{2}\right)\right]=4\left[\cos\left(\frac{\pi}{8}\right)+i\sin\left(\frac{\pi}{8}\right)\right]$$

$$k=1:\ 4\left[\cos\left(\frac{\frac{\pi}{4}+2\pi(1)}{2}\right)+i\sin\left(\frac{\frac{\pi}{4}+2\pi(1)}{2}\right)\right]=4\left[\cos\left(\frac{9\pi}{8}\right)+i\sin\left(\frac{9\pi}{8}\right)\right]$$

Practice problems: *(Answers on page: 760)*

1. Find the cube roots of 125. List the roots in complex form.

2. Find the sixth roots of $-2i$.
3. Find the fourth roots of $-81+81i$.

Review questions: *(Answers to odd questions on page: 761)*

1. True or false: $\sqrt[3]{2}\left(\cos 100° + i\sin 100°\right)$ is a third root of $1 - i\sqrt{3}$.
2. Find the non-real fourth roots of $16 + 0i$ in trigonometric form.
3. Find the cube roots of 8. Which one is in quadrant II?
4. Find the cube roots of $2 + 2i$.
5. Find the cube roots of $1 - i$.

More Roots of Complex Numbers

- **Review**: The nth roots of the complex number $z = r\,(\cos\theta + i\,\sin\theta)$ are given by the formula $\sqrt[n]{r}\left[\cos\left(\frac{\theta + 2\pi k}{n}\right) + i\sin\left(\frac{\theta + 2\pi k}{n}\right)\right]$.
- **Review**: Complex roots always come in **conjugate pairs**. If one of the roots is in the form $a + bi$, there will always be a second root in the form $a–bi$.

Example *Find the cube roots of* -27 • There will be 3 roots. • One of the roots will be -3, because $(-3)(-3)(-3) = 9(-3) = \boxed{-27}$ • The other roots are complex.	Consider the example given here: find the cube roots of –27. One root, –3, is easy to find. How do you find the other roots?
① *Write* -27 *in polar form.* 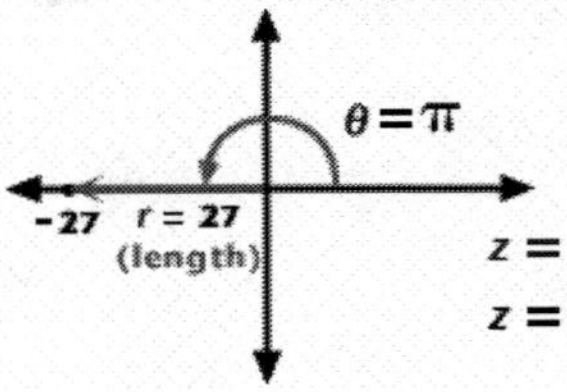 $z = r\,(\cos\theta + i\sin\theta)$ $z = 27\,(\cos\pi + i\sin\pi)$	First, find the **polar form** of the number –27. The best first step is a quick sketch. Notice that $\theta = \pi$ and $r = 27$. **REMEMBER**: $r = 27$, not –27, because length is never negative.
② *Use formula.* $\sqrt[n]{r}\left[\cos\left(\frac{\theta+2\pi k}{n}\right) + i\sin\left(\frac{\theta+2\pi k}{n}\right)\right]$	To find the complex roots, use the formula. **REMEMBER**: The values for k start at 0, not 1, and end at $n - 1$, not at n. In this example, k takes on the values 0, 1, and 2.
when $k = 0$ $3\left[\cos\left(\frac{\pi+2\pi\cdot 0}{3}\right) + i\sin\left(\frac{\pi+2\pi\cdot 0}{3}\right)\right]$ $= 3\,(\cos\frac{\pi}{3} + i\sin\frac{\pi}{3})$ $= 3\left(\frac{1}{2} + i\frac{\sqrt{3}}{2}\right) = \boxed{\frac{3}{2} + \frac{3\sqrt{3}}{2}i}$	When $k = 0$, the angle is $60°$, or $\pi/3$. Substitute the values for cos ($\pi/3$) and sin ($\pi/3$) and note the root.

when $k = 1$ $3\left[\cos\left(\frac{\pi+2\pi\cdot1}{3}\right)+i\sin\left(\frac{\pi+2\pi\cdot1}{3}\right)\right]$ $= 3\left(\cos\frac{3\pi}{3}+i\sin\frac{3\pi}{3}\right)$ $= 3(\cos\pi + i\sin\pi)$ $= 3[-1+i(0)]$ $= \boxed{-3}$	When $k = 1$: The angle is 180°, or π. sin π = 0, so i sin π = 0. cos π = –1. Do the arithmetic. The result, –3, is the only real number root.
when $k = 2$ $3\left[\cos\left(\frac{\pi+2\pi\cdot2}{3}\right)+i\sin\left(\frac{\pi+2\pi\cdot2}{3}\right)\right]$ $= 3\left(\cos\frac{5\pi}{3}+i\sin\frac{5\pi}{3}\right)$ $= 3\left(\frac{1}{2}-i\frac{\sqrt{3}}{2}\right)$ $= \boxed{\frac{3}{2}-\frac{3\sqrt{3}}{2}i}$	Finally, plug in $k = 2$. Once again, substitute in the sine and cosine values and simplify. Notice that this root is the conjugate of the first root found.

Sample problems:

1. Find all roots of $x^3 - 8 = 0$ with answers written in complex form.

<u>Solution:</u> $2,\ -1+i\sqrt{3},\ -1-i\sqrt{3}$

<u>Explanation:</u> If $x^3 - 8 = 0$ then $x^3 = 8$. Express 8 in polar form: $8 = 8(\cos 0 + i\sin 0)$.

Use the formula, $\sqrt[n]{r}\left[\cos\left(\frac{\theta+2\pi k}{n}\right)+i\sin\left(\frac{\theta+2\pi k}{n}\right)\right]$ where $n = 3$, $r = 8$, $\theta = 0$,

and $k = 0,1$ and 2, to find the roots of $x^3 - 8 = 0$. Substitute the values for n, r, and θ into the formula and simplify:

$$\sqrt[3]{8}\left[\cos\left(\frac{0+2\pi k}{3}\right)+i\sin\left(\frac{0+2\pi k}{3}\right)\right]=2\left[\cos\left(\frac{0+2\pi k}{3}\right)+i\sin\left(\frac{0+2\pi k}{3}\right)\right].$$

Evaluate the expression for $k = 0,1$ and 2:

$k = 0$: $2[\cos(0)+i\sin(0)] = 2[1+i(0)] = 2$,

$k = 1$: $2\left[\cos\left(\frac{2\pi}{3}\right)+i\sin\left(\frac{2\pi}{3}\right)\right]=2\left[-\frac{1}{2}+i\left(\frac{\sqrt{3}}{2}\right)\right]=-1+i\sqrt{3}$,

$k = 2$: $2\left[\cos\left(\frac{4\pi}{3}\right)+i\sin\left(\frac{4\pi}{3}\right)\right]=2\left[-\frac{1}{2}+i\left(-\frac{\sqrt{3}}{2}\right)\right]=-1-i\sqrt{3}$.

Thus, $x = 2,\ -1+i\sqrt{3}$, or $-1-i\sqrt{3}$

2. Find all roots of $x^2 + i = 0$ with answers written in complex form.

Solution: $\dfrac{-\sqrt{2}+i\sqrt{2}}{2}$ or $\dfrac{\sqrt{2}-i\sqrt{2}}{2}$

Explanation: If $x^2 + i = 0$ then $x^2 = -i$. Express $-i$ in polar form: $-i = \left(\cos\dfrac{3\pi}{2} + i\sin\dfrac{3\pi}{2}\right)$.

Find the square roots of $-i$ using the formula $\sqrt[n]{r}\left[\cos\left(\dfrac{\frac{3\pi}{2}+2\pi k}{n}\right) + i\sin\left(\dfrac{\frac{3\pi}{2}+2\pi k}{n}\right)\right]$:

$k=0$: $\left[\cos\left(\dfrac{3\pi}{4}\right)+i\sin\left(\dfrac{3\pi}{4}\right)\right] = -\dfrac{\sqrt{2}}{2}+i\left(\dfrac{\sqrt{2}}{2}\right) = \dfrac{-\sqrt{2}+i\sqrt{2}}{2}$,

$k=1$: $\left[\cos\left(\dfrac{7\pi}{4}\right)+i\sin\left(\dfrac{7\pi}{4}\right)\right] = \dfrac{\sqrt{2}}{2}+i\left(-\dfrac{\sqrt{2}}{2}\right) = \dfrac{\sqrt{2}-i\sqrt{2}}{2}$.

Thus, $x = \dfrac{-\sqrt{2}+i\sqrt{2}}{2}$ or $x = \dfrac{\sqrt{2}-i\sqrt{2}}{2}$.

3. Find all roots of $x^3 - 12 = 0$ with answers written in complex form.

Solution: 2.289, $-1.145+1.982i$, or $-1.145-1.982i$

Explanation: If $x^3 - 12 = 0$ then $x^3 = 12$. Express 12 polar form: $12 = 12(\cos 0 + i\sin 0)$.

Find the cube roots of 12:

$k=0$: $\sqrt[3]{12}\left[\cos(0)+i\sin(0)\right] = \left(\sqrt[3]{12}\left[1+i(0)\right]\right) = 2.289$,

$k=1$: $\sqrt[3]{12}\left[\cos\left(\dfrac{2\pi}{3}\right)+i\sin\left(\dfrac{2\pi}{3}\right)\right] = \left(2.289\left[(-0.5)+i(0.866)\right]\right) = -1.145+1.982i$,

$k=2$: $\sqrt[3]{12}\left[\cos\left(\dfrac{4\pi}{3}\right)+i\sin\left(\dfrac{4\pi}{3}\right)\right] = 2.289\left[(-0.5)+i(-0.866)\right] = -1.145-1.982i$.

Thus, $x = 2.289$, $-1.145+1.982i$, or $-1.145-1.982i$.

Practice problems: *(Answers on page: 761)*

1. Find all roots of $x^4 - 16 = 0$ with answers written in complex form.
2. Find all roots of $x^3 + 125 = 0$ with answers written in complex form.
3. Find all roots of $x^6 - 1 = 0$ with answers written in complex form.

Review questions: *(Answers to odd questions on page: 761)*

1. Find all roots of $x^4 - 1 = 0$ with answers written in complex form.
2. Find all roots of $x^4 + 1 = 0$ with answers written in complex form.
3. Find all roots of $x^3 + 64 = 0$ with answers written in complex form.
4. Find all solutions to $x^5 - 1 = 0$. Express solutions in complex form with a and b computed to three decimal places.
5. Find all solutions to $x^3 + 5 = 0$. Express solutions in complex form with a and b computed to three decimal places.

Roots of Unity

- **Review**: The nth roots of the complex number $z = r(\cos\theta + i\sin\theta)$ are given by the formula for $k = 0,1\ldots,(n-1)$:
  $$\sqrt[n]{r}\left[\cos\left(\frac{\theta+2\pi k}{n}\right)+i\sin\left(\frac{\theta+2\pi k}{n}\right)\right].$$
- The **roots of unity** are the complex roots of 1.

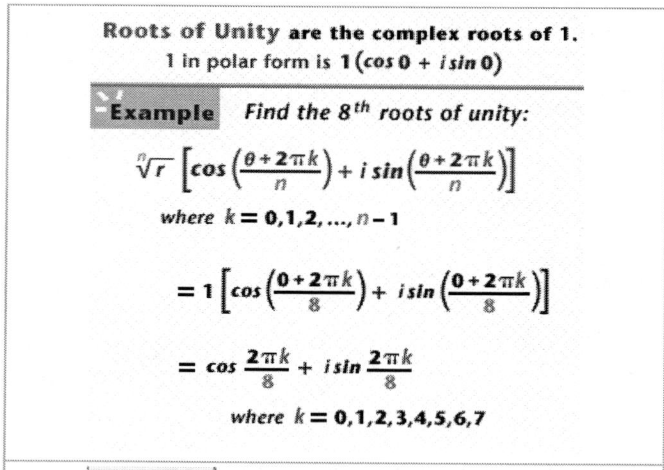

The nth roots of the number 1 are called the **roots of unity**.

Consider the example here, find the 8th roots of unity.

Find them using the formula for finding the roots of complex numbers.

Notice that there will be eight 8th roots of unity.

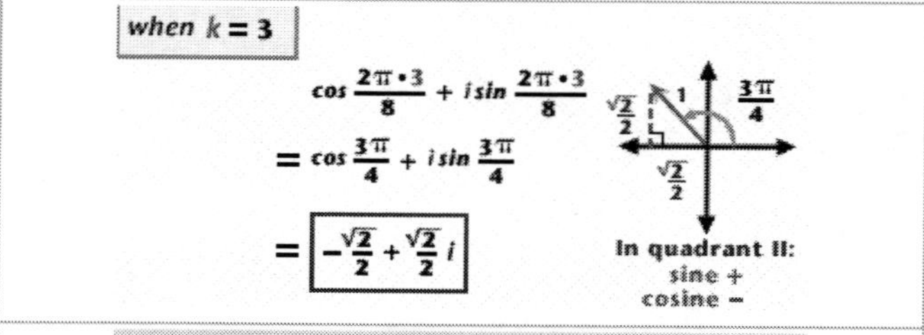

To find the roots, plug in $k = 0, 1, 2, \ldots, 7$ into the formula.

Here are the calculations for $k = 3$.

The answer is one of the 8th roots of unity.

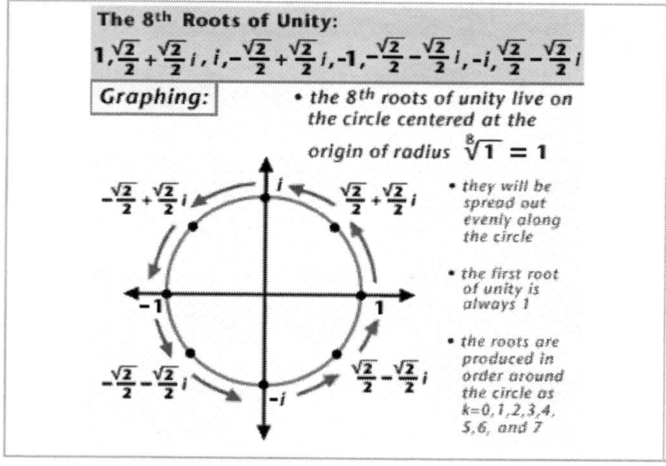

Here are all eight of the 8th roots of unity.

Look at the graph of these roots in the complex plane. Notice they are evenly spread out along the circle of radius 1 centered at the origin.

This will always happen whenever graphing the roots of unity.

Sample problems:

1. Find the five fifth roots of unity. Express the roots in polar form.

   Solution: 1, $\cos 72° + i\sin 72°$, $\cos 144° + i\sin 144°$, $\cos 216° + i\sin 216°$, and $\cos 288° + i\sin 288°$

   Explanation: Evaluate the formula for finding roots of complex numbers, where $\theta = 0$ and $n = 5$, for $k = 0,1,2,3,4$:

   $k = 0$: $\left[\cos\left(\frac{0+2\pi(0)}{5}\right) + i\sin\left(\frac{0+2\pi(0)}{5}\right)\right] = \cos 0° + i\sin 0° = \left[(1) + i(0)\right] = 1.$

   $k = 1$: $\left[\cos\left(\frac{2\pi}{5}\right) + i\sin\left(\frac{2\pi}{5}\right)\right] = \left(\cos 72° + i\sin 72°\right).$

   $k = 2$: $\left[\cos\left(\frac{4\pi}{5}\right) + i\sin\left(\frac{4\pi}{5}\right)\right] = \left(\cos 144° + i\sin 144°\right).$

   $k = 3$: $\left[\cos\left(\frac{6\pi}{5}\right) + i\sin\left(\frac{6\pi}{5}\right)\right] = \left(\cos 216° + i\sin 216°\right).$

   $k = 4$: $\left[\cos\left(\frac{8\pi}{5}\right) + i\sin\left(\frac{8\pi}{5}\right)\right] = \left(\cos 288° + i\sin 288°\right).$

   The five fifth roots of 1 are 1, $\cos 72° + i\sin 72°$, $\cos 144° + i\sin 144°$, $\cos 216° + i\sin 216°$, and $\cos 288° + i\sin 288°$.

2. You know that all the roots of unity are spread evenly around the circle. Calculate the value of the root to which the arrow is pointing.

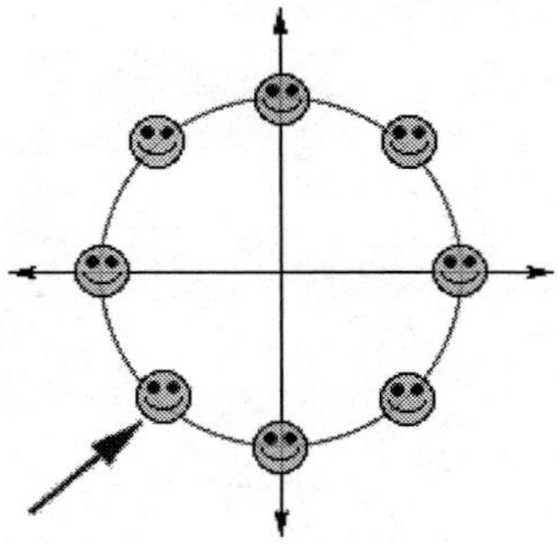

   Solution: $\frac{-\sqrt{2}}{2} - \frac{\sqrt{2}}{2}i$

   Explanation: This is the sixth root out of 8 indicated on this circle. It therefore corresponds to $k = 5$ in the formula for finding the eighth roots of 1:

   $$\cos\left(\frac{0+2\pi(5)}{8}\right) + i\sin\left(\frac{0+2\pi(5)}{8}\right) = \cos\frac{5\pi}{4} + i\sin\frac{5\pi}{4} = \frac{-\sqrt{2}}{2} - \frac{\sqrt{2}}{2}i$$

3. Use the unit circle on the complex plane to find the fourth roots of unity.

   Solution: $1, i, -1, -i$

   Explanation: This will give the four points that lie on the axes on the unit circle in the complex plane.

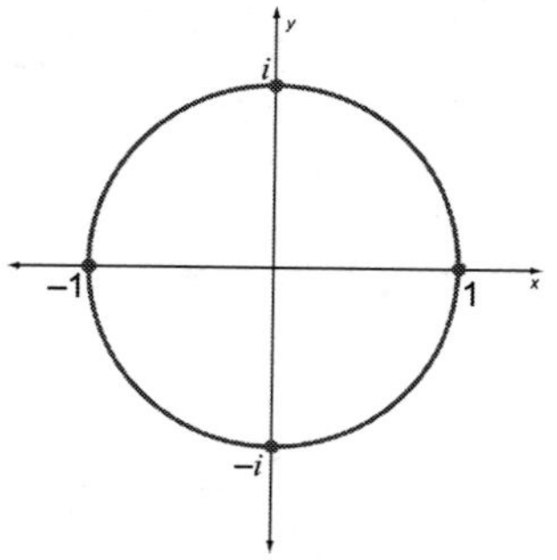

Practice problems: *(Answers on page: 761)*

1. Find the three third roots of unity. Express the roots in complex form.
2. You know that all the roots of unity are spread evenly around the unit circle. Calculate the value of the root to which the arrow is pointing.

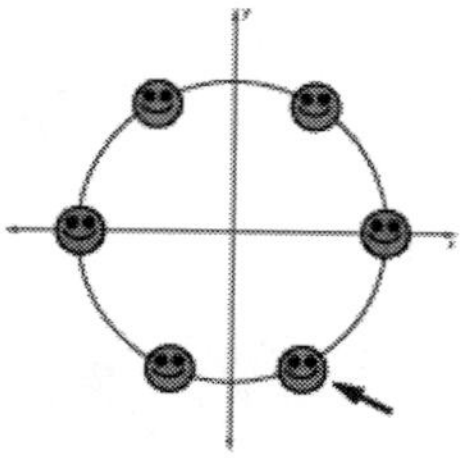

3. You know that all the roots of unity are spread evenly around the unit circle. Calculate the value of the root to which the arrow is pointing.

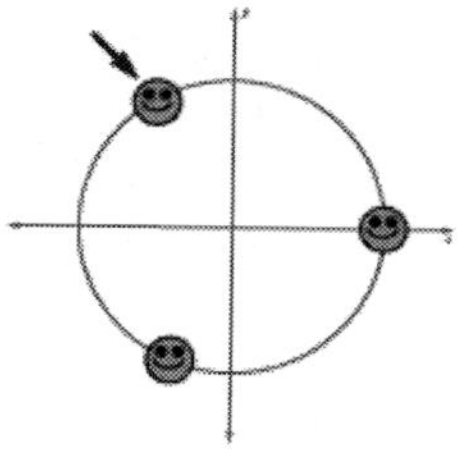

Review questions: *(Answers to odd questions on page: 761)*

1. Find the ten tenth roots of unity. Express the roots in trigonometric form.
2. Find the fifth root of unity that is in the third quadrant.
3. Find the sixth root of unity that is in the second quadrant. Express the answer in complex number form.
4. True or false: 1 is a square root of unity and a cube root of unity.
5. If we graph the ninth roots of unity in the complex plane, how many of them would lie in the second quadrant?

An Introduction to Polar Coordinates

- Instead of describing points using **Cartesian** or **rectangular coordinates**, you can use **polar coordinates** to describe points based on their distance from the origin and their angle from the **polar axis**.
- In polar coordinates, a point is specified by an ordered pair (r, θ), where r is the distance of the point from the origin and θ is the angle of the point from the polar axis. The polar axis is located in the same place as the positive x-axis of a **rectangular coordinate system**.

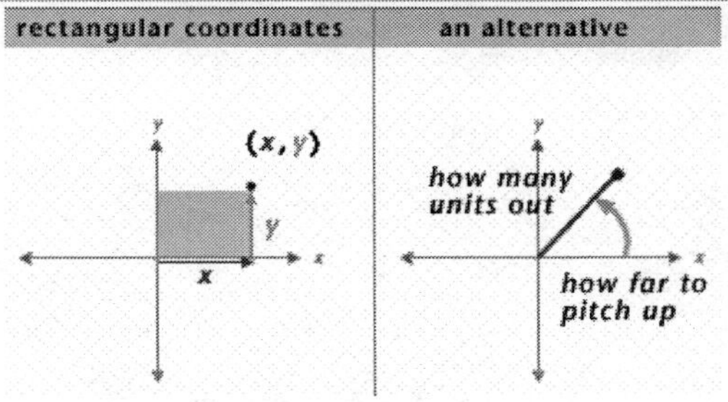

There are many situations where the traditional way of thinking about a rectangular coordinate system is not practical. Consider a radar tower tracking an incoming airplane. The radar tower doesn't calculate the x- and y-components of the plane; instead, it finds the distance of the plane from the tower and its direction from the tower. The radar tower uses what is called **polar coordinates**.

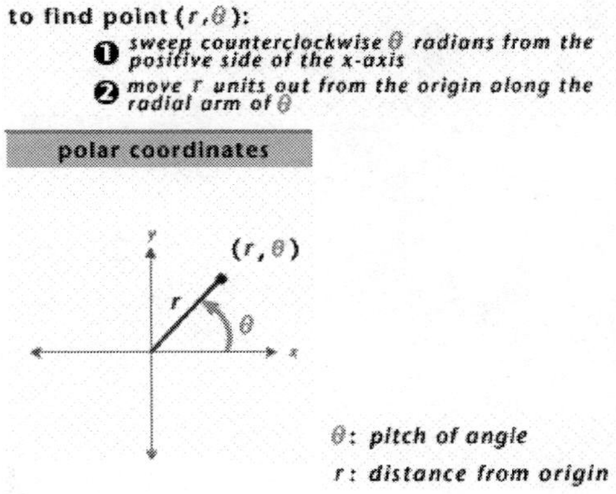

To find the **polar coordinate**s of a point, calculate r, the distance of the point from the origin, and θ, the angle from a set axis known as the **polar axis**.

The polar axis is in the same location as the positive x-axis of the **rectangular coordinate plane**. This is so that the coordinates of the polar graph will match up to the angles of the unit circle.

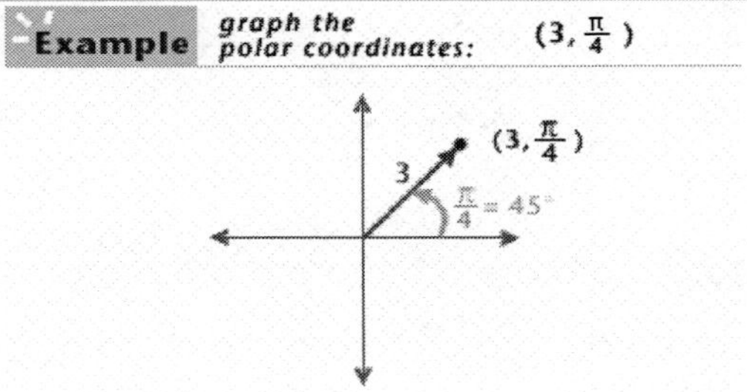

To graph a point in polar coordinates, start by finding the direction of the point from the origin using the angle θ.

Then move a distance of r in that direction.

In this example you're asked to graph the polar coordinate, (3, π/4).

Begin by sweeping up π/4, or 45°. Then, move a distance of 3.

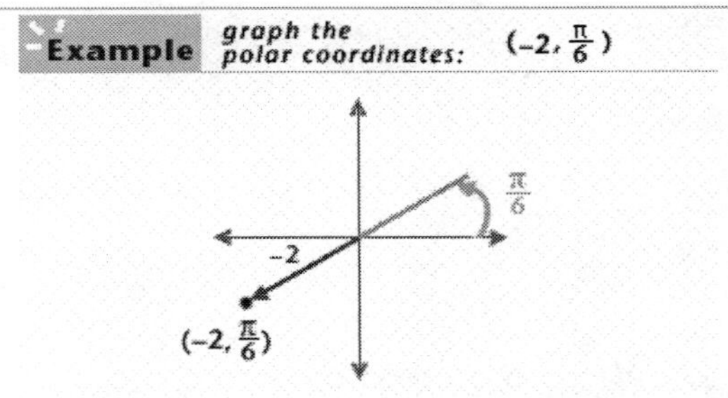

If the r-term is negative, then move in the opposite direction (along the same line) as the angle. Still move the same number of units despite the fact that the value is negative.

Sample problems:

1. State the location of the point defined by the following polar coordinates: $\left(4, \dfrac{\pi}{3}\right)$

   Solution: Quadrant I

   Explanation: $\dfrac{\pi}{3}$ is 60° from the positive x – axis and in the 1st quadrant. The first coordinate defines the distance from the origin. Since 4 is positive, the point is 4 units from the origin along that 60° ray. Thus, $\left(4, \dfrac{\pi}{3}\right)$ is in quadrant I.

2. State the location of the point defined by the following polar coordinates: $\left(-1, \frac{5\pi}{6}\right)$

Solution: Quadrant IV

Explanation: $\frac{5\pi}{6}$ is 150° from the positive x – axis and in the 2nd quadrant. However, the first coordinate is negative, indicating the reverse direction along the 150° ray. Thus, $\left(-1, \frac{5\pi}{6}\right)$ is in quadrant IV.

3. State the location of the point defined by the following polar coordinates: $(-3, 2\pi)$

Solution: negative x – axis

Explanation: 2π indicates that the angle is on the x – axis and -3 indicates a reverse of direction. Thus, $(-3, 2\pi)$ is on the negative side of the x – axis.

Practice problems: *(Answers on page: 761)*

1. State the location of the point defined by the following polar coordinates: $(5, \pi)$
2. State the location of the point defined by the following polar coordinates: $\left(-1, \frac{5\pi}{3}\right)$
3. State the location of the point defined by the following polar coordinates: $\left(0.5, \frac{\pi}{6}\right)$

Review questions: *(Answers to odd questions on page: 761)*

1. Plot the point $P\left(3, \frac{\pi}{2}\right)$ in a polar coordinate system.
2. Plot the point $R\left(-2, \frac{\pi}{2}\right)$ in a polar coordinate system.
3. State the location of the point defined by the following polar coordinates: $\left(3, \frac{11\pi}{6}\right)$
4. State the location of the point defined by the following polar coordinates: $(-2, \pi)$
5. State the location of the point defined by the following polar coordinates: $\left(-1, \frac{7\pi}{6}\right)$

Converting between Polar and Rectangular Coordinates

- To convert from **polar coordinates** to **rectangular coordinates**, use the following: $x = r\cos\theta,\ y = r\sin\theta$.
- To convert from rectangular coordinates to polar coordinates, use the following formula:

$r = \sqrt{x^2 + y^2},\ \theta = \arctan\left(\frac{y}{x}\right)$.

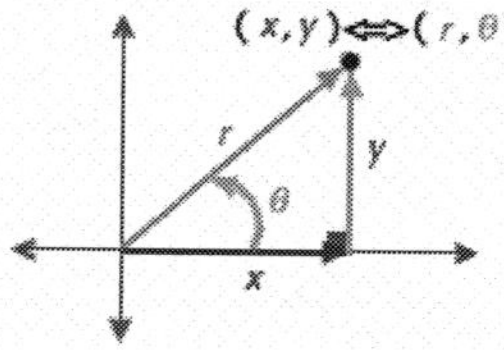	**Polar coordinates** and **rectangular coordinates** both describe points in the plane.

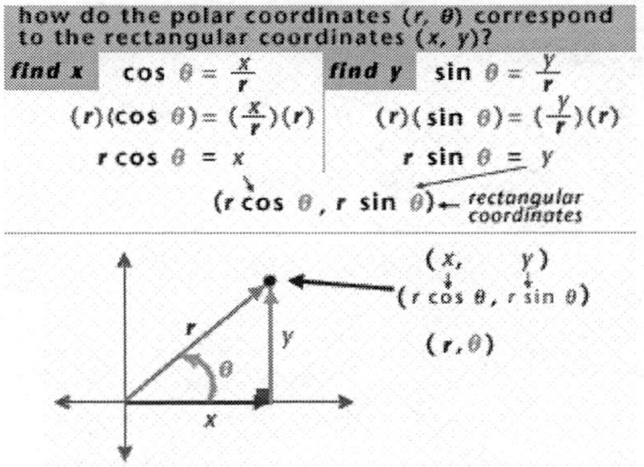

To convert from polar coordinates to rectangular coordinates, use the formulas $x = r\cos\theta$ and $y = r\sin\theta$.

In other words, a point with polar coordinates (r, θ) has rectangular coordinates $(r\cos\theta, r\sin\theta)$.

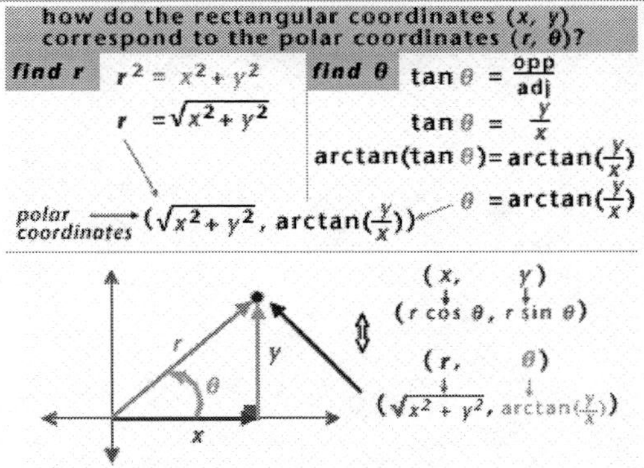

To convert from rectangular coordinates to polar coordinates, use the Pythagorean theorem and one of the **inverse trig functions**.

Use the formulas $r = \sqrt{x^2 + y^2}$ and $\theta = \arctan\left(\dfrac{y}{x}\right)$.

Plug the x- and y-terms into the formula and simplify. The results are the polar coordinates for the point.

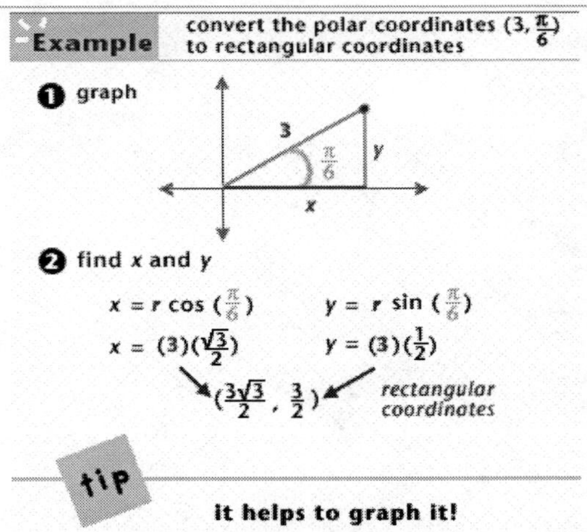

Consider this example, convert the polar coordinates $\left(3, \pi/6\right)$ to rectangular coordinates.

Use the formula for polar coordinates, $(r\cos\theta, r\sin\theta)$. Plug in 3 for r and $\pi/6$ for θ.

Evaluate for cosine and sine and then simplify.

Graphing the point helps identify if the trig functions have the correct signs.

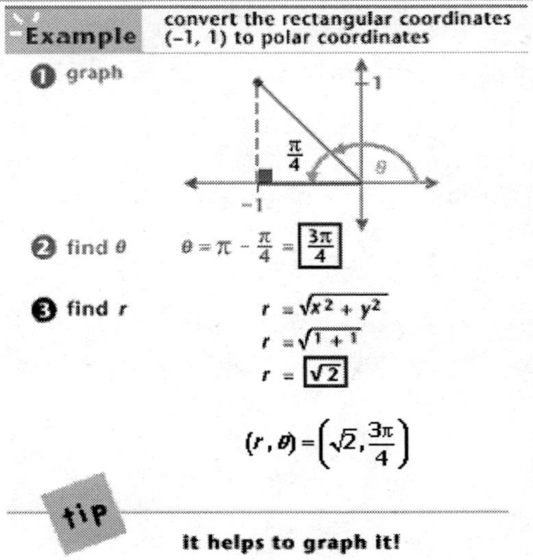

Now try this one: convert the point $(-1, 1)$ from rectangular coordinates to polar coordinates.

Plug the appropriate values into the formula.

Then simplify.

Put the r in the first position and θ in the second position to get the polar coordinates for the point.

Sample problems:

1. Convert the polar coordinates $(-2, -36°)$ to rectangular coordinates.
   Solution: $(-1.6, 1.2)$
   Explanation: Find the x-coordinate: $x = r\cos\theta = -2\cos(-36°) = -2(.8090) = -1.618$. Find the y-coordinate: $y = r\sin\theta = -2\sin(-36°) = -2(-.5878) = 1.176$. Thus, the rectangular coordinates are $(-1.6, 1.2)$.

2. Give polar coordinates of a point whose Cartesian coordinates are $(4, -2)$.
   Solution: $(2\sqrt{5}, 333.4°)$
   Explanation: Find r: $r = \sqrt{x^2 + y^2} = \sqrt{16+4} = \sqrt{20} = 2\sqrt{5}$. Find θ: $y = \tan^{-1}\left(\frac{y}{x}\right) = \tan^{-1}\left(\frac{-2}{4}\right) =$ $-26.565° = 333.435°$. Thus, the polar coordinates are $\left(2\sqrt{5}, 333.4°\right)$.

Practice problems: *(Answers on page: 761)*

1. Give polar coordinates of a point whose Cartesian coordinates are $(-3, -3)$.
   $\left(3\sqrt{2}, \frac{5\pi}{4}\right)$
2. Give the rectangular coordinates of the point whose polar coordinates are $(3, 217°)$.

Review questions: *(Answers to odd questions on page: 761)*

1. Give polar coordinates of a point whose Cartesian coordinates are $(2,2)$.
2. Give polar coordinates of a point whose Cartesian coordinates are $\left(\sqrt{3}, -1\right)$.
3. Give the rectangular coordinates of the point P whose polar coordinates are $\left(4, \frac{\pi}{3}\right)$.
4. Give the rectangular coordinates of the point P whose polar coordinates are $(5, 220°)$.
5. True or false: The rectangular coordinates of the point $P(4, 30°)$ are $x = 2\sqrt{3}$ and $y = 2$.

Graphing Simple Polar Equations

- When graphing in **polar coordinates**:
  - Setting r equal to a constant (as in the equation $r = k$) generates a circle around the origin.
  - Setting θ equal to a constant (as in the equation $\theta = k$) generates a line through the origin.
  - Setting r equal to θ (as in the equation $r = \theta$) generates a spiral.
- To graph a **polar equation** first convert it to **rectangular form**.

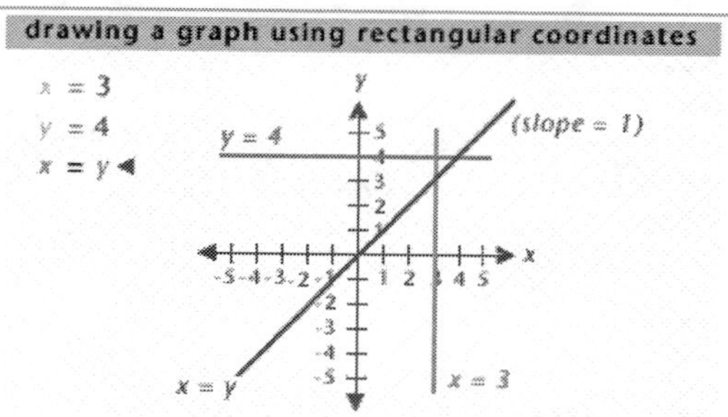

When graphing in **rectangular coordinates**, setting x or y equal to a constant (as in the equations $x = 3$ or $y = 4$) results in a vertical or horizontal line.

Setting the two variables equal to each other generates a line that passes through the origin with a pitch of 45° (or a slope of 1).

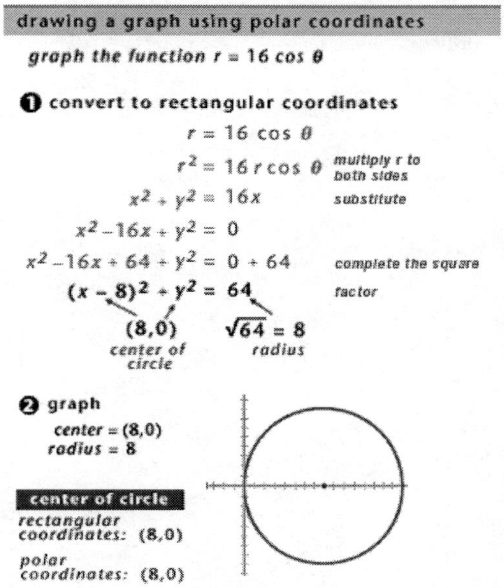

How would you go about graphing $r = 16\cos\theta$?

One way is to first convert the equation to **rectangular coordinates**. Remember that $r\cos\theta = x$ and $r^2 = x^2 + y^2$.

Simplify the expression.

Complete the square for x and y. The result is the equation of a circle with center (8,0) and radius 8.

Graph the center point, find the proper radius, and graph the circle.

Sample problems:

1. Convert $r = 36\sin\theta$ to rectangular form.
   Solution: $x^2 + (y-18)^2 = 324$
   Explanation: Multiply both sides of the equation by r: $r^2 = 36r\sin\theta$. Substitute $r^2 = x^2 + y^2$ and $y = r\sin\theta$: $x^2 + y^2 = 36y$. Set equal to zero and complete the square: $x^2 + y^2 - 36y = 0$; $x^2 + y^2 - 36y + 324 = 324$; $x^2 + (y-18)^2 = 324$.

2. Sketch the polar coordinate graph of $r = 3$.
   Solution:

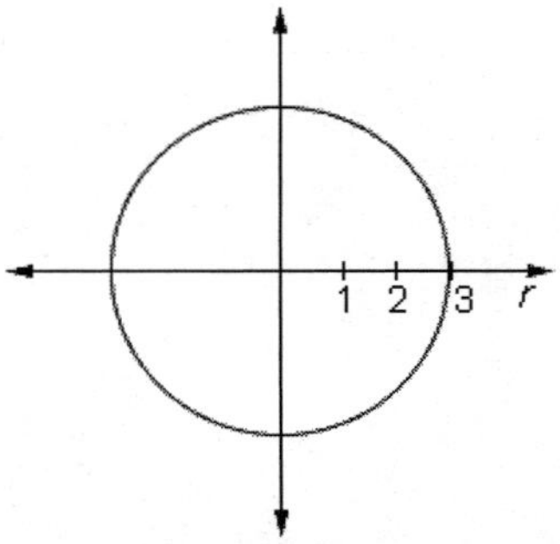

Explanation: Since r is a constant, the distance of the graph from the origin will not change. The angle θ is not restricted though, and can assume any values. Therefore, the equation graphs a circle with its center at the origin and a radius of 3 units.

Practice problems: *(Answers on page: 762)*

1. Convert $r = 4\cos\theta$ to rectangular form.
2. Sketch the polar coordinate graph of $\theta = \frac{\pi}{4}$.

Review questions: *(Answers to odd questions on page: 762)*

1. True or false: The graph of $r = 9\sin\theta$ is a circle with a center or $(3,0)$ and radius 3.
2. Convert $r = 10\sin\theta$ to rectangular form.

3. Convert $r = 12\sin\theta$ to rectangular form.

4. Convert $r = 25\sin\theta$ to rectangular form.

5. Sketch the polar coordinate graph of $r = \frac{1}{2}$.

9

Systems of Equations and Matrices

An Introduction to Linear Systems

- A **system of equations** means that you have more than one equation. A **linear** system of equations means that the graphs of all of the equations in the system are lines.
- The number of times that the graphs of the lines intersect equals the number of solutions that the system of equations can have. For a system of two linear equations, the number of solutions can be zero, one, or infinitely many.

a solution exists when 2 linear equations intersect at one point 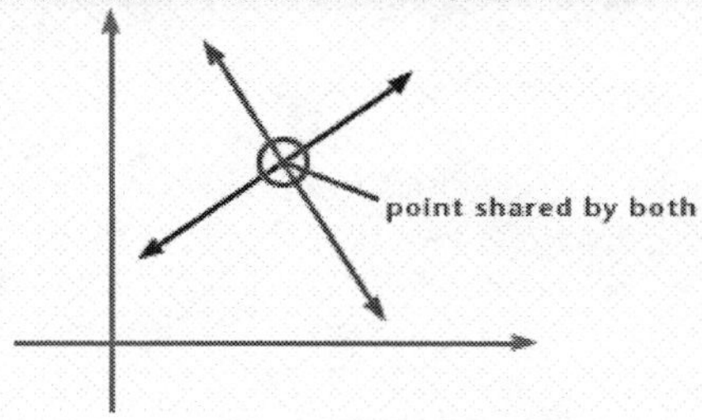 	A **system of linear equations** is simply a group of lines. The points that the lines have in common are the solutions of the system-- that is, the answers that make all the systems true at once. There are three possibilities for how lines can intersect. The first is that they meet at a single point. These systems have a single solution.
no solution exists for 2 parallel linear equations 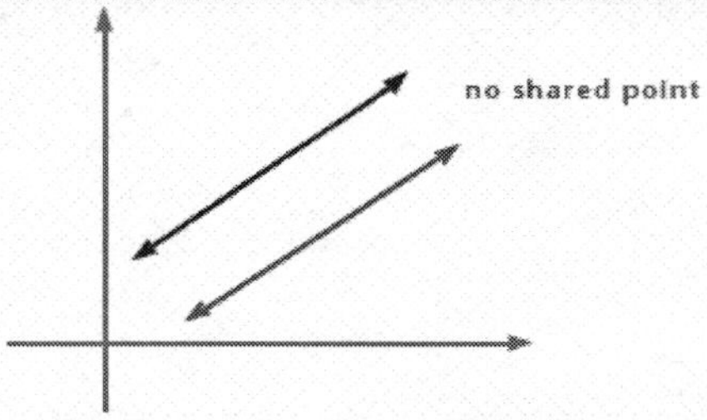 	The next possibility is that the lines never intersect. Lines that never cross are called **parallel lines**. These systems have no solutions.
there are infinite solutions for linear equations that are the same 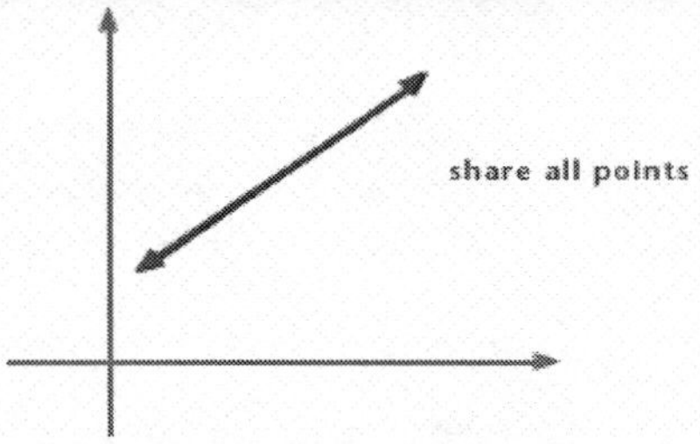 	The final possibility is that the lines are identical, or on top of each other. These lines touch everywhere. Such systems have an infinite number of solutions.
look at the systems algebraically: $A\underline{x} + B\underline{y} = C$ $D\underline{x} + E\underline{y} = F$ find the values for *x* and *y* that satisfy both *at the same time*	**REMEMBER:** The points that the lines have in common are the solutions of the system; that is, the answers that make all the equations true at once.

Solving a System by Substitution

- The **substitution method** is one way to solve a linear system of equations. In the substitution method, start by solving one of the equations for y. Then substitute that expression into the other equation and simplify.
- Finding the solutions to a linear system with two equations gives you the points where the lines intersect.

Example $y = 4x - 3$ $y = 3x - 1$ • solve for y in first equation • substitute answer for y in second equation $y = 4x - 3$ $y = 3x - 1$ $4x - 3 = 3x - 1$ *subtract 3x and add 3 to both sides* $x = 2$	One of the primary uses of algebra is the solving of systems of equations. The **substitution method** is one way to find these solutions. In the substitution method, you solve one of the equations for y and then substitute that expression into the other equation in place of the variable. Solving this one-variable equation will give you a numeric x-value.
$y = 4(2) - 3$ $y = 5$	You aren't done yet! Substitute your new x-value back into one of the original equations to find y.
$x = 2$ lines cross at (2, 5) *substitute for x* $y = 4(2) - 3$ $y = 5$	Now you know the point of intersection, the common solution for the equations in the system.
$y = 4x - 3$ $y = 3x - 1$ $x = 2$ lines cross at (2, 5) *substitute for x* $y = 4(2) - 3$ $y = 5$	Sometimes, you will want to switch the substitution method around and solve for an x-value first. So, rewrite one of the equations as a solution for x. Notice how your x expression substitutes into the other equation. Remember to distribute! Simplify and solve for the y. Once you get y, substitute it into one of the original equations to get your x-value. **Remember:** These values are the coordinates for the point of intersection. They are also the solution common to all the equations in the system.

Sample problems:

1. Solve this system of equations by the substitution method: $\frac{3}{4}x + 4y = 10$, $y = \frac{1}{2}x$.

   Solution: $\left(\frac{40}{11}, \frac{20}{11}\right)$

   Explanation: Substitute $\frac{1}{2}x$ for y in first equation and simplify: $\frac{3}{4}x + 4\left(\frac{1}{2}x\right) = 10$; $\frac{3}{4}x + 2x = 10$. Multiply by 4 to eliminate the denominator: $4\left(\frac{3}{4}x + 2x = 10\right)$; $3x + 8x = 40$. Combine like terms: $11x = 40$. Solve for x. $x = \frac{40}{11}$. Substitute $x = \frac{40}{11}$ into the second equation and simplify: $y = \frac{1}{2}\left(\frac{40}{11}\right) = \frac{20}{11}$.

2. Solve this system of equations by the substitution method: $y = 4x + 8$, $x = -2y + 7$.

   Solution: $(-1, 4)$

   Explanation: Substitute $(-2y + 7)$ for x in the first equation: $y = 4(-2y + 7) + 8$. Distribute: $y = -8y + 28 + 8$. Simplify by combining like terms: $y = -8y + 36$. Solve for y: $9y = 36$; $y = 4$. Substitute $y = 4$ into the second equation: $x = -2(4) + 7 = -8 + 7 = -1$.

3. Solve this system of equations by the substitution method: $x = 2y - 5,\ \ 2x - y = 5$.
   Solution: $(5,5)$
   Explanation: Substitute $(2y-5)$ for x in the second equation and simplify:
   $2(2y-5) - y = 5;\ \ 4y - 10 - y = 5;\ \ 3y - 10 = 5$. Solve for y: $3y = 15;\ \ y = 5$.
   Substitute $y = 5$ into the first equation: $x = 2(5) - 5 = 5$.

Practice problems: *(Answers on page: 762)*

1. Solve this system of equations by the substitution method: $\frac{5}{6}x - 6y = 15,\ x = \frac{3}{5}y$.
2. Solve this system of equations by the substitution method: $4x - 9y = 14,\ x + 3y = 0$.
3. Solve this system of equations by the substitution method: $2x + y = 8,\ y = 2$.

Review questions: *(Answers to odd questions on page: 762)*

1. Solve this system of equations by the subsitution method: $4x + 5y = 2,\ 4x - 5y = 10$.
2. Solve this system of equations by the subsitution method: $x = 4y - 19,\ x = -2y + 5$.
3. Solve this system of equations by the subsitution method: $x = 8 - 7y,\ y = x + 8$.
4. Solve this system of equations by the subsitution method: $3x - y = 7, y = 4x - 11$.
5. Solve this system of equations by the subsitution method: $y = 2x - 7,\ y = x + 1$.

Solving a System by Elimination

- The **elimination method** is another method of solving a linear system of equations.
- In the elimination method, start by manipulating the equations so that the coefficients of the x-terms or the y-terms are equal. Then subtract the two equations to get an equation in only one variable.

Example $3x + 4y = -5$, $x - 5y = -8$ — solve at the same time $3(x - 5y = -8)$ — *multiply through by 3* $3x - 15y = -24$ *same terms* $3x - 15y = -24$, $3x + 4y = -5$ $3x - 15y = -24$ $-(3x + 4y = -5)$ — *subtract equation* $-19y = -19$ $y = 1$ $x - 5(1) = -8$ $x = -3$ — *check answers by plugging in values*	In the elimination method, multiply the equations by constants until one set of the variables match up. Then subtract the equations from each other. Simplify the result and you have the value for one of your variables. Now substitute that value back into one of the original equations (it doesn't matter which) to find the other variable.
$y = 1$ $x = -3$	You now know the coordinates of the point of intersection of the equations of your system, the solution that satisfies all the equations in the system. This is important information.

Example $3x + 2y = 1$, $2x + 3y = 1$ solve at the same time	Here is another example.
$3(3x + 2y = 1)$ $2(2x + 3y = 1)$ multiplying through changes the look not the value	Start by multiplying the equations so that you have matching terms.
$9x + 6y = 3$ $-(4x + 6y = 2)$ $5x = 1$	Then subtract the equations.
$x = \frac{1}{5}$	Simplify to solve for x.
$2(\frac{1}{5}) + 3y = 1$ $\frac{2}{5} + 3y = 1$ $3y = \frac{3}{5}$ $y = \frac{\frac{3}{5}}{3}$	Now that you know x, substitute back into one of the original equations to find y.
$y = \frac{3}{5} \cdot \frac{1}{3}$ $y = \frac{1}{5}$	Now you know the point of intersection and therefore the solution to the system.

Sample problems:

1. Solve the following system of equations by elimination $\frac{3x}{5} + \frac{2y}{3} = 17, \quad -\frac{x}{3} + \frac{y}{2} = 1.$

   Solution: $(15, 12)$

   Explanation: Multiply the first equation by 45: $45\left(\frac{3x}{5} + \frac{2y}{3} = 17\right) = 27x + 30y = 765$. Multiply the second equation by 60: $60\left(-\frac{x}{3} + \frac{y}{2} = 1\right) = -20x + 30y = 60$. Subtract:

   $$\begin{array}{r} 27x + 30y = 765 \\ -(-20x + 30y = 60) \\ \hline 47x \qquad = 705 \\ x = 15 \end{array}$$

   Substitute 15 for x into the second equation; $-\frac{(15)}{3} + \frac{y}{2} = 1$. Solve for y: $-5 + \frac{y}{2} = 1$; $-10 + y = 2$; $y = 12$. Therefore, the solution is $(15, 12)$.

2. Solve the following system of equations by elimination $2x - 3y = 4, \quad 4x - 6y = 10.$

   Solution: No solution

   Explanation: Multiply the first equation by 2: $2(2x - 3y = 4) = 4x - 6y = 8$.

   Subtract the two equations:

   $$\begin{array}{r} 4x - 6y = 8 \\ -(4x - 6y = 10) \\ \hline 0 = -2 \end{array}$$

   This statement is not true; therefore, the system is inconsistent. Inconsistent systems have no solutions.

3. Solve the following system of equations by elimination $\frac{3x-1}{2}-\frac{5y+2}{2}=3,\ x+2y=-8.$

Solution: $(-2,-3)$

Explanation: Multiply the first equation by 2 to eliminate the denominators: $2\left(\frac{3x-1}{2}-\frac{5y+2}{2}=3\right);$ $(3x-1)-(5y+2)=6.$ Simplify: $3x-5y=9.$ So, the revised first equation is $3x-5y=9.$ Multiply the original second equation by 3: $3(x+2y=-8);\ 3x+6y=-24.$ Subtract the equations:

$$\begin{array}{r} 3x-5y=9 \\ \underline{-(3x+6y=-24)} \\ -11y=33 \\ y=-3 \end{array}$$

Substitute $y=-3$ into the original second equation: $x+2(-3)=-8.$ Solve for x: $x-6=-8;\ x=-2.$ Therefore, the solution to this system of equations is $(-2,-3).$

Practice problems: *(Answers on page: 762)*

1. Solve the following system of equations by elimination $2x-3y=4,\ 4x-6y=8.$
2. Solve the following system of equations by elimination $\frac{x}{2}+\frac{2y}{5}=6,\ \frac{x}{2}-\frac{3y}{5}=-14.$
3. Solve the following system of equations by elimination $x-y=-5,\ -x+3y=11.$

Review questions: *(Answers to odd questions on page: 762)*

1. Solve the following system of equations by elimination $x-3y=1,\ -3x+9y=-3.$
2. Solve the following system of equations by elimination $2x-7y=0,\ x-4y=-1.$
3. Solve the following system of equations by elimination $2x+3y=6,\ 3x-y=-13.$
4. Solve the following system of equations by elimination $4x-5y=-6,\ 5x-4y=-3.$
5. Solve the following system of equations by elimination $x+y=0,\ 2y-x=12.$

An Introduction to Linear Systems in Three Variables

- The set of points satisfying a linear equation in three variables is a plane in three-dimensional space.
- The set of points satisfying a system of linear equations in three variables is the intersection of the planes describing each equation in the system.

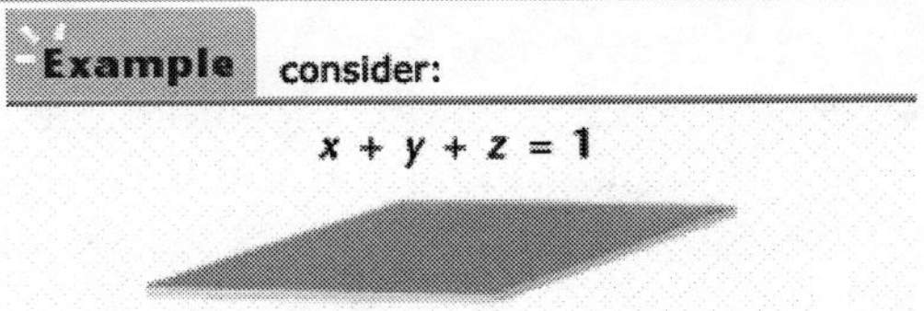

Previously you learned how to solve a system of two linear equations in two variables. What if we add in a third variable?

Consider this linear equation in three variables.

Instead of describing a line in the plane like a linear equation in two variables, a linear equation in three variables describes a plane in three-dimensional space. In other words, the set of points satisfying a linear equation in three variables is a plane.

$$\left.\begin{aligned} x + y + z &= 1 \\ 2x + y - z &= 5 \end{aligned}\right\} \text{ 2 planes}$$

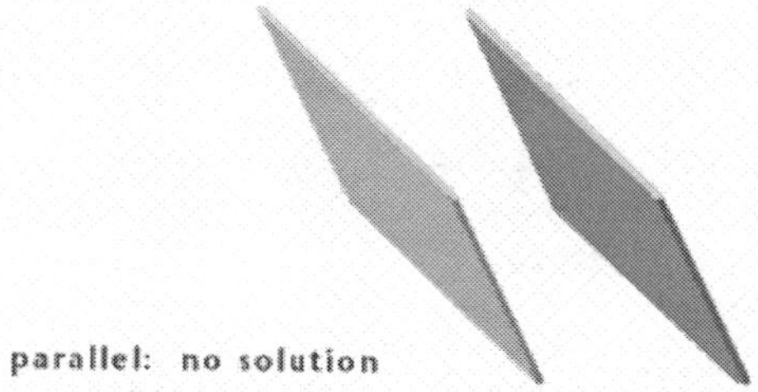

Consider a system of two linear equations in three variables.

Each equation describes a plane in three-space. One possibility is that the planes for the two equations are parallel. In this case, the planes do not intersect each other and there are no solutions to the system of equations.

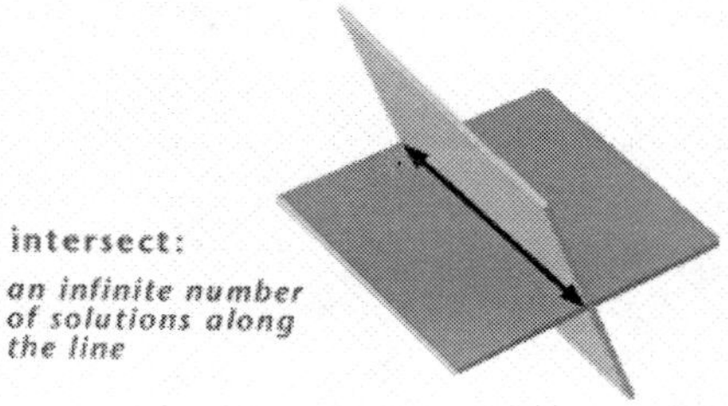

Another possibility is that the planes intersect in a line. Then each point along the line of intersection represents a solution to the system of equations which means for every equation in the system.

Notice that in this case, there are infinitely many solutions!

$$\left.\begin{aligned} x + y + z &= 1 \\ 2x + y - z &= 5 \\ -x + 3y + z &= 7 \end{aligned}\right\} \text{ 3 planes}$$

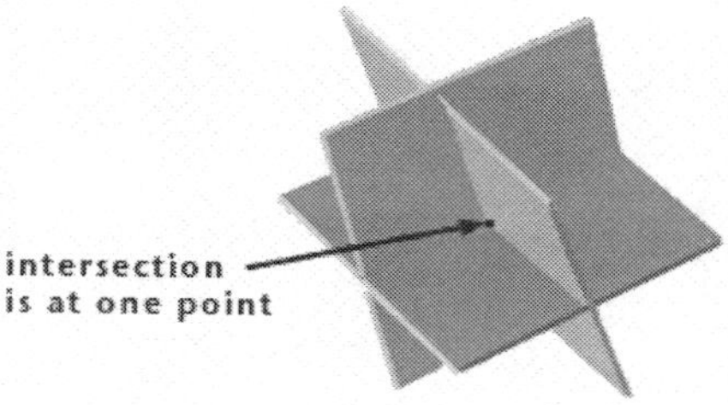

Let's add in one more equation. Now we have a system of three equations in three unknowns.

One possibility is that the three planes describing the three equations all meet at exactly one point. Then this single point is the solution to the system of equations. This point will be the only solution for each equation that is common to all equations in the system.

There are other possibilities, too, which we will consider later.

Solving Linear Systems in Three Variables

- You can solve a system of three linear equations in three variables by eliminating one of the variables and solving the resulting system of two equations.
- An **independent system** of three equations in three unknowns has exactly one solution.
- A **dependent system** of three equations in three unknowns has an infinite number of solutions.
- An **inconsistent system** of three equations in three unknowns has no solutions.

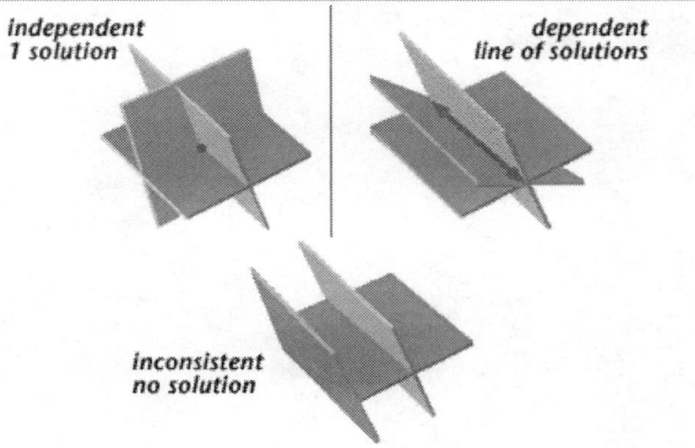

When solving a system of three equations in three variables, there are three distinct possibilities:

1. If the planes describing the equations intersect at exactly one point, then there is exactly one solution. In this case, the system of equations is called an **independent system**.

2. If the planes intersect in a line, then there is an infinite line of solutions. In this case, the system of equations is called a **dependent system**.

3. If the planes do not mutually intersect, then there are no solutions and the system is known as an **inconsistent system**.

Example

$$x + 2y - z = 1$$
$$2x - y + z = 6$$
$$2x - y - z = 0$$

$$\begin{array}{r} x + 2y - z = 1 \\ +\ 2x - y + z = 6 \\ \hline 3x + y \quad = 7 \end{array}$$

add together to eliminate the z's

$$\begin{array}{r} 2x - y + z = 6 \\ +\ 2x - y - z = 0 \\ \hline 4x - 2y \quad = 6 \end{array}$$

add together to eliminate the z's

problem has been reduced to 2 unknowns

$$3x + y = 7$$
$$4x - 2y = 6$$

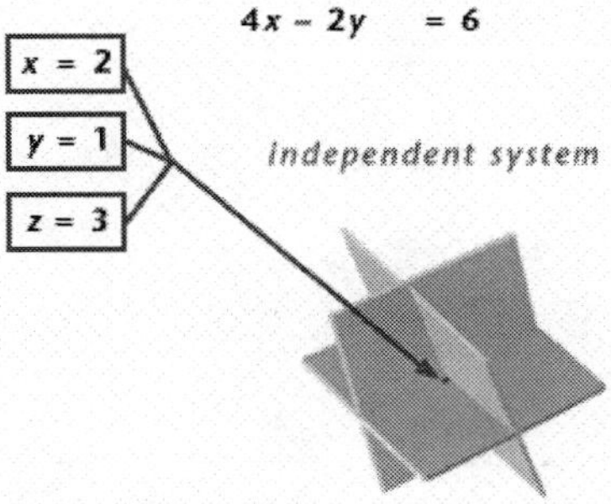

Solving a system of three equations in three unknowns is not much different from solving a system of two equations in two unknowns.
You use the same techniques.

First, add the first two equations in the system to get an equation with no z term.
Then add the second two equations for another equation with no z term.

By eliminating the variable z, you have reduced the problem to a system of two equations in two unknowns. Solve this equation for x and y using any method you like and plug back into one of the original equations to solve for z.

Since this system of equations has the single point (2, 1, 3) as its solution, the system is an independent system.

Sample problems:

1. Solve: (1) $3x+2y+2z=-3$ (2) $2x-4y+z=7$ (3) $10x-4y+2z=-12$
   Solution: $(-3,-2,5)$

Explanation: Multiply equation (2) by 2 and subtract the result from (1) to eliminate z:

$$\begin{array}{lcl} 3x+2y+2z=-3 & & 3x+2y+2z=-3 \\ 2(2x-4y+z=7) & \Rightarrow & \underline{-(4x-8y+2z=14)} \\ & & -x+10y=-17 \end{array}$$

Subtract equation (3) from equation (1) to again eliminate z:

$$\begin{array}{c} 3x+2y+2z=-3 \\ \underline{-(10x-4y+2z=-12)} \\ -7x+6y=9 \end{array}$$

Use elimination to solve the new system, $-x+10y=-17$ and $-7x+6y=9$:

$$\begin{array}{lcl} 7(-x+10y=-17) & & -7x+70y=-119 \\ -7x+6y=9 & \Rightarrow & \underline{-(-7x+6y=9)} \\ & & 64y=-128;\quad y=-2 \end{array}$$

Substitute $y=-2$ into either equation from the new system to find x:
$-x+10y=-17 \Rightarrow -x+10(-2)=-17;\quad -x-20=-17;\quad -x=3;\quad x=-3.$

Substitute the values of x and y into any one of the original equations to find z:
$2x-4y+z=7 \Rightarrow 2(-3)-4(-2)+z=7;\quad -6+8+z=7;\quad z=5.$
Thus, the solution is $x=-3,\ y=-2,$ and $z=5$ or $(-3,-2,5)$.

2. Solve: $(1)\ 3x-2y-2z=9\ \ (2)\ x+4y+3z=5\ \ (3)\ 2x+5y+4z=8$
Solution: $(3,2,-2)$
Explanation: Multiply equation (2) by 3 and subtract it from (1) to eliminate x:

$$\begin{array}{lcl} 3x-2y-2z=9 & & 3x-2y-2z=9 \\ 3(x+4y+3z=5) & \Rightarrow & \underline{-(3x+12y+9z=15)} \\ & & -14y-11z=-6 \end{array}$$

Multiply equation (2) by 2 and subtract equation (3) from this to again eliminate x:

$$\begin{array}{lcl} 2(x+4y+3z=5) & & 2x+8y+6z=10 \\ 2x+5y+4z=8 & \Rightarrow & \underline{-(2x+5y+4z=8)} \\ & & 3y+2z=2 \end{array}$$

Use elimination to solve the new system, $-14y-11z=-6$ and $3y+2z=2$:

$$\begin{array}{lcl} 2(-14y-11z=-6) & & -28y-22z=-12 \\ 11(3y+2z=2) & \Rightarrow & \underline{+(33y+22z=22)} \\ & & 5y=10;\quad y=2 \end{array}$$

Substitute $y=2$ into either equation from the new system to find z:
$3y+2z=2 \Rightarrow 3(2)+2z=2;\quad 6+2z=2;\quad 2z=-4;\quad z=-2.$

Substitute the values of y and z into any one of the orginal equations to find x.
$x+4y+3z=5 \Rightarrow x+4(2)+3(-2)=5;\quad x+8-6=5;\quad x=3.$
Thus, the solution is $x=3,\ y=2,$ and $z=-2$ or $(3,2,-2)$.

3. Solve: $(1)\ 3x+2y+6z=8\ \ (2)\ 2x-4y-3z=5\ \ (3)\ x+2y-3z=5$
Solution: $(3,\ 1/2,\ -1/3)$

Explanation: Multiply equation (2) by 2 and add it to (1) to eliminate z:

$$\begin{array}{lcr} 3x+2y+6z=8 & & 3x+2y+6z=8 \\ 2(2x-4y-3z=5) & \Rightarrow & +(4x-8y-6z=10) \\ \hline & & 7x-6y=18 \end{array}$$

Subtract equation (3) from (2) to again eliminate z:

$$\begin{array}{r} 2x-4y-3z=5 \\ -(x+2y-3z=5) \\ \hline x-6y=0 \end{array}$$

Use elimination to solve the new system, $7x-6y=18$ and $x-6y=0$:

$$\begin{array}{r} 7x-6y=18 \\ -(x-6y=0) \\ \hline 6x=18;\ x=3 \end{array}$$

Substitute $x=3$ into either equation from the new system to find y:

$x-6y=0 \Rightarrow 3-6y=0;\ \ -6y=-3;\ \ y=\frac{1}{2}$

Substitute the values of x and y into any one of the original equations to find z:

$x+2y-3z=5 \Rightarrow 3+2\left(\frac{1}{2}\right)-3z=5;\ 3+1-3z=5;\ \ 4-3z=5;\ \ -3z=1;\ \ z=-\frac{1}{3}$

Thus, the solution is $x=3$, $y=\frac{1}{2}$, and $z=-\frac{1}{3}$ or $(3,\frac{1}{2},-\frac{1}{3})$.

Practice problems: *(Answers on page: 762)*

1. Solve this system for y only: $x-y+z=4,\ \ x-y-z=-6,\ \ 3x+y-2z=3.$
2. Solve: $2x-y+2z=2,\ \ x+2y-3z=10,\ \ x-3y+z=-4$
3. Solve: $x+y+2z=3,\ \ x+y-2z=-5,\ \ x-2y+z=7$

Review questions: *(Answers to odd questions on page: 762)*

1. Solve the following system of equations for x only: $x+2y+z=5,\ \ x+y-z=2,\ \ x+y+z=4.$
2. Solve the following system of equations for z only: $x+3y+z=-5,\ \ x+y-z=-1,\ \ -x+3y-z=-1.$
3. Solve the following system of equations: $x+y+z=4,\ \ x-y+z=2,\ \ x-y-z=-2$
4. Solve the following system of equations: $x+y+z=3,\ \ x-y-2z=-5,\ \ x-2y+3z=4$
5. Solve: $2x-3y-3z=-3,\ \ x-2y-4z=-11,\ \ -3x+4y+4z=3$

Solving Inconsistent Systems

- You can solve a system of three equations in three variables by eliminating one of the variables and solving the resulting system of two equations.
- An inconsistent system of three equations in three unknowns has no solutions.

Example $2x-3y+6z=3$ $x+2y-4z=5$ $3x+4y-8z=7$	There are many different ways you can solve this system of equations. One way is to eliminate the x variable.
$2x-3y+6z=3$ $2(x+2y-4z=5)$ $3x+4y-8z=7$ *eliminate the x's by multiplying through by 2* $2x-3y+6z=3$ $-(2x+4y-8z=10)$ $-7y+14z=-7$ *subtract to eliminate the x's* $\dfrac{-7y+14z=-7}{7}$ *divide through by 7* $\boxed{-y+2z=-1}$ *reduced to 2 variables*	You can take the first equation and subtract 2 times the second equation to get an equation with no x variable. This new equation can be simplified. You have one equation with no x variable, but you will need another in order to solve for y and z.

$2x - 3y + 6z = 3$ $3(x + 2y - 4z = 5)$ $3x + 4y - 8z = 7$ multiply through by 3 $3x + 6y - 12z = 15$ $-(3x + 4y - 8z = 7)$ subtract to eliminate x's $2y - 4z = 8$ $\frac{2y - 4z = 8}{2}$ divide through by 2 $y - 2z = 4$ reduced to 2 variables	Take 3 times the second equation and subtract the last equation to get another equation without an x variable. This equation can be simplified too. Whew! That was a lot of work. But now you finally have a system of two equations in two unknowns.
$-y + 2z = -1$ $+\ y - 2z = 4$ add to eliminate y's ? → $0 = 3$	Adding the two equations results in the "equation" $0 = 3$. This statement is false! These two equations cannot be solved.
Example $-y + 2z = -1$ $y - 2z = 4$ $0 \neq 3$ $2x - 3y + 6z = 3$ $x + 2y - 4z = 5$ $3x + 4y - 8z = 7$ cannot be solved inconsistent system 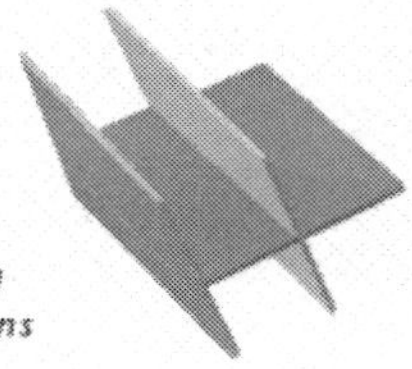 parallel cannot be solved for all 3 equations	Since the system of two equations in two unknowns cannot be solved, the original system cannot be solved either. This system of equations is an inconsistent system, and there is no solution.

Sample problems:

1. True or False: The following system of equations is inconsistent: $x-2y+3z=12$, $3x-y+2z=7$, $6x-7y+11z=10$.

   Solution: True

   Explanation: Multiply the first equation by -3 and add to the second:

   $$\begin{array}{r} -3x+6y-9z=-36 \\ +(3x-y+2z=7) \\ \hline 5y-7z=-29 \end{array}$$

   Multiply the second equation by -2 and add it to the third equation.

   $$\begin{array}{r} -6x+2y-4z=-14 \\ +(6x-7y+11z=10) \\ \hline -5y+7z=-4 \end{array}$$

   Use elimination to solve the new system:

   $$\begin{array}{r} 5y-7z=-29 \\ +(-5y+7z=-4) \\ \hline 0=-33 \end{array}$$

   Since $0=-33$ is a false statement, this system produces no solution and is therefore inconsistent.

2. True or False: The following system of equations is inconsistent: $2x-2y+z=6$, $x-y+z=-2$, $x-y+2z=-6$.
   Solution: True
   Explanation: Subtract the second equations from the first:
   $$\begin{array}{r} 2x-2y+z=6 \\ \underline{-(x-y+z=-2)} \\ x-y=8 \end{array}$$
   Multiply the second equation by 2 and subtract it from the third:
   $$\begin{array}{r} x-y+2z=-6 \\ \underline{-(2x-2y+2z=-4)} \\ -x+y=-2 \end{array}$$
   Use elimination to solve the new system:
   $$\begin{array}{r} x-y=8 \\ \underline{+(-x+y\ =-2)} \\ 0=6 \end{array}$$
   Since $0=6$ is a false statement, this system produces no solution and is therefore inconsistent.

3. True or False: The following system of equations is inconsistent: $2x-y-3z=3$, $3x+2y-2z=5$, $x+y+z=1$.
   Solution: False
   Explanation: Multiply the first equation by 2 and add it to the second equation:
   $$\begin{array}{r} 4x-2y-6z=6 \\ \underline{+(3x+2y-2z=5)} \\ 7x-8z=11 \end{array}$$
   Multiply the third equation by 2 and subtract it from the second equation:
   $$\begin{array}{r} 3x+2y-2z\ =5 \\ \underline{-(2x+2y+2z=2)} \\ x-4z=3 \end{array}$$
   Use elimination to solve the new system (multiply the 2nd equation by 7 and subtract):
   $$\begin{array}{r} 7x-8z=11 \\ \underline{-(7x-28z=21)} \\ 20z=-10;\ z=-\tfrac{1}{2} \end{array}$$
   Find x: $x-4z=3 \Rightarrow x-4\left(-\tfrac{1}{2}\right)=3$; $x+2=3$; $x=1$.
   Since solutions for two of the three variables exist, at least one solution to the system must exist and the system is therefore not inconsistent.

Practice problems: *(Answers on page: 762)*

1. True or false: The following system of equations is inconsistent: $3x+2y+z=8$, $4x+3y+3z=13$, $x+y+2z=12$.
2. True or false: The following system of equations is inconsistent: $x+2y-z=0$, $x+y-2z=-1$, $2x+y-5z=4$.
3. True or false: The following system of equations is inconsistent: $x+5y+4z=0$, $x+y+z=1$, $2x-2y+5z=-3$.

Review questions: *(Answers to odd questions on page: 762)*

1. True or false: The following system of equations is inconsistent: $2x+6y+5z=-5$, $x+5y+4z=5$, $x+y+z=6$.
2. True or false: The following system of equations is inconsistent: $2x+y-3z=5$, $3x+2y-2z=-1$, $x+y+z=3$.

3. True or false: The following system of equations is inconsistent: $x-y+4z=6$, $3x+3y+10z=3$, $-6x+y-22z=1$.
4. True or false: The following system of equations is inconsistent: $2x-2y+z=6$, $x-y+z=-2$, $x-y+2z=-6$.
5. True or false: The following system of equations is inconsistent: $2x+2y-3z=-1$, $x+3y+z=2$, $x+y-2z=3$.

Solving Dependent Systems

- You can solve a system of three equations in three variables by eliminating one of the variables and solving the resulting system of two equations.
- A dependent system of three equations in three unknowns has infinitely many solutions.

Example $2x+y-z=-2$ $3x+2y+3z=21$ $7x+4y+z=17$	Let's work through another problem.
$2(2x+y-z=-2)$ $3x+2y+3z=21$ $7x+4y+z=17$ $4x+2y-2z=-4$ $-(3x+2y+3z=21)$ $\boxed{x-5z=-25}$	You can take 2 times the first equation and subtract the second equation to get an equation with no y-variable.
$2x+y-z=-2$ $2(3x+2y+3z=21)$ $7x+4y+z=17$ $6x+4y+6z=42$ $-(7x+4y+z=17)$ $-1(-x+5z=25)$ $\boxed{x-5z=-25}$	You need another equation in x and z to solve the system. Take 2 times the second equation and subtract the third equation. Now you've reduced the system to a system of two equations in two variables.
$\boxed{x-5z=-25}$ $-\boxed{x-5z=-25}$ $0=0$ can't solve for x and z there is not 1 solution	But the two equations are the same! You cannot solve for x and z. However, this time the system is not inconsistent because you do not get a false statement like $0 = 3$. Instead, this system has more than one solution; it is a dependent system.
let: $c=z$ then: $x-5(c)=-25$ $x=5c-25$ plug in c for z plug in to any equation to find y $2(5c-25)+y-c=-2$ $10c-50+y-c=-2$ $9c+y=48$ $\boxed{y=-9c+48}$	Since this is a dependent system, there will be a solution for any value of z. So, let $c = z$ where c is some number. Then solve for x and y in terms of c.

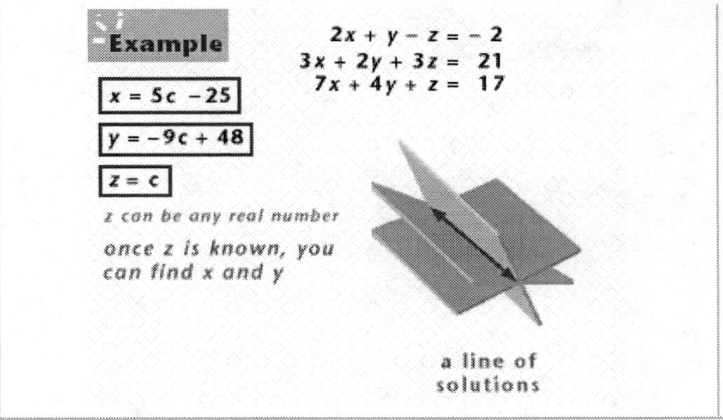

You have found the solution in terms of the parameter c. Notice that there are infinitely many solutions. Each value of c corresponds to a single point on the line of solutions where the three planes intersect.

Sample problems:

1. True or False: $3x+3y+3z=5$; $2x+2y+3z=3$; $x+y+3z=1$ is a dependent system.
   Solution: True
   Explanation: Subtract the second equation from the first:
   $$\begin{array}{r} 3x+3y+3z=5 \\ -(2x+2y+3z=3) \\ \hline x+y=2 \end{array}$$
   Next, subtract the third equation from the second:
   $$\begin{array}{r} 2x+2y+3z=3 \\ -(x+y+3z=1) \\ \hline x+y=2 \end{array}$$
   Finally, subtract the resulting equations:
   $$\begin{array}{r} x+y=2 \\ -(x+y=2) \\ \hline 0=0 \end{array}$$
   There is no single solution for this system, so this system is dependent.

2. True or False: $4x+4y+z=1$; $x+3y+z=-2$; $5x+7y+2z=-1$ is a dependent system.
   Solution: True
   Explanation: Subtract the second equation from the first:
   $$\begin{array}{r} 4x+4y+z=1 \\ -(x+3y+z=-2) \\ \hline 3x+y=3. \end{array}$$
   Next, multiply the second equation by -2 and add to the third:
   $$\begin{array}{r} -2x-6y-2z=4 \\ +(5x+7y+2z=-1) \\ \hline 3x+y=3. \end{array}$$
   Finally, subtract the resulting equations:
   $$\begin{array}{r} 3x+y=3 \\ -(3x+y=3) \\ \hline 0=0. \end{array}$$
   The system is dependent.

3. True or false: $x+6y+7z=1$; $x+2y+2z=0$; $x-2y-3z=0$ is a dependent system.
   Solution: False
   Explanation: Multiply the first equation by -1 and add the second equation:
   $$\begin{array}{r} -x-6y-7z=-1 \\ +(x+2y+2z=0) \\ \hline -4y-5z=-1 \end{array}$$
   Next, multiply the second equation by -1 and add it to the third equation:
   $$\begin{array}{r} -x-2y-2z=0 \\ +\ (x-2y-3z=0) \\ \hline -4y-5z=0 \end{array}$$
   Subtract the resulting equations:
   $$\begin{array}{r} -4y-5z=-1 \\ -(-4y-5z=0) \\ \hline 0=-1 \end{array}$$
   Thus, the system is inconsistent, not dependent.

Practice problems: *(Answers on page: 762)*

1. True or false: $x-2y-z=0$; $2x+y-z=1$; $3x+4y-z=2$ is a dependent system.
2. True or false: $x-y-z=4$; $3x+y-2z=5$; $3x+y-z=2$ is a dependent system.
3. True or false: $2x-2y-2z=3$; $3x-5y-4z=5$; $x-3y-2z=2$ is a dependent system.

Review questions: *(Answers to odd questions on page: 762)*

1. True or false: $x+y+z=-1$; $2x-2y-z=2$; $x-3y-2z=3$ is a dependent system.
2. True or false: $x+3y-2z=2$; $x-2y+2z=-3$; $x-7y+6z=-8$ is a dependent system.
3. True or false: $3x+y+3z=7$; $3x-y+2z=4$; $3x-3y+z=1$ is a dependent system.
4. True or false: $2x+2y-3z=7$; $x-2y-2z=4$; $3x-2y-4z=10$ is a dependent system.
5. True or false: $2x+2z=3$; $-x+y-z=-1$; $4x-2y+3z=5$ is a dependent system:

Solving Systems with Two Equations

- When solving a system of two equations in three unknowns, there are three possibilities:
  1. One solution; i.e., a point of intersection.
  2. Infinitely many solutions; i.e., a line of intersection.
  3. No solutions; i.e., parallel planes.
- You can solve a system of two equations in three unknowns by finding a relationship between two of the variables in terms of the third.

Example $\begin{array}{r} 2x-2y+5z=14 \\ x+4y-3z=-2 \end{array}$	One way to solve this system of only two equations is to find x and y in terms of z. In the case that there are solutions, there will be a solution for any value of z. If you find x and y in terms of z, you will be able to specify the solutions.
$\begin{array}{r} 2x-2y+5z=14 \\ -(2x+8y-6z=-4) \\ \hline \boxed{-10y+11z=18} \end{array}$ *multiply through by 2 and subtract* $\begin{array}{r} 4x-4y+10z=28 \\ x+4y-3z=-2 \\ \hline \boxed{5x+7z=26} \end{array}$ *multiply through by 2* *add*	You can find a relationship between y and z by eliminating the x variable. Now find a relationship between x and z by eliminating the y variable.

suppose: $z = c$

find: x

$$5x + 7c = 26$$
$$5x = 26 - 7c$$
$$x = \frac{26 - 7c}{5}$$

find: y

$$-10y + 11c = 18$$
$$11c = 18 + 10y$$
$$11c - 18 = 10y$$
$$y = \frac{11c - 18}{10}$$

Since no false statements like $0 = 1$ have come up, there are solutions to this system. Suppose that z is equal to some number c. There will be a solution for any value of c.

Find x in terms of c using the relationship between x and z.

Find y in terms of c using the relationship between y and z.

That's it! You have specified the line of solutions in terms of the parameter c.

Example

$$4x - 2y + 6z = 5$$
$$2x - y + 3z = 2 \leftarrow$$ *eliminate a variable*

multiply through by 2

$$4x - 2y + 6z = 5$$
$$-(4x - 2y + 6z = 4)$$
$$0 \quad 0 \quad 0 = 1$$

subtract

$0 = 1$ (crossed out) **no solution**

parallel planes

Take a look at this system of two equations. You can eliminate a variable by subtracting 2 times the second equation from the first equation.

Uh-oh! When you try to eliminate a variable, you get the equation $0 = 1$. This system of equations has no solution.

It is an inconsistent system.

Sample problems:

1. Solve (in terms of y): $x - 2y + 3z = 8$; $x + 3y - z = 2$

   Solution: $\left(\frac{14-7y}{4}, y, \frac{6+5y}{4}\right)$

   Explanation: Since the system is to be solved for y, manipulate the equations so that the other variables are eliminated one at a time.

   Subtract the second equation from the first equation to eliminate x:

   $$x - 2y + 3z = 8$$
   $$-(x + 3y - z = 2)$$
   $$-5y + 4z = 6$$

   Solve for z in terms of y: $-5y + 4z = 6 \Rightarrow 4z = 6 + 5y \Rightarrow z = \frac{6+5y}{4}$

   Multiply the second equation by 3 and add it to the first equation to eliminate z:

   $$x - 2y + 3z = 8$$
   $$+(3x + 9y - 3z = 6)$$
   $$4x + 7y = 14$$

   Solve for x in terms of y: $4x + 7y = 14 \Rightarrow 4x = 14 - 7y \Rightarrow x = \frac{14-7y}{4}$

2. Solve (in terms of x): $4x-2y+z=-3;\ x+y+2z=3$

Solution: $\left(x,\dfrac{7x+9}{5},\dfrac{3-6x}{5}\right)$

Explanation: Multiply the first equation by -2 and add it to the second equation to eliminate z:

$$\begin{array}{l} -8x+4y-2z=6 \\ \underline{+(x+y+2z=3)} \\ \quad -7x+5y=9 \end{array}$$

Solve for y in terms of x: $-7x+5y=9 \Rightarrow 5y=9+7x \Rightarrow y=\dfrac{7x+9}{5}$

Multiply the second equation by 2 and add it to the first equation to eliminate y:

$$\begin{array}{l} 4x-2y+z=-3 \\ \underline{+(2x+2y+4z=6)} \\ \quad 6x+5z=3 \end{array}$$

Solve for z in terms of x: $6x+5z=3 \Rightarrow 5z=3-6x \Rightarrow z=\dfrac{3-6x}{5}$

3. Solve the system of equations in terms of a, where $a=y$:
$-2x-3y+z=2;\ 2x-y-2z=1$

Solution: $\left(\dfrac{-5-7a}{2},a,-3-4a\right)$

Explanation: Let $y=a$. Since the system is to be solved in terms of a, manipulate the equations so that the other variables are eliminated one at at time.
Add the two equations to eliminate x:

$$\begin{array}{l} -2x-3a+z=2 \\ \underline{+(2x-a-2z=1)} \\ \quad -4a-z=3 \end{array}$$

Solve the equation for z in terms of a: $-4a-z=3 \Rightarrow -z=3+4a \Rightarrow z=-3-4a.$
Try a different method for solving for x. Substitute $z=-3-4a$ into either equation and solve for x:

$2x-a-2(-3-4a)=1;\ 2x-a+6+8a=1;\ 2x+6+7a=1;\ 2x=-5-7a;\ x=\dfrac{-5-7a}{2}.$

Practice problems: *(Answers on page: 762)*

1. Solve (in terms of y): $x-6y+z=-4,\ 2x+y-2z=-2$
2. Solve (in terms of x): $4x-2y+z=3,\ 3x+5y-2z=6$
3. Solve (in terms of z): $3x-2y-2z=4,\ 5x-3y+4z=1$

Review questions: *(Answers to odd questions on page: 763)*

1. Solve (in terms of z): $4x-3y+5z=4,\ x-y-5z=-3$
2. Solve (in terms of z): $2x+y-z=4;\ x+y+z=-3$
3. Solve (in terms of y): $x+y+z=8;\ 2x-y+3z=5$
4. Solve (in terms of x): $-2x+3y-z=-1;\ 4x+3y-2z=4$
5. Solve (in terms of y): $x+8y-3z=1;\ 2x-2y+z=3$

Investments

- You can use systems of linear equations to solve many real-world problems.

 *suppose:* **total investment:** $3,000 **stocks:** 4.5% *annual rate of return* **bonds:** 8% *annual rate of return* **total interest:** $177 *how much was invested in the bond fund?*	Suppose that you invested a total of $3,000 in stocks and bonds. Given the rates of return for stock and bonds and the total interest you earned after the first year of your investment, how much did you invest in bonds? You can answer this question by solving a system of linear equations.
S = amount in stocks B = amount in bonds *write down everything you know*	First, define your variables. Use variables to represent the unknown quantities.
$S + B = 3000$ $.045S + .08B = 177$	Now create equations using what you do know. A total of $3,000 was invested. And the total interest for the first year was $177.
solve in terms of B by eliminating S $S + B = 3000$ $S = 3000 - B$ $.045S + .08B = 177$ $.045(3000 - B) + .08B = 177$ $135 - .045B + .08B = 177$ $.035B = 42$ $B = \frac{42}{.035} = \boxed{\$1200}$	You can solve the system of equations any way you like. Here, we use the substitution method to solve for *B*. $1,200 was invested in bonds. Besides being great fun, linear equations can help you solve real problems too!

Sample problems:

1. A department store advertises a limited-time sale, offering 1 pair of shorts for $15 and 2 pairs for $25. A total of 625 shorts are sold and $8,875 is taken in. How many customers purchased 2 pairs of shorts?
Solution: 100
Explanation: Let x = # of customers who bought 1 pair and y = # of customers who bought 2 pairs: $x+2y=625$; $15x+25y=8875$. Solve the first equation for x and substitute in the second equation: $x=625-2y$; $15(625-2y)+25y=8875$. Solve for y: $9,375-30y+25y=8875$; $-5y=-500$; $y=100$. Thus, 100 customers bought 2 pairs of shorts.

2. Joe inherited $30,000 and invested in two bonds, which pay 7% and 9% simple interest. The annual interest is $2,460. Find the amount invested at each rate.
Solution: $12,000, $18,000
Explanation: Let x = amount invested at 7% and y = amount invested at 9%: $x+y=30000$; $0.07x+0.09y=2,460$. Solve the first equation for x and substitute into the second equation: $x=30000-y$; $0.07(30000-y)+0.09y=2460$. Solve for y: $2100-0.07y+0.09y=2460$; $0.02y=360$; $y=18,000$. Substitute $y=18,000$ into $x+y=30,000$ and solve for x: $x+(18,000)=30,000$; $x=12,000$. Thus, $12,000.00 was invested at 7% and $18,000.00 was invested at 9%.

3. One evening, 1500 movie tickets were sold at a theater. Tickets cost $7 for adults and $5 for students. Total reciepts were $9500. How many adult tickets were sold?
Solution: 1000
Explanation: Let x = # of adult tickets and y = # of student tickets: $x+y=1500$; $7x+5y=9500$.
Multiply the 1st equation by 5 and subtract the 2nd equation:
$$\begin{array}{r} 5x+5y=7500 \\ -(7x+5y=9500) \\ \hline -2x=-2000 \end{array}$$
Divide by -2: $x=1000$. Thus, 1000 adult tickets were sold.

Practice problems: *(Answers on page: 763)*

1. A mail-order business shipped 240 packages one day. Customers are charged \$3.50 for each standard-delivery package and \$7.50 for each express-delivery package. Total shipping charges for the day were \$1192. How many express delivery packages were shipped?
2. A home decor store sold 36 lamps one day. Small lamps cost \$12 and large lamps cost \$18. The total for the day was \$522. How many of each kind of lamp was sold?
3. A man had \$4000 dollars to invest. He chose to invest some in stocks paying 8% simple interest and some in growth funds paying 25% simple interest. He earned a total of \$800 for the year. How much did he invest in stocks?

Review questions: *(Answers to odd questions on page: 763)*

1. At a snack shop, peanuts worth \$2.50 per pound were mixed with candy-coated chocolates worth \$7.50 per pound in order to get 20 pounds of a mixture worth \$3.00 per pound. How many pounds of each snack were used?
2. During a promotional campaign, a bank gave either a free ornament or a CD to new customers. It cost the bank \$1 for each ornament and \$2 for each CD. In all, 48 new customers were signed up and the bank's cost for incentives was \$86. How many ornaments were given away?
3. Martha inherits 100,000 and invests it in two certificates of deposit. One certificate pays 6% and the other pays $4\frac{1}{2}$% simple interest annually. If her total interest is \$5,025 per year, how much is invested at each rate?
4. A department store advertises a limited-time sale, offering 1 pair of shoes for \$20 and 2 pairs for \$35. A total of 125 pairs of shoes were sold and \$2,275 was taken in. How many customers purchased 2 pairs of shoes?
5. Jane inherited \$40,000 and invested it in two bonds, which pay 3% and 2% simple interest. The annual interest is \$860. Find the amount invested at each rate.

Solving with Partial Fractions

- You can use the technique of **partial fractions** to write a complicated fraction as the sum of simpler fractions. Applying this technique requires you to solve a system of linear equations.
- Partial fractions help you work backwards to the elements that created the product you have at hand. The process is quite useful in calculus and in practical business situations.

Example $\frac{?}{(3x+5)} + \frac{??}{(x-2)} = \frac{x-5}{(3x+5)(x-2)}$ *what are the numerators?*	In this example, we start by writing an addition problem of fractions. Each of the adding fractions has a variable for its numerator and one of the factors of the longer fraction as its denominator. We assign enough fractions so that each factor of the large denominator is found in its own smaller fraction.
$\frac{A}{3x+5} + \frac{B}{x-2}$ $\frac{A(x-2)}{3x+5(x-2)} + \frac{B(3x+5)}{x-2(3x+5)}$ *find a common denominator* $\frac{Ax-2A+3Bx+5B}{(3x+5)(x-2)}$ *distribute* $\frac{(A+3B)x+(5B-2A)}{(3x+5)(x-2)}$	Let the numerators be represented by the variables A and B. Follow the process for creating a common denominator in the addition problem. Notice that this introduces new elements to the numerator of each of the adding fractions. Add and collect the like terms in the collective numerator. In this example you have $Ax + 3Bx$ and $-2A + 5B$.

what are the numerators? $\frac{?}{(3x+5)} + \frac{??}{(x-2)} = \frac{1x - 5}{(3x+5)(x-2)}$ $\frac{(A+3B)x + (5B-2A)}{(3x+5)(x-2)}$ *2 equations* *2 unknowns*	The sum of the two simpler fractions should be equal to the original complicated fraction. Thus, the coefficients of x in the numerators must be equal. Similarly, the constant terms of both fractions must be equal.
$A + 3B = 1$ $-2A + 5B = -5$ ← *2 equations* *2 unknowns*	This gives you a system of two equations in two unknowns. You can solve the system.
$A = 1 - 3B$ *solve by substitution* $-2(1 - 3B) + 5B = -5$ *substitute for A* $-2 + 6B + 5B = -5$ *distribute* $11B = -3$ $B = \frac{-3}{11}$ $A = 1 - 3B$ $B = \frac{-3}{11}$ $A = 1 - 3(\frac{-3}{11})$ $A = 1 + \frac{9}{11} = \frac{11}{11} + \frac{9}{11}$ $A = \frac{20}{11}$ $\frac{\frac{20}{11}}{(3x+5)} + \frac{\frac{-3}{11}}{(x-2)} = \frac{x-5}{(3x+5)(x-2)}$	Using substitution, you can eliminate A to find B. Substitute B into an "original" equation to find A. Now that you have found the values of A and B, you can write the complicated fraction as the sum of two simpler fractions.

Sample problems:

1. Write the partial fraction decomposition of $\frac{2x+2}{x^2-4}$.

   Solution: $\frac{\frac{1}{2}}{x+2} + \frac{\frac{3}{2}}{x-2}$

   Explanation: Factor denominator: $\frac{2x+2}{x^2-4} = \frac{2x+2}{(x+2)(x-2)}$. Express as a partial fraction: $\frac{2x+2}{(x+2)(x-2)} = \frac{A}{x+2} + \frac{B}{x-2}$.

   Create a common denominator and simplify the numerator: $\frac{A}{x+2} + \frac{B}{x-2} = \frac{A(x-2)}{(x+2)(x-2)} + \frac{B(x+2)}{(x+2)(x-2)} =$

   $\frac{Ax - 2A + Bx + 2B}{(x+2)(x-2)}$. Factor: $\frac{(A+B)x + (-2A+2B)}{(x+2)(x-2)}$. Thus, $A + B = 2$ since the coefficient of x in the original expression was 2, and $-2A + 2B = 2$ since the constant term in the original expression was 2. Solve:

   $2(A+B=2) \qquad 2A+2B=4$
   $-2A+2B=2 \Rightarrow \underline{+(-2A+2B=2)}$

   $$4B = 6;\ B = \frac{3}{2}.$$

   Find A: $A + \frac{3}{2} = 2;\ A = \frac{1}{2}$. So, $\frac{2x+2}{x^2-4} = \frac{\frac{1}{2}}{x+2} + \frac{\frac{3}{2}}{x-2}$.

2. Write the partial fraction decomposition of $\frac{2}{x^2+3x}$.

Solution: $\frac{\frac{2}{3}}{x}+\frac{\frac{-2}{3}}{x+3}$

Explanation: Factor denominator: $\frac{2}{x^2+3x}=\frac{2}{x(x+3)}$. Express as partial fraction: $\frac{2}{x(x+3)}=\frac{A}{x}+\frac{B}{x+3}$.

Create a common denominator and simplify the numerator: $\frac{A(x+3)}{x(x+3)}+\frac{Bx}{x(x+3)}=\frac{Ax+3A+Bx}{x(x+3)}$.

Factor by grouping the x terms: $\frac{Ax+3A+Bx}{x(x+3)}=\frac{(A+B)x+3A}{x(x+3)}$.

$A+B$ must equal the coefficient of x in the original expression, however there is no x term, so $A+B=0$.
The constant term in original expression must equal 3, so $3A=2$.

Solve for A: $A=\frac{2}{3}$. Find B: $\left(\frac{2}{3}\right)+B=0$; $B=-\frac{2}{3}$. Thus, $\frac{2}{x^2+3x}=\frac{\frac{2}{3}}{x}+\frac{\frac{-2}{3}}{x+3}$.

3. Write the partial fraction decomposition of $\frac{-4x+16}{(x-6)(x-2)}$.

Solution: $\frac{-2}{x-6}+\frac{-2}{x-2}$

Explanation: Express as a partial fraction with A and B representing the numerators:
$\frac{-4x+16}{(x-6)(x-2)}=\frac{A}{x-6}+\frac{B}{x-2}$.
Create a common denominator and simplify the numerator:
$\frac{A}{x-6}+\frac{B}{x-2}=\frac{A(x-2)+B(x-6)}{(x-6)(x-2)}=\frac{Ax-2A+Bx-6B}{(x-6)(x-2)}$.
Factor the numerator by grouping the x terms:
$\frac{Ax-2A+Bx-6B}{(x-6)(x-2)}=\frac{Ax+Bx-2A-6B}{(x-6)(x-2)}=\frac{(A+B)x+(-2A-6B)}{(x-6)(x-2)}$.
Thus, $A+B=-4$ since the coefficient of x in the original expression was -4,
and $-2A-6B=16$ since the constant term in the original expression was 16.
Solve the system, $A+B=-4$ and $-2A-6B=16$:

$$\begin{array}{lcl} 2(A+B=-4) & & 2A+2B=-8 \\ -2A-6B=16 & \Rightarrow & \underline{+(-2A-6B=16)} \\ & & -4B=8;\ B=-2. \end{array}$$

Use the value for B to solve for A: $A+B=-4 \Rightarrow$
$A+(-2)=-4$; $A=-2$. So, $\frac{-4x+16}{(x-6)(x-2)}=\frac{-2}{x-6}+\frac{-2}{x-2}$.

Practice problems: *(Answers on page: 763)*

1. Write the partial fraction decomposition of $\frac{3}{x^2+4x+3}$.

2. Write the partial fraction decomposition of $\frac{4}{2x^2-5x-3}$.

3. Write the partial fraction decomposition of $\frac{9x-7}{(x+1)(x-3)}$.

Review questions: *(Answers to odd questions on page: 763)*

1. Write the partial fraction decomposition of $\dfrac{3x-5}{x^2-5x+6}$.
2. Write the partial fraction decomposition of $\dfrac{-3x-9}{(x+1)(x-1)}$.
3. Write the partial fraction decomposition of $\dfrac{2x-3}{x(x+5)}$.
4. Write the partial fraction decomposition of $\dfrac{4x}{2x^2+3x-2}$.
5. Write the partial fraction decomposition of $\dfrac{3x}{x^2-2x-8}$.

Solving Nonlinear Systems Using Elimination

- Linear equations only involve variables raised to the first power.
- Equations that are not linear are called **nonlinear equations**. You can solve systems of nonlinear equations using many of the same methods used to solve systems of linear equations such as substitution or elimination.

<table>
<tr><td>Nonlinear Systems of Equations</td><td>Up to this point we have only looked at systems of linear equations. Linear equations only involve the sums and differences of variables.

Nonlinear equations can involve variables raised to different powers, variables in exponential expressions, trigonometric functions, and any number of other exotic things. The good news is that the methods you have learned to solve linear systems will often work on nonlinear systems.</td></tr>
<tr><td>$\frac{2}{x}+\frac{1}{y}=\frac{3}{2}$
$\frac{3}{x}-\frac{1}{y}=1$
Add equations using elimination method:
$\frac{2}{x}+\cancel{\frac{1}{y}}=\frac{3}{2}$
$+\ \frac{3}{x}-\cancel{\frac{1}{y}}=1$ or $\frac{2}{2}$
$\frac{5}{x}=\frac{5}{2}$
$x=2$</td><td>Here is a system of nonlinear equations. There are xs and ys in the denominators of fractions. How can you solve this system?

Try eliminating the y variable. If you add the two equations, the $1/y$ terms cancel out.

You can use the resulting equation to solve for x. In this case, you can cross multiply to find that $x = 2$.</td></tr>
</table>

How to find y? **Plug 2 into x in either equation and solve for y.** $\frac{2}{x}+\frac{1}{y}=\frac{3}{2} \longrightarrow \frac{2}{2}+\frac{1}{y}=\frac{3}{2}$ $\frac{3}{x}-\frac{1}{y}=1$ subtract $\frac{2}{2}$ from both sides $\frac{1}{y}=\frac{1}{2}$ $y=2$	Now substitute $x=2$ back into one of the equations and solve for y. No sweat!
$\frac{2}{x}+\frac{1}{y}=\frac{3}{2} \longrightarrow \frac{2}{2}+\frac{1}{2}=\frac{3}{2}$ ✓ $\frac{3}{x}-\frac{1}{y}=1 \longrightarrow \frac{3}{2}-\frac{1}{2}=1$ ✓	**REMEMBER:** Whenever you solve a system of equations, you can always check your answers by substituting back into the equations. And it's a good idea to do this.

Sample problems:

1. Solve the system: $x^2+y^2=9$
   $2x^2+3y^2=18$

   Solution: (3, 0); (−3, 0)

   Explanation: Use the elimination method to solve the system. Multiply the fist equation by 3, then subtract the equations:

$$\begin{matrix} 3(x^2+y^2=9) \\ 2x^2+3y^2=18 \end{matrix} \Rightarrow \begin{array}{r} 3x^2+3y^2=27 \\ -(2x^2+3y^2=18) \\ \hline x^2=9 \end{array}$$

   $x^2=9$, so $x=\pm 3$. Now substitute each x value into either equation and solve for y: $x=3 \Rightarrow (3)^2+y^2=9;\ 9+y^2=9;\ y^2=0;\ y=0$, and $x=-3 \Rightarrow (-3)^2+y^2=9;\ 9+y^2=9;\ y^2=0;\ y=0$. Thus, there are 2 solutions: $x=3, y=0$ and $x=-3, y=0$, or (3, 0) and (−3, 0).

2. Solve the system: $x^2+y^2=4$
   $x^2+y^2=9$

   Solution: No Solution

   Explanation: Visualize the graph of each equation: $x^2+y^2=4$ is a circle centered at (0, 0) with radius 2 and $x^2+y^2=9$ is a circle centered at (0, 0) with radius 3. The solution of the system is the point(s) where the graphs intersect. However, these graphs never intersect, thus no solution. Or, solve algebraically using the elimination method:

$$\begin{array}{r} x^2+y^2=4 \\ -(x^2+y^2=9) \\ \hline 0=13 \end{array}$$

   $0=13$. This is a false statement, so the system has no solution.

3. Find all the points where the graphs of $x^2 + y^2 = 5$ and $y = x^2 - 3$ intersect.
Solution: $(1,-2)$; $(-1,-2)$; $(2, 1)$; $(-2, 1)$
Explanation: Visualize the graphs: $x^2 + y^2 = 5$ is a circle and $y = x^2 - 3$ is a parabola. These types of graphs may intersect at 1, 2, 3, or 4 points. The elimination method may be used to solve the system since at least one of the variables in the 2 equations have matching exponents. Arrange the equations for elimination: $x^2 + y^2 = 5 \quad x^2 + y^2 = 5$
$y = x^2 - 3 \Rightarrow -x^2 + y = -3$. Add the equations:
$$\begin{array}{r} x^2 + y^2 = 5 \\ +\left(-x^2 + y = -3\right) \\ \hline y^2 + y = 2. \end{array}$$
Solve this quadratic equation for y: $y^2 + y = 2$; $y^2 + y - 2 = 0$; $(y+2)(y-1) = 0$; $y + 2 = 0$ or $y - 1 = 0$; $y = -2$ or $y = 1$.
Now substitute each y value into either equation and solve for x to find the corresponding x – value(s):
$y = -2 \Rightarrow -2 = x^2 - 3$; $x^2 = 1$; $x = \sqrt{1}$; $x = \pm 1$, and $y = 1 \Rightarrow 1 = x^2 - 3$; $x^2 = 4$; $x = \sqrt{4}$; $x = \pm 2$.
Thus, when $y = -2$, $x = \pm 1$ and when $y = 1$, $x = \pm 2$. So the circle and the parabola intersect at 4 points: $(1,-2)$; $(-1,-2)$; $(2, 1)$; $(-2, 1)$.

Practice problems: *(Answers on page: 763)*

1. Solve the system:
$x^2 + y^2 = 8$
$x^2 - y^2 = 0$
2. Find all the points where
$x^2 + y^2 = 25$ and
$x = 5 - y^2$ intersect.
3. Solve the system:
$3x^2 + 3y^2 = 0$
$x^2 + y^2 = 5$

Review questions: *(Answers to odd questions on page: 763)*

1. Solve the system: $x^2 + 2y^2 = 11$; $3x^2 + 4y = 23$
2. Solve the system: $2x^2 - 3y^2 = 6$; $3x^2 + 2y^2 = 35$
3. Solve the system: $x^2 + y^2 + 2x - y = 14$; $x^2 + y^2 + x - 2y = 9$
4. Solve the system: $3x^2 - y^2 = 11$; $x^2 + 4y^2 = 8$
5. Solve the system: $x^2 + y^2 = 9$; $x^2 - y^2 = 1$

Solving Nonlinear Systems by Substitution

- **Nonlinear equations** can involve such components as variables raised to different powers, variables in exponential expressions, or trigonometric functions. You can solve systems of nonlinear equations using many of the same methods used to solve systems of linear equations such as substitution or elimination.

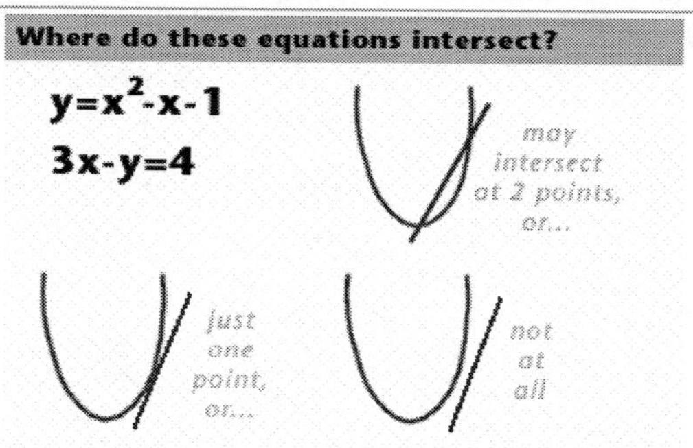

This system of equations is nonlinear because there is an x^2 term in the first equation.

The first equation in the system is described by a parabola and the second equation is described by a line. Depending on how the parabola and line intersect, there may be zero, one, or two solutions to this nonlinear system.

$y=x^2-x-1 \rightarrow 3x-4=x^2-x-1$

$3x-y=4$

$y=\boxed{3x-4}$

$0=x^2-4x+3$

$0=(x-1)(x-3)$

$\boxed{x=1}$ $\boxed{x=3}$

Insert this value for y in first equation to solve for x

You can solve the system by substitution.

Use the second equation to find an expression for y in terms of x. Plug this expression in for y in the first equation. The result is a quadratic equation in x.

Factor the quadratic equation to solve for x. There are two solutions.

$y=x^2-x-1$

$3x-y=4$

$\boxed{x=1}$	$\boxed{x=3}$
plug in to find y:	plug in to find y:
$y=(1)^2-(1)-1$	$y=(3)^2-(3)-1$
$\boxed{y=-1}$	$\boxed{y=5}$

Now look back at the original equations.

To find the values of y that correspond to each value of x, just substitute into one of the equations.

$y=x^2-x-1$

$3x-y=4$

$\boxed{(1,-1) \text{ and } (3,5)}$

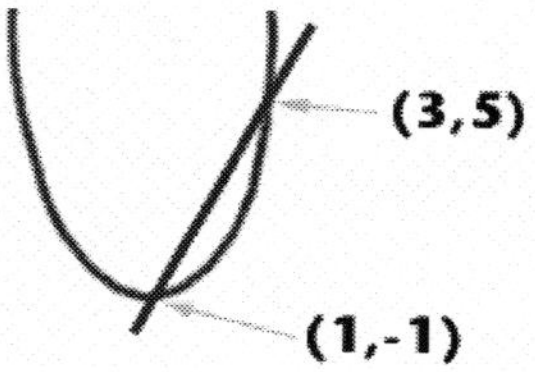

There are two solutions to this nonlinear system: (1, -1) and (3, 5). The parabola and line intersect at two points.

Sample problems:

1. Solve the system: $x^2 - y^2 = 16$
   $x - y = 2$

   Solution: (5, 3)

   Explanation: This system cannot be solved with the elimination method, so use the substitution method. The first step is to solve one of the equations for either x or y, so consider which equation and which variable will produce the simplest equation. Solve the second equation for x: $x - y = 2 \Rightarrow x = y + 2$. Now substitute $(y+2)$ into the other equation for x: $x^2 - y^2 = 16 \Rightarrow (y+2)^2 - y^2 = 16$. Simplify and solve for y: $y^2 + 4y + 4 - y^2 = 16$; $4y + 4 = 16$; $y + 1 = 4$; $y = 3$. Find x by substituting $y = 3$ into the easiest equation, then solve for x: $x - y = 2 \Rightarrow x - 3 = 2$; $x = 5$. Thus the solution is $x = 5$ and $y = 3$, or (5, 3).

2. Find the point(s) where the graphs of $x^2 + y^2 = 1$ and $y = \frac{1}{5}x + 9$ intersect.

   Solution: the graphs do no intersect

   Explanation: Visualize the graphs of each equation. The circle formed by $x^2 + y^2 = 1$ has its center at (0, 0) and the radius is 1. The line formed by $y = \frac{1}{5}x + 9$ crosses the y-axis at 9 and the slope is $\frac{1}{5}$, so it is almost horizontal. Since the line is so high and flat, it is apparent that the two graphs do not intersect. If the system is solved algebraically, the solution is imaginary, thus no real solution.

3. Solve the system: $2x + y = 7$
   $x^2 + xy - 12 = 0$

   Solution: $(4,-1)$; $(3,1)$

   Explanation: Solve the first equation for y: $y = 7 - 2x$. Substitute $(7-2x)$ in the second equation for y, simplify, and solve: $x^2 + xy - 12 = 0 \Rightarrow x^2 + x(7-2x) - 12 = 0$; $x^2 + 7x - 2x^2 - 12 = 0$;
   $-x^2 + 7x - 12 = 0$; $x^2 - 7x + 12 = 0$; $(x-3)(x-4) = 0$; $x - 3 = 0$ or $x - 4 = 0$; $x = 3$ or $x = 4$.
   Substitute each x value into either equation and solve for y:
   $x = 3 \Rightarrow 2(3) + y = 7$; $6 + y = 7$; $y = 1$, and $x = 4 \Rightarrow 2(4) + y = 7$; $8 + y = 7$; $y = -1$.
   Thus, when $x = 3$, $y = 1$ and when $x = 4$, $y = -1$, or $(3,1)$; $(4,-1)$.

Practice problems: *(Answers on page: 763)*

1. Solve the system: $x^2 + y^2 = 9$; $-x + y = 3$
2. Solve the system: $2x^2 + 3y = 33$; $4x + y = -7$
3. Solve the system: $xy = 6$; $2y = 3x - 16$

Review questions: *(Answers to odd questions on page: 763)*

1. Solve the system: $2x^2 - y^2 = 14$; $x - y = 1$
2. Solve the system: $xy + x^2 = 24$; $y - 3x + 4 = 0$
3. Solve the system: $3xy - 10x = y$; $2 - y + x = 0$
4. Solve the system: $x^2 + y^2 = 8$; $x + y = 0$
5. Solve the system: $y + x^2 = 4$; $y + 4x = 16$

An Introduction to Matrices

- A **matrix** is a rectangular block of numbers. The plural of matrix is matrices.
- Systems of linear equations can be represented by matrices.

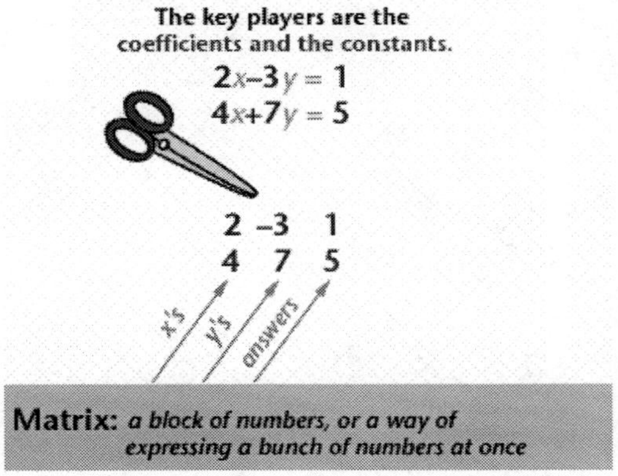

Consider this system of two linear equations. It is the coefficients and constants that differentiate this linear system from any other linear system.

If you write the coefficients and constants in a rectangular block, you can do it in such a way that the first column of numbers contains the coefficients of the x-terms, the second column contains the coefficients of the y-terms, and the third column contains the constants. A rectangular block of numbers such as this one is known as a **matrix**.

$\begin{bmatrix} 1 & 3 & 2 \\ 1 & 4 & 0 \end{bmatrix}$	Here is another matrix. It is a 2 x 3 matrix, or a "two by three matrix," because it has two rows and three columns.
$\begin{bmatrix} 2 & 1 & 0 \\ 3 & -1 & 4 \\ 1 & 1 & 2 \end{bmatrix}$	Here is a 3 x 3 matrix. It has three rows and three columns.
$\begin{bmatrix} 1 \\ 3 \\ -1 \end{bmatrix}$	This is a 3 x 1 matrix. It has three rows and one column.

Sample problems:

1. Represent the following system of equations with an augmented matrix: $\begin{matrix} x+5y=7 \\ 3x-y=0 \end{matrix}$.

   Solution: $\begin{bmatrix} 1 & 5 & 7 \\ 3 & -1 & 0 \end{bmatrix}$

   Explanation: An augmented matrix is a list of the coefficients and constants from a system. List the coefficients and constants of each equation in two rows: $\begin{bmatrix} 1 & 5 & 7 \\ 3 & -1 & 0 \end{bmatrix}$, which is a 2×3 matrix.

2. Write the system of equations that corresponds with the following augmented matrix: $\begin{bmatrix} 5 & 1 & 0 & -6 \\ 3 & -2 & 9 & 0 \\ 4 & \frac{1}{2} & -7 & 1 \end{bmatrix}$.

   Solution: $5x+y=-6;\ 3x-2y+9z=0;\ 4x+\frac{1}{2}y-7z=1$

   Explanation: There are 3 rows in the matrix, so there will be 3 equations in the system. There are 4 columns in the matrix, so there will be 3 variables in the system (use x, y, and z). Apply the coefficients from the matrix to the variables and end each equation with $=$ constant: $5x+y+0z=-6;\ 3x-2y+9z=0;$ $4x+\frac{1}{2}y-7z=1$. Simplify the first equation: $5x+y=-6$.

3. True or False: $\begin{bmatrix} 5 & 1 & -7 \end{bmatrix}$ is a 3×1 matrix.

   Solution: False

   Explanation: A 3×1 matrix has 3 rows and 1 column (rows are horizontal). The matrix $\begin{bmatrix} 5 & 1 & -7 \end{bmatrix}$ has 1 row and 3 columns, thus it is a 1×3 matrix.

Practice problems: *(Answers on page: 763)*

1. Represent the following system with an augmented matrix:
   $7x=4;\ 6x-3y+z=14;\ 2y-z=0$.
2. Write the system that corresponds with the following augmented matrix:
   $\begin{bmatrix} 5 & 1 & -4 & 7 & 0 \end{bmatrix}$.
3. Fill in the blanks:
   $\begin{bmatrix} a_1 & a_2 & a_3 & a_4 \\ b_1 & b_2 & b_3 & b_4 \end{bmatrix}$ is a ____ $\times$ ____ matrix.

Review questions: *(Answers to odd questions on page: 763)*

1. True or false: $\begin{bmatrix} 3 & 4 & 6 & 2 \end{bmatrix}$ is a 1×4 matrix
2. Represent the following system of equations with an augmented matrix: $2x + 6y = 12;\ \ 4x - 2y = 1.$
3. Represent the following system of equations with an augmented matrix: $7x + 9y = 1;\ \ 4y = 12;\ \ 8x + 2y = 5.$
4. Write the system that corresponds with the following augmented matrix:
$$\begin{bmatrix} 4 & 2 & 1 \\ -8 & 0 & 8 \end{bmatrix}$$
5. Write the system that corresponds with the following augmented matrix:
$$\begin{bmatrix} 5 & \frac{1}{2} & 9 & 6 \\ \frac{1}{3} & 0 & 0 & 3 \\ 0 & 4 & 2 & 8 \end{bmatrix}$$

The Arithmetic of Matrices

- To add or subtract **matrices**, they must have the same dimension, or shape. That means they must have the same number of columns and rows.
- Remember to use signs properly, especially when subtracting. The most common mistakes when using matrices occur when signs are incorrect.

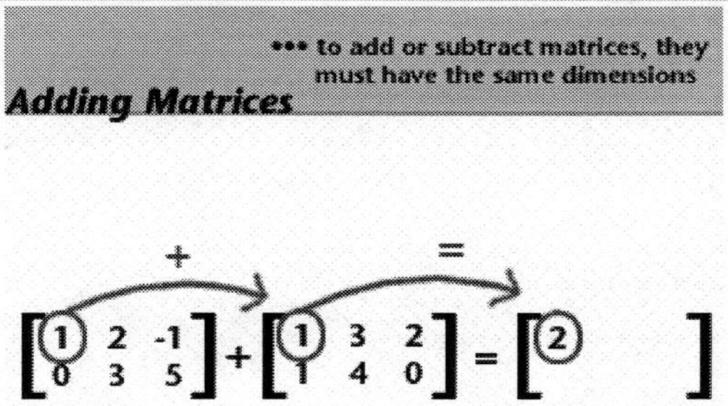	Adding or subtracting is a matter of combining elements in the same position in each matrix.
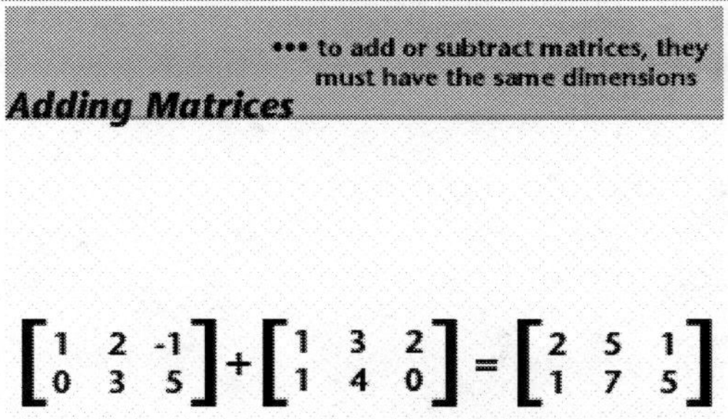	When all the terms have been combined the solution is a new matrix of the same dimension as those in the problems.

Adding Matrices ••• to add or subtract matrices, they must have the same dimensions

$$\begin{bmatrix} 1 & 2 & -1 \\ 0 & 3 & 5 \end{bmatrix} + \begin{bmatrix} 1 & 3 & 2 \\ 1 & 4 & 0 \end{bmatrix} = \begin{bmatrix} 2 & 5 & 1 \\ 1 & 7 & 5 \end{bmatrix}$$

Subtracting Matrices

$$\begin{bmatrix} 1 & 2 & -1 \\ 0 & 3 & 5 \end{bmatrix} - \begin{bmatrix} 1 & 3 & 2 \\ 1 & 4 & 0 \end{bmatrix} = \begin{bmatrix} 0 & -1 & -3 \\ -1 & -1 & 5 \end{bmatrix}$$

Subtracting matrices follows the same process. The terms in the same position combine to form the new term for their position in the solution matrix.

Sample problems:

1. Add: $\begin{bmatrix} 1 & 2 \\ 3 & 4 \end{bmatrix} + \begin{bmatrix} 5 & 6 \\ 7 & 8 \end{bmatrix}$

   Solution: $\begin{bmatrix} 6 & 8 \\ 10 & 12 \end{bmatrix}$

   Explanation: $\begin{bmatrix} 1 & 2 \\ 3 & 4 \end{bmatrix} + \begin{bmatrix} 5 & 6 \\ 7 & 8 \end{bmatrix} = \begin{bmatrix} 1+5 & 2+6 \\ 3+7 & 4+8 \end{bmatrix} = \begin{bmatrix} 6 & 8 \\ 10 & 12 \end{bmatrix}$

2. Subtract: $\begin{bmatrix} -2 & 4 \\ 6 & -3 \\ \frac{1}{4} & -\frac{3}{4} \end{bmatrix} - \begin{bmatrix} 1 & \frac{2}{3} \\ -2 & 5 \\ -\frac{1}{4} & 4 \end{bmatrix}$

   Solution: $\begin{bmatrix} -3 & \frac{10}{3} \\ 8 & -8 \\ \frac{1}{2} & -\frac{19}{4} \end{bmatrix}$

   Explanation: $\begin{bmatrix} -2 & 4 \\ 6 & -3 \\ \frac{1}{4} & -\frac{3}{4} \end{bmatrix} - \begin{bmatrix} 1 & \frac{2}{3} \\ -2 & 5 \\ -\frac{1}{4} & 4 \end{bmatrix} = \begin{bmatrix} -2-1 & 4-\frac{2}{3} \\ 6-(-2) & -3-5 \\ \frac{1}{4}-\left(-\frac{1}{4}\right) & -\frac{3}{4}-4 \end{bmatrix} = \begin{bmatrix} -3 & \frac{10}{3} \\ 8 & -8 \\ \frac{1}{2} & -\frac{19}{4} \end{bmatrix}$

3. Subtract: $\begin{bmatrix} 5 & -3 & 2 \end{bmatrix} - \begin{bmatrix} 1 \\ -2 \\ 7 \end{bmatrix}$.

   Solution: Not possible

   Explanation: In order to add or subtract two matrices, they must have the same dimensions. Since the first matrix is 1×3 and the second is 3×1, these matrices cannot be subtracted.

Practice problems: *(Answers on page: 763)*

1. Add: $\begin{bmatrix} -2 & 4 \\ 6 & -3 \\ \frac{1}{4} & -\frac{3}{4} \end{bmatrix} + \begin{bmatrix} 1 & \frac{2}{3} \\ -2 & 5 \\ -\frac{1}{4} & 4 \end{bmatrix}$

2. Subtract: $\begin{bmatrix} \frac{3}{4} & -3 & 2 \end{bmatrix} - \begin{bmatrix} 1 & \frac{2}{3} \\ -4 & 5 \\ -\frac{1}{4} & 4 \end{bmatrix}$

3. Add: $\begin{bmatrix} 5 & -8 \\ 2 & 3 \\ -5 & 1 \end{bmatrix} + \begin{bmatrix} -3 & 4 \\ 4 & -2 \\ 1 & 7 \end{bmatrix}$

Review questions: *(Answers to odd questions on page: 763)*

1. Add: $\begin{bmatrix} 1 & 3 \\ 5 & 7 \end{bmatrix} + \begin{bmatrix} 2 & 4 \\ 6 & 8 \end{bmatrix}$

2. Subtract: $\begin{bmatrix} 1 & 2 \\ 3 & 4 \end{bmatrix} - \begin{bmatrix} 5 & 6 \\ 7 & 8 \end{bmatrix}$

3. Subtract: $\begin{bmatrix} 2 \\ 3 \\ -8 \end{bmatrix} - \begin{bmatrix} -1 \\ 4 \\ -3 \end{bmatrix}$

4. Add: $\begin{bmatrix} -1 & 4 & 8 \\ 3 & -2 & 1 \\ 5 & 7 & 6 \end{bmatrix} + \begin{bmatrix} \frac{1}{4} & -9 & -2 \\ 1 & \frac{1}{2} & 0 \\ -6 & -5 & 4 \end{bmatrix}$

5. Subtract: $\begin{bmatrix} 1 & 3 \\ 5 & 7 \end{bmatrix} - \begin{bmatrix} 7 \\ 4 \end{bmatrix}$

Multiplying Matrices by a Scalar

- A **scalar** is a single element, a number or constant, by which a matrix is multiplied.
- **Scalar multiplication** of a matrix is the process of multiplying each element of the matrix with the scalar to create a new matrix of enhanced elements.
- You can add and subtract matrices only if they have the same dimension.

$5\begin{bmatrix} 1 \\ 3 \\ -1 \end{bmatrix} = \begin{bmatrix} 5 \\ 15 \\ -5 \end{bmatrix}$ *mulitply along red lines*	Using this 3x1 matrix and multiplying by 5 as the scalar, you have an example of scalar multiplication. The multiplication is marked for you with the lines. Following these lines, you see that the scalar multiplies individually with each term in the matrix to create the terms for the solution matrix.
$4\begin{bmatrix} 1 & 4 \\ 0 & 7 \\ -1 & 2 \end{bmatrix} = \begin{bmatrix} 4 & 16 \\ 0 & 28 \\ -4 & 8 \end{bmatrix}$	This example shows a 3x2 multiplying with 4 to create a new matrix. The first product is marked for you with the line and circles. The remaining terms in the solution matrix are each created in the same way as this first term, by multiplying 4 with the existing term.

$$5\begin{bmatrix} 1 & 3 & 2 \\ 1 & 4 & 0 \end{bmatrix} + 4\begin{bmatrix} 1 & 2 & -1 \\ 0 & 3 & 5 \end{bmatrix}$$

$$\begin{bmatrix} 5 & 15 & 10 \\ 5 & 20 & 0 \end{bmatrix} + \begin{bmatrix} 4 & 8 & -4 \\ 0 & 12 & 20 \end{bmatrix}$$

$$\boxed{\begin{bmatrix} 9 & 23 & 6 \\ 5 & 32 & 20 \end{bmatrix}}$$

In this problem you are adding two matrices after each of them has multiplied with a scalar.

Note that you multiply each matrix first.

Then you add each term position to its matching term to create your final solution matrix.

Sample problems:

1. Multiply: $-5\begin{bmatrix} 1 \\ 3 \\ 5 \end{bmatrix}$

Solution: $\begin{bmatrix} -5 \\ -15 \\ -25 \end{bmatrix}$

Explanation: $-5\begin{bmatrix} 1 \\ 3 \\ 5 \end{bmatrix} = \begin{bmatrix} 1(-5) \\ 3(-5) \\ 5(-5) \end{bmatrix} = \begin{bmatrix} -5 \\ -15 \\ -25 \end{bmatrix}$

2. Multiply: $3\begin{bmatrix} 1 & 2 \\ 3 & 4 \end{bmatrix}$

Solution: $\begin{bmatrix} 3 & 6 \\ 9 & 12 \end{bmatrix}$

Explanation: $3\begin{bmatrix} 1 & 2 \\ 3 & 4 \end{bmatrix} = \begin{bmatrix} 1(3) & 2(3) \\ 3(3) & 4(3) \end{bmatrix} = \begin{bmatrix} 3 & 6 \\ 9 & 12 \end{bmatrix}$

3. Simplify: $\frac{1}{3}\begin{bmatrix} 9 & -1 \\ -3 & 0 \\ \frac{3}{2} & 12 \end{bmatrix} - \frac{1}{2}\begin{bmatrix} 4 & 6 \\ -\frac{2}{3} & -6 \\ 2 & 0 \end{bmatrix}$

Solution: $\begin{bmatrix} 1 & -\frac{10}{3} \\ -\frac{2}{3} & 3 \\ -\frac{1}{2} & 4 \end{bmatrix}$

Explanation: $\frac{1}{3}\begin{bmatrix} 9 & -1 \\ -3 & 0 \\ \frac{3}{2} & 12 \end{bmatrix} - \frac{1}{2}\begin{bmatrix} 4 & 6 \\ -\frac{2}{3} & -6 \\ 2 & 0 \end{bmatrix} = \begin{bmatrix} 9\left(\frac{1}{3}\right) & -1\left(\frac{1}{3}\right) \\ -3\left(\frac{1}{3}\right) & 0\left(\frac{1}{3}\right) \\ \frac{3}{2}\left(\frac{1}{3}\right) & 12\left(\frac{1}{3}\right) \end{bmatrix} - \begin{bmatrix} 4\left(\frac{1}{2}\right) & 6\left(\frac{1}{2}\right) \\ -\frac{2}{3}\left(\frac{1}{2}\right) & -6\left(\frac{1}{2}\right) \\ 2\left(\frac{1}{2}\right) & 0\left(\frac{1}{2}\right) \end{bmatrix}$

$= \begin{bmatrix} 3 & -\frac{1}{3} \\ -1 & 0 \\ \frac{1}{2} & 4 \end{bmatrix} - \begin{bmatrix} 2 & 3 \\ -\frac{1}{3} & -3 \\ 1 & 0 \end{bmatrix} = \begin{bmatrix} 3-2 & -\frac{1}{3}-3 \\ -1+\frac{1}{3} & 0+3 \\ \frac{1}{2}-1 & 4-0 \end{bmatrix} = \begin{bmatrix} 1 & -\frac{10}{3} \\ -\frac{2}{3} & 3 \\ -\frac{1}{2} & 4 \end{bmatrix}$

Practice problems: *(Answers on page: 763)*

1. Multiply: $2\begin{bmatrix} 4 & 6 & 8 \end{bmatrix}$

2. Multiply: $-4\begin{bmatrix} 2 & 4 \\ 6 & 1 \end{bmatrix}$

3. Simplify: $\frac{1}{2}\begin{bmatrix} -1 & 0 \\ -4 & 6 \end{bmatrix}+\frac{1}{3}\begin{bmatrix} 9 & -3 \\ -12 & 3 \end{bmatrix}$

Review questions: *(Answers to odd questions on page: 764)*

1. Multiply: $-\frac{1}{2}\begin{bmatrix} 6 & -5 & -2 \end{bmatrix}$

2. Multiply: $-3\begin{bmatrix} -1 & 6 \\ 3 & -4 \\ -5 & 2 \end{bmatrix}$

3. Multiply: $\frac{1}{4}\begin{bmatrix} 9 & -4 & -\frac{4}{5} \\ -6 & 4 & 0 \\ 2 & \frac{1}{2} & -1 \end{bmatrix}$

4. Simplify: $-5\begin{bmatrix} 3 & 4 & 5 \\ 1 & 2 & -3 \end{bmatrix}+2\begin{bmatrix} 0 & -1 & 5 \\ 1 & 2 & 3 \end{bmatrix}$

5. Simplify: $-5\begin{bmatrix} 3 & 4 & 5 \\ 1 & -2 & -3 \end{bmatrix}-2\begin{bmatrix} 0 & -1 & 5 \\ 1 & 2 & 3 \end{bmatrix}$

Multiplying Matrices

- To successfully multiply two matrices, the number of columns in the left matrix must equal the number of rows in the right matrix.
- It is possible that one matrix can multiply with a second matrix, but not be able to multiply if their positions are reversed.
- The dimension of a matrix is referred to by the number of rows x the number of columns.
- The solution matrix will have the same number of rows as the left matrix and the same number of columns as the right matrix.

$\begin{bmatrix} 1 & 3 & 2 \\ 1 & 4 & 0 \end{bmatrix} \times \begin{bmatrix} 1 & 1 & 2 & -1 \\ 3 & 0 & 0 & 4 \\ -1 & 1 & 5 & 1 \end{bmatrix}$	Matrices are not required to have the same dimension in order to multiply. However, the matrix on the left **must** have the same number of columns as the matrix on the right has number of rows; i.e., **Left # columns = Right #rows**
$\begin{bmatrix} 1 & 3 & 2 \\ 1 & 4 & 0 \end{bmatrix} \times \begin{bmatrix} 1 & 1 & 2 & -1 \\ 3 & 0 & 0 & 4 \\ -1 & 1 & 5 & 1 \end{bmatrix} =$ $(1)(1)+(3)(3)+(2)(-1)=8$ $=\begin{bmatrix} 8 & & & \end{bmatrix}$	To multiply a matrix, create each element in the solution matrix one at a time. To create the first term in the first row: 1. Combine left's row 1 with right's column 1, by multiplying and adding as shown – the first term multiplying with the first term + the second term multiplying with the second term + the third term multiplying with the third term. 2. Write the total, 8, in the position for the first element of the solution matrix.

$= \begin{bmatrix} 8 & \textcircled{3} & & \end{bmatrix}$ (1)(1)+(3)(0)+(2)(1)=3	To create the second term in the first row of the solution matrix, multiply and add left's first row with right's first column in the same manner as above. Your total value is 3 and it is placed in the second position in the first row.
$\begin{bmatrix} 8 & 3 & 12 & \textcircled{13} \end{bmatrix}$ *1st row, 4th column*	Now, in the same manner, complete the first row.

Sample problems:

1. Find the product of the following matrices if possible: $\begin{bmatrix} 1 & 0 & -3 \end{bmatrix} \begin{bmatrix} 2 & 1 & -3 \\ -4 & 3 & 5 \\ 0 & 2 & -1 \end{bmatrix}$.

   Solution: $\begin{bmatrix} 2 & -5 & 0 \end{bmatrix}$
   Explanation: Multiply the entries in row (1) of the first matrix by the entries in column (1) of the second matrix and add the products: $1(2)+0(-4)+(-3)(0)=2+0+0=2$.
   Repeat this procedure for each column of the second matrix to create the first row of the product matrix: $1(1)+0(3)+(-3)(2)=1+0-6=-5$; $1(-3)+0(5)+(-3)(-1)=-3+0+3=0$.
   The product matrix is $\begin{bmatrix} 2 & -5 & 0 \end{bmatrix}$.

2. Find the product of the following matrices if possible: $\begin{bmatrix} 8 & 5 \\ 2 & 7 \\ 4 & 1 \end{bmatrix} \begin{bmatrix} 5 \\ -1 \end{bmatrix}$.

   Solution: $\begin{bmatrix} 35 \\ 3 \\ 19 \end{bmatrix}$
   Explanation: Multiply row (1) of the first matrix by column (1) of the second matrix and add the products: $8(5)+5(-1)=40-5=35$. Repeat for each row to create column (1) of the product matrix: $2(5)+7(-1)=10-7=3$; $4(5)+1(-1)=20-1=19$.
   The product matrix is $\begin{bmatrix} 35 \\ 3 \\ 19 \end{bmatrix}$.

3. Find the product of the following matrices if possible: $\begin{bmatrix} 1 & 0 \\ 3 & 2 \\ 1 & -5 \end{bmatrix}\begin{bmatrix} -2 & 0 & 3 \\ 2 & -3 & 0 \end{bmatrix}$.

<u>Solution:</u> $\begin{bmatrix} -2 & 0 & 3 \\ -2 & -6 & 9 \\ -12 & 15 & 3 \end{bmatrix}$

<u>Explanation:</u> Multiply row (1) of the first matrix by column (1) of the second matrix and add the products: $1(-2)+0(2)=-2+0=-2$. Repeat for each column of the second matrix to create row (1) of the product matrix: $1(0)+0(-3)=0+0=0$; $1(3)+0(0)=3+0=3$, so row (1) of the product matrix is $[-2 \quad 0 \quad 3]$.
Multiply row (2) of the first matrix by column (1) of the second matrix and add the products and repeat for each column of the second matrix to create row (2) of the product matrix: $3(-2)+2(2)=-6+4=-2$; $3(0)+2(-3)=0-6=-6$; $3(3)+2(0)=9+0=9$.
Multiply row (3) of the first matrix by column (1) of the second matrix and add the products and repeat for each column of the second matrix to create row (3) of the product matrix: $1(-2)+(-5)(2)=-2-10=-12$; $1(0)+(-5)(-3)=0+15=15$; $1(3)+(-5)(0)=3+0=3$.

The product matrix is $\begin{bmatrix} -2 & 0 & 3 \\ -2 & -6 & 9 \\ -12 & 15 & 3 \end{bmatrix}$.

Practice problems: *(Answers on page: 764)*

1. Find the product of the following matrices if possible: $\begin{bmatrix} -3 & 6 & 2 \end{bmatrix}\begin{bmatrix} -2 & 4 \\ 0 & -3 \\ 1 & 2 \end{bmatrix}$.

2. Find the product of the following matrices if possible: $\begin{bmatrix} 2 & -1 & 4 & 5 \\ 3 & -2 & 1 & -3 \end{bmatrix}\begin{bmatrix} 2 & 0 \\ -1 & 5 \end{bmatrix}$.

3. Find the product of the following matrices if possible: $\begin{bmatrix} -3 & 3 & -2 \\ 2 & 0 & -2 \\ -1 & 1 & 0 \end{bmatrix}\begin{bmatrix} -3 & 3 & -2 \\ 2 & 0 & -2 \\ -1 & 1 & 0 \end{bmatrix}$.

Review questions: *(Answers to odd questions on page: 764)*

1. Find the product of the following matrices if possible: $\begin{bmatrix} 2 & 3 \\ 5 & 4 \end{bmatrix}\begin{bmatrix} 2 \\ 3 \end{bmatrix}$.

2. Find the product of the following matrices if possible: $\begin{bmatrix} -4 & 6 & -1 \\ 1 & 0 & -2 \end{bmatrix}\begin{bmatrix} 1 \\ 0 \\ -3 \end{bmatrix}$.

3. Find the product of the following matrices if possible: $\begin{bmatrix} 2 & 0 & 3 \\ -1 & 1 & 4 \end{bmatrix}\begin{bmatrix} 1 & 0 \\ -2 & 5 \\ -1 & 3 \end{bmatrix}$.

4. Find the product of the following matrices if possible: $\begin{bmatrix} 2 & 4 \\ 1 & 3 \\ 0 & 5 \end{bmatrix}\begin{bmatrix} 6 & 4 \\ 0 & -1 \end{bmatrix}$.

5. Find the product of the following matrices if possible: $\begin{bmatrix} 1 & 5 & -2 \\ 0 & 4 & 3 \\ 7 & 5 & 1 \end{bmatrix}\begin{bmatrix} 2 & 6 \\ -1 & 1 \\ 4 & -2 \end{bmatrix}$.

Can They Multiply?

- To successfully multiply matrices, the number of columns in the left matrix must equal the number of rows in the right matrix.
- It is possible that one matrix can multiply with a second matrix, but not be able to multiply if their positions are reversed.
- The **dimension of a matrix** is referred to by the number of rows x the number of columns.
- The solution matrix will have the same number of rows as the left matrix and the same number of columns as the right matrix.

To successfully multiply matrices **the number of columns in the left matrix must equal the number of rows in the right matrix** $\begin{bmatrix}2&1&0\\3&-1&4\\1&1&2\end{bmatrix}\begin{bmatrix}1\\3\\-1\end{bmatrix}=$ $=\begin{bmatrix}5\\ \\ \end{bmatrix}$ (2)(1)+(1)(3)+(0)(-1)=5	To multiply, multiply each term in the **row from the left matrix** with its corresponding term in the **column from the right matrix**. Then add all those products for the new term in the solution matrix. In this case, use the first row from the left matrix with the column from the right matrix: 1. 2 multiplies with 1, both in first position. 2. 1 multiplies with 3, both in second position. 3. 0 multiplies with –1, both in third position. Now add those products: the answer is 5 which is the first term in the column for the solution matrix.
$\begin{bmatrix}2&1&0\\3&-1&4\\1&1&2\end{bmatrix}\begin{bmatrix}1\\3\\-1\end{bmatrix}=$ $=\begin{bmatrix}5\\ -4\\ \\ \end{bmatrix}$ (3)(1)+(-1)(3)+(4)(-1)=-4	Next, multiply these from the second row with the column: 1. 3 with 1 (first position) = 3 2. -1 with 3 (second position) = -3 3. 4 with –1 (third position) = -4 Then, add the products = -4 The total is in the second row of the first column of the solution matrix.
$\begin{bmatrix}2&1&0\\3&-1&4\\1&1&2\end{bmatrix}\begin{bmatrix}1\\3\\-1\end{bmatrix}=$ $=\begin{bmatrix}5\\ -4\\ 2\end{bmatrix}$ (1)(1)+(1)(3)+(2)(-1)=2	Next, and last in this case, multiply the third row with the column: 1. 1 with 1 (first position) = 1 2. 1 with 3 (second position) = 3 3. 2 with –1 (third position) = -2 Then, add the products = 2 This is the third and final term of the solution matrix.

Sample problems:

1. True or false: The product of $\begin{bmatrix}3 & -2 & 6\end{bmatrix}$ and $\begin{bmatrix}2 & -3 & 4\end{bmatrix}$ is a 1×3 matrix.
   Solution: False
   Explanation: In order to multiply matrices, the number of columns in the first matrix must equal the number of rows in the second matrix. The first matrix has 3 columns; the second matrix has 1 row. The matrices cannot be multiplied.

2. True or false: The product of $\begin{bmatrix} 1 & 9 & 0 \\ 0 & 1 & 9 \\ 9 & 0 & 1 \end{bmatrix}$ and $\begin{bmatrix} 2 \\ -1 \\ -1 \end{bmatrix}$ is a 3×1 matrix.

<u>Solution:</u> True
<u>Explanation:</u> In order to multiply matrices, the number of columns in the first matrix must equal the number of rows in the second matrix. The first matrix has 3 columns; the second matrix has 3 rows. The matrices can be multiplied. Furthermore, the product matrix will have the same number of rows as the first matrix and the same # of columns as the second. Thus, the product of a 3×3 and a 3×1 is a 3×1 matrix.

3. True or false: The product of $\begin{bmatrix} 2 \\ -1 \\ -1 \end{bmatrix}$ and $\begin{bmatrix} 1 & 9 & 0 \\ 0 & 1 & 9 \\ 9 & 0 & 1 \end{bmatrix}$ is a 3×3 matrix.

<u>Solution:</u> False
<u>Explanation:</u> In order to multiply matrices, the number of columns in the first matrix must equal the number of rows in the second matrix. The first matrix has 1 column; the second matrix has 3 rows. The matrices cannot be multiplied.

Practice problems: *(Answers on page: 764)*

1. True or false: The product of $\begin{bmatrix} 1 & 2 \\ 3 & 4 \end{bmatrix}$ and $\begin{bmatrix} 3 & 9 \\ 0 & 7 \end{bmatrix}$ is a 2×2 matrix.

2. True or false: The product of $\begin{bmatrix} a & b \\ c & d \end{bmatrix}$ and $\begin{bmatrix} e & f \end{bmatrix}$ is a 2×2 matrix.

3. True or false: The product of $\begin{bmatrix} 5 & 2 & 7 & 2 \\ 4 & 3 & 1 & 1 \\ 4 & 5 & 9 & 6 \end{bmatrix}$ and $\begin{bmatrix} 4 & 3 \\ 2 & 5 \\ 8 & 6 \\ 7 & 9 \end{bmatrix}$ is a 3×2 matrix.

Review questions: *(Answers to odd questions on page: 764)*

1. True or false: The product of $\begin{bmatrix} e & g & d & a \end{bmatrix}$ and $\begin{bmatrix} d & f & b & b \end{bmatrix}$ is a 1×1 matrix.

2. True or false: The product of $\begin{bmatrix} 4 & 8 & 7 \\ 1 & 5 & 6 \\ 0 & 9 & 6 \end{bmatrix}$ and $\begin{bmatrix} 1 & 5 & 3 \\ 0 & 3 & 1 \\ 9 & 5 & 0 \end{bmatrix}$ is a 3×3 matrix.

3. True or false: The product of $\begin{bmatrix} 4 & 4 \\ 3 & 5 \end{bmatrix}$ and $\begin{bmatrix} 0 \\ 3 \end{bmatrix}$ is a 2×1 matrix.

4. True or false: The product of $\begin{bmatrix} 3 & 1 \\ 0 & 4 \\ 1 & 1 \end{bmatrix}$ and $\begin{bmatrix} 4 & 2 & 0 \\ 1 & 4 & 4 \end{bmatrix}$ is a 3×3 matrix.

5. True or false: The product of $\begin{bmatrix} x & y \\ w & z \\ z & x \\ z & y \end{bmatrix}$ and $\begin{bmatrix} z & w & x \\ w & x & y \end{bmatrix}$ is a 4×3 matrix.

Using the Gauss-Jordan Method

- The **Gauss-Jordan** method uses matrix manipulations to solve systems of linear equations.
- When using the Gauss-Jordan method, you are allowed to:
  1. Flip the order of rows.
  2. Multiply a row by a constant.
  3. Replace a row by the sum of two rows.
- An **augmented matrix** is a matrix representing a system of linear equations where the constants are included along with the coefficients.

A System of Equations:

$$x + y = 5$$
$$x - y = -1$$

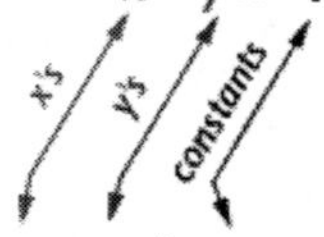

$$\begin{array}{cc:c} 1 & 1 & 5 \\ 1 & -1 & -1 \end{array}$$

** also called an augmented matrix because of the dotted line that divides the x's and y's from the constants*

You can represent a system of linear equations like this one by a matrix where the numbers in the matrix are the coefficients of x and y and the constants.

Such a matrix is called an **augmented matrix** because the constants in the equations are included along with the coefficients of x and y.

A System of Equations:

$$x + y = 5$$
$$x - y = -1$$

$$\left[\begin{array}{cc:c} 1 & 1 & 5 \\ 1 & -1 & -1 \end{array}\right]$$

Allowable operations for the Gauss-Jordan Method:
1) you can flip the order of the rows
2) you can multiply through by a constant
3) you can replace a row with the sum of two rows

Instead of manipulating the actual equations to solve for x and y, you can just manipulate the corresponding augmented matrix.

When using the **Gauss-Jordan method**, there are three allowable operations you can use on the matrix. The idea is to use the allowable operations to manipulate the augmented matrix into a form where the solution can be read directly off the matrix.

$$\left[\begin{array}{cc:c} 1 & 1 & 5 \\ 1 & -1 & -1 \end{array}\right]$$ *Replace top row with the sum of row one (R_1) and row two (R_2)*

$$\left[\begin{array}{cc:c} 2 & 0 & 4 \\ 1 & -1 & -1 \end{array}\right]$$ *$R_1 + R_2$*

$$\left[\begin{array}{cc:c} 1 & 0 & 2 \\ 1 & -1 & -1 \end{array}\right]$$ *divide through R_1 by 2*

$$\left[\begin{array}{cc:c} 1 & 0 & 2 \\ 0 & 1 & 3 \end{array}\right]$$ *$R_1 - R_2$ (subtract row two from row one)*

Let's use the Gauss-Jordan method to solve the system of equations from above.

First, use the third allowable operation -- replacing a row with the sum of two rows -- to replace the top row of the matrix. That gives you the second matrix.

Next, divide the first row by 2 to get the third matrix.

Now, subtract the second row from the first and make that the new second row for the fourth matrix.

$$\left[\begin{array}{cc:c} 1 & 0 & 2 \\ 0 & 1 & 3 \end{array}\right] \quad \begin{array}{l} x = 2 \\ y = 3 \end{array}$$

The solutions to the system can now be read directly off the matrix!

In row 1, the terms indicate that there is $1x + 0y = 2$, so $x = 2$.

In row 2, the terms indicate that there is $0x + 1y = 3$, so $y = 3$.

Sample problems:

1. Given $\begin{bmatrix} 0 & 10 & -5 \end{bmatrix}$, find $\frac{R_1}{10}$, then express that augmented matrix as an equation.

   Solution: $\begin{bmatrix} 0 & 1 & -\frac{1}{2} \end{bmatrix}$; $y = -\frac{1}{2}$

   Explanation: To find $\frac{R_1}{10}$, divide each number by 10: $\frac{R_1}{10} = \begin{bmatrix} 0 & 1 & -\frac{1}{2} \end{bmatrix}$. Since this is an augmented matrix, the corresponding equation will have two variables with 0 and 1 as coefficients, and the equation will $= -\frac{1}{2}$: $\begin{bmatrix} 0 & 1 & -\frac{1}{2} \end{bmatrix} \Rightarrow 0x + 1y = -\frac{1}{2}$ or $y = -\frac{1}{2}$.

2. Express the system $x - 2y = 20$ and $-x - y = 4$ as an augmented matrix, then replace R_1 with $R_1 + R_2$.

   Solution: $\begin{bmatrix} 1 & -2 & 20 \\ -1 & -1 & 4 \end{bmatrix}$; $\begin{bmatrix} 0 & -3 & 24 \\ -1 & -1 & 4 \end{bmatrix}$

   Explanation: To express the system as an augmented matrix, list the coefficients and the constant from the 1st equation in the 1st row, R_1, and list the coefficients and the constant from the 2nd equation in the 2nd row, R_2 : $\begin{matrix} x - 2y = 20 \\ -x - y = 4 \end{matrix} \Rightarrow \begin{bmatrix} 1 & -2 & 20 \\ -1 & -1 & 4 \end{bmatrix}$. Find $R_1 + R_2$ (the sum of the rows) by adding the numbers in each column: $R_1 + R_2 = 0 \quad -3 \quad 24$.

   Replace R_1 with $R_1 + R_2$: $\begin{bmatrix} 0 & -3 & 24 \\ -1 & -1 & 4 \end{bmatrix}$.

3. Use the Gauss-Jordan method to solve the following system: $\begin{matrix} 2x + y = 13 \\ -2x + 3y = -1 \end{matrix}$.

   Solution: $x = 5$ and $y = 3$

   Explanation: Express the system as an augmented matrix: $\begin{bmatrix} 2 & 1 & 13 \\ -2 & 3 & -1 \end{bmatrix}$. In the Guass-Jordan method, the matrix is manipulated by the 3 allowable operations until $R_1 = \begin{bmatrix} 0 & 1 & a \end{bmatrix}$ and $R_2 = \begin{bmatrix} 1 & 0 & b \end{bmatrix}$ (or vice versa), where a and b are any number. Consider the 1st column, if 2 and -2 are added the sum is zero. Thus, the allowable operation "replace a row with the sum of 2 rows" is indicated. Find the sum of the rows: $R_1 + R_2 = 0 \quad 4 \quad 12$. Replace R_1 with $R_1 + R_2$ (replacing R_2 instead of R_1 is allowed, but it makes this problem more complicated): $\begin{bmatrix} 2 & 1 & 13 \\ -2 & 3 & -1 \end{bmatrix} = \begin{bmatrix} 2 & 1 & 13 \\ 0 & 4 & 12 \end{bmatrix}$, so R_2 begins with a 0. To create a 0 in the 2nd column of R_1, divide R_2 by -4, then replace R_1 with $R_1 + R_2$:

   $$\begin{bmatrix} 2 & 1 & 13 \\ 0 & 4 & 12 \end{bmatrix} = \underset{R_2/-4}{\begin{bmatrix} 2 & 1 & 13 \\ 0 & -1 & -3 \end{bmatrix}} = \underset{\text{Replace } R_1 \text{ with } R_1 + R_2}{\begin{bmatrix} 2 & 0 & 10 \\ 0 & -1 & -3 \end{bmatrix}}.$$

   Now the matrix contains the necessary 0's, but not the 1's. To create the 1's, divide R_1 by 2 and divide R_2 by -1: $\begin{bmatrix} 2 & 0 & 10 \\ 0 & -1 & -3 \end{bmatrix} = \underset{R_1/2 \text{ and } R_2/-1}{\begin{bmatrix} 1 & 0 & 5 \\ 0 & 1 & 3 \end{bmatrix}}$.

   Now the matrix contains the necessary 0's and 1's, so express the matrix as a system to reveal the solutions:

   $$\begin{bmatrix} 1 & 0 & 5 \\ 0 & 1 & 3 \end{bmatrix} \Rightarrow \begin{matrix} 1x + 0y = 5 \\ 0x + 1y = 3 \end{matrix} \text{ or } \begin{matrix} x = 5 \\ y = 3 \end{matrix}.$$

Practice problems: *(Answers on page: 764)*

1. Express the system $x + 2y = -2$ and $x - 4y = 4$ with an augmented matrix, then replace R_2 with $R_1 + R_2$.

2. Express the system $4x - y = 10$ and $x - 4y = 10$ with an augmented matrix, then replace R_1 with $R_1/-1$ and replace R_2 with $R_2/-4$.

3. Use the Guass-Jordan method to solve the following system:

   $x + y = 7$
   $-x + y = -5$

Review questions: *(Answers to odd questions on page: 764)*

1. Use the Guass-Jordan method to solve the following system: $x-2y=8;\ \ 3x+y=10$.
2. Use the Guass-Jordan method to solve the following system: $x-y=-5;\ \ -x+3y=11$.
3. Use the Guass-Jordan method to solve the following system: $x+y=11;\ \ 2x-y=13$.
4. Use the Guass-Jordan method to solve the following system: $2x-y=-5;\ \ x+y=8$.
5. Use the Guass-Jordan method to solve the following system: $2x+3y=6;\ \ 3x-y=-13$.

Using Gauss-Jordan: Another Example

- The Gauss-Jordan method uses matrix manipulations to solve systems of linear equations.
- When using the Gauss-Jordan method, you are allowed to:
  1. Flip the order of rows.
  2. Multiply a row by a constant.
  3. Replace a row by the sum of two rows.

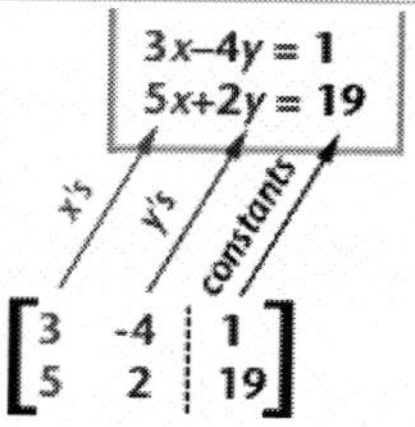	This system of linear equations can be solved using the Gauss-Jordan method. The first step is to write down the augmented matrix representing the system.
Our Goal: $\left[\begin{array}{cc\|c} 1 & 0 & ? \\ 0 & 1 & ? \end{array}\right]$	Next manipulate the augmented matrix using the allowable matrix operations. **REMEMBER**: The goal of the Gauss-Jordan method is to manipulate the augmented matrix into a form where the solutions to the system can be read directly off the matrix.
$\left[\begin{array}{cc\|c} 3 & -4 & 1 \\ 5 & 2 & 19 \end{array}\right]$ $\left[\begin{array}{cc\|c} 13 & 0 & 39 \\ 5 & 2 & 19 \end{array}\right]$ $\left[\begin{array}{cc\|c} 1 & 0 & 3 \\ 5 & 2 & 19 \end{array}\right] R_1/13$ $\left[\begin{array}{cc\|c} 1 & 0 & 3 \\ 0 & 2 & 4 \end{array}\right] R_2-5R_1$	First add 2 times the second row to the first row to replace the first row to produce the second matrix. Then, divide the first row by 13 for the third matrix. Subtract 5 times the first row from the second row to replace the second row for the fourth matrix. Now divide the second row by 2 for the fifth matrix.
$\left[\begin{array}{cc\|c} 1 & 0 & 3 \\ 0 & 1 & 2 \end{array}\right]$ $x=3$ $y=2$	With the augmented matrix in this form, you can just read off the solutions to the system of equations.

Sample problems:

1. Use the Gauss-Jordan method to solve the following system: $\begin{matrix} 2x - y = 5 \\ x + y = -2 \end{matrix}$.

   Solution: $x = 1$ and $y = -3$

   Explanation: Express the system as an augmented matrix: $\begin{bmatrix} 2 & -1 & 5 \\ 1 & 1 & -2 \end{bmatrix}$. Replace R_1 with $R_1 + R_2$: $\begin{bmatrix} 3 & 0 & 3 \\ 1 & 1 & -2 \end{bmatrix}$. Divide R_1 by 3: $\begin{bmatrix} 1 & 0 & 1 \\ 1 & 1 & -2 \end{bmatrix}$. Replace R_2 with $R_2 - R_1$: $\begin{bmatrix} 1 & 0 & 1 \\ 0 & 1 & -3 \end{bmatrix}$. Express the matrix as a system of equations: $x = 1$ and $y = -3$.

2. Use the Guass-Jordan method to solve the following system: $x + 2y = -2$ and $x - y = 4$.

   Solution: $x = 2$ and $y = -2$

   Explanation: Express as an augmented matrix: $\begin{bmatrix} 1 & 2 & -2 \\ 1 & -1 & 4 \end{bmatrix}$. Replace R_1 with $R_1 - R_2$: $\begin{bmatrix} 0 & 3 & -6 \\ 1 & -1 & 4 \end{bmatrix}$. Multiply R_2 by 3: $\begin{bmatrix} 0 & 3 & -6 \\ 3 & -3 & 12 \end{bmatrix}$. Replace R_2 with $R_1 + R_2$: $\begin{bmatrix} 0 & 3 & -6 \\ 3 & 0 & 6 \end{bmatrix}$. Divide R_1 and R_2 by 3: $\begin{bmatrix} 0 & 1 & -2 \\ 1 & 0 & 2 \end{bmatrix}$. Express the matrix as a system: $y = -2$ and $x = 2$.

3. Use the Gauss-Jordan method to solve the following system: $3x - 5y = -2$ and $4x - 3y = -1$.

   Solution: $x = \frac{1}{11}$ and $y = \frac{5}{11}$

   Explanation: Express as an augmented matrix: $\begin{bmatrix} 3 & -5 & -2 \\ 4 & -3 & -1 \end{bmatrix}$. Replace R_1 with $R_2 - R_1$: $\begin{bmatrix} 1 & 2 & 1 \\ 4 & -3 & -1 \end{bmatrix}$. Multiply R_1 by -4: $\begin{bmatrix} -4 & -8 & -4 \\ 4 & -3 & -1 \end{bmatrix}$. Replace R_1 with $R_1 + R_2$: $\begin{bmatrix} 0 & -11 & -5 \\ 4 & -3 & -1 \end{bmatrix}$. Multiply R_1 by $-\frac{3}{11}$: $\begin{bmatrix} 0 & 3 & \frac{15}{11} \\ 4 & -3 & -1 \end{bmatrix}$. Replace R_2 with $R_1 + R_2$: $\begin{bmatrix} 0 & 3 & \frac{15}{11} \\ 4 & 0 & \frac{4}{11} \end{bmatrix}$. Divide R_1 by 3 and R_2 by 4: $\begin{bmatrix} 0 & 1 & \frac{5}{11} \\ 1 & 0 & \frac{1}{11} \end{bmatrix}$. Express as a system: $y = \frac{5}{11}$ and $x = \frac{1}{11}$.

Practice problems: *(Answers on page: 764)*

1. Use the Gauss-Jordan method to solve the following system: $3x + y = 8$ and $2x - y = 12$.
2. Use the Gauss-Jordan method to solve the following system: $x + y = 11$ and $2x - y = 13$.
3. Use the Gauss-Jordan method to solve the following system: $5x + 4y = 20$ and $2x - 5y = -14$.

Review questions: *(Answers to odd questions on page: 764)*

1. Use the Guass-Jordan method to solve the following system: $2x + 3y = 4$; $2x - 3y = -1$.
2. Use the Guass-Jordan method to solve the following system: $3x - 5y = -2$; $4x - 3y = -1$.
3. Use the Guass-Jordan method to solve the following system: $2x - 7y = 0$; $x - 4y = 1$.
4. Use the Guass-Jordan method to solve the following system: $2x + 3y = 6$; $3x - y = -13$.
5. Use the Guass-Jordan method to solve the following system: $4x - 5y = -6$; $5x + 14y = -3$.

Evaluating 2x2 Determinants

- A **determinant** is a number associated with a square matrix.
- A **square matrix** has the same number of columns as rows.
- **Determinant notation**: **det(A)** or |**A**|, where A represents the matrix.
- To calculate the determinant of a matrix, multiply the values on each diagonal from upper left to lower right, and add all the products. Then multiply the values on each diagonal from upper right to lower left. Subtract these products from the sum of the products for the other diagonals.
- A **singular matrix** is one whose determinant is 0.
- A **nonsingular matrix** is one whose determinant is not 0.

det(A) = |A| = when A is a matrix, this means determinant, not absolute value.	Notice the determinant notation. Use context to avoid mistaking this for absolute value.
$\|A\| = \begin{bmatrix} 5 & 3 \\ 8 & 5 \end{bmatrix} = (5)(5)-(3)(8) = 25-24 = 1$	To evaluate the determinant in this case: 1. Multiply the values on the main diagonal: 5 and 5. 2. Multiply the values on the other diagonal: 3 and 8. Finally, subtract the second product from the first product. Det(A) = 1. So A is a nonsingular matrix.
$\|B\| = \begin{bmatrix} 1 & -4 \\ 2 & 10 \end{bmatrix} = (10)(1)-(-4)(2) = 10-\!-8 = 18$	To compute the determinant of B: 1. Multiply the values on the main diagonal: 1 and 10. 2. Multiply the values on the other diagonal: –4 and 2. 3. Subtract the second product from the first product, (10) – (–8) = 18. Det(B) = 18. Thus, B is nonsingular.
$\|C\| = \begin{bmatrix} 2 & 6 \\ 1 & 3 \end{bmatrix} = (2)(3)-(6)(1) = 6-6 = 0$ *C is singular*	To compute the det(C): 1. Multiply the values on the main diagonal: 2 and 3. 2. Multiply the values on the other diagonal: 6 and 1. 3. Subtract the second product from the first product, (6) – (6) = 0. Det(C) = 0. Matrix C is singular.

Sample problems:

1. Find $|A|$ when $A = \begin{bmatrix} 3 & -5 \\ -2 & 0 \end{bmatrix}$.

   Solution: -10

   Explanation: Calculate the products of the numbers on the diagonals, then subtract:
   $(3)(0)-(-5)(-2) = 0-10 = -10.$

2. Find $\det(A)$ when $A = \begin{bmatrix} 2 & a \\ -3 & b \end{bmatrix}$.

   Solution: $2b+3a$

   Explanation: $\begin{bmatrix} 2 & a \\ -3 & b \end{bmatrix} = 2b-(-3a) = 2b+3a.$

3. True or False: $\begin{bmatrix} 3 & 6 \\ -2 & -4 \end{bmatrix}$ is a singular matrix.

   Solution: True

   Explanation: The determinant of a singular matrix is 0. Find the determinant: $3(-4)-6(-2)=-12-(-12)=0$. Thus, it is a singular matrix.

Practice problems: *(Answers on page: 764)*

1. Find $|A|$ when $A=\begin{bmatrix} -2 & 5 \\ 3 & 7 \end{bmatrix}$

2. Find $|B|$ when $B=\begin{bmatrix} 4 & -3 \\ 6 & a \end{bmatrix}$

3. True or False: Given $C=\begin{bmatrix} 5 & 10 \\ 2 & 4 \end{bmatrix}$, C is a nonsingular matrix

Review questions: *(Answers to odd questions on page: 764)*

1. Find $|A|$ when $A=\begin{bmatrix} 2 & 5 \\ 3 & 7 \end{bmatrix}$.

2. Find $|A|$ when $A=\begin{bmatrix} 4 & 1 \\ 3 & 2 \end{bmatrix}$.

3. Find $|A|$ when $A=\begin{bmatrix} 1 & 1 \\ -1 & -1 \end{bmatrix}$.

4. Find $|A|$ when $A=\begin{bmatrix} 3 & -5 \\ 0 & -2 \end{bmatrix}$.

5. Find $|A|$ when $A=\begin{bmatrix} -4 & -3 \\ -2 & -4 \end{bmatrix}$.

Evaluating 3x3 Determinants

- A **determinant** is a number associated with a square matrix.
- A **square matrix** has the same number of columns as rows.
- **Determinant notation**: **det(A)** or **|A|**, where A represents the matrix.

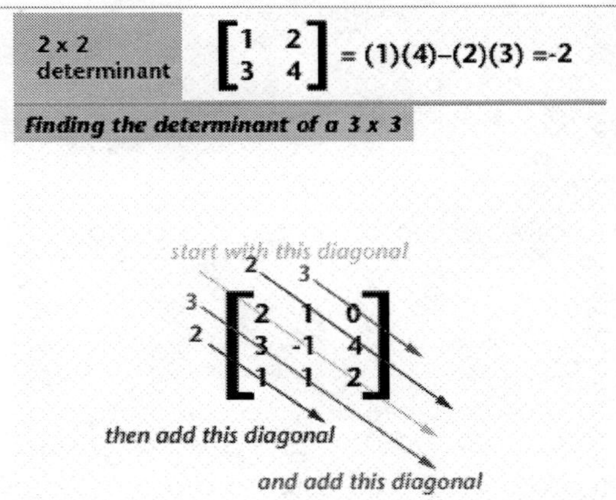

Use the 2x2 method with this 3x3 example.

1. Multiply the entries on the main diagonal: $(2)(-1)(2)=-4$.
2. Multiply the entries on the diagonal labeled 2: $(1)(4)(1)=4$.
3. Multiply the entries on the diagonal labeled 3: $(0)(3)(1)=0$.
4. Add these three products together: $-4+4+0=0$.

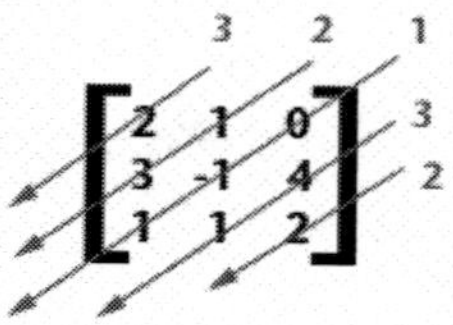 *then subtract these three diagonals*	Repeat the process for the diagonals going the other direction: 1. Multiply the entries on the diagonal labeled 1: $(0)(-1)(1) = 0$. 2. Multiply the entries on the diagonal labeled 2: $(1)(3)(2) = 6$. 3. Multiply the entries on the diagonal labeled 3: $(2)(4)(1) = 8$. 4. Add these three products: $0 + 6 + 8 = 14$.
$\lvert A \rvert = \boxed{-14}$	Subtract the second total from the first total to get the determinant: $\det(A) = -14$.
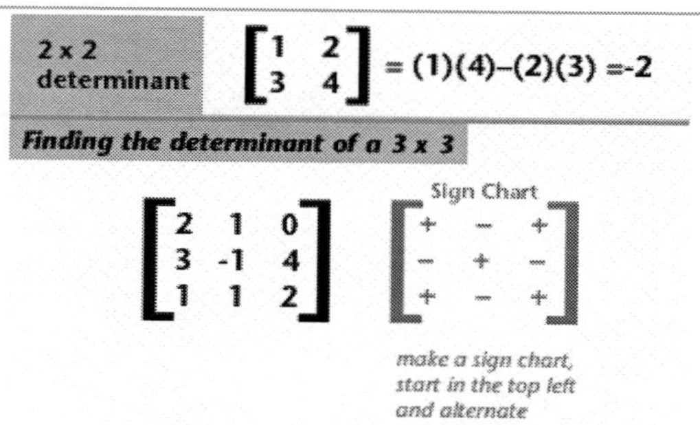	An alternate process is possible. First, create a sign chart with the same dimensions as the determinant. Start in the upper left corner with a "+" and write a sign in every location in the determinant alternating "–" with "+" as you progress.
 *2 times the determinant of this 2 x 2 matrix*	Next choose a row to expand. In this example, the top row was chosen. Cover the first term in that row. In this example, it is 2. Also cover every other term in its row and in its column. This leaves a 2x2 determinant. Evaluate that smaller determinant. In this problem you get $(-1)(2) - (4)(1) = -6$. Then multiply that result with the term you covered up. In this case you covered the 2, so you will multiply $(2)(-6)$ to get -12. Because this term sits in a "+" position on the sign chart, this product will be added.
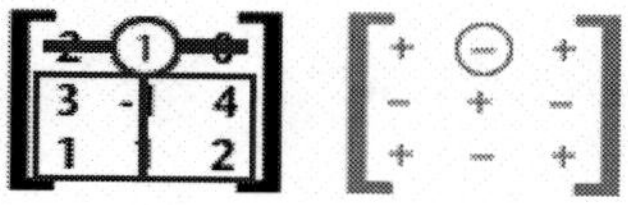	Next, repeat this process with the next term in the row. In this example, that is 1. Again, covering a term and everything in its row and its column leaves a 2x2 determinant. Calculate its value: $(3 \times 2) - (4 \times 1) = 2$. Multiply that total, 2, with the term you covered, 1: $(1)(2) = 2$. This will subtract because the term lies in a "–" position on the sign chart.
	Next repeat the process for the third term in the row. Here this step is easy because the final result of the multiplication will be 0.

$\|A\| = 2[(-1)(2)-(4)(1)]-1[(3)(2)-(1)(4)]+0[(3)(1)-(1)(-1)]$ $= 2(-6) - 1(2) + 0(4)$ $= -12 - 2 + 0 = \boxed{-14}$	Finally, add all these totals using the signs indicated by their location on the sign chart. The total is the determinant, det(A), for the 3x3 matrix. In this case, det(A) = (–12) – (2) + (0) = –14.

Sample problems:

1. Given $A = \begin{bmatrix} 1 & 2 & 3 \\ 4 & 5 & 6 \\ 7 & 8 & 9 \end{bmatrix}$, find det($A$).

   Solution: 0

   Explanation: Find the sum of the products of the right diagonals: $R = 1(5)(9) + 2(6)(7) + 4(8)(3) = 225$. Find the sum of the products of the left diagonals: $L = 3(5)(7) + 2(4)(9) + 1(6)(8) = 225$. Now subtract: $R - L = 225 - 225 = 0$. Thus the det(A) = 0.

2. Given $A = \begin{bmatrix} -3 & 2 & 1 \\ -1 & 1 & 0 \\ 1 & 0 & 1 \end{bmatrix}$, find $|A|$.

   Solution: -2

   Explanation: Find the sum of the right diagonals:
   $R = (-3)(1)(1) + (2)(0)(1) + (-1)(0)(1) = -3 + 0 + 0 = -3$. Find the sum of the left diagonals:
   $L = (1)(1)(1) + (2)(-1)(1) + (-3)(0)(0) = 1 + -2 + 0 = -1$. Subtract: $R - L = -3 - (-1) = -2$.
   Thus, $|A| = -2$

3. Given $M = \begin{bmatrix} a & 2 & 0 \\ 1 & 1 & 1 \\ 1 & 2 & 3 \end{bmatrix}$, find $\det(M)$.

   Solution: $a - 4$

   Explanation: $\det(M) = (3a + 2 + 0) - (0 + 2a + 6) = 3a + 2 - 2a - 6 = a - 4$.

Practice problems: *(Answers on page: 764)*

1. Given $B = \begin{bmatrix} 3 & 2 & 1 \\ -1 & -1 & -1 \\ 1 & 1 & 0 \end{bmatrix}$, find $|B|$.

2. Given $A = \begin{bmatrix} 2 & -1 & 2 \\ 0 & 2 & -1 \\ 2 & 0 & 2 \end{bmatrix}$, find the determinant.

3. Given $P = \begin{bmatrix} a & 2 & b \\ 2 & 1 & 2 \\ 1 & c & 1 \end{bmatrix}$, find $\det(P)$.

Review questions: *(Answers to odd questions on page: 764)*

1. Given $\mathrm{A} = \begin{bmatrix} 1 & 0 & -1 \\ 0 & -1 & 0 \\ -1 & 0 & -1 \end{bmatrix}$, find $|\mathrm{A}|$.

2. Given $C=\begin{bmatrix}1 & 1 & 1\\ 0 & 1 & 1\\ 1 & 1 & 1\end{bmatrix}$, find $|C|$.

3. Given $G=\begin{bmatrix}1 & 2 & 3\\ 1 & -1 & 1\\ 1 & 0 & 1\end{bmatrix}$, find $\det(G)$.

4. Given $V=\begin{bmatrix}1 & 2 & 1\\ 2 & 2 & 0\\ -1 & 0 & -1\end{bmatrix}$ find $\det(V)$.

5. Given $D=\begin{bmatrix}2 & 4 & 1\\ 3 & 2 & 2\\ 1 & 3 & 3\end{bmatrix}$, find $|D|$.

Applying Determinants

- **Determinants** can be used to calculate areas of figures.
- The area of a triangle equals one-half the value of a 3x3 determinant.

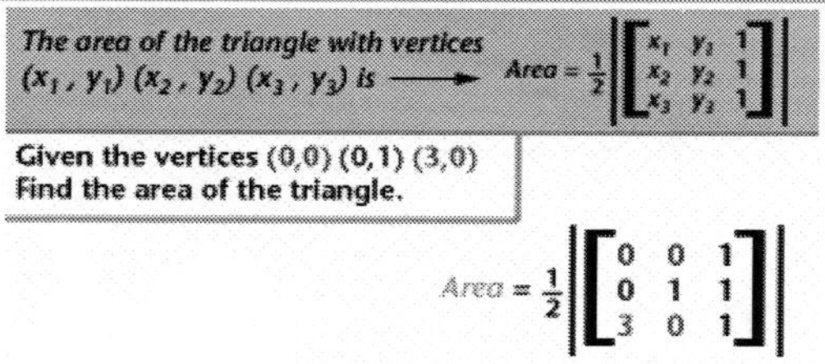	One application of matrices is finding the area of a triangle. Compare the general statement for setting up the matrix with the array for this example. Notice how the coordinates for each vertex are placed in its own row with "1" being the term in the third column on every row. Remember your sign chart as you add your products. Then use your process for evaluating the determinant of a matrix. In this example, the arithmetic will be easy to do because there are so many zeros.
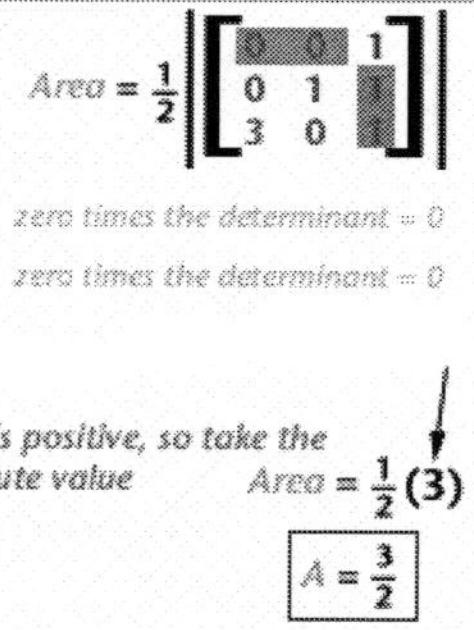	In this case, the area will be: ½{0[(1x1) – (1x0)] – 0[(0x1) – (1x3)] + 1[(0x0) – (1x3)]} = ½(0 – 0 + -3) = ½(-3). Area is always positive, so use the absolute value. The area of the triangle is ½(3) = 3/2..
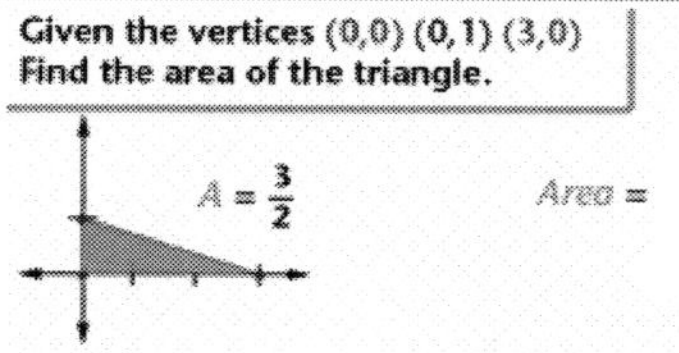	This is an easy area to check because the triangle is half of the rectangle that is 3 units long and 1 unit wide. Therefore, the area of the triangle will be ½(3)(1) = 3/2. That matches what you found using determinants.

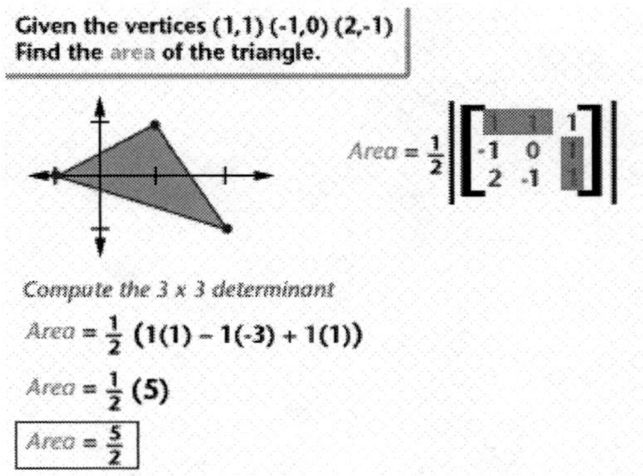

Here is another example.

Once again, the coordinates are placed in the matrix.

The area of the triangle equals: ½{1[(0x1) – (1x–1)] –1[(-1x1) – (1x2)] + 1[(-1x–1) – (0x2)]}. This expression simplifies as shown in the graphic. It results in an area of 5/2.

Sample problems:

1. Find the area of a triangle with the following vertices: $(0,6)$, $(-2,4)$, and $(-1,2)$.
   Solution: 3
   Explanation: The area of a triangle with vertices (x_1, y_1), (x_2, y_2), and (x_3, y_3) is:
   $A = \frac{1}{2}\left\|\begin{bmatrix} x_1 & y_1 & 1 \\ x_2 & y_2 & 1 \\ x_3 & y_3 & 1 \end{bmatrix}\right\|$. Set up the 3×3 matrix and evaluate the determinant: $\left\|\begin{bmatrix} 0 & 6 & 1 \\ -2 & 4 & 1 \\ -1 & 2 & 1 \end{bmatrix}\right\| =$
   $0(4-2)-6(-2--1)+1(-4--4)=0(2)-6(-1)+1(0)=0--6+0=6$. Find the area of the triangle: $A=\frac{1}{2}(6)=3$.

2. Use the determinant to determine if the points (5,5), (0,0), and $(-5,-5)$ are collinear.
   Solution: yes the points are collinear
   Explanation: If the points are collinear then the determinant must equal zero (since the points will not form a triangle, the area is thus 0).
   Set up a 3×3 matrix: $\begin{bmatrix} x_1 & y_1 & 1 \\ x_2 & y_2 & 1 \\ x_3 & y_3 & 1 \end{bmatrix} = \begin{bmatrix} 5 & 5 & 1 \\ 0 & 0 & 1 \\ -5 & -5 & 1 \end{bmatrix}$. Evaluate the determinant: $\begin{vmatrix} 5 & 5 & 1 \\ 0 & 0 & 1 \\ -5 & -5 & 1 \end{vmatrix} =$
   $5(0--5)-5(0--5)+1(0-0)=5(5)-5(5)+1(0)=25-25+0=0$.
   Since the determinant is equal to zero, the points are collinear.

3. Find the area of a polygon with the following vertices listed counterclockwise around the perimeter: $(-2,7),(-3,4),(-1,1),(2,1),(3,4)$.
   Solution: $\frac{45}{2}$
   Explanation: The area of a polygon with vertices (x_1, y_1), (x_2, y_2), (x_3, y_3), ... , (x_n, y_n) listed counterclockwise is: $A=\frac{1}{2}\left\{\begin{vmatrix} x_1 & x_2 \\ y_1 & y_2 \end{vmatrix}+\begin{vmatrix} x_2 & x_3 \\ y_2 & y_3 \end{vmatrix}+\ldots\begin{vmatrix} x_n & x_{n+1} \\ y_n & y_{n+1} \end{vmatrix}\right\}$. The area of this polygon is therefore: $\frac{1}{2}\left\{\begin{vmatrix} -2 & -3 \\ 7 & 4 \end{vmatrix}+\begin{vmatrix} -3 & -1 \\ 4 & 1 \end{vmatrix}+\begin{vmatrix} -1 & 2 \\ 1 & 1 \end{vmatrix}+\begin{vmatrix} 2 & 3 \\ 1 & 4 \end{vmatrix}+\begin{vmatrix} 3 & -2 \\ 4 & 7 \end{vmatrix}\right\}$
   $=\frac{1}{2}\{[(-8-(-21))]+[-3-(-4)]+(-1-2)+(8-3)+[21-(-8)]\}=\frac{1}{2}(13+1-3+5+29)=\frac{1}{2}(45)=\frac{45}{2}$.

Practice problems: *(Answers on page: 764)*

1. Find the area of a triangle with the following vertices: $(3,-1)$, $(-1,0)$, and $(-5,2)$.
2. Use the determinant to determine if the points (2,5), $(-2,3)$, and $(-4,2)$ are collinear.
3. Find the area of a polygon with the following vertices listed counterclockwise around the perimeter: $(1,0),(1,-5),(3,-6),(3,-1)$.

Review questions: *(Answers to odd questions on page: 764)*

1. Find the area of a triangle with the following vertices: $(5,1)$, $(-1,2)$, and $(4,3)$.
2. Find the area of a triangle with the following vertices: $(-3,2)$, $(-4,6)$, and $(5,1)$.
3. Use the determinant to determine if the points $(0,5)$, $(-2,-1)$, and $(-6,-13)$ are collinear.
4. Use the determinant to determine if the points $(-6,-6)$, $(0,3)$, and $(4,-1)$ are collinear.
5. Find the area of a polygon with the following vertices listed counterclockwise around the perimeter: $(0,6),(-2,4),(-1,2),(1,1),(3,4)$.

Using Cramer's Rule

- **Cramer's rule** states that determinants can be used to solve linear systems of equations so long as the number of variables equals the number of equations.
- Solving for x means using the determinant for x, D_x, divided by the determinant of the coefficients.
- Solving for y means using the determinant for y, D_y, divided by the determinant of the coefficients.

You can use Cramer's Rule to solve for variables, as long as: # of equations = # of variables	**Note this requirement:** the number of variables must be the same as the number of equations in the system.
Cramer's Rule $a_1x + b_1y = c_1$, $a_2x + b_2y = c_2$ *generic equations* Set up 3 determinants: $D = \left\|\begin{bmatrix} a_1 & b_1 \\ a_2 & b_2 \end{bmatrix}\right\|$	Using determinants to solve systems of equations involves setting up a matrix using the coefficients of the variables and evaluating its determinant, D. **Note:** This method only works when $D \neq 0$.
$D_x = \left\|\begin{bmatrix} c_1 & b_1 \\ c_2 & b_2 \end{bmatrix}\right\|$ $D_y = \left\|\begin{bmatrix} a_1 & c_1 \\ a_2 & c_2 \end{bmatrix}\right\|$	You also set up a matrix for each variable and compute the determinant. The array for finding x replaces the coefficients of x with the constants from the equations. The array for finding y replaces the coefficients of y with the constants. x will equal the value of D_x divided by D. y will equal the value of D_y divided by D. And now you know why this method cannot work if $D = 0$. You can never divide by 0.
Use Cramer's Rule to solve the following: $5x + 7y = -1$ $6x + 8y = 1$ $D = \left\|\begin{bmatrix} 5 & 7 \\ 6 & 8 \end{bmatrix}\right\| = (5)(8) - (7)(6) = 40 - 42 = -2$ $D_x = \left\|\begin{bmatrix} -1 & 7 \\ 1 & 8 \end{bmatrix}\right\| = (-1)(8) - (7)(1) = -8 - 7 = -15$ $D_y = \left\|\begin{bmatrix} 5 & -1 \\ 6 & 1 \end{bmatrix}\right\| = (5)(1) - (-1)(6) = 5 - -6 = 11$	In this example, first set up D using the coefficients. You calculate that $D = -2$. Then set up D_x replacing the coefficients of x with the constants. You find $D_x = -15$. Thirdly set up D_y replacing the coefficients of y in D with the constants. $D_y = 11$.
Solution: $x = \frac{D_x}{D} = \frac{-15}{-2} = \frac{15}{2}$ $y = \frac{D_y}{D} = \frac{11}{-2}$	Then solve. $x = D_x/D = -15/-2 = 15/2$. $y = D_y/D = 11/-2 = -11/2$.

Sample problems:

1. Use Cramer's rule to solve the system $x+y=11$ and $x-y=5$. If $D=0$, use another method to solve the system.
   Solution: $x=8$ and $y=3$
   Explanation: Write the the 3 matrices and find the determinant of each:
   $$D=\left\|\begin{bmatrix}1 & 1\\ 1 & -1\end{bmatrix}\right\| = (1)(-1)-(1)(1) = -2 \qquad D_x=\left\|\begin{bmatrix}11 & 1\\ 5 & -1\end{bmatrix}\right\| = (11)(-1)-(1)(5) = -16 \qquad D_y=\left\|\begin{bmatrix}1 & 11\\ 1 & 5\end{bmatrix}\right\| = (1)(5)-(11)(1) = -6$$
   Find x: $x=\frac{D_x}{D}=\frac{-16}{-2}=8$. Find y: $y=\frac{D_y}{D}=\frac{-6}{-2}=3$. Thus, $x=8$ and $y=3$.

2. Use Cramer's rule to solve the system $3x+2y=11$ and $9x+6y=33$. If $D=0$, use another method to solve the system.
   Solution: infinitely many solutions
   Explanation: Find D: $D=\left\|\begin{bmatrix}3 & 2\\ 9 & 6\end{bmatrix}\right\|=3(6)-9(2)=18-18=0$. When $D=0$, Cramer's rule cannot be used. Try the elimination method. Multiply the 1st equation by 3, then subtract the equations:
   $$\begin{array}{l}3(3x+2y=11)\\ 9x+6y=33\end{array} \Rightarrow \begin{array}{r}9x+6y=33\\ -(9x+6y=33)\\ \hline 0=0\end{array}$$
   The variables cancel, and the result of subtracting is a true statement.
   Thus, this is a dependent system with infinitely many solutions.

3. Use Cramer's rule to solve the system $3x-5y=9$; $x+2y=-8$. If $D=0$, use another method to solve the system.
   Solution: $x=-2$ and $y=-3$
   Explanation: Write the 3 matrices and find the determinant of each:
   $$D=\left\|\begin{bmatrix}3 & -5\\ 1 & 2\end{bmatrix}\right\| = (3)(2)-(1)(-5) = 11 \qquad D_x=\left\|\begin{bmatrix}9 & -5\\ -8 & 2\end{bmatrix}\right\| = (9)(2)-(-8)(-5) = -22 \qquad D_y=\left\|\begin{bmatrix}3 & 9\\ 1 & -8\end{bmatrix}\right\| = (3)(-8)-(1)(9) = -33$$
   Find x and y: $x=\frac{D_x}{D}=\frac{-22}{11}=-2$ and $y=\frac{D_y}{D}=\frac{-33}{11}=-3$, $x=-2$ and $y=-3$.

Practice problems: *(Answers on page: 764)*

1. Use Cramer's rule to solve the system $x+y=2$ and $3x+y=10$.
   If $D=0$, use another method to solve the system.
2. Use Cramer's rule to solve the system $2x+3y=4$ and $4x-6y=8$.
   If $D=0$, use another method to solve the system.
3. Use Cramer's rule to solve the system $5x+4y=60$ and $5x-6y=-140$.
   If $D=0$, use another method to solve the system.

Review questions: *(Answers to odd questions on page: 764)*

1. Use Cramer's rule to solve the system $x+y=3$ and $3x+2y=7$. If $D=0$, use another method to solve the system.
2. Use Cramer's rule to solve the system $2x+y=2$ and $3x-2y=5$. If $D=0$, use another method to solve the system.
3. Use Cramer's rule to solve the system $2x-7y=0$ and $x-4y=-1$. If $D=0$, use another method to solve the system.

4. Use Cramer's rule to solve the system $2x - y = 5$ and $3x + 3y = -6$. If $D = 0$, use another method to solve the system.

5. Use Cramer's rule to solve the system $x + y = 0$ and $2y - x = 12$. If $D = 0$, use another method to solve the system.

Using Cramer's Rule in a 3x3 Matrix

- **Cramer's rule** states that determinants can be used to solve a system of linear equations so long as the number of variables is the same as the number of equations.
- The solution for any variable, a, in a system of equations is the value of the determinant set up for it, D_a, divided by the value of the determinant set up for all the coefficients, D.

Use Cramer's Rule to solve: $x + y - z = -2$ $2x - y + z = 0$ $x - 2y + 3z = 1$ $D = \left\| \begin{bmatrix} 1 & 1 & -1 \\ 2 & -1 & 1 \\ 1 & -2 & 3 \end{bmatrix} \right\| = 1(-1) - 1(5) + (-1)(-3)$ $= -1 - 5 + 3 = -3$	The first step in this method for solving a system of equations is to use the coefficients to set up a matrix whose determinant is D. Notice that the coefficients for each variable are used to create the columns of the matrix, while the coefficients across each equation make up the rows. **Remember:** If $\det(D) = 0$, you must stop this process.
$D_x = \left\| \begin{bmatrix} -2 & 1 & -1 \\ 0 & -1 & 1 \\ 1 & -2 & 3 \end{bmatrix} \right\| = -2(-1) - 1(-1) + (-1)(1)$ $= 2 + 1 - 1 = 2$	Next create the matrix for the variable, x. Replace the coefficients of x in the first matrix with the constants from the equations, keeping each constant in the row for its equation. Then, evaluate the determinant of the matrix. In this case, $\det(D_x) = 2$.
$D_y = \left\| \begin{bmatrix} 1 & -2 & -1 \\ 2 & 0 & 1 \\ 1 & 1 & 3 \end{bmatrix} \right\| = 1(-1) - (-2)(5) + (-1)(2)$ $= -1 + 10 - 2 = 7$ $D_z = \left\| \begin{bmatrix} 1 & 1 & -2 \\ 2 & -1 & 0 \\ 1 & -2 & 1 \end{bmatrix} \right\| = 1(-1) - 1(2) + (-2)(-3)$ $= -1 - 2 + 6 = 3$	Next, repeat the process to find the values of the determinants for each of the other two variables, y and z. The determinants are denoted D_y and D_z.
$D = -3 \quad D_x = 2 \quad D_y = 7 \quad D_z = 3$	When you are done you have four determinant values: one for the system and one each for the three variables.
$x = \frac{D_x}{D} = -\frac{2}{3}$ $y = \frac{D_y}{D} = -\frac{7}{3}$ $z = \frac{D_z}{D} = -\frac{3}{3} = -1$	Finally, solve for each variable by dividing the corresponding determinant by the value D.

Sample problems:

1. Use Cramer's Rule to solve the system $3x+2y+2z=-3,\ 2x-4y+z=7,$ and $5x-2y+z=-6.$
   If $D=0$, use another method to solve the system.
   Solution: $x=-3,\ y=-2,$ and $z=5.$

   Explanation: $D=\left|\begin{bmatrix} 3 & 2 & 2 \\ 2 & -4 & 1 \\ 5 & -2 & 1 \end{bmatrix}\right|=32.$

   $$D_x=\left|\begin{bmatrix} -3 & 2 & 2 \\ 7 & -4 & 1 \\ -6 & -2 & 1 \end{bmatrix}\right|=-96;\ x=\frac{-96}{32}=-3.$$

   $$D_y=\left|\begin{bmatrix} 3 & -3 & 2 \\ 2 & 7 & 1 \\ 5 & -6 & 1 \end{bmatrix}\right|=-64;\ y=\frac{-64}{32}=-2.$$

   $$D_z=\left|\begin{bmatrix} 3 & 2 & -3 \\ 2 & -4 & 7 \\ 5 & -2 & -6 \end{bmatrix}\right|=160;\ y=\frac{160}{32}=5.$$

2. Use Cramer's Rule to solve the system $2x-3y-3z=-3,\ x-2y-4z=-11,$ and $-3x+4y+4z=3.$
   If $D=0$, use another method to solve the system.
   Solution: $x=3,\ y=-1,$ and $z=4.$

   Explanation: $D=\left|\begin{bmatrix} 2 & -3 & -3 \\ 1 & -2 & -4 \\ -3 & 4 & 4 \end{bmatrix}\right|=-2.$

   $$D_x=\left|\begin{bmatrix} -3 & -3 & -3 \\ -11 & -2 & -4 \\ 3 & 4 & 4 \end{bmatrix}\right|=-6;\ x=\frac{-6}{-2}=3.$$

   $$D_y=\left|\begin{bmatrix} 2 & -3 & -3 \\ 1 & -11 & -4 \\ -3 & 3 & 4 \end{bmatrix}\right|=2;\ y=\frac{2}{-2}=-1.$$

   $$D_z=\left|\begin{bmatrix} 2 & -3 & -3 \\ 1 & -2 & -11 \\ -3 & 4 & 3 \end{bmatrix}\right|=-8;\ y=\frac{-8}{-2}=4.$$

3. Use Cramer's Rule to solve the system $x+y+2z=3,\ x+y-2z=-5,$ and $x-2y+z=7.$
   If $D=0$, use another method to solve the system.
   Solution: $x=1,\ y=-2,\ z=2.$

   Explanation: $D=\left|\begin{bmatrix} 1 & 1 & 2 \\ 1 & 1 & -2 \\ 1 & -2 & 1 \end{bmatrix}\right|=-12.$

   $$D_x=\left|\begin{bmatrix} 3 & 1 & 2 \\ -5 & 1 & -2 \\ 7 & -2 & 1 \end{bmatrix}\right|=-12;\ x=\frac{-12}{-12}=1.$$

   $$D_y=\left|\begin{bmatrix} 1 & 3 & 2 \\ 1 & -5 & -2 \\ 1 & 7 & 1 \end{bmatrix}\right|=24;\ y=\frac{24}{-12}=-2.$$

   $$D_z=\left|\begin{bmatrix} 1 & 1 & 3 \\ 1 & 1 & -5 \\ 1 & -2 & 7 \end{bmatrix}\right|=-24;\ y=\frac{-24}{-12}=2.$$

Practice problems: *(Answers on page: 764)*

1. Use Cramer's rule to solve the system $3x-2y-2z=9,\ x+4y+3z=5,$ and $2x+5y+4z=8.$ If $D=0$, use another method to solve the system.

2. Use Cramer's rule to solve the system $3x+5y=27$, $2x+7z=22$, and $4y+3z=18$. If $D=0$, use another method to solve the system.
3. Use Cramer's rule to solve the system $x+3y+z=-5, x+y-z=-1$, and $-x+3y-z=-1$. If $D=0$, use another method to solve the system.

Review questions: *(Answers to odd questions on page: 764)*

1. Use Cramer's rule to solve the system. If $D=0$, use another method to solve the system.
$5x-y=13;\ \ 3x+2z=11;\ \ 4y+3z=11$
2. Use Cramer's rule to solve the system. If $D=0$, use another method to solve the system.
$x+2y=13;\ \ 3x+4z=27;\ \ -y-z=-7$
3. Use Cramer's rule to solve the system. If $D=0$, use another method to solve the system.
$3x+2y+6z=8;\ \ 2x-4y-3z=5;\ \ x+2y-3z=5$
4. Use Cramer's rule to solve the system. If $D=0$, use another method to solve the system.
$2x-y+2z=2;\ \ x+2y-3z=10;\ \ x-3y+z=-4$
5. Use Cramer's rule to solve the system. If $D=0$, use another method to solve the system.
$2x-3y-3z=-3;\ \ x-2y-4z=-11;\ \ -3x+4y+4z=3$

An Introduction to Inverses

- The **multiplicative identity** of any number is 1 because when any number multiplies with 1 the product is the number itself.
- The **multiplicative inverse** of any number is the value that, if you multiply it with the given number, produces 1. Usually this is the reciprocal of the number.
- The **identity matrix** is the one that will produce a given matrix when that matrix multiplies with the identity matrix. The identity matrix has the characteristic that all of its terms are 0 except those that lie on the main diagonal from the upper left corner to the lower right corner.
- The **inverse matrix** is the one that will produce the identity matrix when multiplied with a given matrix. The only matrices which have inverses are those which are non-singular; i.e. those whose determinants do not equal zero.

multiplicative identity (a.k.a. 1): a # times this = the # (itself) $5 \cdot 1 = 5$ $1 \cdot 5 = 5$ multiplicative identity	Multiplying with the **identity** yields the original number as the product. In this example, 5 multiplies with **1**, the identity, to produce 5.
multiplicative inverse: a # times this = the identity (1) $5 \cdot {}^{1}/_{5} = 1$ multiplicative inverse	Multiplying with the **inverse** yields the identity as the product. The identity in the case of a number is 1.

identity matrix $\begin{bmatrix} 1 & 0 & \dots\dots & \\ 0 & 1 & 0 & \dots\dots \\ 0 & 0 & 1 & 0 \\ \text{.and so on.....} & & & \\ \dots\dots & 0 & 0 & 1 \end{bmatrix}$ *has 1's along the diagonal and 0's everywhere else* 2 x 2 identity matrix $\begin{bmatrix} 1 & 0 \\ 0 & 1 \end{bmatrix}$	The identity in the case of a matrix is the matrix of the same dimension that has all of its terms being zeros except on the main diagonal from the upper left to the lower right. On this diagonal, all the terms are 1s.
Inverse of a Matrix $\begin{bmatrix} 3 & 5 \\ 5 & 8 \end{bmatrix} \begin{bmatrix} -8 & 5 \\ 5 & -3 \end{bmatrix} = \begin{bmatrix} 1 & 0 \\ 0 & 1 \end{bmatrix}$ *the determinant of this is -1, which is not zero, so this matrix does have an inverse*	From left to right, the first matrix is the inverse of the second matrix. They produce the identity matrix when they multiply together, no matter what order they are in. **Remember:** A matrix M will have an inverse matrix only if it is non-singular; i.e., only if $\det(M) \neq 0$.

Inverses: 2x2 Matrices

- An **inverse matrix** is one that, when multiplied with its original matrix, yields the identity matrix.
- The only matrices that have inverses are those which are square and nonsingular:
  - A **square matrix** has the same number of columns as rows.
  - A **nonsingular matrix** is one whose determinant (D) is not 0.
- To check whether one matrix is the inverse of another, multiply the original matrix with the proposed inverse matrix. If the answer is the identity matrix, then the second matrix is the inverse of the first matrix.
- To find the inverse of a 2x2 matrix: $A = \begin{bmatrix} a & b \\ -c & d \end{bmatrix}$
  - Compute its determinant, D.
  - Determine the reciprocal of D.
  - Multiply the reciprocal with the matrix that has the positions and signs of its elements altered as shown:

$$A^{-1} = \left|\frac{1}{D}\right| \begin{bmatrix} d & -b \\ -c & a \end{bmatrix}$$

Example ***What is the inverse of A?*** $A = \begin{bmatrix} 1 & 3 \\ -1 & 5 \end{bmatrix}$ $\quad \lvert A \rvert = 8$ $A^{-1} = \frac{1}{8} \begin{bmatrix} 5 & -3 \\ 1 & 1 \end{bmatrix}$ $A^{-1} = \begin{bmatrix} \frac{5}{8} & \frac{-3}{8} \\ \frac{1}{8} & \frac{1}{8} \end{bmatrix}$ *A inverse*	In this example, first find D, the determinant of A. To do that, calculate: (1 x 5) – (3 x –1) = 5 + 3 = 8. The reciprocal of the determinant 8 is 1/8. Reverse the position of the elements on the main diagonal; i.e., switch 5 and 1. Change the signs of the elements on the other diagonal; i.e. 3 and –1 become –3 and 1. Multiply the new matrix by the scalar 1/8. The resulting matrix is the inverse of A, noted A^{-1}.
$\begin{bmatrix} 1 & 3 \\ -1 & 5 \end{bmatrix} \begin{bmatrix} \frac{5}{8} & \frac{-3}{8} \\ \frac{1}{8} & \frac{1}{8} \end{bmatrix} = \begin{bmatrix} 1 & 0 \\ 0 & 1 \end{bmatrix}$ **this IS the identity** **so this IS the inverse**	Multiply A by its inverse, A^{-1}. (1 x 5/8) + (3 x 1/8) = 1 (first row, left) (1 x -3/8) + (3 x 1/8) = 0 (first row, right) (-1 x 5/8) + (5 x 1/8) = 0 (second row, left) (-1 x -3/8) + (5 x 1/8) = 1 (second row, right) The result is the identity matrix. If you switch the order and multiply, the result would still be the identity matrix. Thus, the new matrix is the inverse of the original matrix.

Sample problems:

1. True or False: Given $A=\begin{bmatrix}-1 & 5\\ -2 & 10\end{bmatrix}$, A^{-1} exists.

   Solution: False

   Explanation: Find the determinant of *A*: $|A|=\left|\begin{bmatrix}-1 & 5\\ -2 & 10\end{bmatrix}\right|=-1(10)-(-2)(5)=0.$

   The determinant of this matrix is zero, so the inverse does not exist.

2. Given $A=\begin{bmatrix}-4 & -1\\ 2 & -1\end{bmatrix}$, find A^{-1} if it exists.

   Solution: $\begin{bmatrix}-\frac{1}{6} & \frac{1}{6}\\ -\frac{1}{3} & -\frac{2}{3}\end{bmatrix}$

   Explanation: Calculate $|A|$: $|A|=(-4)(-1)-(2)(-1)=6.$

   Calculate A^{-1}: $A^{-1}=\frac{1}{6}\begin{bmatrix}-1 & 1\\ -2 & -4\end{bmatrix}=\begin{bmatrix}-\frac{1}{6} & \frac{1}{6}\\ -\frac{1}{3} & -\frac{2}{3}\end{bmatrix}.$

3. Given $A=\begin{bmatrix}-2 & 2\\ 3 & -3\end{bmatrix}$, find A^{-1} if it exists.

   Solution: Inverse does not exist

   Explanation: Calculate $|A|$: $|A|=(-2)(-3)-(2)(3)=6-6=0.$

   Since $|A|=0$, the matrix is singular and therefore has no inverse.

Practice problems: *(Answers on page: 765)*

1. True or False: Given $A=\begin{bmatrix}1 & 3\\ -2 & 6\end{bmatrix}$, A^{-1} exists.

2. Given $A=\begin{bmatrix}6 & 2\\ 2 & 1\end{bmatrix}$, find A^{-1} if it exists.

3. Given $A=\begin{bmatrix}-5 & 1\\ 2 & -1\end{bmatrix}$, find A^{-1} if it exists.

Review questions: *(Answers to odd questions on page: 765)*

1. Given $A=\begin{bmatrix}8 & 3\\ 2 & 1\end{bmatrix}$, find A^{-1} if it exists.

2. Given $A=\begin{bmatrix}5 & 1\\ 5 & 1\end{bmatrix}$, find A^{-1} if it exists.

3. Given $A=\begin{bmatrix}-3 & 1\\ 2 & 2\end{bmatrix}$, find A^{-1} if it exists.

4. Given $A=\begin{bmatrix}-1 & 1\\ 1 & -1\end{bmatrix}$, find A^{-1} if it exists.

5. Given $A=\begin{bmatrix}3 & 5\\ 1 & 2\end{bmatrix}$, find A^{-1} if it exists.

Another Look at 2x2 Inverses

- An **inverse matrix** is one that, when multiplied with its original matrix, yields the identity matrix.
- The only matrices that have inverses are those which are square and nonsingular:
  - A **square matrix** has the same number of columns as rows.
  - A **nonsingular matrix** is one whose determinant (D) is not 0
- To check whether one matrix is the inverse of another, multiply the original matrix with the proposed inverse matrix. If the answer is the identity matrix, then the second matrix is the inverse of the first matrix.
- To find the inverse of a 2x2 matrix: $A = \begin{bmatrix} a & b \\ -c & d \end{bmatrix}$
  - Compute its determinant, D.
  - Determine the reciprocal of D.
  - Multiply the reciprocal with the matrix that has the positions and signs of its elements altered as shown:

$$A^{-1} = \left|\frac{1}{D}\right| \begin{bmatrix} d & -b \\ -c & a \end{bmatrix}$$

- To find the inverse of any matrix:
  1. Set up a matrix alternating "+" and "-"
  2. For each position in the new matrix:
     (a) block out the element in that position in the original matrix plus everything in both its row and its column.
     (b) Evaluate the determinant of whatever is still uncovered.
     (c) Write that value in the new matrix; change its sign if it lies in a "–" position.
  3. Flip this new matrix over the main diagonal, which runs from the upper left to the lower right.
  4. Multiply this new matrix by the reciprocal of the determinant of the original matrix.

$A = \begin{bmatrix} 1 & 3 \\ -1 & 5 \end{bmatrix}$ $A^{-1} = \frac{1}{8}\begin{bmatrix} 5 & -3 \\ 1 & 1 \end{bmatrix}$	One way to derive the inverse of a 2x2 matrix: 1. Switch the elements on the main diagonal. 2. Change the signs along the other diagonal. 3. Multiply the new matrix by the reciprocal of the determinant of the original matrix.
New Method $N = \begin{bmatrix} + & - \\ - & + \end{bmatrix}$ *alternating signs*	An alternate method of deriving an inverse can be used with a square matrix of any size. First, write out a matrix of signs, alternating "+" and "–".
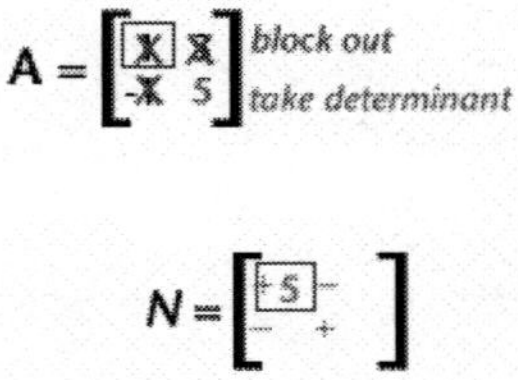	To determine the element for each position in the inverse: 1. Cover that position. In this example cover the 1, and everything in both its row and its column. 2. Evaluate the determinant of what is not covered; in this example, the 5. 3. Write the new value in the matrix of signs; change signs in the "-" positions. In this example, write the 5 without changing its sign because it is in a "+" position.
$N = \begin{bmatrix} 5 & 1 \\ -3 & 1 \end{bmatrix}$	Block out and evaluate in this way for every position in the new matrix.

$N=\begin{bmatrix}5 & 1\\ -3 & 1\end{bmatrix}=\begin{bmatrix}5 & -3\\ 1 & 1\end{bmatrix}$ $\frac{1}{8}\begin{bmatrix}5 & -3\\ 1 & 1\end{bmatrix}$ $\begin{bmatrix}\frac{5}{8} & -\frac{3}{8}\\ \frac{1}{8} & \frac{1}{8}\end{bmatrix}=A^{-1}$	Finally, flip the elements in the new matrix over the main diagonal. Multiply that result by the reciprocal of the determinant of the original matrix to arrive at the inverse matrix.

Sample problems:

1. Given $A=\begin{bmatrix}-5 & 6\\ 1 & -2\end{bmatrix}$, find A^{-1} if it exists.

   Solution: $\begin{bmatrix}-\frac{1}{2} & -\frac{3}{2}\\ -\frac{1}{4} & -\frac{5}{4}\end{bmatrix}$

   Explanation: Find the determinant of A: $|A|=\left|\begin{bmatrix}-5 & 6\\ 1 & -2\end{bmatrix}\right|=10-6=4$.

   Find the "new" matrix: $N=\begin{bmatrix}+ & -\\ - & +\end{bmatrix}=\begin{bmatrix}+(-2) & -1\\ -6 & +(-5)\end{bmatrix}=\begin{bmatrix}-2 & -1\\ -6 & -5\end{bmatrix}$.

   Reflect the "new" matrix across the diagonal: $N=\begin{bmatrix}-2 & -6\\ -1 & -5\end{bmatrix}$.

   Multiply N by $\frac{1}{|A|}$: $A^{-1}=\frac{1}{4}\begin{bmatrix}-2 & -6\\ -1 & -5\end{bmatrix}=\begin{bmatrix}-\frac{1}{2} & -\frac{3}{2}\\ -\frac{1}{4} & -\frac{5}{4}\end{bmatrix}$.

2. Given $A=\begin{bmatrix}-3 & -1\\ -1 & -4\end{bmatrix}$, find A^{-1} if it exists.

   Solution: $\begin{bmatrix}-\frac{4}{11} & \frac{1}{11}\\ \frac{1}{11} & -\frac{3}{11}\end{bmatrix}$

   Explanation: $|A|=\left|\begin{bmatrix}-3 & -1\\ -1 & -4\end{bmatrix}\right|=12-(-1)=11$; $N=\begin{bmatrix}+ & -\\ - & +\end{bmatrix}=\begin{bmatrix}+(-4) & -(-1)\\ -(-1) & +(-3)\end{bmatrix}=\begin{bmatrix}-4 & 1\\ 1 & -3\end{bmatrix}$.

   $A^{-1}=\frac{1}{11}\begin{bmatrix}-4 & 1\\ 1 & -3\end{bmatrix}=\begin{bmatrix}-\frac{4}{11} & \frac{1}{11}\\ \frac{1}{11} & -\frac{3}{11}\end{bmatrix}$.

3. Given $A=\begin{bmatrix}-3 & 6\\ 1 & -2\end{bmatrix}$, find A^{-1} if it exists.

   Solution: The inverse does not exist.

   Explanation: Find the determinant of A: $|A|=\left|\begin{bmatrix}-3 & 6\\ 1 & -2\end{bmatrix}\right|=6-6=0$.

   Since $|A|=0$, the matrix is singular and therefore has no inverse.

Practice problems: *(Answers on page: 765)*

1. Given $A=\begin{bmatrix}7 & -1\\ 3 & 1\end{bmatrix}$, find A^{-1} if it exists.

2. Given $A = \begin{bmatrix} 8 & -2 \\ -4 & 1 \end{bmatrix}$, find A^{-1} if it exists.

3. Given $A = \begin{bmatrix} -5 & -1 \\ 13 & 3 \end{bmatrix}$, find A^{-1} if it exists.

Review questions: *(Answers to odd questions on page: 765)*

1. Given $A = \begin{bmatrix} 5 & 2 \\ 3 & 1 \end{bmatrix}$, find A^{-1} if it exists.

2. Given $A = \begin{bmatrix} 7 & -3 \\ -2 & 1 \end{bmatrix}$, find A^{-1} if it exists.

3. Given $A = \begin{bmatrix} -9 & 6 \\ -3 & 2 \end{bmatrix}$, find A^{-1} if it exists.

4. Given $A = \begin{bmatrix} -12 & -6 \\ -2 & -1 \end{bmatrix}$, find A^{-1} if it exists.

5. Given $A = \begin{bmatrix} -5 & 2 \\ -4 & 2 \end{bmatrix}$, find A^{-1} if it exists.

Inverses: 3x3 Matrices

- A **3x3 matrix** is an array with three columns and three rows.
- An **inverse matrix** is one that, when multiplied with its original matrix, yields the identity matrix.
- The only matrices that have inverses are those which are **square** and **nonsingular** :
- To check whether one matrix is the inverse of another, multiply the original matrix with the proposed inverse matrix. If the answer is the identity matrix, then the second matrix is the inverse of the first matrix.
- To find the inverse of any matrix:
  1. Set up a matrix alternating "+" and "-."
  2. Compute the determinant of the matrix.
  3. For each position in the new matrix:
     (a) block out the element in that position in the original matrix plus everything in both its row and its column.
     (b) Evaluate the determinant of whatever is still uncovered.
     (c) Write that value in the new matrix; change its sign if it lies in a "–" position.
  3. Flip this new matrix over the main diagonal, which runs from the upper left to the lower right.
  4. Multiply this new matrix by the reciprocal of the determinant of the original matrix.

<table>
<tr>
<td>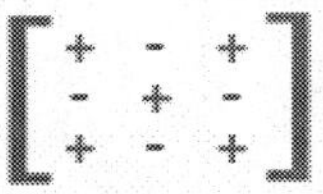
</td>
<td>Step One: Set up a 3x3 sign chart for this matrix.</td>
</tr>
<tr>
<td>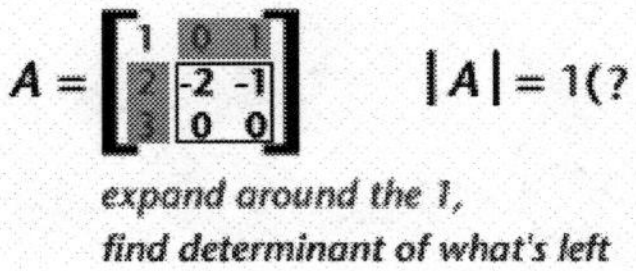
</td>
<td>Step Two: Compute the determinant of the matrix.
1. Find the first value. Cover the first row and column, then evaluate the determinant of the 2x2 matrix that is still uncovered: []. The determinant, 0, is multiplied with the uncovered 1.
2. Find the second value, remembering that its sign is "-". In this case, multiply (0) , i.e., [] 0(3).
3. Find the third value. Multiply (1) [] , i.e., 1(6). The determinant |A|, is 0 – 0 + 6 = 6.</td>
</tr>
</table>

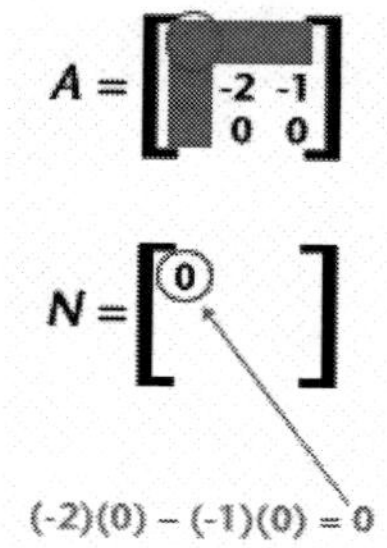	**Step Three:** Develop the inverse. Start with the first element of the first row. Cover the first element in the original matrix and everything in its row and column. Evaluate the determinant of the remaining matrix and write that value in the first position of the new matrix, *N*. **Caution:** Do not multiply with the original term itself. Use only the value derived from evaluating the terms that were not covered.
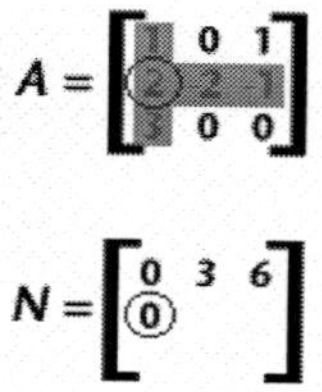	Repeat that process for every term in *N*. The determinant of each of these smaller matrices is called the minor of the corresponding element in the first row.
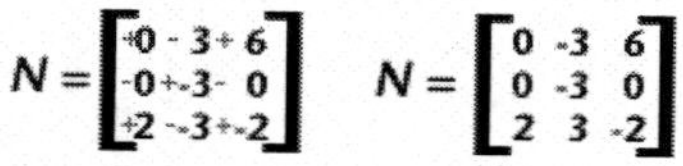	Check your signs against the sign chart. Change the sign of any term that lies in a "–" position. In this example, you can see that the top and bottom 3s in the middle column change signs.
	Next, flip the matrix *N* over its main diagonal. In this example, you can see the 6 and the 2 switch places, the –3 and the 0 on the left of the diagonal switch places, and the 0 on the right of the diagonal and the 3 switch places.
$A^{-1}=\frac{1}{6}\begin{bmatrix}0&0&2\\-3&-3&3\\6&0&-2\end{bmatrix}$ $A^{-1}=\begin{bmatrix}0&0&\frac{1}{3}\\-\frac{1}{2}&-\frac{1}{2}&\frac{1}{2}\\1&0&-\frac{1}{3}\end{bmatrix}$	Finally, the determinant of the original matrix is 6. So, its reciprocal is 1/6. To find the inverse, multiply 1/6 with the matrix you have just created. The final result is the inverse of *A*, noted A^{-1}.

Sample problems:

1. Given $A=\begin{bmatrix}-1&2&0\\0&3&2\\0&1&4\end{bmatrix}$, find A^{-1} if it exists.

<u>Solution:</u> $\begin{bmatrix}-1&\frac{4}{5}&-\frac{2}{5}\\0&\frac{2}{5}&-\frac{1}{5}\\0&-\frac{1}{10}&\frac{3}{10}\end{bmatrix}$

Explanation: Find the determinant: $|A| = -1(12-2) - 2(0-0) + 0(0-0) = -10 - 0 + 0 = -10.$

Create a new matrix: $N = \begin{bmatrix} +\begin{bmatrix} 3 & 2 \\ 1 & 4 \end{bmatrix} & -\begin{bmatrix} 0 & 2 \\ 0 & 4 \end{bmatrix} & +\begin{bmatrix} 0 & 3 \\ 0 & 1 \end{bmatrix} \\ -\begin{bmatrix} 2 & 0 \\ 1 & 4 \end{bmatrix} & +\begin{bmatrix} -1 & 0 \\ 0 & 4 \end{bmatrix} & -\begin{bmatrix} -1 & 2 \\ 0 & 1 \end{bmatrix} \\ +\begin{bmatrix} 2 & 0 \\ 3 & 2 \end{bmatrix} & -\begin{bmatrix} -1 & 0 \\ 0 & 2 \end{bmatrix} & +\begin{bmatrix} -1 & 2 \\ 0 & 3 \end{bmatrix} \end{bmatrix} = \begin{bmatrix} +10 & -0 & +0 \\ -8 & -4 & -(-1) \\ +4 & -(-2) & +(-3) \end{bmatrix} = \begin{bmatrix} 10 & 0 & 0 \\ -8 & -4 & 1 \\ 4 & 2 & -3 \end{bmatrix}.$

Reflect across the diagonal and multiply by $\frac{1}{|A|}$: $A^{-1} = \frac{1}{-10}\begin{bmatrix} 10 & -8 & 4 \\ 0 & -4 & 2 \\ 0 & 1 & -3 \end{bmatrix} = \begin{bmatrix} -1 & \frac{4}{5} & -\frac{2}{5} \\ 0 & \frac{2}{5} & -\frac{1}{5} \\ 0 & -\frac{1}{10} & \frac{3}{10} \end{bmatrix}.$

2. Given $A = \begin{bmatrix} 1 & -2 & 2 \\ 2 & 1 & 0 \\ 0 & -1 & -1 \end{bmatrix}$, find A^{-1} if it exists.

Solution: $\begin{bmatrix} \frac{1}{9} & \frac{4}{9} & \frac{2}{9} \\ -\frac{2}{9} & \frac{1}{9} & -\frac{4}{9} \\ \frac{2}{9} & -\frac{1}{9} & -\frac{5}{9} \end{bmatrix}$

Explanation: Find the determinant: $|A| = 1(-1-0) - -2(-2-0) + 2(-2-0) = -9.$

Create a new matrix: $N = \begin{bmatrix} +\begin{bmatrix} 1 & 0 \\ -1 & -1 \end{bmatrix} & -\begin{bmatrix} 2 & 0 \\ 0 & -1 \end{bmatrix} & +\begin{bmatrix} 2 & 1 \\ 0 & -1 \end{bmatrix} \\ -\begin{bmatrix} -2 & 2 \\ -1 & -1 \end{bmatrix} & +\begin{bmatrix} 1 & 2 \\ 0 & -1 \end{bmatrix} & -\begin{bmatrix} 1 & -2 \\ 0 & -1 \end{bmatrix} \\ +\begin{bmatrix} -2 & 2 \\ 1 & 0 \end{bmatrix} & -\begin{bmatrix} 1 & 2 \\ 2 & 0 \end{bmatrix} & +\begin{bmatrix} 1 & -2 \\ 2 & 1 \end{bmatrix} \end{bmatrix} = \begin{bmatrix} -1 & 2 & -2 \\ -4 & -1 & 1 \\ -2 & 4 & 5 \end{bmatrix}.$

Reflect across the diagonal and multiply by $\frac{1}{|A|}$: $A^{-1} = \frac{1}{-9}\begin{bmatrix} -1 & -4 & -2 \\ 2 & -1 & 4 \\ -2 & 1 & 5 \end{bmatrix} = \begin{bmatrix} \frac{1}{9} & \frac{4}{9} & \frac{2}{9} \\ -\frac{2}{9} & \frac{1}{9} & -\frac{4}{9} \\ \frac{2}{9} & -\frac{1}{9} & -\frac{5}{9} \end{bmatrix}.$

3. Given $A = \begin{bmatrix} 0 & 1 & 2 \\ 1 & -2 & -1 \\ 1 & 2 & -2 \end{bmatrix}$, find A^{-1} if it exists.

Solution: $\begin{bmatrix} \frac{2}{3} & \frac{2}{3} & \frac{1}{3} \\ \frac{1}{9} & -\frac{2}{9} & \frac{2}{9} \\ \frac{4}{9} & \frac{1}{9} & -\frac{1}{9} \end{bmatrix}$

Explanation: Find the determinant: $|A| = 0(4--2) - 1(-2--1) + 2(2--2) = 9$.

Create a new matrix: $N = \begin{bmatrix} +\begin{bmatrix} -2 & -1 \\ 2 & -2 \end{bmatrix} & -\begin{bmatrix} 1 & -1 \\ 1 & -2 \end{bmatrix} & +\begin{bmatrix} 1 & -2 \\ 1 & 2 \end{bmatrix} \\ -\begin{bmatrix} 1 & 2 \\ 2 & -2 \end{bmatrix} & +\begin{bmatrix} 0 & 2 \\ 1 & -2 \end{bmatrix} & -\begin{bmatrix} 0 & 1 \\ 1 & 2 \end{bmatrix} \\ +\begin{bmatrix} 1 & 2 \\ -2 & -1 \end{bmatrix} & -\begin{bmatrix} 0 & 2 \\ 1 & -1 \end{bmatrix} & +\begin{bmatrix} 0 & 1 \\ 1 & -2 \end{bmatrix} \end{bmatrix} = \begin{bmatrix} 6 & 6 & 3 \\ 6 & -2 & 1 \\ 3 & 2 & -1 \end{bmatrix}$.

Reflect across the diagonal and multiply: $A^{-1} = \frac{1}{9}\begin{bmatrix} 6 & 6 & 3 \\ 1 & -2 & 2 \\ 4 & 1 & -1 \end{bmatrix} = \begin{bmatrix} \frac{2}{3} & \frac{2}{3} & \frac{1}{3} \\ \frac{1}{9} & -\frac{2}{9} & \frac{2}{9} \\ \frac{4}{9} & \frac{1}{9} & -\frac{1}{9} \end{bmatrix}$.

Practice problems: *(Answers on page: 765)*

1. Given $A = \begin{bmatrix} 1 & 0 & 2 \\ 1 & 2 & 0 \\ 1 & 2 & 3 \end{bmatrix}$, find A^{-1} if it exists.

2. Given $A = \begin{bmatrix} 0 & 2 & 0 \\ 1 & 2 & -1 \\ 0 & 4 & 0 \end{bmatrix}$, find A^{-1} if it exists.

3. Given $A = \begin{bmatrix} 2 & 0 & 1 \\ -1 & 1 & 0 \\ 0 & 2 & 0 \end{bmatrix}$, find A^{-1} if it exists.

Review questions: *(Answers to odd questions on page: 765)*

1. Given $A = \begin{bmatrix} -1 & 3 & 0 \\ 1 & 4 & 2 \\ 1 & 3 & 2 \end{bmatrix}$, find A^{-1} if it exists.

2. Given $A = \begin{bmatrix} 2 & 0 & 1 \\ 1 & 5 & 4 \\ 4 & 0 & 2 \end{bmatrix}$, find A^{-1} if it exists.

3. Given $A = \begin{bmatrix} -3 & 1 & 2 \\ -1 & 0 & 1 \\ 1 & 2 & -1 \end{bmatrix}$, find A^{-1} if it exists.

4. Given $A = \begin{bmatrix} -1 & 0 & \frac{1}{2} \\ 0 & 0 & \frac{1}{2} \\ 2 & 1 & -1 \end{bmatrix}$, find A^{-1} if it exists.

5. Given $A = \begin{bmatrix} -1 & 0 & 3 \\ 0 & 5 & 7 \\ -2 & 0 & 6 \end{bmatrix}$, find A^{-1} if it exists.

Solving a System of Equations with Inverses

- An **inverse matrix** is one that, when multiplied with its original matrix, yields the identity matrix.
- The only matrices that have inverses are those that are square and nonsingular.
  - A **square matrix** has the same number of columns as it has rows.
  - A **nonsingular matrix** is one whose determinant *D* is not 0.
- The inverse of a 2x2 matrix $A=\begin{bmatrix} a & b \\ -c & d \end{bmatrix}$: $A^{-1}=\left|\frac{1}{D}\right|\begin{bmatrix} d & -b \\ -c & a \end{bmatrix}$,where *D* is the determinant of *A*.

Given $a_1x+b_1y=c_1$ $a_2x+b_2y=c_2$ $\begin{bmatrix} a_1 & b_1 \\ a_2 & b_2 \end{bmatrix}\begin{bmatrix} x \\ y \end{bmatrix}=\begin{bmatrix} c_1 \\ c_2 \end{bmatrix}$ $A\begin{bmatrix} x \\ y \end{bmatrix}=\begin{bmatrix} c_1 \\ c_2 \end{bmatrix}$ $\begin{bmatrix} x \\ y \end{bmatrix}=A^{-1}\begin{bmatrix} c_1 \\ c_2 \end{bmatrix}$	Consider a system of two linear equations with two unknowns *x* and *y*. Let a_1, b_1, c_1, a_2, b_2, and c_2 be the constants and coefficients. Represent this system of equations using the matrix *A*. You now have an equation in terms of matrices. You can solve for the matrix on the left. Multiply both sides of the equation by the inverse of *A*.
Example $-x+y=1$ $2x-y=1$ 1) create matrix A from coefficients of the system 2) set up equation 3) find A^{-1} $A=\begin{bmatrix} -1 & 1 \\ 2 & -1 \end{bmatrix}$ $\begin{bmatrix} x \\ y \end{bmatrix}=A^{-1}\begin{bmatrix} 1 \\ 1 \end{bmatrix}$ $A^{-1}=\frac{1}{-1}\begin{bmatrix} -1 & -1 \\ -2 & -1 \end{bmatrix}$ switch places switch signs $\begin{bmatrix} x \\ y \end{bmatrix}=\begin{bmatrix} 1 & 1 \\ 2 & 1 \end{bmatrix}\begin{bmatrix} 1 \\ 1 \end{bmatrix}$ $A^{-1}=\begin{bmatrix} 1 & 1 \\ 2 & 1 \end{bmatrix}$ $\begin{bmatrix} x \\ y \end{bmatrix}=\begin{bmatrix} 2 \\ 3 \end{bmatrix}$	Here is an example. First write the matrix *A* using the coefficients of *x* and *y* from the two equations. The matrix formed by the unknowns will be equal to the product of A^{-1} and the matrix formed by the constants 1 and 1. Determine A^{-1} by first calculating the determinant of *A*, which is –1. Then switch signs and positions inside the matrix using the method you already learned. Finally, distribute 1/–1, which is the reciprocal of the determinant. When you multiply A_{-1} by the matrix with 1 and 1, you get the solution matrix. So $x = 2$ and $y = 3$.
a simple version of what we just did: $ax = t$ *a represents a matrix* $a^{-1}(ax) = a^{-1}t$ *for which we can find* $x = a^{-1}t$ *an inverse*	Actually, you have just solved this matrix equation in the same way you solve equations of the form $ax = t$. The only difference is that with real numbers like *a* the multiplicative inverse is written as the fraction $1/a$.

Sample problems:

1. Solve the system of equations using the inverse of the coefficient matrix: $9x-6y=-12;\ x+y=3$.

   Solution: $x=\frac{2}{5},\ y=\frac{13}{5}$

   Explanation: Write the coefficient matrix: $A=\begin{bmatrix} 9 & -6 \\ 1 & 1 \end{bmatrix}$.

   Find the inverse: $A^{-1}=\frac{1}{|A|}\begin{bmatrix} b_2 & -b_2 \\ -a_1 & a_1 \end{bmatrix}=\frac{1}{15}\begin{bmatrix} 1 & 6 \\ -1 & 9 \end{bmatrix}=\begin{bmatrix} \frac{1}{15} & \frac{2}{5} \\ -\frac{1}{15} & \frac{3}{5} \end{bmatrix}$.

   Multiply A^{-1} by $\begin{bmatrix} -12 \\ 3 \end{bmatrix}$ to solve for *x* and *y*: $\begin{bmatrix} x \\ y \end{bmatrix}=\begin{bmatrix} \frac{1}{15} & \frac{2}{5} \\ -\frac{1}{15} & \frac{3}{5} \end{bmatrix}\begin{bmatrix} -12 \\ 3 \end{bmatrix}=\begin{bmatrix} \frac{2}{5} \\ \frac{13}{5} \end{bmatrix}$.

2. Solve the system of equations using the inverse of the coefficient matrix: $x-4y=14$; $2x+5y=15$.
Solution: $x=10,\ y=-1$

Explanation: Write the coefficient matrix: $A=\begin{bmatrix}1 & -4\\ 2 & 5\end{bmatrix}$.

Find the inverse: $A^{-1}=\frac{1}{|A|}\begin{bmatrix}b_2 & -b_2\\ -a_1 & a_1\end{bmatrix}=\frac{1}{13}\begin{bmatrix}5 & 4\\ -2 & 1\end{bmatrix}=\begin{bmatrix}\frac{5}{13} & \frac{4}{13}\\ -\frac{2}{13} & \frac{1}{13}\end{bmatrix}$.

Multiply A^{-1} by $\begin{bmatrix}14\\ 15\end{bmatrix}$ to solve for x and y: $\begin{bmatrix}x\\ y\end{bmatrix}=\begin{bmatrix}\frac{5}{13} & \frac{4}{13}\\ -\frac{2}{13} & \frac{1}{13}\end{bmatrix}\begin{bmatrix}14\\ 15\end{bmatrix}=\begin{bmatrix}10\\ -1\end{bmatrix}$.

3. Solve the system of equations using the inverse of the coefficient matrix:
$-x+7y=-10$; $-2x-3y=14$.
Solution: $x=-4,\ y=-2$

Explanation: Write the coefficient matrix: $A=\begin{bmatrix}-1 & 7\\ -2 & -3\end{bmatrix}$.

Find the inverse: $A^{-1}=\frac{1}{|A|}\begin{bmatrix}b_2 & -b_2\\ -a_1 & a_1\end{bmatrix}=\frac{1}{17}\begin{bmatrix}-3 & -7\\ 2 & -1\end{bmatrix}=\begin{bmatrix}-\frac{3}{17} & -\frac{7}{17}\\ \frac{2}{17} & -\frac{1}{17}\end{bmatrix}$.

Multiply A^{-1} by $\begin{bmatrix}-10\\ 14\end{bmatrix}$ to solve for x and y: $\begin{bmatrix}x\\ y\end{bmatrix}=\begin{bmatrix}-\frac{3}{17} & -\frac{7}{17}\\ \frac{2}{17} & -\frac{1}{17}\end{bmatrix}\begin{bmatrix}-10\\ 14\end{bmatrix}=\begin{bmatrix}-4\\ -2\end{bmatrix}$.

Practice problems: *(Answers on page: 765)*

1. Solve the system of equations using the inverse of the coefficient matrix: $2x+3y=5$; $x+y=8$.
2. Solve the system of equations using the inverse of the coefficient matrix: $-x+5y=0$; $4x+y=7$.
3. Solve the system of equations using the inverse of the coefficient matrix: $-4x-y=1$; $2x+3y=5$.

Review questions: *(Answers to odd questions on page: 765)*

1. Solve the system of equations using the inverse of the coefficient matrix: $x+y=8$; $x-y=2$.
2. Solve the system of equations using the inverse of the coefficient matrix: $6x+y=12$; $2x+y=10$.
3. Solve the system of equations using the inverse of the coefficient matrix: $-x-y=1$; $2x-3y=0$.
4. Solve the system of equations using the inverse of the coefficient matrix: $4x-y=11$; $3x+y=3$.
5. Solve the system of equations using the inverse of the coefficient matrix: $5x+2y=3$; $x+2y=1$.

An Introduction to Systems of Inequalities

- A **system of inequalities** means that you have more than one inequality, or an inequality mixed in with regular equations.
- When **graphing inequalities**, start by drawing the equation normally. The equation should divide the coordinate system into several regions. Use a solid-line graph only if the inequality can equal the points on the curve. Then pick a point off the curve to find out which region is the correct side for your inequality.

Relationships other than equalities do occur in mathematics. These relationships are called inequalities, and they can be graphed.

Notice that any given line will divide the co-ordinate plane into two regions. This idea will help us **graph inequalities**.

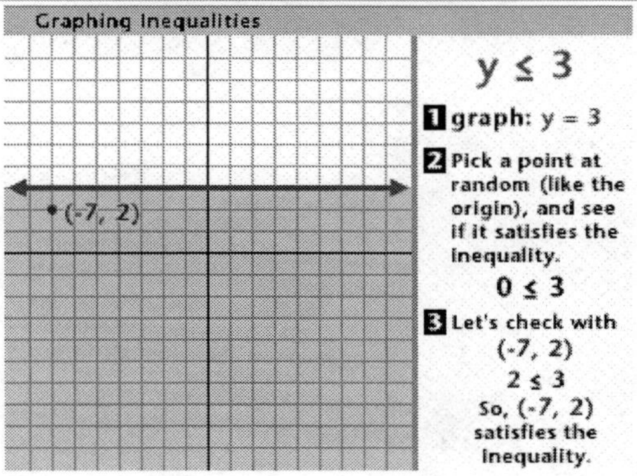

Consider the inequality $y \leq 3$. To graph the inequality, start by graphing what the line would be if you had an equation.

Graph with a solid line because this inequality includes the "or equal to" in its notation.

This line divides the graph into 2 parts.

Pick a point on the plane but not on the line. Substitute that point's coordinates into the inequality. If you have a true statement, then that entire region represents the solution for the inequality.

x > -1

What about inequalities that do not include the "or equal to" in their statement? These inequalities do not include the points on the curves graphed. Use a dotted or dashed line to represent these inequalities.

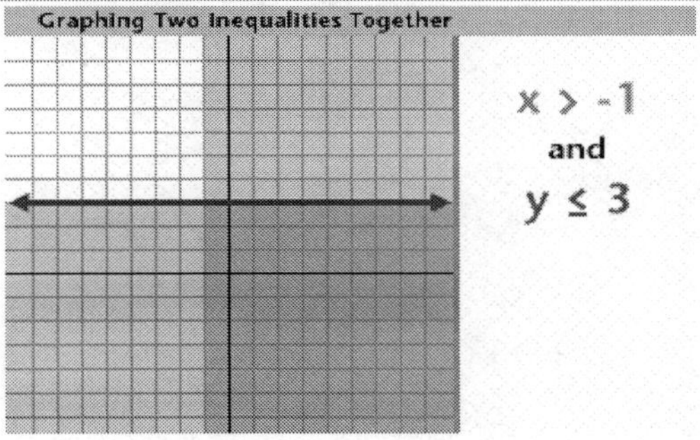

Sometimes you have two inequalities. You are asked to determine what solution satisfies both statements.

In that case, graph each inequality separately. Your system solution is the region where the individual solutions overlap.

In this case, the system solution is the region to the right of $x = -1$ and beneath or equal to $y = 3$.

Sample problems:

1. True or false: The graph of $x \leq -2$ is a solid, vertical line with shading to the left of the line.
   Solution: True
   Explanation: Since the inequality contains "or equal to", the line is solid. The graph of $x = -2$ is indeed a vertical line. The solution region includes all points where the x value is "less than or equal to" -2, these points are located to the left of the line $x = -2$.

2. True or false: The point $(-5, 0)$ is included in the solution region of $y > 0$.
   Solution: False
   Explanation: Determine if the point satifies the inquality $y > 0$, by substituting the y value from the point into the inequality: $y > 0 \Rightarrow 0 > 0$, false. Thus, $(-5, 0)$ is not in the solution region of $y > 0$.

3. True or false: The solution region of $x \leq 1$ and $y \geq 5$ includes $(-4, 7)$.
   Solution: True
   Explanation: Substitute the x and y values from the point into each inequality: $x \leq 1 \Rightarrow -4 \leq 1$, true and $y \geq 5 \Rightarrow 7 \geq 5$, true. Since both inequalities are true statements, $(-4, 7)$ is in the solution region of $x \leq 1$ and $y \geq 5$.

Practice problems: *(Answers on page: 765)*

1. True or false: The solution region of $y \le 3$ is the region below the line $y = 3$, including the line $y = 3$.
2. True or false: The solution region of $y \le -4$ includes $(0,-3)$.
3. True or false: The solution region of $x < 5$ and $y \le -1$ includes $(5,-2)$.

Review questions: *(Answers to odd questions on page: 765)*

1. True or false: The solution region of $y \ge 2$ is the region below the line $y = 2$, including the line $y = 2$.
2. True or false: The solution region of $y < 3$ is the region below the line $y = 3$, not including the line $y = 3$.
3. True or false: The solution region of $y \ge 8$ includes (0, 8).
4. True or false: The solution region of $y < 4$ includes (5, -4).
5. True or false: The solution region of $y \ge 2$ includes (2, 1).

Graphing Systems of Inequalities

- When **graphing inequalities**, start by drawing the equation normally. The equation should divide the coordinate system into two regions. Then pick a point to find out which region is the correct side for your inequality. The actual equation is part of the solution only if the inequality was $\le$ or $\ge$.

$2x - 3y \ge 1$ **1 Graph:** $2x - 3y = 1$ $2x - 1 = 3y$ $y = \frac{2}{3}x - \frac{1}{3}$ **2 Pick a point at random (like the origin), and see if it satisfies the inequality.** **(0, 0)** $2(0) - 3(0) \ge 1$ $0 \ge 1$? 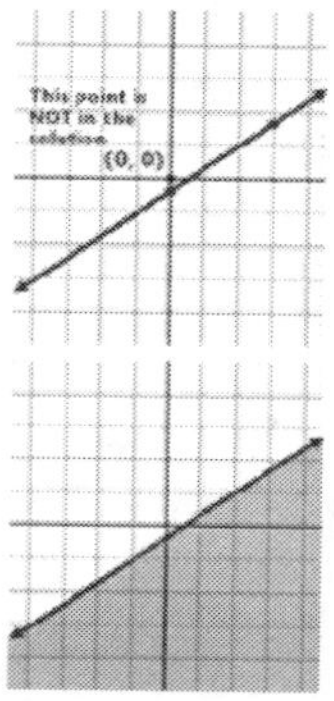	You can graph inequalities that are not horizontal or vertical lines too. The process is the same. Start by drawing the graph as though it were an equality. Pick a point somewhere not on the line and plug it into the inequality. If this point makes the inequality true, then everything on that side of the line satisfies the inequality. Shade it in! Otherwise, shade in the region you did NOT try; it's the solution. Remember, the line itself is a member only if the inequality is $\le$ or $\ge$.
$x + y < 3$ **1 Graph:** $x + y = 3$ $y = -x + 3$ **2 Pick a point at random (like the origin), and see if it satisfies the inequality.** (0, 0) $0 + 0 < 3$ $0 < 3$ 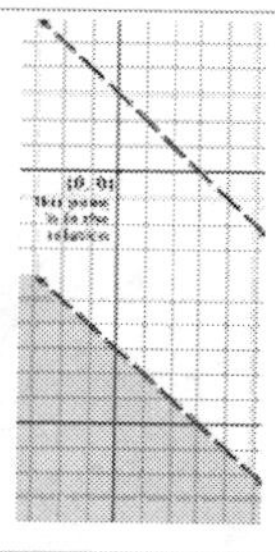	Here is another linear example. Start by drawing the graph as though it were an equality. Pick a point not on the line and plug it into the inequality. Shade the appropriate region. In this case, the line itself does not satisfy the inequality, since it is < or >.
$y < x^2$ **1 Graph:** $y = x^2$ **2 Pick a point at random, and see if it satisfies the inequality. (You can't use the origin because the curve passes through it.)** **(0, 1)** $1 < 0$? 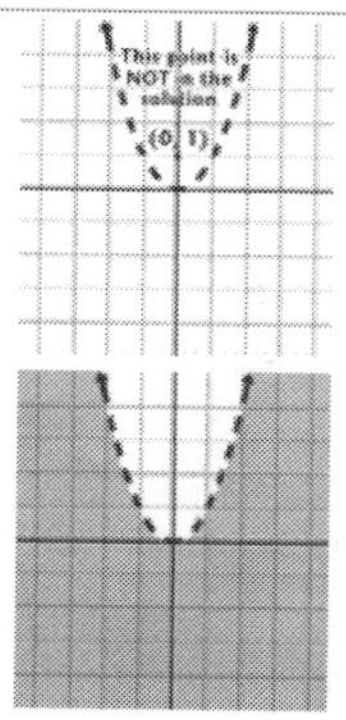	This process works with higher-order inequalities too. Consider this parabola. Start by graphing it as though it were an equality. Notice that since the solution will not include the parabola, the graph is dashed instead of solid. Pick a point and see if it is true. Shade in the correct region!

Sample problems:

1. True or False: The graph of $y \ge -2x^2$ is correctly represented below.

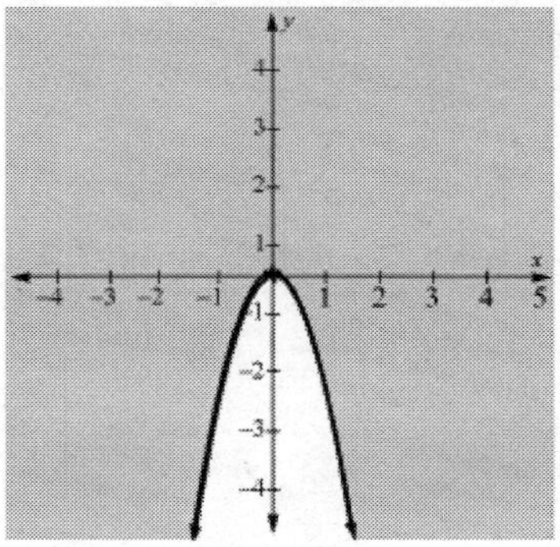

Solution: True

Explanation: First graph the parabola $y = -2x^2$. This curve splits the plane into two separate regions, inside and outside of the parabola. Pick a point not on the curve, say, $(0,-1)$. Substituting $(0,-1)$ into the inequality results in $-1 \ge 2(0)^2$; $-1 \ge 0$, which is not a true statement. Since the point $(0,-1)$ does not satisfy the inequality, the region of the plane not containing the point $(0,-1)$ is the solution set for the inequality, so shade outside the parabola. Note that the line is solid because the inequality is "greater than or equal to."

2. True or False: The graph of $y \ge \frac{2}{3}x^2$ is correctly represented below.

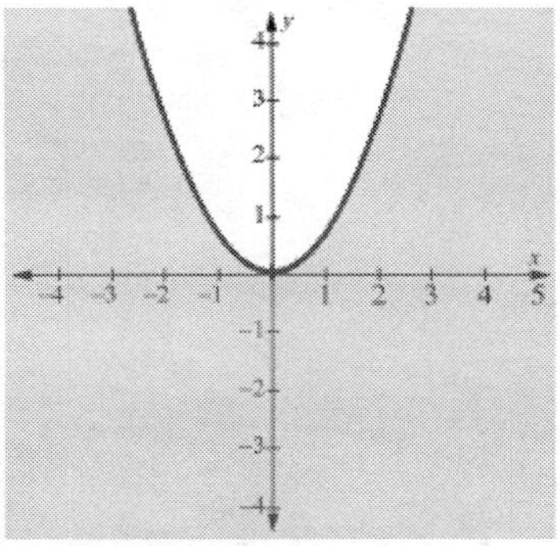

Solution: False

Explanation: The inequality $y \ge \frac{2}{3}x^2$ represents a parabola and all the points inside that curve. First graph the parabola. Use a solid line since the inequality includes the concept of "or equal to". The plane is now split into two regions, inside the parabola and outside the parabola. To choose which region is the solution region try a random point, $(0,2)$, in the inequality: $(2) \ge \frac{2}{3}(0)^2$; $2 \ge 0$. The point yields a true statement. So, shade in its region, the inside of the parabola, to indicate the solution set for the parabola.

3. True or False: The graph of $y \ge x^3$ is correctly represented below.

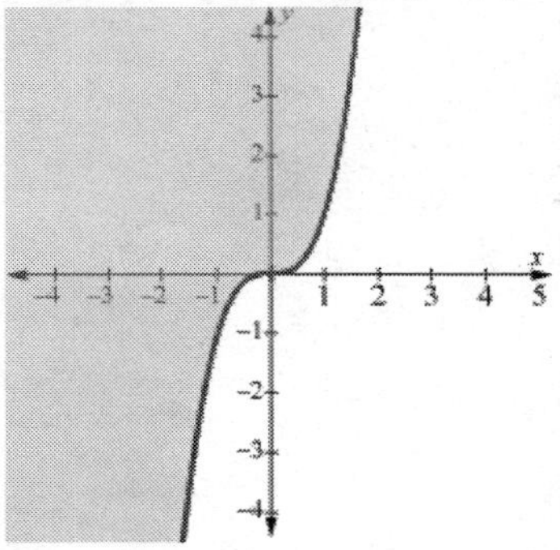

Solution: True

Explanation: $y \geq x^3$ is a cubic curve that passes through the origin. Choosing a point off the curve, for example $(0,2)$, and substituting its coordinates into the inequality indicates that the region above the curve contains the solution points, since $2 \geq 0^3$. Note that the solid line is used since the inequality is "or equal to".

Practice problems: *(Answers on page: 766)*

1. Graph the inequality: $x \geq -3$
2. Graph the inequality: $3x + 4y \geq 12$
3. Graph the inequality: $y \leq -x^2 - 2$

Review questions: *(Answers to odd questions on page: 766)*

1. True or false: The graph below represents the inequality $-3x - 5y \leq -15$.

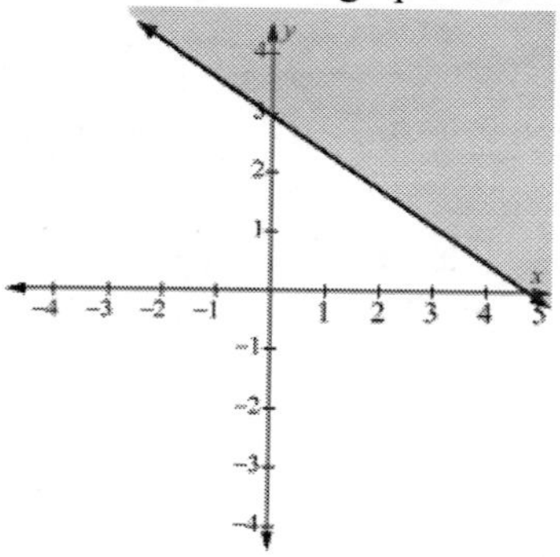

2. True or false: The graph below represents the inequality $-2x - 4y \geq 8$.

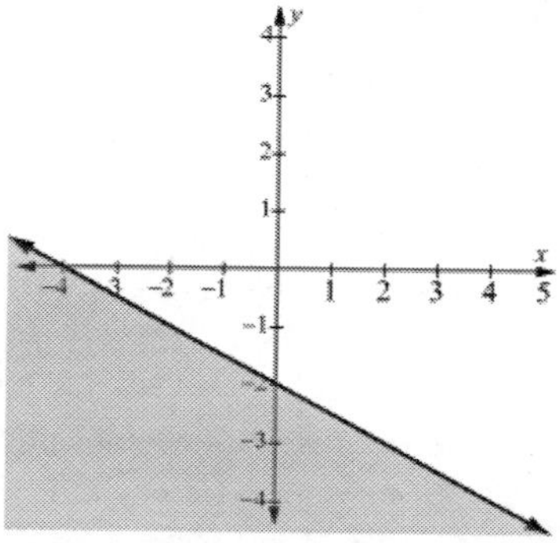

3. True or false: The graph below represents the inequality $x - y < 5$.

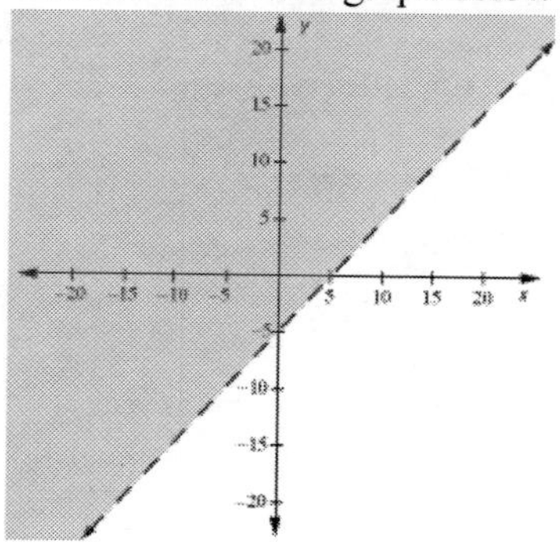

4. True or false: The graph below represents the inequality $x^2 + y^2 \leq 4$.

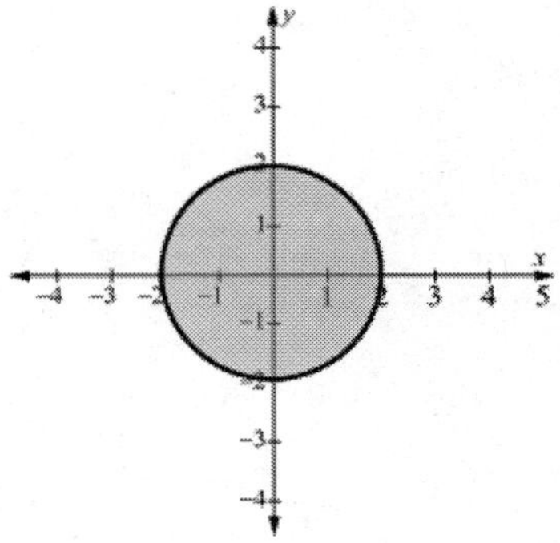

5. True or false: The graph below represents the inequality $y \leq -x^2 - 2$.

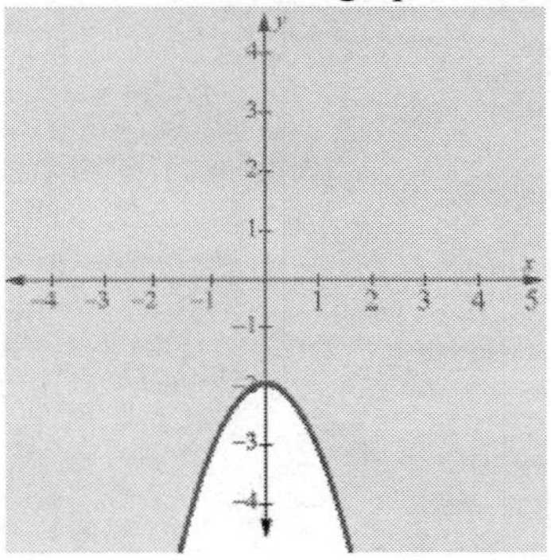

Graphing the Solution Set of a System of Inequalities

- **Systems of inequalities** might divide the coordinate plane into numerous regions. When graphing them, see where the regions overlap. That is your solution!

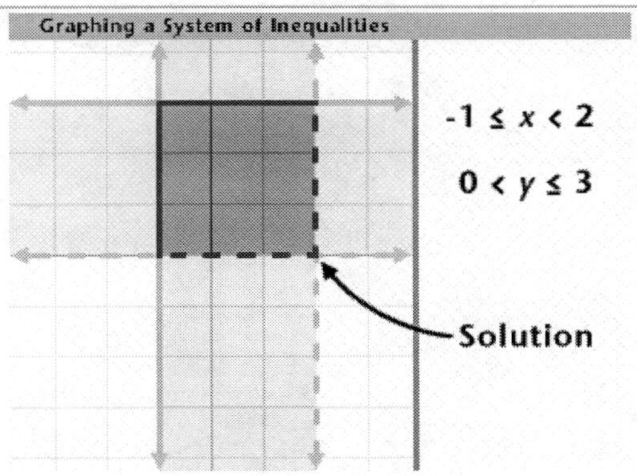

Inequalities are sometimes represented in three pieces instead of the usual two. When dealing with these inequalities, you have to think of them as two separate inequalities and graph each piece separately.

In this example, you actually have to graph four lines and find the solution regions in pairs, one region for each of the compound inequalities.

Remember: The solution is where the inequalities overlap.

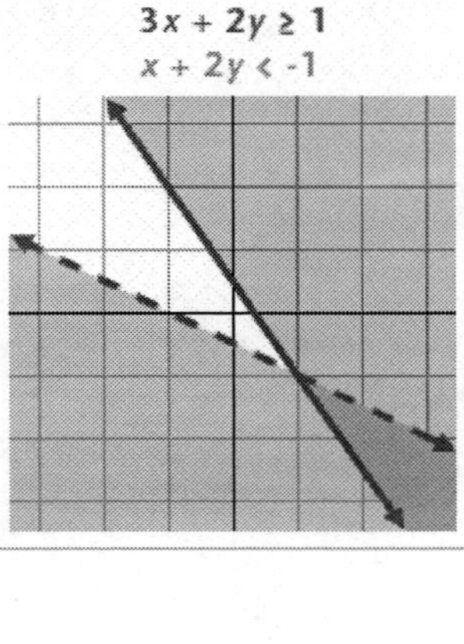

Inequalities can be intersecting regions of lines too. Treat these just like any other inequality problem.

First graph the regions of each piece.
Then find where the regions overlap.

This is your solution!

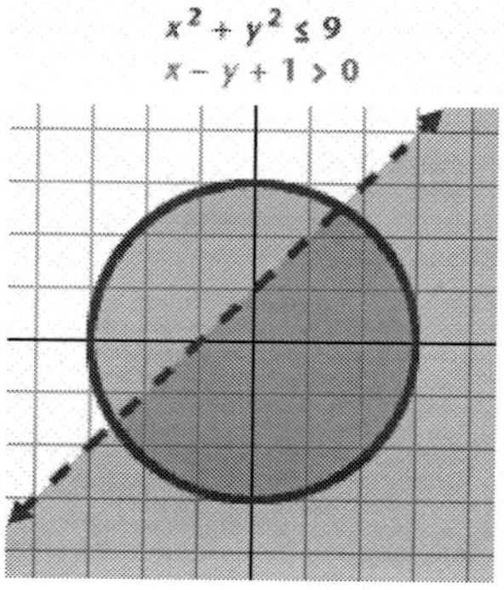

What if you get something more complicated than a line?

No problem! Use the same steps.

Graph the individual inequalities.
Then find where the regions overlap.

You have your answer!

Sample problems:

1. True or False: The solution of this system of inequalities, $3x + 2y \le -6$ and $x > 1$, is correctly represented below.

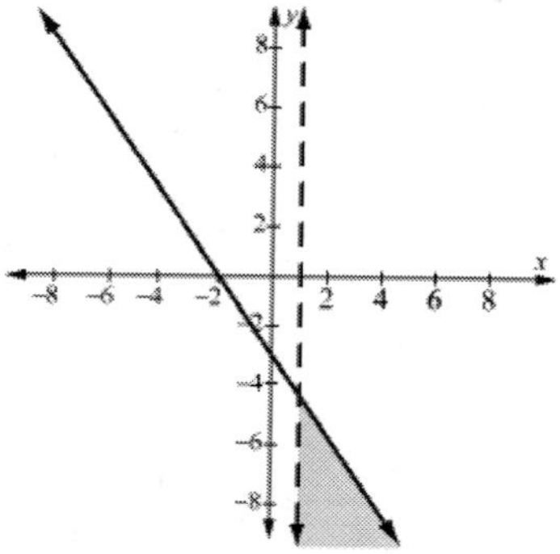

Solution: True

Explanation: Solve the first inequality for y: $y \le -\frac{3}{2}x - 3$. Graph the equation with a solid line and shade below the line. The second inequality is already solved for the variable, $x > 1$. Graph the equation with a broken line and shade to the right of the line. The intersection of the shaded regions is the solution to the system.

2. True or False: The solution of this system of inequalities, $y \le (x-3)^2$ and $x - y > -1$, is correctly represented below.

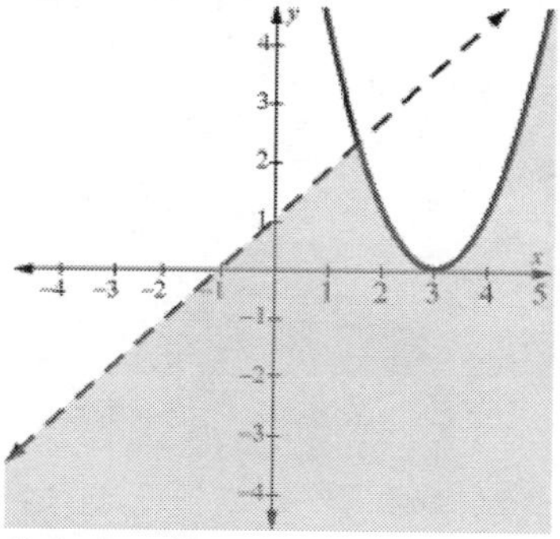

Solution: True

Explanation: Graph the first inequality: $y \le (x-3)^2$. The graph is a parabola (formed with a solid line) with the vertex at (3, 0) and the solution region is outside the parabola. Solve the second inequality for y: $x - y > -1 \Rightarrow -y > -x - 1 \Rightarrow y < x + 1$ (remember to flip the inequality). The graph of $y < x + 1$ is a broken line and the solution region is below the line. The solution region of the system of inequalities is the intersection of the shaded regions: below the line, but not including the inside of the parabola.

3. True or False: The solution of this system of inequalities, $x^2 + y \le 2$ and $x - y > 2$, is correctly represented below.

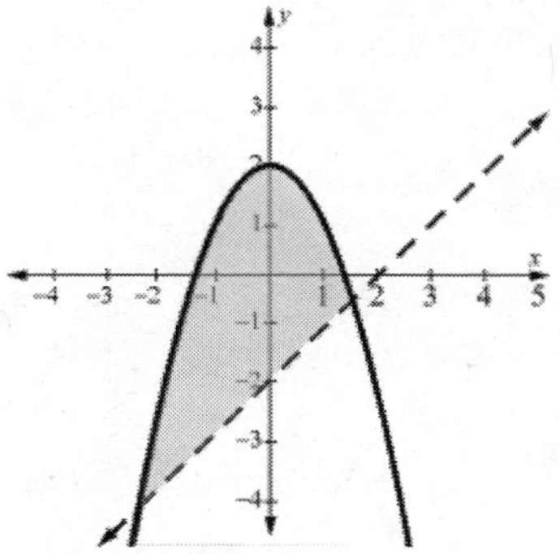

Solution: False

Explanation : Solve the first inequality for y: $y \leq -x^2 + 2$. Graph the equation with a solid line and shade inside the parabola. Solve the second inequality for y: $y < x - 2$. Graph the equation with a broken line and shade below the line. The intersection of the shaded regions is the solution to the system: below the line including the inside of the parabola. The solution region in the graph is above the line, thus false.

Practice problems: *(Answers on page: 766)*

1. Graph the solution of this system of inequalities:
   $x^2 - y \leq 0$
   $x < -\frac{1}{2}$
2. Graph the solution of this system of inequalities:
   $3x + 2y \leq -6$
   $x - 1 > 0$
3. Graph the solution of this system of inequalities:
   $x + 3y < 6$
   $x - 3y < 6$

Review questions: *(Answers to odd questions on page: 766)*

1. True or False: The solution of this system of inequalities, $x + 2y \geq 2$; $x - y \leq 0$, is correctly represented below.

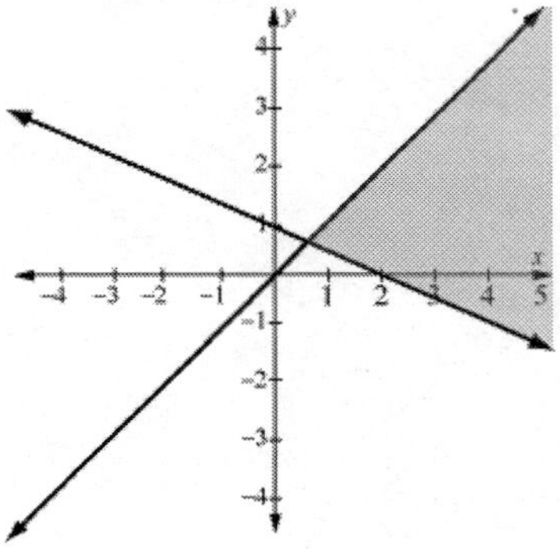

2. True or False: The solution of this system of inequalities, $x^2 + y < 3;\ \ x - y < 2,$ is correctly represented below.

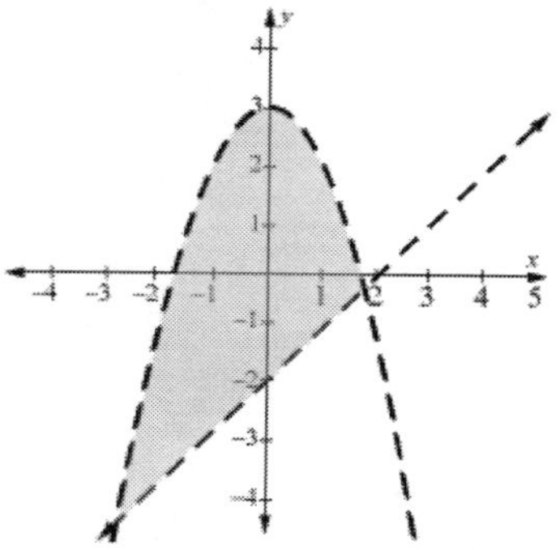

3. True or false: The solution for this system of inequalities, $3x - 2y \geq -6;\ \ x - 1 < 0,$ is correctly represented below.

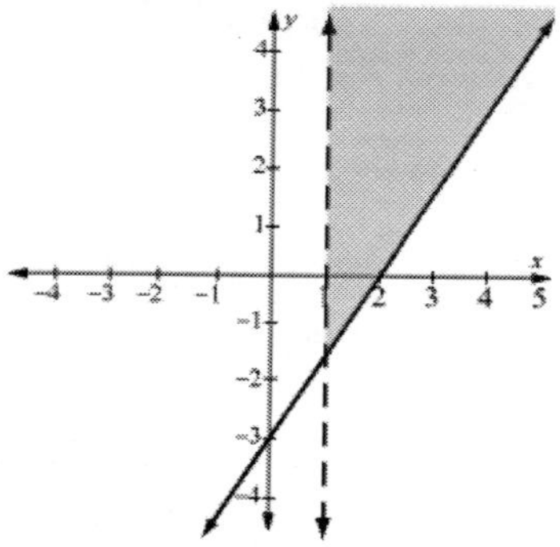

4. True or false: The solution for this system of inequalities, $2x + y \leq 4;\ \ y - 1 < 0,$ is correctly represented below.

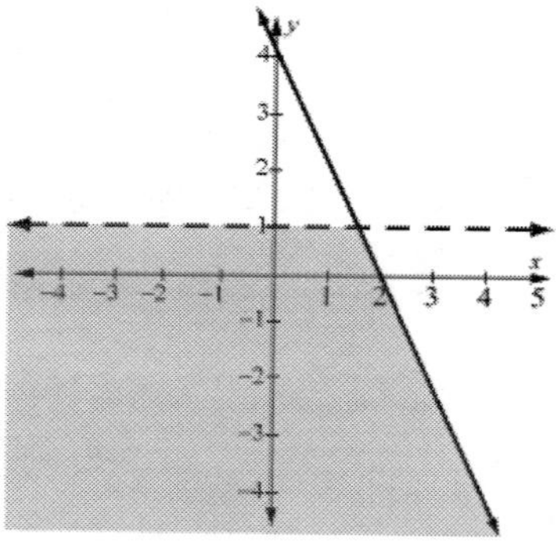

5. True or false: The solution for this system of inequalities, $x^2 + y^2 \leq 16;\ \ 2x - y > 2,$ is correctly represented below.

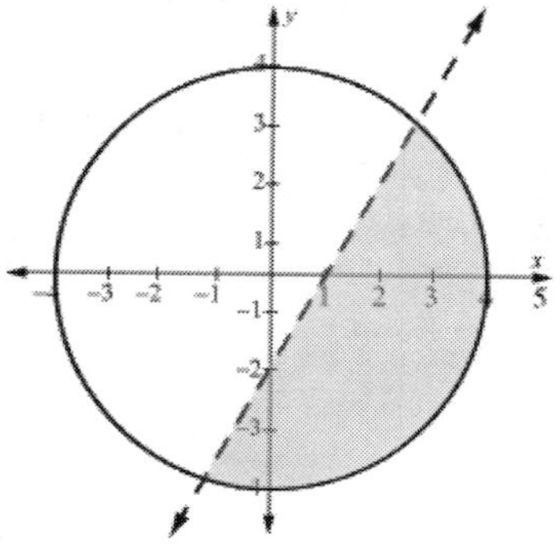

Solving for Maxima-Minima

- Using **linear programming**, you can apply constraints in the form of inequalities onto functions. This allows you to determine maximum and minimum points, a very useful activity for many business applications.
- To do so, graph the system of inequalities and find the vertex points of the region created by the system. Substitute the coordinates of these vertex points into the main equation. The greatest answer is the **maximum** of the function; the smallest answer is the **minimum**.

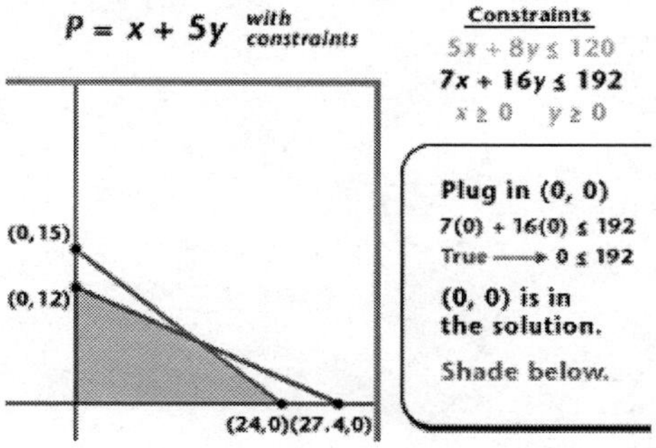

In this example, profit is determined by the equation $P = x + 5y$. There are four constraints upon the variables, represented by the system of inequalities.

The process of solving these situations is called linear programming.

The first step is to graph the system of inequalities.

Analyzing your graph, note the coordinates of the points that are vertices of the shaded region. These include (0,12), (0,0), (24,0) and the point of intersection of the two lines.

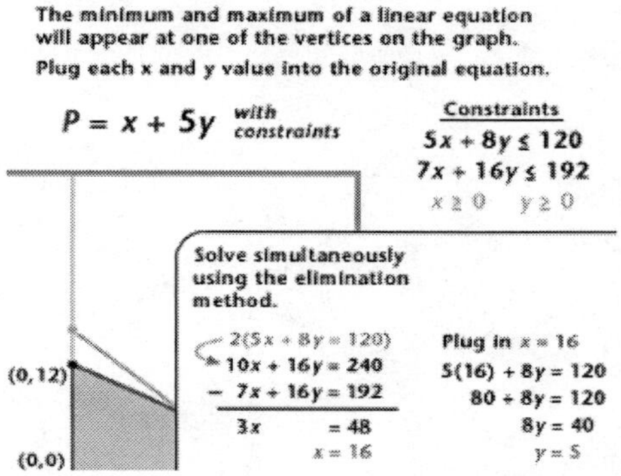

You must solve for the coordinates of the vertex that is the intersection point. To do so, set the lines equal to each other and solve for x and y. You find the point (16,5).

The minimum and maximum values of the function will occur at one of these vertices. This fact only applies to linear equations—higher order equations require the use of calculus.

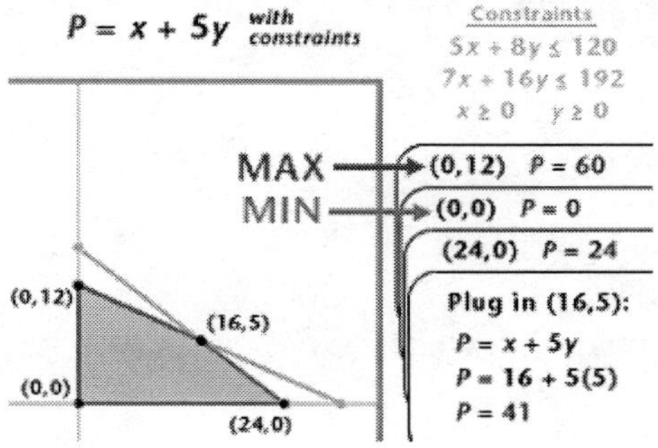

Now that you know all of the vertices, simply substitute their coordinates into the profit equation.

Whichever point results in the greatest profit is the **maximum** point.

Whichever point results in the least profit is the **minimum** point.

Sample problems:

1. Maximize $C = 5x + y$ with the following constraints: $x \ge 0, y \ge 0, -x + 2y \le 4, 2x + y \le 8$.
   Solution: $(4,0)$
   Explanation: Graph all the constraints on the same axis: $x \ge 0,\ y \ge 0;\ -x + 2y \le 4;\ 2x + y \le 8$.
   Find the coordinates of the vertices of the bounded region: $(0,2)$, $(0,0)$, and $(4,0)$.
   Solve the system formed by $-x + 2y = 4$ and $2x + y = 8$ to find the fourth vertex:
   $2(-x + 2y = 4) \qquad -2x + 4y = 8$
   $2x + y = 8 \quad \rightarrow \quad +(2x + y = 8)$
   $5y = 16;\ y = \frac{16}{5}$. Find x: $2x + \frac{16}{5} = 8;\ x = \frac{12}{5}$.
   Substitute each of the vertices of the bounded regions into C to determine the maxima:
   $(0,2) \rightarrow C = 5(0) + 2 = 2;$
   $(0,0) \rightarrow C = 5(0) + 0 = 0;$
   $(4,0) \rightarrow C = 5(4) + 0 = 20;$
   $\left(\frac{12}{5}, \frac{16}{5}\right) \rightarrow C = 5\left(\frac{12}{5}\right) + \frac{16}{5} = \frac{76}{5} = 15\frac{1}{5}.$
   The maximum value of C corresponds with $(4,0)$.

2. Minimize $C = x + y$ with the following constraints: $x \le 4,\ y \le 4,\ 2x - 3y \le -1,\ -x + y \ge 0$.
   Solution: $\left(0, \frac{1}{3}\right)$
   Explanation: Graph all the constraints on the same axis: $x \le 4,\ y \le 4,\ 2x - 3y \le -1,\ -x + y \ge 0$.
   Find the coordinates of the vertices of the bounded region: $(0,4)$, $(4,4)$, $\left(0, \frac{1}{3}\right)$ and $(1,1)$.
   Substitute each of the vertices of the bounded regions into C to determine the minima:
   $(0,4) \rightarrow C = 0 + 4 = 4;\ (4,4) \rightarrow C = 4 + 4 = 8;\ \left(0, \frac{1}{3}\right) \rightarrow C = 0 + \frac{1}{3} = \frac{1}{3};$
   $(1,1) \rightarrow C = 1 + 1 = 2$. The minimum value of C corresponds with $\left(0, \frac{1}{3}\right)$.

3. Maximize $C = x + 3y$ with the following constraints: $0 \le x \le 6,\ 0 \le y \le 6,\ -6x + 3y \le 12,\ 6x + y \ge 4$.
   Solution: $(6,6)$
   Explanation: Graph all the constraints on the same axis and find the coordinates of the vertices of the bounded region: $\left(\frac{2}{3}, 0\right)$, $(0,4)$, $(1,2)$, $(6,6)$ and $(6,0)$.
   Substitute each of the vertices of the bounded regions into C to determine the maxima.
   The maximum value of C corresponds with $(6,6)$.

Practice problems: *(Answers on page: 766)*

1. Maximize $C = x + y$ with the following constraints:
   $x \ge 0,\ y \ge 0$
   $4x + 2y \le 8$
   $2x - y \le 0$
2. Minimize $C = 2x + 2y$ with the following constraints:
   $x \le 6,\ y \le 6$
   $3x + y \ge 6$
   $4x - 2y \ge 8$
3. Maximize $C = 2x + 2y$ with the following constraints:
   $x \ge 0,\ y \ge 0$
   $-6x + 3y \le 12$
   $6x + y \le 4$

Review questions: *(Answers to odd questions on page: 766)*

1. Maximize $C = 2x + y$ with the following constraints:
   $x \geq 0,\ y \geq 0$
   $x + y \leq 6$
   $x + y \geq 1$
2. Minimize $C = 2x + 5y$ with the following constraints:
   $0 \leq x \leq 5$
   $0 \leq y \leq 3$
   $x + y \geq 2$
3. Maximize $C = 3x + 5y$ with the following constraints:
   $x \geq 0$
   $y \geq 0$
   $x + y \geq 2$
   $2x + 3y \leq 12$
   $3x + 2y \leq 12$
4. Minimize $C = 5x + 4y$ with the following constraints:
   $x \geq 0$
   $y \geq 0$
   $x + y \geq 2$
   $2x + 3y \leq 12$
   $3x + y \leq 12$
5. Minimize $C = 2x + 3y$ with the following constraints:
   $0 \leq x \leq 6$
   $0 \leq y \leq 5$
   $x + y \geq 2$

Applying Linear Programming

- **Review:** Using linear programming, you can determine the maximum and minimum value for a function within certain constraints (or inequalities). To do so, graph the system of inequalities and find the vertex points of that figure. Then plug these vertex points into the main equation. The greatest answer is the maximum of the function; the smallest answer is the minimum.

The Problem

As a farmer growing mangos and kiwis, you can earn a profit of $70/acre for mangos and $50/acre for kiwis. To cultivate one acre of mango land requires 3 hours of plowing and 2 hours of tilling. One acre of kiwi land requires 4 hours of plowing and 1 hour of tilling. You can rent the plow for a maximum of 200 hours and the tiller for a maximum of 100 hours. How many acres of each type of fruit should you grow to maximize profits?

m = acres of mangos
k = acres of kiwis

Profit is defined as:
$P = 70m + 50k$

Constraints
Plow: $3m + 4k \leq 200$
Tiller: $2m + k \leq 100$

Take a look at this problem requiring the use of linear programming. The objective is to maximize your profits as a mango and kiwi farmer.

The first step is to assign your variables and write down the profit function. This is the function you will try to maximize.

You face two constraints, which you need to write as inequalities:
1. You can rent the plot for a maximum of 200 hours.
2. You can rent the tiller for a maximum of 100 hours.

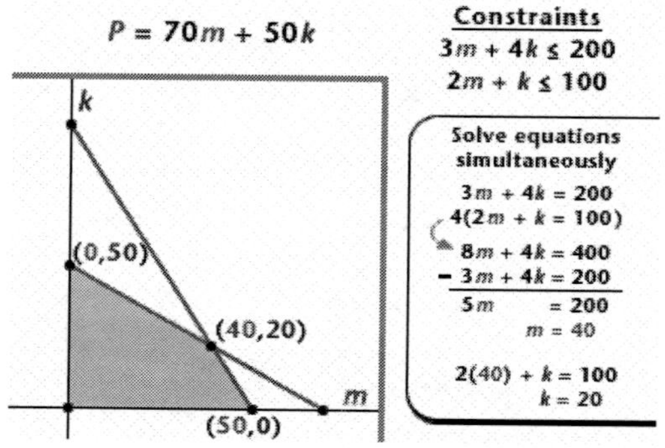	Graph the constraints. The maximum profit will occur at once of the vertices of the shaded region, so you need to solve for the point of intersection of the lines.
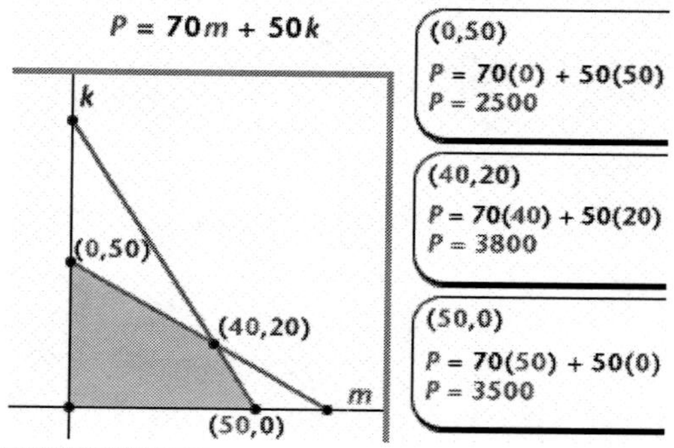	Now plug back into the profit equation to find the amount of profit at each of the vertices. The maximum profit occurs at the point (40, 20), so you should grow 40 acres of mangos and 20 acres of kiwis.

Sample problems:

1. An office supply company manufactures desks and chairs. In a given week, the company can assemble 400 units. They must assemble at least 100 desks and 150 chairs to meet their usual demands. Their profit is \$30 per desk and \$20 per chair. How many units of each should they assemble to maximize their profit?
Solution: $x = 250, y = 150$; 250 desks and 150 chairs
Explanation: Let x = number of desks and y = number of chairs.
Write the constraint inequalities:
"at least 100 desks" $\rightarrow x \geq 100$;
"at least 150 chairs" $\rightarrow y \geq 150$;
"can assemble 400 units" $\rightarrow x + y \leq 400$.
The profit function is $P = 30x + 20y$.
Graph each of the constraint inequalities on a single plane (first quadrant only) and find the coordinates of all vertices formed by the region determined by the constraints. Substitute these coordinates into the profit function:
$(100,300) \rightarrow 30(100) + 20(300) = 9000$;
$(250,150) \rightarrow 30(250) + 20(150) = 10,500$;
$(150,200) \rightarrow 30(150) + 20(200) = 8500$.
The coordinates yielding the largest value represent the number of each type of unit which should be assembled to maximize profits. Therefore, they should assemble 250 desks and 150 chairs.

2. Family Foods makes jumbo cookies and regular cookies. The oven can make at most 200 cookies per day. Each jumbo cookie requires 2 oz flour, each regular cookie requires 1 oz flour. There are 300 oz of flour available. The income from each jumbo cookie is 10 cents, and from each regular cookie is 8 cents. How many of each size cookie should be made to maximize income?
Solution: $x = 100, y = 100$; 100 of each size cookie
Explanation: Let x = number of jumbo cookies and y = number of regular cookies.
Write the constraint inequalities:
"at most 200 cookies per day" $\rightarrow x + y \leq 200$;
"jumbo require 2 oz flour, regular require 1 oz flour, 300 oz available" $\rightarrow 2x + y \leq 300$.
Find the coordinates of all vertices formed by the region determined by the constraints.
Substitute the coordinates in the profit function $P = .10x + .08y$.
$(0,0) \rightarrow P = 10(0) + .08(0) = 0$;
$(0,200) \rightarrow P = .10(0) + .08(200) = 16$;
$(100,100) \rightarrow P = .10(100) + .08(100) = 18$;
$(150,0) \rightarrow P = .10(150) + .08(0) = 15$.
The coordinates yielding the largest value represent the number of each type of cookie which should be assembled to maximize profits. Based on results, for maximum profit 100 of each size cookie should be made.

3. A florist designs two high profit arrangements - a funeral wreath and a bridal centerpiece. The company's employees can complete up to 14 arrangements each day using up to 24 total man-hours of labor. It takes 4 man-hours to complete one funeral wreath, and 7 man-hours to complete one bridal arrangement. How many of each type of arrangement should the florist produce daily for maximum profit, if the profit on funeral wreath is \$75 and the profit on a bridal arrangement is \$40?
Solution: $x = 6, y = 0$; 6 funeral wreaths and no bridal centerpieces
Explanation: Let x = number of funeral wreaths and y = number of bridal centerpieces.
Write the constraint inequalities:
"up to 14 arrangements each day" $\rightarrow x + y \leq 14$;
"4 hours for a wreath, 7 hours for a centerpiece, up to 24 hours total" $\rightarrow 4x + 7y \leq 24$.
Find the coordinates of all vertices formed by the region determined by the constraints.
Substitute the coordinates in the profit function $P = 75x + 40y$.
$(0,0) \rightarrow P = 75(0) + 40(0) = 0$;
$(14,0) \rightarrow P = 75(14) + 40(0) = 1050$;
$(0,\frac{24}{7}) \rightarrow P = 75(0) + 40(\frac{24}{7}) = \frac{960}{7} = 137 - \frac{1}{7}$;
$(\frac{4}{3},\frac{8}{3}) \rightarrow P = 75(\frac{4}{3}) + 40(\frac{8}{3}) = \frac{620}{3} = 206 - \frac{2}{3}$.
Based on results, the maximum profit derives when the florist produces 6 funeral wreaths and no bridal centerpieces in a day.

Practice problems: *(Answers on page: 766)*

1. An office supply company manufactures desks and chairs. In a given week, the company can assemble 500 units. They must assemble at least 150 desks and 200 chairs to meet their usual demands . Their profit is \$50 per desk and \$ 40 per chair . How many units of each should they assemble to maximize their profit?

2. Family Foods makes jumbo cookies and regular cookies. The oven can make at most 200 cookies per day. Each jumbo cookie requires 2 oz of flour, each regular cookie requires 1 oz of flour. There are 300 oz of flour available. The income from each jumbo cookie is 13 cents, and from each regular cookie is 7 cents. How many of each size cookie should be made to maximize income?

3. Angus Farms encompasses 240 acres. The owner will plant wheat and oats. The profit per acre of wheat is \$40, and the profit per acre of oats is \$30. He has workers who will provide 320 hours of labor. Each acre of wheat requires 2 hr of labor and each acre of oats requires 1 hr of labor. How many acres of each should he plant to maximize his profit?

Review questions: *(Answers to odd questions on page: 766)*

1. A music production company is promoting new CDs by one of its biggest artists. There are 12,000 of the CDs already burned and ready to sell. As a marketing ploy some of the CDs are being packed as one-disk units while others are being packed as two-disk albums. Given that the net gain for the company on the one-disk units is $.87 each and on the two-disk albums is $1.13 each, how should they pack the CDs for maximum profit?
2. Joe owns a car and a dirt bike. He has sufficient funds for 12 gal of fuel to be split between the car and dirt bike. Joe's car gets 20 mpg and holds a maximum of 10 gal of fuel. His dirt bike gets 100 mpg and hold a maximum of 3 gal of fuel. How many gallons of fuel should he purchase for each vehicle to travel the greatest distance?
3. Joe owns a car and a dirt bike. He has sufficient funds for 12 gal of fuel to be split between the car and dirt bike. Joe's car gets 15 mpg and holds up to 10 gal of fuel. His dirt bike gets 100 mpg and holds a maximum of 3 gal of fuel. How many gallons of fuel should he purchase for each vehicle to travel the greatest distance?
4. A motorcyle business manufactures two popular models -- a heavy-duty road bike and an errand-running about-town model. The company employees can complete up to 5 motorcyles each day using up to 200 total man-hours of labor. It takes 75 man-hours to complete one heavy-duty bike and picture, and 60 man-hours to complete an about-town bike. How many of each type should be made daily to maximize the company's profit, if the profit on a heavy-duty bike is $3500 and the profit on an around-town model is $3200?
5. A pet company designs two types of pet collars - one with rhinestones and one training collar. The company employees can complete 180 collars each day using up to 400 total man-hours of labor. It takes 6 man-hours to complete one rhinestone collar, and 2 man-hours to complete one training collar. How many of each type of collar should be made daily to maximize the company's profit, if the profit on a rhinestone collar is $18 and the profit on an training collar is $4?

10

Special Topics

An Introduction to Conic Sections

- A **conic section** is a curve made by intersecting a cone with a plane. The conic sections include the **point**, **line**, **circle**, **ellipse**, **parabola**, and **hyperbola**.

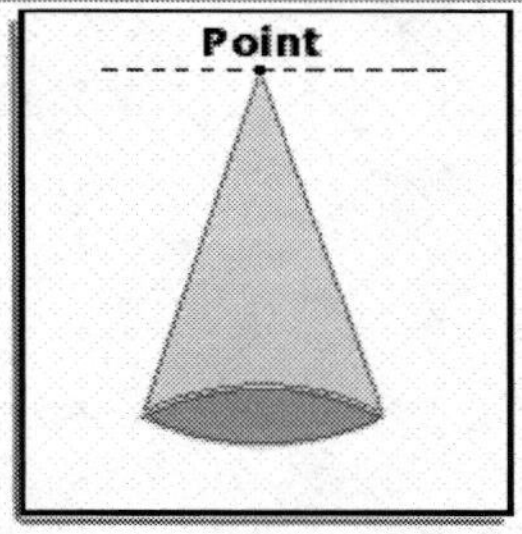	By slicing a cone with a plane in different ways, you can generate various **conic sections**. Here the cone is sliced at its very tip. The result is a single **point**.
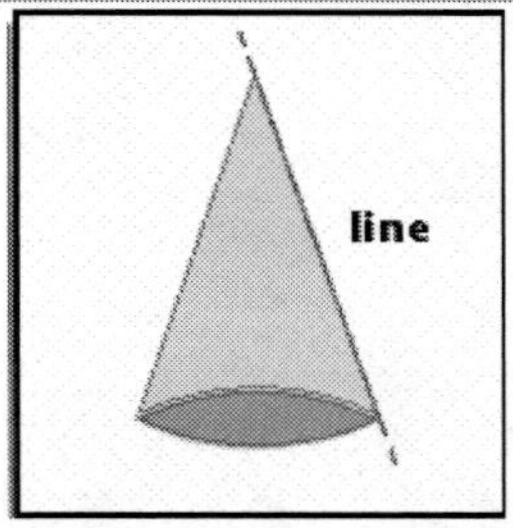	If the cone is sliced alone its side, the result is a **line**.
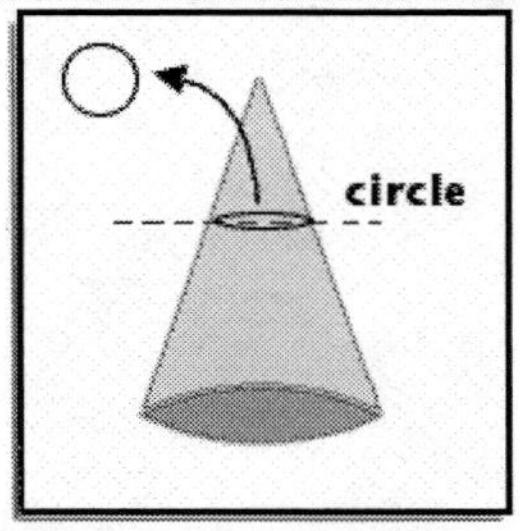	Here the cone is sliced horizontally. The result is a **circle**.
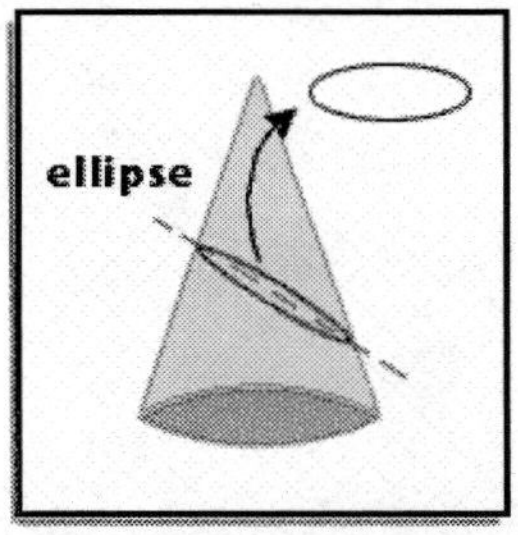	If the cone is sliced at an angle, the result is not a circle but an **ellipse**.
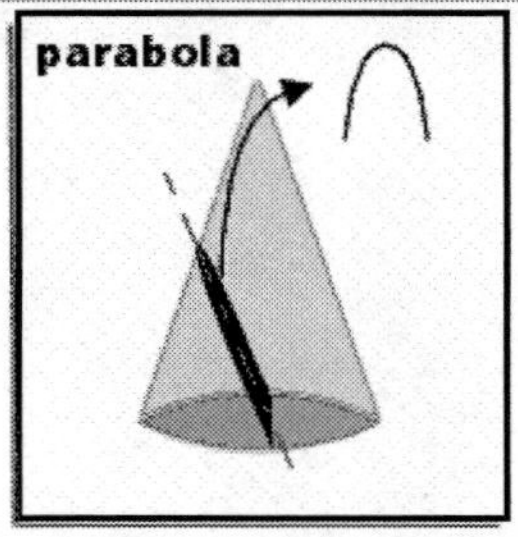	If the slice is made parallel to the side of the cone, then the result is a **parabola**.
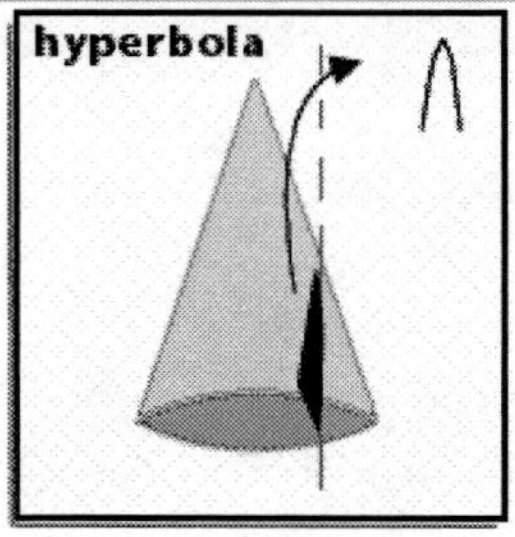	When the slice is made vertically, the result is a **hyperbola**.

An Introduction to Parabolas

- A parabola consists of the set of points that are equidistant from a point called the **focus** and a line called the **directrix**.

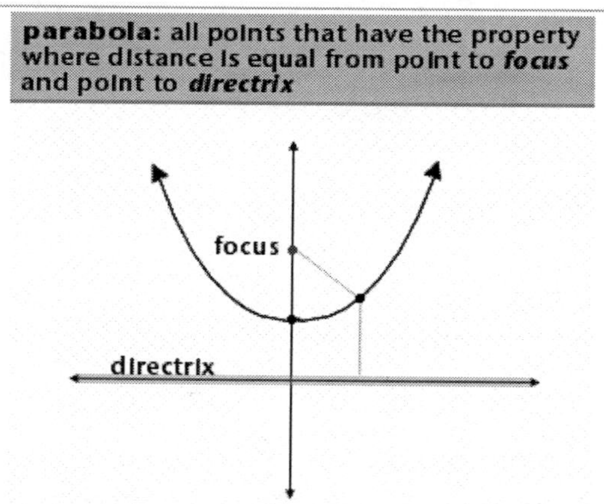

Associated with every parabola is a point called the focus and a line called the directrix.

The parabola itself is the set of points equidistant from the focus and the directrix. Any point on the parabola is as far away from the focus as it is from the directrix. Notice how the focus is inside the curve of the parabola and the directrix is outside.

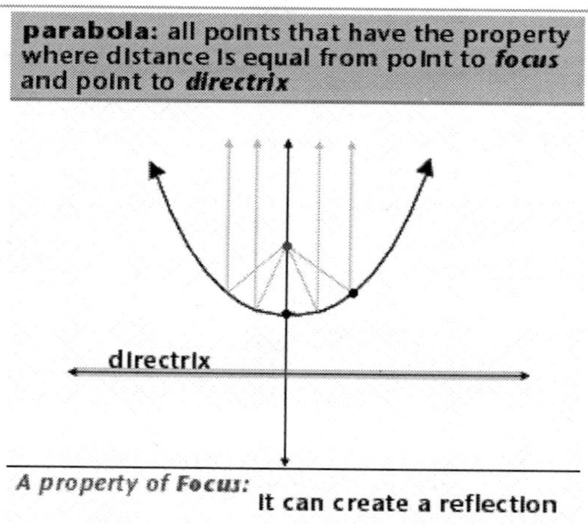

Parabolas have many interesting properties. For example, if a light is placed at the focus of a reflective parabola, the parabola will reflect the light rays directly outwards. This fact is put to good use in flashlights, satellite dishes, and other objects in the real world.

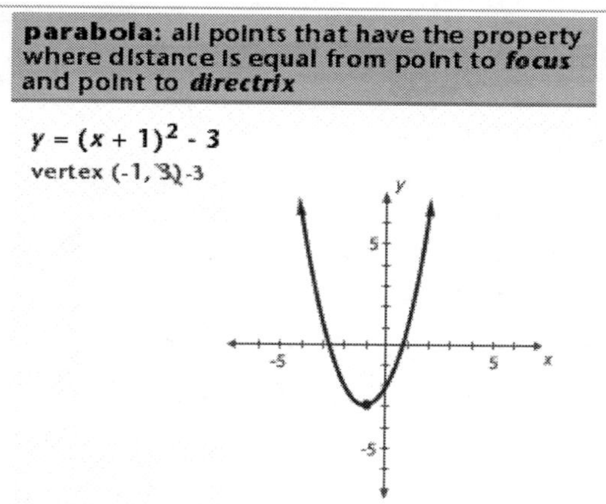

As you probably recall, parabolas are described algebraically by quadratic functions. This example is described by the equation, $y = (x + 1)^2 - 3$.

The curve of a parabola graphed in the Cartesian plane is the same as the curve of a parabola generated by slicing a cone!

Sample problems:

1. Describe the graph of $y = (x-3)^2 + 5$ in terms of the parabola's direction and vertex.
   Solution: direction: parabola opens up, vertex: (3, 5).
   Explanation: The equation is in vertex form, $y = a(x-h)^2 + k$, so $a = 1$, $h = 3$, and $k = 5$. The direction of a parabola is described by the value of a: if a is positive, the parabola opens up, if a is negative, the parabola opens down. Thus the parabola opens up since a is positive. The vertex is located at (h, k), so the vertex is at (3, 5).

2. True or false: The graph of $y = -x^2 + 2x - 1$ is a parabola that opens down, the vertex is at (1,0), the y-intercept is -1, and it has 2 roots.
Solution: False
Explanation: The equation is in standard form, $y = ax^2 + bx + c$, so $a = -1$, $b = 2$, and $c = -1$. Since a is negative the parabola does open down. The vertex of a parabola in standard form is at (h, k) where $h = \frac{b}{2a}$ and $k = f(h)$. Find the vertex: $h = \frac{2}{-2(-1)} = 1$ and $k = -(1)^2 + 2(1) - 1 = 0$, so (1, 0) is the vertex. The y-intercept is the value of y when $x = 0$, or c for all quadratic equations in standard form, so the y-intercept is -1. The root of the parabola is the x-intercept(s). The vertex of this parabola is on the x-axis, therefore there is only one x-intercept, or one root, not two.

3. Does the equation $y = x^2 + 2$ match the following graph?

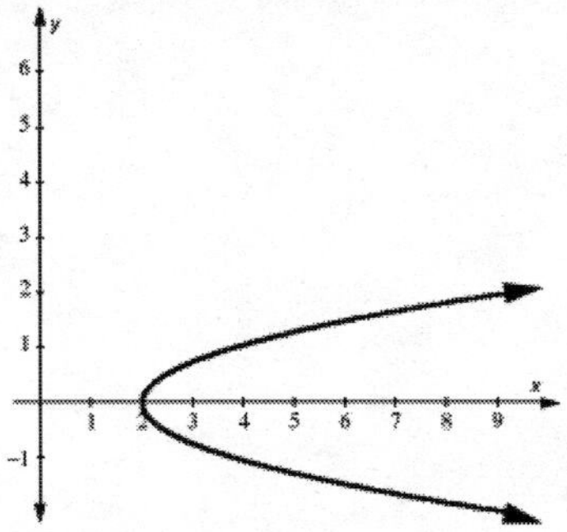

Solution: No
Explanation: The parabola opens sideways, so the y term in the equation must be squared, not the x term.

Practice problems: *(Answers on page: 767)*

1. True or false: The graph of $f(x) = 3x^2$ is a parabola that opens up with its vertex is at (0,0).
2. Graph $y = x^2$.
3. True or false: The following graph represents the equation $y^2 + 2y + x = 0$.

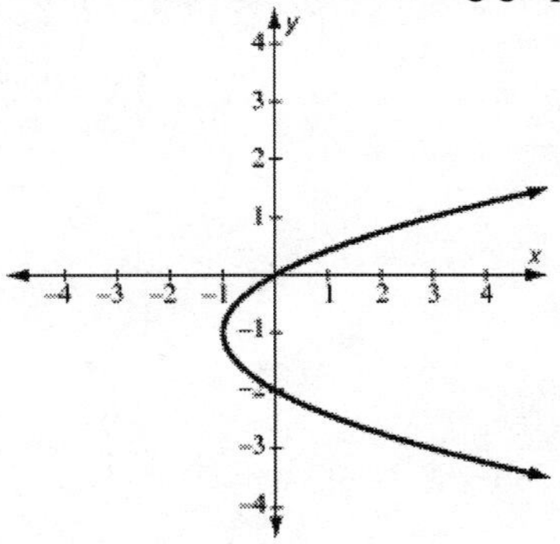

Review questions: *(Answers to odd questions on page: 767)*

1. Describe the graph of $y = (x+1)^2$ in terms of the parabola's direction and vertex.
2. True or false: The graph of $y = -x^2 + 4x + 3$ is a parabola that opens down, the vertex is at $(2, 7)$, and the y-intercept is -3.
3. True or false: The graph of $y = 4x^2 + 6x - 1$ is a parabola that opens up, the vertex is at $\left(-\frac{3}{4}, \frac{13}{4}\right)$, and the y-intercept is -1.
4. True or false: The graph of $x = -\frac{1}{2}y^2$ is a parabola that opens sideways.

5. True or false: The graph of $y = -x^2 + 6x - 1$ is a parabola that opens down, the vertex is at (3,8), the y-intercept is -1, and it has 2 roots.

Determining Information about a Parabola from Its Equation

- A parabola consists of the set of points that are equidistant from a point called the focus and a line called the directrix.
- A parabola of the form $y = cx^2$ has its focus at the point $(0, \frac{1}{4c})$ and its directrix along the line $y = -\frac{1}{4c}$.

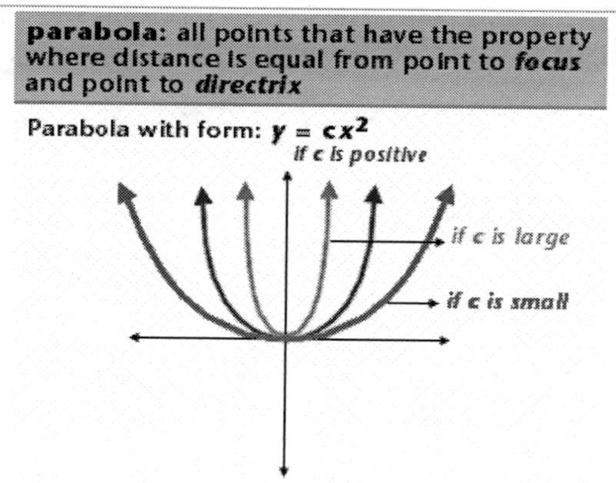

REMEMBER: If $|c| > 1$, then the parabola is narrow as compared to $y = x^2$. If $|c| < 1$, then the parabola is wider than $y = x^2$.

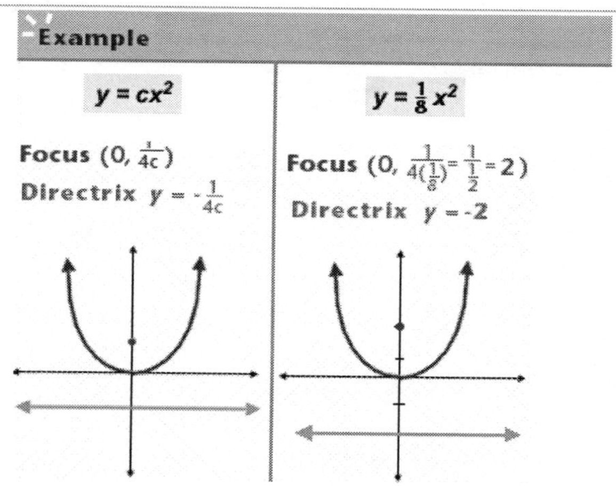

It is relatively easy to find the focus and directrix of a parabola of the form $y = cx^2$. In general, for a parabola of the form $y = cx^2$, the focus is located at the point $\left(0, \dfrac{1}{4c}\right)$ and the directrix is the line described by the equation $y = -\dfrac{1}{4c}$.

You can apply these general formulas for a specific parabola like $y = \dfrac{1}{8}x^2$.

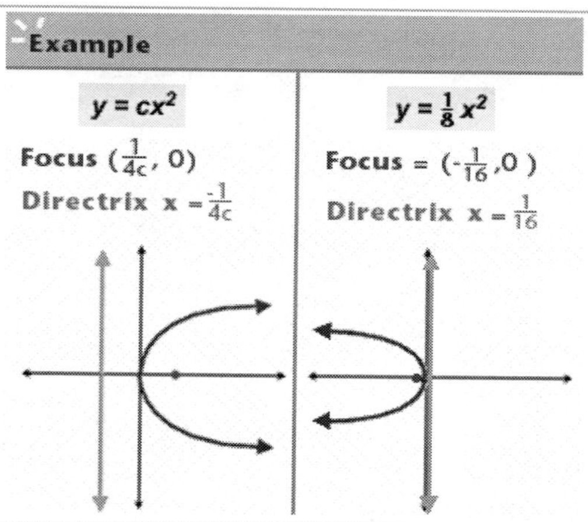

Similar formulas exist for the focus and directrix of a parabola of the form $x = cy^2$.

For a parabola of the form $x = cy^2$, the focus is located at the point $\left(\dfrac{1}{4c}, 0\right)$ and the directrix is the line $x = -\dfrac{1}{4c}$.

Sample problems:

1. Identify the focus and directrix of the parabola described by $x = -\frac{5}{6}y^2$.

   Solution: Focus: $\left(-\frac{3}{10}, 0\right)$, directrix: $x = \frac{3}{10}$

   Explanation: The graph of $x = -\frac{5}{6}y^2$ is a parabola of the form $y = cy^2$, so the focus is at $\left(\frac{1}{4c}, 0\right)$ and the directrix is the line $x = -\frac{1}{4c}$. Find the focus: $\frac{1}{4c} = \frac{1}{4\left(-\frac{5}{6}\right)} = -\frac{1}{2\left(\frac{5}{3}\right)} = -\frac{1}{\frac{10}{3}} = -\frac{3}{10}$, so the focus is the point $\left(-\frac{3}{10}, 0\right)$. Find the directrix: $-\frac{1}{4c} = -\left(-\frac{3}{10}\right) = \frac{3}{10}$, so the directrix is the line $x = \frac{3}{10}$.

2. Consider a parabola with the vertex at the origin, that opens up, and that passes through the point $(-3, 18)$. Find the focus of that parabola.

   Solution: $\left(0, \frac{1}{8}\right)$

   Explanation: To determine the focus, first write the equation that describes that parabola using vertex form. Substitute the (h, k) values from the vertex and the (x, y) values from the point into $y = a(x-h)^2 + k$ (this is the correct form since the parabola opens up, not sideways): $18 = a(-3-0)^2 + 0$. Solve for a: $18 = 9a$; $a = 2$. Next substitute a, h, and k back into vertex form to write the equation of the parabola: $y = 2(x-0)^2 + 0$; $y = 2x^2$. Now, substitute that coefficient into the formula for the focus: $\frac{1}{4c} = \frac{1}{4(2)} = \frac{1}{8}$, so the focus is at $\left(0, \frac{1}{8}\right)$.

3. Identify the focus and directrix of the parabola whose equation is $y = 3x^2$.

   Solution: Focus: $\left(0, \frac{1}{12}\right)$, directrix: $y = -\frac{1}{12}$

   Explanation: The graph of $y = 3x^2$ is a parabola of the form $y = cx^2$, so the focus is at $\left(0, \frac{1}{4c}\right)$ and the directrix is the line $y = \frac{1}{4c}$. Find the focus: $\frac{1}{4c} = \frac{1}{4 \cdot 3} = \frac{1}{12}$, so the focus is the point $\left(0, \frac{1}{12}\right)$. Find the directrix: $-\frac{1}{4c} = -\frac{1}{12}$, so the directrix is the line $y = -\frac{1}{12}$.

Practice problems: *(Answers on page: 767)*

1. Consider the parabola $x = \frac{2}{3}y^2$. Identify the vertex and the focus.
2. Consider the parabola $y = -\frac{1}{4}x^2$. Identify the focus and the directrix.
3. Consider a parabola with the vertex at the origin, that opens sideways, and passes through the point (8,4). Identify the focus.

Review questions: *(Answers to odd questions on page: 767)*

1. Consider the parabola $8x^2 = y$. Identify the vertex and focus.
2. Consider the parabola $x = -\frac{1}{3}y^2$. Identify the vertex and focus.
3. Consider the parabola $y = -\frac{3}{4}x^2$. Identify the focus and the directrix.

4. Consider a parabola with the vertex at the origin, that opens up, and that passes through the point $(6,18)$. Find the focus of that parabola.

5. Consider a parabola with the vertex at the origin, that opens to the right, and that passes through the point $(-12,-6)$. Find the focus of that parabola.

Writing an Equation for a Parabola

- A parabola consists of the set of points that are equidistant from a point called the focus and a line called the directrix.
- The vertex of a parabola is the point where the curve of the parabola changes direction. It is either the highest or lowest point of the parabola (or the leftmost or rightmost point, depending on the direction that the parabola opens).
- A parabola with vertex at (h, k) and focus at a distance of $\pm p$ from the vertex is described by the equation $(x-h)^2 = 4p(y-k)$ or $(y-k)^2 = 4p(x-h)$, depending on the direction that the parabola opens.

vertex *(h,k)* **Focus** *distance* **±p** *away then:* $(x-h)^2 = 4p(y-k)$ $(y-k)^2 = 4p(x-h)$ 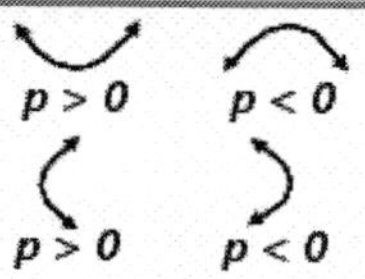	You probably recall that the vertex of a parabola is the point where the curve of the parabola changes direction. For a parabola that opens up or down, it is the lowest or highest point on the graph, respectively. For a parabola that opens left or right, it is the rightmost or leftmost point, respectively. Using these general equations, it is possible to write the equation for a specific parabola given its vertex and focus.
Example *write an equation for a parabola* $V = (0,0)$ $F = (4,0)$ $(y-0)^2 = 4p(x-0)$ $y^2 = 4 \cdot 4(x)$ $\boxed{y^2 = 16x}$ 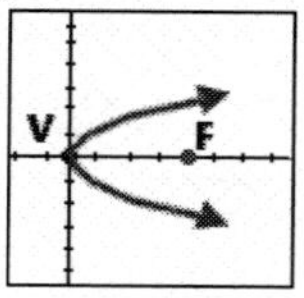	It's always a good idea to sketch a rough picture first. Since the vertex is at (0, 0), $h = 0$ and $k = 0$. The focus is 4 units away from the vertex and the parabola opens to the right, so $p = 4$. (If the parabola opened to the left, then p would equal -4). Substitute these values into the general equation and the result is the equation for this specific parabola.
Example *write an equation for a parabola* $V = (4,3)$ $F = (4,0)$ $(x-4)^2 = 4 \cdot -3(y-3)$ $\boxed{(x-4)^2 = -12(y-3)}$ 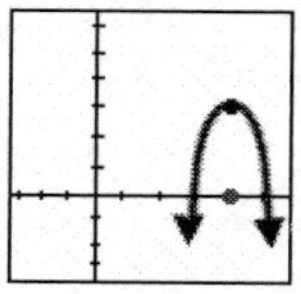	The first step is to sketch a picture. You can see that this parabola opens downwards. Since the parabola opens downwards and the distance between the vertex and the focus is 3, $p = -3$. Since the vertex is at (4, 3), $h = 4$ and $k = 3$. Substitute into the formula to find the equation for the parabola.

Sample problems:

1. Identify the vertex and focus of the parabola whose equation is $(x-2)^2 = -8(y-1)$.
   Solution: vertex: $(2,1)$, focus: $(2,-1)$
   Explanation: This equation is in the form $(x-h)^2 = 4p(y-k)$, so the vertex, (h,k), is at $(2,1)$. The focus is p units away from the vertex, so find p: $4p = -8$; $p = -2$. Therefore, the focus is two units below the vertex, so it is at $(2,-1)$.

2. Find the equation for the parabola with its vertex on the origin and its focus at $(0,3)$.
   Solution: $y = \frac{1}{12}x^2$
   Explanation: The parabola opens up, so use standard form $(x-h)^2 = 4p(y-k)$ to write the equation. Determine p: the focus is at $(0,3)$ which is 3 units away from the vertex, so $p = 3$. Now substitute the values of p and (h,k) (from the vertex) into $(x-h)^2 = 4p(y-k)$, simplify, and solve for y: $(x-0)^2 = 4 \cdot 3(y-0)$; $x^2 = 12y$; $y = \frac{1}{12}x^2$.

3. Find the equation for the parabola with its vertex at $(-2,5)$ and its focus at $(-6,5)$.
   Solution: $(y-5)^2 = -16(x+2)$
   Explanation: The parabola opens to the left, so use $(y-k)^2 = 4p(x-h)$ to write the equation. Find p: the focus is -4 units away from the vertex, so $p = -4$. Now substitute the values of p and (h,k) into $(y-k)^2 = 4p(x-h)$ and simplify: $(y-5)^2 = 4(-4)(x-(-2))$; $(y-5)^2 = -16(x+2)$.

Practice problems: *(Answers on page: 767)*

1. Find the equation for the parabola with its vertex on the origin and its focus at $(-3,0)$.
2. Write the equation for the parabola whose vertex is at (3,5) and focus is at (3,7).
3. Identify the vertex and focus of the parabola whose equation is $(y+5)^2 = 4(x-3)$.

Review questions: *(Answers to odd questions on page: 767)*

1. Find the equation for the parabola with its vertex on the origin and its focus at $\left(0,\frac{3}{2}\right)$.
2. Find the equation for the parabola with its vertex on the origin and its focus at $(-5,0)$.
3. Determine the vertex of the parabola $(y-3)^2 = -8(x-2)$.
4. Write an equation for the parabola with vertex $(3,5)$ and focus $(3,1)$.
5. Write an equation for the parabola with vertex $(2,-5)$ and focus $(7,-5)$.

An Introduction to Ellipses

- An ellipse consists of the set of points, the sum of whose distances from two fixed points is always the same. The two fixed points are called the **foci** of the ellipse. The singular form of **foci** is focus.
- The standard equation for an ellipse centered at the origin is $\frac{x^2}{a^2}+\frac{y^2}{b^2}=1$, where the x-intercepts are at $\pm a$ and the y-intercepts are at $\pm b$.
- The standard equation for an ellipse centered at (h, k) is $\frac{(x-h)^2}{a^2}+\frac{(y-k)^2}{b^2}=1$.
- The long axis of an ellipse is called the **major axis**. The short axis of an ellipse is called the **minor axis**.

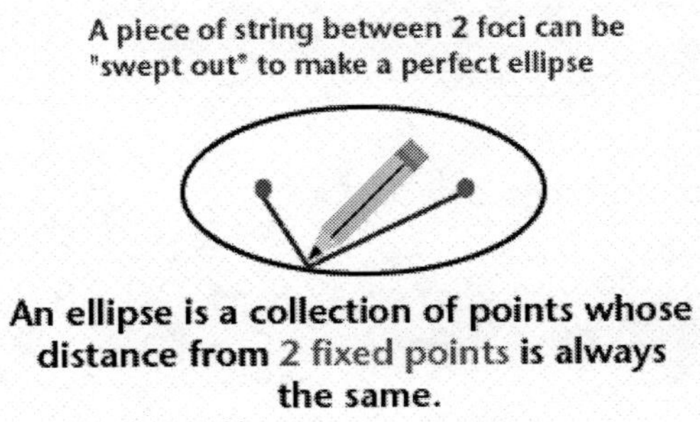

Since it is a conic section, an ellipse can be obtained by intersecting a plane with a cone. However, an ellipse can also be defined as a locus of points in the plane: Every ellipse is the set of points whose total distance from two fixed points, called the foci, is the same.

You can construct an ellipse using a piece of string and a pencil.

An analytical point of view of an ellipse

$$\frac{x^2}{\boxed{25}} + \frac{y^2}{\boxed{9}} = 1$$

x intercepts = $\pm\sqrt{25}$ y intercepts = $\pm\sqrt{9}$

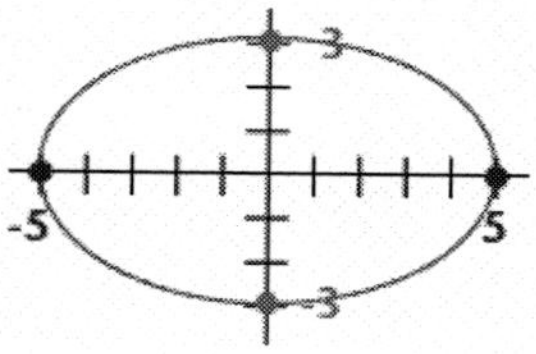

Here is a typical equation describing an ellipse centered at the origin.

An easy way to graph the ellipse described by this equation is to find the x and y-intercepts. You can find them by taking the plus and minus square roots of the coefficients under the x^2 and y^2 terms.

The long axis of the ellipse is called the major axis. In this case the major axis has a length of 10. The short axis, called the minor axis, has a length of 6.

What if the ellipse is not centered at the origin?

center = (h, k)

$$\frac{(x-h)^2}{a^2} + \frac{(y-k)^2}{\boxed{b^2}} = 1$$

The major axis can be the y axis if this number is larger.

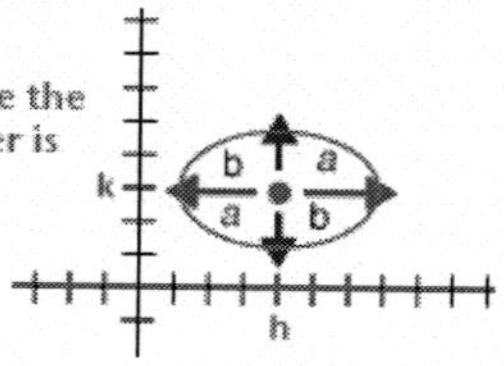

What if the ellipse is centered at (h, k) instead of the origin?

This is the standard equation describing an ellipse centered at (h, k).

To graph the ellipse described by this equation, first find the center of the ellipse. Then you can go a units to the left and right to find the left and right ends of the ellipse. Similarly, you can go b units up and down to find the vertical ends of the ellipse.

Sample problems:

1. Identify the center and x and y-intercepts of the ellipse described by $\frac{x^2}{16}+\frac{y^2}{36}=1$.

   Solution: Center: (0, 0); x-intercepts: ± 4; y-intercepts: ± 6

   Explanation: Since the equation $\frac{x^2}{16}+\frac{y^2}{36}=1$ is in the standard form of an ellipse, $\frac{x^2}{a^2}+\frac{y^2}{b^2}=1$, the center must be the origin, (0, 0).
   The x-intercepts are at $\pm a$: $a^2=16$; $a=\sqrt{16}=\pm 4$.
   The y-intercepts are at $\pm b$: $b^2=36$; $b=\sqrt{36}=\pm 6$.

2. Express the equation $4x^2+3y^2+8x-6y-29=0$ in the standard form of an ellipse, then identify the center of the ellipse.

   Solution: $\frac{(x+1)^2}{9}+\frac{(y-1)^2}{12}=1$; center: $(-1, 1)$

   Explanation: Group the x-terms and y-terms on the left and the constant on the right: $4x^2+8x+3y^2-6y=29$. Factor a 4 from the x-terms and a 3 from the y-terms: $4(x^2+2x)+3(y^2-2y)=29$. Complete the square for x and y (remember to add the product of the constant and the factor to the right side to keep the equation balanced): $4(x^2+2x+\_\_)+3(y^2-2y+\_\_)=29+4(\_)+3(\_)$; $4(x^2+2x+1)+3(y^2-2y+1)=29+4\cdot 1+3\cdot 1$.
   Factor and simplify: $4(x+1)^2+3(y-1)^2=36$.
   Consider the standard form of an ellipse: $\frac{(x-h)^2}{a^2}+\frac{(y-k)^2}{b^2}=1$. Notice that in standard form the right side is 1, so divide the equation by 36 to produce 1 on the right side: $\frac{4(x+1)^2}{36}+\frac{3(y-1)^2}{36}=\frac{36}{36}$; $\frac{(x+1)^2}{9}+\frac{(y-1)^2}{12}=1$.
   Now the equation is expressed in standard form. Identify the center, or the (h, k), values in the equation: $(-1, 1)$.

3. Given the ellipse $\frac{(x-3)^2}{4}+\frac{(y+1)^2}{9}=1$, find the endpoints of the major axis and the endpoints of the minor axis.
Solution: Major axis: (3, 2) and (3, − 4); minor axis: (5, − 1) and (1, − 1)
Explanation: Identify the center, $(h,\ k)$ from the equation: $(3,-1)$. The endpoints of the major and minor axes are located $\pm a$ units horizontally and $\pm b$ units vertically from the center. Find a and b: $a^2=4$; $a=\sqrt{4}=\pm 2$ and $b^2=9$; $b=\sqrt{9}=\pm 3$. Since $b>a$ the vertical axis is the major axis. Find the endpoints of the major axis by moving vertically ± 3 units from the center: $(3,-1+3)$ and $(3,-1-3)$; (3, 2) and (3, − 4). Find the endpoints of the minor axis by moving horizontally ± 2 units from the center: $(3+2,-1)$ and $(3-2,-1)$; $(5,-1)$ and $(1,-1)$.

Practice problems: *(Answers on page: 767)*

1. Find the center and the length of the minor axis of the ellipse described by $\frac{(x-4)^2}{9}+(y+3)^2=1$.
2. Find the center and the lengths of the major and minor axes of the ellipse described by: $7x^2+28x+4y^2=0$.
3. Sketch the graph of $\frac{x^2}{4}+\frac{y^2}{16}=1$.

Review questions: *(Answers to odd questions on page: 767)*

1. Express the equation $4x^2+y^2-40x+6y+105=0$ in the standard form of an ellipse and identify the center of the ellipse.
2. Identify the center and x and y-intercepts of the ellipse described by $\frac{x^2}{25}+y^2=1$.
3. Find the lengths of the major and minor axes of the ellipse represented by this equation: $\frac{(x+2)^2}{15}+\frac{y^2}{64}=1$.
4. Given $\frac{(x-1)^2}{9}+\frac{(y+3)^2}{16}=1$, state the center and intercepts for this graph.
5. Identify the center of the ellipse described by $5x^2+40x+3y^2-6y+68=0$.

Finding the Equation for an Ellipse

- An ellipse consists of the set of points, the sum of whose distances from two fixed points is always the same. The two fixed points are called the foci of the ellipse.
- The standard equation for an ellipse centered at $(h,\ k)$ is $\frac{(x-h)^2}{a^2}+\frac{(y-k)^2}{b^2}=1$.

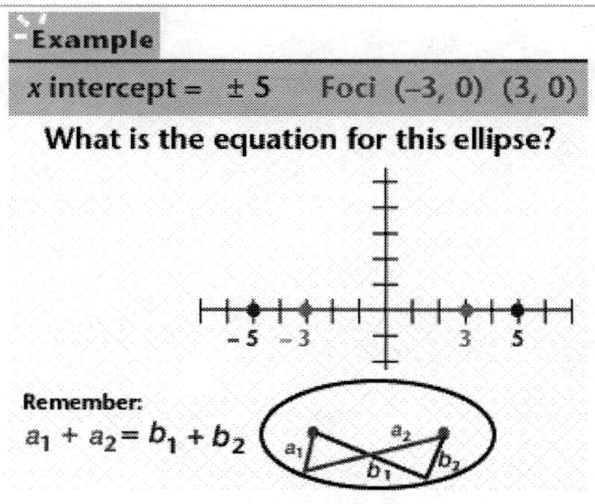

How can you find the equation for this ellipse given its x-intercepts and foci?

By plotting the x-intercepts and foci, you can see that the ellipse is centered at the origin. If you can find the y-intercepts of the ellipse, you will know everything you need to know to write its equation.

The key to finding the y-intercepts is to remember that for any point on an ellipse, the sum of the distances from that point to the two foci is a constant.

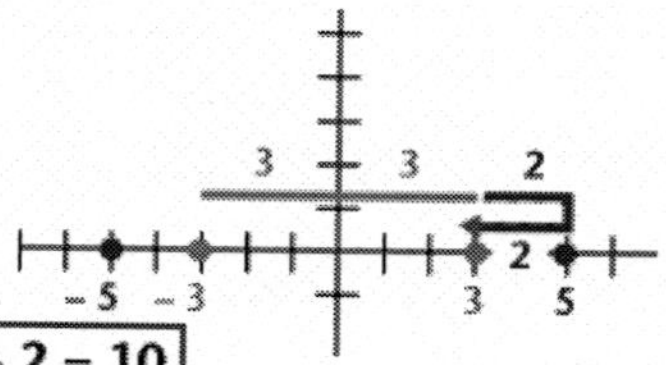

3 + 3 + 2 + 2 = 10

What would the length of the string be from the first focus, out to the +5*x* intercept, and back to the second focus?

Since you know that the point (5,0) is on the ellipse, you can calculate the sum of the distances from that point to the two foci.

If you remember how you can create an ellipse using a piece of string and a pencil, you can think of this distance as the length of that string.

In this case, the sum is equal to 2 + 8, or 10.

Where does the string cross on the y axis?

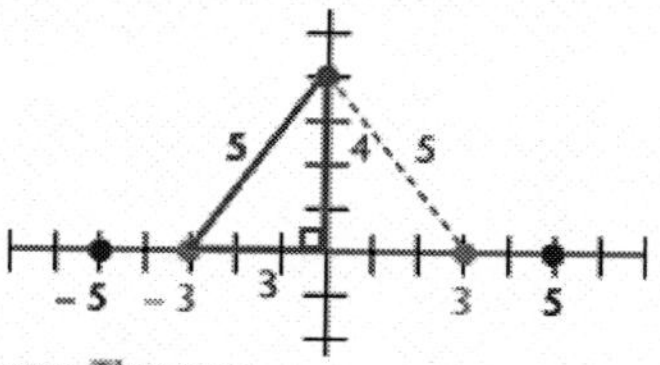

Use the Pythagorean Theorem to find the height of the ellipse.

$3^2 + 4^2 = 5^2$

The sum of the distances from a y-intercept of the ellipse to the two foci will also equal 10. Since the two distances are the same for a *y*-intercept of the ellipse because it is centered at (0,0), the distance from the y-intercept to each of the foci is 5.

You can calculate the location of the y-intercept using the Pythagorean theorem. You place it at (0,±4).

$$\frac{x^2}{a^2} + \frac{y^2}{b^2} = 1$$

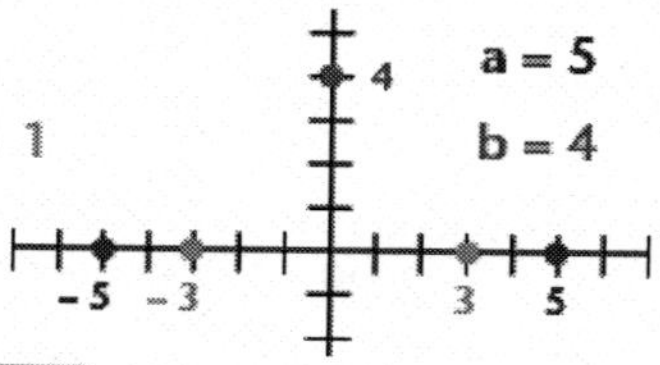

a = 5

b = 4

$$\frac{x^2}{25} + \frac{y^2}{16} = 1$$

Now just substitute into the standard equation for an ellipse centered at the origin.

This is the equation describing the ellipse.

Sample problems:

1. The foci of an ellipse are at $(-8,0)$ and $(8, 0)$ and the x-intercepts are at ± 10. Write the equation of this ellipse.

   Solution: $\frac{x^2}{100} + \frac{y^2}{36} = 1$

   Explanation: Since the foci are centered around the origin, the center of the ellipse must be (0, 0). Therefore, the equation is in the form $\frac{x^2}{a^2} + \frac{y^2}{b^2} = 1$, where a represents the x-intercepts, so $a \pm 10$. Find b, the y-intercepts. The total distance from any point to the foci must be 20, since $8 + 8 + 2 + 2 = 20$. Since the 2 distances are the same for the y-intercepts, the distance from the focus (8, 0) to the positive y-intercept is 10 (half of 20). Set up a right triangle and use the Pythagorean Theorem to solve for b, the y-intercept: $8^2 + b^2 = 10^2$; $b^2 = 100 - 64$; $b^2 = 36$; $b = \sqrt{36} = \pm 6$. Substitute the a and b values into the standard equation of an ellipse: $\frac{x^2}{(\pm 10)^2} + \frac{y^2}{(\pm 6)^2} = 1$; $\frac{x^2}{100} + \frac{y^2}{36} = 1$.

2. The foci of an ellipse are at $(0, 3)$ and $(0, -3)$ and the y-intercepts are at ± 5. Write the equation of this ellipse.

   Solution: $\frac{x^2}{16} + \frac{y^2}{25} = 1$

   Explanation: Set up a right triangle and use the Pythagorean Theorem to find the x-intercepts: $a^2 + 9 = 25$; $a^2 = 16$; $a = \pm 4$. Substitute the a and b values into the standard form of an ellipse, $\frac{x^2}{a^2} + \frac{y^2}{b^2} = 1$; $\frac{x^2}{(\pm 4)^2} + \frac{y^2}{25} = 1$; $\frac{x^2}{16} + \frac{y^2}{25} = 1$.

3. True or false: The equation $(x-4)^2+\dfrac{(y+5)^2}{4}=1$ describes an ellipse centered at $(4,-5)$.

   Solution: True

   Explanation: The equation $(x-4)^2+\dfrac{(y+5)^2}{4}=1$ is expressed in the standard form of an ellipse, $\dfrac{(x-h)^2}{a^2}+\dfrac{(y-k)^2}{b^2}=1$, centered at (h,k). Thus, the center is indeed $(4,-5)$.

Practice problems: *(Answers on page: 767)*

1. The foci of an ellipse are at $(-5,0)$ and $(5,0)$ and the x-intercepts are at ± 13. Write the equation of this ellipse.
2. The x-intercepts of an ellipse are at ± 2 and the y-intercepts are at ± 3. Write the equation of this ellipse.
3. Find center of the ellipse described by $\dfrac{(x+4)^2}{9}+\dfrac{y^2}{5}=1$.

Review questions: *(Answers to odd questions on page: 767)*

1. Find the foci of the ellipse represented by the equation $\dfrac{x^2}{10}+\dfrac{y^2}{7}=1$.
2. Find the equation of an ellipse with y-intercepts at ± 4 and x-intercepts at ± 2.
3. The foci of an ellipse are at $(0,-4)$ and $(0,4)$ and the y-intercepts are at ± 5. Write the equation of this ellipse.
4. The foci of an ellipse are at $(-\sqrt{21},0)$ and $(\sqrt{21},0)$ and the x-intercepts are at ± 5. Write the equation of this ellipse.
5. Find center of the ellipse described by $(x-1)^2+\dfrac{y^2}{3}=1$.

Applying Ellipses: Satellites

- The standard equation for an ellipse centered at the origin is $\dfrac{x^2}{a^2}+\dfrac{y^2}{b^2}=1$, where the x-intercepts are at $\pm a$ and the y-intercepts are at $\pm b$. If $a \geq b$, the foci of the ellipse are located at $(\pm c, 0)$, where $c^2 = a^2 - b^2$. If $b < c$, the foci of the ellipse are located at $(0, \pm c)$, where $c^2 = b^2 - a^2$.

The generic formula for an ellipse $\dfrac{x^2}{a^2}+\dfrac{y^2}{b^2}=1$

If a ≥ b, then the foci are $(\pm c, 0)$.

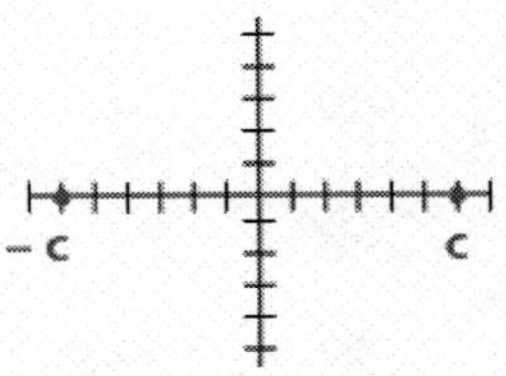

$c^2 = a^2 - b^2$

Previously you learned the general equation describing an ellipse centered at the origin.

If a is greater than or equal to b in the equation, then the foci are located on the x-axis at $(+c, 0)$, and $(-c, 0)$.

You can calculate where the foci are located exactly using this formula for c^2.

If b ≥ a, then the foci are (0, ±c). 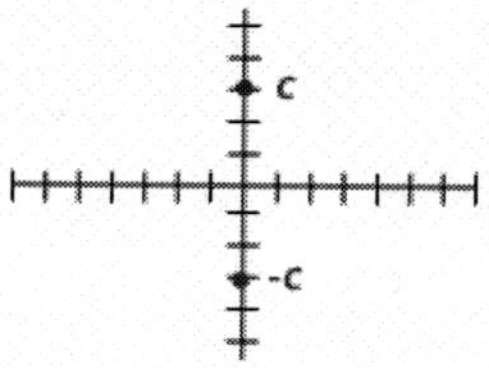 $c^2 = b^2 - a^2$	If b is greater than a in the equation, then the foci are located on the y-axis at $(0, \pm c)$. Use the formula $c^2 = b^2 - a^2$ to find c when $b > a$.
Example **Consider space:** **The coordinates for the satellite (in miles) can be described by the regular equation for an ellipse.** $\frac{x^2}{a^2} + \frac{y^2}{b^2} = 1$ a = 4465 miles, b = 4462 miles 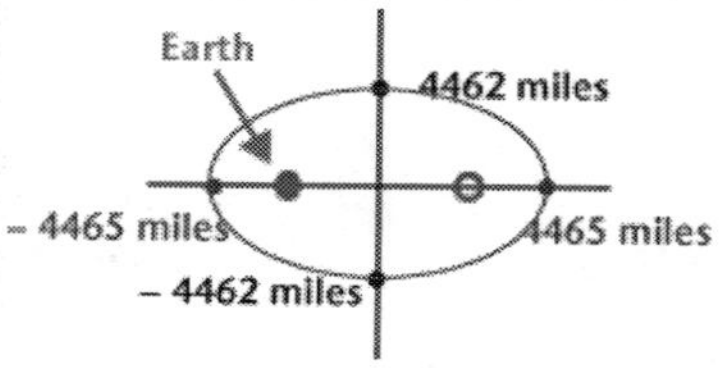 	Try this real-world problem. Suppose that an ellipse describes the orbit of a satellite around the Earth with the Earth at a focus. What are the maximum and minimum distances between the satellite and the Earth?
Plug a and b into the generic equation for the ellipse. $\frac{x^2}{4465^2} + \frac{y^2}{4462^2} = 1$	First, find the equation of the ellipse describing the satellite's orbit using the x and y-intercepts.
Find the foci by using the formula: $c^2 = a^2 - b^2$ **Use a calculator to find:** $c^2 = 4465^2 - 4462^2$ $c^2 = 26781$ $c = 163.64$	Now you can find the location of the Earth by finding the location of the foci using the formula from above.
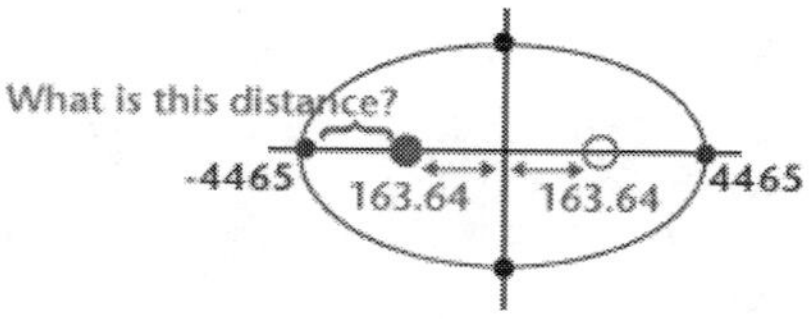 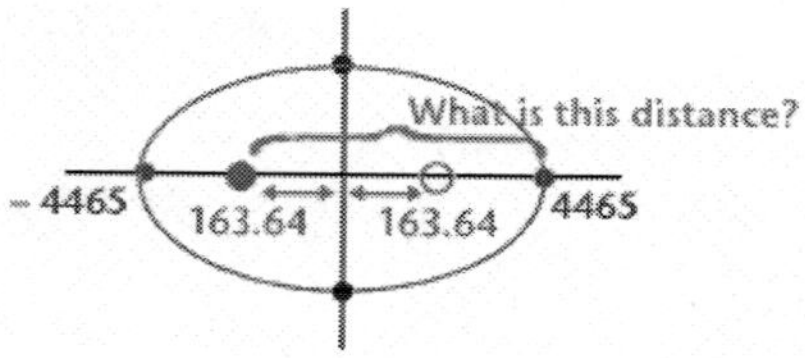 **4465 – 163.64 = 4301.36** $c = 163.64$ **minimum distance**	Once you know where the Earth is located, just do a little adding and subtracting to find the maximum and minimum distances between the Earth and the satellite. Ellipses come up frequently in the real world!

Sample problems:

1. Given $x^2 + \frac{y^2}{16} = 1$, where are the foci of the ellipse?
   Solution: $(0, -\sqrt{15})$ and $(0, \sqrt{15})$
   Explanation: Identify a and b from the equation: $a^2 = 1;\ a = \sqrt{1} = \pm 1$ and $b^2 = 16;\ b = \sqrt{16} = \pm 4$.
   Since $b > a$ the foci are at $(0, \pm c)$. use the formula $c^2 = b^2 - a^2$ to determine c: $c^2 = 16 - 1$;
   $c^2 = 15;\ c = \sqrt{15}$. So the foci are at $(0, -\sqrt{15})$ and $(0, \sqrt{15})$.

2. Given the ellipse $\frac{x^2}{25} + \frac{y^2}{9} = 1$, what are the curve's foci?
   Solution: $(4,0)$ and $(-4,0)$
   Explanation: Since $a \geq b$, the foci are $\left(\pm\sqrt{c}, 0\right)$, where $c^2 = a^2 - b^2$. Use the equation to find c:
   $c^2 = 25 - 9;\ c = \sqrt{16} = \pm 4$. Therefore, the foci are at $(4,0)$ and $(-4,0)$.

3. Suppose that an ellipse describes the orbit of a satellite around the Earth with the Earth at a focus. If horizontal and vertical axes are centered through the orbit, the satellite passes through (5000, 0) and (0, 4500). Find the minimum distance between the satellite and the Earth.
   Solution: 2324.55
   Explanation: Substitute 5,000 and 4,500 into the standard equation of an ellipse for a and b respectively:
   $\frac{x^2}{(5{,}000)} + \frac{y^2}{(4{,}500)} = 1$. Since $a \geq b$, use the equation $c^2 = a^2 - b^2$ to find c:
   $c^2 = (5{,}000)^2 - (4{,}500)^2;\ c^2 = 4{,}750{,}000;\ c = \pm 2179.45$.
   So the minimum distance must be $4{,}500 - 2179.45 = 2324.55$ miles.

Practice problems: *(Answers on page: 767)*

1. Given $\frac{x^2}{36} + \frac{y^2}{9} = 1$, where are the foci of the ellipse?
2. Given $\frac{x^2}{20} + \frac{y^2}{45} = 1$, where are the foci of the ellipse?
3. Suppose that an ellipse describes the orbit of a satellite around the Earth with the Earth at a focus. If horizontal and vertical axes are centered through the orbit, the satellite passes through (0, 3800) and (4000, 0). Find the maximum distance between the satellite and the Earth.

Review questions: *(Answers to odd questions on page: 767)*

1. Given $\frac{x^2}{100} + \frac{y^2}{36} = 1$, where are the foci of the ellipse?
2. Given $\frac{(x-6)^2}{64} + \frac{y^2}{6.25} = 1$, where are the foci of the ellipse?
3. Given $\frac{(x-4)^2}{9} + (y+3)^2 = 1$, where are the foci of the ellipse?
4. A room is elliptical. If it is 40 feet long and 20 feet wide, how far apart would two people be if they are standing at the foci?
5. The Oval Office of the President of the US is in the shape of an ellipse. The room is 36 feet long by 28 feet wide. Write the equation for this ellipse.

An Introduction to Hyperbolas

- A **hyperbola** consists of the set of points, the difference of whose distances from two fixed points is a constant. The two fixed points are called the **foci** of the hyperbola. The singular form of foci is focus.
- The standard equation for a hyperbola centered at the origin that opens to the left and right is $\frac{x^2}{a^2}-\frac{y^2}{b^2}=1$ where the x-intercepts are at $\pm a$. The foci of the hyperbola are located at $(\pm c, 0)$, where $c^2 = a^2 + b^2$.
- The standard equation for a hyperbola centered at the origin that open up and down is $\frac{x^2}{a^2}-\frac{y^2}{b^2}=1$ where the y-intercepts are at $\pm b$. The foci of the hyperbola are located at $(0, \pm c)$, where $c^2 = a^2 + b^2$.
- In either case, the hyperbola has asymptotes along the lines $y=\pm\frac{b}{a}x$.

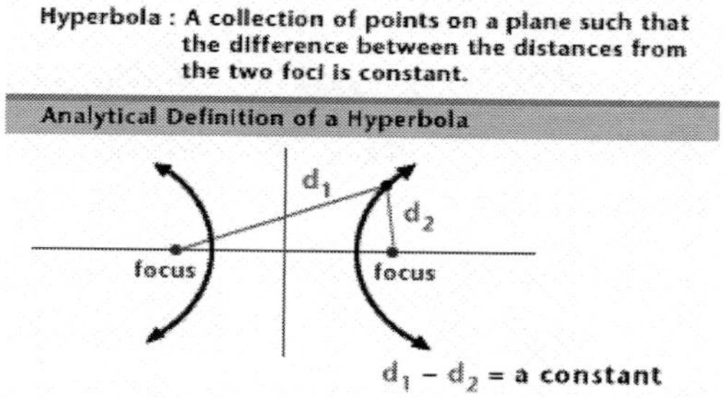

A hyperbola has a definition very similar to the definition of an ellipse. The major difference is that hyperbolae deal with a constant difference in the distances to two fixed points, rather than a constant sum.

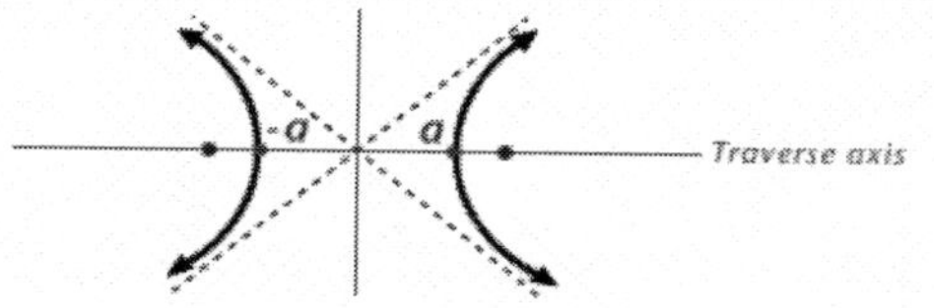

Hyperbolas reintroduce asymptotes, which you remember from earlier curves. The lines represent limits on the values used by the points in the hyperbolae since the curves approach the lines but never touch or intersect them.

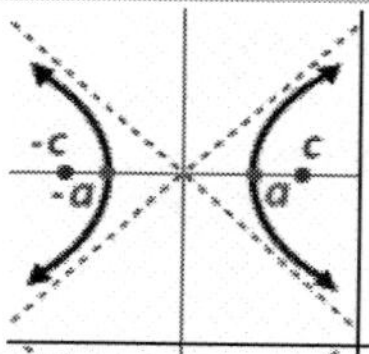

Equation: $\frac{x^2}{a^2}-\frac{y^2}{b^2}=1$

Foci: $c^2=a^2+b^2$ $(\pm c, 0)$

Asymptotes: $y=\pm\frac{b}{a}x$

Here is a summary of the formulas for a hyperbola that opens to the left and right.

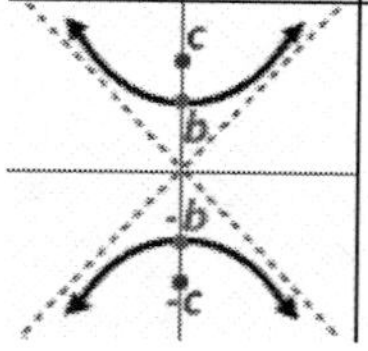

Equation: $\frac{y^2}{b^2}-\frac{x^2}{a^2}=1$

Foci: $c^2=a^2+b^2$ $(0, \pm c)$

Asymptotes: $y=\pm\frac{b}{a}x$

Similar formulas exist for a hyperbola that opens upwards and downwards.

Sample problems:

1. State the equations for the asymptotes of the hyperbola: $\frac{y^2}{36}-\frac{x^2}{25}=1$.

   Solution: $y=\pm\frac{6}{5}x$

   Explanation: The hyperbola defined by $\frac{y^2}{36}-\frac{x^2}{25}=1$ is a up/down hyperbola centered at the origin. Therefore, to find the equations of the asymptotes, use the formula $y=\pm\frac{a}{b}x$. Consider the standard form of a hyperbola, $\frac{y^2}{a^2}-\frac{x^2}{b^2}=1$ to identify a and b: $a^2=36$; $a=\sqrt{36}=\pm 6$ and $b^2=25$; $b=\sqrt{25}=\pm 5$. Substitute a and b into $y=\pm\frac{a}{b}x$: $y=\pm\frac{6}{5}x$.

2. State the foci of the hyperbola: $\dfrac{x^2}{15}-\dfrac{y^2}{5}=1$.

Solution: $(\pm 2\sqrt{5},\ 0)$

Explanation: The equation $\frac{x^2}{15}-\frac{y^2}{5}=1$ is in the standard form of a left/right hyperbola, so the foci are located at $(\pm c,\ 0)$ where $c^2=a^2+b^2$. Identify a^2+b^2 from the equation, $a^2=15$ and $b^2=5$. Substitute the a^2+b^2 values into $c^2=a^2+b^2$ to determine c: $c^2=15+5$; $c^2=20$; $c=\sqrt{20}$; $c=2\sqrt{5}$. So the foci are at $(\pm 2\sqrt{5},\ 0)$.

3. State the foci and equation for the asymptotes of the hyperbola: $4y^2-9x^2=36$.

Solution: foci: $(0,\pm\sqrt{13})$; asymptotes: $y=\pm\dfrac{3}{2}x$

Explanation: Express the equation in standard form by dividing by 36: $\frac{4y^2}{36}-\frac{9x^2}{36}=\frac{36}{36}$; $\frac{y^2}{9}-\frac{x^2}{4}=1$. Determine c to locate the foci: $c^2=a^2+b^2$; $c^2=9+4$; $c^2=13$; $c=\sqrt{13}$. So, the foci are at $(0,\pm\sqrt{13})$ since this is a up/down hyperbola. Find the equation of the asymptotes: $y=\pm\frac{a}{b}x$; $y=\pm\frac{3}{2}$.

Practice problems: *(Answers on page: 768)*

1. State the equations for the asymptotes of the hyperbola: $x^2-\dfrac{y^2}{25}=1$.
2. State the foci of the hyperbola: $y^2-25x^2=100$.
3. State the foci and the equations for the asymptotes of the hyperbola: $4x^2-y^2=16$.

Review questions: *(Answers to odd questions on page: 768)*

1. State the foci of the hyperbola: $\dfrac{x^2}{9}-\dfrac{y^2}{25}=1$.
2. State the foci of the hyperbola: $\dfrac{y^2}{36}-\dfrac{x^2}{1}=1$.
3. State the foci of the hyperbola: $\dfrac{x^2}{7}-\dfrac{y^2}{2}=1$.
4. State the equations for the asymptotes of the hyperbola: $9x^2-4y^2=36$.
5. State the foci of the hyperbola: $5y^2-4x^2=20$.

Finding the Equation for a Hyperbola

- The standard equation for a hyperbola centered at the origin that opens to the left and right is $\frac{x^2}{a^2}-\frac{y^2}{b^2}=1$ where the x-intercepts are at $\pm a$. The foci of the hyperbola are located at $(\pm c, 0)$, where $c^2 = a^2 + b^2$. For a hyperbola that opens upwards and downwards, the standard equation is $\frac{y^2}{a^2}-\frac{x^2}{b^2}=1$, and the foci are located at $(0, \pm c)$.
- The standard equation for a hyperbola centered at the origin that opens to the left and right is $\frac{x^2}{a^2}-\frac{y^2}{b^2}=1$ where the x-intercepts are at $\pm a$. The foci of the hyperbola are located at $(\pm c, 0)$, where $c^2 = a^2 + b^2$.
- The standard equation for a hyperbola centered at the origin that open up and down is $\frac{x^2}{a^2}-\frac{y^2}{b^2}=1$, where the y-intercepts are at $\pm b$. The foci of the hyperbola are located at $(0, \pm c)$, where $c^2 = a^2 + b^2$.
- In either case, the hyperbola has asymptotes along the lines $y=\pm\frac{b}{a}x$.

Example Write the hyperbola's equation, given:
x intercept = ±4
Foci at (±5, 0)

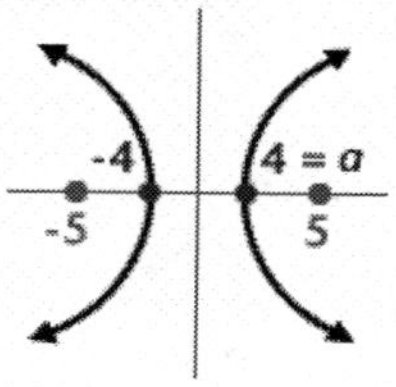

$$\frac{x^2}{16}-\frac{y^2}{b^2}=1$$

In this example problem you are asked to write the equation describing a hyperbola given the location of its x-intercepts and foci.

A good first step is to draw a rough sketch of the hyperbola.

You can see that the hyperbola opens to the left and right, so the general equation is $\frac{x^2}{a^2}-\frac{y^2}{b^2}=1$.
Since you already know the value of a in the standard equation for a hyperbola, all you need to find is the value of b^2.

$$c^2 = a^2 + b^2$$
$$25 = 16 + b^2$$
$$9 = b^2$$

$$\frac{x^2}{16}-\frac{y^2}{b^2}=1 \qquad \boxed{\frac{x^2}{16}-\frac{y^2}{9}=1}$$

To find the value of b^2, use the formula $c^2 = a^2 + b^2$.

Substitute b^2 into the standard equation for a hyperbola that opens to the left and right and you're done.

Example Write the hyperbola's equation, given:
y intercept = ±9
Foci at (0, ±15)

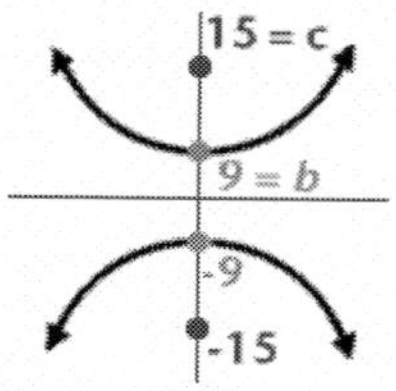

$$c^2 = a^2 + b^2$$
$$225 = a^2 + 81$$
$$144 = a^2$$

$$\frac{y^2}{81}-\frac{x^2}{a^2}=1 \qquad \boxed{\frac{y^2}{81}-\frac{x^2}{144}=1}$$

Here is another problem along the same lines.

First sketch a rough picture. This hyperbola opens upwards and downwards, so the general equation is $\frac{x^2}{a^2}-\frac{y^2}{b^2}=1$.

Now find the value of a^2 using $c^2 = a^2 - b^2$.

Substitute into the standard equation for a hyperbola that opens upwards and downwards.

Sample problems:

1. Write the equation of a hyperbola given that the y-intercepts are ± 4 and the foci are at $(0, \pm 9)$.

Solution: $\frac{y^2}{16} - \frac{x^2}{65} = 1$

Explanation: Sketch the hyperbola. The general form of the equation is $\frac{y^2}{b^2} - \frac{x^2}{a^2} = 1$, since it is an up/down parabola. Substitute 4 into the equation for b: $\frac{y^2}{4^2} - \frac{x^2}{a^2} = 1$. Use the equation $c^2 = a^2 + b^2$ to determine a: $9^2 = a^2 + 4^2$; $81 = a^2 + 16$; $a^2 = 65$; $a = \sqrt{165}$. Substitute $\sqrt{65}$ into the equation of the hyperbola for a and simplify: $\frac{y^2}{4^2} - \frac{x^2}{\sqrt{65}^2} = 1$; $\frac{y^2}{16} - \frac{x^2}{65} = 1$.

2. Write the equation of a hyperbola given that the x-intercepts are ± 2 and the foci are at $(\pm 5,\ 0)$.

Solution: $\frac{x^2}{4} - \frac{y^2}{16} = 1$

Explanation: Since this is a left/right hyperbola, the general equation is $\frac{x^2}{a^2} - \frac{y^2}{b^2} = 1$, where the x-intercepts are $\pm a$. Substitute 2 into the equation for a: $\frac{x^2}{2^2} - \frac{y^2}{b^2} = 1$. Find b: $c^2 = a^2 + b^2$; $5^2 = 2^2 + b^2$; $25 = 4 + b^2$; $b^2 = 16$; $b = \sqrt{16} = \pm 4$. Therefore, the equation of the hyperbola is $\frac{x^2}{4} - \frac{y^2}{16} = 1$.

3. Write the equation of a hyperbola given that the x-intercepts are ± 4 and it passes through the point (5, 3.75).

Solution: $\frac{x^2}{16} - \frac{y^2}{25} = 1$

Explanation: Since the x-intercepts are ± 4, begin with the equation $\frac{x^2}{16} - \frac{y^2}{b^2} = 1$. Find b by substituting the x and y-values from the point (5, 3.75) into the equation and solving for b: $\frac{(5)^2}{16} - \frac{(3.75)}{b^2} = 1$; $\frac{25}{16} - \frac{14.0625}{b^2} = 1$; $-\frac{14.0625}{b^2} = 1 - \frac{25}{16}$; $-\frac{14.0625}{b^2} = -\frac{9}{6}$; $9b^2 = 16(14.0625)$; $b^2 = 25$; $b = \sqrt{25}$; $b = \pm 5$. So the equation of the hyperbola is $\frac{x^2}{16} - \frac{y^2}{25} = 1$.

Practice problems: *(Answers on page: 768)*

1. Write the equation of a hyperbola given that the x-intercepts are ± 6 and the foci are at $(\pm 10,\ 0)$.
2. Write the equation of a hyperbola given that the y-intercepts are ± 1 and the foci are at $(0, \pm 3)$.
3. A hyperbola's x-intercepts are located at $(4,0)$ and $(-4,0)$, and it passes through the point $(-5,5)$. Write the equation of this hyperbola.

Review questions: *(Answers to odd questions on page: 768)*

1. Write the equation of a hyperbola given that the y-intercepts are $(0,2)$ and $(0,-2)$ and the foci are at $(0,3)$ and $(0,-3)$.
2. Write the equation of a hyperbola given that the x-intercepts are $(7,0)$ and $(-7,0)$ and the foci are at $(10,0)$ and $(-10,0)$.
3. Write the equation of a hyperbola given that the y-intercepts are $(0,3)$ and $(0,-3)$ that passes through the point $(-2,5)$.

4. Write the equation of a hyperbola given that the x-intercepts are $(2,0)$ and $(-2,0)$ that passes through the point $(3,\sqrt{3})$.

5. Write the equation of a hyperbola given that the x-intercepts are $(4,0)$ and $(-4,0)$ that passes through the point $(\sqrt{32},1)$.

Applying Hyperbolas: Navigation

- Hyperbolas are useful in many real-world situations. One such situation is the navigation of ships at sea.
- The standard equation for a hyperbola centered at the origin that opens to the left and right is $\frac{x^2}{a^2}-\frac{y^2}{b^2}=1$, where the x-intercepts are at $\pm a$. The foci of the hyperbola are located at $(\pm c, 0)$, where $c^2 = a^2 + b^2$.
- The standard equation for a hyperbola centered at the origin that open up and down is $\frac{x^2}{a^2}-\frac{y^2}{b^2}=1$, where the y-intercepts are at $\pm b$. The foci of the hyperbola are located at $(0, \pm c)$, where $c^2 = a^2 + b^2$.
- In either case, the hyperbola has asymptotes along the lines $y=\pm\frac{b}{a}x$.

Example

Find the equation for the hyperbola that has foci at T_1 and T_2 and contains the ship.

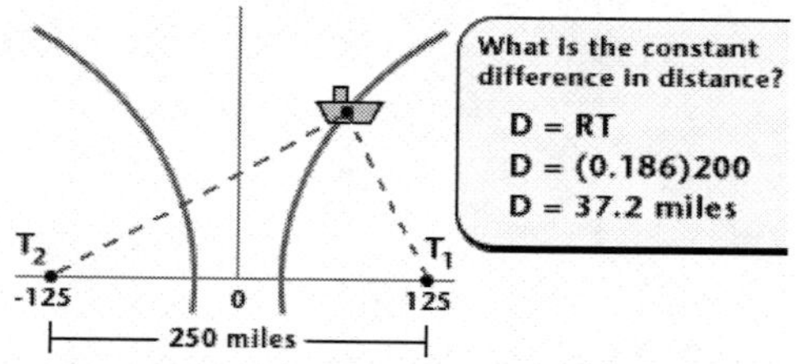

The T_2 signal is received 200 μsec after the T_1 signal.
The signals travel at 0.186 miles / μsec

A ship can determine its location at sea using radio signals sent from two separate locations on shore.

Since one signal will reach the ship before the other, it is possible to calculate the difference in distances between the ship and the two points on shore given the speed of the radio signal.

The calculations show us that the difference between when the two signals are received indicates a difference in distance from the ship to the two beacons of 37.2 miles.

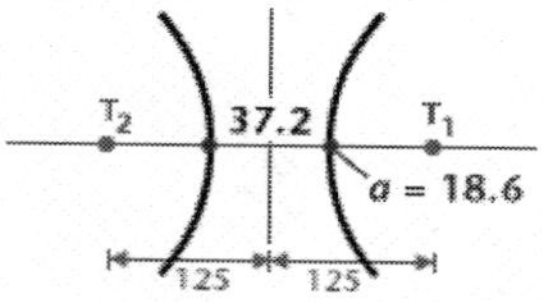

$$\frac{x^2}{a^2}-\frac{y^2}{b^2}=1$$

$$\frac{x^2}{345.96}-\frac{y^2}{b^2}=1$$

You can find the equation for this hyperbola using a little algebra.

Since you know the location of the foci of the hyperbola and you know the difference in distances between a point on the hyperbola and the two foci, you can find the value of a, the x-intercept of the hyperbola.

$c^2 = a^2 + b^2$
$125^2 = 18.6^2 + b^2$
$15{,}625 = 345.96 + b^2$
$b^2 = 15{,}279.04$

$$\frac{x^2}{345.96}-\frac{y^2}{b^2}=1$$

$$\boxed{\frac{x^2}{345.96}-\frac{y^2}{15{,}279.04}=1}$$

Using $c^2 = a^2 + b^2$, you can determine b^2. Just substitute these values into the standard equation for a hyperbola.

Example

If the ship is 100 miles east of the y axis, then how far is it from shore (the x axis)?

$$\frac{x^2}{345.96} - \frac{y^2}{15{,}279.04} = 1$$

Just plug in 100 for x.

$$\frac{10{,}000}{345.96} - \frac{y^2}{15{,}279.04} = 1$$

$$\frac{y^2}{15{,}279.04} = \frac{10{,}000}{345.96} - 1$$

$$\frac{y^2}{15{,}279.04} = 27.9\ldots$$

$$y^2 = 426{,}362.7\ldots$$

$$y = 652.9 \text{ miles}$$

Once you have found the equation for the hyperbola, it is easy to answer the question to the left. Just plug in $x = 100$ and solve for y.

Bring the constants to one side to isolate the y variable.

Do you see how hyperbolas can be very useful in the real world?

Sample problems:

1. Suppose 2 Loran stations, T_1 and T_2, are positioned 200 miles apart and the signals they are sending travel 186,000 miles per second. A ship, traveling along a hyperbola with the stations as a foci, records a .00038 second time difference between the signals. Write the equation of the hyperbola that contains the ship.

   Solution: $\frac{x^2}{1248.92} - \frac{y^2}{8751.08} = 1$

   Explanation: The shore and the stations are on the x-axis and the center of the stations is the origin. Since the stations are 200 miles apart, the foci must be $T_1 = (-100,\ 0)$ and $T_2 = (100,\ 0)$. Use $d = rt$ to determine the constant difference in distance: $d = (186{,}000)(.00038) = 70.68$. Therefore, the distance between the x-intercepts must also be 70.68. Since the x-intercepts are centered around the origin and the distance between them is 70.68, the x-intercepts are located at $\pm\frac{70.68}{2}$, or ± 35.35. So, $a = 35.35$ and $a^2 = 1248.92$. Determine b^2 using $c^2 = a^2 + b^2$: $100^2 = 1248.92 + b^2$; $b^2 = 8751.08$. Substitute a^2 and b^2 into the standard equation of a hyperbola, $\frac{x^2}{a^2} - \frac{y^2}{b^2} = 1$: $\frac{x^2}{1248.92} - \frac{y^2}{8751.08} = 1$.

2. Use the situation in sample problem #1 to determine the distance of the ship from the shore when it is 50 miles east of the y-axis.

   Solution: Approximately 94 miles

   Explanation: Substitute 50 into the equation from #1 for x and solve for y:

   $\frac{(50)^2}{1248.92} - \frac{y^2}{8751.08} = 1$; $2.002 - \frac{y^2}{8751.08} = 1$; $\frac{y^2}{8751.08} = 1.002$; $y^2 = 8768.58$; $y = 93.64$.

   So the ship is almost 94 miles from the shore.

Practice problems: *(Answers on page: 768)*

1. Suppose 2 Loran stations, T_1 and T_2, are positioned 250 miles apart and the signals they are sending travel 186,000 miles per second. A ship, traveling along a hyperbola with the stations as a foci, records a .00032 second time difference between the signals. Write the equation of the hyperbola that contains the ship.

2. Use the situation in problem #1 to determine the distance of the ship from the shore when it is 75 miles east of the y-axis.

Review questions: *(Answers to odd questions on page: 768)*

1. Suppose 2 Loran stations, T_1 and T_2, are positioned150 miles apart and the signals they are sending travel 195,000 miles per second. A ship, traveling along a hyperbola with the stations as a foci, records a .00024 second time difference between the signals. Write the equation of the hyperbola that contains the ship.
2. Use the situation in problem #1 to determine the distance of the ship from the shore when it is 40 miles east of the y-axis.

Identifying a Conic

- You can determine whether an equation describes a conic section and which conic section an equation describes by completing the square for the x and y variables and factoring.
- **Review**: The standard equation for a **parabola** centered at (h,k) is $(x - h)^2 = 4p(y - k)$
- **Review**: The standard equation for a **circle** centered at (h,k) is $(x - h)^2 + (y - k)^2 = r^2$
- **Review**: The standard equation for an **ellipse** centered at (h,k) is $\frac{(x-h)^2}{a^2}+\frac{(y-k)^2}{b^2}=1$.
- **Review**: The standard equation for a **hyperbola** centered at the origin that opens to the left and right is $\frac{x^2}{a^2}-\frac{y^2}{b^2}=1$. For a hyperbola that opens upwards and downwards, the standard equation is $\frac{y^2}{a^2}-\frac{x^2}{b^2}=1$.

Example

By completing the square , we can recognize whether or not an algebraic expression is a conic section.

$$4x^2 + 9y^2 - 16x - 36y + 16 = 0$$

Complete the square:

$$4(x^2 - 4x + 4 - 4) + 9(y^2 - 4y + 4 - 4) + 16 = 0$$

$$4(x - 2)^2 - 16 + 9(y - 2)^2 - 36 + 16 = 0$$

$$4(x-2)^2 + 9(y-2)^2 = 36$$

This is an ellipse $\frac{(x - 2)^2}{9} + \frac{(y - 2)^2}{4} = 1$

Express the equation in a standard form through some algebraic manipulation. First, collect x terms and the y terms.
Factor out any constants within each group.
Complete the square for x and also for y.
Move the unattached constants to the other side of the equation.
Divide by the constant coefficients of each square.

Now you have the equation in standard form! This particular equation describes an ellipse.

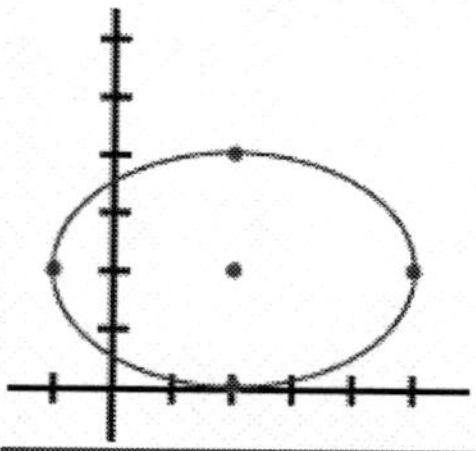

$$\frac{(x - 2)^2}{9} + \frac{(y - 2)^2}{4} = 1$$

Let's review how to graph the ellipse.

First, find its center. In this case the center is (2, 2). The a^2 tells you to go 3 units to the sides. Similarly, the b^2 tells you to go 2 units up and down.

With these points plotted, it's a snap to sketch in the ellipse.

Sample problems:

1. Express the following equation in standard form, identify the conic, and state the location of its center or vertex: $-9x^2+4y^2=36$.

   Solution: $\frac{y^2}{9}-\frac{x^2}{4}=1$; hyperbola with center (0, 0)

   Explanation: The equation appears to be a hyperbola since it is similar to $\frac{y^2}{a^2}-\frac{x^2}{b^2}=1$.

   Switch the x and y terms and divide the equation by 36: $\frac{4y^2}{36}-\frac{9x^2}{36}=\frac{36}{36}$; $\frac{y^2}{9}-\frac{x^2}{4}=1$.
   Therefore, it is an up/down hyperbola with center at (0, 0).

2. Express the following equation in standard form, identify the conic, and state the location of its center or vertex: $x^2-6x+y^2+8y=5$.
   Solution: $(x-3)^2+(y-4)^2=30$; circle with center $(3,-4)$
   Explanation: The equation appears to be a circle. Complete the square for $x+y$:
   $(x^2-6x+9)+(y^2+8y+16)=5+9+16$. Factor and simplify: $(x-3)^2+(y+4)^2=30$.
   Therefore, since this equation is in the form $(x-h)^2+(y-k)^2=r^2$, the conic is a circle and the center is $(3,-4)$.

3. Express the following equation in standard form, identify the conic, and state the location of its center or vertex: $x^2-10x-8y+17=0$.
   Solution: $(x-5)^2=8(y+1)$; parabola with vertex $(5,-1)$
   Explanation: The equation appears to be a parabola since x is squared, but y is not.
   So, manipulate the equation to express it in the standard form of a parabola, $(x-h)^2=4p(y-k)$.
   Move the y-term and the constant term to the right side: $x^2-10x=8y-17$.
   Complete the square for x: $x^2-10x+25=8y-17+25$. Factor and simplify: $(x-5)^2=8y+8$.
   Factor an 8 out of the right side: $(x-5)^2=8(y+1)$. So, the conic is a parabola and the vertex is at $(5,-1)$.

Practice problems: *(Answers on page: 768)*

1. Express the following equation in standard form, identify the conic, and state the location of its center or vertex: $-x^2+4y^2-6x-8y-21=0$.
2. Express the following equation in standard form, identify the conic, and state the location of its center or vertex: $9x^2+36y^2-36=0$.
3. Express the following equation in standard form, identify the conic, and state the location of its center or vertex: $2x^2-8x-20y=52$.

Review questions: *(Answers to odd questions on page: 768)*

1. Express the following equation in standard form, identify the conic, and state the location of its center or vertex: $-4x^2-12y^2+16x-36y+5=0$.
2. Express the following equation in standard form, identify the conic, and state the location of its center or vertex: $3x^2-12x+3y^2-6=0$.
3. Express the following equation in standard form, identify the conic, and state the location of its center or vertex: $3y^2-x+15y+11=0$.
4. Express the following equation in standard form, identify the conic, and state the location of its center or vertex: $x^2-6x-4y^2+12y-5=0$.

5. Express the following equation in standard form, identify the conic, and state the location of its center or vertex: $x^2 - 4y + 8 = 0$.

Name That Conic

- You can determine whether an equation describes a conic section and which conic section an equation describes by completing the square for the x and y variables and factoring.
- The standard equation for a **parabola** centered at (h,k) is $\mathbf{(x - h)^2 = 4p(y - k)}$
- The standard equation for a **circle** centered at (h,k) is $\mathbf{(x - h)^2 + (y - k)^2 = r^2}$
- The standard equation for an **ellipse** centered at (h,k) is $\frac{(x-h)^2}{a^2} + \frac{(y-k)^2}{b^2} = 1$.
- The standard equation for a **hyperbola** centered at the origin that opens to the left and right is $\frac{x^2}{a^2} - \frac{y^2}{b^2} = 1$.
- For a hyperbola that opens upwards and downwards, the standard equation is $\frac{y^2}{a^2} - \frac{x^2}{b^2} = 1$.

Example **Original Equation:** $9x^2 - 25y^2 - 18x + 50y = 0$ Complete the square: $9(x^2 - 2x + 1 - 1) - 25(y^2 - 2y + 1 - 1) = 0$ $9(x-1)^2 - 9 - 25(y-1)^2 + 25 = 0$ $9(x-1)^2 - 25(y-1)^2 = -16$ $\frac{9(x-1)^2}{-16} + \frac{25(y-1)^2}{16} = 1$	What conic section does this equation represent? First collect the x and y terms together. Factor any constants from each group. Watch out for those negative signs! Then, complete the square. Remove any unattached constants to the other side of the equation. Divide everything by the constant coefficients. Things are starting to look more familiar now.
$\frac{9(x-1)^2}{-16} + \frac{25(y-1)^2}{16} = 1$ $\frac{(y-1)^2}{(\frac{4}{5})^2} - \frac{(x-1)^2}{(\frac{4}{3})^2} = 1$	To finish things off, use a compound fraction to put the constant coefficients entirely in the denominators. You can see that the equation is now in the standard form for a hyperbola that opens upwards and downwards.
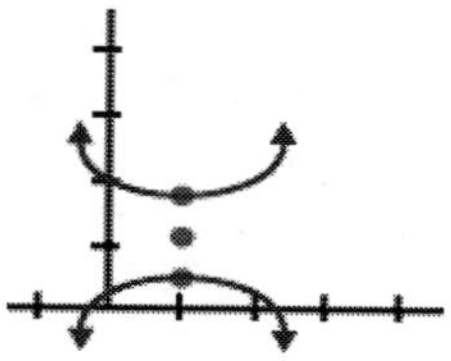 $\frac{(y-1)^2}{(\frac{4}{5})^2} - \frac{(x-1)^2}{(\frac{4}{3})^2} = 1$	To graph the hyperbola, notice first that its center is at (1, 1). Then, the coefficient of $(4/5)^2$ under the y term tells you to go up and down from the center by 4/5 units. With these points plotted, you can make a rough graph of the hyperbola.

Sample problems:

1. Identify the type of conic section represented by $3x^2 - 30x - 4y + 67 = 0$.
   Solution: Parabola
   Explanation: Since the x-term is squared, but the y-term is not, the conic must be a parabola. The same result is obtained when the equation is expressed in standard form by separating the terms and completing the square: $3x^2 - 30x = 4y - 67$; $3(x^2 - 10x) = 4y - 67$; $3(x^2 - 10x + 25)4y - 67 + 75$; $3(x-5)^2 = 4y + 8$; $(x-5)^2 = \frac{4}{3}(y+2)$. So, this is the standard form of a parabola, $(x-h)^2 = 4p(y-k)$.

2. Identify the type of conic section represented by $x^2 + 22 = 10x - y^2 - 2y$.
   Solution: Circle
   Explanation: Express the equation in standard form. Since x and y are squared, it is not a parabola. It appears to be a circle or an ellipse since x and y are squared and they will have the same sign when both on the right. So, manipulate the equation into the standard equation of a circle: $(x-h)^2 + (y-k)^2 = r^2$. Move the y-terms to the left and the constant to the right: $x^2 - 10x + y^2 + 2y = -22$. Complete the square for x and y: $x^2 + 10x + 25 + y^2 + 2y + 1$ $= -22 + 25 + 1$. Factor and simplify: $(x-5)^2 + (y+1)^2 = 4$. So, the conic is a circle.

3. Identify the type of conic section represented by $3x^2 - 18y^2 = 36$.
   Solution: Hyperbola
   Explanation: This equation appears to be a hyperbola since x and y are squared and they have opposite signs. Manipulate the equation into the standard form of a hyperbola. Divide the equation by 36, so that it will equal 1: $\frac{3x^2}{36} - \frac{18y^2}{36} = \frac{36}{36}$; $\frac{x^2}{12} - \frac{y^2}{12} - \frac{y^2}{2} = 1$. So, the conic is a hyperbola.

Practice problems: *(Answers on page: 768)*

1. Identify the type of conic section represented by $x^2 + y^2 - 14x + 6y = 42$.
2. Identify the type of conic section represented by $15y^2 + 14x^2 = 90$.
3. Identify the type of conic section represented by $-2x^2 + 3x + 7y = 0$.

Review questions: *(Answers to odd questions on page: 768)*

1. Identify the type of conic section represented by $3x = 2y^2 + 7y - 11$.
2. Identify the type of conic section represented by $4x^2 - 6x + 9y^2 + 15y - 1 = 0$.
3. Identify the type of conic section represented by $3x^2 + 15x - 3y^2 = 0$.
4. Identify the type of conic section represented by $\frac{(x-7)^2}{20} + \frac{(y+3)^2}{20} = 1$.
5. Identify the type of conic section represented by $15y^2 + 14x^2 = 90$.

Using the Binomial Theorem

- **Pascal's triangle** is a group of numbers in a very special pattern. The triangle's terms are found by adding the terms above on either side of the term you want.
- The **binomial theorem** states that the coefficients in a binomial expansion follow directly from Pascal's triangle.

Binomial $x + y$ (two terms) $(x + y)^2 = (x + y)(x + y) = x^2 + 2xy + y^2$ $(x + y)^3 = (x+y)(x+y)(x+y) = x^3+3x^2y+3xy^2+y^3$ $(x + y)^{101} = ?$	You have already learned how to **FOIL** binomial expressions when the exponents are low. But what do you do when the exponents start getting bigger?
Example $1x + 1y$ 1 1 ← coefficients $(x + y)^2$ $1x^2 + 2xy + 1y^2$ 1 2 1 $(x + y)^3$ 1 3 3 1 $1x^3 + 3x^2y + 3xy^2 + 1y^3$	When mathematicians look for shortcuts they start by looking for patterns. Take a look at how the coefficients of these binomial expressions change. Do you see any patterns?
Example **Rule:** always start with a 1 and end with a 1 $(x + y)$ 1 1 $(x + y)^2$ 1 2 1 $(x + y)^3$ 1 3 3 1	The most obvious pattern is that the coefficient of the first and the last term is always 1. Is there another pattern here?
$(x + y)$ 1 1 $(x + y)^2$ 1 + 2 = 1 $(x + y)^3$ 1 3 3 1	Check this out! Each inner term is equal to the sum of the two previous adjacent terms.
$(x + y)$ 1 1 $(x + y)^2$ 1 2 1 $(x + y)^3$ 1 3 3 1 $(x + y)^4$ 1 4 6 4 1 $(x + y)^5$ 1 5 10 10 5 1	This pattern holds true for all the inner terms. The figure that this pattern creates is called **Pascal's triangle**.
Example $(x + y)^4 = 1x^4+4x^3y+6x^2y^2+4xy^3+1y^4$ $(x + y)$ 1 1 $(x + y)^2$ 1 2 1 $(x + y)^3$ 1 3 3 1 $(x + y)^4$ 1 4 6 4 1 $(x + y)^5$ 1 5 10 10 5 1	By using Pascal's triangle, the **binomial theorem** states that you can find the coefficient of each term in the expansion. Start with the first term of the binomial raised to the same power as the binomial, in this example that's x^4. Each successive term will have one power less of the first term and one more of the second term. Now you can expand large binomials!

Sample problems:

1. Expand the binomial: $(5x+4y)^3$.
   Solution: $125x^3+300x^2y+240xy^2+64y^3$
   Explanation: Generate the 3rd row of Pascal's triangle, since the exponent is 3: 1331. There are 4 numbers in the 3rd row, so there will be 4 terms in the expansion. Make a skeleton of the espansion polynomial where each term contains the appropriate coefficient: $(5x+4y)^3 = (1) \quad +(3) \quad +(3) \quad +(1)$. Insert the decreasing powers of $5x$, begin in the 1st term with $(5x)^3$: $(5x+4y)^3 = (1)(5x)^3 \; +(3)(5x)^2 \; +(3)(5x)^1 \; +1$. Inset increasing powers of $4y$, begin with $(4y)^1$ in the 2nd term: $(5x+4y)^3 = (1)(5x)^3+(3)(5x)^2(4y)^1+(3)(5x)(4y)^2+(1)(4y)^3$. Simplify: $(5x+4y)^3 = (1)(5x)x^3+(3)(5^2)(4^1)x^2y = (3)(5^1)(4^2)xy^2+(1)(4^3)y^3 = 125x^3+300x^2y+240xy^2+64y^3$.

2. Expand the binomial: $(3x-2y)^4$

   Solution: $81x^4-216x^3y+216x^2y^2-96xy^3+16y^4$

   Explanation: Generate the 4th row of Pascal's triangle: 1 4 6 4 1. Insert the coefficients into the skeleton: $(1)\ \ +(4)\ \ +(6)\ \ +(4)\ \ (1)$. Insert decreasing powers of $3x$:
   $1(3x)^4\ \ +4(3x)^3\ \ +6(3x)^2\ \ +4(3x)^1\ \ +(1)$. Insert increasing powers of $-2y$, begin in the 2nd term:
   $=(1)(3x)^4+(4)(3x)^3(-2y)+(6)(3x)^2(-2y)^2+(4)(3x)(-2y)^3+(1)(-2y)^4$. Simplify:
   $(3x-2y)^4=81x^4-216x^3y+216x^2y^2-96xy^3+16y^4$.

3. Expand the binomial: $\left(2x^3+4\sqrt{y}\right)^5$.

   Solution: $32x^{15}+320x^{12}\sqrt{y}+1280x^9y+2560x^6\sqrt{y}^3+2560x^3y^2+1024\sqrt{y}^5$

   Explanation: Generate the 5th row of Pascal's triangle and insert those coefficients into the skeleton:
   $(1)\ \ +(5)\ \ +(10)\ \ +(10)\ \ +(5)\ \ +(1)$. Insert decreasing powers of $2x^3$:
   $(1)\left(2x^3\right)^5\ \ +(5)\left(2x^3\right)^4\ \ +(10)\left(2x^3\right)^3\ \ +(10)\left(2x^3\right)^2+(5)\left(2x^3\right)^1\ \ +(1)$. Insert increasing powers of $4\sqrt{y}$:
   $(1)\left(2x^3\right)^5+(5)\left(2x^3\right)^4\left(4\sqrt{y}\right)^1+(10)\left(2x^3\right)^3\left(4\sqrt{y}\right)^2+(10)\left(2x^3\right)^2\left(4\sqrt{y}\right)^3+(5)\left(2x^3\right)^1\left(4\sqrt{y}\right)^4+(1)\left(4\sqrt{y}\right)^5$.
   Simplify: $\left(2^5\right)x^{15}(5)\left(2^4\right)\left(4^1\right)x^{12}\sqrt{y}+(10)\left(2^3\right)\left(4^2\right)x^9\sqrt{y}^2+(10)\left(2^2\right)\left(4^3\right)x^6\sqrt{y}^3+5\left(2^1\right)\left(4^4\right)x^3\sqrt{y}^4+4^5\sqrt{y}^5=$
   $32x^{15}+320x^{12}\sqrt{y}+1280x^9y+2560x^6\sqrt{y}^3+2560x^3y^2+1024\sqrt{y}^5$.
   Note the pattern in the exponents $\{15, 12, 9, 6, 3\}$ and $\left\{\frac{1}{2}, 1, \frac{3}{2}, 2, \frac{5}{2}\right\}$.

Practice problems: *(Answers on page: 768)*

1. Expand the binomial: $(2-y)^5$.
2. Let the expression equal y and then change the equation to exponential form: $\log_{64}16$
3. Expand the binomial: $\left(4\sqrt{x}+3y^2\right)^4$

Review questions: *(Answers to odd questions on page: 768)*

1. Expand the binomial: $(5-\mathrm{y})^4$.
2. Expand the binomial: $(2x^3+y^2)^5$.
3. Expand the binomial: $(x-y)^3$.
4. Expand the binomial: $(x-4)^5$.
5. Expand the binomial: $(x-3\sqrt{y})^3$.

Binomial Coefficients

- The **factorial** is a function that takes an integer and multiplies it by all the positive integers that are less than it is. Factorials are represented by exclamation points (!).
- The **binomial coefficient formula**: $\binom{n}{m}=\dfrac{n!}{m!(n-m)!}$
- The **binomial theorem**: $(x+y)^n=x^n+\binom{n}{1}x^{n-2}y^2...\binom{n}{n-1}xy^{n-1}+\binom{n}{n}y^n$

Pascal's Triangle $(x+y)$: 1 1 $(x+y)^2$: 1 2 1 $(x+y)^3$: 1 3 3 1 $(x+y)^4$: 1 4 6 4 1 $(x+y)^5$: 1 5 10 10 5 1 ↓ ↓ $(x+y)^{101}$ 1 . . .	You can use **Pascal's triangle** to find the coefficients of a binomial expansion pretty easily if the power is small enough. But what about those cases where the power is really large? Is there a shortcut?
Factorial: n! *(reads: n factorial)* $n! = n(n-1)(n-2)\ldots 2\cdot 1$ $0! = 1$ $4! = \boxed{4\cdot 3\cdot 2\cdot 1} = 24$ $4(4-1)(4-2)(4-3)$ $5! = 5\cdot\boxed{4\cdot 3\cdot 2\cdot 1}$ $5(5-1)(5-2)(5-3)(5-4)$ $= 5(4!) = 120$	The **factorial** function is a shorthand way to say "multiply this integer by all of the positive integers less than it is." The exclamation point (**!**) is read as "factorial". Notice how 5! includes 4! by its very definition? This fact might be helpful later on when you try to cancel and eliminate terms. Sometimes you can do less arithmetic than you might expect.
Binomial Coefficients: $\binom{n}{m} = \frac{n!}{m!\,(n-m)!}$ ***reads:*** *binomial coefficient n m or n choose m* **Note:** $n \geq m$	Any particular binomial coefficient can be found by using the **binomial coefficient formula**. *n* is equal to the power you are raising the binomial to. *m* is one less than the number of the term you are creating.
Example $\binom{4}{2} = \frac{4!}{2!\,(4-2)!} = \frac{4!}{2!\,2!} = \frac{4\cdot 3\cdot 2\cdot 1}{2\cdot 1\cdot 2\cdot 1} = 6$	This example asks you to find the third term of a fourth-power binomial expansion. Notice how easily the factors are cancelled? It required very little calculation.
Binomial Theorem $(x+y)^n = x^n + \binom{n}{1}x^{n-1}y + \binom{n}{2}x^{n-2}y^2 +$ $\binom{n}{3}x^{n-3}y^3 \ldots \binom{n}{n-1}xy^{n-1} + \binom{n}{n}y^n$	This is the official form of the **binomial theorem**. Be very careful when trying to create specific terms! Notice that the number on the bottom in each set of parentheses is equal to the power of the *y*-term associated with that parenthesis. This is a great way to keep track of which coefficient goes where.

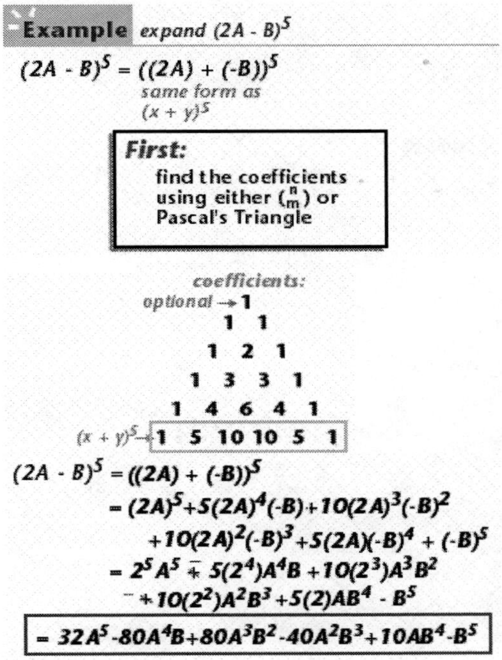

Here is an example of the binomial theorem in action.

First, find the coefficients.

In this case, the power is low enough that you can use Pascal's triangle. If the power was much higher, you would want to use the binomial coefficient formula.

First, put the binomial into the correct form. It has to look like the formula.

Expand the binomial out according to the binomial theorem using the coefficients.

Simplify the expansion and group the numbers together.

Notice the two sign errors on the terms with b and b^3. Just checking to make sure you are being careful too.

Here is your answer!

Sample problems:

1. Evaluate: $\binom{7}{4}$.

   Solution: 35

   Explanation: Use $\binom{n}{m} = \dfrac{n!}{m!(n-m)!}$ to find "7 choose 4", where $n = 7$ and $m = 4$:

   $$\binom{7}{4} = \frac{7!}{4!3!} = \frac{7\cdot6\cdot5\cdot4\cdot3\cdot2\cdot1}{4\cdot3\cdot2\cdot1(3\cdot2\cdot1)} = \frac{7\cdot6\cdot5}{3\cdot2\cdot1} = \frac{35}{1} = 35.$$

2. Expand the binomial using the binomial theorem: $(3x+5)^3$.

   Solution: $27x^3 + 135x^2 + 225x + 125$

   Explanation: Find each coefficient: $c_1 = 1$, $c_2 = \binom{3}{1} = \dfrac{3!}{1!2!} = 3$, $c_3 = \dfrac{3}{2} = \dfrac{3!}{2!1!} = 3$, $c_4 = 1$. Note that these coefficients are the same as the 3rd row of Pascal's triangle. Insert the coefficients into the skeleton: $(1)\quad +(3)\quad +(3)\quad +(1)$. Insert decreasing powers of $3x$ and decreasing poewrs of 5: $(1)(3x)^3\,(3)(3x)^2(5) + (3)(3x)(5)^2 + (1)(5)^3$. Simplify: $(3x+5)^3 = 27x^3 + 135x^2 + 225x + 125$.

3. Expand the binomial using the binomial theorem: $(3x^2 + y^3)^4$.

   Solution: $81x^8 + 108x^6y^3 + 54x^4y^6 + 12x^2y^9 + y^{12}$

   Explanation: Find each coefficient: $c_1 = 1$, $c_2 = \binom{4}{1} = \dfrac{4!}{1!3!} = 4$, $c_3 = \binom{4}{2} = \dfrac{4}{2!2!} = 6$, $c_4 = \binom{4}{3} = \dfrac{4!}{3!1!} = 4$, $c_5 = 1$. Insert the coefficients, along with decreasing powers of $3x^2$ and increasing powers of y^3, into the skeleton, the simplify: $(3x^2+y^3)^4 = 1(3x^2)^4 + 4(3x^2)^3(y^3) + 6(3x^2)^2(y^3)^2 + 4(3x^2)(y^3)^3 + 1(y^3)^4$ $= 81x^8 + 108x^6y^3 + 54x^4y^6 + 12x^2y^9 + y^{12}$.

Practice problems: *(Answers on page: 768)*

1. Evaluate: $\binom{8}{5}$.

2. Expand the binomial using the binomial theorem: $(2x-5y)^5$

3. Expand the binomial using the binomial theorem: $\left(2x^3-3\sqrt{y}\right)^4$.

Review questions: *(Answers to odd questions on page: 768)*

1. Expand the binomial using the binomial theorem: $\left(2\sqrt{x}-3\sqrt{y}\right)^4$.
2. Expand the binomial using the binomial theorem: $\left(3\sqrt{x}+y^2\right)^5$.
3. Expand the binomial using the binomial theorem: $\left(2x^3-3y\right)^4$.
4. Calculate the binomial coefficient: (6^8).
5. Calculate the binomial coefficient: (5^9).

Understanding Sequence Problems

- A **sequence** is an ordered collection of numbers.
- An **inductive sequence** uses a pattern based upon previous terms.
- The **Fibonacci sequence**: $a_1=1$, $a_2=1$, $a_n=a_{n-1}+a_{n-2}$.

Sequence: an ordered collection of numbers *counting order* 1, 2, 3, 4, 5, 6 . . . *powers of two* 1, 2, 4, 8, 16, 32 . . . 1 x 2 = 2 x 2 = 4 *no pattern* 1, -3, 9, 103, 2 . . .	A **sequence** is just a collection of numbers listed in a specific order. The order is very important, however. You can't change it! Some sequences have a pattern to the way their terms change. Other sequences have no pattern. This is why it is important to keep them in order.
Formula for a Sequence $\{a_n\}$ = Sequence *a* term *n* $a_1, a_2, a_3, a_4 \ldots$ *means 4th term in sequence a*	Sequences are so important in mathematics that they have their own notation. In this example, the letter "*a*" names the sequence. The subscript tells you which term of the sequence you are looking at. So a_3 means the third term of the sequence.
Example *let* $a_1 = 1$ *general term* $a_n = 2n - 1$ $a_2 = (2\cdot2) - 1 = 3$ $a_3 = (2\cdot3) - 1 = 5$ $a_4 = (2\cdot4) - 1 = 7$ *Formula allows you to find any term in the sequence* $a_{20} = (2\cdot20) - 1 = 39$	Some sequences work a lot like functions. To find out the value of a specific term, you can just plug that number into the sequence. You can plug in whichever value you want!

Example let $a_1 = 1$
general term $a_n = 2(a_{n-1}) + 1$
(2 times the previous term plus 1)

term	a_1	a_2	a_3	a_4	a_5
value $a_n=2(a_{n-1})+1$	1	3	7	15	31

Other sequences require that you know the value of earlier terms to calculate a new term. If the formula for the sequence requires you to know previous terms, then the sequence is called an **inductive sequence** or a **recursive sequence**.

Fibonacci Sequence: adding the two previous terms gives you the next term
1, 1, 2, 3, 5, 8, 13 . . .

One famous example of an inductive sequence is the **Fibonacci sequence**. A given term of this sequence is equal to the sum of the two previous terms.

Fibonacci sequences actually appear in nature. For example, pineapples and pinecones grow rings in accordance with this pattern.

Sample problems:

1. Find the first 3 terms and the 20 th term of the sequence that has the given n^{th} term: $a_n = 5n-7$.
Solution: $a_1 = -2,\ a_2 = 3,\ a_3 = 8,\ a_{20} = 93$
Eplanation: Given the formula $a_n = 5n-7;\ a_1 = 5(1)-7 = -2;\ a_2 = 5(2)-7 = 3;\ a_3 = 5(3)-7 = 8;$ $a_{20} = 5(20)-7 = 93.$

2. Find the 3rd and 4th terms of the recursive sequence given $a_1 = 3,\ a_2 = 7,$ and $a_n = 2a_{(n-1)}a_{(n-2)}$.
Solution: $a_3 = 42$ and $a_4 = 588$
Explanation: Find a_3 : $a_3 = 2a_{(3-1)}a_{(3-2)} = 2a_2a_1 = 2(3)(7) = 42.$ Find a_4 : $a_4 = 2a_{(4-1)}a_{(4-2)}$ $= 2a_3a_2 = 2(42)(7) = 588.$

3. Write an expression for the nth term of the sequence: $a_1 = \frac{1}{2},\ a_2 = \frac{-1}{4},\ a_3 = \frac{1}{8},\ a_4 = \frac{-1}{16}...$
Solution: $a_n = \frac{(-1)^{n+1}}{2^n}$ or $a_n = \frac{(-1)^{n-1}}{2^n}$
Explanation: Consider the sequence in 2 parts, numerator and denominator. The pattern in the numerator is just 1's with alternating signs. Notice that $(-1)^2 = 1$ and $(-1)^3 = -1$, the sign of one continues to alternate for increasing values of the exponent. The pattern in the denominator, $\{2, 4, 8, 16\}$, is increasing powers of 2: $2 = 2^1,\ 4 = 2^2,\ 8 = 2^3$, and $16 = 2^4$. Try $a_n = \frac{(-1)^n}{2^n}$:
$a_1 = \frac{(-1)^1}{2^1} = -\frac{1}{2}$, which has the wrong sign. Try $a_n = \frac{(-1)^{n+1}}{2^n}$: $a_1 = \frac{(-1)^{1+1}}{2^1} = \frac{(-1)^2}{2} = \frac{1}{2}$,
$a_2 = \frac{(-1)^{2+1}}{2^2} = \frac{(-1)^3}{4} = \frac{-1}{4}$, $a_3 = \frac{(-1)^{3+1}}{2^3} = \frac{(-1)^4}{8} = \frac{1}{8}$. So, the nth term of the sequence is given by $a_n = \frac{(-1)^{n+1}}{2^n}$. Notice that $a_n = \frac{(-1)^{n-1}}{2^n}$ works as well.

Practice problems: *(Answers on page: 769)*

1. Find the first 3 terms and the 20th term of the sequence that has the given n^{th} term: $a_n = (-1)^n(n-3)^2$
2. Find the 4th and 5th terms of the recursive sequence given $a_1 = 2, a_2 = 5, a_n = 3a_{n-1} - 2a_{n-2}$.
3. Write an expression for the nth term of the sequence: $a_1 = 3\sqrt{7},\ a_2 = 6\sqrt{7},\ a_3 = 9\sqrt{7}...$

Review questions: *(Answers to odd questions on page: 769)*

1. Write an expression for the nth term of the sequence: $1, 4, 7, 10, \ldots$.
2. Write an expression for the nth term of the sequence: $3, 4, 5, 6, \ldots$.
3. Find the first 3 terms and the 20th term of the sequence that has the given n^{th} term: $a_n = n+5$.
4. Find the first 3 terms and the 20th term of the sequence that has the given n^{th} term: $a_n = n(n-1)^n$.
5. Write an expression for the nth term of the sequence: $-4, 9, -16, 25, \ldots$

Solving Problems Involving Arithmetic Sequences

- An **arithmetical sequence** is a sequence in which the difference between any two consecutive terms is a constant.
- Arithmetical sequences follow the formula: $a_n = a_1 + (n-1)d$.

Arithmetical Sequence a fixed number is added to each term $3, 8, 13, 18, 23, \ldots$ (differences: 5, 5, 5, 5) *the difference between any two consecutive terms is 5*	The pattern of some sequences is simply that each term is a constant number more than the last. If the difference between any two consecutive terms is the same, then the sequence is called an **arithmetical sequence**.
*Write a formula for an arithmetic sequence in which each term is increased by **d*** $a_1 \rightarrow a_1$; $a_1 + d \rightarrow a_2$; $a_1 + 2d \rightarrow a_3$; $a_1 + 3d \rightarrow a_4$ *To find the **n** term:* $a_n = a_1 + (n-1)d$	Each term in an arithmetical sequence is equal to the original term plus a factor times the constant, *d*. You can generalize arithmetical sequences to this formula. If you know the first term and the amount the sequence changes by, you can find the value of any term you want!
Example find a_6 *given:* $a_1 = 3$, $d = 2$ $a_6 = 3 + (6-1)2$ $= 3 + 10$ $\boxed{a_6 = 13}$	In this example, you are given the value of the first term as well as the value of *d*. Since you want to know the sixth term of the sequence, simply plug the numbers you know into the formula and simplify. So the answer is 13.
Example *set up an equation and solve* *given:* $a_{15} = 6$, $a_{17} = 2$ $a_n = a_1 + (n-1)d$ *plug in what you already know* $a_{15} = 6 = a_1 + (14)d$ $-\ a_{17} = 2 = a_1 + (16)d$ *solve for one unknown* $4 = -2d$ $\boxed{d = -2}$ $\rightarrow 6 = a_1 - 28$ *plug -2 in for d* $\boxed{a_1 = 34}$	You can solve arithmetical sequences even if the terms you are given are not consecutive. Using the formula, simply plug in what you know. Subtracting the two equations will cancel the a_1 term, leaving you with *d*. Next, just plug the value of *d* into one of the above equations. Now you have all the pieces you need for the general formula!

Sample problems:

1. Find the 16th term of the arithmetic sequence where $a_1 = 4$ and $d = 3$.
   Solution: 49
   Explanation: Substitute $a_1 = 4$ and $d = 3$ into the general form of an arithmetic series: $a_n = a_1 + d(n-1)$: $a_n = 4 + 3(n-1)$. To find the 16th term, substitute $n = 16$ into $a_n = 4 + 3(n-1)$ and simplify: $a_{16} = 4 + 3(16-1) = 4 + 3(15) = 49$.

2. Given an arithmetic sequence where $a_7 = 31$ and $a_{20} = 96$, find the common difference, d.
   Solution: 5
   Explanation: To find d, write a system of equations, one equation using $a_7 = 31$ and the second equation using $a_{20} = 96$, then solve the system for d with the elimination method. Write the 1st equation by substituting $a_n = 31$ and $n = 7$ into the general form of an arithmetic series, then simplify: $31 = a_1 + d(7-1)$; $31 = a_1 + 6d$. Similarly, the 2nd equation is $96 = a_1 + 19d$. Now solve the system using the elimination method:

$$\begin{array}{lll} 31 = a_1 + 6d \Rightarrow & \text{subtract:} & 31 = \not{a}_1 + 6d \\ 96 = a_1 + 19d \Rightarrow & & \underline{-96 = -\not{a}_1 - 19d} \\ & & -65 = -13d;\ d = 5. \end{array}$$

3. Given an arithmetic sequence where $a_{11} = 23$ and $a_{40} = 81$, find the 1650th term.
   Solution: 3301
   Explanation: Use $a_{11} = 23$ and $a_{40} = 81$ to write a system (as was done in #2), then solve for a_1 and d:

$$\begin{array}{ll} 23 = a_1 + 10d \Rightarrow & 23 = \not{a}_1 + 10d \\ 81 = a_1 + 39d \Rightarrow & \underline{-81 = \not{a}_1 - 39d} \\ & -58 = -29d;\ d = 2. \end{array}$$

   Now substitute $d = 5$ into either equation and solve for a_1: $23 = a_1 + 10(2)$; $23 = a_1 + 20$; $a_1 = 3$. Write the arithmetic sequence where $a_1 = 3$ and $d = 2$: $a_n = 3 + 2(n-1)$. Substitute $n = 1650$ into this equation and simplify to find the 1650th term: $a_{1650} = 3 + 2(1650-1) = 3301$.

Practice problems: *(Answers on page: 769)*

1. Find the 25th term of the arithmetic sequence where $a_1 = 1$ and $d = 15$.
2. Find the common difference of the arithmetic sequence where $a_{10} = 83$ and $a_{15} = 118$.
3. Given an arithmetic sequence where $a_{21} = 93$ and $a_{30} = 133$, find the 107th term.

Review questions: *(Answers to odd questions on page: 769)*

1. Find the general term of the arithmetic sequence where $a_1 = 7$ and $d = 10$.
2. Find the general term of the arithmetic sequence where $a_1 = 95$ and $d = 3$.
3. Find the general term of the arithmetic sequence where $a_4 = 95$ and $a_7 = 110$.
4. Find the general term of the arithmetic sequence where $a_{15} = 60$ and $a_{22} = 88$.
5. Find the twentieth term in an arithmetic sequence if $a_{36} = 78$ and $a_{42} = 90$.

Solving Problems Involving Geometric Sequences

- A **geometric sequence** is a sequence in which any given term in the sequence is equal to the previous term multiplied by a constant. Geometric sequences follow the formula: $a_n = a_1 r^{n-1}$.

$3, 12, 48, 192 \ldots$ ×4 ×4 ×4 each term is multiplied by 4 $3 \quad 3(4) \quad 3(4)^2 \quad 3(4)^3 \quad 3(4)^4 \ldots$ $a_1 \quad a_2 \quad a_3 \quad a_4 \quad a_5$ What is the pattern? $r = \frac{a_{n+1}}{a_n}$ when any term is divided by its previous term, the ratio should be constant $\boxed{a_n = a_1 r^{n-1}}$	The pattern of some sequences is simply that each term is some constant number times the previous term. These sequences are called **geometric sequences**. In such cases, there is a ratio r that each term divided by its previous term will equal. If you know the ratio and the first term, this formula will enable you to find any value in the sequence you want!
Example find a_4 *given:* $a_1 = 4 \quad a_2 = 20$ *find the value for r* $a_2 = 20 = 4r^{2-1}$ $20 = 4r$ $5 = r$ *formula for this sequence* $a_n = 4(5^{n-1})$ *solve for a_4* $a_4 = 4(5^{4-1})$ $= 4(5^3)$ $= 4(125)$ $\boxed{a_4 = 500}$	In this example, you are given the first two terms of a geometric sequence. Using the general formula, solve for r. Now plug r back into the general formula. This will allow you to solve for any term in the sequence. You were asked to find the fourth term. So plug 4 into the general form. You're done!
Example *Write formula for the sequence* *given:* $a_3 = 5 \quad a_8 = \frac{1}{625}$ $a_3 = 5 = a_1 r^2 \Rightarrow a_1 = \frac{5}{r^2}$ *solve for a_1* $a_8 = \frac{1}{625} = a_1 r^7$ *substitute in a_1 value* $\frac{1}{625} = \frac{5 \cdot r^7}{r^2}$ *cancel out the powers* $\frac{1}{625} = 5r^5$ *divide by 5* $\frac{1}{5} \cdot \frac{1}{625} = r^5$ $\frac{1}{3125} = r^5$ *take 5th root* $\boxed{\frac{1}{5} = r}$ $\Rightarrow a_1 = \frac{5}{r^2} = \frac{5}{(\frac{1}{5})^2} = \frac{5}{\frac{1}{25}} = 5 \cdot \frac{25}{1}$ $\boxed{a_1 = 125}$ ***formula for this sequence:*** $a_n = 125(\frac{1}{5})^{n-1}$	What if you are given non-consecutive terms? You can still find r and solve for a_1. Plug in what you know for both terms. Then solve one of the terms for a_1 and substitute that value into the other equation. Now solve for r. Once you have r, plug that value into one of the equations to find a value for a_1. Plug a_1 and r into the general formula and you are done!

Sample problems:

1. Find the 9th term of the geometric sequences: $2, 1, \frac{1}{2}, \frac{1}{4}, \ldots$
   Solution: $\frac{1}{128}$
   Explanation: Since $a_1 = 2$ and $a_2 = 1$, the common ratio is $\frac{1}{2}$. Substituting into the formula, $a_n = 2\left(\frac{1}{2}\right)^{n-1}$ using $n = 9$, we obtain $a_9 = 2\left(\frac{1}{2}\right)^{9-1} = \frac{1}{128}$.

2. Find the formula for the nth term of the geometric sequence in which the 5th term is $-\frac{32}{81}$ and the 9th term is $-\frac{512}{6,561}$.

Solution: $a_n = -2\left(\frac{2}{3}\right)^{n-1}$

Explanation: Given the 5th term is $-\frac{32}{81}$, $a_n = a_1 r^{n-1}$ becomes $-\frac{32}{81} = a_1 r^4$. Given the 9th term, $n = 9$ substitutes into the formula $a_n = a_1 r^{n-1}$ to obtain $-\frac{521}{6,561} = a_1 r^8$. Solving the first equation for a_1; $a_1 = -\frac{32}{81r^4}$. Substituting this value of a_1 into the other equation, $\left(-\frac{512}{6,561}\right)\left(-\frac{81}{32}\right) = r^4$. Solving for r; $r = \frac{2}{3}$. Substituting back into the first equation; $-\frac{32}{81} = a_1\left(\frac{2}{3}\right)^4$. Solving for a_1; $a_1 = -2$. Substituting a_1 and r into the general formula; $a_n = -2\left(\frac{2}{3}\right)^{n-1}$.

3. Find the 20th term of the geometric sequence in which the 3rd term is $\frac{3}{2}$ and the 6th term is $\frac{3}{16}$.

Solution: $6\left(\frac{1}{2}\right)^{19}$

Explanation: Given the 3rd term is $\frac{3}{2}$, $\frac{3}{2} = a_1 r^2$. Given the 6th term is $\frac{3}{16}$, $\frac{3}{16} = a_1 r^5$. Solving the first equation for a_1; $a_1 = \frac{3}{2r^2}$. Substituting this value for a_1 into the other equation; $\frac{3}{16} = \frac{3}{\left(2r^2\right)} r^5$. Solving for r; $r = \frac{1}{2}$. Substituting back into the first equation; $a_1 = \frac{3}{2\left(\frac{1}{2}\right)^2} = 6$. Substituting a_1 and r into the general formula; $a_n = 6\left(\frac{1}{2}\right)n-1$. Therefore a_{20} is $6\left(\frac{1}{2}\right)19$.

Practice problems: *(Answers on page: 769)*

1. Find the 15th term of the geometric sequence in which the 4th term is 250 and the 7th term is 31,250.
2. Find the 100th term of the geometric sequence in which the 4th term is 81 and the 7th term is 2,187.
3. Find the formula for the nth term of the geometric sequence in which the 3rd term is -36 and the 7th term is $-2,916$.

Review questions: *(Answers to odd questions on page: 769)*

1. Find the common ratio in the geometric sequence in which the first term is 3 and the sixth term is 729.
2. Find the 12th term in the following geometric sequence: $2, 1, \frac{1}{2}, \frac{1}{4}, \ldots$
3. Find the 18th term of the geometric sequence in which the first term is 5 and the fifth term is 405.
4. Find the formula for the nth term of the geometric sequence $3, 2, \frac{4}{3}, \frac{8}{9}, \ldots$
5. Find the formula for the nth term of the geometric sequence $4, -2, 1, -\frac{1}{2}, \ldots$

Proving Formulas Using Mathematical Induction

- **Mathematical induction** is a way of proving a list of statements is true by showing that the first statement is true and then showing that if one of the statements is true, then the statement that follows it is also true.

Math is all about proving things true	Mathematics is all about rules. How do you know that the rules work? Because a mathematician proved them. So math is actually all about proof.

Suppose you have a list of statements:

Given 1: The first statement is true.

Given 2: If any statement is true, then it forces the statement that follows to be true.

	True	False	
Statement 1	✓		← Given 1
Statement 2	✓		Because of given 2
Statement 3	✓		Because of given 2
Statement 4	✓		Because of given 2

Therefore: All of the statements are true.

A list of statements is entirely true if:
1. You can demonstrate that the first statement is true.
2. If you assume that any particular statement is true, you can demonstrate that the next statement is true.

Why?

Think of this process as an ongoing loop--each time you show one fact true, it proves the next one. That proves the next one, and so on. This concept is called **mathematical induction.**

Example

Given 1:
The first domino falls.

Given 2:
If any domino falls, then it forces the domino that follows to fall.

Therefore:
All of the dominoes fall.

Mathematical induction is a lot like setting up a stack of dominoes. You basically show that the first domino can fall.

Then you show that if a domino falls, it knocks over the domino after it.

By doing so, you knock all the dominoes down. You have found mathematical proof!

Examples of Induction

- When proving something by **mathematical induction**, first show the statement is true for $n = 1$. Then assume that the statement is true for $n = k$ and show that it is true for $n = k + 1$. Doing this proves the statement true for every n.

Prove that: $1 + 2 + \ldots + n = \frac{n(n+1)}{2}$

Proof: Base Case $n = 1$

$$1 = \frac{1(2)}{2} = 1 \checkmark$$

Assume that the formula holds when $n = k$

Now show that the formula holds when $n = k + 1$

Assume:

$$1 + 2 + \ldots + k = \frac{k(k+1)}{2}$$

Prove:

$$1 + 2 + \ldots + k + (k+1) =$$

$$\frac{k(k+1)}{2} + \frac{2(k+1)}{2} = \frac{k(k+1) + 2(k+1)}{2}$$

$$= \frac{(k+1)(k+2)}{2}$$

We just proved that the formula holds true for $k + 1$.

When asked to prove something by **mathematical induction**, there are a few steps you have to follow.

First, you must start by showing that the base case (when $n = 1$) is true. This basically gives induction a place to start.

Now that the base case is true, you can assume that the statement is true for some value of k.

What you want to do next is show that since the statement is true for k, then it is true for $k + 1$. Notice how the expression for k can be substituted into the $k + 1$ expression?

Now it is just a matter of simplifying the expression and trying to get it into the same form as the original statement.

The dominoes fall.
The statement is true for all n!

Example

Prove that: $2+4+8+\ldots+2^n = 2(2^n-1)$

Proof: Base Case $n=1$ $2=2(1)$ ✓

Assume:

$2+4+8+\ldots+2^k = 2(2^k-1)$

Prove:

$2+4+8+\ldots+2^k + 2^{k+1} =$

Prove:

$2+4+8+\ldots+2^k+2^{k+1} = 2(2^k-1)+2^{k+1}$

$2^{k+1}-2+2^{k+1} = 2(2^{k+1})-2$

$= 2(2^{k+1}-1)$

We've proven that the formula holds true for 2^{k+1}.

So, by induction, the formula holds true for all powers of 2.

Here is another example.

Start by showing that the statement is true for the base case.

Now you can assume that the statement is true for $n = k$.

Write out the statement for $n = k+1$.

Substitute the expression for $n = k$ and simplify.

Factoring out a 2 leaves the expression in the form we need.

Therefore, the statement is true for all n!

Sample problems:

1. Use the principle of mathematical induction to prove the following statement for all natural numbers n: $5+9+13+\ldots+4n+1 = n(2n+3)$.
   Solution: The base case is $n=1$ so $5 = 1(2(1)+3)$. Assume that the statement is true for $n = k$. Show that the statement is true for $n = k+1$. $(5+9+13+\ldots+4k+1)+4(k+1) = (k+1)(2(k+1)+3)$. Substituting $k(2k+3)$ for $5+9+13+\ldots+4k+1$, we obtain $k(2k+3)+4(k+1)+1 = (k+1)(2(k+1)+3)$; $2k^2+3k+4k+5 = (k+1)(2k+5)$. By the principle of mathematical induction, $5+9+13+\ldots+4n+1 = n(2n+3)$ for all natural numbers n

2. Use the principle of mathematical induction to prove the following statement for all natural numbers n: $3+9+27+\ldots+3^n = \frac{3}{2}(3^n-1)$.
   Solution: The base case is $n=1$ so $3 = \frac{3}{2}(3-1)$. Assume that the statement is true for $n = k$. Show that the statement is true for $n = k+1$. $(3+9+27+\ldots+3^k)+3^{k+1} = \frac{3}{2}(3^{k+1}-1)$. Substituting $\frac{3}{2}(3^k-1)$ for $3+9+27+\ldots+3^k$, we obtain $\frac{3}{2}(3^k-1)+3^{k+1} = \frac{3}{2}(3^{k+1}-1)$; $3(3^k-1)+2(3^{k+1}) = 3(3^{k+1}-1)$; $3^{k+1}-3+2(3^{k+1}-1)$. By the principal of mathematical induction, $3+9+27+\ldots+3^n = \frac{3}{2}(3^n-1)$ for all natural numbers n.

3. Use the principle of mathematical induction to prove the following statements for all natural numbers n: $1+3+57+\ldots+2n-1 = n^2$.
   Solution: The base case is $n=1$ so $1 = 1^2$. Assume that the statement is true for $n = k$. Show that the statement is true for $n = k+1$. $(1+3+5+\ldots+2k = 1+2(k+1))-1 = (k+1)^2$. Substituting k^2 for $1+3+5+\ldots+2k-1$, we obtain $k^2+2k+1 = (k+1)^2$. By the principle of mathematical induction, $1+3+5+\ldots+2n-1 = n^2$ for all natural numbers n.

Practice problems: *(Answers on page: ?)*

1. Use the principle of mathematical induction to prove the following statements for all natural numbers n: $(xy)^n = x^n y^n$.
2. Use the principle of mathematical induction to prove the following statements for all natural numbers n: $n^2+1 < (n+1)^2$.
3. Use the principle of mathematical induction to prove the following statements for all natural numbers n: $1+5+25+\ldots+5^{n-1} = \frac{1}{4}(5n-1)$.

Review questions: *(Answers to odd questions on page: 769)*

1. Use the principle of mathematical induction to prove the following statements for all natural numbers n: $1+3+5+...+2n-1=n^2$.
2. Use the principle of mathematical induction to prove the following statement for all natural numbers n: $3+7+11+...+4n-1=n(2n+1)$.
3. Use the principle of mathematical induction to prove the following statement for all natural numbers n: $2+4+6+...+2n=n(n+1)$.
4. Use the principle of mathematical induction to prove the following statement for all natural numbers n: $5+10+20+...+5(2^{n-1})=5(2^n-1)$.
5. Use the principle of mathematical induction to prove the following statement for all natural numbers n: $2+8+32+...+2^{2n-1}=\frac{2}{3}(4^n-1)$.

Solving Problems Involving Permutations

- A **combination** is a way of selecting distinct objects from a collection when order is not important. Combinations can cover several permutations.
- The combination formula: $c(n,r)=\dfrac{n!}{r!(n-r)!}$.

 There are 3 ways of picking 2 of the blocks when order doesn't matter. B Y G B G Y Y B G Y G B G Y B G B Y	**REVIEW**: To find all the possible permutations of a collection of distinct objects, you just have to find n! But what if the order doesn't matter? For example, what if picking blue then yellow was just as good as picking yellow then blue? This isn't unrealistic; order is unimportant in lotteries and card games. Notice how the possible permutations duplicate answers when the order isn't important.
$c\,(n, r)=$ "*c* of *n* choose *r*" $c\,(n, r)=\dfrac{n!}{r!(n-r)!}$ *The binomial coefficient formula*	There is a great formula for finding the number of possible combinations. This notation is read "*c* of *n* choose *r*". In a collection of n items, r is the number of items in the combination. The c tells you that you are looking for combinations. The equation matches the binomial coefficient formula almost exactly!
Example $c\,(52, 5)=\dfrac{52!}{5!(47)!}$ $=\dfrac{52\cdot51\cdot50\cdot49\cdot48\cdot\cancel{47!}}{5\cdot4\cdot3\cdot2\cdot1\cancel{(47)!}}$ $=\boxed{2,598,960}$ 	Here is an example of combinations at work. There are 52 distinct cards in a deck. Therefore, $n=52$. You are dealt 5 cards. So your combination has $r=5$. Plug these values into the combination formula. Notice how a large chunk of the factorial cancels. You are left with relatively few pieces to multiply out. So there are 2,598,960 possible combinations.

Sample problems:

1. Twenty-five people at a party are eligible for four different door prizes. In how many ways can the door prizes be given?
   Solution: 303,600
   Explanation: Your are selecting 4 people from 25 people and then ordering them to assign the different door prizes, so use $25n\,\mathrm{Pr}\,4 = 303{,}600$ using a calculator, or $\frac{25!}{(25-4)!} = 303{,}600$.

2. Four different acting roles need to be filled for a play. If ten people audition for the play, in how many different ways can the roles be assigned?
   Solution: 5,040
   Explanation: Your are selecting 4 people from the 10 people that auditioned and then ordering them to assign the roles, so use $10n\,\mathrm{Pr}\,4 = 5{,}040$ using a calculator, or $\frac{10!}{(10-4)!} = 5{,}040$.

3. A multiple choice exam has twelve different questions. In how many ways can the questions be ordered to form different versions of the exam?
   Solution: 479,001,600
   Explanation: You are ordering all 12 questions, so use $12n\,\mathrm{Pr}\,12 = 479{,}001{,}600$ using a calculator, or $\frac{12!}{(12-12)!} = 479{,}001{,}600$.

Practice problems: *(Answers on page: 769)*

1. Evaluate the expression: $P(8,6)$
2. Six people volunteer to help on a project. If there are six different jobs, in how many ways can the six jobs be assigned to the six people?
3. How many permutations are there of the set $\{1,2,3\}$?

Review questions: *(Answers to odd questions on page: 769)*

1. Evaluate the expression: $P(12,7)$
2. In how many ways can ten books be arranged on a book shelf?
3. Eight dogs run in a race at the track. In how many ways can the first, second, and third place finishers be chosen?
4. A club has 15 members. In how many ways can a president, vice president, secretary, and treasurer be chosen?
5. How many possible arrangements are there of the letters $\{a,b,c,d,e\}$?

Solving Problems Involving Combinations

- **Probability** is a mathematical measurement that tells you how likely an event is.
- A **permutation** is a way of arranging objects in a particular order. n distinct objects have $n!$ complete permutations.
- The permutation formula: $P(n,r) = \dfrac{n!}{(n-r)!}$.

Probability- gives the means of putting a measurement of likelihood to certain events that you just don't know about.	You can't be certain about the future. But mathematicians do study the likelihood of certain events using **probability**.

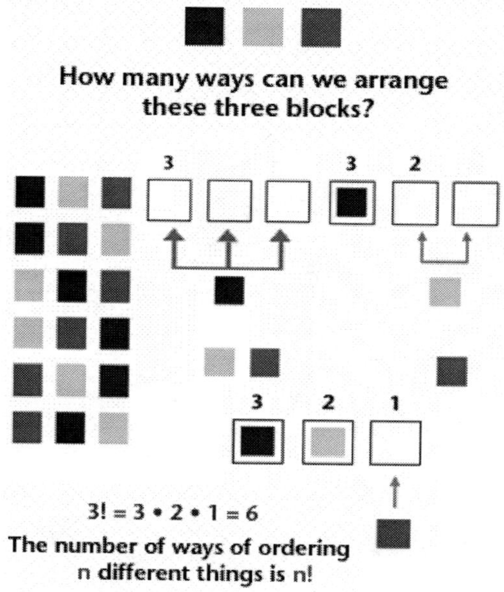

One of the main applications of probability is to determine the number of different ways in which distinct objects can be arranged.

Notice in this example that the blue object could be in any of the 3 slots. Once you pick a slot, that leaves only 2 choices for the yellow object. Finally, the green object gets no choice. This process creates 6 distinct arrangements of the blocks.

Hey! The number of the objects factorial is equal to the number of possible complete arrangements!

Permutation- arrangement of distinct objects in a definite order.

Each possible arrangement of the objects is called a **permutation**.

Consider a fish race:

There are 4!, or 24, ways of ordering these 4 fish.

What if you wanted to know all of the possible first and second place combinations?

$$P(n,r) = \frac{n!}{(n-r)!}$$

$$P(4,2) = \frac{4!}{(4-2)!} = \frac{4!}{2!} = \frac{4 \cdot 3 \cdot \cancel{2 \cdot 1}}{\cancel{2 \cdot 1}} = 12$$

In many cases, you aren't going to be interested in the complete arrangement. You might just want to know how two or three of the slots could be filled. For example, how many different combinations are there for the first and second place finishers of this fish race?

If n is the total number of objects and r is the number of slots you are interested in, you can use this permutation formula to find out how many possibilities there are. Just plug n and r into the formula and simplify.

So there are 12 different ways that the fish can finish first or second place.

Sample problems:

1. Evaluate the expression: $C(9,5)$.
   Solution: 126

   Explanation: Evaluate $C(9,5)$: $C(9,5) = \frac{9!}{5!(9-5)!} = \frac{9!}{5!4!} = \frac{9 \cdot 8 \cdot 7 \cdot 6 \cdot 5 \cdot 4 \cdot 3 \cdot 2 \cdot 1!}{(5 \cdot 4 \cdot 3 \cdot 2 \cdot 1)(4 \cdot 3 \cdot 2 \cdot 1)} = \frac{9 \cdot \cancel{8} \cdot 7 \cdot \cancel{6}^2 \cdot \cancel{5 \cdot 4 \cdot 3 \cdot 2 \cdot 1}}{(\cancel{5 \cdot 4 \cdot 3 \cdot 2 \cdot 1})(\cancel{4 \cdot 3 \cdot 2 \cdot 1})}$;

   $9 \cdot 7 \cdot 2 = 126$.

2. A summer reading list contains 15 titles. In how many ways can 5 titles be chosen from the list?
   Solution: 3,003

   Explanation: Evaluate $C(15,5)$: $C(15,5) = \frac{15!}{5!(15-5)!} = \frac{15!}{5!10!} = \frac{15 \cdot 14 \cdot 13 \cdot 12 \cdot 11 \cdot 10 \cdot 9 \cdot 8 \cdot 7 \cdot 6 \cdot 5 \cdot 4 \cdot 3 \cdot 2 \cdot 1}{(5 \cdot 4 \cdot 3 \cdot 2 \cdot 1)(4 \cdot 3 \cdot 2 \cdot 1)}$;

   $\frac{\cancel{15}^3 \cdot \cancel{14}^7 \cdot 13 \cdot \cancel{12} \cdot 11 \cdot \cancel{10 \cdot 9 \cdot 8 \cdot 7 \cdot 6 \cdot 5 \cdot 4 \cdot 3 \cdot 2 \cdot 1}}{(\cancel{5 \cdot 4 \cdot 3 \cdot 2} \cdot 1)(\cancel{10 \cdot 9 \cdot 8 \cdot 7 \cdot 6 \cdot 5 \cdot 4 \cdot 3 \cdot 2 \cdot 1})} = 3 \cdot 7 \cdot 13 \cdot 11 = 3{,}003$.

3. Five cards are selected from an ordinary deck of 52 cards. How many different hands are possible?
   Solution: 2,598,960
   Explanation: Evaluate $C(52,5)$: $C(52,5) = \frac{52!}{5!(52-5)!} = \frac{52!}{5!47!} = \frac{52\cdot51\cdot50\cdot49\cdot48\cdot47!}{(5\cdot4\cdot3\cdot2\cdot1)(47!)}$

   $= \frac{52\cdot51\cdot\cancel{50}^{10}\cdot49\cdot\cancel{48}^{2}\cdot\cancel{47!}}{(\cancel{5\cdot4\cdot3\cdot2\cdot1})(\cancel{47!})}$; $52\cdot51\cdot10\cdot49\cdot2 = 2{,}598{,}960$.

Practice problems: *(Answers on page: 769)*

1. Evaluate the expression: $C(11,4)$
2. How many five member subcommittees are possibly chosen from the 100 U.S. senators?
3. You have 14 different shirts. In how many ways can you choose 8 shirts for a trip?

Review questions: *(Answers to odd questions on page: 769)*

1. Evaluate the expression: $C(10,3)$
2. 16 teams qualify for a tournament. How many possible ways can the final two teams result?
3. In how many ways can a costume designer choose four different fabrics from a group of seven fabrics?
4. In how many ways can you select 10 questions from an exam containing 13 questions?
5. In how many ways can three people be selected from a group of eight people?

Solving for Probability and Odds: Dice Rolls

- **Probability** is defined as the ratio of the number of ways an event can be successful divided by the total number of possible outcomes.

Consider a coin toss **Q: What is the probability of having a quarter land heads up?** **A: 1 out of 2, or $\frac{1}{2}$.** **Whenever you have an event where all of the outcomes are equally likely, then probability is:** $\frac{\text{The number of ways of a successful outcome}}{\text{The total number of all outcomes}}$	When you toss a coin in the air, it will land either heads up or tails up. There are only 2 possible outcomes. There is only one way that the coin can land heads up. This makes the probability one out of two. **Probability** is simply a fraction with the number of possible ways of success in the numerator and the number of total possible outcomes in the denominator.
Example What is the probability that a coin will land heads up all 3 times? **All possible outcomes**: HHH, HHT, HTH, HTT, THH, THT, TTH, TTT $\frac{\text{Number of successes}}{\text{Total possible outcomes}} = \frac{1}{8}$ ... exactly 2 heads? $\frac{\text{Number of successes}}{\text{Total possible outcomes}} = \frac{3}{8}$ ... at least 1 tail? $\frac{\text{Number of successes}}{\text{Total possible outcomes}} = \frac{7}{8}$ 	When asked to calculate a probability, put the number of ways the event is a success in the numerator. Then put the total number of outcomes in the denominator. The resulting fraction will be less than 1. This is the probability of a successful event actually occurring.

Example What is the probability of rolling 2 dice and rolling a 7?

36 possible outcomes

	1	2	3	4	5	6
1	2	3	4	5	6	7
2	3	4	5	6	7	8
3	4	5	6	7	8	9
4	5	6	7	8	9	10
5	6	7	8	9	10	11
6	7	8	9	10	11	12

$\frac{6}{36} = \frac{1}{6}$ **6 successful outcomes**

Start probability questions by determining the number of possible outcomes.

Rolling two dice gives you 36 possible results. This number goes in the denominator.

Next, determine how many ways that the outcomes can be successful.

You will find that constructing a table will be very helpful when working with many probability problems.

Since there are 6 ways to roll a 7, put 6 in the numerator. The probability is 6/36, or 1/6.

Sample problems:

1. Find the probability of getting a sum of 5 when two fair dice are rolled.

   Solution: $\frac{1}{9}$

   Explanation: When rolling a pair of dice there are 36 possible outcomes and there are 4 ways to roll a sum of 5. Find the probability of rolling a sum of 5: $\frac{\text{successful outcomes}}{\text{possible outcomes}} = \frac{4}{36} = \frac{1}{9}$.

2. Find the probability of getting at least 3 heads when 4 fair coins are tossed.

   Solution: $\frac{5}{16}$

   Explanation: If a fair coin is tossed 4 times there are 16 possible outcomes $(2 \cdot 2 \cdot 2 \cdot 2 = 16)$. Three heads can occur in 4 different ways (HHHT, HHTH, HTHH, THHH) and 4 heads can occur in only one way. Thus, there are 5 successful outcomes.

   Find the probability: $\frac{\text{successful outcomes}}{\text{possible outcomes}} = \frac{5}{16}$.

3. Find the probability rolling a sum of at least 8 when 2 fair dice are rolled.

   Solution: $\frac{5}{12}$

   Explanation: There are 36 possible outcomes when two dice are rolled. If the sum on the dice is at least 8, then it could be 8,9,10,11 or 12. There are 5 ways to get an 8, 4 ways to get a 9, 3 ways to get a 10, 2 ways to get an 11, and 1 way to get a 12. Thus, there are $5+4+3+2+1=15$ successful outcomes. Find the probability: $\frac{\text{successful outcomes}}{\text{possible outcomes}} = \frac{15}{36} = \frac{5}{12}$.

Practice problems: *(Answers on page: 769)*

1. Find the probability of seeing exactly one head when 4 fair coins are tossed.
2. Find the probability of seeing less than 6 dots when 2 fair dice are rolled.
3. Find the probability of seeing at least 6 dots, but less than 10 dots when 2 fair dice are rolled.

Review questions: *(Answers to odd questions on page: 769)*

1. Find the probability of seeing exactly 2 tails when 3 fair coins are tossed.
2. Find the probability of seeing an even number of dots when a fair die is rolled.
3. Find the probability of not seeing a head when a fair coin is tossed.

4. Find the probability of seeing at least 2 dots when a fair dice is rolled.
5. Find the probability of seeing at most 5 dots, but an odd # dots when 2 fair dice are rolled.

Solving for Probability and Odds: Decks of Cards

- **REVIEW**: **Probability** is defined as the ratio of the number of ways an event can be successful divided by the total number of possible outcomes.

To calculate probability: $\frac{\text{Number of successful outcomes}}{\text{Total number of equally possible outcomes}}$	**REVIEW**: Probability is a fraction with the number of possible ways of success in the numerator and the number of total possible outcomes in the denominator.
Example What is the probability of pulling an Ace out of the deck? 4 successful outcomes 52 possible outcomes  $\frac{\text{Number of successes}}{\text{Total possible outcomes}} = \frac{4}{52} = \frac{1}{13}$	A deck of cards has 52 possible outcomes.How many aces are there? A regular deck of cards has 4 aces.So divide the number of aces by the number of cards. The probability is 1/13!
Example What is the probability of drawing a red card out of the deck? 26 successful outcomes 52 possible outcomes  $\frac{\text{Number of successes}}{\text{Total possible outcomes}} = \frac{26}{52} = \frac{1}{2}$	There are 26 red cards in a deck. 26/52 gives you a probability of 1/2.
Example What is the probability of picking the King of Clubs out of the deck? 1 successful outcome 52 possible outcomes  $\frac{\text{Number of successes}}{\text{Total possible outcomes}} = \frac{1}{52}$	There is only 1 King of Clubs in a deck. The probability is equal to 1/52.

Sample problems:

1. Find the probability of drawing a red king from a standard deck of 52 playing cards.

   Solution: $\frac{1}{26}$

   Explanation: There are two red kings in a standard deck.

   Find the probability of drawing a red king: $\frac{\text{successful outcomes}}{\text{possible outcomes}} = \frac{2}{52} = \frac{1}{26}$.

2. Find the probability of drawing a jack or a black ace from a standard deck of 52 playing cards.

   Solution: $\frac{3}{26}$

   Explanation: There are four jacks and two black aces in a standard deck.

   Find the probability: $\frac{\text{successful outcomes}}{\text{possible outcomes}} = \frac{6}{52} = \frac{3}{26}$.

3. Find the probability of drawing a black card which is greater than 3 and less than 9 from a standard deck of 52 playing cards.

   Solution: $\frac{5}{26}$

   Explanation: There are 10 black cards that are greater than 3 and less than 9. Find the probability: $\frac{\text{successful outcomes}}{\text{possible outcomes}} = \frac{10}{52} = \frac{5}{26}$.

Practice problems: *(Answers on page: 769)*

1. Find the probability of pulling out a black diamond from a standard deck of 52 playing cards.
2. Find the probability of pulling out a red card or a diamond from a standard deck of 52 playing cards.
3. Find the probability of pulling out a heart or a diamond from a standard deck of 52 playing cards.

Review questions: *(Answers to odd questions on page: 769)*

1. Find the probability of drawing an ace or a 10 from a standard deck of 52 playing cards.
2. Find the probability of drawing a jack or a club from a standard deck of 52 playing cards.
3. Find the probability of drawing a red card or a black card from a standard deck of 52 playing cards.
4. Find the probability of drawing an ace or a red card from a standard deck of 52 playing cards.
5. Find the probability of drawing a red king or red queen from a standard deck of 52 playing cards.

Answer Key:

Basic Algebra Review

Concepts of Inequality *p.23*

Practice: **1.** True **2.** True **3.** False

Review: **1.** True **3.** False **5.** False

Inequalities and Interval Notation *p.25*

Practice: **1.** True **2.** True **3.** False

Review: **1.** True **3.** True **5.** True

Properties of Absolute Value *p.26*

Practice: **1.** 52 **2.** –28 **3.** $\frac{1}{12}$

Review: **1.** 13 **3.** 9 **5.** 1

Evaluating Absolute Value Expressions *p.28*

Practice: **1.** $-4x+1$ **2.** π **3.** $3x-5$

Review: **1.** $1-x$ **3.** $11-2x$ **5.** $\frac{1}{3}$

An Introduction to Exponents *p.30*

Practice: **1.** 29 **2.** 189 **3.** 16

Review: **1.** 125 **3.** –49 **5.** False

Evaluating Exponential Expressions *p.31*

Practice: **1.** 4 **2.** –19 **3.** –105

Review: **1.** –48 **3.** 14,856,594 **5.** 4

Applying the Rules of Exponents *p.32*

Practice: **1.** True **2.** y^{10} **3.** $675x^{12}y^{11}z^{20}$

Review: **1.** True **3.** $9x^4y^2$ **5.** $-8a^6b^3c^9$

Evaluating Expressions with Negative Exponents *p.34*

Practice: **1.** $\frac{1}{48}$ **2.** $\frac{4x^5y}{3z}$ **3.** $\frac{b^3c^2}{a^8}$

Review: **1.** True **3.** True **5.** $\frac{a^{11}}{8}$

Converting between Decimal and Scientific Notation *p.36*

Practice: **1.** True **2.** 5.4×10^7 **3.** 6.5094×10^{-11}

Review: **1.** 381,000,000 **3.** True **5.** 5.74×10^{-6}

Converting Rational Exponents and Radicals *p.37*

Practice: **1.** 10 **2.** False **3.** $\frac{1}{8}$

Review: **1.** 3 **3.** $\frac{1}{7}$ **5.** $\frac{1}{5}$

Simplifying Radical Expressions *p.39*

Practice: **1.** 6 **2.** 8 **3.** $\frac{1}{2}$

Review: **1.** 7 **3.** $\frac{\sqrt{41}}{9}$ **5.** $\frac{125}{512}$

Simplifying Radical Expressions with Variables *p.40*

Practice: **1.** $6b^2\sqrt{a}$ **2.** $\frac{2u\sqrt{2v}}{t^3}$ **3.** $2x^3y^2z\sqrt[3]{y^2}$

Review: **1.** $\frac{1}{5}$ **3.** $\frac{10x\sqrt{x}}{y}$ **5.** $5x^2y^3$

Rationalizing Denominators *p.43*

Practice: **1.** $11\sqrt{2}+11$ **2.** $\frac{67-16\sqrt{3}}{61}$ **3.** $\frac{-21+3\sqrt{2-y}}{-y-47}$

Review: **1.** $3\sqrt{2}$ **3.** $\sqrt{6}+\sqrt{3}$ **5.** $3\sqrt{7}+3$

Determining Components and Degree *p.45*

Practice: **1.** True **2.** False **3.** False

Review: **1.** False **3.** False **5.** False

Adding, Subtracting, and Multiplying Polynomials *p.46*

Practice: **1.** $3x^3-11x^2-10x-5$ **2.** $3x^3+7x^2+17x+5$ **3.** $81-90p+25p^2$

Review: **1.** $13ab^2-8ab^2$ **3.** $18a^3b^2+33a^2b^3-15a^3b^3$ **5.** $4x^2-28x+49$

Multiplying Big Products *p.48*

Practice: **1.** $-x^4+5x^3+3x^2+18x$ **2.** $6x^4+7x^3+5x^2+21x-4$ **3.** $3a+11+a^{-1}+7a^{-2}+2a^{-3}$

Review: **1.** $w^2-10w+9$ **3.** $2x^4+2x^3+x+1$ **5.** $-3x^3+23x^2+44x-72$

Using Special Products *p.49*

Practice: **1.** $9w^4-6v^5w^2+v^{10}$ **2.** $y^4+6xy^2-2y^2+9x^2-6x+1$ **3.** $x^3-9x^2y+27xy^2-27y^3$

Review: **1.** $y^3+3y+3y^{-1}+y^{-3}$ **3.** $4c^2+44cd+121d^2$ **5.** $25x^2y^6-70x^3y^3+49x^4$

Factoring Using the Greatest Common Factor *p.51*

Practice: **1.** $12a^2b^4(5a+3b)$ **2.** $(y-13)(2x^3+x-1)$ **3.** $6a^4(1-b)(2a-1)$

Review: **1.** $3(2x-13)$ **3.** $5a^2b^2(3a-10b+17b^3)$ **5.** $(8p+1)(10p)$

Factoring by Grouping *p.52*

Practice: **1.** $(6v+5)(t^5+8v)$ **2.** $3x(2y-1)(z+5)$ **3.** $5a^2b[(2-b)(1-c)]$

Review: **1.** $(2w-3)(4v+15)$ **3.** $(3rs+5)(3r-11)$ **5.** $(7y+1)(3y^2-1)$

Factoring Trinomials *p.54*

Practice: **1.** $3(g+2)(g-8)$ **2.** $(d-2)(2d-1)$ **3.** $(3x+y)(5x+8y)$

Review: **1.** $(x-2)(x+1)$ **3.** $(x-5)(x-2)$ **5.** $(2y+1)(5y+2)$

Factoring Perfect Square Trinomials *p.56*

Practice: **1.** $(w+t)^2$ **2.** $(9s-6)^2$ **3.** $[(3a+b)^2-10]^2$

Review: **1.** $(x-4)^2$ **3.** $(3x+2)^2$ **5.** $\left[(m-2n)-2\right]^2$

Factoring the Difference of Two Squares *p.58*

Practice: **1.** $(a+2b)(a-2b)$ **2.** $(5r^2+3s^3)(5r^2-3s^3)$ **3.** $[(y-3)+11][(y-3)-11]$

Review: **1.** $(x+3)(x-3)$ **3.** $(3x+1)(3x-1)$ **5.** $\left[(x-7)+4\right]\left[(x-7)-4\right]$

Factoring the Sums and Differences of Cubes *p.59*

Practice:

1. $(3+z)(9-3z+z^2)$

2. $(5-4z)(25+20z+16z^2)$

3. $[(a-b)-4c^2][(a-b)^2+4c^2(a-b)+16c^4]$

Review: **1.** $(x+2)(x^2-2x+4)$ **3.** $(2x+yz)(4x^2-2xyz+y^2z^2)$ **5.** $\left[(a-b)-4\right]\left[(a-b)^2+4(a-b)+16\right]$

Factoring by Any Method *p.61*

Practice:

1. $(5x-3)(25x^2+15x+9)$

2. $(2+y)(4-2y+y^2)(3x+5)(2x-1)$

3. $2xz(3x^3+5y)(3x^3-5y)(w-1)(w^2+w+1)$

Review: **1.** $(x+2)(x-4)$ **3.** $(2p-5)(p+3)$ **5.** $(2k^2-3)(a+6b)$

Rational Expressions and Domain *p.63*

Practice: **1.** True **2.** True **3.** All real numbers except $-4, -1$, and 1

Review: **1.** True **3.** False **5.** True

Working with Fractions *p.65*

Practice: **1.** $\frac{3}{2}$ **2.** $\frac{33}{10}$ **3.** $\frac{7}{3}$

Review: **1.** $-\frac{1}{3}$ **3.** 40 **5.** $\frac{-74}{15}$

Writing Rational Expressions in Lowest Terms *p.67*

Practice: **1.** $\frac{t-4}{2t+3},\ t\neq -\frac{2}{3}, -\frac{3}{2}$ **2.** $\frac{z+3}{z-3},\ z\neq 3,-3$ **3.** $\frac{a^2+3a+9}{a+3},\ a\neq 3,\ -3$

Review: **1.** $\frac{6}{a+2}, a\neq -2,-4$ **3.** $\frac{5}{7}, x\neq 1$ **5.** $\frac{a^2+3a+9}{a+3}, a\neq 3,-3$

Multiplying and Dividing Rational Expressions *p.69*

Practice:

1. $\frac{t-4}{t+6},\ t\neq -4,\ t\neq 5,\ t\neq -3,\ t\neq -6$

2. $\frac{x+4}{2x-6},\ x\neq -3,\ x\neq 0,\ x\neq 2,\ x\neq 3,\ x\neq 4$

3. 1

Review: **1.** $\frac{x+2}{2}, x\neq 0$ **3.** $\frac{4w}{w-1}, w\neq -1, w\neq -3, w\neq 1$ **5.** $1, v\neq 3, v\neq -11, v\neq -\frac{1}{2}, v\neq 2$

Adding and Subtracting Rational Expressions *p.71*

Practice: **1.** $\frac{-48}{(k+8)(k-8)}$ **2.** $\frac{3x^2+2x-19}{(x+1)(x-2)}$ **3.** $\frac{x^2-x+15}{(x+4)(x-4)(x+5)}$

Review: **1.** $\frac{16}{3}$ **3.** $\frac{4t-2}{3t(t-2)}$ **5.** $\frac{y^2+38y-7}{4y(y+7)(y-1)}$

Rewriting Complex Fractions *p.73*

Practice: **1.** $\frac{3-2n}{3-n}$ **2.** $\frac{x}{x+5}$ **3.** $\frac{2x^2-3x-44}{5x+7}$

Review: **1.** $\frac{3}{4}$ **3.** $\frac{xy}{y-x}$ **5.** $\frac{4x+3}{7x+3}$

Introducing and Writing Complex Numbers *p.76*

Practice: **1.** $2i\sqrt{5}$ **2.** $9+3i\sqrt{2}$ **3.** $30i\sqrt{3}$

Review: **1.** $11i$ **3.** $7+i$ **5.** $2\sqrt{5}(5i+7)$

Rewriting Powers of i *p.77*

Practice: **1.** i **2.** $-i$ **3.** -1

Review: **1.** 1 **3.** $-i$ **5.** -1

Adding and Subtracting Complex Numbers *p.79*

Practice: **1.** $8i-3$ **2.** $-4i+3$ **3.** $14i+42$

Review: **1.** 3 **3.** $-3-7i$ **5.** i

Multiplying Complex Numbers *p.80*

Practice: **1.** $21+20i$ **2.** 6 **3.** $-3-7i$

Review: **1.** $2i$ **3.** $12i$ **5.** $7+6i$

Dividing Complex Numbers *p.81*

Practice: **1.** $\frac{12}{13}+\frac{5}{13}i$ **2.** $\frac{11}{10}+\frac{13}{10}i$ **3.** $\frac{67}{113}+\frac{12}{113}i$

Review: **1.** $\frac{1}{5}+\frac{1}{5}i$ **3.** $\frac{3}{5}-\frac{4}{5}i$ **5.** $\frac{27}{61}+\frac{8}{61}i$

Equations and Inequalities

An Introduction to Solving Equations *p.87*

Practice: **1.** -11 **2.** True **3.** -8

Review: **1.** -16 **3.** $\frac{4p+t}{2}$ **5.** $-8/7$

Solving a Linear Equation *p.88*

Practice: **1.** $\frac{1}{10}$ **2.** -4 **3.** 3

Review: **1.** 3 **3.** $-\frac{3}{5}$ **5.** $-\frac{1}{11}$

Solving a Linear Equation with Rationals *p.90*

Practice: **1.** 4 **2.** 4 **3.** -5

Review: **1.** $\frac{9}{5}$ **3.** $-\frac{19}{12}$ **5.** No Solution

Solving a Linear Equation That Has Restrictions *p.93*

Practice: **1.** –27 **2.** No Solution **3.** $-\frac{1}{13}$

Review: **1.** –3 **3.** No Solution **5.** No Solution

An Introduction to Solving Word Problems *p.95*

Solving for Perimeter *p.96*

Practice: **1.** 10 **2.** 5 inches **3.** 16 or 20

Review: **1.** 35 ft **3.** 12 inches **5.** 14 ft

Solving a Linear Geometry Problem *p.97*

Practice: **1.** 9 cm **2.** 12, 22, 10, and 20 cm **3.** 1008 in^2

Review: **1.** 38.5 cm^2 **3.** 12, 4, and 9 cm **5.** 6 in

Solving for Consecutive Numbers *p.99*

Practice: **1.** 23, 24, 25, 26 **2.** 10, 12, 14, 16 **3.** 18,20

Review: **1.** 43, 44 **3.** 2, 4 **5.** 106, 108

Solving to Find the Average *p.101*

Practice: **1.** 12 games **2.** 91 **3.** 30, 40, 80, 85

Review: **1.** 6 hours **3.** 92 **5.** 6 hours

Solving for Constant Velocity *p.102*

Practice: **1.** 2880 m **2.** 9 miles **3.** 36mph

Review: **1.** 48 mph **3.** $\frac{6}{5}$ hr. = 1 hr. 12 min. **5.** 2.5 mph

Solving a Problem about Work *p.104*

Practice: **1.** 24 minutes **2.** 4 hr 48 min **3.** 1 hr 9 min

Review: **1.** 1 hr 12 min **3.** 22 hr 30 min **5.** 3 hr 20 min

Solving a Mixture Problem *p.107*

Practice: **1.** 1 liter **2.** 50 **3.** $1\frac{1}{2}$ cups

Review: **1.** 7.7 g **3.** 1.5 liters **5.** 36 ml

Solving an Investment Problem *p.108*

Practice: **1.** \$750, \$2250 **2.** \$6000 at 14% and \$4500 at 11% **3.** 6.7%

Review: **1.** \$560 **3.** \$300 at 2%, \$500 at 5% **5.** 4% and 5%

Solving Business Problems *p.110*

Practice: **1.** \$10.95 **2.** 60 necklaces **3.** 100 chairs

Review: **1.** \$40.00 **3.** 39 bunches **5.** 2000 baskets

Solving Quadratics by Factoring *p.112*

Practice: **1.** 12 or -2 **2.** 3 **3.** $\frac{2}{5}$ or 6

Review: **1.** $-2, 4$ **3.** $-\frac{4}{3}, \frac{1}{2}$ **5.** $-1, 0, 4$

Solving Quadratics by Completing the Square *p.113*

Practice: **1.** -24 or -6 **2.** 1 or -7 **3.** 13 or -9

Review: **1.** -1 or 4 **3.** 2 or 4 **5.** $3-\sqrt{13}$ or $3+\sqrt{13}$

Completing the Square: Another Example *p.115*

Practice: **1.** -3 **2.** $\frac{5}{3}$ **3.** $\frac{1+\sqrt{17}}{2}$ or $\frac{1-\sqrt{17}}{2}$

Review: **1.** $3+\sqrt{19}$ or $3-\sqrt{19}$ **3.** 1 or $-\frac{1}{2}$ **5.** $\frac{3+\sqrt{2}}{2}$ or $\frac{3-\sqrt{2}}{2}$

Proving the Quadratic Formula *p.117*

Using the Quadratic Formula *p.118*

Practice: **1.** $\frac{-3\pm\sqrt{13}}{2}$ or $\frac{-3-\sqrt{13}}{2}$ **2.** $\frac{-1\pm i\sqrt{3}}{2}$ or $\frac{-1-i\sqrt{3}}{2}$ **3.** $\frac{-5+\sqrt{65}}{4}$ or $\frac{-5-\sqrt{65}}{4}$

Review: **1.** $-2+\sqrt{13}$ or $-2-\sqrt{13}$ **3.** $\frac{2+i\sqrt{2}}{3}$ or $\frac{2-i\sqrt{2}}{3}$ **5.** $\frac{1+2i\sqrt{5}}{3}$ or $\frac{1-2i\sqrt{5}}{3}$

Predicting the Type of Solutions Using the Discriminant *p.120*

Practice: **1.** 2 distinct real solutions **2.** 1 real solution **3.** 2 complex solutions

Review: **1.** 0 **3.** 2 distinct real solutions **5.** 2 complex solutions

Solving for a Squared Variable *p.121*

Practice:

1. $\frac{-2wx+y\sqrt{x}}{x}$ or $\frac{-2wx-y\sqrt{x}}{x}$

2. $\frac{-y+\sqrt{y^2-48}}{6}$ or $\frac{-y-\sqrt{y^2-48}}{6}$

3. $\frac{1-R+\sqrt{(R-1)^2+4g^2}}{2g}$ or $\frac{1-R-\sqrt{(R-1)^2+4g^2}}{2g}$

Review: **1.** $y=\sqrt{-22-x}$ or $y=-\sqrt{-22-x}$ **3.** 1 or -9 **5.** $r=\frac{-1-s\pm\sqrt{(1+5)^2-16p^2}}{2p}$

Finding Real Number Restrictions *p.123*

Practice: **1.** 2 **2.** none **3.** none

Review: **1.** 4 and 9 **3.** -4 and 1 **5.** none

Solving Fancy Quadratics *p.125*

Practice: **1.** $\sqrt[3]{4}$ or -1 **2.** $\frac{2}{3}$ or -3 **3.** $\frac{1}{25}$ or 4

Review: **1.** $-\frac{8}{3}$ or $-\frac{5}{3}$ **3.** $2,\ -2,\ \sqrt{\frac{1}{2}},\ -\sqrt{\frac{1}{2}}$ **5.** -6 or $-\frac{1}{3}$

Solving a Quadratic Geometry Problem *p.126*

Practice: **1.** 8 **2.** $10\text{ in}\times12\text{ in}$ **3.** $200\text{m}\times350\text{m}$

Review: **1.** $7\text{in}\times11\text{ in}$ **3.** $5\times11\text{ in}^2$ **5.** $20\text{ yards}\times10\text{ yards}$

Solving with the Pythagorean Theorem *p.129*

Practice: **1.** 10 **2.** 7 ft **3.** 120 mph

Review: **1.** $6\sqrt{2}$ **3.** 20 **5.** 36 ft

Solving a Motion Problem *p.132*

Practice: **1.** 50 mph **2.** 100 miles/hr **3.** 20 miles/hr

Review: **1.** 65 miles/hr **3.** $\frac{5}{4}$ hr = 1 hr 15 min **5.** 8 hrs

Solving a Projectile Problem *p.134*

Practice: **1.** 336 feet **2.** 4 seconds **3.** $1+\sqrt{3}$ seconds

Review: **1.** 8 seconds **3.** 5 seconds **5.** 1.30 seconds

Solving Other Problems *p.136*

Practice: **1.** 80,000 **2.** 12,450 **3.** \$52

Review: **1.** 3400 units **3.** 11.3 seconds **5.** $P \le \$268.8$ million

Determining Extraneous Roots *p.138*

Solving an Equation Containing a Radical *p.139*

Practice: **1.** 8 **2.** $\frac{11}{3}$ **3.** 5

Review: **1.** 4 **3.** $\frac{7}{2}$ **5.** 4

Solving an Equation with Two Radicals *p.141*

Practice: **1.** 12 **2.** 5 or 8 **3.** 10, 46

Review: **1.** 4 **3.** −1 **5.** 25

Solving an Equation with Rational Exponents *p.142*

Practice: **1.** $\frac{1}{3}$ or 4 **2.** -3 or $\frac{1}{2}$ **3.** $0, \frac{1}{16}, -\frac{1}{16}$

Review: **1.** 29 or −25 **3.** 2 **5.** $\frac{3}{2}$ or −1

An Introduction to Variation *p.145*

Direct Proportion *p.145*

Practice: **1.** \$11,760 **2.** 51 feet **3.** 36

Review: **1.** 42.3 km **3.** 78 cm **5.** 57 liters

Inverse Proportion *p.147*

Practice: **1.** 9.4 candela **2.** 0.34 **3.** $f_2 = \frac{1}{2} f_1$

Review: **1.** 2,400 watts **3.** 5.5 decibels **5.** 0.37L

An Introduction to Solving Inequalities *p.149*

Practice: **1.** $[\frac{2}{11}, \infty)$ **2.** $\left(-\infty, -\frac{43}{3}\right)$ **3.** $[-2, \infty]$

Review: **1.** $(5, \infty)$ **3.** $[8, \infty)$ **5.** $\left(-\infty, -\frac{9}{4}\right]$

Solving Compound Inequalities *p.150*

Practice: **1.** $[7,10)$ **2.** $[3.5,4)$ **3.** $(-\infty,0]\cup(1,\infty)$

Review: **1.** $(-\infty,\infty)$ **3.** $[1,\infty)$ **5.** $\left(6, \frac{20}{3}\right]$

More on Compound Inequalities *p.151*

Practice: **1.** $(1, 5)$ **2.** $[-23, 5)$ **3.** True

Review: **1.** $\left[\frac{3}{5}, 2\right)$ **3.** $(-\infty, \infty)$ **5.** $(-\infty, \infty)$

Solving Word Problems Involving Inequalities *p.153*

Practice: **1.** 500 miles or more **2.** 38 **3.** 1,945 bowls

Review: **1.** 80 cars/year **3.** 1429 yo-yos **5.** 16

Solving Quadratic Inequalities *p.155*

Practice: **1.** $\left(-\infty, -\frac{1}{2}\right] \cup [9, \infty)$ **2.** $(-2, 3)$ **3.** $\left(-\frac{7}{3}, 11\right)$

Review: **1.** $(-\infty, -2) \cup (3, \infty)$ **3.** $(-\infty, -5) \cup (4, \infty)$ **5.** $\left(-\infty, -\frac{5}{2}\right] \cup [3, \infty)$

Solving Quadratic Inequalities: Another Example *p.156*

Practice: **1.** $(-\infty, -6] \cup [-1, \infty)$ **2.** $\left(\frac{-5}{2}, \frac{5}{2}\right)$ **3.** $\left(-\infty, \frac{-3}{4}\right) \cup \left(\frac{1}{6}, \infty\right)$

Review: **1.** $\left[-3, \frac{-2}{5}\right]$ **3.** $[-6, -2]$ **5.** $\left(-\infty, -\frac{5}{3}\right] \cup \left[\frac{7}{2}, \infty\right)$

Solving Rational Inequalities *p.158*

Practice: **1.** $\left(-\frac{7}{2}, 5\right]$ **2.** $(-\infty, -15] \cup (-6, \infty)$ **3.** $(-3, -1) \cup [7, \infty)$

Review: **1.** $(-\infty, -7] \cup (11, \infty)$ **3.** $(-\infty, 3) \cup (7, \infty)$ **5.** $(-\infty, 0) \cup \left(\frac{1}{7}, \frac{1}{4}\right)$

Solving Rational Inequalities: Another Example *p.160*

Practice: **1.** $(-\infty, -3) \cup [4, 6]$ **2.** $(-\infty, -5] \cup [-2, 3)$ **3.** $(-\infty, -3) \cup \left(-\frac{5}{2}, -2\right] \cup [1, \infty)$

Review: **1.** $[-3] \cup (4, \infty)$ **3.** $(-\infty, -3)$ **5.** $(-\infty, -3) \cup (-1, 1) \cup (2, \infty)$

Determining the Domains of Expressions with Radicals *p.162*

Practice: **1.** $(-\infty, -3] \cup [5, \infty)$ **2.** $(-2, 1]$ **3.** $[-3, 2) \cup [7, \infty)$

Review: **1.** $\left(-\infty, \frac{3}{2}\right] \cup [6, \infty)$ **3.** $\left(-\infty, -\frac{5}{3}\right) \cup \left[\frac{7}{2}, \infty\right)$ **5.** $\left(-2, -\frac{1}{2}\right] \cup [7, \infty)$

Matching Number Lines with Absolute Values *p.164*

Practice: **1.** True **2.** False **3.** True

Review: **1.** True. **3.** True **5.** False: The absolute value of x can never be negative.

Solving Absolute Value Equations *p.166*

Practice: **1.** -9 or 11 **2.** 3 or -1 **3.** -3 or 3

Review: **1.** 17 or -17 **3.** -4 or 10 **5.** -1 or 11

Solving Equations with Two Absolute Value Expressions *p.168*

Practice: **1.** $\frac{3}{2}$ or $-\frac{1}{4}$ **2.** 1 or -11 **3.** -2, 1, or 2

Review: **1.** 1 **3.** 3 or 7 **5.** No solutions

Solving Absolute Value Inequalities *p.169*

Practice: **1.** $w \le -8$ or $w \ge 13$ **2.** $5 \le y \le 7$ **3.** $x \le -\frac{4}{3}$ or $x \ge \frac{10}{3}$

Review: **1.** $-1 \le x \le 1$ **3.** $x \le -2$ or $x \ge 3$ **5.** $-\frac{4}{5} \le x \le 2$

Solving Absolute Value Inequalities: More Examples *p.171*

Practice: **1.** $-16 \le x \le 11$ **2.** $x < -2$ or $x > \frac{8}{5}$ **3.** $x \le \frac{11}{6}$ or $x \ge \frac{19}{6}$

Review: **1.** $-2 < x < 4$ **3.** $p \le -4$ or $p \ge 10$ **5.** $x < -\frac{1}{3}$ or $x > \frac{1}{7}$

Relations and Functions

Using the Cartesian System *p.175*

Practice: **1.** True **2.** quadrant IV **3.** $(-2,2)$

Review: **1.** False **3.** $(5,-5)$ **5.** the fourth quadrant

Thinking Visually *p.177*

Finding the Distance between Two Points *p.178*

Practice: **1.** 14.8 **2.** $5\sqrt{7}$ **3.** (1997, 7900)

Review: **1.** $(-3,-7)$ **3.** 17.37 **5.** 14.8

Finding the Second Endpoint of a Segment *p.180*

Practice: **1.** $\left(\frac{1}{2},-1\right)$ **2.** 10 **3.** $(3n+1,-n)$

Review: **1.** $(1,12)$ **3.** 1 **5.** $\left(\frac{2z}{3},0\right)$

Collinearity and Distance *p.182*

Practice: **1.** yes **2.** no **3.** yes

Review: **1.** yes **3.** yes **5.** yes

Triangles *p.183*

Practice: **1.** True **2.** yes **3.** no

Review: **1.** yes **3.** no **5.** no

Finding the Center-Radius Form of the Equation of a Circle *p.185*

Practice: **1.** $(x-3)^2+(y+2)^2=5$ **2.** $x^2+y^2=25$ **3.** False

Review: **1.** $(x+4)^2+(y-2)^2=25$ **3.** $x^2+(y-3)^2=9$ **5.** $(x-4)^2+(y-2)^2=9$

Finding the Center and Radius of a Circle *p.187*

Practice: **1.** $(3,-1)$; $r=\sqrt{13}$ **2.** $\left(\frac{1}{3},\frac{2}{3}\right)$; $r=2$ **3.** $\left(\frac{2}{3},\frac{1}{2}\right)$; $r=1$

Review: **1.** $(3,-4)$; radius $=4\sqrt{2}$ **3.** $(-2\sqrt{3},-\sqrt{3})$; radius $=3$ **5.** $\left(\frac{1}{2},-\frac{1}{3}\right)$; radius $=\frac{1}{2}$

Decoding the Circle Formula *p.189*

Practice: **1.** $(2, 0);\ r = 3$ **2.**

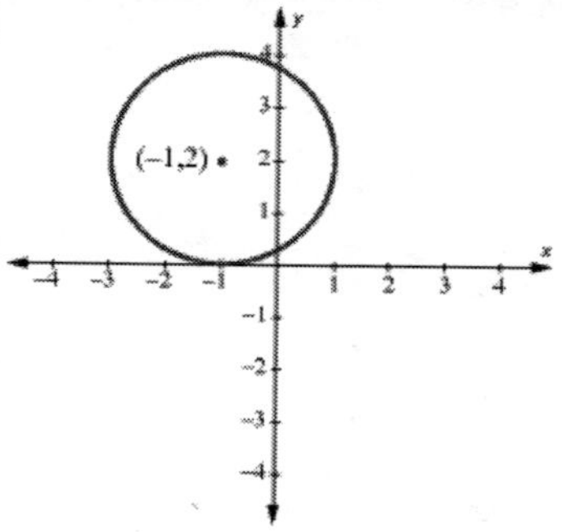

3. $(-4, 1);\ r = \sqrt{5}$

Review: **1.** $(3,4)$; radius $=\sqrt{3}$ **3.** $(9,3)$; radius $=6$ **5.** $(0,-4)$; radius $= 121$

Solving Word Problems Involving Circles *p.190*

Practice: **1.** $(7,-7)$ and $(-1, 1)$ **2.** $(x-4)^2 + (y-1)^2 = 25$ **3.** $(x-\frac{1}{2})^2 + (y-\frac{1}{2})^2 = 2$

Review: **1.** $(x-3)^2 + (y-5)^2 = 8$ **3.** $73 = (x-1)^2 + (y+2)^2$ **5.** 20

Graphing Equations by Locating Points *p.193*

Practice: **1.**

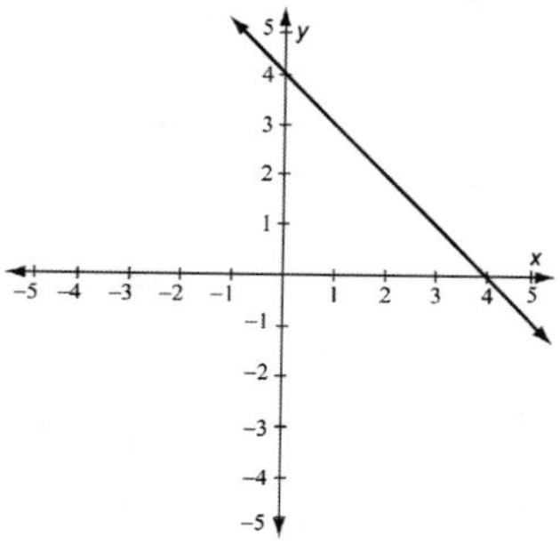

2.

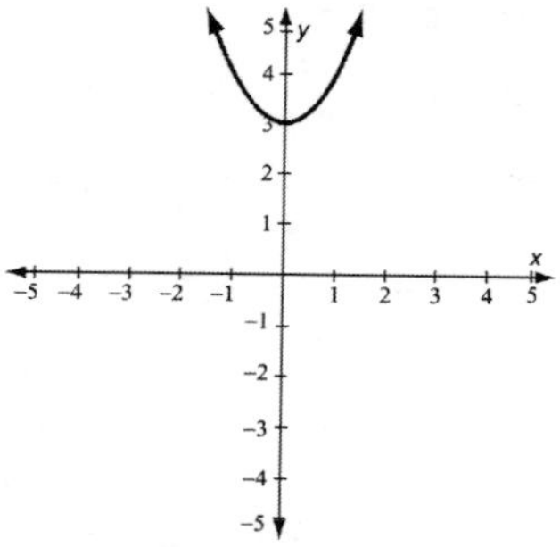

3.

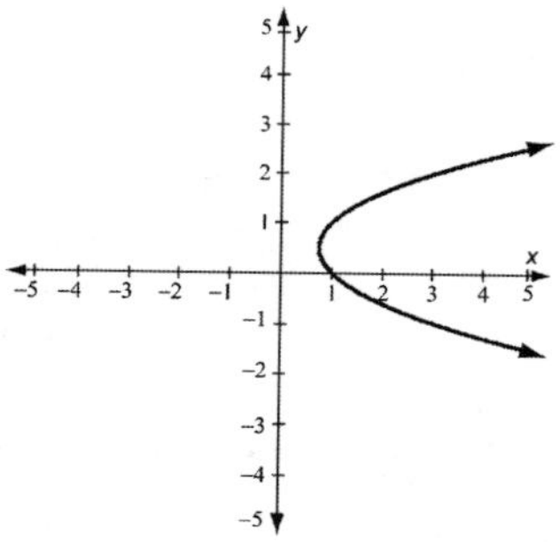

Review: **1.**

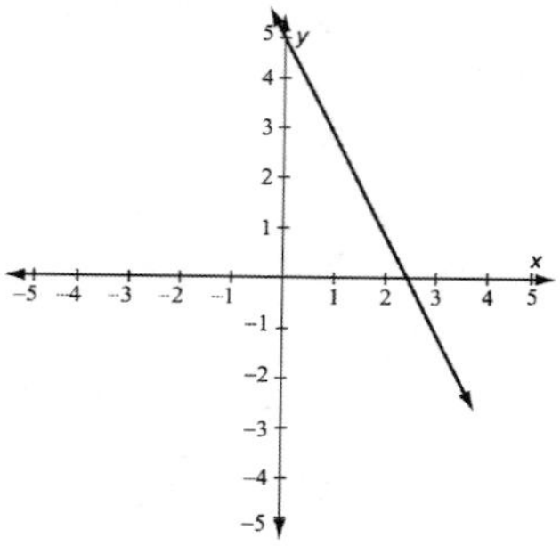

3.

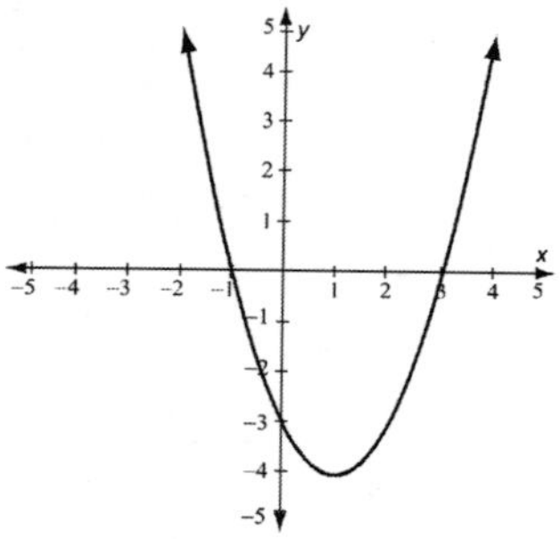

5.

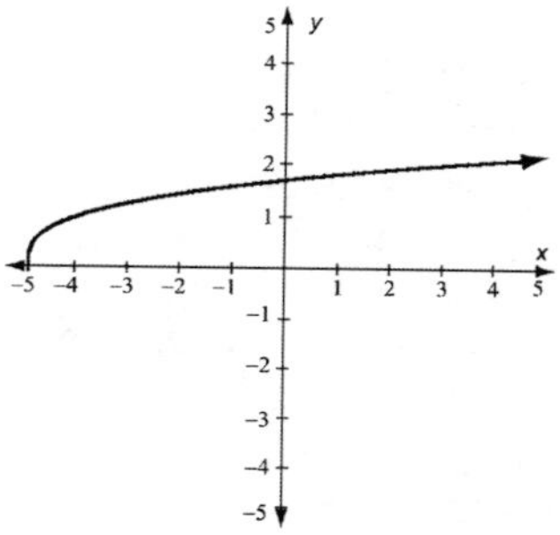

Finding the x- and y-Intercepts of an Equation *p.196*

Practice: **1.** $1, -3$ **2.** $\frac{5}{3}$ **3.** 2 or -2

Review: **1.** -8 **3.** $0, 3$ **5.** 3

Functions and the Vertical Line Test *p.198*

Practice: **1.** False **2.** True **3.** True

Review: **1.** Yes **3.** False **5.** True

Identifying Functions *p.201*

Practice: **1.** y is a function of x **2.** y is not a function of x **3.** y is a function of x

Review: **1.** y is a function of x **3.** y is not a function of x **5.** y is a function of x

Function Notation and Finding Function Values *p.203*

Practice: **1.** $\frac{a^2+2a+3}{a+1}$ **2.** $x^2+2hx+h^2-2x-2h$ **3.** $x+1$

Review: **1.** 0 **3.** 4 **5.** $\frac{2x-5}{6x}$

Determining Intervals Over Which a Function Is Increasing *p.205*

Practice: **1.** $(0,\infty)$ **2.** $(-\infty,\infty)$ **3.** $(-3,1)$

Review: **1.** $(0,\infty)$ **3.** $(-\infty,\infty)$ **5.** $(2,3)$

Evaluating Piecewise-Defined Functions for Given Values *p.209*

Practice: **1.** $(-\infty,-1]$ and $[1,\infty)$ **2.** $-\frac{1}{3}$ **3.** -2

Review: **1.** $(0,1)$ **3.** -10 **5.** -8

Solving Word Problems Involving Functions *p.211*

Practice: **1.** 64 units^2 **2.** $V=\frac{4}{3}\pi\left(\frac{S}{4\pi}\right)^{\frac{3}{2}}$ **3.** $A=10w-w^2$

Review: **1.** 55 units^2 **3.** $\frac{C^2}{2\pi}$ **5.** $4x(5-x)(4-x)$

Finding the Domain and Range of a Function *p.213*

Practice: **1.** $-\infty < x < \infty$ **2.** $x \le 6$ **3.** domain: $x < 15$; range: $y \ge -3$

Review: **1.** $y \ge 4$ **3.** All real numbers **5.** All real numbers

Domain and Range: One Explicit Example *p.218*

Practice: **1.** All real numbers except -4 **2.** All real numbers ≥ 5 **3.** Domain: $\mathbb{R}$; Range: $y \le 0$

Review: **1.** All real numbers **3.** domain: All real numbers; range: All real numbers **5.** domain: All real numbers except 3; range: All real numbers except 0

Satisfying the Domain of a Function *p.220*

Practice: **1.** $x \ge -5$ **2.** $\mathbb{R}\setminus\{-3\}$ **3.** $x < 5\setminus\{-4\}$

Review: **1.** $\mathbb{R}\setminus\{4\}$ **3.** $-3 \le x \le 3$ **5.** $[-2,3)\cup(3,\infty)$

An Introduction to Slope *p.222*

Finding the Slope of a Line Given Two Points *p.222*

Practice: **1.** $-\frac{9}{2}$ **2.** 1 **3.** -1

Review: **1.** $\frac{1}{3}$ **3.** $\frac{13}{22}$ **5.** $\frac{1}{3}$

Interpreting Slope from a Graph *p.224*

Practice: **1.** undefined **2.** increase **3.** decrease

Review: **1.** -8 **3.** increase **5.** decrease

Graphing a Line Using Point and Slope *p.226*

Practice: **1.** (0, 8) **2.**

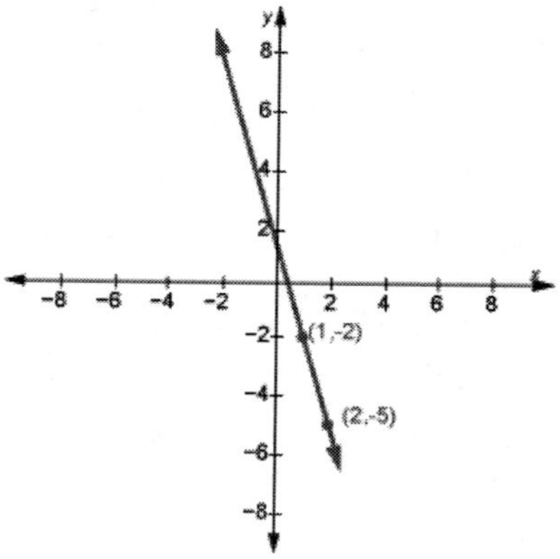

3. No

Review:

1.

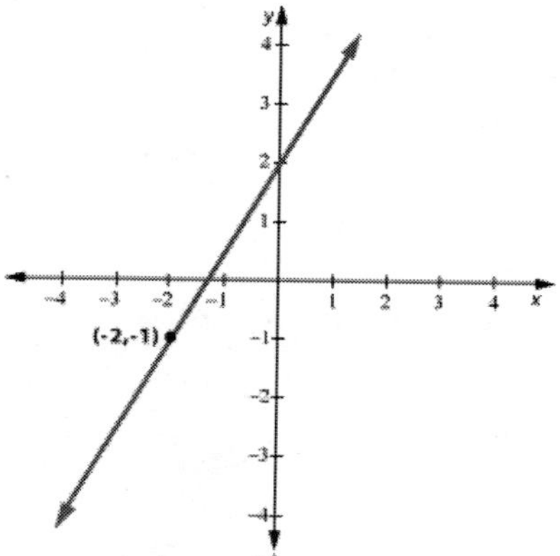

3.

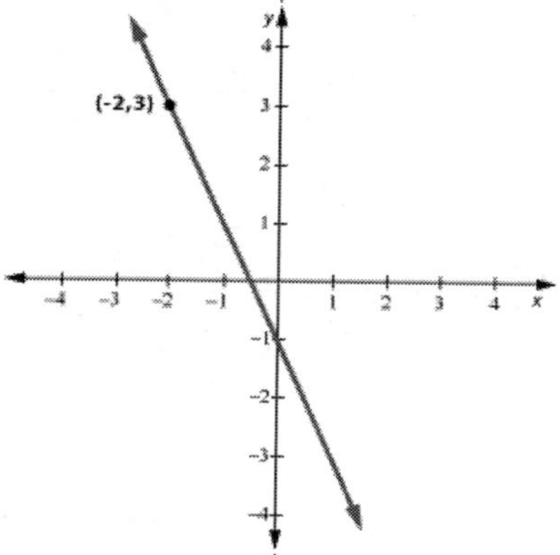

5.

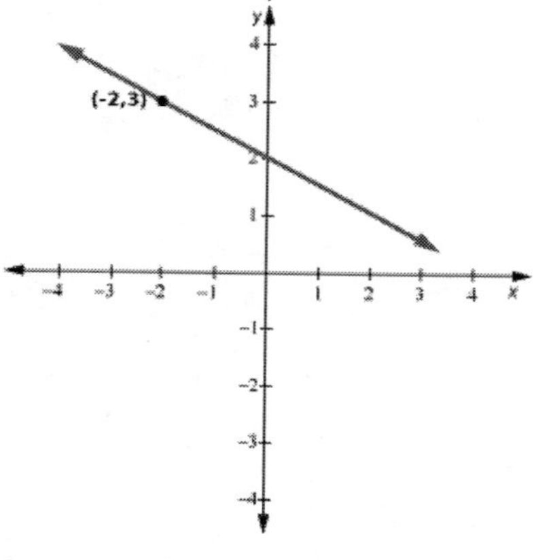

Writing an Equation in Slope-Intercept Form *p.228*

Practice: **1.** $y = \frac{4}{3}x - 1$ **2.** $m = -1$ and $b = 2$ **3.** $y = 3x$

Review: **1.** $y = -3x + 4$ **3.** $y = \frac{2}{3}x - 2$ **5.** $y = \frac{1}{3}x$

Writing an Equation Given Two Points *p.230*

Practice: **1.** $y = 22x + 29$ **2.** $y = -x$ **3.** $y = \frac{14}{13}x - \frac{37}{13}$

Review: **1.** $y = 2x$ **3.** $y = -2x$ **5.** $y = -\frac{1}{3}x + 7$

Writing an Equation in Point-Slope Form *p.231*

Practice: **1.** $y = 4(x - 3)$ **2.** $y - 5 = -2(x + 1)$ **3.** $y - 2 = 3(x + 3)$

Review: **1.** $y - 5 = 4(x - 2)$ **3.** $y = -(x - 4)$ **5.** $\left(y + \frac{2}{3}\right) = \frac{5}{3}\left(x - \frac{3}{4}\right)$

Matching a Slope-Intercept Equation with Its Graph *p.233*

Practice: **1.** Yes **2.** Yes **3.** $y = -\frac{3}{4}x + 4$

Review: **1.** Yes **3.** $y = \frac{3}{2}x + 3$ **5.** Yes

Slope for Parallel and Perpendicular Lines *p.237*

Practice: **1.** 2 **2.** −2 **3.** $y = -\frac{3}{2}x + 5$

Review: **1.** $\frac{1}{2}$ **3.** $y = \frac{5}{2}x + \frac{1}{2}$ **5.** $y = -\frac{1}{2}x - \frac{11}{2}$

Constructing Linear Function Models of Data *p.239*

Practice: **1.** decrease, \$5/year **2.** \$55.00 **3.** 2013

Review: **1.** −1400 **3.** True **5.** 2005

Linear Cost and Revenue Functions *p.242*

Practice: **1.** \$3,120 **2.** 24 temps **3.** 19

Review: **1.** \$96,400 **3.** 21 **5.** 64

Graphing Some Important Functions *p.244*

Practice: **1.** $f(x) = \sqrt{x}$ **2.** $y = x^2$ **3.** I and IV

Review: **1.** False **3.** $y = x$ **5.** True

Graphing Piecewise-Defined Functions *p.246*

Practice: **1.** $[0, \infty)$ **2.**

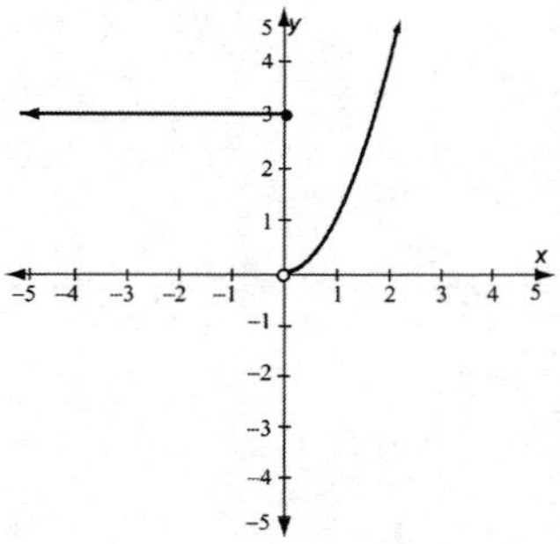

3.

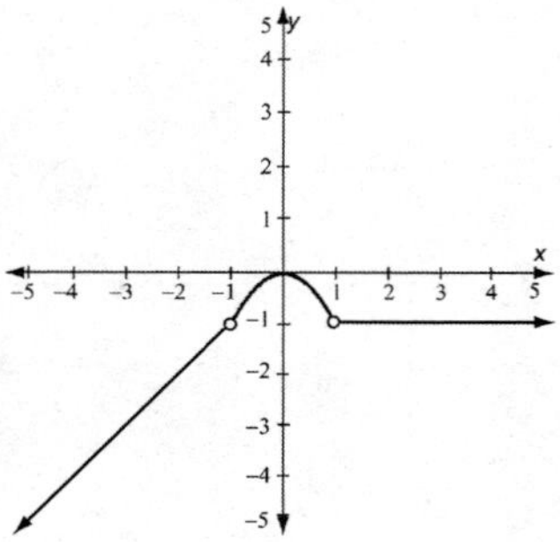

Review: **1.** 3 **3.** All positive numbers. **5.**

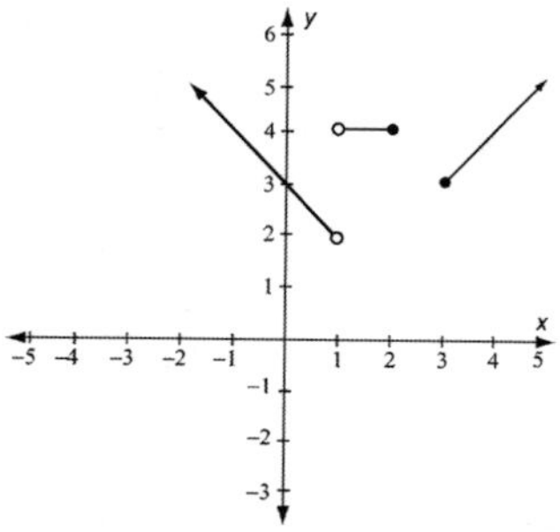

Matching Equations with Their Graphs *p.248*

Practice: **1.** $y = |x|$ **2.** $x = y^2$ **3.** $y = \dfrac{1}{x}$

Review: **1.** $y = x$ **3.** $y = x^3$ **5.** $y = 2^x$

The Greatest Integer Function *p.252*

Practice: **1.** –2 **2.** 19 **3.** 19

Review: **1.** –7 **3.** 2 **5.** –7

Graphing the Greatest Integer Function *p.253*

Practice:

1.

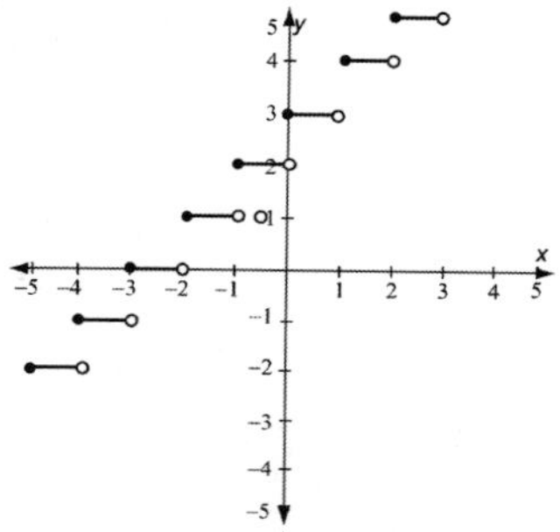

2.

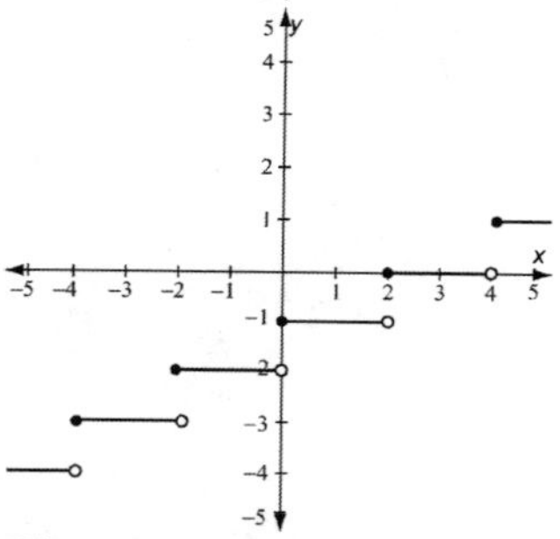

3. The graph of $y = [-x]$ is the reflection of $y = [x]$ across the y-axis.

Review: **1.**

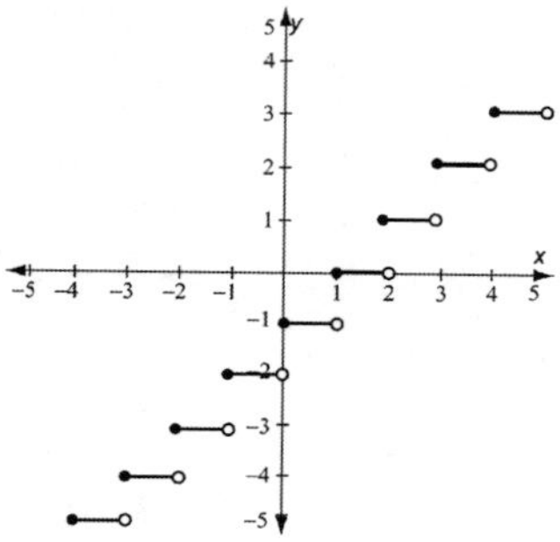

3.

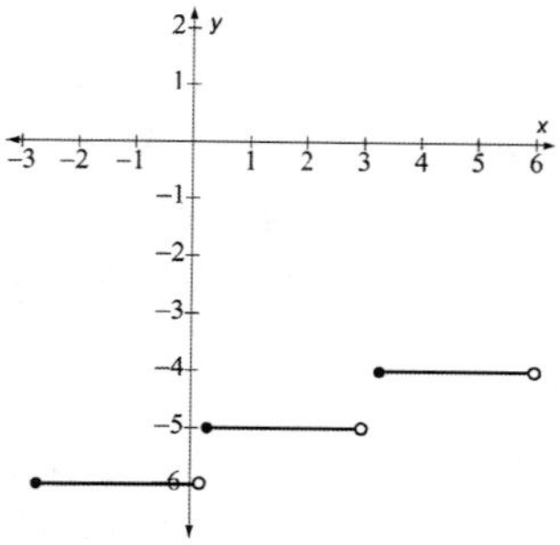

5. True

Deconstructing the Graph of a Quadratic Function *p.255*

Practice: **1.** 2 units to the left and one unit down **2.** $(-5,0)$, maximum **3.** $y \geq -3$

Review: **1.** $\frac{1}{2}$ units to the right and three units up **3.** $(7,1)$, minimum **5.** $y \le 2$

Nice-Looking Parabolas *p.257*

Practice: **1.** down, (0, 5) **2.** up, (2, 0) **3.** up, $(-3, -7)$

Review: **1.** up, $(0,-8)$ **3.** down, $(3,-2)$ **5.** up, $(-1,1)$

Using Discriminants to Graph Parabolas *p.259*

Practice:

1. False, the discriminant is positive.
2. the vertex is on the x-axis and the parabola opens down
3. the dicriminant is >0

Review: **1.** False, the discriminant is zero. **3.** True **5.** the discriminant is 0 and a is negative

Maximum Height in the Real World *p.262*

Practice: **1.** 7.5 sec. **2.** 5 sec., 400 ft. **3.** 10 seconds

Review: **1.** $500 **3.** $1\frac{7}{8}$ second **5.** 2.5

Finding the Vertex by Completing the Square *p.264*

Practice: **1.** $\left(\frac{1}{4},-\frac{15}{16}\right)$ **2.** $(-2,9)$ **3.** $\left(\frac{1}{4},-\frac{11}{4}\right)$

Review: **1.** $(1, 5)$ **3.** $(-1, -1)$ **5.** $\left(\frac{1}{2}, 1\right)$

Using the Vertex to Write the Quadratic Equation *p.266*

Practice: **1.** $y=(x-3)^2+1$ **2.** $y=2(x+3)^2-5$ **3.** $y=3x^2-6x+1$

Review: **1.** $y=(x-4)^2+1$ **3.** $y=5(x+1)^2+2$ **5.** $f(x)=3x^2-18x+1$

Finding the Maximum or Minimum of a Quadratic *p.268*

Practice: **1.** 1 **2.** $-\frac{35}{64}$ **3.** True

Review: **1.** 2 **3.** –6.05 **5.** $\frac{25}{12}$

Graphing Parabolas *p.269*

Practice:

1. vertex: (0, 0); direction: up; x and y-intercepts: (0, 0)
2. vertex: (4,0); direction: up; x-intercept: (4,0); y-intercept: (0,8)
3. vertex: $\left(-\frac{1}{3}, \frac{16}{3}\right)$; direction: down; x-intercept: $\left(-\frac{5}{3}, 0\right)$ and (1, 0); y-intercept: (0, 5)

Review:

1. vertex: (0, 0); direction: up; x and y-intercepts: (0, 0)
3. vertex: $(-1,-7)$; direction: up; x-intercepts: $-1\pm\sqrt{7}$; y-intercept: $(0,-6)$
5. vertex: $\left(\frac{3}{2},\frac{3}{2}\right)$; opens down; x-intercepts: $\frac{-3\pm\sqrt{3}}{2}$; y-intercept: -3

Shifting Curves along Axes *p.272*

Practice:

1. Add +2 to the function's expression;
   therefore $f(x)=x^2-2$ becomes $f(x)=x^2$
2. Add +3 to the expression

3. $y = x^2$

Review: **1.** Add +7 to the function **3.** True **5.** $y = (x+4)^2 - 2$

Shifting or Translating Curves along Axes *p.273*

Practice: **1.** $f(x) = \frac{5}{4}(x-7)^2 + \frac{17}{4}$ **2.** $f(x) = 2(x+3)^2 - 5$ **3.** $b = 4;\ c = -14$

Review: **1.** $f(x) = 5(x - 2\frac{1}{2})^2 - 1$ **3.** $f(x) = -(x + 3\frac{2}{5})^2 + 3$ **5.** $b = 0$ and $c = 6$

Stretching a Graph *p.275*

Practice: **1.** True **2.** False **3.** True

Review: **1.** True **3.** False **5.** The curve becomes narrower and gets flipped upside down

Graphing Quadratics Using Patterns *p.277*

Practice: **1.** $y = \frac{10}{3}(x+7)^2$ **2.** $y = (x-3.25)^2 + 1.5$ **3.** $y = (x+8)^2 - 3$

Review: **1.** $y = 4(x+2)^2 + 5$ **3.** $y = -(x+3)^2 + 4$ **5.** $y = (x+8)^2 - 3$

Determining Symmetry *p.279*

Practice: **1.** $(4,-1)$ and $(-5,0)$ **2.** $(-2,0)$ and $(5,1)$ **3.** Odd

Review: **1.** $(-3,-2)$ and $(0,-1)$ **3.** $(-13,4)$ and $(7,1)$ **5.** Neither

Reflections *p.281*

Practice: **1.** $(-5,2)$, $(1,7)$, and $(0,2)$ **2.** $(a-1, b-d)$ and $(d-c, e)$ **3.**

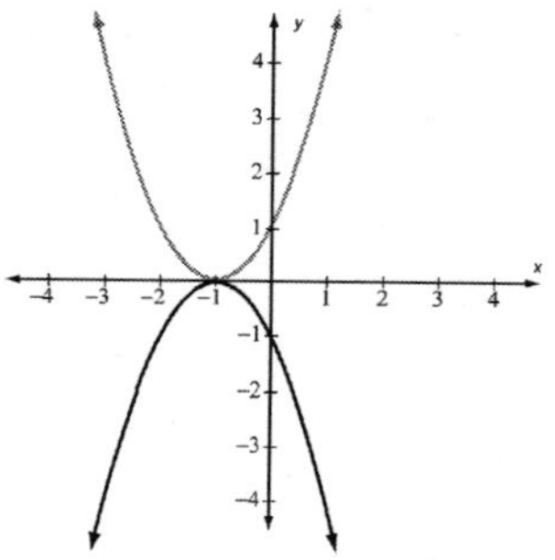

Review: **1.** $(-10,-2)$, $(1,3)$, and $(0,0)$ **3.** $(2a+x, y-1)$ and $(z-w, -1-z)$ **5.**

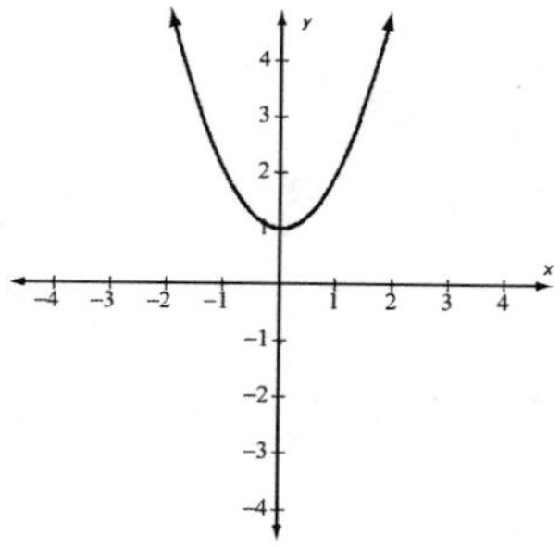

Reflecting Specific Functions *p.283*

Practice: **1.** $(-1,3)$ and $(1,3)$ **2.** $g(x) = -2x^2 + x - 1$ **3.** $g(x) = \frac{1+x^3}{x^2}$

Review: **1.** $(2,-6)$ and $(-2,-6)$ **3.** $g(x) = x^3 + x^2 - x$ **5.** $g(x) = 1 + x - x^3$

Using Operations on Functions *p.285*

Practice: **1.** $28x^3 - 7x^2$ **2.** $10x + 10$ **3.** $3x^2 + 7x + 6xh - 7h + 3h^2 - 3$

Review: **1.** True **3.** $\frac{1}{(x-5)}$, $x \neq \pm 5$ **5.** $4x^3 - x^2 - 7x + 3$

Composite Functions *p.286*

Practice: **1.** 16 **2.** 9 **3.** $\frac{5}{4}$

Review: **1.** 4 **3.** $2x^2 + 11$ **5.** 15

Components of Composite Functions *p.288*

Practice: **1.** $180x^2 + 240x + 80$ **2.** $x^2 - 10x + 30$ **3.** $-3x^2 - 6x + 6$

Review: **1.** –50 **3.** $18x^2 - 48x + 35$ **5.** $12x^2 + 12x + 8$

Finding Functions That Form a Given Composite *p.289*

Practice: **1.** $g(x) = 3x - 1, f(x) = 2x^2$ **2.** $g(x) = x^2, f(x) = -x^2 + 5x$ **3.** $g(x) = x^3, f(x) = \frac{1}{2}x^2 - 3x + 1$

Review: **1.** $g(x) = 1 - x, f(x) = 3x^5$ **3.** $g(x) = 2x, f(x) = 3x^6 + 3x^3 - x$ **5.** $g(x) = x^4, f(x) = x^2 - x$

Finding the Difference Quotient of a Function *p.291*

Practice: **1.** $5h^2 + 10hx + 2h$ **2.** $2x + h + 2,\ h \neq 0$ **3.** $4x + 2h - 3,\ h \neq 0$

Review: **1.** $h^2 + 2hx$ **3.** $2x + h - 6,\ h \neq 0$ **5.** $-3x^2 - h^2 - 3hx + 5,\ h \neq 0$

Polynomial and Rational Functions

Using Long Division with Polynomials *p.295*

Practice: **1.** $-x^2 + 4x - 14$, R (49) **2.** 5, R $(12x + 2)$ **3.** $2x^3 - 1$

Review: **1.** $x - 2$, R(-2) **3.** $x^2 - 3x + 1$, R(-1) **5.** $x + 2$, R$(8x - 1)$

Long Division: Another Example *p.297*

Practice: **1.** $4x^2 - 8x + 19$, R $(-38x - 1)$ **2.** $-3x^2 - 6x^2 - 12x - 24$, R$\left(\frac{-48}{x-2}\right)$ **3.** $\frac{5}{2}x^3 - \frac{5}{4}x^2 + \frac{1}{2}x + \frac{1}{4}$, R$(-\frac{1}{4})$

Review: **1.** $x^3 - 2x^2 + 5x - 9$, R(19) **3.** $5x^3 - 10x^2 + 20x - 46$, R(84) **5.** $-x^2 - 4x - 11$, R$(-26x + 5)$

Using Synthetic Division with Polynomials *p.299*

Practice: **1.** $x^3 + 2x^2 + 10x + 13$, R(38) **2.** $y^2 - y + 2$, R(-24) **3.** $8x - 2$, R$(\frac{3}{2})$

Review: **1.** $x^2 + 3x$ **3.** $x^3 - x^2 + 2x - 3$, R(6) **5.** $6x^5 - x^4 + 5x^3 - 2x^2 + 4x - 3$, R(4)

More Synthetic Division *p.302*

Practice: **1.** $x^3 - 3x^2 - x + 1$, R(1) **2.** $x^2 - 8x + 64$ **3.** $x^2 - \frac{1}{2}x + \frac{1}{4}$, R$(-\frac{1}{8})$

Review: **1.** $x^2 + 5x + 7$, R(4) **3.** $x^2 - 2x - 2$, R(-9) **5.** $6x^3 + 12x^2 - 8x + 2$

The Remainder Theorem *p.304*

Practice: **1.** 970 **2.** $\frac{47}{16}$ **3.** $\frac{17}{18}$

Review: **1.** –3 **3.** –7 **5.** 2159

More on the Remainder Theorem *p.306*

Practice: **1.** 21 **2.** –35 **3.** 5

Review: **1.** -2 **3.** -3 **5.** -8.279

The Factor Theorem and Its Uses *p.308*

Practice:

1. $x-5$ is not a factor of $5x^4+x^2-3x+18$
2. $x-1$ is a factor of $2x^5-2x^4-5x^2+6x-1$
3. $x+7$ is a not factor of $x^6-x^2+2x-10$

Review:

1. $x+1$ is a factor of $2x^4+2x^3-x^2+7x+8$
3. $x+5$ is not a factor of $4x^5-7x^2+20x-13$
5. $x+4$ is not a factor of $7x^6-2x^5-3x^2-x-7$

Factoring a Polynomial Given a Zero *p.309*

Practice: **1.** $x=10,\ x=2$ **2.** $x=-3,\ x=1,\ x=-1$ **3.** $x=5,\ x=-4,\ x=\frac{1}{2}$

Review: **1.** $x=-12,\ x=5$ **3.** $x=-1,\ x=-2,\ x=2$ **5.** $x=6,\ x=-\frac{2}{3},\ x=\frac{1}{2}$

Presenting the Rational Zero Theorem *p.311*

Practice: **1.** $\pm1,\ \pm2,\ \pm3,\ \pm6$ **2.** $\pm1,\ \pm5,\ \pm\frac{1}{5}$ **3.** $\pm\frac{1}{2},\ \pm1,\ \pm2,\ \pm\frac{7}{2},\ \pm7,\ \pm14$

Review: **1.** $\pm1,\ \pm2,\ \pm5,\ \pm10$ **3.** $\pm1,\ \pm3,\ \pm9,\ \pm\frac{1}{3}$ **5.** $\pm\frac{1}{5},\ \pm\frac{2}{5},\ \pm1,\ \pm2,\ \pm5,\ \pm10$

Considering Possible Solutions *p.313*

Practice: **1.** 21 **2.** 11 **3.** 25

Review: **1.** 12 **3.** 4 **5.** 24

Finding Polynomials Given Zeros, Degree, and One Point *p.315*

Practice: **1.** $f(x)=3x^3-15x^2-3x+15$ **2.** $f(x)=\frac{1}{2}x^3+2x^2+\frac{1}{2}x-3$ **3.** $f(x)=-3x^3-12x^2+21x+30$

Review: **1.** $f(x)=2x^3-14x^2+20x$ **3.** $f(x)=\frac{3}{5}x^3+\frac{6}{5}x^2-15x-30$ **5.** $f(x)=\frac{2}{3}x^3-\frac{4}{3}x^2-14x-12$

Finding all Zeros and Multiplicities of a Polynomial *p.316*

Practice:

1. $x=-2$, multiplicity 3; $x=1$, multiplicity 2
2. $x=0$, multiplicity 2; $x=-1$, multiplicity 5; $x=-4$, multiplicity 2
3. $x=\frac{1}{3}$, multiplicity 2; $x=i$, multiplicity 3; $x=-i$, multiplicity 3

Review:

1. $x=0$, multiplicity 5
3. $x=0$, multiplicity 1; $x=2$, multiplicity 1; $x=-1$, multiplicity 3
5. $x=0$, multiplicity 3; $x=\frac{5}{2}$, multiplicity 4; $x=3i$, multiplicity 1; $x=-3i$, multiplicity 1

Finding the Real Zeros for a Polynomial *p.318*

Practice: **1.** $x=0,\ x=\pm10$ **2.** $x=0,\ x=1,\ x=\pm\frac{-5+\sqrt{13}}{2}$ **3.** $x=0,\ x=\pm3$

Review: **1.** $x=\pm\frac{1}{2}$ **3.** $x=0,\ x=1,\ x=\pm\frac{3+\sqrt{5}}{2}$ **5.** no real zeros

Using Descartes' Rule of Signs *p.320*

Practice: **1.** 1 positive; 1 negative **2.** 2 or 0 positive; 1 negative **3.** 3 or 1 positive; 3 or 1 negative

Review: **1.** 3 or 1 positive; 2 or 0 negative **3.** 2 or 0 positive; 1 negative **5.** 0 positive; 3 or 1 negative

Finding the Zeros of a Polynomial from Start to Finish *p.321*

Practice: **1.** $x = -1, 3, -7$ **2.** $x = 2, 4, \frac{3}{2}$ **3.** $x = -2, -3, -4, -\frac{5}{2}$

Review: **1.** $x = -1, -3, 1$ **3.** $x = -1, -3, -\frac{4}{5}$ **5.** $x = -2, -5, 5, \frac{1}{3}$

Matching Graphs to Polynomial Functions *p.324*

Practice: **1.** zero **2.** True **3.** False

Review: **1.** zero **3.** True **5.** negative coefficient, even degree, no real roots

Sketching the Graphs of Basic Polynomial Functions *p.327*

Practice: **1.**

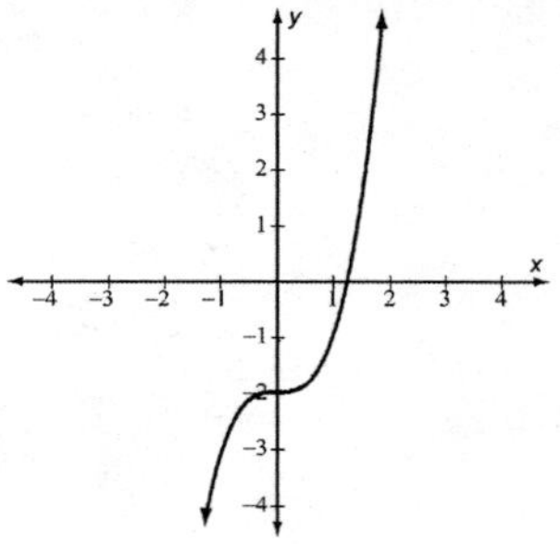

2.

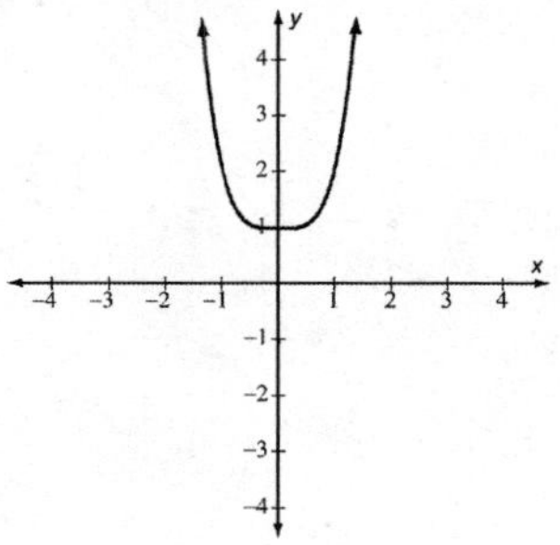

3. U-shaped, opening down

Review: **1.**

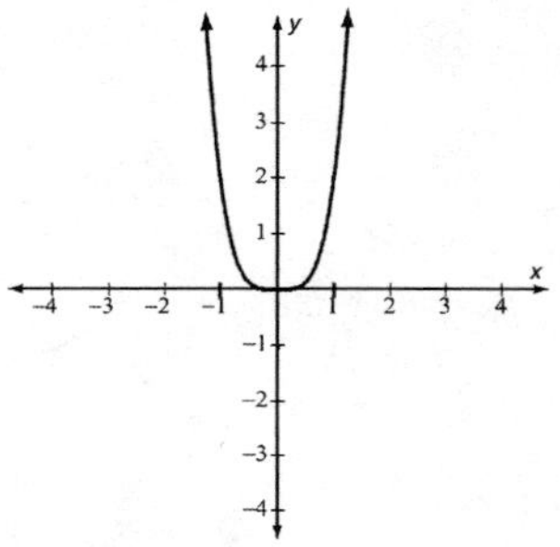

3.

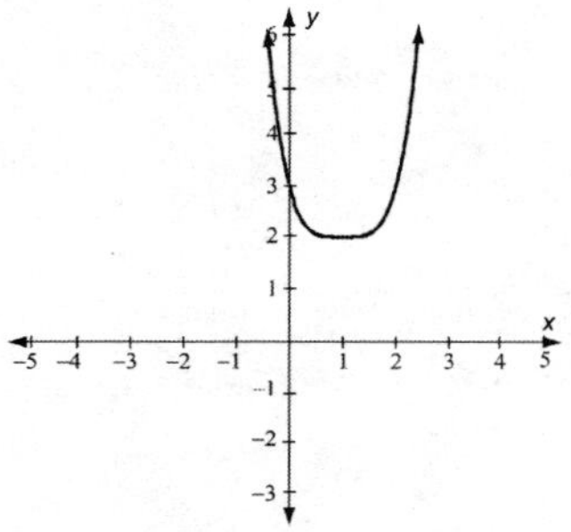

5.

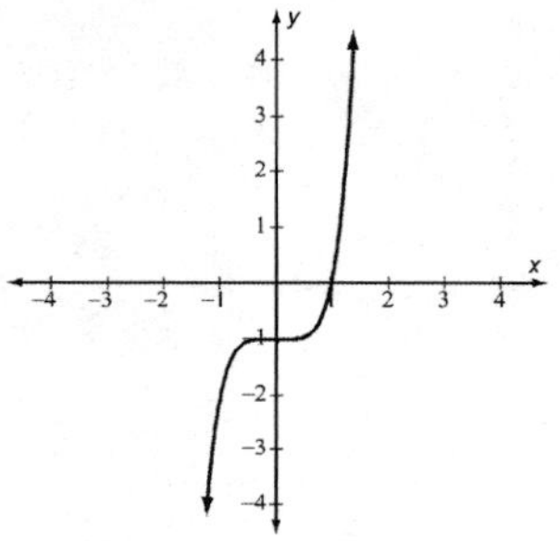

Understanding Rational Functions *p.329*

Practice:

1. Domain: all real numbers x such that $x \neq 4$
Range: all real numbers y such that $y \neq -2$

2. Domain: all real numbers x such that $x \neq -2$
Range: all real numbers y such that $y \neq -3$

3. $y = 0$ and $x = 0$

Review:

1. Domain: all real numbers x such that $x \neq 2$
Range: all real numbers y such that $y \neq 3$

3. Domain: all real numbers x such that $x \neq -4$
Range: all real numbers y such that $y \neq -3$

5. $y = -2$ and $x = 3$

Basic Rational Functions *p.333*

Practice: **1.**

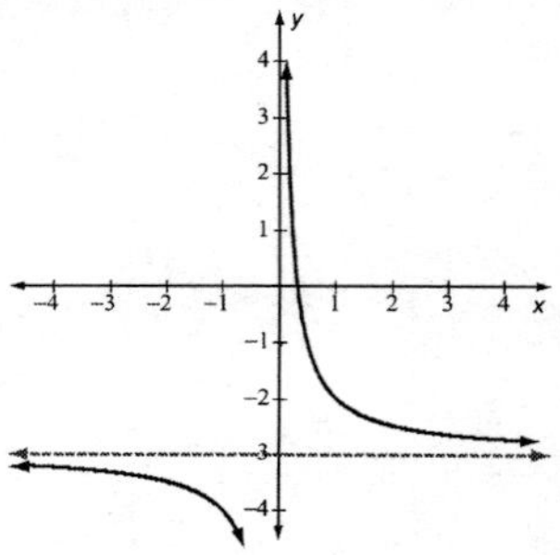

2.

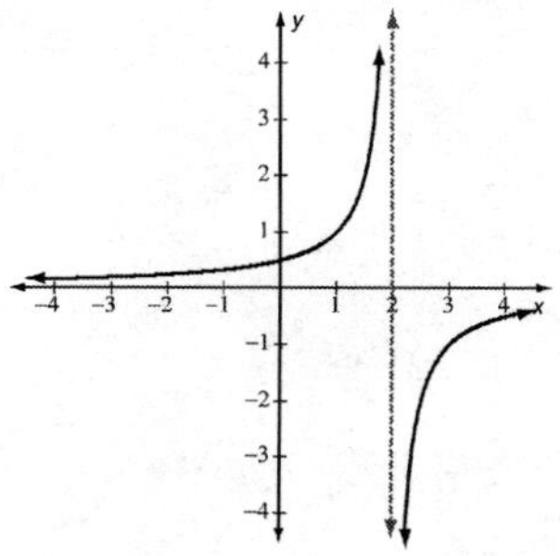

3.

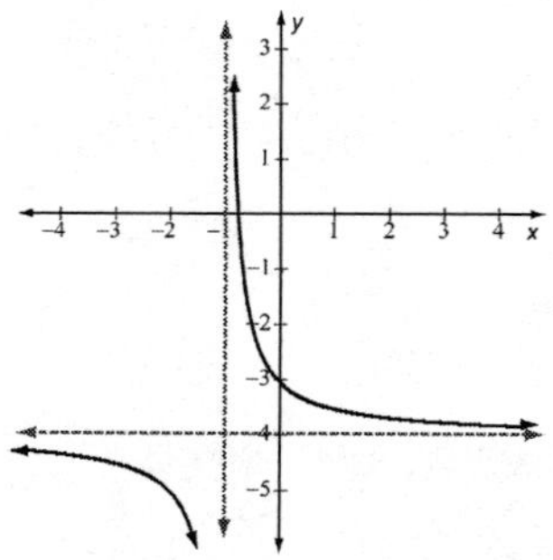

Review: **1.** 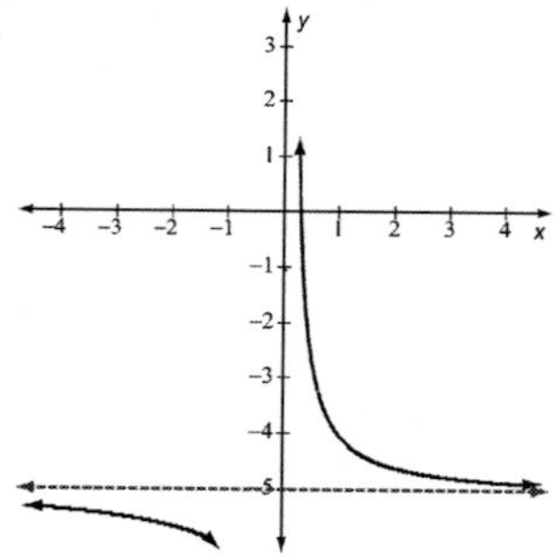 **3.** 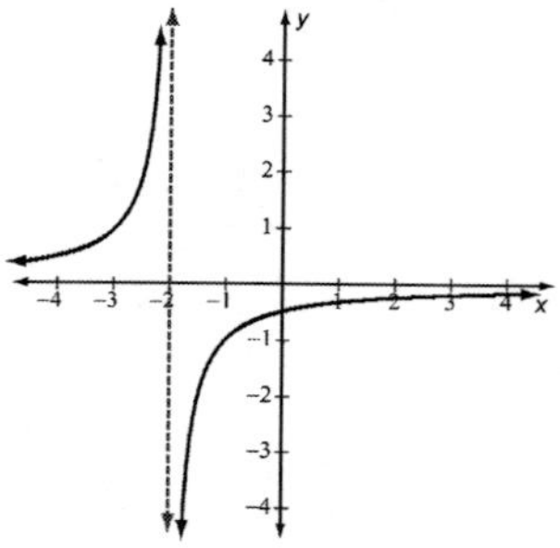 **5.** 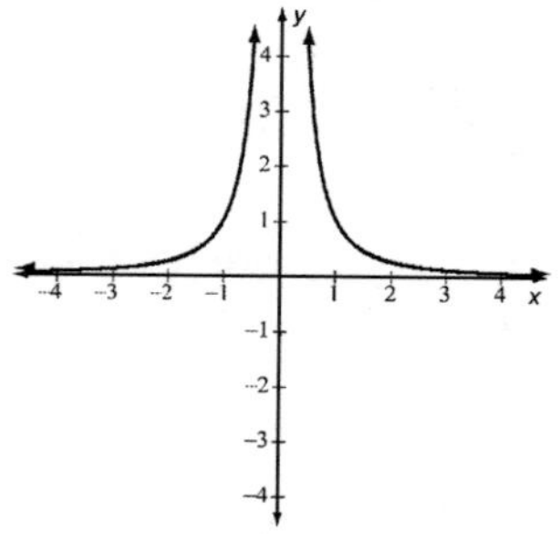

Vertical Asymptotes *p.335*

Practice: **1.** $x = -7$ **2.** $x = 3$ and $x = -3$ **3.** no vertical asymptotes

Review: **1.** $x = 0$ **3.** $x = 5$ and $x = -5$ **5.** no vertical asymptotes

Horizontal Asymptotes *p.337*

Practice: **1.** $y = 0$ **2.** $y = 0$ **3.** $y = \frac{1}{4}$

Review: **1.** $y = 0$ **3.** $y = 1$ **5.** does not exist

Graphing Rational Functions *p.338*

Practice: **1.** 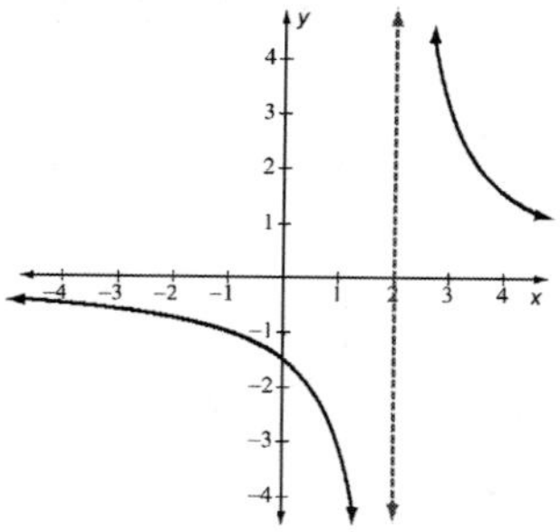 **2.** 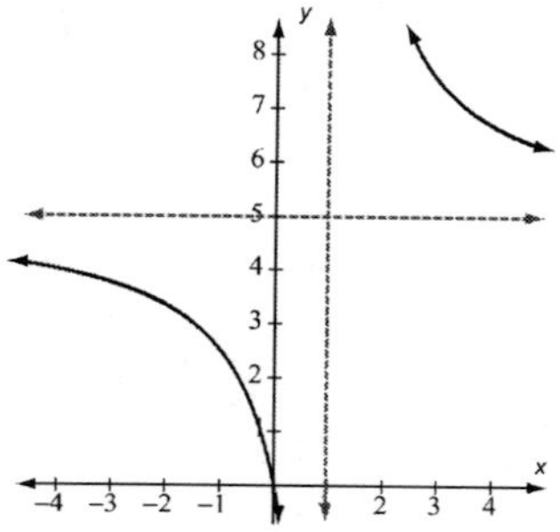 **3.** 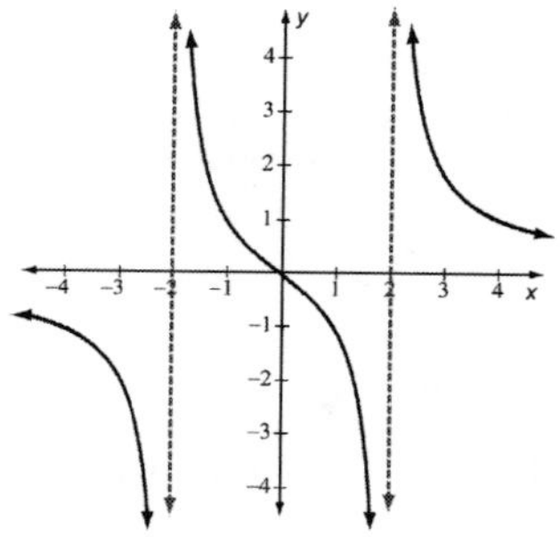

Review: **1.** 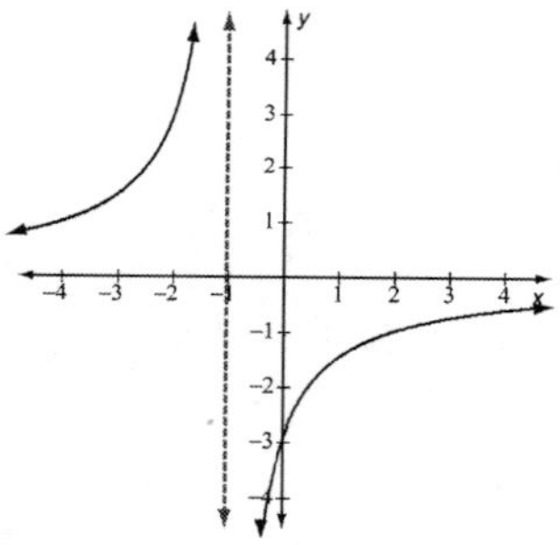 **3.** 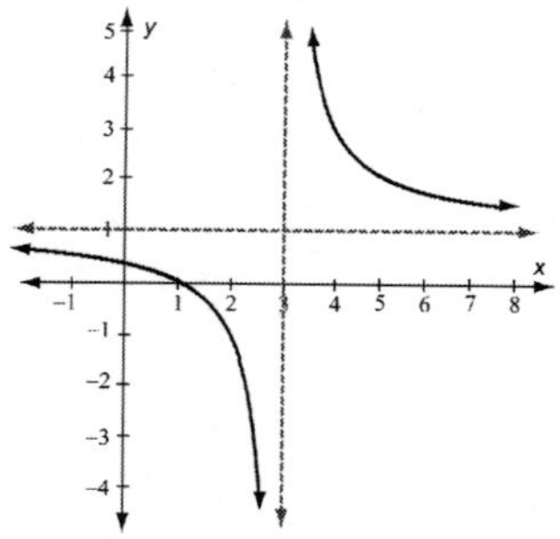 **5.** 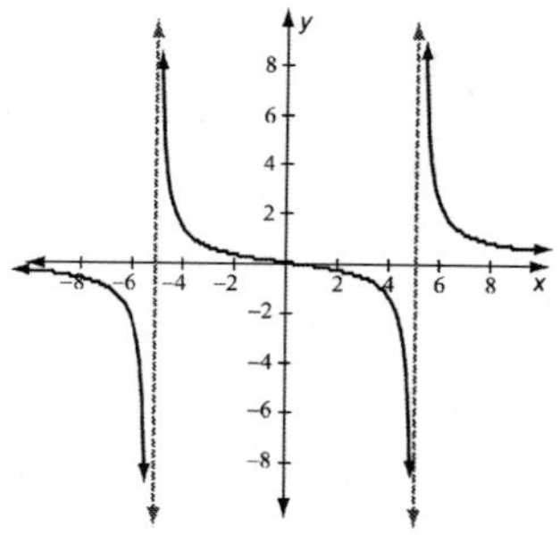

Examples with Quadratics *p.341*

Practice: **1.** 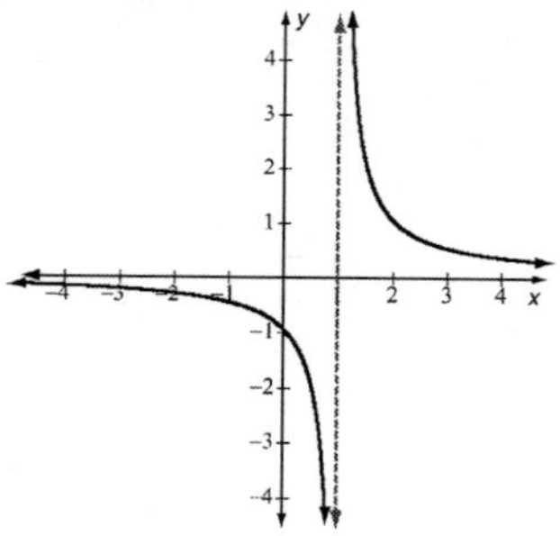 **2.** 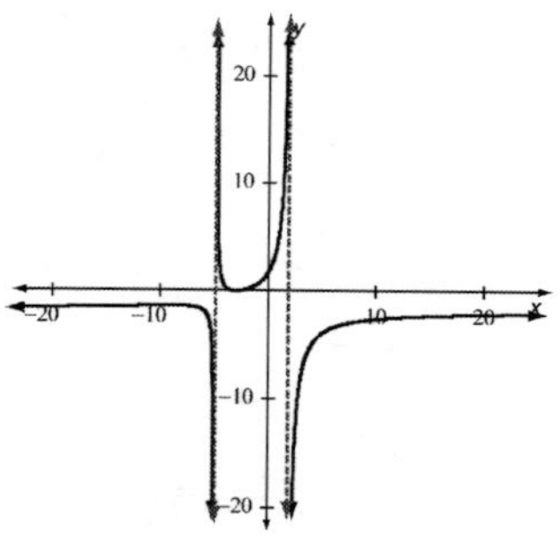 **3.** 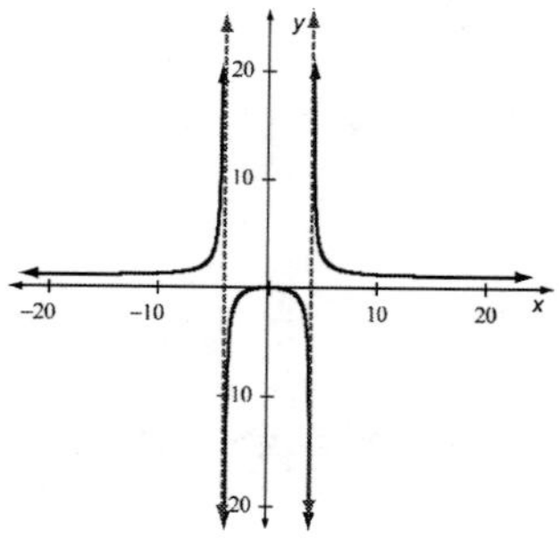

Review: **1.**

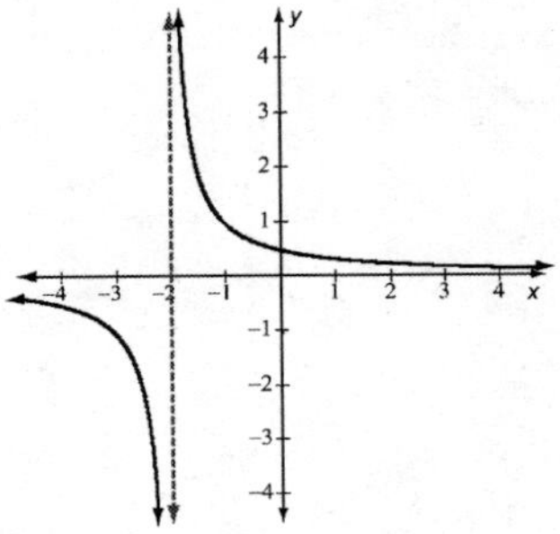

3.

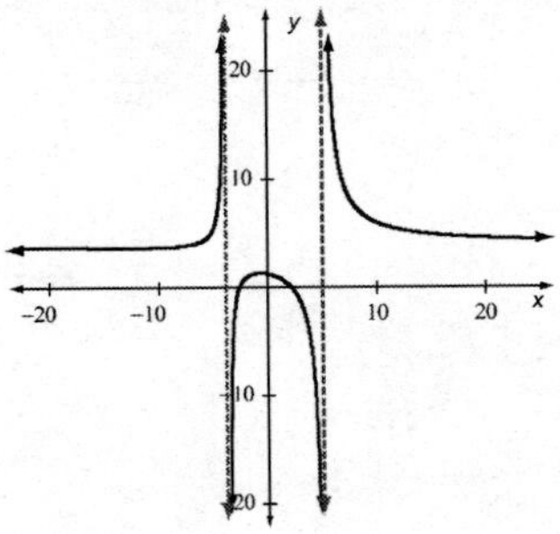

5.

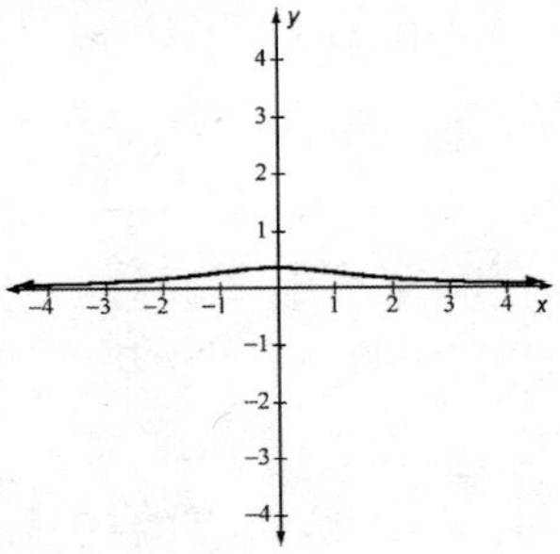

Exponential and Logarithmic Functions

Understanding Inverse Functions *p.347*

Practice: **1.** –4 **2.** –3 **3.** 5

Review: **1.** 12 **3.** 5 **5.** 17.5

The Horizontal Line Test *p.348*

Practice: **1.** yes **2.** False **3.** True

Review: **1.** No **3.** False **5.** False

Are Two Functions Inverses of Each Other? *p.350*

Practice: **1.** Yes, the two functions are inverses. **2.** True **3.** True

Review: **1.** Yes **3.** No **5.** True

Graphing the Inverse *p.353*

Practice: **1.**

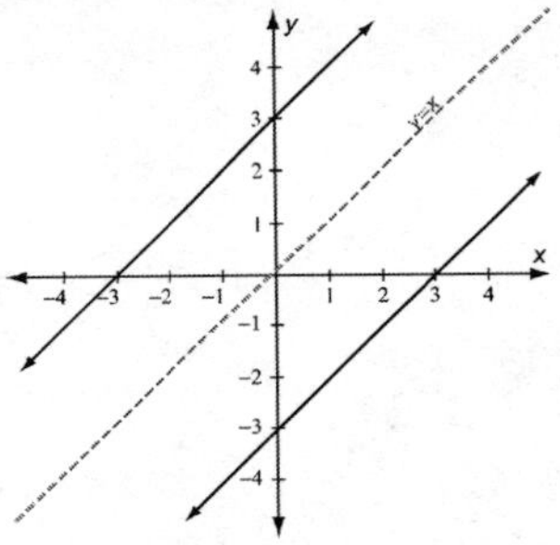

2.

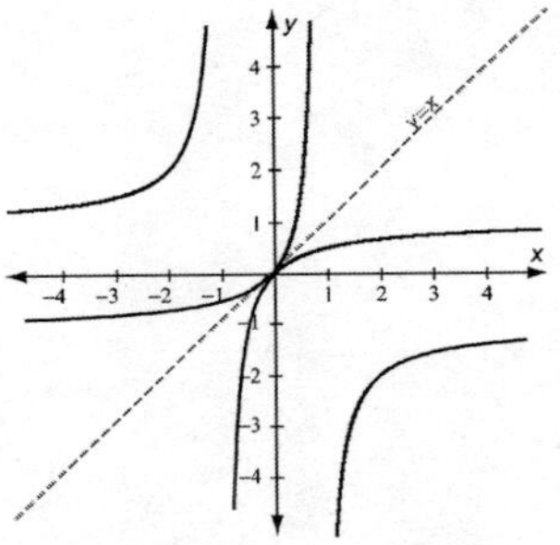

3.

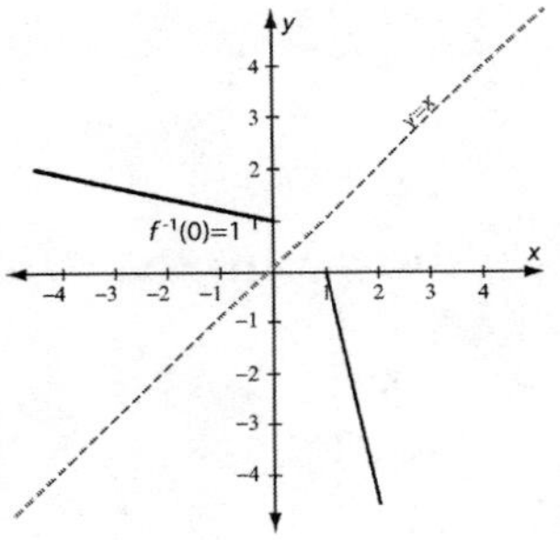

Review: **1.**

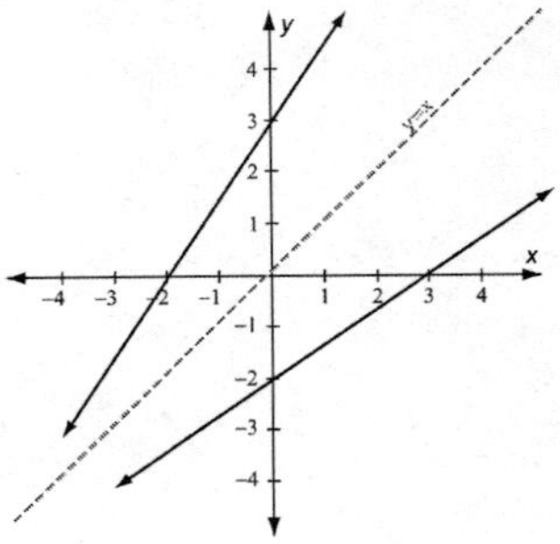

3.

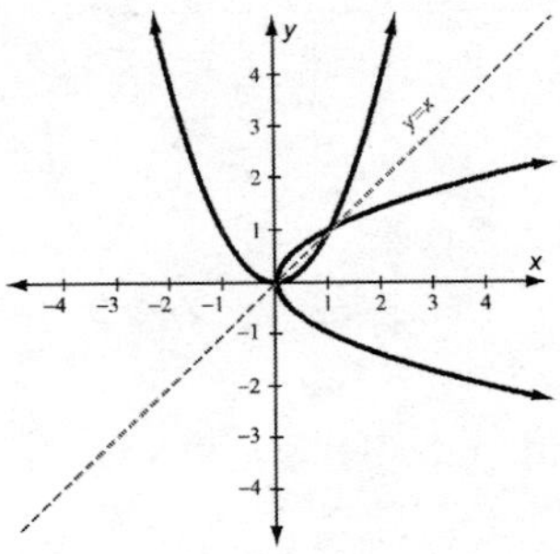

5.

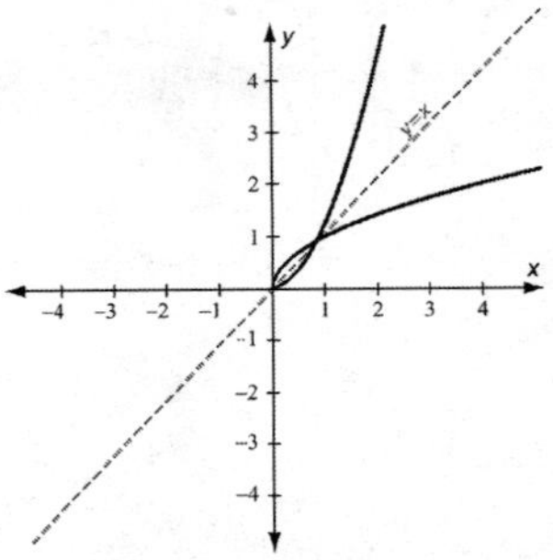

Finding the Inverse of a Function *p.357*

Practice:

1. $g^{-1}(x) = \dfrac{5}{2} - \dfrac{7x}{6}.$

2. The function is not invertible because it is not one-to-one.

3. $p^{-1}(x) = 5x^2$;
$p^{-1}(3) = 45$ feet;
If the period is 3 seconds
then the length is 45 feet.

Review: **1.** $f^{-1}x = \frac{1}{2}(x-1);\ f^{-1}(5) = 2$ **3.** $f^{-1} = \sqrt{\frac{(x+5)}{2}},\quad x \geq -5$ **5.** $t^{-1}(5)$ is how many rescuers are required to find a hiker in 5 hours.

$t^{-1}(5) = \frac{80}{x}$ again; $t^{-1}(5) = 16$ rescuers

Finding the Inverse of a Function with Higher Powers *p.359*

Practice:

1. $f^{-1}(x) = \frac{\sqrt[3]{x}}{3} - 5$ and $f^{-1}(-8) = -\frac{17}{3}$

2. $f(x)$ is not invertible because it is not one-to-one

3. $T^{-1}(1)$ is the amount of poison (grams) in the blood 1 hour after ingestion.

$T^{-1}(x) = 2 - \frac{x^4}{500}$

$T^{-1}(1) = 1.998$ grams

Review:

1. $f^{-1}(x) = 1 + \sqrt[3]{2x}$ and $f^{-1}(4) = 3$

3. $f(x)$ is not invertible because it is not one-to-one

5. $S^{-1}(10)$ is the power produced by a 10 mph wind.

$S^{-1}(p) = \frac{p^3}{20}.$

$S^{-1}(10) = 50$ watts.

An Introduction to Exponential Functions *p.361*

Practice: **1.** True **2.** $c(x)$ **3.** $f(x)$

Review: **1.** 0.06157 **3.** False **5.** $g(x) = \frac{1}{3}^x$

Graphing Exponential Functions: Useful Patterns *p.363*

Practice: **1.** Neither **2.** $h(x) = 8^x$ **3.** For all x-values

Review: **1.** $h(x) = 6^x$ **3.** $g(x) = 4^x$ **5.** $g(x) = \left(\frac{3}{2}\right)^x$

Graphing Exponential Functions: More Examples *p.365*

Practice:

1. True

2. Shift to the left 1 unit and up 3 units.

3. $y = 4^x + 2$

Review: **1.** $b(x) = 9 \cdot 3^x$ **3.** $f(x) = 6^x$ is shifted to the left 8 units to form $g(x)$ **5.** $y = 2^{x-1} - 6$

Using Properties of Exponents to Solve Exponential Equations *p.367*

Practice: **1.** $x = \frac{3}{7}$ **2.** $x = 8$ **3.** $x = \frac{1}{10}$

Review: **1.** $h = 8$ **3.** $x = -1.2$ **5.** $x = \frac{4}{3}$

Finding Present Value and Future Value *p.368*

Practice: **1.** 613,136.41 yen **2.** \$1,160.18 **3.** \$16,286.10

Review: **1.** \$212,557.18 **3.** \$4,646.43 **5.** \$100,418.07

Finding an Interest Rate to Match Given Goals *p.370*

Practice: **1.** 7.29% **2.** 21.8% **3.** 3.37%

Review: **1.** 4.19% **3.** 15.6% **5.** 5.7%

e *p.372*

Applying Exponential Functions *p.373*

Practice: **1.** 254 people **2.** 8.6% **3.** 11.3%

Review: **1.** 2.3 billion **3.** 82.2 % **5.** 59.8 %

An Introduction to Logarithmic Functions *p.374*

Practice: **1.** –1 **2.** True **3.** –3

Review: **1.** 2 **3.** –3 **5.** $\frac{2}{3}$

Converting between Exponential and Logarithmic Functions *p.376*

Practice: **1.** $\log_6 36 = 2$ **2.** $\log_m k = z$ **3.** $16^{\frac{1}{4}} = 2$

Review: **1.** $7^0 = 1$ **3.** $10^{-2} = 0.01$ **5.** $\log_4 0.125 = -\frac{3}{2}$

Finding the Value of a Logarithmic Function *p.377*

Practice: **1.** –2 **2.** 6 **3.** $-\frac{1}{8}$

Review: **1.** 7 **3.** 1 **5.** –1

Solving for x in Logarithmic Equations *p.379*

Practice: **1.** No solution **2.** $x = \frac{4}{5}$ **3.** $x = \frac{4}{3}$

Review: **1.** $x = 10$ **3.** $x = 8$ **5.** $x = \frac{1}{4}$

Graphing Logarithmic Functions *p.381*

Practice: **1.** True **2.** (1, 0) **3.** $g(4) = -7$

Review: **1.**

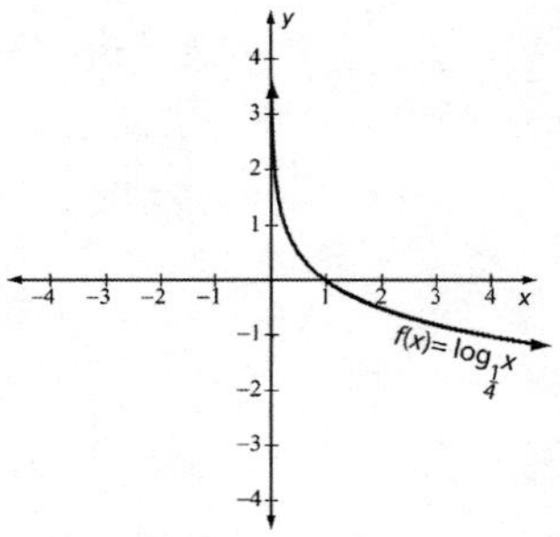

3. (1,0) **5.** $f(x)\log_{10} x$

Matching Logarithmic Functions with Their Graphs *p.383*

Practice: **1.** $y = \log_9(7x)$ **2.** The curve is shifted 2 units to the right. **3.** 1

Review: **1.** False **3.**

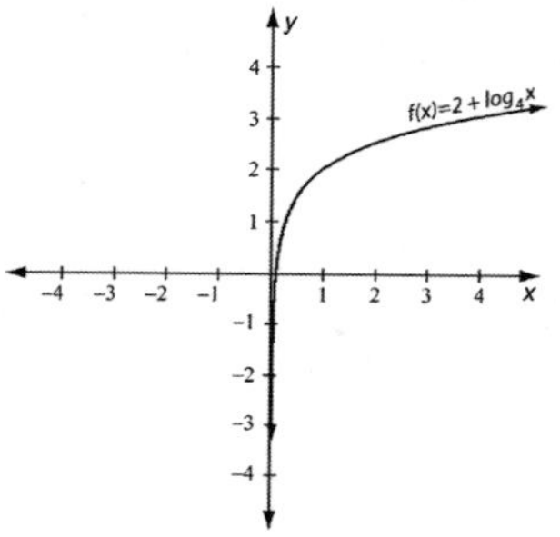

5.

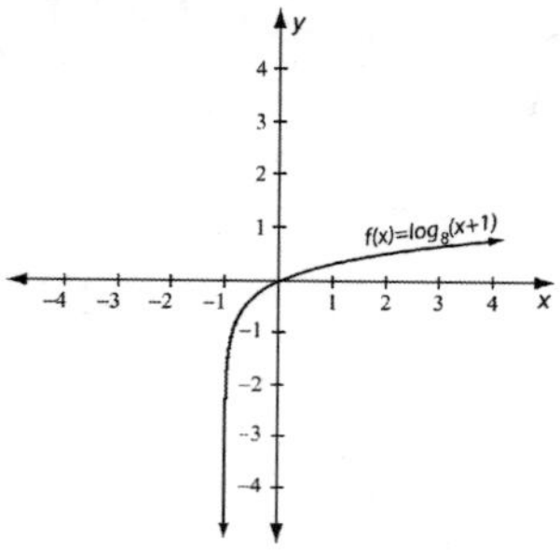

Properties of Logarithms *p.386*

Practice: **1.** $\log_1 x + 3\log_1 y$ **2.** $1+\log_2 p - \log_2 q$ **3.** $\log_6(x-2)-\log_6 y$

Review: **1.** $\log_4 j + \frac{1}{6}\log_4 k$ **3.** $3\log_5 x - 1$ **5.** $\log_2 t - 3$

Expanding a Logarithmic Expression Using Properties *p.388*

Practice: **1.** $\frac{1}{2}\cdot\log_{10} 2 + \frac{1}{2}\cdot\log_{10} p - 6\log_{10} h$ **2.** Cannot be expanded or simplified. **3.** $3+4\log_2 t - \log_2 3 - 2\log_2 n$

Review: **1.** $2\log_4 d + 7\log_4 g - 1 - 3\log_4 m$ **3.** Cannot be expanded or simplified. **5.** $\frac{1}{3}\cdot\log_e a - \frac{1}{3}\cdot\log_e b$ or $\frac{(\log_e a - \log_e b)}{3}$

Combining Logarithmic Expressions *p.390*

Practice: **1.** $\log\sqrt[4]{(a^2x)-3}$ **2.** $\log_6\left[\frac{y^3}{(y+5)}\right]+2$ **3.** $1+\ln\frac{x^5}{8}$

Review: **1.** $\log_b(a-t)$ **3.** $\log_2\left(\sqrt{u^3}\cdot\sqrt[4]{w^3}\right)$ **5.** $\ln\left(\frac{x^2y^4}{z^3}\right)$

Evaluating Logarithmic Functions Using a Calculator *p.392*

Practice: **1.** 0.7597 **2.** 4.4031 **3.** –4.5659

Review: **1.** 1.5465 **3.** –0.1761 **5.** 3.2308

Using the Change of Base Formula *p.394*

Practice: **1.** $\frac{\log\frac{1541}{3.29}}{\log 20}$ **2.** $\frac{\ln 0.287}{\ln 4}$ **3.** True

Review: **1.** $\frac{\ln 20}{\ln 9}$ **3.** $\frac{\log 35}{\log 9}$ **5.** $\frac{\log 8}{\log\frac{1}{2}}$

The Richter Scale *p.395*

Practice: **1.** 6.95 **2.** 7.87 **3.** 6.73

Review: **1.** 6.48 **3.** 7.31 **5.** 8.26

The Distance Modulus Formula *p.397*

Practice: **1.** 4.502 **2.** 5.57 parsecs **3.** 2.2 million light years

Review: **1.** 5.11 **3.** 28.97 parsecs **5.** 93 million light years

Solving Exponential Equations *p.398*

Practice: **1.** $x=\pm 2$ **2.** $x=-0.5544$ **3.** $x=-4.0107$

Review: **1.** $x=2$ **3.** $x=-\frac{1}{2}$ **5.** $x=-3.212$

Solving Logarithmic Equations *p.400*

Practice: **1.** 5 **2.** 5 **3.** 3

Review: **1.** 17 **3.** 3 **5.** –4.3891

Solving Equations with Logarithmic Exponents *p.402*

Practice: **1.** 1 **2.** $\frac{1}{3}$ **3.** $\frac{3}{10}$

Review: **1.** 3 **3.** $\frac{3}{2}$ **5.** 103

Compound Interest *p.403*

Practice: **1.** $12,555.40 **2.** 6.2% **3.** 17 years

Review: **1.** 7.9 years **3.** 2.285 years **5.** $11,410.66

Predicting Change *p.405*

Practice: **1.** .01 moles per liter **2.** 2004 **3.** 1998

Review: **1.** 1245.8 **3.** 15 watts **5.** 63.41%

An Introduction to Exponential Growth and Decay *p.407*

Practice: **1.** 60,744 **2.** 14.5 years **3.** 1957 and 1958

Review: **1.** 30,248 **3.** 19,700 **5.** 785 pounds

Half-Life *p.409*

Practice: **1.** 88% **2.** 2.0 hours **3.** 9.797 grams

Review: **1.** 16 years **3.** 45.8% **5.** $A(t) = 80e^{-.00578t}$

Newton's Law of Cooling *p.412*

Practice: **1.** 49 degrees **2.** 102 minutes **3.** $T(t) = 40 + 35e^{-0.01352t}$

Review: **1.** 133°F **3.** 83° **5.** about 1 hour

Continuously Compounded Interest *p.414*

Practice: **1.** $39,967 **2.** $4\frac{1}{2}$ years **3.** 7 years

Review: **1.** 7.4% **3.** 9.1% **5.** The 8% account will double faster.

The Trigonometric Functions

Finding the Quadrant in Which an Angle Lies *p.419*

Practice: **1.** Quadrant I **2.** Quadrant III **3.** True

Review: **1.** Quadrant II **3.** Quadrant I **5.** False

Finding Coterminal Angles *p.421*

Practice: **1.** False **2.** False **3.** 285°

Review: **1.** True **3.** True **5.** –173°

Finding the Complement and Supplement of an Angle *p.423*

Practice: **1.** False **2.** $180° - x$ **3.** 32.7°

Review: **1.** False **3.** 122° **5.** 36°

Converting between Degrees and Radians *p.425*

Practice: **1.** $\frac{540}{\pi}°$ **2.** –1200° **3.** $\frac{2\pi}{3}$ radians

Review: **1.** $\frac{\pi}{4}$ rad **3.** $\frac{11\pi}{15}$ rad **5.** 1 radian

Using the Arc Length Formula *p.426*

Practice: **1.** 1.75 meters **2.** 19.635 ft **3.** 2.749 in.

Review: **1.** The length of the arc **3.** 0.586 ft **5.** 9.00 in

An Introduction to the Trigonometric Functions *p.429*

Practice: **1.** False **2.** $\frac{4}{3}$ **3.** $\frac{5}{17}$

Review: **1.** True **3.** $\frac{7}{5}$ **5.** $\frac{1}{4}$

Evaluating Trigonometric Functions for an Angle in a Right Triangle *p.433*

Practice: **1.** $\frac{16}{\sqrt{31}}$ **2.** $\frac{\sqrt{55}}{3}$ **3.** $\frac{9\sqrt{3}}{2}$

Review: **1.** $\frac{5}{4}$ **3.** $\frac{\sqrt{61}}{5}$ **5.** False

Finding an Angle Given the Value of a Trigonometric Function *p.436*

Practice: **1.** 30° **2.** $\frac{\pi}{6}$ rad **3.** $\frac{\pi}{3}$ rad

Review: **1.** $\frac{\pi}{3}$ rad **3.** $\frac{\pi}{3}$ rad **5.** 30° or $\frac{\pi}{6}$

Using Trigonometric Functions to Find Unknown Sides of Right Triangles *p.439*

Practice: **1.** 11.4 **2.** 5.6 **3.** 47.0 ft

Review: **1.** tangent **3.** 8.6 **5.** 427 ft

Finding the Height of a Building *p.442*

Practice: **1.** 1300 ft **2.** 69 yd **3.** 27 feet

Review: **1.** True **3.** 3239 ft **5.** 0.265 miles

Evaluating Trigonometric Functions for an Angle in the Coordinate Plane *p.446*

Practice: **1.** True **2.** $\frac{4}{5}$ **3.** $\sin\theta = -\frac{\sqrt{5}}{5}$; $\cos\theta = \frac{2\sqrt{5}}{5}$

Review: **1.** $\frac{4}{3}$ **3.** Quadrant IV **5.** $\frac{4}{5}$

Evaluating Trigonometric Functions Using the Reference Angle *p.447*

Practice: **1.** 10° **2.** $\frac{1}{2}$ **3.** True

Review: **1.** 30° **3.** 50° **5.** $\frac{1}{2}$

Finding the Value of Trigonometric Functions Given Information about the Values of Other Trigonometric Functions *p.449*

Practice: **1.** $\sin\theta = -\frac{12}{13}$; $\cos\theta = \frac{5}{13}$ **2.** $\sin\theta = \frac{4}{5}$; $\tan\theta = -\frac{4}{3}$ **3.** $-\sqrt{2}$

Review: **1.** Quadrants I and III **3.** $\frac{2}{\sqrt{5}}$ **5.** $\frac{1}{2}$

Trigonometric Functions of Important Angles *p.451*

Practice: **1.** 1 **2.** $-\sqrt{3}$ **3.** 1

Review: **1.** 0 **3.** $\frac{\sqrt{3}}{2}$ **5.** $\frac{\sqrt{3}}{3}$

An Introduction to the Graphs of Sine and Cosine Functions *p.453*

Practice: **1.** $y = \sin x$ **2.** 3 **3.** 6π

Review: **1.** False **3.** True **5.** True

Graphing Sine or Cosine Functions with Different Coefficients *p.456*

Practice:

1. 4

2. The period is $\frac{2\pi}{5}$, and the amplitude is 2.

3. True

Review: **1.** 4π **3.** 2 **5.** False

Finding Maximum and Minimum Values and Zeros of Sine and Cosine *p.458*

Practice: **1.** 3 **2.** –2 **3.** 35

Review: **1.** 4 **3.** 3 **5.** 5

Solving Word Problems Involving Sine or Cosine Functions *p.460*

Practice: **1.** 4 feet per second **2.** 68.18 mi **3.** 3.5 hours

Review: **1.** 1,584 mph **3.** Cannot be determined **5.** 97°F

Graphing Sine and Cosine Functions with Phase Shifts *p.462*

Practice: **1.** 3 to the right **2.** True **3.** True

Review: **1.** False **3.** $\frac{\pi}{2}$ units to the left **5.** 4 to the left

Fancy Graphing: Changes in Period, Amplitude, Vertical Shift, and Phase Shift *p.464*

Practice: **1.** $\frac{\pi}{6}$ to the left **2.** $y = 4\cos(x-3)+2$ **3.** $y = 3\sin(x-\pi)-1$

Review: **1.** down 4 units **3.** True **5.** False

Graphing the Tangent, Secant, Cosecant, and Cotangent Functions *p.466*

Practice: **1.** $\frac{\pi}{2}$ **2.** $x = k\pi$ (multiples of π) **3.** True

Review: **1.** π **3.** $x = k\pi$ (multiples of π) **5.** True

Fancy Graphing: Tangent, Secant, Cosecant, and Cotangent *p.469*

Practice:

1. True

2. $\frac{\pi}{3}$

3. The graph of $y = 2\sec x$ is stretched vertically by 2 and the graph of $y = 2\sec x$ has a period change from 2π to π.

Review:

1. $\frac{\pi}{6}$
3. False
5. The coefficient 3 stretches the graph vertically by a factor of 3 and the negative flips it.

Identifying a Trigonometric Function from its Graph *p.472*

Practice: **1.** $y = \cot x + 1$ **2.** False **3.** True

Review: **1.** $y = -\sec x$ **3.** $y = -\tan x - 3$ **5.** True

An Introduction to Inverse Trigonometric Functions *p.477*

Practice: **1.** True **2.** $-1 \le t \le 1$ **3.** True

Review: **1.** True **3.** False **5.** $-\frac{\pi}{6} < y < \frac{\pi}{6}$

Evaluating Inverse Trigonometric Functions *p.480*

Practice: **1.** 78° **2.** 30° **3.** $\frac{3\pi}{4}$

Review: **1.** 0.853 **3.** No such number exists. **5.** $\frac{\pi}{4}$

Solving an Equation Involving an Inverse Trigonometric Function *p.481*

Practice: **1.** $\frac{\pi}{2} + 2\pi n$ **2.** $-\frac{\pi}{4} + \pi n$ **3.** $\frac{5\pi}{6} + 2\pi n$ and $\frac{7\pi}{6} + 2\pi n$

Review: **1.** –2 **3.** πn **5.** $\frac{5\pi}{3} + 2\pi n$ and $\frac{\pi}{3} + 2\pi n$

Evaluating the Composition of a Trigonometric Function and Its Inverse *p.483*

Practice: **1.** $-\frac{\pi}{3}$ **2.** $\frac{\pi}{3}$ **3.** $\frac{\pi}{6}$

Review: **1.** 1.7 **3.** $\frac{\pi}{3}$ **5.** $-\frac{\pi}{6}$

Applying Trigonometric Functions: Is He Speeding? *p.486*

Practice: **1.** 5.3 mi **2.** 60.7 mph **3.** This horse is slower by 5.86 mph.

Review: **1.** 1492.8 ft **3.** 0.0695 miles **5.** 3.93 mph over the speed limit

Trigonometric Identities

Fundamental Trigonometric Identities *p.495*

Practice: **1.** True **2.** False **3.** $4x^2 + 12x + 9$

Review: **1.** True **3.** True **5.** $25x^2 - 30x + 9$

Finding All Function Values *p.497*

Practice: **1.** $\frac{\sqrt{3}}{2}$ **2.** $\frac{\sqrt{5}}{2}$ **3.** $-\sqrt{35}$

Review: **1.** $\sqrt{3}$ **3.** .86 **5.** 2

Simplifying a Trigonometric Expression Using Trigonometric Identities *p.499*

Practice: **1.** $\sin^2 x$ **2.** $\sin^2 t$ **3.** 1

Review: **1.** $\sec\theta$ **3.** $\tan^2 x$ **5.** 1

Simplifying Trigonometric Expressions Involving Fractions *p.501*

Practice: **1.** $1+\tan\theta$ **2.** $\cot^2\theta$ **3.** $\dfrac{1}{\cos^2 x\sin^2 x}$

Review: **1.** 1 **3.** $\tan^3\theta$ **5.** 1

Simplifying Products of Binomials Involving Trigonometric Functions *p.503*

Practice: **1.** $2+\cot^2\theta$ **2.** $\tan^2 t\cdot\sin^2 t$ **3.** $\cot^2\theta-1$

Review: **1.** $-\cos^2 x$ **3.** $\tan^2 x-\sin^2 x$ **5.** $\cot^2\csc^2$

Factoring Trigonometric Expressions *p.505*

Practice: **1.** $2(\cos\theta+2)(\cos\theta+3)$ **2.** $\csc\theta$ **3.** $1+\cot a$

Review: **1.** 1 **3.** 1 **5.** 1

Determining Whether a Trigonometric Function Is Odd, Even, or Neither *p.506*

Practice: **1.** Even **2.** Odd **3.** The function is odd.

Review: **1.** Odd **3.** Neither **5.** Neither

Proving an Identity *p.508*

Practice: **1.** True **2.** True **3.** True

Review: **1.** True **3.** True **5.** True

Proving an Identity: Other Examples *p.511*

Practice: **1.** $\csc^2\theta-\csc^2\theta\sin\theta=\cot^2\theta$ **2.** $\dfrac{1}{\cot x}+\cot x=\dfrac{1}{\sin x\cos x}$ **3.** $\dfrac{1+2\tan^2 x+\tan^4 x}{1-\tan^2 x}=\dfrac{\sec^4 x}{1-\tan^2 x}$

Review: **1.** $\tan x$ **3.** $\tan^2 x+\sin^2 x$ **5.** $\csc\theta-\cot\theta$

Solving Trigonometric Equations *p.513*

Practice: **1.** $x=\dfrac{\pi}{4}+2\pi n$ and $x=\dfrac{7\pi}{4}+2\pi n$ **2.** $x=\pi+2\pi n$ **3.** πn

Review: **1.** $x=\pi+2\pi n$ **3.** True **5.** $\dfrac{\pi}{4}+\pi n$

Solving Trigonometric Equations by Factoring *p.516*

Practice: **1.** $\theta=0,\dfrac{\pi}{6},\dfrac{5\pi}{6}$, or π **2.** $x=0,\ \dfrac{\pi}{4},\ \pi$, or $\dfrac{5\pi}{4}$ **3.** $x=0,\ \dfrac{\pi}{2}$, or π

Review: **1.** $x=0$ or π **3.** $x=0,\ \dfrac{\pi}{2},\ \pi,\ \dfrac{3\pi}{2}$, or 2π **5.** $x=\dfrac{\pi}{3},\ \pi,\ \dfrac{5\pi}{3}$

Solving Trigonometric Equations with Coefficients in the Argument *p.518*

Practice: **1.** $\dfrac{\pi}{12},\dfrac{5\pi}{12},\dfrac{13\pi}{12}$, or $\dfrac{17\pi}{12}$ **2.** $\dfrac{3\pi}{4}$ **3.** $\dfrac{4\pi}{9},\dfrac{8\pi}{9}$, or $\dfrac{16\pi}{9}$

Review: **1.** $\dfrac{\pi}{12},\dfrac{5\pi}{12},\dfrac{7\pi}{12},\dfrac{11\pi}{12},\dfrac{13\pi}{12},\dfrac{17\pi}{12},\dfrac{19\pi}{12}$, and $\dfrac{23\pi}{12}$ **3.** $\dfrac{\pi}{6},\dfrac{5\pi}{6},\dfrac{7\pi}{6}$, and $\dfrac{11\pi}{6}$ **5.** π

Solving Trigonometric Equations Using the Quadratic Formula *p.520*

Practice:

1. .373, 1.721, 2.467, 3.815, 4.561, and 5.909 radians
2. 3.553 or 5.872
3. 0.196, 1.375, 3.338, or 4.516

Review: **1.** 1.922, 2.791, 5.064, and 5.933 radians **3.** True **5.** 1.179 or 5.104

Solving Word Problems Involving Trigonometric Equations *p.522*

Practice: **1.** $\frac{1}{3}$ **2.** 4.429 seconds **3.** $t = .2793 + \frac{\pi}{2}n$ for $0 \le n \le 38$

Review: **1.** 15° **3.** 13 seconds **5.** 5.854 seconds

Identities for Sums and Differences of Angles *p.525*

Practice: **1.** $\frac{\sqrt{2}-\sqrt{6}}{4}$ **2.** $\frac{-\sqrt{2}-\sqrt{6}}{4}$ **3.** -1.31

Review: **1.** True **3.** $\frac{\sqrt{6}+\sqrt{2}}{4}$ **5.** 0.43

Using Sum and Difference Identities *p.527*

Practice: **1.** $\frac{\sqrt{6}+\sqrt{2}}{4}$ **2.** $-2+\sqrt{3}$ **3.** $-\frac{63}{16}$

Review: **1.** $\frac{\sqrt{6}-\sqrt{2}}{4}$ **3.** $2+\sqrt{3}$ **5.** $\frac{16}{65}$

Using Sum and Difference Identities to Simplify an Expression *p.529*

Practice: **1.** 0 **2.** $\frac{\sqrt{3}}{3}$ **3.** $\frac{1}{2}$

Review: **1.** $\frac{1}{2}$ **3.** $\frac{\sqrt{3}}{2}$ **5.** $\cos x$

Confirming a Double-Angle Identity *p.530*

Practice: **1.** $\sqrt{3}$ **2.** $\frac{12}{13}$ **3.** $\cos^2 2x$

Review: **1.** 0 **3.** $\frac{120}{119}$ **5.** $\frac{24}{25}$

Using Double-Angle Identities *p.532*

Practice: **1.** $0, \pi$ **2.** $0,\ \pi,\ \frac{\pi}{6},\ \frac{5\pi}{6}$ **3.** 0

Review: **1.** $\frac{\pi}{4}, \frac{3\pi}{4}, \frac{5\pi}{4}$, or $\frac{7\pi}{4}$ **3.** $\frac{2\pi}{3}$ or $\frac{4\pi}{3}$ **5.** $\frac{\pi}{2}$ or $\frac{3\pi}{2}$

Solving Word Problems Involving Multiple-Angle Identities *p.534*

Practice: **1.** $2y$ **2.** $\frac{\pi}{2}$ **3.** $\frac{\pi}{4}$ or 45°

Review: **1.** $x = 5\cos\theta, y = 5\sin\theta$ **3.** $x = 20\cos\theta,\ y = 20\sin\theta$ **5.** $72\sin\theta\cos\theta$

Using a Cofunction Identity *p.538*

Practice: **1.** $-\tan x$ **2.** $\tan x$ **3.** $-\sin x$

Review: **1.** $\sin x$ **3.** $\sin x$ **5.** $-\tan x$

Using a Power-Reducing Identity *p.540*

Practice: **1.** $\cos 2t$ **2.** $\frac{\pi}{8}, \frac{3\pi}{8}, \frac{5\pi}{8}$, or $\frac{7\pi}{8}$ **3.** $\frac{3-4\cos 2t+\cos 4t}{3+4\cos 2t+\cos 4t}$

Review: **1.** $\left(\frac{1}{2}\right)(\sin t - \sin t\cos 2t)$ **3.** $\left(\frac{1}{8}\right)(-1+\cos 4t)$ **5.** $\frac{3-4\cos 2t+\cos 4t}{12+16\cos 2t+4\cos 4t}$

Using Half-Angle Identities to Solve a Trigonometric Equation *p.542*

Practice: **1.** $\frac{1}{7}$ **2.** $\frac{\sqrt{26}}{26}$ **3.** $\frac{\sqrt{2-\left(\sqrt{2+\sqrt{3}}\right)}}{2}$

Review: **1.** $\frac{\sqrt{2+\sqrt{3}}}{2}$ **3.** $\sqrt{2}-1$ **5.** $\frac{\sqrt{\left(2+\sqrt{2}\right)}}{2}$

Applications of Trigonometry

The Law of Sines *p.547*

Practice: **1.** $a = 73$ mm, $b = 200$ mm **2.** 237 mm **3.** 4.3

Review: **1.** 13.5m **3.** 2.87 cm **5.** 22.0 in

Solving a Triangle Given Two Sides and One Angle *p.549*

Practice: **1.** 25.7° **2.** 31° **3.** $a = 22.2$, $b = 36.5$

Review: **1.** 64.19° **3.** $a = 23.67$ in, $A = 80.34°$ **5.** $b = 20.5$ in and $B = 78.65°$

Solving a Triangle (SAS): Another Example *p.551*

Practice: **1.** $\angle 1 = 109°$, $\angle 2 = 71°$ **2.** 104.88° or 21.12° **3.** $12.89 < a < 15.75$

Review: **1.** $C = 50.61°$, $b = 17.10$ ft **3.** 12.76° or 105.24° **5.** no solution

The Law of Sines: An Application *p.554*

Practice: **1.** 103.95 m **2.** 189 miles **3.** 53.21'

Review: **1.** 1615 ft **3.** 11.5 miles **5.** 14 miles

The Law of Cosines *p.558*

Practice: **1.** An angle and its two adjacent sides **2.** 5.04 **3.** 6.6

Review: **1.** 3.6 **3.** 11.67 **5.** 12.12 m

The Law of Cosines (SSS) *p.560*

Practice:

1. 34.8°
2. 53.13°
3. $\gamma = 114.974°$, $\alpha = 22.191°$, and $\beta = 42.835°$

Review: **1.** 22.33° **3.** 36.1° **5.** 34.047°

The Law of Cosines (SAS): An Application *p.562*

Practice: **1.** 3.4 mm **2.** 14.5 cm **3.** 114.57 km

Review: **1.** 3460 m **3.** 3.1 cm **5.** 424.5 km

Heron's Formula *p.565*

Practice: **1.** 63 **2.** 242.9 sq. in. **3.** 309.0 mm^2

Review: **1.** 54 in^2 **3.** 42 cm^2 **5.** 10859.3 sq ft

An Introduction to Vectors *p.568*

Practice: **1.** $< 9,5 >$ **2.** Vectors **a** and **w**. **3.** $\langle 6,-2 \rangle$

Review: **1.** $< 2,5 >$ **3.** $< 7,10 >$ **5.** $< -4,2 >$

Finding the Magnitude and Direction of a Vector *p.571*

Practice: **1.** 329.036° **2.** 273.8° **3.** 3

Review: **1.** $\sqrt{41}$ **3.** $3\sqrt{2}$ or 4.24 **5.** 234.46°

Vector Addition and Scalar Multiplication *p.574*

Practice: **1.** $\langle -18,22\rangle$ **2.** $\langle -4,16\rangle$ **3.** $\langle 0,-6\rangle$

Review: **1.** $\langle 9,-21\rangle$ **3.** $\langle 6,-9\rangle$ **5.** $\langle 23,-13\rangle$

Finding the Components of a Vector *p.576*

Practice: **1.** $(-\sqrt{3},-1)$ **2.** $(-15,15)$ **3.** $\langle -6.31,-9.01\rangle$

Review: **1.** $\langle 5,5\sqrt{3}\rangle$ **3.** $\langle 6\sqrt{2},6\sqrt{2}\rangle$ **5.** $\langle 9.66,-2.59\rangle$

Finding a Unit Vector *p.579*

Practice: **1.** $\left\langle \frac{-3\sqrt{58}}{58},\frac{-7\sqrt{58}}{58}\right\rangle$ **2.** $\langle 1,0\rangle$ **3.** 1

Review: **1.** $\left\langle -\frac{5}{13},\frac{12}{13}\right\rangle$ **3.** $\left\langle -\frac{\sqrt{2}}{2},\frac{\sqrt{2}}{2}\right\rangle$ **5.** $\left\langle \frac{7}{25},\frac{-24}{25}\right\rangle$

Solving Word Problems Involving Velocity or Forces *p.581*

Practice: **1.** $90\langle -\sqrt{3},1\rangle$ **2.** 225° **3.** 119.8

Review: **1.** $\langle 125,125\sqrt{3}\rangle$ **3.** $v=\langle 12.7,27.2\rangle$ **5.** The plane is moving 493 mph on a bearing of 33.4°

Graphing a Complex Number and Finding Its Absolute Value *p.584*

Practice: **1.** 5 **2.** False. **3.** $5\sqrt{5}$

Review: **1.** True **3.** 10 **5.** $\sqrt{290}$

Expressing a Complex Number in Trigonometric or Polar Form *p.586*

Practice: **1.** $7(\cos 270°+i\sin 270°)$ **2.** $5\sqrt{2}\left(\cos\frac{3\pi}{4}+i\sin\frac{3\pi}{4}\right)$ **3.** $-2\sqrt{2}-i2\sqrt{2}$

Review: **1.** $4\sqrt{2}(\cos 45°+i\sin 45°)$ **3.** $9(\cos 90°+i\sin 90°)$ **5.** -3

Multiplying and Dividing Complex Numbers in Trigonometric or Polar Form *p.588*

Practice: **1.** $8(\cos 210°+i\sin 210°)$ **2.** $3(\cos(-240°)+i\sin(-240°))$ **3.** $-1-i\sqrt{3}$

Review: **1.** $12(\cos 150°+i\sin 150°)$ **3.** $15(\cos 90°+i\sin 90°)$ **5.** -24 or $-24+0i$

Using DeMoivre's Theorem to Raise a Complex Number to a Power *p.591*

Practice: **1.** $64(\cos 120°+i\sin 120°)$ **2.** $32(\cos 150°+i\sin 150°)$ **3.** $8(\cos 270°+i\sin 270°)$

Review: **1.** $16(\cos 500°+i\sin 500°)$ **3.** $16(\cos 1200°+i\sin 1200°)$ **5.** $-32-32i\sqrt{3}$

Roots of Complex Numbers *p.593*

Practice:

1. $5,\ \frac{-5+5i\sqrt{3}}{2},\ \frac{-5-5i\sqrt{3}}{2}$

2. $\sqrt[6]{2}\left(\cos\frac{\pi}{4}+i\sin\frac{\pi}{4}\right),\ \sqrt[6]{2}\left(\cos\frac{7\pi}{12}+i\sin\frac{7\pi}{12}\right),$
$\sqrt[6]{2}\left(\cos\frac{11\pi}{12}+i\sin\frac{11\pi}{12}\right),\ \sqrt[6]{2}\left(\cos\frac{5\pi}{4}+i\sin\frac{5\pi}{4}\right),$
$\sqrt[6]{2}\left(\cos\frac{19\pi}{12}+i\sin\frac{19\pi}{12}\right),\ \sqrt[6]{2}\left(\cos\frac{23\pi}{12}+i\sin\frac{23\pi}{12}\right)$

3. $3\sqrt[8]{2}\left(\cos\frac{3\pi}{16}+i\sin\frac{3\pi}{16}\right)$, $3\sqrt[8]{2}\left(\cos\frac{11\pi}{16}+i\sin\frac{11\pi}{16}\right)$,
$3\sqrt[8]{2}\left(\cos\frac{19\pi}{16}+i\sin\frac{19\pi}{16}\right)$, $3\sqrt[8]{2}\left(\cos\frac{27\pi}{16}+i\sin\frac{27\pi}{16}\right)$

Review:

1. True

3. $2\left(\cos\frac{2\pi}{3}+i\sin\frac{2\pi}{3}\right)$

5. $\sqrt[6]{2}\left(\cos\frac{7\pi}{12}+i\sin\frac{7\pi}{12}\right)$, $\sqrt[6]{2}\left(\cos\frac{5\pi}{4}+i\sin\frac{5\pi}{4}\right)$, $\sqrt[6]{2}\left(\cos\frac{23\pi}{12}+i\sin\frac{23\pi}{12}\right)$

More Roots of Complex Numbers *p.597*

Practice:

1. $2,-2,2i,-2i$

2. $-5,\frac{5-5\sqrt{3}}{2},\frac{5+5i\sqrt{3}}{2}$

3. $1,\frac{1+i\sqrt{3}}{2},\frac{-1+i\sqrt{3}}{2}-1,\frac{-1-i\sqrt{3}}{2},\frac{1-i\sqrt{3}}{2}$

Review: **1.** $1,i,-1,-i$ **3.** $-4,2+2i\sqrt{3},2-2i\sqrt{3}$ **5.** $0.855+1.481i,-1.710,0.855-1.481i$

Roots of Unity *p.600*

Practice: **1.** $1,\ -\frac{1}{2}+\frac{i\sqrt{3}}{2},\ -\frac{1}{2}-\frac{i\sqrt{3}}{2}$ **2.** $0.5-0.866i$ **3.** $-0.5+0.866i$

Review:

1. $\cos 0+i\sin 0$, $\cos 36+i\sin 36$, $\cos 72+i\sin 72$, $\cos 108+i\sin 108$, $\cos 144+i\sin 144$, $\cos 180+i\sin 180$, $\cos 216+i\sin 216$, $\cos 252+i\sin 252$, $\cos 288+i\sin 288$, $\cos 324+i\sin 324$

3. $-\frac{1}{2}+\frac{\sqrt{3}}{2}i$

5. 2

An Introduction to Polar Coordinates *p.602*

Practice: **1.** negative $x-$axis **2.** Quadrant II **3.** Quadrant I

Review: **1.**

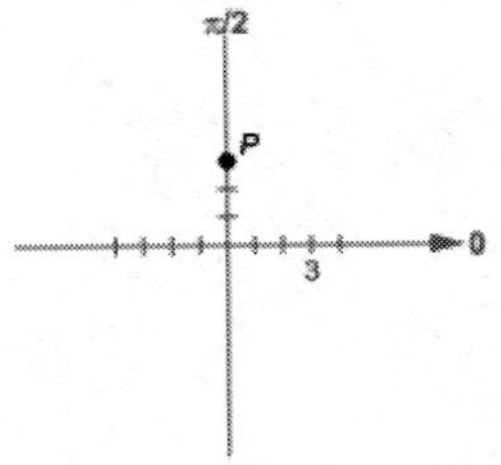

3. Quadrant IV **5.** Quadrant I

Converting between Polar and Rectangular Coordinates *p.604*

Practice: **1.** 2 $(-2.4,-1.8)$

Review: **1.** $(2\sqrt{2},45°)$ **3.** $(2,2\sqrt{3})$ **5.** True

Graphing Simple Polar Equations *p.606*

Practice: **1.** $(x-2)^2+y^2=4$ **2.**

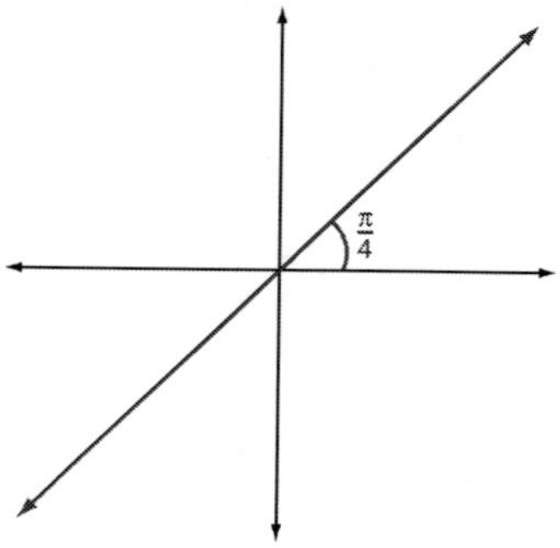

Review: **1.** False **3.** $x^2+(y-6)^2=36$ **5.**

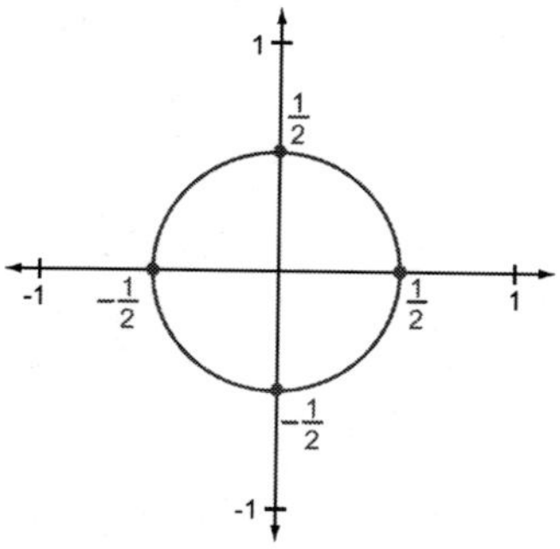

Systems of Equations and Matrices

An Introduction to Linear Systems *p.611*

Solving a System by Substitution *p.611*

Practice: **1.** $\left(-\frac{18}{11},-\frac{30}{11}\right)$ **2.** $\left(2,-\frac{2}{3}\right)$ **3.** $(3,2)$

Review: **1.** $\left(\frac{3}{2},-\frac{4}{5}\right)$ **3.** $(-6,2)$ **5.** $(8,9)$

Solving a System by Elimination *p.613*

Practice: **1.** Infinitely Many Solutions **2.** $(-4,20)$ **3.** $(-2,3)$

Review: **1.** Infinitely many solutions **3.** $(-3,4)$ **5.** $(-4,4)$

An Introduction to Linear Systems in Three Variables *p.615*

Solving Linear Systems in Three Variables *p.616*

Practice: **1.** $y=4$ **2.** $(3,2,-1)$ **3.** $(1,-2,2)$

Review: **1.** $x=2$ **3.** $(1,1,2)$ **5.** $(3,-1,4)$

Solving Inconsistent Systems *p.619*

Practice: **1.** True **2.** True **3.** False

Review: **1.** True **3.** False **5.** False

Solving Dependent Systems *p.622*

Practice: **1.** True **2.** False **3.** True

Review: **1.** True **3.** True **5.** False

Solving Systems with Two Equations *p.624*

Practice: **1.** $\left(\frac{11y-10}{4},y,\frac{13y-6}{4}\right)$ **2.** $(x,12-11x,27-26x)$ **3.** $(-14z-10,-22z-17,z)$

Review: **1.** $(13-20z,\ 16-25z,\ z)$ **3.** $(19-4y, y, -11+3y)$ **5.** $\left(\frac{10-2y}{7}, y, \frac{1+18y}{7}\right)$

Investments *p.626*

Practice: **1.** 88 **2.** (21,15) **3.** \$1176.47

Review: **1.** $(18,\ 2)$ **3.** \$35,000 at 6% and \$65,000 at $4\frac{1}{2}$% **5.** \$34,000 at 2% and \$6,000 at 3%

Solving with Partial Fractions *p.628*

Practice: **1.** $\frac{-3/2}{x+3}+\frac{3/2}{x+1}$ **2.** $\frac{-8/7}{2x+1}+\frac{4/7}{x-3}$ **3.** $\frac{4}{x+1}+\frac{5}{x-3}$

Review: **1.** $\frac{-1}{x-2}+\frac{4}{x-3}$ **3.** $\frac{-3/5}{x}+\frac{13/5}{x+5}$ **5.** $\frac{2}{x-4}+\frac{1}{x+2}$

Solving Nonlinear Systems Using Elimination *p.631*

Practice: **1.** (2, 2); (2,−2); (−2, 2); (−2,−2) **2.** (5, 0); (−4, 3); (−4,−3) **3.** No solution

Review:

1. $(3,\ -1);\ (-3,\ -1);\ \left(\frac{7}{3}, \frac{5}{3}\right);\ \left(-\frac{7}{3}, \frac{5}{3}\right)$

3. $\left(\frac{3}{2}, \frac{7}{2}\right);\ (2, 3)$

5. $\left(\sqrt{5}, 2\right);\ \left(\sqrt{5}, -2\right);\ \left(-\sqrt{5}, 2\right);\ \left(-\sqrt{5}, -2\right)$

Solving Nonlinear Systems by Substitution *p.633*

Practice: **1.** (−3, 0); (0, 3) **2.** (9,−43); (−3,5) **3.** $(6,\ 1);\ (-\frac{2}{3}, -9)$

Review: **1.** $(3, 2);\ (-5, -6)$ **3.** $(2, 4);\ \left(-\frac{1}{3}, \frac{5}{3}\right)$ **5.** No real solution

An Introduction to Matrices *p.635*

Practice: **1.** $\begin{bmatrix} 7 & 0 & 0 & 4 \\ 6 & -3 & 1 & 14 \\ 0 & 2 & -1 & 0 \end{bmatrix}$ **2.** $5x+y-4z+7w=0$ **3.** 2×4

Review: **1.** True **3.** $\begin{bmatrix} 7 & 9 & 1 \\ 0 & 4 & 12 \\ 8 & 2 & 5 \end{bmatrix}$ **5.** $5x+\frac{1}{2}y+9z=6;\ \frac{1}{3}x=3;\ 4y+2z=8$

The Arithmetic of Matrices *p.637*

Practice: **1.** $\begin{bmatrix} -1 & \frac{14}{3} \\ 4 & 2 \\ 0 & \frac{13}{4} \end{bmatrix}$ **2.** not possible **3.** $\begin{bmatrix} 2 & -4 \\ 6 & 1 \\ -4 & 8 \end{bmatrix}$

Review: **1.** $\begin{bmatrix} 3 & 7 \\ 11 & 15 \end{bmatrix}$ **3.** $\begin{bmatrix} 3 \\ -1 \\ -5 \end{bmatrix}$ **5.** not possible

Multiplying Matrices by a Scalar *p.639*

Practice: **1.** $\begin{bmatrix} 8 & 12 & 16 \end{bmatrix}$ **2.** $\begin{bmatrix} -8 & -16 \\ -24 & -4 \end{bmatrix}$ **3.** $\begin{bmatrix} \frac{5}{2} & -1 \\ -6 & 4 \end{bmatrix}$

Review: **1.** $\begin{bmatrix} -3 & \frac{5}{2} & 1 \end{bmatrix}$ **3.** $\begin{bmatrix} \frac{9}{4} & -1 & -\frac{1}{5} \\ -\frac{3}{2} & 1 & 0 \\ \frac{1}{2} & \frac{1}{8} & -\frac{1}{4} \end{bmatrix}$ **5.** $\begin{bmatrix} -15 & -18 & -35 \\ -7 & 6 & 9 \end{bmatrix}$

Multiplying Matrices *p.641*

Practice: **1.** $\begin{bmatrix} 8 & -26 \end{bmatrix}$ **2.** not possible **3.** $\begin{bmatrix} 17 & -11 & 0 \\ -4 & 4 & -4 \\ 5 & -3 & 0 \end{bmatrix}$

Review: **1.** $\begin{bmatrix} 13 \\ 22 \end{bmatrix}$ **3.** $\begin{bmatrix} -1 & 9 \\ -7 & 17 \end{bmatrix}$ **5.** $\begin{bmatrix} -8 & 12 \\ 8 & -2 \\ 13 & 45 \end{bmatrix}$

Can They Multiply? *p.644*

Practice: **1.** True **2.** False **3.** True

Review: **1.** False **3.** False **5.** True

Using the Gauss-Jordan Method *p.646*

Practice: **1.** $\begin{bmatrix} 1 & 2 & -2 \\ 1 & -4 & 4 \end{bmatrix}$; $\begin{bmatrix} 1 & 2 & -2 \\ 2 & -2 & 2 \end{bmatrix}$ **2.** $\begin{bmatrix} 4 & -1 & 10 \\ 1 & -4 & 10 \end{bmatrix}$; $\begin{bmatrix} -4 & 1 & -10 \\ -\frac{1}{4} & 1 & -\frac{5}{2} \end{bmatrix}$ **3.** $x = 6$ and $y = 1$

Review: **1.** $x = 4,\ y = -2$ **3.** $x = 8,\ y = 3$ **5.** $x = -3,\ y = 4$

Using Gauss-Jordan: Another Example *p.648*

Practice: **1.** $x = 4$ and $y = -4$ **2.** $x = 8$ and $y = 3$ **3.** $x = \frac{4}{3}$ and $y = \frac{10}{3}$

Review: **1.** $x = \frac{3}{4},\ y = \frac{5}{6}$ **3.** $x = -7,\ y = -2$ **5.** $x = -\frac{11}{9},\ y = \frac{2}{9}$

Evaluating 2x2 Determinants *p.650*

Practice: **1.** –29 **2.** $4a + 18$ **3.** False

Review: **1.** –1 **3.** 0 **5.** 10

Evaluating 3x3 Determinants *p.651*

Practice: **1.** 1 **2.** 2 **3.** $a - 2ac + 2bc - b$

Review: **1.** 2 **3.** 2 **5.** –21

Applying Determinants *p.654*

Practice: **1.** 2 **2.** yes the points are collinear **3.** 10

Review: **1.** 5.5 **3.** yes the points are collinear **5.** 14

Using Cramer's Rule *p.656*

Practice: **1.** $x = 4,\ y = -2$ **2.** $x = 2, y = 0$ **3.** $x = -4, y = 20$

Review: **1.** $x = 1,\ y = 2$ **3.** $x = 7,\ y = 2$ **5.** $x = -4,\ y = 4$

Using Cramer's Rule in a 3x3 Matrix *p.658*

Practice: **1.** $x = 3,\ y = 2,\ z = -2$ **2.** $x = 4,\ y = 3,\ z = 2$ **3.** $x = -1,\ y = -1,\ z = -1$

Review: **1.** $x = 3,\ y = 2,\ z = 1$ **3.** $x = 3,\ y = \frac{1}{2},\ z = -\frac{1}{3}$ **5.** $x = 3,\ y = -1,\ z = 4$

An Introduction to Inverses *p.660*

Inverses: 2x2 Matrices *p.661*

Practice: **1.** True **2.** $\begin{bmatrix} \frac{1}{2} & -1 \\ -1 & 3 \end{bmatrix}$ **3.** $\begin{bmatrix} -\frac{1}{3} & -\frac{1}{3} \\ -\frac{2}{3} & -\frac{5}{3} \end{bmatrix}$

Review: **1.** $\begin{bmatrix} \frac{1}{2} & -\frac{3}{2} \\ -1 & 4 \end{bmatrix}$ **3.** $\begin{bmatrix} -\frac{1}{4} & \frac{1}{8} \\ \frac{1}{4} & \frac{3}{8} \end{bmatrix}$ **5.** $\begin{bmatrix} 2 & -5 \\ -1 & 3 \end{bmatrix}$

Another Look at 2x2 Inverses *p.663*

Practice: **1.** $\begin{bmatrix} \frac{1}{10} & \frac{1}{10} \\ -\frac{3}{10} & \frac{7}{10} \end{bmatrix}$ **2.** The inverse does not exist. **3.** $\begin{bmatrix} -\frac{3}{2} & -\frac{1}{2} \\ \frac{13}{2} & \frac{5}{2} \end{bmatrix}$

Review: **1.** $\begin{bmatrix} -1 & 2 \\ 3 & -5 \end{bmatrix}$ **3.** The inverse does not exist. **5.** $\begin{bmatrix} -1 & 1 \\ -2 & \frac{5}{2} \end{bmatrix}$

Inverses: 3x3 Matrices *p.665*

Practice: **1.** $\begin{bmatrix} 1 & \frac{2}{3} & -\frac{2}{3} \\ -\frac{1}{2} & \frac{1}{6} & \frac{1}{3} \\ 0 & -\frac{1}{3} & \frac{1}{3} \end{bmatrix}$ **2.** The inverse does not exist. **3.** $\begin{bmatrix} 0 & -1 & \frac{1}{2} \\ 0 & 0 & \frac{1}{2} \\ 1 & 2 & -1 \end{bmatrix}$

Review: **1.** $\begin{bmatrix} -1 & 3 & -3 \\ 0 & 1 & -1 \\ \frac{1}{2} & -3 & \frac{7}{2} \end{bmatrix}$ **3.** $\begin{bmatrix} -1 & \frac{5}{2} & \frac{1}{2} \\ 0 & \frac{1}{2} & \frac{1}{2} \\ -1 & \frac{7}{2} & \frac{1}{2} \end{bmatrix}$ **5.** The inverse does not exist.

Solving a System of Equations with Inverses *p.669*

Practice: **1.** $x = 19,\ y = -11$ **2.** $x = \frac{5}{3},\ y = \frac{1}{3}$ **3.** $x = -\frac{4}{5},\ y = \frac{11}{5}$

Review: **1.** $x = 5,\ y = 3$ **3.** $x = -\frac{3}{5},\ y = -\frac{2}{5}$ **5.** $x = \frac{1}{2},\ y = \frac{1}{4}$

An Introduction to Systems of Inequalities *p.670*

Practice: **1.** True **2.** False **3.** False

Review: **1.** False **3.** True **5.** False

Graphing Systems of Inequalities *p.672*

Practice: **1.**

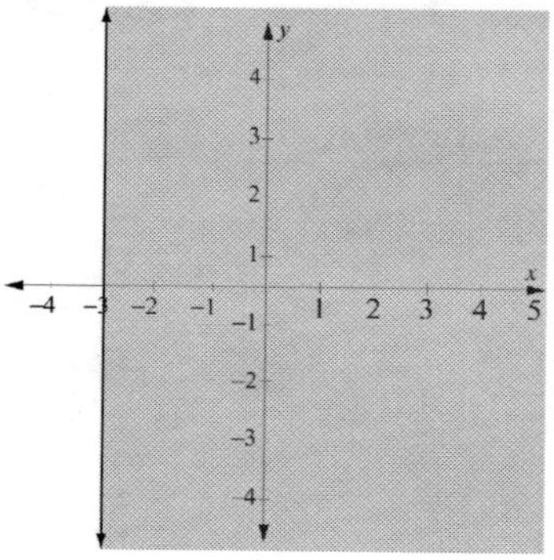

2.

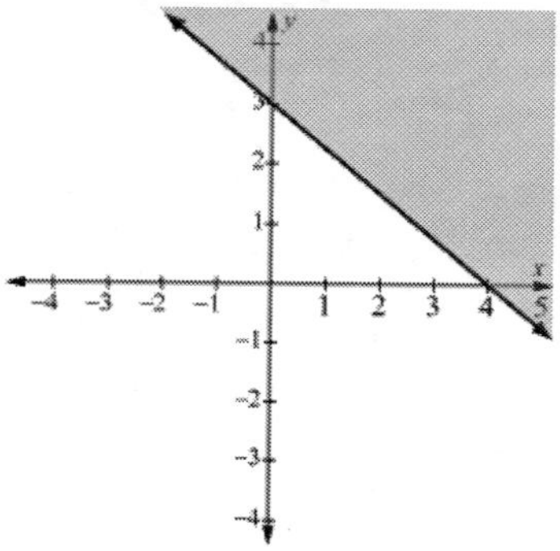

3.

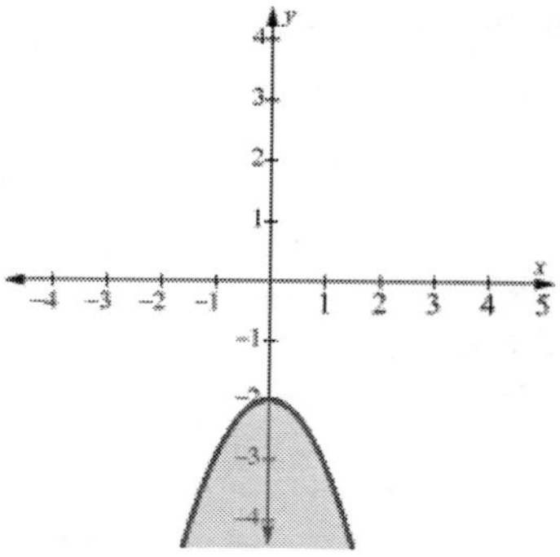

Review: **1.** True **3.** True **5.** False

Graphing the Solution Set of a System of Inequalities *p.675*

Practice: **1.**

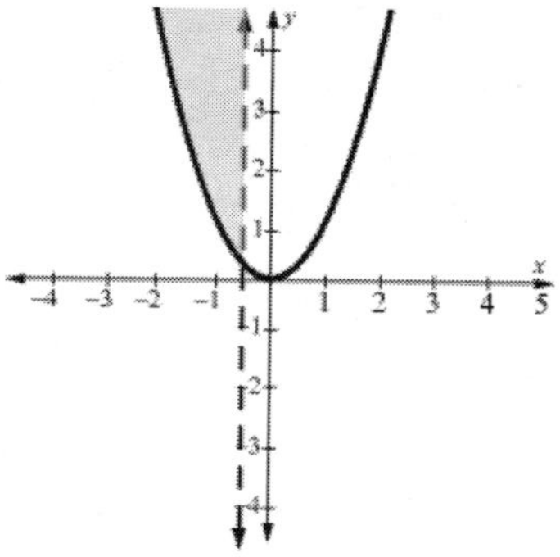

2.

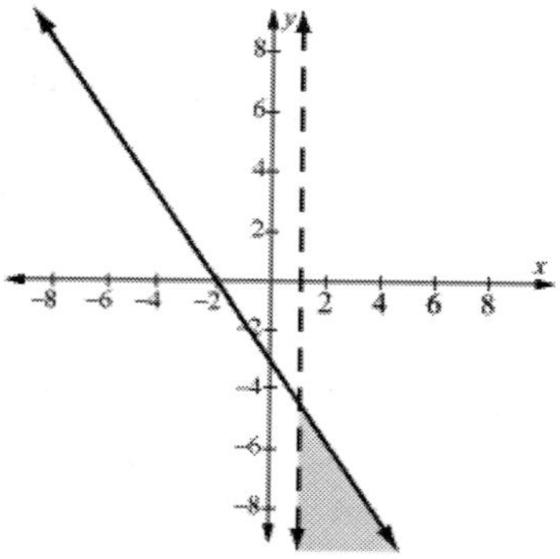

3.

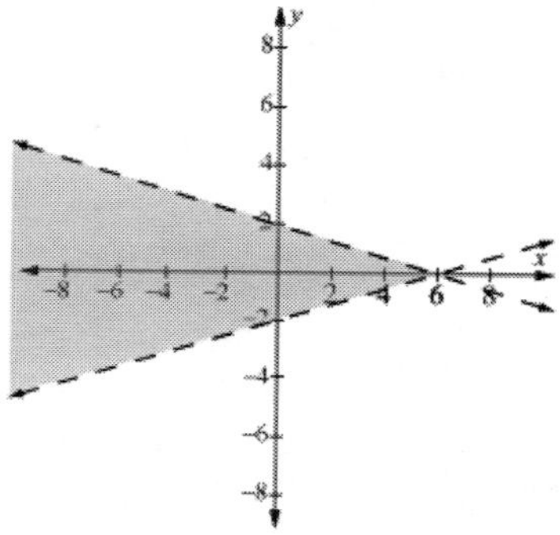

Review: **1.** False **3.** False **5.** True

Solving for Maxima-Minima *p.679*

Practice: **1.** $(0,4)$ **2.** $(2,0)$ **3.** $(0,4)$

Review: **1.** $(6,0)$ **3.** $(0,4)$ **5.** $(2,0)$

Applying Linear Programming *p.681*

Practice:

1. $x = 300$, $y = 200$;
i.e., 300 desks and 200 chairs.

2. $x = 100$, $y = 100$;
i.e., 100 of each kind of cookie.

3. $x = 80$, $y = 160$;
i.e., plant 80 acres of wheat with 160 acres of oats.

Review:

1. $x = 12{,}000$, $y = 0$;
i.e., 12,000 one-disk units and no two-disk albums.

3. $x = 9$, $y = 3$;
i.e., 9 gallons for the car and 3 gallons for the dirt bike.

5. $x = 66 - 2/3$, $y = 0$;
i.e., $66 - 2/3$ rhinestone collars and no training collars.

Special Topics

An Introduction to Conic Sections *p.687*

An Introduction to Parabolas *p.688*

Practice: **1.** True **2.**

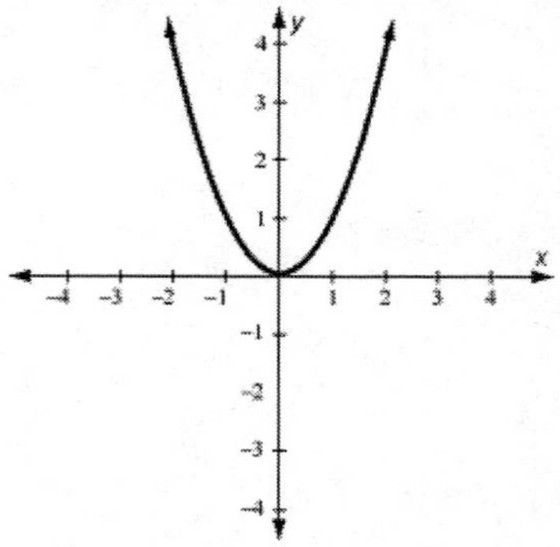

3. True

Review: **1.** direction: parabola opens up, vertex: $(-1, 0)$. **3.** True **5.** True

Determining Information about a Parabola from Its Equation *p.690*

Practice: **1.** vertex $(0,0)$; focus $\left(\frac{3}{8},0\right)$ **2.** focus: $(0,-1)$; directrix: $y=1$ **3.** focus: $(\frac{1}{2},0)$

Review: **1.** vertex $(0,0)$; focus $\left(0,\frac{1}{32}\right)$ **3.** Focus: $\left(0,-\frac{1}{3}\right)$, directrix: $y=\frac{1}{3}$ **5.** $\left(-\frac{3}{4},0\right)$

Writing an Equation for a Parabola *p.692*

Practice: **1.** $y^2=-12x$ **2.** $(x-3)^2=8(y-5)$ **3.** vertex: $(3,-5)$; focus: $(4,-5)$

Review: **1.** $x^2=6y$ **3.** $(2,3)$ **5.** $(y+5)^2=20(x-2)$

An Introduction to Ellipses *p.693*

Practice:

1. Center: $(4,-3)$; Minor axis: 2
2. Center: $(-2,0)$; Major axis: $2\sqrt{7}$; Minor axis: 4
3.

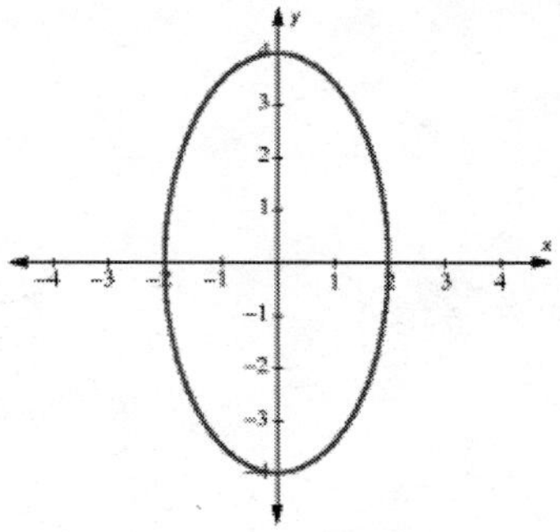

Review: **1.** $(x-5)^2+\frac{(y+3)^2}{4}=1$ center: $(5,-3)$ **3.** Major axis $=16$; minor axis $=2\sqrt{15}$ **5.** $(-4, 1)$

Finding the Equation for an Ellipse *p.695*

Practice: **1.** $\frac{x^2}{169}+\frac{y^2}{144}=1$ **2.** $\frac{x^2}{4}+\frac{y^2}{9}=1$ **3.** $(-4,0)$

Review: **1.** $\left(\sqrt{3},0\right)$ and $\left(-\sqrt{3},0\right)$ **3.** $\frac{x^2}{9}+\frac{y^2}{25}=1$ **5.** $(1,0)$

Applying Ellipses: Satellites *p.697*

Practice: **1.** $(\pm 3\sqrt{3},\ 0)$ **2.** $(0,\ \pm 5)$ **3.** 5,249 miles

Review: **1.** $(8,0)$ and $(-8,0)$ **3.** $(4+2\sqrt{2},-3)$ and $(4-2\sqrt{2},-3)$ **5.** $\frac{x^2}{18^2}+\frac{y^2}{14^2}=1$

An Introduction to Hyperbolas *p. 700*

Practice:

1. $y = \pm 5x$

2. $(0, \pm\sqrt{29})$

3. Foci: $(\pm 2\sqrt{5},\ 0)$; Asymptotes: $y = \pm 2x$

Review: **1.** $\left(\pm\sqrt{34}, 0\right)$ **3.** $(\pm 3, 0)$ **5.** $(0, \pm 3)$

Finding the Equation for a Hyperbola *p. 702*

Practice: **1.** $\frac{x^2}{36} - \frac{y^2}{64} = 1$ **2.** $y^2 - \frac{x^2}{8} = 1$ **3.** $\frac{x^2}{16} - \frac{y^2}{\frac{400}{9}} = 1.$

Review: **1.** $\frac{x^2}{49} - \frac{y^2}{25} = 1$ **3.** $\frac{y^2}{9} - \frac{4x^2}{9} = 1$ **5.** $\frac{x^2}{16} - \frac{y^2}{12} = 1$

Applying Hyperbolas: Navigation *p. 704*

Practice: **1.** $\frac{x^2}{885.66} - \frac{y^2}{14739.34} = 1$ **2.** Approximately 281 miles

Review: **1.** $\frac{x^2}{547.56} - \frac{y^2}{5077.44} = 1$

Identifying a Conic *p. 706*

Practice: **1.** $\frac{(y-1)^2}{4} - \frac{(x+3)^2}{16} = 1$; hyperbola with center $(-3,1)$ **2.** $\frac{x^2}{4} + y^2 = 1$; ellipse with center $(0,0)$. **3.** $(x-2)^2 = 10(y+3)$; parabola with vertex $(2,-3)$

Review:

1. $\frac{(x-2)^2}{12} + \frac{\left(y+\frac{3}{2}\right)^2}{4} = 1$; ellipse with center $\left(2, -\frac{3}{2}\right)$

3. $\left(y+\frac{5}{2}\right)^2 = \frac{1}{3}\left(x+\frac{31}{4}\right)$; parabola with vertex $\left(-\frac{31}{4}, -\frac{5}{2}\right)$

5. $x^2 = 4(y-2)$; parabola with vertex $(0,2)$

Name That Conic *p. 708*

Practice: **1.** Circle **2.** Ellipse **3.** Parabola

Review: **1.** Parabola **3.** Hyperbola **5.** Ellipse

Using the Binomial Theorem *p. 709*

Practice: **1.** $32 - 80y + 80y^2 - 40y^3 + 10y^4 - y^5$ **2.** $32x^{15} + 80x^{12}y^2 + 80x^9y^4 + 40x^6y^6 + 10x^3y^8 + y^{10}$ **3.** $256x^2 + 768\sqrt{x}^3y^2 + 864xy^4 + 432\sqrt{x}y^6 + 81y^8$

Review: **1.** $625 - 500y + 150y^2 - 20y^3 + y^4$ **3.** $x^3 - 3x^2y + 3xy^2 - y^3$ **5.** $x^3 - 9x^2\sqrt{y} + 27xy - 27y^{3/2}$

Binomial Coefficients *p. 711*

Practice: **1.** 56 **2.** $32x^5 - 400x^4y + 2000x^3y^2 - 5000x^2y^3 + 6250xy^4 - 3125y^5$ **3.** $16x^{12} - 96x^9\sqrt{y} + 216x^6y - 216x^3\sqrt{y}^3 + 81y^2$

Review: **1.** $16x^2 - 96x^{3/2}\sqrt{y} + 216xy - 216\sqrt{x}y^{3/2} + 81y^2$ **3.** $16x^{12} - 96x^9y + 216x^6y^2 - 216x^3y^3 + 81y^4$ **5.** 126

Understanding Sequence Problems *p. 714*

Practice: **1.** $a_1 = -4,\ a_2 = 1,\ a_3 = 0,\ a_{20} = 289$ **2.** $a_4 = 23$ and $a_5 = 47$ **3.** $a_n = 3n\sqrt{7}$

Review: **1.** $a_n = 3n - 2$ **3.** $a_1 = 6,\ a_2 = 7,\ a_3 = 8,\ a_{20} = 25$ **5.** $a_n = (-1)^n(n+1)^2$

Solving Problems Involving Arithmetic Sequences *p.716*

Practice: **1.** 361 **2.** 7 **3.** 441

Review: **1.** $a_n = 7 + 10(n-1)$ **3.** $a_n = 80 + 5(n-1)$ **5.** 46

Solving Problems Involving Geometric Sequences *p.717*

Practice: **1.** $2(5)^{14}$ **2.** 3^{100} **3.** $a_n = -4(3)^{n-1}$

Review: **1.** 3 **3.** $5(3)^{17}$ **5.** $a_n = 4\left(-\frac{1}{2}\right)^{n-1}$

Proving Formulas Using Mathematical Induction *p.719*

Examples of Induction *p.720*

Review: **1.** **3** **5.**

Solving Problems Involving Permutations *p.722*

Practice: **1.** 20,160 **2.** 720 **3.** 6

Review: **1.** 3,991,680 **3.** 336 **5.** 120

Solving Problems Involving Combinations *p.723*

Practice: **1.** 330 **2.** 75,287,520 **3.** 3,003

Review: **1.** 120 **3.** 35 **5.** 56

Solving for Probability and Odds: Dice Rolls *p.725*

Practice: **1.** $\frac{1}{4}$ **2.** $\frac{5}{18}$ **3.** $\frac{5}{9}$

Review: **1.** $\frac{3}{8}$ **3.** $\frac{1}{2}$ **5.** $\frac{1}{6}$

Solving for Probability and Odds: Decks of Cards *p.727*

Practice: **1.** 0 **2.** $\frac{1}{2}$ **3.** $\frac{1}{2}$

Review: **1.** $\frac{2}{13}$ **3.** 1 **5.** $\frac{1}{13}$

Glossary:

absolute value	the measured distance on a number line from one location to the origin (0).
absolute value with greater than	all the solution values are outside the endpoints away from zero; $\|A\| > B$ means $A < -B$ or $A > B$
absolute value with less than	all the solution values are between the endpoints and zero: $\|A\| < B$ means $-B < A < B$
adding complex numbers	combine like terms, the real numbers with themselves and the imaginary numbers with themselves
adding polynomials	combining all like terms in an algebraic expression
algebra of functions	process of adding, subtracting, multiplying or dividing functions with functions
amplitude	half the difference between the maximum and minimum values of a periodic function; in effect, the maximum displacement of a periodic function from equilibrium
and	connector used with inequalities to indicate that the solution set will include only values which satisfy both inequalities in the problem; sometimes referred to as an intersection.
angle of depression	the angle measured downwards from the horizontal to a point or an object
angle of elevation	the angle measured upwards from the horizontal to a point or an object
approximation	a line or curve created to approximately represent the pattern produced by graphing single pieces of data on a plane.
arc	a portion of a circle or other curve
argument	the expression that a function operates on
arithmetic sequence	an ordered collection of numbers in which the difference between any two consecutive terms is a constant (d); these sequences follow the pattern $a_n = a_1 + (n - 1)d$
asymptote	a line that the graph of a function approaches but never reaches. Asymptotes can be either horizontal or vertical
augmented matrix	an array for a system of equations which utilizes as elements both the coefficients of the variables and the constants in the equations
average	one number used to represent a group of values, calculated by adding all the values in the group then dividing by the number of values included in the group
axis of symmetry	the imaginary line that passes through the vertex of a parabola and is parallel to the axis along which the curve is opening
b	variable used to represent the y-intercept in the slope-intercept equation for a line.
base	the number or variable to which an exponent is attached
bearing	the direction of an object measured clockwise from north; also called compass direction
binomial	an algebraic expression composed of two monomial terms linked by addition or subtraction
cancellation	dividing both a numerator and a denominator by the same number so long as the numbers being divided are either both in the same fraction or are in fractions which are multiplying with each other.
Cartesian coordinates	the ordered pair, usualy (x,y), that designates the location of a point on a Cartesian plane
Cartesian plane	the flat surface created by two number lines which intersect at right angles
Center of a circle	the fixed point that is a set distance from each point in the set of points that is the circle; usually designated as the ordered pair (h, k) where h is the x-value and k is the y-value of the point.
circle	the set of all the points at a fixed distance, the radius (r), from a specified point, the center (h,k); a completely symmetrical figure
clearing the denominator	practice of elminating a radical from the denominator of a fraction

coefficient	a constant multiplying with an algebraic variable
collinear	any two or more points that fall on the same line
common denominator	a number that can be used as the denominator for every fraction in a problem; generally it is the lowest multiple common to all the existing denominators in the problem
compass direction	the direction of an object measured clockwise from north; also called bearing
complement	the positive angle that, when added to a given angle, results in a right angle
completing the square	the process of isolating on one side of the equation the terms containing the variable being solved for, then adding the value necessary for that side to be a perfect square to both sides of the equation, then factoring or taking the square root of both sides, and finally performing arithmetic as needed to solve for the variable.
complex fraction	a fraction which has one or more fractions in its numerator, denominator or both.
complex number	a value composed of both a real number and an imaginary number. Complex numbers are often written in the form $a + bi$, where a is the real number and bi is the imaginary number.
complex plane	a coordinate system for graphing complex numbers where the horizontal axis is the real axis and the vertical axis is the imaginary axis
composite function	a function that results from first applying one function, and then another.
composition	multiple functions acting on each other in a specified order.
compound inequality	two inequalities linked by *and* or *or*
compound interest formula	$A = P(1 + {}^{r}/_{m})^{mt}$
conic section	any curve which is derived by intersecting a cone with a plane, such figures include: the point (the plane touches the tip of the cone) line (the plane is tangent to the side of the cone) parabola (the plane intersects the cone parallel to its side) circle (the plane intersects the cone parallel to the base of the cone) ellipse (the plane intersects the cone at an angle), and hyperbola (the plane intersects the cone vertically).
conjugate pair	a pair of numbers of the form $a + b$ and $a - b$ where a or b (or both) is often a radical or imaginary number
consecutive even numbers	even numbers that follow one another when counting, i.e., 2, 4, 6, ... or x, x + 2, x + 4, ...
consecutive numbers	numbers that follow one another when counting; i.e., 3, 4, 5, ... or x, x + 1, x + 2, ...
consecutive odd numbers	odd numbers that follow one another when counting, i.e., 3, 5, 7, ..., or 2x + 1, 2x + 3, 2x + 5, ..., or x, x + 2, x + 4 ... given that x is an odd number
constant	a number which always has the same value, i.e., 7; the value in a function which does not change
constant velocity	a constant change in position with respect to time; traveling a distance over some amount of time at an even speed, can be determined using a formula that specifies that speed equals distance traveled divided by time used travelling
coordinate plane	a plane on which points can be identified using a set of values that uniquely specifies their location
cosine	one of the six trigonometric functions, denoted cos. In a right triangle, the cosine of an angle is equal to the adjacent side divided by the hypotenuse.
coterminal angles	angles that have the same initial and terminal sides. Coterminal angles have measures that differ by a multiple of 360°.
Cramer's rule	a process utilizing determinants to solve systems of linear equations
cross-multiplying	a practice used to eliminate denominators when one or more fractions are found in an equation; the procedure involves multiplying the common denominator from one side of the equation with the numerators on the other side of the equation with the result that the multiplying denominator disappears into the receiving numerator

curve fitting	superimposing a line or curve over the graph of single points of data to approximately represent the pattern produced in the graph
decreasing	a function or an interval for a function whose value is becoming smaller as viewed on its graph from left to right; a function may decrease over some intervals but not others
degree	the highest power used in any of the terms of an algebraic expression
degree of polynomial	highest power used in any of the terms of the algebraic expression
denominator	number or expression on the bottom, or doing the dividing, of a fraction
dependent system	a group of three equations in three unknowns that has an infinite number of solutions; the planes for the three equations intersect in a line
dependent variable	the quantity in an algebraic expession whose value changes as calculations are made subsequent to one or more substitutions for the independent variable, i.e., the variable whose value "depends" on what is substituted in for the other, or "independent," variable.
Descartes' rule of signs	a method for determining the number of positive and negative real roots for a polynomial; first arrange the polynomial in descending order with the highest power first, then substitute in "x" and note the number of times the sign changes between terms, then repeat the process using "-x". In each case the number of real number solutions of the type substituted will equal the number of sign changes or that number minus some even number.
determinant	|D|, det(D), a number, or scalar, that represents the value of a matrix
dimension of a matrix	the number of rows "x" the number of columns
direct proportion	two or more quantities increase or decrease in the same way to the same degree, each in accordance with its size
direct variation	two or more quantities increase or decrease in the same way to the same degree, each quantity in accordance with its size
direction angle	the angle measured counterclockwise from the positive x-axis to a vector
distance modulus formula	M = 5logr - 5; used in astronomy to find large distances.
distributive property	(of multiplication over addition), $a(b + c) = ab + ac$, where a, b, and c are real numbers.
domain	the set of all values that the independent variable for a function, usually x, can use in that function
domain of a rational	the set of all values available for the variable such that the denominator of the rational never equals zero
e	the base of the natural logarithm, approximately 2.71828; a number important in calculating population growth, decay, and many other practical things, also known as Napier's number
elimination	a process for solving systems of equations by combining two of the equations in such a way that one of the variables adds or subtracts away, with steps following to solve the new equation(s) for the remaining variable(s) until a value has been discovered for each variable in the system.
empty set	a solution with no values which indicates that there are no numbers which satisfy the equation or inequality
equation	a mathematical sentence in which one term or expression is linked, using "=", to another of exactly the same value
equation of a line	ax + by = c
even function	a function whose graph is symmetric about the y-axis; a function $f(x)$ that satisfies the expression $f(-x) = f(x)$.
exponent	the superscripted number or term attached to the right side of an algebraic term or parentheses (the base) which indicates how many times the base is expected to multiply with itself in the problem
exponentiation	the practice of using exponents, or superscripted numerical indicators, rather than writing what is required in words

extraneous root a value found for the variable that cannot be considered part of the solution because it gives a false statement when substituted into the original equation.

factor theorem the expression (x - c) must be a factor of a polynomial, p(x), if it divides into the polynomial with a remainder of zero; for (x - c) to be a factor of f(x), f(c) = 0.

factorial (n!) (n!) a process of multiplying the given integer with every positive integer smaller than itself

factoring process for solving algebraic expressions by reversing multiplication to discover the elements which produced the expression; steps include first "unmultiplying" any number or variable which is common to all the terms in the expression, then looking for ways to group terms in multiplying expressions, then breaking up higher-power terms

Fibonacci sequence a series of numbers that starts out with 1 and 1, then each succeeding term is the sum of the two terms that precede it; the early terms in the sequence are 1, 1, 2, 3, 5, 8, 13, ...; the sequence is found many times in nature.

FOIL method a process for multiplying two binomial expressions: multiply the two First terms (F), then the two Outer terms (O), then the two Inner terms (I), and finally the two Last terms (L). Finish by combining like terms.

formula a generalized equation in one or more variables used to measure a characteristic or action in every situation of its kind

fraction a division problem written vertically with the number on top (numerator) being divided by the number on the bottom (denominator)

function a set of ordered pairs in which any given *x*-value is paired with exactly one *y*-value; an expression for which each *x*-value produces exactly one *y*-value

function notation f(x) read "f of x." If a value, say 2, is substituted into the function for x, then f(x) becomes f(2) and is read "f at 2;" "f(x)" is used instead of "y" to show that the y-value varies depending on the choices made for x.

Gauss-Jordan method a process for solving linear equations which uses matrix manipulations such as flipping the order of rows, multiplying rows by constants, and replacing a row by the sum of two rows

graph a visual representation of data on a line or plane, or in a higher-dimensional space

graphing inequalities graph the inequality as an equation which divides the plane into two regions and show the graph as a broken line unless the "equal to" is part of the inequality, then pick a point off the curve and substitute it into the inequality checking to see if what results is a true statement. If the statement is true, shade in the region which included that point for that region will contain all the points and only those points which make the statement true while, if the statement is false, shade in the opposite region knowing that its points are those needed for the solution set.

greater than (>) a linking concept which indicates that the number or expression on the left side of a mathematical sentence is larger than the number or expression on the right side of the sentence.

greatest integer function assigns as the y-value the greatest integer that is less than or equal to the value produced by each x, graphs as a "step function" meaning that its graph appears in short horizontal bars rising one after another when viewed from left to right

grouping with exponents setting all the bases within a term which carry the same exponent within parentheses to which the exponent is attached

half-angle identity a trigonometric identity used to rewrite trigonometric functions of angle A/2 in terms of angle A.

harmonic motion the motion of an object that moves back and forth regularly

Hooke's law provides a formula to measure the distance a spring stretches and shows that the distance varies directly with the force applied

horizontal axis measures horizontal distance from the origin on a plane; it is usually designated by x and referred to as the x-axis.

horizontal line test	a test to determine whether a function is one-to-one. The horizontal line test states that if every horizontal line that intersects the graph of a function does so at most once, then the function has an inverse.
hyperbola	consists of the set of points the difference of whose distance from two fixed points (foci) is constant
identity	an equation that is true for all meaningful values of the variable(s) involved
identity matrix	the array which will produce the given matrix when the given matrix multiplies with the identity matrix; an array made up of 0s and 1s such that the 1s form a diagonal from upper left to lower right in the array, and 0s fill in all the other places in the array
imaginary number	the square root of a negative number
imaginary part of a complex number	the part of a complex number measured along the imaginary axis in the complex plane; the imaginary part of the complex number $a + bi$ is b
inconsistent system	a group of three equations in three unknowns that has no solution; i.e., the planes for the three equations do not intersect
increasing	a term used to describe the behavior of a function over an interval. A curve is increasing if $f(x_1) < f(x_2)$ whenever $x_1 < x_2$; a graph that appears to be rising when viewed from the left to the right; In calculus, a function is increasing over an interval if the first derivative is positive over that entire interval.
independent system	a group of three equations in three unknowns that has exactly one solution; i.e., the planes for the three equations intersect in a single point
independent variable	the quantity in an algebraic expression whose value must be set before the value of the entire expression can be determined
indirect proportion	two or more quantities increase or decrease in opposite ways to the same degree each in accordance with its size; sometimes called inverse proportion
induction	a method of proving a list of statements is true by showing that the first statement is true, then showing that if one of the statements is true then the next one that follows is also true; i.e., each time one fact is shown to be true it proves the next one is true; when using this method first show the statement is true for n = 1, then assume that the statement is true for n = k and show that it is true for = k + 1 thereby proving that the statement is true for every n.
inductive sequence	an ordered collection of numbers which uses a pattern based upon previous terms
inequality	the concept that one side of a mathematical sentence is a different size than the other side, generally denoted with the less than and greater than symbols
infinity	the value derived by adding one more to the value at each end of the number line thereby extending the number line one more unit in either direction. The ability to keep performing this extension process for the number line means that the possible number values never end either as very large numbers or as very small numbers.
intercept	the point(s) at which a line or curve crosses one of the axes of the plane
interval	the range of values on a number line which are solutions for a given variable in a given problem situation; the range of x-values for a function over which the graph of the function is being considered in some aspect
interval notation	[a,b] indicates that the variable can be any of the values between the two given numbers including the end numbers. (a,b) indicates that the variable can be any of the values between the two given numbers except the end numbers.
inverse function	a function which undoes another function; if g(x) is the inverse of f(x), then g[f(x)] = x; not all functions have an inverse
inverse matrix	the array which will produce the identity matrix when multiplied with a given matrix; to have an inverse a matrix must be nonsingular; i.e., its determinant will be other than zero.
inverse proportion	two or more quantities increase or decrease in opposite ways to the same degree each quantity in accordance with its size; sometimes called indirect proportion or inverse variation

inverse trigonometric function a function that undoes a trigonometric function; e.g. arcsine, arccosine, arctangent

inverse variation two or more quantities increase or decrease in opposite ways to the same degree each quantity in accordance with its size; also called indirect proportion

investment problem usually a word problem related to interest on sums of money

k the constant of change, a value used with variation problems; a value fixed within each type of problem depending on the materials and situations involved in the problem

least common denominator (LCD) (LCD) the smallest multiple common to all the denominators in the problem

less than (<) a linking concept which indicates that the number or expression on the left side of a mathematical sentence is smaller than the number or expression on the right side of the sentence

less than or equal to (<) a linking concept which indicates that the expression on the left of the mathematical sentence is smaller than or the same size as the expression on the right side of the sentence

like term all monomials in an expression which contain exactly the same variables each to the same degree

line the shortest distance between two points in Euclidean geometry; the straight path passing through and beyond any two points

linear equation a mathematical sentence in which all variables are at the first power level, the equation graphs as a line

linear function a function whose graph is a line

linear programming a process for using systems of inequalities to determine maximum and minimum possibilities in business and other concrete situations; each inequality is graphed and the region bounded by the system is noted, then the vertex points of this region are substituted into the function to determine the maximum and minimum points

linear system of equations solving a group of linear equations for a solution to each variable that is common to every equation in the group

linear work problem usually a word problem designed to calculate work performed at an average rate over a period of time by one or more workers

ln A the natural logarithm evaluated at A; the logarithm with base e evaluated at the number A

logarithmic function function which has a logarithm as one of the elements; never equals zero; all of these functions graph to the same basic shape with the only unique pieces being the x-intercept and the altitude the curve attains.

major axis the long axis of an ellipse

mathematical induction a method of proving a list of statements is true by showing that the first statement is true, then showing that if one of the statements is true then the statement that follows is also true; i.e., each time one fact is shown to be true it proves the next one is true; when using this method to prove something first show the statement is true for $n = 1$, then assume that the statement is true for $n = k$ and show that it is true for $n = k + 1$ thereby proving that the statement is true for every n

matrices more than one matrix

matrix a rectangular block or array of numbers

maxima the plural form of maximum; the points on a graph where the function changes from increasing to decreasing

maximum a point where a function attains its greatest value on an open interval; the high point on the graph of a curve; the point where a function which has been increasing in value begins to decrease; in calculus, the point in an open interval where the derivative of a function changes from positive to negative

midpoint of a line the point that lies equidistant from the two endpoints of the line segment

minima the plural form of minimum; the points on a graph where the function changes from decreasing to increasing

minimum	a point where a function attains its smallest value on an open interval; a low point on the graph of a curve; the point where a function which has been decreasing in value begins to increase; in calculus, the point in an interval where the derivative changes from negative to positive
minor axis	the short axis of an ellipse
mixture problem	usually a word problem designed to calculate quantities or strengths of substances mixed together
monomial	an algebraic term composed of numbers and variables that multiply or divide with each other, but do not add or subtract with each other
multiplicative identity	the number which multiplies with the given number for a product that is the given number; i.e., 1
multiplicative inverse	the number which multiplies with the given number for a product of 1
multiplicity	number of times a specific value is used as a solution for a polynomial
multiplying binomials	the process of multiplying individually each term in one binomial with each term in the other binomial followed by combining like terms
multiplying matrices	creating a new matrix by multiplying elements in the columns of one matrix with elements in the rows of the other matrix; for two matrices to be able to multiply, the number of columns in the left matrix must match the number of rows in the right matrix; the solution matrix will have the same number of rows as the left matrix and the same number of columns as the right matrix
multiplying polynomials	the process of multiplying individually each term in one polynomial with each term in the other polynomial followed by combining like terms
multiplying with exponents	since exponents actually count how often the base numbers multiply with themselves, multiplying with exponents involves adding the exponents attached to the same bases within a multiplication problem
Napier's number	the number e, or the base of the natural logarithm
natural log	a logarithm with base e
negative exponent	requires that the reciprocal of its base number be used in the problem
negative slope	indicates that the line falls, or loses value, when viewed from left to right.
nonlinear system of equations	a group of equations, all of which graph something other than a line, which are being processed for solutions that work in all the equations
nonsingular determinant	the value for a matrix equal to something other than zero
nth roots	the complex *n*th roots of a number k are those complex numbers z that satisfy the equation $z^n = k$. There are n complex *n*th roots of any number.
number line	a scale that represents the sequence of numbers from the smallest values and negative infinity on the left end to the largest values and positive infinity on the right end.
numerator	the number on top, or being divided, in a fraction
odd function	a function whose graph is symmetric about the origin; a function $f(x)$ that satisfies the equation $f(-x) = -f(x)$
one-to-one function	a function which satisfies the horizontal line test; every y-value output by the function comes from exactly one x-value input into the function
or	used with inequalities to indicate that the solution set will include values which satisfy one or the other inequalities, but not necessarily both; sometimes referred to as a union
order of operations	established practice for deriving consistent answers when doing arithmetic that requires whatever arithmetic is enclosed within parentheses be done first, followed by the arithmetic required to satisfy exponents, followed by multiplication and division from left to right across the expression, followed by addition and subraction across the expression

ordered pair	two numbers in the form (x, y), usually representing the coordinates of a point; the two numbers which locate a point on the Cartesian plane by indicating with the first number (x) the horizontal distance of the point from the origin and with the second number (y) the vertical distance of the point from the origin
origin	the center of the rectangular or Cartesian coordinate system, located at (0,0); the point of intersection of the two number lines used to create a Cartesian plane
parabola	one of the conic sections; the set of points equidistant from a fixed point (the focus) and a fixed line (the directrix)
parallel	indicates that two lines or planes will never intersect; i.e., they have no points in common; predicted by two lines having the same slope and different y-intercepts
partial fraction	a fraction which represents part of a more complicated fraction and which uses as its denominator one factor from the denominator of the more complicated fraction; one element of a process using a system of linear equations to simplify a complicated fraction as the sum of a group of simpler fractions
Pascal's triangle	a group of numbers which form and are derived from a unique pattern such that every row starts and ends with 1 while all the other terms are derived by adding the two elements above their position in the triangle
period	the smallest length of time or distance along the x-axis required for a periodic function to repeat itself
periodic function	a function that repeats itself
perpendicular	a concept that indicates that two lines or planes intersect at right angles; predicted when the slopes of two lines are the negative reciprocals of each other, which is to say that their slopes will multiply to give the answer -1.
phase shift	a horizontal translation of a periodic function
pi	(p) an irrational number, approximately equal to 3.14159..., that is the ratio of the circumference of a circle to its diameter ($p = C/d$).
piecewise function	function which is defined differently across various intervals of the x-axis with the result that its graph may be discontinuous and present more than one type of curve
pitch	a measure of the steepness with which a line or curve increases or decreases over an interval
plane	a two-dimensional surface considered to have height and width, but no depth; a plane is created whenever two axes intersect
plotting a point	the process of locating a point on a number line or axis system
point	a location in space with no width, depth or height; a location specified on the Cartesian plane by the ordered pair (x,y) which details the point's horizontal and vertical distance from the central point (0,0)
point of inflection	a point on a curve where the concavity changes; also called an inflection point
polar axis	the number line used to measure change in distance on the polar plane
polar coordinate system	a system for locating points on the plane by specifying their angle from a polar axis and their distance from a central point
polynomial	a sum of monomials; monomial terms linked by positive and negative signs
polynomial function	a function defined by a polynomial expression; often described by its degree n where n is a nonnegative integer
position function	a function describing the position or location of an object as a function of time t
positive slope	indicates that the line rises, or gains value, when viewed from left to right
power	an exponent attached to a base; the power of a polynomial or function equals the largest exponent attached to a variable in the expression
power-reducing identity	a trigonometric function used to rewrite powers of trigonometric identities

probability	a mathematical measurement as to the likelihood that a given event will occur
proving an answer	using the value found for each variable, substitute into the equation to validate they create a true mathematical sentence
Pythagorean theorem	the sum of the squares of the lengths of the legs of a right triangle equals the square of the length of the hypotenuse; $a^2 + b^2 = c^2$
quadrant	one of the four regions of the Cartesian plane. Starting with quadrant I in the upper-right, they are counted counterclockwise.
quadratic equation	a mathematical sentence which contains one variable to the second degree; an equation whose graph presents a parabola
quadratic function	a function defined by a quadratic, or second-degree expression; a function whose graph presents a parabola
radical	a notation indicating that the number under the symbol is to be reduced to the root prescribed by the index
radicand	the value or expression under a radical sign
radius	the distance from the center of a circle to any point on the circle
range	the set of all output values that can be taken by a function; the set of all values possible for the dependent variable of a function
rational	a number written in fraction form
rational exponent	a small superscripted number attached to a base number or term which is in fraction form whose numerator stipulates the power of the base and whose denominator stipulates what root of the base is desired
rational expression	a fraction with a polynomial in the numerator, the denominator, or both
rational function	a function in the form of a fraction with a polynomial in the numerator and another in the denominator, with the stipulation that the polynomial in the denominator is not equal to 0
real element of a complex number	the part of a complex number measured along the real axis in the complex plane. The real part of the complex number $a + bi$ is a.
rectangular coordinate plane	the plane containing the rectangular coordinate system
rectangular coordinate system	a system for locating points on the plane by specifying their horizontal and vertical components
rectangular coordinates	the ordered pair (x,y) used to denote the location of points on a Cartesian plane
rectangular form of a complex number	the a + bi form of a complex number, as opposed to the trigonometric form; also called standard form
recursive sequence	an ordered collection of numbers which uses a pattern based upon previous terms; an inductive sequence
reference angle	the positive, acute angle formed by the terminal side of an angle and the x-axis
reflecting a curve	this procedure turns a graph matching every point (x, y) with a point (x, -y) if the reflection is over the x-axis or matching every point (x, y) with a point (-x, y) if the reflection is over the y-axis
region	for graphing, one of the four quadrants of the Cartesian plane; for inequalities, one of the several areas created by the graphs of the related equations one of which, and possibly its boundaries, contains all the solution values for the inequality or system of inequalities.
relation	a set of ordered pairs in which any given x-value may be paired with multiple y-values; an equation that does not necessarily satify the vertical line test (as opposed to a function)
remainder theorem	if a polynomial p(x) is divided by (x - c), then the remainder will be p(c); this concept is useful for determining factors in that their remainder is always zero
right circular cylinder	the shape of a can with a round top and bottom that are the same size with its sides perpendicular to the top and bottom

root	a number derived when a given number is reduced according to its exponents; an x-value where a function or polynomial is equal to zero; also called a zero
roots of unity	the complex roots of 1, or the solutions to the equation $z^n = 1$.There are *n n*th roots of unity.
scalar	a single number which can multiply with a matrix or vector
sequence	an ordered collection of numbers
shifting a curve	adding a value to the equation of a curve with the result that the curve moves to a new location on its plane
similar	having the same shape and proportions
sine	one of the six trigonometric functions, denoted sin. In a right triangle, the sine of an angle is equal to the opposite side divided by the hypotenuse.
singular determinant	an array value equal to zero
sinusoidal	having the shape or characteristics of a sine curve
slope of a horizontal line	this value is zero because the difference between the y-values in the numerator is zero
slope of a vertical line	this value is undefined because the difference between the x-values in the denominator is zero
solution set	all the values that satisfy the terms required for an equation or inequality to be valid
solving an equation	finding the value(s) for the variable(s) that makes an equation true
solving an inequality	determining the set of values that can be used by the variables so that the inequality is a true statement
spiral	a path in a plane traced around a central point while continuously receding from or approaching it
square matrix	an array with the same number of rows as columns
standard form of a complex number	a + bi; also called rectangular form as opposed to the trigonometric form
step function	a function that graphs its values as short horizontal bars rising or falling one after another when viewed from left to right
substitution method	a process for solving systems of equations by distilling two of the equations to a value for one of the variables, then substituting that value back into one of the original equations to help solve for another variable, until a value has been discovered for each variable in the system
subtracting polynomials	changing the signs on the subtracting terms, then combining like terms; distributing the negative sign as appropriate, then combining like terms
supplement	an angle that, when added to a given angle, results in a straight angle
symmetry	when half the graph of a function is an exact mirror image of the other half
synthetic division	a shorthand method for dividing polynomials when the divisor is in the form (x + c). This method works only when the coefficient of x equals 1
system of inequalities	a group of inequalities or a group of inequalities mixed with equations
system of linear equations	a group of equations that is processed for solutions that work in all the equations
tangent	one of the six trigonometric functions, denoted tan. In a right triangle, the tangent of an angle is equal to the opposite side divided by the adjacent side.
terminal side	the position of the ray sweeping out an angle after rotation through the angle
transitive property	a concept for comparing numbers which states that if one number is larger than a second number, and the second number is larger than a third number, then the first number is also larger than the third number. The same property holds true if the numbers are smaller than each other. Other transitive properties exist (such as one for the equality of numbers).

translation	movement of the graph of an entire curve in some direction; sometimes called a shift
trigonometric function	a function of angle measure based on the ratios of the sides of right triangles; the six trigonometric functions are sine, cosine, tangent, cosecant, secant, and cotangent
trigonometric identity	an equation involving trigonometric functions that is true for all meaningful values of the variable involved
trinomial	an algebraic expression composed of three monomial terms linked by addition or subtraction
undefined	a rational expression whose value cannot be determined because its denominator has a value equal to zero.
ungrouping with exponents	removing a set of parentheses around a group of terms by attaching the parentheses' exponent to each individual term within the group
union	the solution set for two inequalities linked by "or"; a set formed by combining the elements of two or more sets
unit vector	a vector that has a magnitude of 1
variable	an unknown value in an expression or equation that is usually represented by a letter
variation	when two or more quantities increase or decrease in relation to each other
vector	a mathematical object made up of a magnitude (length) and a direction
velocity	the speed and direction of the motion of an object; the rate of change of position with respect to time.
vertex	(h, k) is the turning point of a parabola; the vertex is the minimum point if the parabola opens up along the y-axis or the maximum point if the parabola opens down along the y-axis; the coordinates of the vertex can be discovered by using information from the standard equation, h = -b/2a; k = f(h)
vertical axis	a scale to measure vertical distance from the origin on a plane; usually designated by y and referred to as the y-axis.
vertical line test	used to determine if a relation is a function; if a vertical line passes through the graph of a relation more than once at any specific point, then the relation fails the vertical line test and is not a function
vertical shift	the rigid motion (or translation) of the graph of a function upwards or downwards; changing the location of an entire curve upwards or downwards from its original location or from the origin on a Cartesian plane
volume	a measurement of 3-dimensional space; involves multiplying the three dimensions of the object as in height x width x depth for a rectangular prism, or pi x radius x radius x height for a right cylinder
word problem	a sentence or paragraph presenting a mathematical situation to solve; the solution procedure involves defining variables, discerning known facts, creating an equation, solving the equation, and checking the answer
x	letter most commonly used as a variable in algebraic expressions
x-axis	the number line used to measure horizontal change on a Cartesian plane
x-intercept	the *x*-value where a graph crosses or touches the *x*-axis
x-value	the number used for *x* within a given point (*x,y*) to indicate where the point is located horizontally on the Cartesian plane; in general, the value of the variable *x*
y-axis	the number line used to measure vertical change on the Cartesian plane
y-intercept	the *y*-value where a graph passes through or touches the *y*-axis
y-value	the number used for *y* in a given point (*x,y*) to indicate where the point is located vertically on the Cartesian plane; in general, the value of the variable *y*
zero of a function	an x-value where a function equals zero; the point(s) at which a function has an x-intercept

zero of a polynomial function an x-value where a polynomial p(x) is equal to zero, i.e. any number c that satisfies p(c)=0; any point where the graph of a polynomial crosses or touches the x-axis